MARTIN HOTINE

1898–1968

Martin Hotine's death on November 12, 1968, ended a brilliant career; his energetic leadership in geodesy will be missed. Although seriously ill, his drive and enthusiasm enabled him to complete the manuscript of this monograph, *Mathematical Geodesy*—a fitting climax to a lifetime of geodetic research and application.

During the 50-year span of Martin Hotine's professional career, he provided numerous valuable contributions of lasting significance to basic research and practical applications of geodesy. Among the many achievements from his surveying and mapping career in England, two contributions are most outstanding—the retriangulation of Great Britain under his direction from 1935 until its completion in 1962, and the surveys and mapping of underdeveloped countries, initiated and directed by him in 1946 and still continuing with his high standards of accuracy. Martin Hotine was truly a builder of worldwide geodetic networks.

A firm belief in international geodetic cooperation was one of Martin Hotine's convictions. This was manifested by his leadership of the Commonwealth Survey Officers Conferences from 1955 to 1963, by his intense participation in the general assemblies of the International Association of Geodesy, and most notably by his collaboration with Professor Antonio Marussi of Italy in the formation of three symposia on three-dimensional and mathematical geodesy. He was heavily involved in the program planning for the fourth symposium to be held in May 1969.

Many significant theoretical contributions to the science of geodesy were made by Martin Hotine. He expanded the classical theoretical limitations of the current geodetic horizon by insisting on a unified three-dimensional approach to geodetic measurements and principles, and by applying the most relevant mathematical tools, such as the tensor calculus, to exploit these concepts properly. Many of the papers on these subjects never appeared in print. However, by being presented at various international meetings, they were well publicized and proved very influential in their impact on other geodesists.

It was thus fortunate that while employed at ESSA, Martin Hotine was able to combine and expand these ideas, formulated over the years, into this treatise on mathematical geodesy. In recognition of his service to the United States Government, Martin Hotine was awarded posthumously the Gold Medal of the Department of Commerce "for highly distinguished and productive authorship of exceptional quality and extraordinary importance to science: for outstanding leadership in assisting ESSA in formalizing its geodetic research program." Mrs. Hotine accepted the award at the American Embassy in London on January 24, 1969.

essa
MONOGRAPH
2

Mathematical Geodesy

by Martin Hotine

U.S. DEPARTMENT OF COMMERCE, Maurice H. Stans, *Secretary*

ENVIRONMENTAL SCIENCE SERVICES ADMINISTRATION, Robert M. White, *Administrator*

Washington, D.C., 1969

ESSA MONOGRAPHS

Editors

William O. Davis, Miles F. Harris, and Fergus J. Wood

Consulting Editor

Bernard H. Chovitz

Editorial Board

Editors of the ESSA Monographs, Environmental Science Services Administration, Rockville, Md. 20852, invite readers to submit to them all errors or omissions noted in the text for correction in future reprints of this book.

UDC 528:51(021)
    528 Geodesy
    51 Mathematical
    (021) Comprehensive manual

Library of Congress Catalog Card Number: 73–602618

For sale by the Superintendent of Documents, U.S. Government Printing Office, Washington, D.C. 20402.   Price $5.50

Foreword

In 1963, Martin Hotine completed a distinguished career of government service — both military and civil — in Great Britain. He attained the military rank of Brigadier, and later as a civil servant he was Director of the Directorate of Overseas Surveys and Advisor on Surveys to the Secretary of the Department of Technical Cooperation. In November 1963, he accepted an invitation of Rear Admiral H. Arnold Karo, Director of the U.S. Coast and Geodetic Survey, to join his scientific staff as a research geodesist. When ESSA was formed in 1965, Martin Hotine became a member of the Earth Sciences Laboratories in Boulder, where he remained until his return to England in August 1968. During these 5 years in the United States, Martin Hotine devoted his attention to new concepts in the geodetic sciences and continued the work that led to his recognition as one of the world's foremost authorities on geodesy.

To compile scientific thought within a particular specialty of any discipline is never an easy task. Only an individual who has a proficiency in his field gained through years of practical experience and one who is dedicated to the advancement of science would undertake such a difficult task. Martin Hotine was such an individual, and the result of his efforts provides a foundation in basic theory and current thought in mathematical geodesy and another step from which the science of geodesy can progress.

ESSA is highly honored and extremely fortunate to be able to include this volume in its monograph series. The purpose of this series is to add authoritative information to the depository of total scientific knowledge. *Mathematical Geodesy* is such a treatise.

Robert M. White
Administrator

Preface

This book is an attempt to free geodesy from its centuries-long bondage in two dimensions. This does not mean that any geodesist, from Eratosthenes to modern contenders for the title, has ever considered the Earth to be flat; the two dimensions, such as latitude and longitude, have always been non-Euclidian and have been taken as coordinates on a curved reference surface. It has been usual, nevertheless, to project points from the topographic surface of the Earth to the reference surface and thereafter to work entirely between points on the reference surface. The third dimension of height above the reference surface is, after all, small compared with the mean radius of the Earth; this fact has made it possible to avoid any precise definition of the actual process of projection or of the exact location and orientation of the reference surface in relation to points on the topographic surface. The main process of projecting the line of observation into curves of normal section on the reference surface (usually a spheroid or ellipsoid of revolution), combining these curves into a spheroidal geodesic, and solving geodesic triangles does give sufficiently accurate results from fairly simple formulas over short lines. Unfortunately, the process involves an element of indiscipline which could bring the subject into disrepute; for example, the author's own interest was aroused some years ago by an argument in print between two leading European geodesists on the correct application of Laplace azimuth adjustment, between points not located on the reference surface, which showed that neither geodesist had clearly defined what he meant by a geodetic azimuth at points in space. The classical process could not, in any case, deal with the longer lines of observation in flare triangulation, stellar triangulation, and now satellite triangulation without excessive complication; it is actually simpler to consider the line of observation as a line in three dimensions and to carry out all computations and network adjustments in three dimensions.

It can be said that one form of the classical process was first introduced for the reduction of a survey of Hanover, Germany, by the celebrated Karl Friedrich Gauss who also introduced the differential geometry of curved surfaces. There is little doubt that Gauss, faced with modern geodetic problems, would have antedated Ricci and others by extending his differential geometry to three or more dimensions. The first geodetic application of these extended methods was made in 1949, far too many years after Gauss, by Marussi of the University of Trieste. (See, Marussi (1949), "Fondements de Géométrie Différentielle Absolue du Champ Potentiel Terrestre," *Bulletin Géodésique*, new series, no. 14, pp. 411–439.)

Cartesian coordinates in three dimensional space are not suitable for all geodetic processes. We are led inevitably to consider more general curvilinear systems, and to publish a book requiring the differential geometry of such systems without using the tensor calculus (including vector calculus in index notation) would indeed be an archaism. Unfortunately, very few geodesists have yet studied this important branch of mathematics, and the older generation is now unlikely ever to do so.

Geodesists are by no means alone in their conservatism. Most new and advanced texts on mathematical physics are still being published in the old dot-and-cross boldface-type vector notation, which is peculiarly suitable for only a very few applications; this notation is much more restricted than the use of index notation even for vectors considered as first-order tensors. Index notation is a practical necessity for tensors of higher order than the second; for the derivation of results, particularly those involving differentiation, which are true in any coordinate system; for generalized curvilinear coordinate systems and other applications requiring a mixture of both vectors and higher order tensors; and for the notion of curved space required not only in relativity but also in such applications as generalized conformal transformations. Nevertheless, physicists have still to acquire the no less difficult dot-and-cross boldface-type vector and dyadic notation for use in the more elementary applications. For more advanced work, they also need index notation which would serve all purposes. The waste of effort involved in using one notation for first-order tensors and an altogether different notation when tensors of higher order are required should be avoided in geodesy, which already requires the use of higher order tensors in quite elementary applications.

It is still possible to obtain a master's degree *in mathematics* at most universities without any knowledge of the tensor calculus, but we may expect less conservatism in the future now that the subject is being taught to undergraduates in some universities and is being included in a growing number of special courses in applied mathematics. Moreover, many simplified texts have been made available since Eddington in 1923 sought a wide English-speaking audience with his *Mathematical Theory of Relativity*.

Part I of this book attempts to introduce tensor calculus to geodesists and to cover the ground required for present and foreseeable future geodetic applications. It has been written only after searching the readily available literature in the hope of recommending instead a single text containing all the required material and written by someone with teaching experience. It is not surprising that none suitable for the purpose could be found among the many excellent books which are now available. Many of these books are naturally written to cover in outline a wide range of applications, and those that specialize are usually relativity-oriented. Moreover, most books on the subject have been written by mathematicians who are compelled to treat the subject rigorously; whereas the geodesist, who has to keep up to date in many other areas, is prepared to take much on trust, and is able to do so because he deals only with such well-behaved functions as Newtonian potentials in free space or with very regular functions suitable as coordinates. Even so, the treatment in Part I, necessarily compressed in a book which is required to cover even in outline the entire ground of theoretical geodesy, may prove too difficult for the beginner. It is recommended that he read a more elementary account of the broad basis of the subject first; for example, the first 83 pages of Spain's (1953) *Tensor Calculus* or Chapters 2 and 5 of Lawden's (1968, 2d ed.) *An Introduction to Tensor Calculus and Relativity*. It is always better to read two books on a subject, one more general than the other, instead of one specialized book twice. Much, but by no means all, of the subject matter of Part I is covered by McConnell's (1931) *Applications of the Absolute Differential Calculus* (also published in a 1957 Dover edition as *Applications of Tensor Analysis*). The reader who requires a more elegant and rigorous treatment—and some geodesists demand rigor—might read Guggenheimer's (1963) *Differential Geometry*.

Part I was first drafted as a collection of formulas to save the reader from the annoyance of continual reference to several other books and also to include some formulas which are not to be found readily, if at all, in books or papers. By the time the formulas and the notation had been explained, the manuscript had reached perhaps half of its present size; it was then decided to derive, or at least indicate how to derive, the results and to expand the explanation of some points likely to prove difficult. In the writer's experience, for example, most geodesists shy at the notion of covariance and contravariance, which seems to be the counterpart of the Euclidian *pons asinorum*, perhaps because geodesists usually acquire some knowledge of statistics in which covariance means something quite different. In these days of aids to rapid reading, the expert need lose no time over such elementary exposition, but he is, nevertheless, advised to skim through Part I, if his knowledge is rusty, to get the feel of the notation and the conventions.

The temptation to include indefinite metrics, requiring little more explanation and leading straight into relativity, has been resisted. Apart from measurements based on the position of stars, geodetic measurements have not yet been made beyond the Moon and relativistic corrections for high velocities in the solar system can be, if necessary, applied quite simply without much knowledge of relativity theory. (See, for example, Walker, in a letter to *Nature*, v. 168, December 1, 1951, pp. 961–962.) The methods used in relativity, like the tensor calculus itself, may, nevertheless, become important to the research geodesist who, if he knows or acquires Part I will have no difficulty in extracting keen enjoyment from Synge and Schild's (1949) *Tensor Calculus*, to prepare himself for Synge's two master-pieces on relativity.

Some consideration has also been given to including in Part I a short account of more general deformations of space than the conformal transformations of Chapter 10. This will come, together perhaps with some geodetic excursions into non-Riemannian geometry, but the geodetic application of this subject is still young and publication in book form would probably be premature. Meanwhile, some account has been given in §30–19 of a method of systematically deforming one member of a general family of surfaces into another member of the family for a particular application.

Part II deals with coordinate systems of special interest in geodesy. In Chapter 12, the properties of a general class of three-dimensional systems are developed from a single-valued, continuous and differentiable scalar N which serves as one coordinate, while the other two coordinates are defined by the direction of the gradient of N. In Chapters 15 through 18, the scalar N is restricted to provide simpler systems, whose properties can then be derived at once from the general results of Chapter 12. Transformations between members of the general class for different values of N are treated in Chapter 19. Another advantage of treating the subject in this way is that the scalar N can also be given a physical meaning (for example, the gravitational potential in Chapter 20) so that Chapter 12 also provides the geometry of the gravitational field.

In case it should be required to transfer the values of point functions from a point in space to a particular N-surface, which is the rigorous counterpart of several operations of classical geodesy, methods of transfer along the isozenithals (the N-coordinate lines) and along the normals to the N-surfaces are worked out for each coordinate system in Part II, following a general discussion in Chapters 13 and 14. The process is connected intimately with Gaussian spherical representation, which is developed in this context, following a more general discussion in Chapter 11, and is extended to nonspherical representation in Chapter 13. Such methods of projection are seldom any simpler than three-dimensional methods, although they are put to occasional special use in Part III, but it is as well that the process should be more fully understood in the future.

Part III deals with the main geodetic applications of the mathematics in Parts I and II. Geometry, which used to mean literally the science of Earth measurements, is no longer confined to geodesy, but there is, nevertheless, still a considerable overlap, more so perhaps than the overlap with physics, and we cannot expect a rigid division between the two subjects. For example, the differential geometry of Chapter 12 contains all the metrical properties of the gravitational field used in geodesy if we restrict one coordinate in accordance with a physical law. As another example, the transformation between two members of a class of coordinate systems in Chapter 19 includes the process of switching between geodetic and astronomical systems. Part III simply attempts to show how these mathematical concepts can be used today in attacking the main problems in geodesy. The treatment is not complete; for example, nothing is included on the formation and solution of normal equations in least-square adjustments, which are adequately treated in existing literature. Nor does the treatment cover all possible applications; few geodesists have so far worked on these lines, and future developments may be considerable. For example, the reader cannot expect to learn all about so-called physical geodesy (which in fact is again mostly geometry) from Chapters 29 and 30, although it is hoped that he will acquire a clear idea of the basic theory which will enable him to follow the considerable literature of the subject more easily and critically. The same applies to satellite geodesy in earlier chapters.

Manipulative skill in any branch of mathematics cannot be obtained by reading alone. In most cases, the work has been shortened by omitting several steps leading to a result, but full references are given to enable the reader to fill in the missing steps, if he so desires. It is hoped that this procedure will serve the purpose of the examples and problems in textbooks which would be quite out of place here. The experts, no doubt, will omit the whole procedure and will take the results on trust.

References to other publications are given only as required by the text. They do not provide anything like a complete bibliography or any indication of priority or relative importance. For example, Marussi's classical paper noted earlier in this preface is referenced only once in the text, although it can be considered the foundation stone of modern theoretical geodesy. However, the reader who looks at the references, particularly those to books, will soon find that he has access through them to a considerable bibliography.

The question of credits and priorities is particularly difficult in this subject. Classical results are given a nametag to help identify them in the literature, but the name is that normally associated with the result in English, without attempting to assess priority between, for example, Gauss, Green, and Ostrogradskii. Some of the named results seem almost trivial when derived by modern methods, but it is hoped this will not dim the luster of great men who unearthed them with less serviceable tools. Credit is also given, when known, for particular recent results, but such credits are few because not many geodesists as yet have worked in this area. To offset what must seem like cavalier treatment, no priority is claimed for any results, although it is believed that some are new, either in content or in presentation.

The title of the book requires some explanation. An attempt has been made to cover only the basic mathematical discipline of geodesy, excluding such specialized matters as routine computer programs and including only such references to instrumentation and field (or laboratory) procedures as may be necessary to a full appreciation of the underlying theory. The book accordingly bears much the same relation to the whole of geodesy as numerous books entitled "Mathematical Physics" do to the whole of physics. Various alternatives have been considered and rejected; for example, the title would be some variant of "Higher Geodesy" if published on the European continent, but the content of the book is quite different from any other book bearing that title.

The terminology and symbolism used in the book cannot be expected to command universal acceptance. For example, there is a growing tendency in geodesy to call an ellipsoid of revolution simply an ellipsoid and to reserve the term spheroid for an equipotential surface of the standard gravitational field. This convention can cause confusion whenever reference is made to mathematical literature in English where a spheroid is defined geometrically as an ellipsoid of revolution and an ellipsoid in general means a quartic with three unequal axes; for example, the treatment of spheroidal and ellipsoidal harmonics in Hobson's standard work on the subject is based on this definition, which is clearly stated in the Van Nostrand (1968, 3d ed.) publication, *Mathematics Dictionary*, edited by James and James. In a mainly mathematical book, it has accordingly been decided to retain the mathematical convention, which incidentally is also used by most English-speaking geodesists. In much the same way, the physical sign convention has been used for a Newtonian potential, although the fact that the potential is invariably negative in terrestrial applications has led most geodesists to change the sign. No good can come through willfully discarding scientific conventions universally accepted in a parent subject which has every right to prescribe the convention. Adoption of the physical convention for potential not only facilitates reference to the literature of physics, but also accords better with the geometrical basis of this book.

Most geodesists use the symbol λ for longitude. However, in a book using vectors, there is an overriding need for an orthogonal triad λ_r, μ_r, ν_r frequently used in mathematical literature. In the geodetic applications, λ_r is associated with longitude, but it is not the gradient of the longitude as the use of λ for the scalar longitude would imply. The symbol ω, usually associated with a rotation, is accordingly used for longitude. Whenever possible, however, the symbolism most generally adopted by the best literature in a particular branch of the subject has been used to facilitate wider reading although this often results in using the same symbol for different purposes in different chapters. The Index of Symbols at the end of the book indicates the *general* use of a symbol, any departure from which is invariably noted in the text. For example, α and β are generally used for azimuth and zenith distance, which differ in different coordinate systems, but the context will show which coordinate system is being used. The same applies to latitude and longitude, and this arrangement enables us to dispense with special symbolism for particular coordinate systems, such as spherical (geocentric) and spheroidal (geodetic) systems. Following standard mathematical conventions in English, right-handed systems are used throughout the book, and sign conventions are adopted to conform. In general, some warning or comment is given in the text whenever there is a departure from standard mathematical or physical conventions in the geodetic literature; for example, the use of left-handed systems imported from photogrammetry into satellite triangulation.

To facilitate reference, summaries of main formulas are collected as a Summary of Formulas at the end of the book. In some cases, a particular chapter suggests a particular arrangement; for example, some formulas in the summary for Chapter 17 are obtained by specializing the results of earlier chapters at sight and are not given in the text of Chapter 17, although they do apply to the subject matter of Chapter 17. The best way of using the Summary of Formulas is to look first at the chapter headings or subheadings for the required subject matter. Each equation in the index carries a reference to the text which gives the derivation and symbolism. Back references in the text are always to the text, but a reference to the Summary of Formulas may be sufficient and quicker; however, if the back reference is not given in the index, it will be necessary to refer to the text.

It is difficult to make adequate acknowledgment covering a lifetime of study, discussion, and collaboration. The author's main source of inspiration in the subject of this book has been Professor Antonio Marussi of the University of Trieste, not only for the range and originality of his ideas but also for continual advice and encouragement. The book and its writer owe much to the two official reviewers, Mr. Bernard H. Chovitz of the Earth Sciences Laboratories of ESSA and Professor Ivan I. Mueller of the Ohio State University, for careful reading and checking and for many improvements. In addition, specialist reviews and information have been freely provided by Professor Arne Bjerhammar and his associates of the Royal Institute of Technology, Stockholm; Mr. Robert H. Hanson of the Earth Sciences Laboratories of ESSA; Dr. Karl-Rudolf Koch of the Ohio State University; Professor Helmut Moritz of the Technical University of Berlin; Mr. F. Foster Morrison of the Earth Sciences Laboratories of ESSA; Mr. Allen J. Pope of the Coast and Geodetic Survey of ESSA; Professor Erik Tengström of the University of Uppsala; Dr. Moody C. Thompson of the Institute for Telecommunication Sciences of ESSA; and Mr. John Wright of the Directorate of Overseas Surveys of Great Britain. None of these distinquished men, especially neither of the official reviewers, is responsible for any remaining errors and omissions.

The difficult and unrewarding task of editing such a specialized book has been successfully undertaken throughout by Mr. John R. Bernick. The index has been compiled by Jean S. Campbell. The production coordination of the publication has been accomplished by Mr. Edward W. Koehler and the manuscript has been marked for printing by Miss Lila Paavola and Mrs. Helen Hoener.

Last, but far from least, the manuscript has been typed and retyped most expeditiously and efficiently by Mrs. Nancy Durazzo and Mrs. Judy Shore.

August 1968   MARTIN HOTINE

Contents

PART III

CONTENTS

Part I

1

Vectors

CARTESIAN VECTORS

1. Geometrically, a length in a certain direction defines a vector $\overrightarrow{OP}$. In ordinary three-dimensional space, we can, for instance, take O as the origin of a rectangular Cartesian coordinate system and specify the vector completely by the three coordinates of P. Or, if we wish to define a number of vectors at different points in the space, we can take a fixed origin and define the vector by the differences in rectangular coordinates over the length OP, that is, by the orthogonal projection of OP on the coordinate axes. These three quantities, known as the rectangular Cartesian *components* of the vector, will depend on the choice of coordinate system; but the sum of their squares will be the square of the length OP, which does not depend on the coordinate system. If the vector is of unit length, or if we divide the components by the length, the components become the direction cosines of the direction OP, and the vector is known as a unit vector.

2. The matter becomes more complicated when we consider inclined coordinate axes. For the present, we shall continue to consider a Cartesian system; that is, a system in which the coordinates are actual lengths along straight coordinate axes. For ease of illustration, we shall consider a vector $\overrightarrow{OP}$ in relation to coordinate axes OX, OY (fig. 1) in two dimensions, but similar conclusions will apply in three or more dimensions. We can still specify the vector by its orthogonal projections OQ, OR on the coordinate axes, in which case the components of a unit vector in the direction OP will still be the direction cosines of OP. We call these *covariant* components and write

$$l_1 = OQ = OP \cos \theta_1$$

1.01 $$l_2 = OR = OP \cos \theta_2,$$

making use of *index notation* l_1, l_2 for the components.

3. Alternatively, we could specify the vector completely by taking the differences in coordinates OS, OT as components, which we shall call the *contravariant* components. We distinguish them from the covariant components by using superscript indices and write

$$l^1 = OS = OP \sin \theta_2 / \sin (\theta_1 + \theta_2)$$

1.02 $$l^2 = OT = OP \sin \theta_1 / \sin (\theta_1 + \theta_2).$$

We can no longer square and add either set of components as a means of obtaining the length or *magnitude* of the vector, but the above formulas

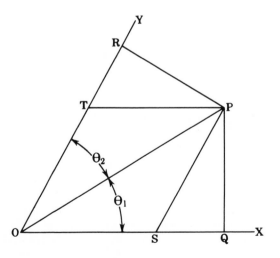

Figure 1.

lead at once to the result

$$l^1l_1 + l^2l_2 = OP^2.$$

As a form of shorthand whose value will become more apparent later, we can write this as

1.03 $l^\alpha l_\alpha = OP^2$

in which we use the *summation convention*. Whenever a superscript and a subscript index are the same, we assume that this index takes all possible values (in this case $\alpha = 1, 2$), and the results are then summed.

4. Next, suppose we have two vectors $\overrightarrow{OL}$, $\overrightarrow{OM}$ (fig. 2), and that the angles giving the direction of

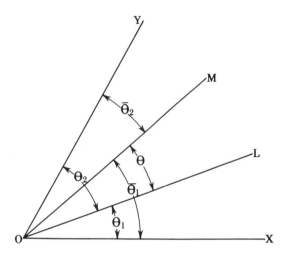

Figure 2.

$\overrightarrow{OM}$ are distinguished by overbars. We have

$$l^1m_1 + l^2m_2 = l^\alpha m_\alpha$$

$$= \frac{OL \cdot OM \,(\sin \theta_2 \cos \bar\theta_1 + \sin \theta_1 \cos \bar\theta_2)}{\sin (\theta_1 + \theta_2)}$$

$$= OL \cdot OM \cos \theta,$$

and we can obtain the same result from $l_\alpha m^\alpha$. We call this the *scalar product* of the two vectors and write

1.04 $l^\alpha m_\alpha = l_\alpha m^\alpha = OL \cdot OM \cos \theta.$

Or, to phrase this in words, the scalar product is the product of the two magnitudes and of the cosine of the angle between the two vectors. The scalar product of two perpendicular vectors is clearly zero. Also, Equation 1.03 is a special case of Equation 1.04 in which the two vectors coincide.

5. The reader with an inclination for spherical trigonometry can verify that Equation 1.04 holds

equally well in three dimensions. A simpler method is to assume that

$$l^r m_r \qquad (r = 1, 2, 3)$$

has the same value in all coordinate systems—or, in other words, is *invariant* under coordinate transformations—as we found $l^\alpha m_\alpha$ to be in two dimensions, and to evaluate the expression in a special coordinate system. We choose OX to coincide with OL and leave OY, OZ arbitrary. In that case, $l^1 = OL$ and l^2, l^3 are both zero because the y- and z-coordinates do not change in the direction OL. Consequently, we have

$$l^r m_r = OL \cdot m_1 = OL \cdot OM \cos \theta.$$

By choosing a coordinate axis along OM, we find that $l_r m^r$ is the same so that we have

1.05 $l^r m_r = l_r m^r = OL \cdot OM \cos \theta.$

6. Throughout this book, we shall adopt Greek indices for the two-dimensional components of vectors and Roman indices for three dimensions. The index notation for a vector l^r need not be confused with the rth-power of a quantity l. The context will usually distinguish between the two without explanation, but in cases where confusion could arise, we shall use and shall describe special notation for a power index. In the same way, numerical subscripts will often be used to distinguish certain quantities. Covariant vectors will usually have a literal subscript; but if a numerical subscript has to be used for a particular component, attention will, if necessary, be called to the fact.

7. It will be clear from the definitions of the covariant and contravariant components of a vector that the two sets of components are equal in rectangular Cartesian coordinates, but are not equal in inclined Cartesian coordinates. By introducing the two sets of components, however, we have been able to ensure that such results as Equation 1.05 apply in both rectangular and inclined Cartesian coordinates.

VECTORS IN CURVILINEAR COORDINATES

8. We have now to generalize the matter still further by considering curvilinear coordinate systems. Through each point in some region of three-dimensional space, there will still be three unique coordinate lines along each of which only one coordinate varies, the other two being constant; but the coordinate lines may be curved as well as

inclined, and will not, as a rule, be parallel to the directions of the corresponding coordinate lines at other points. The space itself may be curved, like the surface of a sphere in two dimensions, and in that case, the space can only be described in curvilinear coordinates; we should be unable to find a Cartesian system which would give the positions of points in an extended region of the space. Finally, a curvilinear coordinate will no longer necessarily be an actual length measured along a coordinate line, as in the case of Cartesian coordinates, although lengths and coordinates must obviously be related in some way because a displacement over a given length in a certain direction must involve a unique change in coordinates.

9. This relation, which may vary from point to point, is expressed by the *metric* or *line element* of the space; the square of an element of length ds in a small neighborhood of a point can be expressed in terms of the changes in coordinates dx^r over the element of length by a relation of the form

1.06
$$ds^2 = g_{rs}\, dx^r dx^s \qquad (r, s = 1, 2, 3).$$

We assume that the summation convention is used in this formula, which accordingly may contain nine coefficients g_{rs} in three dimensions to go with all possible combinations of the coordinates. We do not need, however, more than six and can take g_{rs} as symmetrical so that we have $g_{12} = g_{21}$, for example. We can then expand Equation 1.06 as

$$ds^2 = g_{11}(dx^1)^2 + g_{22}(dx^2)^2 + g_{33}(dx^3)^2$$
$$+ 2g_{12}dx^1 dx^2 + 2g_{13}dx^1 dx^3 + 2g_{23}dx^2 dx^3.$$

Throughout this book, we shall use only what are known as *positive-definite* metrics; that is, for any real and nonzero displacement dx^r, the value of the quadratic form in Equation 1.06 is positive and not zero. Only in this way can the form represent the square of a real element of length. Relativity metrics in four dimensions, on the other hand, are usually *indefinite*, in the sense that ds^2 may be zero without all the dx^r being zero.

10. The numbers g_{rs} (totaling nine, of which six may have different values) will vary continuously from point to point, but will be defined uniquely at each point for a particular coordinate system; in other words, they will be functions of the coordinates x^r, or *functions of position*. This array of numbers is known as the *metric tensor*, for reasons which will appear later. In rectangular Cartesian coordinates, the metric must reduce to the Pythagorean form

$$ds^2 = (dx)^2 + (dy)^2 + (dz)^2$$
1.07
$$= (dx^1)^2 + (dx^2)^2 + (dx^3)^2$$

in which case we have

$$g_{rs} = 1 \quad (r=s); \qquad g_{rs} = 0 \quad (r \neq s).$$

In inclined Cartesian coordinates, the g_{rs} $(r \neq s)$ are functions of the angles enclosed by the coordinate axes and are therefore the same at all points, but are not zero.

11. As a simple example of curvilinear coordinates, we take spherical polar coordinates (ω, ϕ, r), defined by

$$x = r \cos \phi \cos \omega$$
$$y = r \cos \phi \sin \omega$$
$$z = r \sin \phi.$$

By straight differentiation and substitution in Equation 1.07, we have the metric

$$ds^2 = (r^2 \cos^2 \phi)d\omega^2 + r^2 d\phi^2 + dr^2,$$

and the components of the metric tensor are

$$g_{11} = r^2 \cos^2 \phi ; \qquad g_{22} = r^2 ; \qquad g_{33} = 1$$
$$g_{rs} = 0 \quad (r \neq s).$$

The ω-coordinate lines, along which ϕ and r are constant, are circles parallel to the xy-plane and centered on the z-axis; the ϕ-coordinate lines are circles centered on the Cartesian origin whose planes contain the z-axis; and the r-coordinate lines are radial lines from the Cartesian origin. Alternatively, we can say that the ω-coordinate *surfaces* (over any one of which ω is a constant) are planes containing the z-axis, the ϕ-coordinate surfaces are cones whose common axis is the z-axis, and the r-coordinate surfaces are spheres centering on the Cartesian origin. In a Cartesian system, all the coordinate lines would be straight and all the coordinate surfaces would be planes.

12. Over short distances, we can, nevertheless, consider that the coordinate lines are straight in a curvilinear system. By analogy with the Cartesian definition, we still can say that a small change in coordinates

$$dx^r \qquad (r = 1, 2, 3)$$

represents the three contravariant components of a small vector of length ds, and that in the limit, the ratios

1.08
$$\frac{dx^r}{ds} = l^r \qquad (r = 1, 2, 3)$$

are the contravariant components of a unit vector

l^r. Although we are no longer dealing with finite lengths, it is easy to see that this definition of a contravariant unit vector agrees with the Cartesian definition. We can also define a nonunit vector of magnitude λ, in the same direction as the unit vector l^r, as

1.09 $$L^r = \lambda l^r,$$

without contradicting the Cartesian conception, although we may no longer be able to interpret λ as a finite length.

13. The covariant components, however, need further consideration because they were defined in Cartesian coordinates as lengths along the axes. By dividing Equation 1.06 by ds^2 and substituting Equation 1.08, we have

1.10 $$g_{rs} l^r l^s = 1.$$

To preserve the Cartesian conception of a covariant vector as far as possible, we may use Equation 1.05 and write for a unit vector

1.11 $$l_s l^s = 1.$$

However, if both Equations 1.10 and 1.11 are to hold for all directions at a point, that is, for arbitrary values of the contravariant components l^s, we must have

1.12 $$l_s = g_{rs} l^r$$

as the definition of the covariant components of a unit vector. From Equation 1.09, we have also

$$g_{rs} L^r L^s = \lambda^2 g_{rs} l^r l^s = \lambda^2.$$

However, to preserve the Cartesian conception corresponding to Equation 1.05, this must equal $L_r L^r$ so that a general covariant vector can be written as

1.13 $$L_r = g_{rs} L^s = \lambda l_r.$$

Comparing this with Equation 1.09, we see that multiplication by g_{rs} and use of the summation convention have *lowered the indices* of the vector Equation 1.09. It is easy to see that the same operation would lower the free (not summed) index in any vector equation.

14. We now consider whether the above definition of a generalized covariant vector agrees completely with the Cartesian conception, in the sense that a Cartesian system provides a special case. For ease of illustration, we shall again consider the case of two dimensions. In figure 3, we take a small displacement of length ds, made up of displacements

of length $\sqrt{a_{11}} dx^1$ and $\sqrt{a_{22}} dx^2$ along the coordinate axes, obtained, respectively, by making $dx^2 = 0$ and $dx^1 = 0$ in the metric

$$ds^2 = a_{11}(dx^1)^2 + 2a_{12} dx^1 dx^2 + a_{22}(dx^2)^2.$$

From the figure, we have at once

$$ds^2 = a_{11}(dx^1)^2 + a_{22}(dx^2)^2 \\ + 2\sqrt{a_{11}}\sqrt{a_{22}} dx^1 dx^2 \cos(\theta_1 + \theta_2).$$

By comparing these two forms of the metric, we have

1.14 $$\cos(\theta_1 + \theta_2) = a_{12}/\sqrt{a_{11}a_{22}}.$$

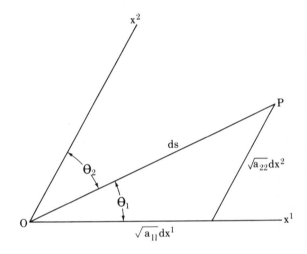

Figure 3.

Using the generalized definition of the covariant components l_α of $\overrightarrow{OP}$ and evaluating dx^1/ds, etc., from triangles in figure 3, we have

$$l_1 = a_{1\beta} l^\beta = a_{11}(dx^1/ds) + a_{12}(dx^2/ds)$$
$$= \frac{\sqrt{a_{11}}\sin\theta_2}{\sin(\theta_1 + \theta_2)} + \frac{a_{12}}{\sqrt{a_{22}}}\frac{\sin\theta_1}{\sin(\theta_1 + \theta_2)}$$

1.15 $$= \sqrt{a_{11}}\cos\theta_1,$$

on substitution of a_{12} from Equation 1.14 and expansion. In the same way, we have

1.16 $$l_2 = \sqrt{a_{22}}\cos\theta_2.$$

If the coordinate system were Cartesian ($a_{11} = a_{22} = 1$), this would agree exactly with Equations 1.01 for a unit vector. We can obtain the same result in three dimensions. We can accordingly claim to have generalized the conception of contravariant and covariant vectors for a general curvilinear coordinate system and to have shown that previous results in Cartesian coordinates are merely special cases.

15. It will be noted that we use the symbol

$$a_{\alpha\beta} \qquad (\alpha, \beta = 1, 2)$$

for the metric tensor in a two-dimensional space instead of the three-dimensional g_{rs}. We shall adopt this convention as standard.

16. We are now able to conclude in much the same way that Equation 1.05 holds equally well in curvilinear coordinates. If L^r, M^r are two vectors in the directions of unit vectors l^r, m^r and of magnitudes λ, μ, we can write

$$L_r M^r = g_{rs} L^r M^s = \lambda\mu g_{rs} l^r m^s$$
$$= \lambda\mu l^r m_r$$

1.17 $$= \lambda\mu \cos\theta$$

where θ is the angle between the two vectors. This generalizes the scalar product of two vectors, which again is zero for two perpendicular vectors.

TRANSFORMATION OF VECTORS

17. We now consider the effect on the components of a vector when the coordinate system is changed. We shall denote the new coordinates $\bar{x}^r$ and the new components by overbars. For a contravariant unit vector, we have at once

1.18 $$\bar{l}^r = \frac{\partial \bar{x}^r}{\partial s} = \frac{\partial \bar{x}^r}{\partial x^s}\frac{\partial x^s}{\partial s} = \frac{\partial \bar{x}^r}{\partial x^s} l^s$$

in which, of course, the summation convention is applied to the index s, and we have used the chain rule of elementary calculus. The same formula clearly will apply to nonunit vectors $\bar{L}^r$, L^s.

18. In the case of a covariant vector, we form the scalar product with an arbitrary vector $\bar{A}^r$. The result is an invariant, which has the same value in either coordinate system, because it depends only on the magnitudes of the two vectors and the angle between them so that we may write

$$\bar{l}_r \bar{A}^r = l_s A^s = l_s (\partial x^s / \partial \bar{x}^r) \bar{A}^r,$$

using Equation 1.18 for the vector A^r. Since this relation holds for any arbitrary vector $\bar{A}^r$, we must have

1.19 $$\bar{l}_r = \frac{\partial x^s}{\partial \bar{x}^r} l_s,$$

which is the required transformation. The same formula will apply to nonunit vectors $\bar{L}_r$, L_s.

19. We could define a vector as a set of three quantities (in three dimensions) which transform in this way. To illustrate the point, we take a continuous differentiable *scalar* N; that is, a real number which has a unique value at all points of a region of space and can therefore be considered a function of the coordinates. The scalar N is also an *invariant* whose value at a particular point is the same whatever the coordinate system. Most physical quantities, such as potential or gravity, are scalar invariants. We differentiate N with respect to each coordinate x^r and write

$$N_r = \partial N / \partial x^r.$$

But because N is an invariant ($\bar{N} = N$), we can write

1.20 $$\bar{N}_r = \frac{\partial \bar{N}}{\partial \bar{x}^r} = \frac{\partial N}{\partial \bar{x}^r} = \frac{\partial N}{\partial x^s}\frac{\partial x^s}{\partial \bar{x}^r} = \frac{\partial x^s}{\partial \bar{x}^r} N_s$$

so that N_r transforms like a covariant vector and can be taken as a covariant vector. It is called the *gradient* of N. Because N is differentiable, there will be some directions l^r in which N is constant so that we have

$$N_r l^r = \partial N / \partial s = 0.$$

The gradient of N is accordingly perpendicular to all such directions. If N is constant over a surface, its gradient is perpendicular to all surface directions at a point and is therefore in the direction of the unit *normal* ν_r to the surface. We can then write

1.21 $$N_r = n\nu_r$$

where n is the magnitude of the gradient vector. In this discussion, we have, of course, assumed that at least some of the derivatives of N exist, even though N itself may be zero; otherwise, the gradient of N and therefore ν_r would be undefined. The assumption is justified in the case of surfaces dealt with in this book.

20. If, in three dimensions, we know the components in both coordinate systems of three mutually perpendicular unit vectors λ_r, μ_r, ν_r, we can derive the set of transformation factors from the formulas

$$\partial \bar{x}^r / \partial x^s = \bar{\lambda}^r \lambda_s + \bar{\mu}^r \mu_s + \bar{\nu}^r \nu_s$$

1.22 $$\partial x^r / \partial \bar{x}^s = \lambda^r \bar{\lambda}_s + \mu^r \bar{\mu}_s + \nu^r \bar{\nu}_s.$$

To verify these formulas, we multiply the first equation by λ^s, for example, use Equation 1.11 and the fact that the scalar product of two perpendicular vectors is zero, and so recover Equation 1.18.

21. We can also show that the scalar product of any two vectors is an invariant,

1.23 $\bar{A}_r\bar{B}^r = \dfrac{\partial x^s}{\partial \bar{x}^r} A_s \dfrac{\partial \bar{x}^r}{\partial x^t} B^t = \delta_t^s A_s B^t = A_t B^t = A_r B^r.$

Here we have used the *Kronecker delta*

$$\delta_t^s = 1 \quad (s = t)$$

1.24 $\qquad\qquad \delta_t^s = 0 \quad (s \neq t)$

so that the only value of s which contributes to the summation is t, and we accordingly may write t for s in Equation 1.23. We have also used the chain rule in partial differentiation, that is,

$$\frac{\partial x^s}{\partial \bar{x}^r} \frac{\partial \bar{x}^r}{\partial x^t} = \frac{\partial x^s}{\partial x^t} = \delta_t^s.$$

22. We shall often want to set up a *right-handed* set of three vectors λ_r, μ_r, ν_r in three dimensions. If the three vectors are mutually orthogonal, we say that the set is right handed in the order given if their directions are the same as the usual right-handed conventions for the (x, y, z) coordinate axes of a rectangular Cartesian coordinate system. If, for example, the direction of ν_r is toward the reader, the set in figure 4 is right handed in the order λ_r, μ_r, ν_r.

Figure 4.

However, it is not necessary for the vectors to be orthogonal, so long as the rotation from one vector to another is in the same general sense. Looking along λ_r, for instance, ν_r must be to the right of μ_r. We shall arrange for the coordinate axes, even curvilinear, to be a right-handed system in the order (x^1, x^2, x^3) or $(1, 2, 3)$.

CHAPTER 2

Tensors

GENERAL RULES

1. A matrix or set of quantities, defined in a particular coordinate system in 3-dimensional space, such as

$$A_{rs} \qquad (r, s = 1, 2, 3),$$

is considered as a tensor if it transforms like a vector for each index so that we have

2.01 $$\bar{A}_{rs} = \frac{\partial x^p}{\partial \bar{x}^r} \frac{\partial x^q}{\partial \bar{x}^s} A_{pq}$$

in which the summation convention applies to the indices p, q. We may have covariant tensors like the above, or contravariant tensors like

2.02 $$\bar{A}^{rs} = \frac{\partial \bar{x}^r}{\partial x^p} \frac{\partial \bar{x}^s}{\partial x^q} A^{pq},$$

or mixed tensors like

2.03 $$\bar{A}^r_s = \frac{\partial \bar{x}^r}{\partial x^p} \frac{\partial x^q}{\partial \bar{x}^s} A^p_q,$$

and we may have any number of indices. The order of the tensor is the number of free (not summed) indices; all the above examples being of the second order. A vector is accordingly a first-order tensor, and an invariant is a tensor of zero order.

2. It is evident from the transformation formulas that, if all the components of a tensor at a point are zero in one coordinate system, they are all zero in any other coordinate system. This implies, for instance, that the tensor equation

$$A_{rs} = 0$$

is true in any coordinate system, if it is true in one.

We shall see later that all tensor equations have this property.

3. It will also be apparent from the formulas that a tensor transformation is *transitive*. If we transform from a coordinate system (a) to another (b), and then to a third (c), the result will be the same as a transformation direct from (a) to (c).

4. We can add tensors of the same order and type. For example, the sum of two mixed third-order tensors

$$A^r_{st} + B^r_{st}$$

is obtained by adding corresponding *components*, such as

$$A^1_{23} + B^1_{23},$$

to provide the corresponding component of the sum

$$C^1_{23}$$

so that we can write

2.04 $$C^r_{st} = A^r_{st} + B^r_{st} \qquad (r, s, t = 1, 2, 3).$$

If we multiply this equation across by the appropriate transformation factors, we have

$$\frac{\partial \bar{x}^k}{\partial x^r} \frac{\partial x^s}{\partial \bar{x}^l} \frac{\partial x^t}{\partial \bar{x}^m} C^r_{st} = \bar{A}^k_{lm} + \bar{B}^k_{lm} = \bar{C}^k_{lm}$$

in which the components of the transformed sum

$$\bar{C}^k_{lm}$$

are obtained in the same way by adding corresponding components of the transformed tensors. The sum accordingly obeys the transformation law for tensors and is therefore a tensor.

5. We can similarly multiply two tensors, not

9

necessarily of the same order and type, and can show that the result is a tensor of higher order. We can write the product, for example, as

2.05 $$C^r_{st} = A_{st}B^r$$

in which all the indices are free, and can obtain each component, for instance,

$$C^1_{23},$$

of the product by multiplying the components

$$A_{23}, B^1.$$

6. If an upper and lower index of a product are the same, then we must apply the summation convention, and the result will be a *contracted* tensor of lower order containing only the remaining free indices. For instance, we have

2.06 $$C_s = A_{st}B^t$$

in which each component of the contracted product is now obtained as, for example (in three dimensions),

$$C_1 = A_{11}B^1 + A_{12}B^2 + A_{13}B^3.$$

We can prove the tensor character of the contracted product Equation 2.06 as follows,

$$\bar{A}_{st}\bar{B}^t = A_{jk}B^l \frac{\partial x^j}{\partial \bar{x}^s}\frac{\partial x^k}{\partial \bar{x}^t}\frac{\partial \bar{x}^t}{\partial x^l}.$$

$$= A_{jk}B^l \frac{\partial x^j}{\partial \bar{x}^s}\, \delta^k_l$$

$$= A_{jk}B^k \frac{\partial x^j}{\partial \bar{x}^s}$$

$$= C_j \frac{\partial x^j}{\partial \bar{x}^s}$$

$$= \bar{C}_s.$$

7. Any letter can be chosen for a summation or *dummy* index, so long as it is not one of the free indices, because it will, in any case, assume all values during the summation. We can accordingly alter or can exchange dummy indices as, for example,

$$A^r_{st}B^sC^t = A^r_{ts}B^tC^s = A^r_{pq}B^pC^q,$$

so long as we do not confuse them with the free indices (*r* in this example).

8. It is evident that any scalar formed by tensor contraction will be an *invariant*, whose value will be the same in any coordinate system.

9. A tensor is said to be *symmetric* in two indices, both upper or both lower, if it remains the same on interchanging those two indices. For example, if

$$A^r_{stu} = A^r_{sut},$$

then the tensor is symmetric in the second- and third-covariant indices. If its value remains the same but the sign changes, for example,

$$B^r_{stu} = -B^r_{sut},$$

then it is said to be *skew-symmetric* or *antisymmetric* in the two indices. These properties are retained on change of coordinates because, for example, all components of the tensors

$$(A^r_{stu} - A^r_{sut}) \quad \text{or} \quad (B^r_{stu} + B^r_{sut})$$

are zero in one coordinate system and must therefore be zero in any other.

10. Any second-order tensor can be expressed as a sum of a symmetric and a skew-symmetric tensor, as is evident from the identity

$$A_{rs} = \tfrac{1}{2}(A_{rs} + A_{sr}) + \tfrac{1}{2}(A_{rs} - A_{sr}),$$

the first tensor within parentheses being symmetric and the second being skew-symmetric.

11. If we contract the product of a symmetric tensor A_{rs} and a skew-symmetric tensor B^{jrs} on the symmetric and skew-symmetric indices, the result will be zero because

$$B^{jrs}A_{rs} = -B^{jsr}A_{sr} = -B^{jrs}A_{rs}$$

on interchanging the dummy indices so that we have

$$B^{jrs}A_{rs} = 0.$$

12. The relations, Equations 2.04, 2.05, and 2.06, are examples of *tensor equations*. If we take any such equation relating the components of tensors in one system of coordinates and multiply across by the transformation factors for the free indices as was done, for example, with Equation 2.04, we see at once that the same equation holds between components in the transformed coordinate system. In other words, if a tensor equation is true in one coordinate system, it is true in any coordinate system. This fact is of fundamental importance in all applications of the subject, particularly the physical applications, because a physical law must, from its very nature, be independent of a man-chosen coordinate system and so is best expressed in tensor form. We can very often set up a tensor equation in a simple coordinate system, for instance Cartesian, and immediately can assert that it is true in a complicated system, whereas it would be very difficult to find it or to prove it in the complicated

system alone; we have merely to make quite sure that all the terms in the equation are tensors.

TENSOR CHARACTER

13. Tests for tensor character are for this reason most important. Ultimately, these must require the set of quantities in question to obey the transformation law, but we can derive some simple rules to avoid having to resort to the transformation law in each case. If, for example, the given set of quantities form an invariant when contracted to a scalar with *arbitrary* nonzero vectors, then it will be a tensor. In that case, we have, for example,

$$a_{rs}A^rB^s = \bar{a}_{rs}\bar{A}^r\bar{B}^s = \bar{a}_{jk}\bar{A}^j\bar{B}^k$$

in which a_{rs} is the set under test and A^r, B^s are arbitrary vectors. Transforming the vectors, we have

$$\left(a_{rs} - \bar{a}_{jk}\frac{\partial \bar{x}^j}{\partial x^r}\frac{\partial \bar{x}^k}{\partial x^s}\right)A^rB^s = 0.$$

In three dimensions, this is an equation with nine arbitrary coefficients A^1B^2, etc., connecting the nine components of the matrix within parentheses. Nine or more of these equations containing different values of the arbitrary coefficients can only be satisfied if each component of the matrix within parentheses is zero, that is,

$$a_{rs} = \bar{a}_{jk}\frac{\partial \bar{x}^j}{\partial x^r}\frac{\partial \bar{x}^k}{\partial x^s},$$

which proves the tensor character of a_{rs}. We could not say this if A^r, B^s were the same vector because we should have then only six independent coefficients connecting the nine components of the matrix. We could, however, interchange the indices r, s and add the result to provide an equation of the form

$$\left(a_{rs} + a_{sr} - \bar{a}_{jk}\frac{\partial \bar{x}^j}{\partial x^r}\frac{\partial \bar{x}^k}{\partial x^s} - \bar{a}_{jk}\frac{\partial \bar{x}^j}{\partial x^s}\frac{\partial \bar{x}^j}{\partial x^r}\right)A^rA^s = 0$$

in which there are now six distinct components of the matrix and six arbitrary coefficients $(A^1)^2$, A^1A^2, etc. We now can say that

$$a_{rs} + a_{sr} = \bar{a}_{jk}\frac{\partial \bar{x}^j}{\partial x^r}\frac{\partial \bar{x}^k}{\partial x^s} + \bar{a}_{jk}\frac{\partial \bar{x}^j}{\partial x^s}\frac{\partial \bar{x}^k}{\partial x^r}$$

$$= (\bar{a}_{jk} + \bar{a}_{kj})\frac{\partial \bar{x}^j}{\partial x^r}\frac{\partial \bar{x}^k}{\partial x^s}$$

on interchanging the dummy indices j, k in the last term. This shows that

$$(a_{rs} + a_{sr})$$

is a tensor, and so is a_{rs} if a_{rs} and $\bar{a}_{jk}$ are symmetric, that is, if

$$a_{rs} = a_{sr}$$

in all coordinate systems. In that case, a_{rs} is a tensor if it forms an invariant with only one arbitrary nonzero vector.

14. It is evident from the working that, instead of two arbitrary vectors A^r, B^s, we could equally well have used an arbitrary tensor C^{rs}; and that this could be an arbitrary symmetric tensor when a_{rs} is symmetric in all coordinate systems. Moreover, it is not necessary that the operation of contraction should result in an invariant. It is sufficient if contraction with an arbitrary vector results in a tensor, but the proof of this, on much the same lines as above, is left to the reader.

15. We must now prove that the metric tensor is in fact a tensor. From Equation 1.17, we can say that if L^r, M^s are arbitrary vectors, we have

$$g_{rs}L^rM^s = \bar{g}_{rs}\bar{L}^r\bar{M}^s$$

because the magnitudes of the vectors and the angle between them are obviously unaffected by the choice of coordinate system. Therefore, g_{rs} forms an invariant with any two arbitrary vectors (even though not the same invariant for different vectors), and is accordingly a tensor. Again, the square of the line element ds^2 is clearly independent of the coordinate system so that

$$g_{rs}dx^rdx^s$$

is an invariant for an arbitrary small vector dx^r. Because g_{rs} is symmetric in all coordinate systems, it is therefore a tensor. Yet again, we have from Equation 1.13, in the case of an arbitrary vector L^r,

$$g_{rs}L^s = L_r,$$

and this again shows that g_{rs} is a tensor.

16. The *Kronecker delta* is a mixed tensor because

$$\delta_s^r\frac{\partial \bar{x}^p}{\partial x^r}\frac{\partial x^s}{\partial \bar{x}^q} = \frac{\partial \bar{x}^p}{\partial x^r}\frac{\partial x^r}{\partial \bar{x}^q} = \frac{\partial \bar{x}^p}{\partial \bar{x}^q} = \bar{\delta}_q^p$$

straight from the transformation law.

17. Now suppose that we have a mutually orthogonal triad of unit vectors $(\lambda^r, \mu^r, \nu^r)$ and consider the tensor

$$\lambda^r\lambda_s + \mu^r\mu_s + \nu^r\nu_s.$$

In rectangular Cartesian coordinates whose axes

are in the direction of these vectors, their components are

$$\lambda^r \quad \text{or} \quad \lambda_s \quad (1, 0, 0)$$
$$\mu^r \quad \text{or} \quad \mu_s \quad (0, 1, 0)$$
$$\nu^r \quad \text{or} \quad \nu_s \quad (0, 0, 1),$$

and we can see in this Cartesian system that

2.07 $\qquad \lambda^r\lambda_s + \mu^r\mu_s + \nu^r\nu_s = \delta^r_s.$

But this is a tensor equation because we have seen above that the right-hand side is a tensor and the left-hand side is formed by the multiplication of vectors. Consequently, this equation is true in any coordinates for any orthogonal triad of vectors.

THE ASSOCIATED METRIC TENSOR

18. If, in the same Cartesian system, we consider the tensor

$$\lambda_r\lambda_s + \mu_r\mu_s + \nu_r\nu_s,$$

we find that it is equivalent to the metric tensor g_{rs}, which in this system is unity for $r = s$ and is zero for $r \neq s$. Consequently, we can say that the tensor equation

2.08 $\qquad g_{rs} = \lambda_r\lambda_s + \mu_r\mu_s + \nu_r\nu_s$

is true for the metric tensor in any coordinates for any orthogonal triad. If we know the components of such a triad in any coordinate system, we can find the components of the metric tensor in the same coordinates at once.

19. Using the same triad of unit vectors, we now inquire what meaning should be attached to the tensor

2.09 $\qquad g^{rt} = \lambda^r\lambda^t + \mu^r\mu^t + \nu^r\nu^t.$

If we multiply Equations 2.08 and 2.09 and remember that the vectors are unit perpendicular vectors so that $\lambda^r\lambda_r = 1$, $\lambda^r\mu_r = 0$, etc., we have

$$g^{rt}g_{rs} = \lambda^t\lambda_s + \mu^t\mu_s + \nu^t\nu_s = \delta^t_s.$$

Next, we multiply this equation by G^{ks}, the cofactor of g_{ks} in the determinant formed by the components of the metric tensor which we shall denote by g. Using the ordinary rules for expanding a determinant and applying the summation convention, we then have

$$g^{rt}\delta^k_r g = \delta^t_s G^{ks} = G^{kt}$$

so that

2.10 $\qquad g^{kt} = G^{kt}/g,$

which enables us to calculate all the components of this tensor from the components of the metric tensor. We see from Equation 2.09 that g^{kt} *is a tensor* and *is* symmetric. It is called the *associated or conjugate metric tensor*.

We can easily show that the determinant of the associated tensor is $1/g$.

In deriving these results, we have assumed that g is not zero. It can be shown [1] that in the case of the positive-definite metrics used throughout this book, g is positive and never zero.

20. We can use the associated tensor to raise the index of a vector and to determine its contravariant from the covariant components in the same way as we use the metric tensor to lower the indices. An arbitrary vector L_r, whose Cartesian components relative to the axes $(\lambda_r, \mu_r, \nu_r)$ are (a, b, c), can be written as

$$L_r = a\lambda_r + b\mu_r + c\nu_r$$

or

$$L^r = a\lambda^r + b\mu^r + c\nu^r,$$

both of which are vector equations true for any coordinates. If, in a general coordinate system, we multiply the first of these equations by Equation 2.09, we have

2.11 $\qquad g^{rt}L_r = a\lambda^t + b\mu^t + c\nu^t = L^t,$

which raises the index of the vector.

21. The process is not confined to vectors, and we can raise or lower the indices of tensors in the same way. By the ordinary multiplication rules for tensors, we have, for example,

$$g^{rs}A_{rt} = B^s_{\cdot t}$$

where B is some tensor of the type and order indicated. If we multiply this across by g_{sk} and sum, we have

$$\delta^r_k A_{rt} = A_{kt} = g_{sk}B^s_{\cdot t} = C_{kt},$$

for instance, in which all components of A and C are equal so that they are the same tensor. The result of raising an index and then of lowering it again is similar to recovering the original tensor; therefore, we are justified in considering B as simply another form of A, just as the covariant and contravariant components are considered as describing the same vector. We may accordingly write

$$g^{rs}A_{rt} = A^s_{\cdot t}.$$

But, because A_{rt} is not, in general, the same as

---

[1] Levi–Cività (1926), *The Absolute Differential Calculus*, 90.

A_{tr}, we must be careful to leave a space or a dot to show from where the raised index came so that it may be returned later to the right place. If there is likely to be any confusion, it is best to write any tensor so that no superscript is vertically above a subscript.

THE PERMUTATION SYMBOLS IN THREE DIMENSIONS

22. We now introduce a system e_{rst} or e^{rst} in three dimensions, defined as follows:

(a) When any two indices are the same, the system is zero—for example, $e^{112} = 0$.

(b) When the arrangement of indices is 123, or the cyclic order 231 or 312—that is, an even permutation of 123—it is $+1$.

(c) In all other cases, that is, an odd permutation of 123, it is -1—for example, $e^{213} = -1$.

In short, the systems are skew-symmetric in any two indices.

23. If A_r^i is a term in any third-order determinant, the superscript being the row and the subscript the column, it is not difficult to verify that the value of the determinant A is given in terms of these e-systems by the formula

2.12 $A e_{rst} = e_{ijk} A_r^i A_s^j A_t^k,$

using, as always, the summation convention. If the terms of the determinant are the tensor transformation matrix, this is

2.13 [2] $\left| \dfrac{\partial x^p}{\partial \bar{x}^q} \right| e_{rst} = e_{ijk} \dfrac{\partial x^i}{\partial \bar{x}^r} \dfrac{\partial x^j}{\partial \bar{x}^s} \dfrac{\partial x^k}{\partial \bar{x}^t}.$

But the values of the e-systems are the same in all coordinates and, in consequence, the left-hand side cannot, in general, be $\bar{e}_{rst}$. The e-systems are accordingly not absolute tensors, although systems which transform like Equation 2.13 are often called relative tensors.

24. We now take the unbarred coordinates to be rectangular Cartesian. The metric tensor of the transformed space is

$$\bar{g}_{rs} = \dfrac{\partial x^p}{\partial \bar{x}^r} \dfrac{\partial x^q}{\partial \bar{x}^s} g_{pq}.$$

By taking the determinant of this and using the ordinary rule for the multiplication of determinants with $|g_{pq}| = 1$, we find that

---

[2] Throughout this book, side-line notation will be used, as here, for determinants. In a few cases, which will be clear from the context, side lining may indicate an absolute value.

$$\left| \dfrac{\partial x^p}{\partial \bar{x}^r} \right| = \sqrt{\bar{g}}.$$

Consequently, if we write

2.14 $\bar{\epsilon}_{rst} = \sqrt{\bar{g}}\, e_{rst},$

we can make Equation 2.13 into

$$\bar{\epsilon}_{rst} = \epsilon_{ijk} \dfrac{\partial x^i}{\partial \bar{x}^r} \dfrac{\partial x^j}{\partial \bar{x}^s} \dfrac{\partial x^k}{\partial \bar{x}^t}$$

so that for this transformation from Cartesian to general coordinates, the covariant ϵ-system behaves like an absolute tensor. But if ϵ_{rst} is a tensor in one general coordinate system, it is a tensor in any other. In much the same way, using the fact that the determinant of the associated tensor g^{rs} is $1/g$, we can show that

2.15 $\epsilon^{rst} = e^{rst}/\sqrt{g}$

is an absolute tensor.

25. We can write Equation 2.12 for the expansion of a determinant in the alternative form

2.16 $3! A = e^{ijk} e^{rst} A_{ir} A_{js} A_{kt}$

or

$$3! A/g = \epsilon^{ijk} \epsilon^{rst} A_{ir} A_{js} A_{kt},$$

which shows that if A_{ir} is a tensor, then A/g is an absolute invariant which has the same value in any coordinate system.

26. We can also write cofactors A^{ir} of the determinant in the form

2.17 $2! A^{ir} = e^{ijk} e^{rst} A_{js} A_{kt},$

which can easily be verified from the ordinary rules. Equation 2.17 shows that if A_{js} is a tensor, then A^{ir}/g is an absolute tensor. We have met one example of this in the metric tensor itself.

GENERALIZED KRONECKER DELTAS

27. Next, we introduce a *generalized Kronecker delta* formed by multiplying ϵ-systems and defined as

2.18 $\delta_{rst}^{lmn} = \epsilon^{lmn} \epsilon_{rst} = e^{lmn} e_{rst}.$

28. If we contract on, for instance, the indices (l, r), we have yet another form of the Kronecker delta defined as

2.19 $\delta_{st}^{mn} = \delta_{stp}^{mnp} = \delta_{st1}^{mn1} + \delta_{st2}^{mn2} + \delta_{st3}^{mn3}$

in which we have, of course, applied the summation convention. By combining Equations 2.18 and 2.19 and using the rules for the e-system, we can verify without difficulty that Equation 2.19 equals

(a) $+1$ when (m, n) and (s, t) are the same two numbers in the same order $(m \neq n$ and $t \neq s)$, for example,

$$\delta^{12}_{12} = \delta^{31}_{31} = +1;$$

(b) -1 when (m, n) and (s, t) are the same two numbers in the opposite order $(m \neq n$ and $t \neq s)$, for example,

$$\delta^{12}_{21} = \delta^{31}_{13} = -1; \quad \text{and}$$

(c) otherwise zero.

If we contract a tensor with this δ-system, it is not difficult to verify such results as

2.20 $\delta^{mn}_{st}A_{mnp} = A_{stp} - A_{tsp}$

2.21 $\delta^{mn}_{st}A^{st}_{\cdot\cdot p} = A^{mn}_{\cdot\cdot p} - A^{nm}_{\cdot\cdot p}.$

29. We can further contract Equation 2.19 into the ordinary two-index Kronecker delta, but, in this case, to square with the previous definition in Equations 1.24, we shall need a factor of $(\frac{1}{2})$ so that

2.22 $\delta^{m}_{s} = \frac{1}{2} \delta^{mn}_{sn} = \frac{1}{2} (\delta^{m1}_{s1} + \delta^{m2}_{s2} + \delta^{m3}_{s3}),$

which can easily be verified.

VECTOR PRODUCTS

30. We shall often meet a contracted product of the ϵ-systems with two vectors, and shall now consider what this means.

We revert to the mutually orthogonal triad of vectors $(\lambda_r, \mu_r, \nu_r)$ discussed above, and again take these temporarily as rectangular Cartesian axes as in § 2–17. Then the tensor equations

$$\lambda^r = \epsilon^{rst}\mu_s\nu_t ; \qquad \mu^r = \epsilon^{rst}\nu_s\lambda_t ; \qquad \nu^r = \epsilon^{rst}\lambda_s\mu_t$$

2.23

are evidently true in these coordinates and are accordingly true in any coordinate system, as we have seen in § 2–12.

We now take a unit vector $\bar{\mu}_s$ in the plane of μ_s and ν_s, and making an angle θ with ν_s so that

$$\bar{\mu}_s = \mu_s \sin\theta + \nu_s \cos\theta,$$

we evaluate

$$\epsilon^{rst}\bar{\mu}_s\nu_t = \epsilon^{rst}\mu_s\nu_t \sin\theta + \epsilon^{rst}\nu_s\nu_t \cos\theta.$$

But all components of the last term are zero in the Cartesian system, owing to the skew-symmetry of the ϵ-systems, and must therefore be zero in any coordinate system. We may therefore write

$$\epsilon^{rst}\bar{\mu}_s\nu_t = \lambda^r \sin\theta.$$

But μ_s, ν_t are quite general unit vectors, and λ^r is perpendicular to both. Instead of these unit vectors, we can also introduce nonunit vectors A_s, B_t of magnitudes a, b and write

2.24 $\epsilon^{rst}A_sB_t = (ab \sin\theta)\lambda^r$

in which λ^r is a unit vector perpendicular to both A_s and B_t. If we go back over the derivation, we see that λ^r, A_s, B_t must be a right-handed system in that order like λ^r, μ_s, ν_t, even though two of them are no longer orthogonal. The expression on the left of Equation 2.24 is a generalized *vector product* in tensor notation. Its components in Cartesian coordinates become the usual definition of a vector product of Cartesian vectors.

31. If we multiply Equation 2.24 by a third vector C_r and contract, we have

2.25 $\epsilon^{str}A_sB_tC_r = abc \sin\theta \sin\phi$

in which ϕ is the angle C_r makes with the plane of A_s, B_t. The expression on the left of Equation 2.25 is known as a *scalar triple product*. For the product to be positive, the three vectors must be right-handed in the order of the ϵ-system indices. If any two of the vectors have the same direction, the scalar triple product will be zero because either θ or ϕ will be zero. This also follows from § 2–11.

32. It is evident from Equation 2.25 that, if $(\lambda_r, \mu_r, \nu_r)$ is any right-handed mutually orthogonal triad of unit vectors, we have

2.26 $\epsilon^{rst}\lambda_r\mu_s\nu_t = 1.$

The sign of this product will be changed if any two of the vectors are interchanged; the product will be zero if any two of the vectors are the same. We can accordingly express the ϵ-systems as products of the three vectors as follows,

$$\epsilon^{rst} = \lambda^r(\mu^s\nu^t - \nu^s\mu^t) + \mu^r(\nu^s\lambda^t - \lambda^s\nu^t)$$

2.27 $+ \nu^r(\lambda^s\mu^t - \mu^s\lambda^t),$

with a covariant equation obtained by simply lowering all the indices.

33. By multiplying two tensors of the form Equation 2.27 and contracting with the metric tensor, we have

$$g_{ri}\epsilon^{rst}\epsilon^{ijk} = (\mu^s\nu^t - \nu^s\mu^t)(\mu^j\nu^k - \nu^j\mu^k)$$

$$+ \text{ two similar terms.}$$

Multiplying this out and using Equation 2.09, we have finally

2.28 $g_{ri}\epsilon^{rst}\epsilon^{ijk} = g^{sj}g^{tk} - g^{sk}g^{jt},$

with a similar equation obtained by raising or lowering each index.

THE PERMUTATION SYMBOLS AND THE METRIC TENSOR IN TWO DIMENSIONS

34. One advantage of the tensor calculus is that if we have a tensor equation in three dimensions, for instance, then it is likely that a similar equation exists in two or four or any number of dimensions. In many cases, the equation will be exactly the same with the Greek indices of two dimensions as it is in the Roman indices of three dimensions. The reason for this is that the defining and transformation equations of tensors are of the same form in any number of dimensions. Thus corresponding to Equation 2.01, for example, we should have

2.29 $$\overline{A}_{\alpha\beta} = \frac{\partial x^\gamma}{\partial \bar{x}^\alpha} \frac{\partial x^\delta}{\partial \bar{x}^\beta} A_{\gamma\delta} \qquad (\alpha, \beta, \gamma, \delta = 1, 2).$$

35. There will, of course, be fewer components in two dimensions because fewer numbers can be assigned to the indices, and this may affect the form of the tensor. For instance, we cannot have

$$\epsilon^{\alpha\beta\gamma} \qquad (\alpha, \beta, \gamma = 1, 2)$$

defined in the same way as the ϵ-systems in three dimensions because all its components would be zero. We can, however, have

$$\epsilon^{\alpha\beta}, \ \epsilon_{\alpha\beta} \qquad (\alpha, \beta = 1, 2)$$

defined in the same way, that is,

2.30 $$\epsilon^{\alpha\beta} = e^{\alpha\beta}/\sqrt{a} \ ; \qquad \epsilon_{\alpha\beta} = \sqrt{a} \, e_{\alpha\beta}$$

in which a is the determinant of the two-dimensional metric tensor $a_{\alpha\beta}$ and the $e_{\alpha\beta}$- or $e^{\alpha\beta}$-systems are defined as equal to
(a) zero if $\alpha = \beta$,
(b) $+1$ if $(\alpha, \beta) = (1, 2)$, and
(c) -1 if $(\alpha, \beta) = (2, 1)$.

36. By analogy with Equation 2.26, we should expect

2.31 $$\epsilon^{\alpha\beta} \lambda_\alpha \mu_\beta = 1,$$

if $(\lambda_\alpha, \mu_\beta)$ are any two mutually orthogonal vectors in the order of the coordinates (1, 2), just as the triad $(\lambda_r, \mu_r, \nu_r)$ in three dimensions is arranged in order of the coordinates (1, 2, 3) to give a right-handed system. The rotation of λ_α to μ_β must be in the same direction as the rotation of the x^1-coordinate line to the x^2-coordinate line. We may also expect, using the same arguments as for Equation

2.27, that the following tensor equations should hold,

2.32 $$\begin{aligned} \epsilon^{\alpha\beta} &= \lambda^\alpha \mu^\beta - \mu^\alpha \lambda^\beta \\ \epsilon_{\alpha\beta} &= \lambda_\alpha \mu_\beta - \mu_\alpha \lambda_\beta. \end{aligned}$$

37. Both Equations 2.31 and 2.32 can easily be verified, remembering that as tensor equations we have only to verify them in one particular coordinate system. If we take λ^α, μ^β as unit vectors in the directions of the coordinate lines in the orthogonal metric

$$ds^2 = a_{11}(dx^1)^2 + a_{22}(dx^2)^2,$$

their components are

2.33 $$\begin{aligned} \lambda^\alpha &= (1/\sqrt{a_{11}}, 0) & \mu^\alpha &= (0, 1/\sqrt{a_{22}}) \\ \lambda_\alpha &= (\sqrt{a_{11}}, 0) & \mu_\alpha &= (0, \sqrt{a_{22}}), \end{aligned}$$

and Equations 2.31 and 2.32 are verified at once.

38. In this same coordinate system, defining $a^{\alpha\beta}$ as the cofactor of $a_{\alpha\beta}$ in the determinant $|a_{\alpha\beta}|$, divided by the value of the determinant $a = a_{11}a_{22}$, we can at once verify that

2.34 $$a_{\alpha\beta} = \lambda_\alpha \lambda_\beta + \mu_\alpha \mu_\beta$$

2.35 $$a^{\alpha\beta} = \lambda^\alpha \lambda^\beta + \mu^\alpha \mu^\beta$$

2.36 $$a^{\alpha\beta} a_{\beta\gamma} = \lambda^\alpha \lambda_\gamma + \mu^\alpha \mu_\gamma = \delta^\alpha_\gamma$$

correspond to the three-dimensional Equations 2.08 and 2.09. Since these are tensor equations, they are true in any coordinate system and for any pair of orthogonal vectors. It should be noted that we have not appealed to Cartesian coordinates (in the plane) in order to prove them.

39. The equations in Equations 2.32 are of particular importance because, given a surface vector λ_α, we can define an orthogonal surface vector in terms of it as

2.37 $$\mu_\beta = \epsilon_{\alpha\beta} \lambda^\alpha, \qquad \text{etc.}$$

40. As in three dimensions, we can form generalized Kronecker deltas from products of the ϵ-systems, that is,

2.38 $$\delta^{\alpha\beta}_{\gamma\delta} = \epsilon^{\alpha\beta} \epsilon_{\gamma\delta},$$

and we can contract this to

2.39 $$\delta^{\alpha\beta}_{\alpha\delta} = \delta^{1\beta}_{1\delta} + \delta^{2\beta}_{2\delta} = \delta^\beta_\delta,$$

which defines the ordinary Kronecker delta (Equations 1.24), that is,

2.40 $$\begin{aligned} \delta^\alpha_\beta &= 1 & (\alpha = \beta) \\ \delta^\alpha_\beta &= 0 & (\alpha \neq \beta). \end{aligned}$$

41. Corresponding to Equation 2.20, we have also, for example,

$$\textbf{2.41} \qquad \delta_{\gamma\delta}^{\alpha\beta} A_{\alpha\beta\rho\sigma} = A_{\gamma\delta\rho\sigma} - A_{\delta\gamma\rho\sigma}$$

in which A is any tensor.

42. Corresponding to Equation 2.16, we have for the expansion of a second-order determinant

$$\textbf{2.42} \qquad 2!A = e^{\alpha\gamma} e^{\beta\delta} A_{\alpha\beta} A_{\gamma\delta},$$

which shows that if $A_{\alpha\beta}$ is a surface tensor, then A/a is a surface invariant, having the same value in any coordinate system. The cofactors are given by

$$\textbf{2.43} \qquad A^{\alpha\beta} = e^{\alpha\gamma} e^{\beta\delta} A_{\gamma\delta},$$

which shows that if $A_{\gamma\delta}$ is a surface tensor, then so is $A^{\alpha\beta}/a$. If $A_{\gamma\delta}$ is the metric tensor, then we have

$$\textbf{2.44} \qquad a^{\alpha\beta} = \epsilon^{\alpha\gamma} \epsilon^{\beta\delta} a_{\gamma\delta},$$

a tensor equation in which we can raise and lower indices to obtain also

$$\textbf{2.45} \qquad a_{\alpha\beta} = \epsilon_{\alpha\gamma} \epsilon_{\beta\delta} a^{\gamma\delta}.$$

CHAPTER 3

Covariant Differentiation

THE CHRISTOFFEL SYMBOLS

1. We have considered a tensor as a set of point functions defined at a number of discrete points in space, and we must now consider how its components vary from point to point — in other words, how to differentiate a tensor with respect to a small displacement of the coordinates dx^r. The differentials of a general tensor must clearly involve the differentials of the metric tensor whose components will also vary, in general, from point to point. We shall see that the analysis inevitably leads to the following grouping of differentials of the metric tensor, requiring the special symbols on the left,

3.01 $$[ij, k] = \tfrac{1}{2}\left(\frac{\partial g_{jk}}{\partial x^i} + \frac{\partial g_{ik}}{\partial x^j} - \frac{\partial g_{ij}}{\partial x^k}\right)$$

3.02 $$\Gamma^l_{ij} = g^{lk}[ij, k].$$

These special symbols are known as the *Christoffel symbols* of the first and second kinds, respectively. We note that both Christoffel symbols are symmetric in (i, j).

In Cartesian coordinates, all components of the metric tensor are constants and therefore all the Christoffel symbols are zero.

2. In the case of a transformation from Cartesian coordinates (overbarred), we have

$$g_{jk} = \bar{g}_{mn}\frac{\partial \bar{x}^m}{\partial x^j}\frac{\partial \bar{x}^n}{\partial x^k}$$

in which the $\bar{g}_{mn}$ are constants; and by direct differentiation and substitution, we find that

3.03 $$[ij, k] = \bar{g}_{mn}\frac{\partial^2 \bar{x}^m}{\partial x^i \partial x^j}\frac{\partial \bar{x}^n}{\partial x^k}.$$

Multiplying this across by

$$g^{kl} = \bar{g}^{pq}\frac{\partial x^k}{\partial \bar{x}^p}\frac{\partial x^l}{\partial \bar{x}^q},$$

we have after some simplification

3.04 $$\Gamma^l_{ij} = \frac{\partial^2 \bar{x}^m}{\partial x^i \partial x^j}\frac{\partial x^l}{\partial \bar{x}^m}.$$

3. We can now take a field of parallel unit vectors A^r whose Cartesian components (still denoted by overbars) are the same at any point in space and are given by

$$\bar{A}^m = A^i \frac{\partial \bar{x}^m}{\partial x^i}.$$

If we differentiate this equation with respect to each of the coordinates x^j in turn, then no matter what the corresponding change in the Cartesian coordinates may be, the differentials of the constant Cartesian components on the left will be zero; we may write the complete set of resulting equations as

$$\frac{\partial A^i}{\partial x^j}\frac{\partial \bar{x}^m}{\partial x^i} + A^i \frac{\partial^2 \bar{x}^m}{\partial x^i \partial x^j} = 0.$$

If we multiply this result across by $\partial x^l/\partial \bar{x}^m$ and use Equation 3.04, we have

3.05 $$\frac{\partial A^l}{\partial x^j} + \Gamma^l_{ij}A^i = 0,$$

which are the differential equations of a set of parallel vectors A^l in general coordinates. In much the same way, by differentiating

$$A_i = \frac{\partial \bar{x}^m}{\partial x^i}\bar{A}_m,$$

17

we have

$$\frac{\partial A_i}{\partial x^j} = \frac{\partial^2 \bar{x}^m}{\partial x^i \partial x^j} \, \bar{A}_m = \frac{\partial^2 \bar{x}^m}{\partial x^i \partial x^j} \, \frac{\partial x^l}{\partial \bar{x}^m} \, A_l$$

so that

3.06 $\qquad\qquad \dfrac{\partial A_i}{\partial x^j} - \Gamma^l_{ij} A_l = 0,$

which is the covariant form of Equation 3.05.

COVARIANT DERIVATIVES

4. Next, we take a general vector field λ^i (defined in some way at all points of a region of space), which may vary in both magnitude and direction from point to point. We also define an arbitrary set of unit parallel vectors A_i over the same region as, for instance, a field of unit vectors all parallel to a Cartesian axis. We differentiate the scalar product of the two vectors with respect to each coordinate x^j and use Equation 3.06 to give

$$\frac{\partial(\lambda^i A_i)}{\partial x^j} = \frac{\partial \lambda^i}{\partial x^j} A_i + \lambda^i \Gamma^l_{ij} A_l$$

$$= \left(\frac{\partial \lambda^i}{\partial x^j} + \Gamma^i_{jk} \lambda^k \right) A_i$$

on changing the dummy indices. But we have already seen in § 1–19 that the differentials of an invariant form a covariant vector, so that the left-hand side of this equation is a covariant vector as is also the right-hand side. Because A_i is arbitrary, this means that the expression within the parentheses is a mixed tensor. This we call the *covariant derivative* of the contravariant vector λ^i with respect to the coordinate x^j, which we write as

3.07 $\qquad\qquad \lambda^i_j = \dfrac{\partial \lambda^i}{\partial x^j} + \Gamma^i_{jk} \lambda^k.$

In exactly the same way, we can find the covariant derivative of the covariant vector λ_i as

3.08 $\qquad\qquad \lambda_{ij} = \dfrac{\partial \lambda_i}{\partial x^j} - \Gamma^l_{ij} \lambda_l.$

Covariant derivatives are sometimes distinguished from other tensors by writing a comma or a bar before the index of differentiation, thus

$$\lambda_{i,\,j} \quad \text{or} \quad \lambda_{i/j}.$$

But we shall not do this where the context clearly indicates that the tensor has been formed by covariant differentiation, or where the distinction is immaterial.

5. We can similarly derive an expression for the covariant derivative of a tensor of any order or type by reduction to an invariant with a number of arbitrary parallel vector fields. For example, ordinary differentiation of the invariant

$$\lambda^r_{st} A_r B^s C^t$$

will show that the covariant derivative of the tensor is

3.09 $\qquad \lambda^r_{stu} = \dfrac{\partial \lambda^r_{st}}{\partial x^u} + \Gamma^r_{uj} \lambda^j_{st} - \Gamma^j_{us} \lambda^r_{jt} - \Gamma^j_{ut} \lambda^r_{sj}.$

The rule is to place each index of the original tensor inside a Christoffel symbol at the same level. The sign of the Christoffel symbol is positive for a transferred contravariant index and is negative for a transferred covariant index. The place of the transferred index is taken by a dummy (summation) index (j), which must also be inserted at the opposite level in the Christoffel symbol. The Christoffel symbol is completed with the derivative index (u in the above example).

6. The covariant derivative of the gradient of a scalar ϕ can be written as

3.10 $\qquad\qquad \phi_{r,\,s} = \dfrac{\partial^2 \phi}{\partial x^r \partial x^s} - \Gamma^t_{rs} \phi_t,$

which is evidently symmetric in (r, s) because the Christoffel symbols are symmetric in these indices and the ordinary derivatives commute. We can accordingly write in this case

3.11 $\qquad\qquad \phi_{r,\,s} = \phi_{s,\,r}.$

7. Compared with ordinary differentiation of the separate components, the great advantage of covariant differentiation is that it results in a tensor. If we differentiate a tensor equation covariantly, we get another tensor equation which remains true in any coordinate system and retains all the other advantages of working in tensors.

8. The Christoffel symbols are not tensors, even though their addition to the ordinary derivatives, which are not tensors either, produces a derived tensor of a higher order. From Equations 3.01 and 3.02, it is clear that the Christoffel symbols are all zero in Cartesian coordinates; if they were components of a tensor, they would have to be zero in all coordinate systems. That this is not so, we can observe from Equation 3.04.

The fact that all the Christoffel symbols are zero in Cartesian coordinates implies that covariant derivatives become ordinary derivatives in Cartesian coordinates. This fact is apparent at once from Equation 3.09.

DIFFERENTIAL INVARIANTS

9. Suppose we form the second covariant derivative of a scalar F, or the first covariant derivative of its gradient F_r, and then contract the derivative with the associated metric tensor to form the invariant

$$g^{rs} F_{rs},$$

which, as an invariant, will have the same value in all coordinate systems. In rectangular Cartesian coordinates (x, y, z),

$$g^{rs} = 1 \quad (r = s) \quad \text{and} \quad g^{rs} = 0 \quad (r \neq s)$$

and the covariant derivatives become ordinary derivatives so that the invariant is

$$\frac{\partial^2 F}{\partial x^2} + \frac{\partial^2 F}{\partial y^2} + \frac{\partial^2 F}{\partial z^2}.$$

This is well known as the *Laplacian* of F, which we shall write as ΔF. Accordingly, in any coordinate system, we can write

3.12 $$\Delta F = g^{rs} F_{rs} = F^s_{\cdot s},$$

whether F_r is a general vector or the gradient of a scalar. If it is a general vector, the Laplacian is called its *divergence*.

10. Other differential invariants, which we shall meet often, are given with their Cartesian equivalents as

3.13 $$\nabla(F) = g^{rs} F_r F_s = \left(\frac{\partial F}{\partial x}\right)^2 + \left(\frac{\partial F}{\partial y}\right)^2 + \left(\frac{\partial F}{\partial z}\right)^2$$

$$\nabla(F, G) = g^{rs} F_r G_s$$

3.14 $$= \left(\frac{\partial F}{\partial x}\right)\left(\frac{\partial G}{\partial x}\right) + \left(\frac{\partial F}{\partial y}\right)\left(\frac{\partial G}{\partial y}\right) + \left(\frac{\partial F}{\partial z}\right)\left(\frac{\partial G}{\partial z}\right).$$

11. Again, if F_t is a vector and we expand the contravariant vector

3.15 $$\epsilon^{rst} F_{ts}$$

in rectangular Cartesian coordinates (x^1, x^2, x^3), we have a vector whose components are

$$\left(\frac{\partial F_3}{\partial x^2} - \frac{\partial F_2}{\partial x^3}\right), \quad \left(\frac{\partial F_1}{\partial x^3} - \frac{\partial F_3}{\partial x^1}\right), \quad \left(\frac{\partial F_2}{\partial x^1} - \frac{\partial F_1}{\partial x^2}\right).$$

which are usually known as the *curl* of the original vector. Accordingly, we take Equation 3.15 as the curl of a vector in general coordinates.

RULES FOR COVARIANT DIFFERENTIATION

12. A few rules for covariant differentiation may be noted rapidly. Since all components of the tensor

$$\epsilon_{rst,\,u}$$

are zero in Cartesian coordinates where the ϵ_{rst} are constants, they must be zero also in any coordinates, which means that the ϵ-systems, covariant and contravariant, behave as constants under *covariant* differentiation. For the same reason, the metric tensor and its associate and the Kronecker deltas behave as constants.

13. Expansion of these results leads to a number of useful formulas. For example, we have

$$\epsilon_{123,\,u} = 0 = \frac{\partial \sqrt{g}}{\partial x^u} - \Gamma^k_{1u}\epsilon_{k\cdot 23} - \Gamma^k_{2u}\epsilon_{1k3} - \Gamma^k_{3u}\epsilon_{12k}$$

$$= \frac{\partial \sqrt{g}}{\partial x^u} - \sqrt{g}(\Gamma^1_{1u} + \Gamma^2_{2u} + \Gamma^3_{3u})$$

so that

3.16 $$\frac{\partial(\ln \sqrt{g})}{\partial x^u} = \Gamma^k_{ku},$$

which enables us to write the divergence of a vector F_r in the form

3.17 $$F^r_{\cdot r} = \frac{1}{\sqrt{g}} \frac{\partial}{\partial x^r}(\sqrt{g} F^r),$$

or the Laplacian of a scalar F in the form

3.18 $$\Delta F = \frac{1}{\sqrt{g}} \frac{\partial}{\partial x^r}(\sqrt{g} g^{rs} F_s).$$

14. The sum or products of tensors can be differentiated covariantly by the same rules as those for ordinary differentiation. To establish this fact, we have only to remember that covariant differentiation is the same as ordinary differentiation in Cartesian coordinates. Thus, the product

$$A^p_q B^q_{st},$$

differentiated covariantly, is

$$(A^p_q B^q_{st})_u = A^p_{q,\,u} B^q_{st} + A^p_q B^q_{st,\,u}.$$

This, with ordinary differentials, is clearly the correct result in Cartesian coordinates and must also be true in any coordinates because it is a tensor equation.

15. If l^r is any *unit* vector, we have from Equation 1.11

$$l^r l_r = 1;$$

differentiating this covariantly, we have

$$l^r_{,s} l_r + l^r l_{r,s} = 0.$$

By raising and lowering indices in the first term, we find that

3.19 $$l_{r,s} l^r = 0.$$

Similarly, if l^r, j^r are two unit perpendicular vectors, then we have

$$l^r j_r = 0$$

and

3.20 $$l_{r,s} j^r = -j_{r,s} l^r.$$

These two simple equations will be in constant use.

CHAPTER 4

Intrinsic Properties of Curves

CURVES IN THREE DIMENSIONS

1. We have determined the covariant derivatives with respect to each coordinate, which means that the tensor being differentiated must be defined in space. If the tensor is merely defined along a line, we can use the same formulas (as if we were dealing with a *family or congruence* of lines in space) and can restrict their application to a particular line by contracting with the unit tangent vector of the line. For example, the differential of a tensor A_{st}^r along a curve whose unit tangent is l^u is

4.01 $$A_{st,u}^r l^u = A_{st,u}^r (dx^u/dl)$$

where dl is the arc element of the curve. This is known as the *intrinsic* derivative of the tensor, with respect to the arc length of the curve, and is written as

$$\frac{\delta}{\delta l}(A_{st}^r).$$

In place of the arc element, we could use equally well any parameter (q) defined along the curve because this parameter would be some function of the arc. In that case,

$$\frac{\delta}{\delta q}(A_{st}^r)$$

would be the intrinsic derivative with respect to the parameter.

2. The intrinsic derivative of the unit tangent itself is

$$l_{rs}l^s$$

and is called the *vector curvature* of the line; it represents the arc rate-of-change in the tangent vector along the line and so is a generalization of the notion of curvature for plane curves. If the vector curvature is zero throughout, the curve is said to be a *geodesic* of the space—that is, a straight line in flat space—although it would not necessarily be "straight" in a curved space, such as a curved two-dimensional surface.

3. We can write the vector curvature as

4.02 $$l_{rs}l^s = \chi m_r$$

in which m_r is a unit vector, known as the *principal normal* to the curve. The magnitude of the vector curvature is the scalar invariant

$$\chi = l_{rs}m^r l^s,$$

and is known as the *first* or *principal curvature*, or simply the *curvature* of the curve. If we multiply Equation 4.02 by $g^{rt}l_t$ and use Equation 3.19, we have

$$\chi g^{rt}l_t m_r = l_{rs}l^r l^s = 0$$

which shows that unless $\chi = 0$, the principal normal is perpendicular to the unit tangent. If $\chi = 0$, the curve is a geodesic, and its principal normal is indeterminate.

4. In the case of a curve in three dimensions, we can associate another unit vector n_r with the curve, such that (l_r, m_r, n_r) form a mutually orthogonal right-handed system. This third vector, known as the *binormal*, is perpendicular to the *osculating plane* of the curve defined by l_r and m_r and will therefore remain parallel to itself along a *plane curve*. However, if the curve is not a plane but a *twisted curve*, the binormal will not remain parallel

to itself but will have an intrinsic derivative
$$n_{r,s}l^s,$$
which is a vector and can therefore be written in the form

4.03 $\qquad\qquad n_{rs}l^s = -\tau p_r$

where τ is the magnitude of the unit vector p_r (the negative sign is simply a convention). If we take $(l_r,\ m_r,\ n_r)$ as temporary coordinate axes, it is clear that p_r must be expressible as

$$p_r = Al_r + Bm_r + Cn_r$$

in which A, B, C are the components of p_r. Using Equation 3.20, we then have

$$-\tau A = -\tau p_r l^r = n_{rs}l^r l^s = -l_{rs}n^r l^s,$$

which from Equation 4.02 is zero because n^r is perpendicular to m^r; also we have

$$-\tau C = -\tau p_r n^r = n_{rs}n^r l^s,$$

which is zero from Equation 3.19. Because τ is not, in general, zero, we have

$$A = C = 0$$
and thus
$$p_r = m_r,$$

both being unit vectors. We may accordingly rewrite Equation 4.03 as

4.04 $\qquad\qquad n_{rs}l^s = -\tau m_r.$

The magnitude τ of this vector is called the second curvature or *torsion* of the curve.

5. The variation of the principal normal along the curve is settled by the variation of the tangent and binormal because, by definition, the principal normal remains perpendicular to both. We cannot, therefore, obtain an independent expression for the variation of the principal normal, but it is, nevertheless, useful to express the variation in terms of Equations 4.02 and 4.04. Proceeding on the same lines as above, we write

$$m_{rs}l^s = Cl_r + Dm_r + En_r$$

in which D is zero from Equation 3.19 and

$$C = m_{rs}l^s l^r = -l_{rs}m^r l^s = -\chi$$

from Equations 3.20 and 4.02. Also, we have

$$E = m_{rs}n^r l^s = -n_{rs}m^r l^s = \tau,$$

so that we have finally

4.05 $\qquad\qquad m_{rs}l^s = -\chi l_r + \tau n_r.$

The three Equations 4.02, 4.04, and 4.05, two of which are independent, are known as the *Frenet* equations of the curve and are collected for easier reference as

$$l_{rs}l^s = \chi m_r$$

$$m_{rs}l^s = -\chi l_r + \tau n_r$$

4.06 $\qquad\qquad n_{rs}l^s = -\tau m_r.$

CURVES IN TWO DIMENSIONS

6. In the case of a curve contained wholly on a surface, the vector curvature can similarly be defined as

4.07 $\qquad\qquad l_{\alpha\beta}l^\beta = \sigma j_\alpha \qquad\qquad (\alpha,\ \beta = 1,\ 2)$

in which the covariant derivative of the unit tangent l_α is taken with respect to the two-dimensional surface metric. If we multiply Equation 4.07 by l^α and use the two-dimensional form of Equation 3.19, we find that the unit surface vector j_α is perpendicular to the unit tangent l_α and is known as the *normal* to the curve. The magnitude σ of the vector curvature is called the *geodesic curvature* of the curve. If σ is zero, the curve is called a *geodesic* of the surface, paralleling the definition of a three-dimensional geodesic in §4–2. We must remember, however, that the curve is also a curve in the surrounding space and will have a first or principal curvature in three dimensions as well as geodesic curvature in two dimensions. The curve will not be a geodesic of the surrounding space unless its principal curvature is zero. We shall see later that the principal curvature and geodesic curvature are related; but for the present, we shall consider only the intrinsic curvature properties of surface curves and shall defer consideration of them as curves in the surrounding space.

7. If we confine our attention to the surface alone, it is clear that the curve can have no surface binormal because there is no *surface* direction perpendicular to both l_α and j_α. The only independent Frenet equation is accordingly Equation 4.07. We can, however, derive a useful dependent equation in much the same way as we derived the second Frenet equation in 3-space from the other two. We write

$$j_{\alpha\beta}l^\beta = Al_\alpha + Bj_\alpha$$

and note at once that $B = 0$ from the two-dimensional

form of Equation 3.19. Further, we use Equation 3.20 and find that

$$A = j_{\alpha\beta} l^{\alpha} l^{\beta} = -l_{\alpha\beta} j^{\alpha} l^{\beta} = -\sigma$$

from Equation 4.07, so that finally we have

4.08
$$j_{\alpha\beta} l^{\beta} = -\sigma l_{\alpha}.$$

8. Suppose that l_{α} is defined over some finite region of the surface as the unit tangent to a family of curves. The unit tangent to the orthogonal trajectories of the family will be j_{α}. In that case, the j_{α} can be differentiated over the surface and will have a geodesic curvature σ^* defined as

4.09
$$j_{\alpha\beta} j^{\beta} = -\sigma^* l_{\alpha}.$$

In obtaining this equation from Equation 4.07, we must preserve the same sense of the rotation from l_{α} to j_{α} for the rotation from j_{α} to *its* normal, which is accordingly minus l_{α}. Corresponding to Equation 4.08, we have also

4.10
$$l_{\alpha\beta} j^{\beta} = +\sigma^* j_{\alpha}.$$

We can finally express $l_{\alpha\beta}$ and $j_{\alpha\beta}$ as products of vectors in the form

$$l_{\alpha\beta} = \sigma j_{\alpha} l_{\beta} + \sigma^* j_{\alpha} j_{\beta}$$

4.11
$$j_{\alpha\beta} = -\sigma l_{\alpha} l_{\beta} - \sigma^* l_{\alpha} j_{\beta},$$

remembering that, because of Equation 3.19, there can be no l_{α}-terms in, for example, the expansion of $l_{\alpha\beta}$.

9. If, as we shall assume throughout, the rotation from l_{α} to j_{α} is made in the same sense as the rotation from the x^1- to the x^2-coordinate line and we use Equations 2.31 or 2.32, then we have

$$\epsilon^{\alpha\beta} l_{\alpha\beta} = -\sigma$$

4.12
$$\epsilon^{\alpha\beta} j_{\alpha\beta} = -\sigma^*$$

CHAPTER 5

Intrinsic Curvature of Space

THE CURVATURE TENSOR

1. We shall consider briefly the second covariant derivatives of a vector λ_r, that is,

$$\lambda_{r,\,st}.$$

In flat space, defined as a space which can be expressed in Cartesian coordinates, the resulting third-order tensor reduces to the ordinary derivatives of the components,

$$\frac{\partial^2 \lambda_r}{\partial x^s \partial x^t}$$

in Cartesian coordinates; and because the ordinary derivatives commute, we can write

5.01 $$\lambda_{r,\,st} = \lambda_{r,\,ts}$$

as a tensor equation, which is true in any coordinates but applies only in flat space.

2. It is possible to conceive a space which is not flat, in the sense that it cannot be expressed over a finite region in Cartesian coordinates. For example, in two dimensions, the surface of a sphere is not flat, and the relative positions of points on such a surface cannot be described in Cartesian coordinates as they can be on a plane. The line element or metric of the space is, nevertheless, still expressible by means of a symmetric covariant tensor of the second order. A space with this form of metric is known as a *Riemannian space*; it may be flat or curved, and of any number of dimensions.

3. We first consider whether the second covariant derivatives of a vector commute in such a space.

We have

$$\lambda_{i,\,jk} = \frac{\partial \lambda_{ij}}{\partial x^k} - \Gamma^m_{ik}\lambda_{mj} - \Gamma^m_{jk}\lambda_{im}.$$

Interchanging $(j,\,k)$, subtracting, and remembering the symmetrical property of the Christoffel symbols, we have

$$\lambda_{i,\,jk} - \lambda_{i,\,kj} = \frac{\partial}{\partial x^k}\left(\frac{\partial \lambda_i}{\partial x^j} - \Gamma^l_{ij}\lambda_l\right) - \Gamma^m_{ik}\left(\frac{\partial \lambda_m}{\partial x^j} - \Gamma^l_{mj}\lambda_l\right)$$

$$- \frac{\partial}{\partial x^j}\left(\frac{\partial \lambda_i}{\partial x^k} - \Gamma^l_{ik}\lambda_l\right) + \Gamma^m_{ij}\left(\frac{\partial \lambda_m}{\partial x^k} - \Gamma^l_{mk}\lambda_l\right)$$

5.02 $$= R^l_{\cdot ijk}\lambda_l$$

if, after some simplification and change of dummy indices, we write

5.03 $$R^l_{\cdot ijk} = \frac{\partial}{\partial x^j}\Gamma^l_{ik} - \frac{\partial}{\partial x^k}\Gamma^l_{ij} + \Gamma^m_{ik}\Gamma^l_{mj} - \Gamma^m_{ij}\Gamma^l_{mk}.$$

Because λ_l is an arbitrary vector and the left-hand side of Equation 5.02 is a third-order tensor, then it follows that Equation 5.03 is a fourth-order tensor, known as the *Riemann-Christoffel* or curvature tensor. If the space is flat, there exists a Cartesian coordinate system in which all the Christoffel symbols in Equation 5.03 are zero; therefore, all components of the Riemann-Christoffel tensor are zero. All components of this tensor are then zero in any coordinate system. The vanishing of the Riemann-Christoffel tensor is accordingly a necessary condition for flat space, and it can be shown that the vanishing of the tensor is also a sufficient condition.

4. From Equation 5.03, we can see at once that the tensor is skew-symmetric in $(j,\,k)$ so that

we have

5.04 $$R^l_{\cdot ijk} = -R^l_{\cdot ikj}.$$

Further, by straight substitution, we can also show that

5.05 $$R^l_{\cdot ijk} + R^l_{\cdot jki} + R^l_{\cdot kij} = 0$$

in which the three lower indices are given a cyclic permutation.

5. There is also a covariant form of the Riemann-Christoffel tensor, obtained by lowering the superscript and written as

5.06 $$R_{mijk} = g_{lm} R^l_{\cdot ijk}.$$

With a little manipulation, the covariant tensor can be written in either of the following forms,

$$R_{mijk} = \frac{\partial}{\partial x^j}[ik, m] - \frac{\partial}{\partial x^k}[ij, m]$$

5.07 $$+ \Gamma^l_{ij}[mk, l] - \Gamma^l_{ik}[mj, l]$$

or

$$R_{mijk} = \tfrac{1}{2}\left(\frac{\partial^2 g_{mk}}{\partial x^i \partial x^j} + \frac{\partial^2 g_{ij}}{\partial x^m \partial x^k} - \frac{\partial^2 g_{mj}}{\partial x^i \partial x^k} - \frac{\partial^2 g_{ik}}{\partial x^m \partial x^j}\right)$$

5.08 $$+ g^{pq}\{[mk, p][ij, q] - [mj, p][ik, q]\}$$

in which the Christoffel symbols are given by Equations 3.01 and 3.02. The covariant form has the same properties as the mixed form in Equations 5.04 and 5.05 with the superscript lowered. In addition, the covariant form is skew-symmetric in the first two indices (m, i) and symmetric with respect to the two pairs of indices, that is,

5.09 $$R_{mijk} = R_{jkmi}.$$

LOCALLY CARTESIAN SYSTEMS

6. In earlier sections, we have derived a number of results such as Equations 2.23 by assuming a Cartesian coordinate system; the question arises whether these results are true only in flat space. It is apparent from Equation 5.03 that the curvature of the space enters the question only when we differentiate the Christoffel symbols—that is, when we compare their values at different points in space. There is nothing to stop our choosing a coordinate system in which the Christoffel symbols are zero at one particular point; it is only when we insist on these symbols remaining zero at all other points that we require the space to be flat. A coordinate system in which all the Christoffel symbols

are zero at one point of the space is known as a *locally Cartesian* system. In such a system, the curvature tensor would be

$$R^l_{\cdot ijk} = \frac{\partial}{\partial x^j}\Gamma^l_{ik} - \frac{\partial}{\partial x^k}\Gamma^l_{ij},$$

but only at the origin, or the point where the Christoffel symbols are zero. If the space is curved, the symbols are not, in general, zero elsewhere, and we should use the full formula of Equation 5.03 for the curvature tensor.

7. Clearly, any result obtained by applying a Cartesian system to tensor point functions, such as those in Equation 2.05, is valid because we could have obtained the same result by choosing a locally Cartesian system at the point under consideration. Any results containing the first covariant derivatives of a tensor (or the second covariant derivatives of a scalar) are valid because they do not contain derivatives of the Christoffel symbols. In short, all results, given prior to this chapter, are valid in curved space. We cannot, however, verify a tensor equation containing higher covariant derivatives by an appeal to Cartesian coordinates unless the space is flat.

8. In a locally Cartesian system, the first ordinary derivatives of components of the metric tensor are zero at the origin of the system because the Christoffel symbols and the covariant derivatives of the metric tensor are zero. We can accordingly say that the system is Cartesian to a first order, or in the immediate neighborhood of the origin where the Christoffel symbols are zero.

9. Fermi[1] has proved further that a locally Cartesian system need not be confined to the neighborhood of one point assigned beforehand; it is possible to choose a Cartesian system in curved space which applies in the immediate neighborhood of all points of a given line assigned beforehand. This extension is sometimes useful.

SPECIAL FORMS OF THE CURVATURE TENSOR

10. It can be shown[2] that the number of independent components of the covariant curvature tensor in a space of N dimensions is

---

[1] Levi-Cività (1926), *The Absolute Differential Calculus*, 167.

[2] See for example, Synge and Schild (corrected reprint of 1964), *Tensor Calculus*, original ed. of 1949, 86.

5.10 $\qquad N^2(N^2-1)/12.$

This means that in three dimensions there are only six independent components; thus, all the curvature properties should be expressible in terms of a simpler symmetric second-order tensor formed by contracting the full curvature tensor.

11. One such contraction, known as the *Ricci* tensor, is formed by contracting the first and last indices, thus we have

5.11 $\qquad R_{ij}=g^{mk}R_{mijk}=R^k_{\cdot ijk}.$

Using the symmetrical and skew-symmetrical properties of the curvature tensor, this can also be written as

$$g^{mk}R_{imkj}=g^{mk}R_{kjim}=R_{ji},$$

which shows that the Ricci tensor is symmetric. The tensor has therefore six independent components and can represent all the curvature properties of 3-space.

By direct contraction of Equation 5.03 on the indices (l, k) and use of Equation 3.16, we can write the Ricci tensor as

5.12 $\qquad R_{ij}=\dfrac{\partial}{\partial x^j}\,\Gamma^l_{il}-\dfrac{\partial}{\partial x^l}\,\Gamma^l_{ij}+\Gamma^m_{il}\Gamma^l_{mj}-\Gamma^m_{ij}\Gamma^l_{ml}$

in which the first and last terms are

$$\frac{\partial^2(\ln\sqrt{g})}{\partial x^i\partial x^j}-\Gamma^m_{ij}\frac{\partial(\ln\sqrt{g})}{\partial x^m}=(\ln\sqrt{g})_{ij}.$$

In this last expression, g is the determinant of the metric tensor which is obviously not an invariant, although in a particular coordinate system, the determinant will be a function of the coordinates; and we can accordingly take its gradient and second covariant derivative.

12. Another contraction of the curvature tensor in three dimensions is

5.13 $\qquad S^{pq}=\tfrac{1}{4}\epsilon^{pmi}\epsilon^{qjk}R_{mijk}.$

If we multiply this by

$$\epsilon_{prs}\epsilon_{qtu}$$

and use Equation 2.20 and the skew-symmetrical properties of the curvature tensor, we have an alternative form

5.14 $\qquad \epsilon_{prs}\epsilon_{qtu}S^{pq}=R_{rstu}.$

We can also write Equation 5.13 as

$$S^{pq}=\tfrac{1}{4}\epsilon^{pmi}\epsilon^{qjk}R_{jkmi}=S^{qp},$$

showing that the tensor is symmetric with six independent components, which again can represent all the curvature properties of 3-space. We shall call this the *Lamé* tensor because, when all of its components are set equal to zero in flat 3-space, the tensor gives the well-known six Lamé equations which must be satisfied by the metric of any coordinate system in flat 3-space.

13. We shall finally relate the Ricci and Lamé tensors from Equations 5.11 and 5.14 as

$$\begin{aligned}R_{ij}&=g^{mk}\epsilon_{pmi}\epsilon_{qjk}S^{pq}\\&=g^{mk}\epsilon_{mip}\epsilon_{kqj}S^{pq}\\&=(g_{iq}g_{pj}-g_{ij}g_{pq})S^{pq},\end{aligned}$$

using Equation 2.28, so that if S is the contraction $g_{pq}S^{pq}$, we have

5.15 $\qquad R_{ij}=S_{ij}-Sg_{ij}.$

CURVATURE IN TWO DIMENSIONS

14. The idea of curved space is difficult because we are accustomed to think of "space" as the ordinary Euclidian flat space of three dimensions. We are more familiar with curved spaces of two dimensions, or curved "surfaces," because we can measure the curvature from the outside. As far as the tensor calculus is concerned, there is no essential difference between spaces of two- and three- or n-dimensions, except in the number of components which tensors can have in such spaces. A curved space of two dimensions has intrinsic curvature properties which do not depend on outside measurements. We can define the curvature tensor of two-dimensional curved space, as in Equation 5.03, by simply substituting Greek indices for Roman and restricting them to the numbers (1, 2). However, reference to Equation 5.10 will show that in two dimensions, the curvature tensor has only one independent component. The intrinsic curvature properties of a two-dimensional surface can accordingly be completely exhibited by an invariant, just as those of a 3-space can be completely specified by the six independent components of a symmetric second-order tensor. We denote this invariant by K and call it the Gaussian or specific curvature of the surface, defined by the following contraction of the curvature tensor,

5.16 $\qquad K=\tfrac{1}{4}\epsilon^{\alpha\beta}\epsilon^{\gamma\delta}R_{\alpha\beta\gamma\delta},$

corresponding to Equation 5.13.

15. We could, of course, have contracted the curvature tensor in another manner and so have defined K differently; but, if we had used a symmetric tensor, such as $a^{\alpha\beta}$ in the same way as $\epsilon^{\alpha\beta}$, the result would have been zero because of the skew-symmetry of the curvature tensor. By substituting for the ϵ-systems from Equations 2.30 and using the skew-symmetry of the curvature tensor, we can reduce Equation 5.16 to

5.17 $$K = R_{1212}/a,$$

which, in conjunction with Equation 5.07 or 5.08, enables us to calculate K for any given metric. The sheer labor of substitution is lightened if we choose orthogonal coordinates, so that $a_{12} = 0$ and the metric is

$$ds^2 = a_{11}(dx^1)^2 + a_{22}(dx^2)^2.$$

In that case, if we form the Christoffel symbols directly from the definitions of Equation 3.01 and substitute in Equation 5.08, we can express the result as

$$K = -\frac{1}{2\sqrt{a}}\left[\frac{\partial}{\partial x^1}\left(\frac{1}{\sqrt{a}}\frac{\partial a_{22}}{\partial x^1}\right) + \frac{\partial}{\partial x^2}\left(\frac{1}{\sqrt{a}}\frac{\partial a_{11}}{\partial x^2}\right)\right].$$

5.18

16. Multiplying Equation 5.16 by $\epsilon_{\epsilon\rho}\epsilon_{\sigma\tau}$ and using Equations 2.40, we have

5.19 $$R_{\epsilon\rho\sigma\tau} = K\epsilon_{\epsilon\rho}\epsilon_{\sigma\tau}$$

as an alternative expression which is sometimes useful. If we contract this equation to form the Ricci tensor in two dimensions and use Equations 2.32 and 2.34 for two arbitrary orthogonal vectors λ_α, μ_α, we have

$$R_{\rho\sigma} = Ka^{\epsilon\tau}(\lambda_\epsilon\mu_\rho - \mu_\epsilon\lambda_\rho)(\lambda_\sigma\mu_\tau - \mu_\sigma\lambda_\tau)$$
$$= -K(\lambda_\rho\lambda_\sigma + \mu_\rho\mu_\sigma)$$

5.20 $$= -Ka_{\rho\sigma}.$$

We could accordingly have defined K by contracting the Ricci tensor as

5.21 $$a^{\rho\sigma}R_{\rho\sigma} = -K\delta^\rho_\rho = -2K,$$

which gives us another way of calculating K from the two-dimensional equivalent of Equation 5.12.

17. Corresponding to Equation 5.02, we have for an arbitrary vector λ_α,

5.22 $$\lambda_{\alpha,\beta\gamma} - \lambda_{\alpha,\gamma\beta} = \lambda_\delta R^\delta_{.\alpha\beta\gamma} = \lambda^\delta R_{\delta\alpha\beta\gamma}.$$

If we substitute Equation 5.19 and use Equation 2.36, we have

5.23 $$\lambda_{\alpha,\beta\gamma} - \lambda_{\alpha,\gamma\beta} = K\mu_\alpha\epsilon_{\beta\gamma}$$

in which μ_α is the usual vector orthogonal to λ_α. If we multiply this by $\epsilon^{\beta\gamma}$ and use Equation 2.38, we have after some interchange of dummy indices

5.24 $$\epsilon^{\beta\gamma}\lambda_{\alpha,\beta\gamma} = K\mu_\alpha.$$

These equations enable us to interchange indices in the second covariant derivatives of surface vectors.

18. It should be noted that in this chapter we have derived only properties of a surface which depend on the metric tensor and its derivatives. Such properties are called *intrinsic*. They usually have counterparts in the intrinsic properties of spaces of more than two dimensions, which is one of the great advantages of the tensor calculus. A surface can also have *extrinsic* properties, derived from the space in which it is embedded. We shall consider these properties later.

RIEMANNIAN CURVATURE

19. We can simplify the notion of curvature of a general space by considering the curvature of surfaces within it.
We take a pair of unit orthogonal vectors λ^r, μ^r at a point P in the space and let the pair define a *section* of the space, so that any other unit vector in the section is given in terms of a parameter θ by the relation

$$l^r = \lambda^r \sin\theta + \mu^r \cos\theta.$$

The geodesics of the space in all these directions, l^r, will form a definite surface whose Gaussian curvature is called the *Riemannian curvature* of the space for the section defined by λ^r, μ^r. If the space is flat, all the geodesics would be straight lines; and the Gaussian curvature of all the section planes is zero, so that the Riemannian curvature for all sections would be zero.
Working from this definition, it can be shown[3] that the Riemannian curvature of the section, defined by the unit orthogonal vectors (λ^r, μ^r), is given by

5.25 $$C = R_{mijk}\lambda^m\mu^i\lambda^j\mu^k.$$

20. In two dimensions, the only "section" of the space in this sense is the space itself; and the geodesic surface formed by geodesics of the space — that is, by geodesics of the surface — is again the

[3] Levi-Città, *op. cit. supra* note 1, 196.

surface itself. Accordingly, we may write the Riemannian curvature as

$$C = K = R_{\alpha\beta\gamma\delta}\lambda^{\alpha}\mu^{\beta}\lambda^{\gamma}\mu^{\delta}.$$

Evaluating this invariant for the special coordinate system of Equations 2.33 gives

$$C = K = R_{1212}/a,$$

which agrees with Equation 5.17. This result does not, of course, prove the more general formula of Equation 5.25, but does demonstrate the consistency of Equation 5.25.

21. Now suppose that in three dimensions we complete the orthogonal triad with a third vector ν^{r}, such that $(\lambda^{r}, \mu^{r}, \nu^{r})$ is a right-handed system. If we multiply Equation 5.14 by $\lambda^{r}\mu^{s}\lambda^{t}\mu^{u}$ and use

Equations 2.23, we have

$$S^{pq}\nu_{p}\nu_{q} = R_{rstu}\lambda^{r}\mu^{s}\lambda^{t}\mu^{u}$$

so that the Riemannian curvature in three dimensions can be written in terms of the Lamé tensor as

5.26 $$C = S^{pq}\nu_{p}\nu_{q} = S_{pq}\nu^{p}\nu^{q}.$$

It should be noted that the geodesic surface, whose Gaussian curvature is C, is now formed by all the geodesics perpendicular to the direction ν^{p}. It can be shown [4] that, in general, there will be three mutually orthogonal *principal directions* at a point which give rise in this way to stationary (usually maximum or minimum) values of the Riemannian curvature known as the *principal curvatures*. The analogy with a curved surface will become clear later. We can also consider the Riemannian curvature as analogous to inertia or strain, the only difference being the nature of the tensor S_{pq}.

[4] *Ibid.*, 201.

CHAPTER 6

Extrinsic Properties of Surfaces

FORMS OF SURFACE EQUATIONS

1. We have considered the intrinsic properties of surfaces as two-dimensional spaces in their own right. We have now to consider the properties of the same surfaces when embedded in space of three dimensions.

2. The link between the two sets of properties will be an infinitesimal displacement on the surface, which can be described either as dx^r in the space coordinates or as dx^α in the surface coordinates, following the convention introduced in § 1–6 and §2–34. The two are related by the ordinary formula for total differentiation

6.01 $$dx^r = \frac{\partial x^r}{\partial x^\alpha}\, dx^\alpha$$

in which the partial derivatives are considered as known from the equations of the surface, so that each space coordinate is expressed in terms of the two surface coordinates—either explicitly or implicitly. For example, the equations of a spherical surface of constant radius r are given in terms of latitude (ϕ) and longitude (ω) as

$$x = r \cos \phi \cos \omega$$
$$y = r \cos \phi \sin \omega$$
$$z = r \sin \phi.$$

In these equations, the x^r are (x, y, z) and the x^α are (ω, ϕ). We can obtain the $\partial x^r/\partial x^\alpha$ by direct differentiation as, for example,

$$\frac{\partial x}{\partial \phi} = -r \sin \phi \cos \omega.$$

3. These partial derivatives occur so often that it is usual to give them the special symbol

6.02 $$\frac{\partial x^r}{\partial x^\alpha} = x_\alpha^r.$$

Evidently, the set of these quantities will transform like a contravariant space vector for each value of α and like a covariant surface vector for each value of r. This last point can be illustrated by considering each space coordinate as a scalar defined over the surface, in which case the corresponding x_α^r becomes the surface gradient of the scalar.

4. The equations of a surface in relation to the surrounding space may be given in one of three forms. The first, or Gauss' form, expresses each space coordinate as some function of the two surface coordinates (u^1, u^2). In symbols, this form is usually shown as

6.03 $$x^r = x^r(u^1, u^2) \qquad (r = 1, 2, 3),$$

much as the equations of a sphere are expressed above.

5. The second, or Monge's form, expresses one space coordinate as a function of the other two as, for example,

6.04 $$x^3 = f(x^1, x^2),$$

which similarly imposes a restriction on what points of the space can form the surface. We could take (x^1, x^2) as surface coordinates, in which case the form is equivalent to the Gauss form

$$x^3 = f(u^1, u^2)$$
$$x^2 = u^2$$
$$x^1 = u^1$$

If, for example, the surface is given by

$$z = f(x, y)$$

in rectangular Cartesian coordinates, then y or u^2 is constant over the xz-plane, and the x- or u^1-surface coordinate lines are accordingly the intersection of the surface with the xz-planes. We then have

$$x_1^3 = \partial f / \partial u^1 = \partial f / \partial x$$

and similarly

$$x_2^3 = \partial f / \partial u^2 = \partial f / \partial y,$$

while the other components are given by

$$x_\alpha^r = \delta_\alpha^r \qquad (r = 1, 2).$$

It should be noted, however, that this last equation is not a tensor equation, but is merely a relation between *some* components of the tensor x_α^r in a particular coordinate system. We cannot manipulate this last equation as a tensor equation by, for example, taking its covariant derivative.

6. This device of taking two of the space coordinates as surface coordinates often leads quickly to simple results, and we shall use this device throughout Part II. We lose no generality by doing so, but we must check the results for tensor character, as in the case of x_α^r above, before manipulating the results further as tensors.

7. The third form of surface equation expresses some functional relation between the three space coordinates, which are accordingly restricted in value at points on the surface. In this case, we may write

6.05 $$f(x^1, x^2, x^3) = N$$

in which N is a constant over the surface. By assigning different values to N, we should have different surfaces which would, nevertheless, have some properties in common, dictated by the form of the function f. This third form, or its equivalent

$$f(x^1, x^2, x^3, N) = 0,$$

is accordingly most useful when we are required to express a *family* of surfaces. If we are not given the surface coordinates in terms of the space coordinates, we could, as in Monge's form, take x^1, x^2 as surface coordinates. By partial differentiation of Equation 6.05 over the surface with x^2 and x^1, respectively, constant, we then have

$$\frac{\partial f}{\partial x^1} + \frac{\partial f}{\partial x^3} x_1^3 = 0$$

$$\frac{\partial f}{\partial x^2} + \frac{\partial f}{\partial x^3} x_2^3 = 0,$$

which give the x_α^3; the other components are given as before by

$$x_\alpha^r = \delta_\alpha^r \qquad (r = 1, 2).$$

8. Finally, we could take N in Equation 6.05 as one of the space coordinates. The other two space coordinates, which could be adopted as surface coordinates on the family of constant N-surfaces, must then be chosen in such a way that they can vary independently of N and of each other; this implies that the gradient of each coordinate must be perpendicular to the other two coordinate lines. This arrangement is adopted for Part II, where it will be explained in greater detail.

9. The functions in the three forms of surface equations and their derivatives must satisfy certain conditions if the functions are to represent a real nondegenerate surface, and even then there may be singular points on the surface.[1] This need not present too much of a problem because the surfaces with which we shall be dealing will either satisfy these conditions or will be prescribed as existing surfaces by the physical conditions.

THE METRIC TENSORS

10. We can easily relate the space and surface metric tensors, g_{rs} and $a_{\alpha\beta}$, by considering a small surface line element ds. Considered as a displacement in space, this is

$$ds^2 = g_{rs} dx^r dx^s = g_{rs} x_\alpha^r x_\beta^s dx^\alpha dx^\beta$$

in which we have used Equations 6.01 and 6.02. But considered as a displacement on the surface, it is

$$ds^2 = a_{\alpha\beta} dx^\alpha dx^\beta,$$

and because the two invariant displacements are the same for any arbitrary dx^α and the tensors multiplying the dx^α are symmetric, we must have, as in § 2–13,

6.06 $$a_{\alpha\beta} = g_{rs} x_\alpha^r x_\beta^s.$$

SURFACE VECTORS

11. If we suppose that the changes in coordinates in Equation 6.01 take place over an arc length ds in

[1] See, for example, Kreyszig (revised reprint of 1964), *Differential Geometry*, English ed. of 1959, 1–117. This is a free translation of "Differentialgeometrie," printed in 1957 in *Mathematik und ihre Anwendungen in Physik und Technik*, series A, v. 25, 1–143.

the direction of a unit surface vector whose space components are l^r and whose surface components are l^α and then divide Equation 6.01 by ds, we have

6.07 $$l^r = x^r_\alpha l^\alpha,$$

which relates the space and surface contravariant components of any unit surface vector. If we multiply Equation 6.07 by $g_{rs}x^s_\beta$ and use Equation 6.06, we have

6.08 $$l_s x^s_\beta = a_{\alpha\beta} l^\alpha = l_\beta,$$

which relates the covariant components.

12. We have seen that the x^r_α are equivalent to the contravariant space components and the covariant surface components of a surface vector and must therefore be expressible in terms of any two mutually orthogonal surface vectors l^r or l_α and j^r or j_α. We can easily verify from Equations 6.07 and 6.08 that this expression is

6.09 $$x^r_\alpha = l^r l_\alpha + j^r j_\alpha.$$

We note that the two vectors in this tensor equation are quite arbitrary. If we know the space and surface components of any two orthogonal unit surface vectors in a particular coordinate system, then we have all the x^r_α in the same system.

THE UNIT NORMAL

13. We shall normally be dealing with closed surfaces, and we denote the unit vector normal to the surface by ν^r and define its direction as *outward*

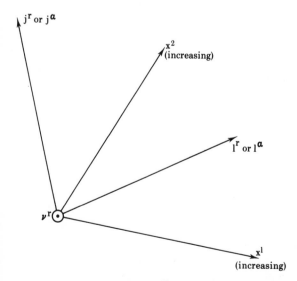

Figure 5.

from a closed surface, that is, away from the region of space enclosed by the surface. We shall consider that the two surface vectors in Equation 6.09 form a right-handed orthogonal triad with ν^r in the order (l^r, j^r, ν^r), and the rotation from l^r to j^r is in the same sense as the rotation of the positive direction of the x^1-surface coordinate line toward the x^2-surface coordinate line. The diagram (fig. 5) illustrates the situation if the paper represents a tangent plane to the surface and if the unit normal points toward the reader.

14. We are now able to obtain a relation between the contravariant metric tensors corresponding to Equation 6.06. Using Equations 2.09 and 2.35, we have

$$g^{rs} = l^r l^s + j^r j^s + \nu^r \nu^s$$
$$= x^r_\alpha x^s_\beta (l^\alpha l^\beta + j^\alpha j^\beta) + \nu^r \nu^s$$
6.10 $$= a^{\alpha\beta} x^r_\alpha x^s_\beta + \nu^r \nu^s.$$

15. Next, we shall express the unit normal in terms of the x^r_α. Using Equations 2.27 and 2.32, we have

$$\nu_r \epsilon^{rst} = l^s j^t - j^s l^t = x^s_\alpha x^t_\beta (l^\alpha j^\beta - j^\alpha l^\beta)$$
6.11 $$= \epsilon^{\alpha\beta} x^s_\alpha x^t_\beta.$$

Multiplying this by ϵ_{pst} and using Equations 2.19 and 2.22, we have

6.12 $$\nu_p = \tfrac{1}{2} \epsilon^{\alpha\beta} \epsilon_{pst} x^s_\alpha x^t_\beta,$$

showing that ν_p, besides being a covariant space vector, is a surface invariant; its components do not change if the surface coordinates are transformed independently of the space coordinates.

SURFACE COVARIANT DERIVATIVES

16. All the formulas in Chapter 3 on covariant differentiation can be obtained in exactly the same way in two dimensions, in regard to the differentiation of tensors which are defined only on the surface. We have only to form the surface Christoffel symbols from the metric $a_{\alpha\beta}$ instead of g_{rs} and to restrict the indices (α, β) to (1, 2). In cases where we used locally Cartesian coordinates $\bar{x}^r$ in the course of a proof, we now use locally Cartesian coordinates $\bar{x}^\alpha$ in two dimensions, when all components of the metric tensor $a_{\alpha\beta}$ will be constants *at the point considered*. The metric tensor $a_{\alpha\beta}$ and

its associated tensor $a^{\alpha\beta}$, the ϵ-systems $\epsilon^{\alpha\beta}$ and $\epsilon_{\alpha\beta}$, and the Kronecker deltas all behave as constants under covariant differentiation in two dimensions, just as their counterparts did in three dimensions. We can immediately write down, for instance, the counterpart of the Equation 3.16 as

6.13
$$\frac{\partial(\ln\sqrt{a})}{\partial x^\alpha} = \Gamma^\beta_{\alpha\beta}.$$

17. In the case of tensors defined in space, the procedure is much the same. First, we differentiate the tensors covariantly with the respect to the space metric g_{rs} in order to discover the variation of the tensor for a change in the space coordinates dx^r; and then second, we restrict this change to a displacement on the surface, just as we did along a line in § 4–1. For example, the change in a space tensor A_{rs} for a change in the space coordinates dx^t is

$$A_{rs,\,t}\,dx^t.$$

But if the change in the space coordinates results from a displacement on the surface corresponding to a change dx^α in the surface coordinates, this is

$$A_{rs,\,t}\,x^t_\alpha dx^\alpha.$$

We call the new tensor

$$A_{rs,\,t}\,x^t_\alpha,$$

the surface covariant derivatives of the space tensor A_{rs} with respect to the surface coordinates x^α.

18. It is at once evident that g_{rs}, g^{rs}, ϵ^{rst}, ϵ_{rst} and all the Kronecker deltas formed from the three-index ϵ-systems behave as constants under surface covariant differentiation. For example, the surface covariant derivative of g_{rs} is

$$g_{rst}x^t_\alpha = 0$$

because g_{rst} is zero.

19. As an example, we take the surface covariant derivative of x^r_α with respect to x^β, which we shall write as $x^r_{\alpha\beta}$, from the tensor Equation 6.09,

$$x^r_\alpha = l^r l_\alpha + j^r j_\alpha.$$

We then have

$$x^r_{\alpha\beta} = l^r_s x^s_\beta l_\alpha + l^r l_{\alpha\beta} + j^r_s x^s_\beta j_\alpha + j^r j_{\alpha\beta}.$$

By expanding the covariant derivatives and rearranging terms, this expression becomes

$$\frac{\partial}{\partial x^\beta}(l^r l_\alpha + j^r j_\alpha) + \Gamma^r_{st}(l^t l_\alpha + j^t j_\alpha)x^s_\beta - \Gamma^\gamma_{\alpha\beta}(l^r l_\gamma + j^r j_\gamma)$$

so that finally we have

6.14
$$x^r_{\alpha\beta} = \frac{\partial^2 x^r}{\partial x^\alpha \partial x^\beta} + \Gamma^r_{st}x^t_\alpha x^s_\beta - \Gamma^\gamma_{\alpha\beta}x^r_\gamma$$

in which the space Christoffel symbols formed from g_{rs} are given Roman indices; and the surface Christoffel symbols formed from $a_{\alpha\beta}$ are given Greek indices. It should be noted that $x^r_{\alpha\beta}$ is symmetric in the Greek indices.

20. The rules for surface covariant differentiation of mixed space and surface tensors are illustrated by Equation 6.14 for the tensor x^r_α. To obtain the terms containing the space Christoffel symbols, we simply treat the tensor as a space tensor with respect to each of its Roman indices and hold the Greek indices fixed. If we are differentiating with respect to the surface coordinate x^γ, we complete the term with x^u_γ in which u is a dummy index appearing also in the space Christoffel symbol. The terms containing surface Christoffel symbols are obtained by treating the tensor as a surface tensor with respect to each of its Greek indices while holding the Roman indices fixed. Thus, the surface covariant derivative of $A^{rs}_{\alpha\beta}$ is

$$A^{rs}_{\alpha\beta,\,\gamma} = \frac{\partial A^{rs}_{\alpha\beta}}{\partial x^\gamma} + \Gamma^r_{tu}A^{ts}_{\alpha\beta}x^u_\gamma + \Gamma^s_{tu}A^{rt}_{\alpha\beta}x^u_\gamma$$
$$- \Gamma^\delta_{\alpha\gamma}A^{rs}_{\delta\beta} - \Gamma^\delta_{\beta\gamma}A^{rs}_{\alpha\delta}.$$

21. It is of no consequence if a space tensor is defined over one surface only, such as the surface vector whose space components are l^r, or the vector ν^r normal to one given surface. We can always suppose that the given surface belongs to some family of surfaces in which case, for example, the ν^r would become a unit vector field, differentiable in any direction in space. When we multiply by x^r_α, we restrict the variation to displacements on one particular surface, and we can forget the other members of the family. We have already used this device to find the variation of tensors defined along a line in Chapter 4.

22. We shall often denote surface covariant differentiation, with or without a comma, by simply adding a Greek subscript, particularly when all the Roman indices are superscripts, for example,

$$\nu^r_\alpha = \nu^r_{,\alpha} = \nu^r_{,s}x^s_\alpha = \nu^r_s x^s_\alpha.$$

The commas will be dropped if it is clear from the context or from the usage that covariant differentiation is involved.

THE GAUSS EQUATIONS

23. If we take the surface covariant derivative of Equation 6.06, we have

$$g_{rs}x_{\alpha\gamma}^r x_\beta^s + g_{rs}x_\alpha^r x_{\beta\gamma}^s = 0.$$

By cyclic permutation of the free surface indices (α, β, γ), we have also

$$g_{rs}x_{\beta\alpha}^r x_\gamma^s + g_{rs}x_\beta^r x_{\gamma\alpha}^s = 0$$

$$g_{rs}x_{\gamma\beta}^r x_\alpha^s + g_{rs}x_\gamma^r x_{\alpha\beta}^s = 0.$$

Adding the first two, subtracting the third, and remembering that $x_{\alpha\beta}^r$ is symmetric in (α, β) and that g_{rs} is symmetric, we have

6.15 $\qquad g_{rs}x_{\alpha\gamma}^r x_\beta^s = 0.$

If we consider the space coordinates, it is apparent from Equation 6.09 that x_β^s is an arbitrary surface vector; therefore, $x_{\alpha\gamma}^r$ must be a space vector in the direction of the normal. We can then write

6.16 $\qquad x_{\alpha\gamma}^r = b_{\alpha\gamma}\nu^r$

in which $b_{\alpha\gamma}$ is evidently a symmetric surface tensor like $x_{\alpha\gamma}^r$. These equations are usually known as the Gauss equations of the surface (not a very distinctive name in this subject), and the tensor $b_{\alpha\gamma}$ is known as the *second fundamental form* of the surface. (The metric tensor $a_{\alpha\gamma}$ is sometimes known as the *first fundamental form*.) We shall see later that the second fundamental form settles the extrinsic curvatures of the surface.

THE WEINGARTEN EQUATIONS

24. We take next the surface covariant derivative of Equation 6.10 as

$$0 = a^{\alpha\beta}(x_{\alpha\gamma}^r x_\beta^s + x_\alpha^r x_{\beta\gamma}^s) + \nu_\gamma^r \nu^s + \nu^r \nu_\gamma^s.$$

If we multiply this by ν_s and use Equation 3.19, we shall have

$$\nu_s \nu_\gamma^s = \nu_s \nu_t^s x_\gamma^t = 0$$

and, from Equation 6.09,

$$\nu_s x_\beta^s = 0,$$

so that finally, using Equation 6.16, we have

6.17 $\qquad \nu_\gamma^r = -a^{\alpha\beta}b_{\beta\gamma}x_\alpha^r.$

These equations, giving the surface derivatives of the normal, are known as the *Weingarten* equations of the surface. They give rise to a *third fundamental*

form of the surface which we define as

$$c_{\alpha\beta} = g_{rs}\nu_\alpha^r \nu_\beta^s.$$

If we substitute Equation 6.17 and use Equations 6.06 and 2.36, we have also

$$c_{\alpha\beta} = a^{\gamma\delta}b_{\alpha\gamma}b_{\beta\delta}.$$

25. We shall see later that the three fundamental forms $a_{\alpha\beta}$, $b_{\alpha\beta}$, $c_{\alpha\beta}$ are not independent; corresponding components are connected by a linear relation.

26. If we contract the Weingarten Equation 6.17 with $g_{rs}x_\delta^s$, we have

$$g_{rs}\nu_\gamma^r x_\delta^s = -a^{\alpha\beta}b_{\beta\gamma}a_{\alpha\delta} = -\delta_\delta^\beta b_{\beta\gamma} = -b_{\gamma\delta}$$

as an alternative expression for the second fundamental form. Comparable expressions for all three fundamental forms are collected here for easy reference as

$$a_{\alpha\beta} = g_{rs}x_\alpha^r x_\beta^s$$

$$b_{\alpha\beta} = -g_{rs}x_\alpha^r \nu_\beta^s$$

6.18 $\qquad c_{\alpha\beta} = g_{rs}\nu_\alpha^r \nu_\beta^s = a^{\gamma\delta}b_{\alpha\gamma}b_{\beta\delta}.$

THE MAINARDI-CODAZZI EQUATIONS

27. We have so far not considered the sort of space in which the surface is embedded; it could be either curved or flat. As we have seen, this question involves the second covariant derivatives of a space vector, for which we shall take the unit normal.

28. We start with the relation $\nu_r x_\alpha^r = 0$, obtainable from Equation 6.09, because ν_r is perpendicular to all surface vectors. Taking the surface covariant derivative and using Equation 6.16, we have

6.19 $\qquad \nu_{rs}x_\alpha^r x_\beta^s = -b_{\alpha\beta};$

differentiating again, we have

6.20 $\qquad \nu_{rst}x_\alpha^r x_\beta^s x_\gamma^t + \nu_{rs}x_\alpha^r \nu^s b_{\beta\gamma} = -b_{\alpha\beta\gamma}$

in which we have used Equations 3.19 and 6.16. We shall now interchange (β, γ). In the first term, we can also interchange (s, t) *if the space is flat* because, as we have seen in Equation 5.01,

$$\nu_{rst} = \nu_{rts},$$

so that the first term remains unchanged. The second term also remains unchanged because $b_{\beta\gamma}$ is symmetric. We conclude therefore that if the space in the immediate neighborhood of the surface is flat, we have

6.21 $b_{\alpha\beta\gamma} = b_{\alpha\gamma\beta}.$

These are known as the *Mainardi-Codazzi* equations. Owing to the symmetry of the $b_{\alpha\beta}$, there are only two independent equations, namely,

$$b_{112} = b_{121}$$

$$b_{212} = b_{221}.$$

We have shown that the Mainardi-Codazzi equations are necessary conditions for the surface to be embedded in flat space. They can take various forms, which we shall derive later, sometimes by considering the second covariant derivatives of space vectors other than ν_r; but all these forms are equivalent to the simple relation in Equation 6.21 between the surface covariant derivatives of the $b_{\alpha\beta}$.

29. It should be noted that while the $b_{\alpha\beta\gamma}$ are first covariant derivatives of the surface tensor $b_{\alpha\beta}$, it is evident from the Gauss Equation 6.16 or from Equation 6.20 that they are connected with the second derivatives of space vectors and, for this reason, are affected by the curvature of the surrounding space.

In flat space, the surface tensor $b_{\alpha\beta\gamma}$ is symmetric in any two indices because of the Codazzi Equation 6.21 and also because $b_{\alpha\beta}$ is symmetric.

30. However, if the surface is embedded in space whose curvature tensor is R_{urst}, we can use Equation 5.02 and make the necessary modifications in working from Equation 6.20 to show that the "Mainardi-Codazzi" equations would then take the form

6.22 $b_{\alpha\beta\gamma} = b_{\alpha\gamma\beta} - R_{urst}\nu^u x_\alpha^r x_\beta^s x_\gamma^t.$

This equation reduces to Equation 6.21 when the space is flat. If the curvature tensor is specified, as it usually will be by the conditions of the problem, then these equations, although different, are just as restrictive as Equation 6.21.

THE GAUSSIAN CURVATURE

31. We shall see later that the $b_{\alpha\beta}$ determine the curvatures of the surface, so that there must be a relation between the $b_{\alpha\beta}$ and the intrinsic curvature of the surface considered as a space of two dimensions—that is, the Gaussian or specific curvature which we defined in Equation 5.16.

We start with Equation 6.08 for an arbitrary unit surface vector

$$l_\alpha = l_r x_\alpha^r$$

and take its surface covariant derivative

6.23 $l_{\alpha\beta} = l_{rs} x_\alpha^r x_\beta^s + (l_r \nu^r) b_{\alpha\beta},$

the last term being zero because l_r is perpendicular to ν^r. Again, we differentiate and have

6.24 $l_{\alpha\beta\gamma} = l_{rst} x_\alpha^r x_\beta^s x_\gamma^t + l_{rs} x_\alpha^r x_{\beta\gamma}^s + l_{rs} x_\beta^s \nu^r b_{\alpha\gamma}.$

If we interchange (β, γ), the first term on the right remains the same if the surrounding space is flat because, in that case, we have $l_{rst} = l_{rts}$ from Equation 5.01. The second term remains the same anyway because $x_{\beta\gamma}^s$ is symmetric in (β, γ). We then have

$$l_{\alpha\beta\gamma} - l_{\alpha\gamma\beta} = l_{rs}\nu^r x_\beta^s b_{\alpha\gamma} - l_{rs}\nu^r x_\gamma^s b_{\alpha\beta}$$

6.25 $= -\nu_{rs} x_\delta^r x_\beta^s b_{\alpha\gamma} l^\delta + \nu_{rs} x_\delta^r x_\gamma^s b_{\alpha\beta} l^\delta,$

using Equations 3.19 and 6.07. If we now introduce Equations 6.19 and 5.22, we have

$$R_{\delta\alpha\beta\gamma} l^\delta = (b_{\alpha\gamma} b_{\beta\delta} - b_{\delta\gamma} b_{\alpha\beta}) l^\delta.$$

Because l^δ is arbitrary, we have also

6.26 $K\epsilon_{\delta\alpha}\epsilon_{\beta\gamma} = R_{\delta\alpha\beta\gamma} = (b_{\alpha\gamma} b_{\beta\delta} - b_{\delta\gamma} b_{\alpha\beta}),$

the only nonzero form of which, introducing Equation 5.17, is

6.27 $aK = R_{1212} = b_{11} b_{22} - (b_{12})^2 = b.$

In Equation 6.27, we write b for the determinant of the $b_{\alpha\beta}$, while a is as usual the determinant of the metric tensor $a_{\alpha\beta}$. This remarkable result relates the $b_{\alpha\beta}$ to the expression of K or R_{1212} in terms of differentials of the $a_{\alpha\beta}$ (for example, Equation 5.18). This result is again due to Gauss and is in fact equivalent to his "theorema egregium." The form

$$b = R_{1212},$$

when expanded, is sometimes known as the *Gauss characteristic equation*.

32. It should be noted, however, that this result is true only if the surface is embedded in flat space. If we make the necessary modifications and from Equation 5.02 use

$$l_{rst} - l_{rts} = R_{urst} l^u,$$

we find that for a surface embedded in space whose curvature tensor is R_{urst}, the combination of Equation 6.26 with Equation 5.19 would be

$$K\epsilon_{\delta\alpha}\epsilon_{\beta\gamma} = R_{\delta\alpha\beta\gamma} = b_{\alpha\gamma}b_{\beta\delta} - b_{\delta\gamma}b_{\alpha\beta} + R_{urst}x_\delta^u x_\alpha^r x_\beta^s x_\gamma^t.$$

6.28

The Gaussian curvature K, being intrinsic to the surface, is the same whether the space is curved or flat. We conclude therefore that the $b_{\alpha\beta}$ must change with the curvature of the space. We shall consider this further in §8–19 through §8–26.

33. According to a theorem of Bonnet, any six quantities $a_{\alpha\beta}$ and $b_{\alpha\beta}$, together with their derivatives, which satisfy the Gauss characteristic equation and the two Mainardi-Codazzi equations, determine a surface uniquely except for its position and orientation in space. The theorem is usually proved for a surface in flat space,[2] but is obviously true also in curved space, provided the curvature tensor is specified and the full Codazzi and Gauss equations, Equations 6.22 and 6.28, are used. We cannot expect therefore to derive any other independent properties of a surface; indeed, some of the quantities we have already derived, such as the $c_{\alpha\beta}$, cannot be independent. They are, nevertheless, useful tools, so long as we do not expect them to unearth a completely new result which could not be obtained otherwise.

---

[2] See, for instance, Forsyth (reprint of 1920), *Lectures on the Differential Geometry of Curves and Surfaces*, original ed. of 1912, 51.

CHAPTER 7

Extrinsic Properties of Surface Curves

THE TANGENT VECTORS

1. We shall now investigate the properties of surface curves considered both as curves on the surface and in space. The unit tangent to the curve will be either l^r or l^α, depending on whether we consider the unit tangent to be a space or a surface vector, and the orthogonal surface vector will be j^r or j^α as in figure 5 (see §6–13). As before, we shall also consider, as we can do without any loss of generality, that the two vectors are the unit tangents, respectively, to a family of surface curves and to their orthogonal trajectories, defined in some way over a finite region of the surface, in which case we can differentiate the vectors with respect to the surface coordinates without confining our attention to one particular curve.

CURVATURE

2. As in Equation 6.07, the space and surface components of the unit tangent are connected by

$$l^r = x_\alpha^r l^\alpha.$$

We differentiate this with respect to the surface coordinate x^β and use Equation 6.16 to obtain

$$l_s^r x_\beta^s = \nu^r(b_{\alpha\beta}l^\alpha) + x_\alpha^r l_\beta^\alpha.$$

In the last term, we substitute Equation 6.09 for x_α^r and introduce the (intrinsic) geodesic curvatures σ, σ^* of the l_α-curves and of their j_α-trajectories from Equations 4.11. We then have

7.01 $\qquad l_s^r x_\beta^s = \nu^r(b_{\alpha\beta}l^\alpha) + j^r(\sigma l_\beta + \sigma^* j_\beta).$

We are now able to introduce the principal normal m^r and the curvature χ of l^r considered as a curve in space from Equations 4.06; we do so by contracting the last equation with l^β. We then have

7.02 $\qquad l_s^r l^s = \chi m^r = (b_{\alpha\beta}l^\alpha l^\beta)\nu^r + \sigma j^r,$

which shows that the principal normal to the space curve lies in the plane containing the surface normal ν^r and j^r. Moreover, l^r must be perpendicular to this plane because l^r is perpendicular to all three space vectors in Equation 7.02, so that the plane also contains the binormal n^r. The situation is shown with the appropriate conventions in figure 6, which represents the plane perpendicular to l^r.

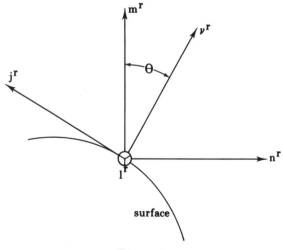

Figure 6.

39

If θ, as shown in figure 6, is the positive rotation from m^r to ν^r about l^r, then we have at once from Equations 3.20 and 7.02

7.03 $\qquad l_{rs}\nu^r l^s = -\nu_{rs}l^r l^s = b_{\alpha\beta}l^\alpha l^\beta = \chi \cos \theta = k$

7.04 $\qquad l_{rs}j^r l^s = \sigma = \chi \sin \theta.$

From this last equation and Equation 4.07, it is evident that

$$l_{rs}j^r l^s = l_{\alpha\beta}j^\alpha l^\beta$$

for any pair of surface vectors. This expression is a special case of a more general proposition which we shall obtain in Equation 8.25.

3. Equations 7.03 and 7.04 are usually attributed to Meusnier. The quantity k in the first equation depends only on $b_{\alpha\beta}$, which is a surface tensor point function, and on the direction l^α; it does not depend on the curvature of any particular curve in this direction. Consequently, the quantity k is the same for all surface curves in this initial direction (l^α) and is therefore a property of the surface in this direction. It is called the *normal curvature* of the surface in the direction l^α.

4. If the curve l^α is a geodesic of the surface, as previously defined by $\sigma = 0$ in § 4–6, then because it is not, in general, a geodesic also of the space, $\chi \neq 0$, we must have $\theta = 0$. The principal normal to a surface geodesic accordingly coincides with the surface normal. Also from the first Meusnier equation, we determine that the normal curvature of the surface in a given direction is the space curvature of the geodesic in that direction.

TORSION

5. We have now to consider the torsion τ of the curve l^r. From figure 6, we can express the binormal as

$$n_r = \nu_r \sin \theta - j_r \cos \theta,$$

and by differentiating this along the curve (arc element ds), we have, using Equations 4.06,

$$n_{rs}l^s = -\tau m_r = \nu_{rs}l^s \sin \theta - j_{rs}l^s \cos \theta$$
$$+ (\nu_r \cos \theta + j_r \sin \theta)(d\theta/ds).$$

If we contract with j^r (or ν^r), we have

7.05 $\qquad \tau + (d\theta/ds) = -\nu_{rs}j^r l^s.$

Contraction with l^r would give us nothing new, but if we contract Equation 6.19 with $l^\alpha j^\beta$ or $l^\beta j^\alpha$, we have, because $b_{\alpha\beta}$ is symmetric,

7.06 $\qquad \nu_{rs}j^r l^s = \nu_{rs}l^r j^s = -b_{\alpha\beta}l^\alpha j^\beta.$

Combining these last two equations, we have

7.07 $\qquad \tau + (d\theta/ds) = b_{\alpha\beta}l^\alpha j^\beta.$

But the expression on the right, like $b_{\alpha\beta}l^\alpha l^\beta = k$, depends only on the direction l^α and not on any particular curve in this direction, and so expresses a property of the surface in the direction l^α which is the same for all curves in that direction. For the geodesic in the direction l^α, we have $\theta = 0$, so that the expression on the right of Equation 7.07 is the space torsion of this geodesic. For this reason, the expression on the right of Equation 7.07 is known as the *geodesic torsion* (t) of the surface in the direction l^α. Collecting all the relevant formulas, we have

$$t = \tau + (d\theta/ds) = b_{\alpha\beta}l^\alpha j^\beta = b_{\alpha\beta}j^\alpha l^\beta$$
7.08 $\qquad\qquad = -\nu_{rs}l^r j^s = -\nu_{rs}j^r l^s.$

6. The geodesic torsion in the direction j^α is similarly

$$b_{\alpha\beta}j^\alpha(-l^\beta) = -t,$$

so that the sum of the geodesic torsions in any two perpendicular directions is zero.

7. From Equations 7.03 and 7.08, we obtain at once a useful formula for the intrinsic change of the unit normal vector along a line whose unit tangent is l^s,

7.09 $\qquad \nu_{rs}l^s = -kl_r - tj_r,$

having noted that the vector on the left can have no ν_r-component because of Equation 3.19, together with the corresponding two-dimensional formula

7.10 $\qquad b_{\alpha\beta}l^\beta = +kl_\alpha + tj_\alpha.$

8. If the normal curvature in the j^β-direction is k^*, the corresponding equation to Equation 7.10 for the direction j^β is

7.11 $\qquad b_{\alpha\beta}j^\beta = k^*j_\alpha + tl_\alpha.$

In deriving this equation, we have used the fact that the geodesic torsion in the direction j^β is minus t; also that the direction corresponding to j_α in Equation 7.10 is now minus l_α. Equations 7.10 and 7.11 lead to the explicit expression of the second fundamental form in terms of any two orthogonal surface vectors as

7.12 $\qquad b_{\alpha\beta} = kl_\alpha l_\beta + t(l_\alpha j_\beta + j_\alpha l_\beta) + k^*j_\alpha j_\beta,$

which may easily be verified by contracting with l^β and j^β in turn. This last equation may be compared with the corresponding formula for the metric tensor in Equation 2.34, that is,

7.13 $$a_{\alpha\beta} = l_\alpha l_\beta + j_\alpha j_\beta.$$

We can also obtain the corresponding formula for the third fundamental form by substituting two equations of the form of Equation 7.12 in Equations 6.18, and we find without difficulty that

$$c_{\alpha\beta} = (k^2 + t^2)l_\alpha l_\beta + 2Ht(l_\alpha j_\beta + j_\alpha l_\beta) + (k^{*2} + t^2)j_\alpha j_\beta$$

7.14

in which, anticipating the next section, we have written $2H$ for $(k + k^*)$.

CURVATURE INVARIANTS

9. From Equations 2.35 and 7.12, it is easy to form the invariant

7.15 $$a^{\alpha\beta}b_{\alpha\beta} = k + k^* = 2H,$$

which no longer depends on the particular pair of orthogonal directions l_α, j_α. We conclude that the sum of the normal curvatures for any pair of orthogonal directions is the same, and we call H the *mean curvature* of the surface.

10. To relate the normal curvatures in flat space to the Gaussian intrinsic curvature of the surface, we need to find the determinant b from Equation 7.12 for substitution in Equation 6.27. The simplest way of doing this is to take l^α, j^α as orthogonal coordinate axes, in which case we have, as in Equations 2.33,

$$l_\alpha = (\sqrt{a_{11}}, 0) \qquad j_\alpha = (0, \sqrt{a_{22}})$$

and, from Equation 7.12,

$$b_{11} = ka_{11}, \quad b_{12} = t\sqrt{a_{11}}\sqrt{a_{22}}, \quad b_{22} = k^*a_{22},$$

so that we have

7.16 $$b = (kk^* - t^2)a_{11}a_{22} = (kk^* - t^2)a$$

and finally

7.17 $$K = kk^* - t^2.$$

We conclude that the right-hand side of Equation 7.17 must be the same for any pair of orthogonal directions because K is an invariant which has the same value in any coordinate system, not only in the temporary system used above.

11. The same temporary coordinate system applied to Equation 7.14 gives

$$c_{11} = (k^2 + t^2)a_{11}$$
$$c_{12} = 2Ht\sqrt{a_{11}}\sqrt{a_{22}}$$
$$c_{22} = (k^{*2} + t^2)a_{22},$$

leading to the determinant

$$c = (kk^* - t^2)^2 a = aK^2.$$

Because K is a surface invariant, so is c/a which accordingly has the same value in any coordinate system. We can then write

7.18 $$K = b/a = c/b = (kk^* - t^2)$$

and can assert that these relations are true in any coordinate system and for any pair of orthogonal directions.

12. An alternative formula for the mean curvature can be found at once from Equations 7.03 and 2.09 as

7.19 $$2H = -\nu^r_{,r},$$

which is the negative of the divergence of the unit normal.

13. The components of the three fundamental forms are not independent, but are related by means of the curvature invariants. From Equations 7.12, 7.13, and 7.14, we find at once that

7.20 $$Ka_{\alpha\beta} - 2Hb_{\alpha\beta} + c_{\alpha\beta} = 0.$$

PRINCIPAL CURVATURES

14. We consider next the maxima and minima of the normal curvature for different directions around a fixed point. For this purpose, we take a pair of *fixed* unit orthogonal surface vectors A^α, B^α at the point. If l^α makes an angle a with A^α, we can write

$$l^\alpha = A^\alpha \cos a + B^\alpha \sin a$$
$$j^\alpha = -A^\alpha \sin a + B^\alpha \cos a;$$

and if we differentiate the components with respect to a as a parameter, we have

$$\frac{dl^\alpha}{da} = -A^\alpha \sin a + B^\alpha \cos a = j^\alpha.$$

Now we differentiate the normal curvature

$$k = b_{\alpha\beta}l^\alpha l^\beta,$$

keeping $b_{\alpha\beta}$ constant because we are merely going to alter direction, not position. For stationary values of k, we must have

$$b_{\alpha\beta}j^\alpha l^\beta + b_{\alpha\beta}l^\alpha j^\beta = 0,$$

or, because $b_{\alpha\beta}$ is symmetric, we have

$$b_{\alpha\beta}j^\alpha l^\beta = t = 0.$$

But if t is zero in the l^α-direction, it must also be zero in the j^α-direction because we have seen that the sum of the geodesic torsions in the two directions is zero. We conclude, in general, that there are two orthogonal directions in which the geodesic torsions are zero, and the normal curvatures are either a maximum or a minimum.[1] Moreover, proceeding on the above lines, or differentiating $(2H)$ which is the same for all pairs of directions, we find that

$$\frac{d^2k}{da^2} = -\frac{d^2k^*}{da^2} = 2(k^* - k),$$

which shows that the normal curvature is a maximum in one direction and a minimum in the other. We call these directions the *principal directions* u_α, v_α, and the corresponding normal curvatures the *principal curvatures* κ_1, κ_2.

15. Because $t = 0$ for the principal directions, the curvature invariants can be expressed as

7.21 $$2H = \kappa_1 + \kappa_2$$

7.22 $$K = \kappa_1\kappa_2.$$

---

[1] For a more rigorous solution, not confined to two dimensions, see Levi-Cività (1926), *The Absolute Differential Calculus*, 204.

The three fundamental forms become

7.23 $$a_{\alpha\beta} = u_\alpha u_\beta + v_\alpha v_\beta$$

7.24 $$b_{\alpha\beta} = \kappa_1 u_\alpha u_\beta + \kappa_2 v_\alpha v_\beta$$

7.25 $$c_{\alpha\beta} = \kappa_1^2 u_\alpha u_\beta + \kappa_2^2 v_\alpha v_\beta.$$

From Equation 7.09, we can also write

7.26 $$\nu_{rs} u^s = -\kappa_1 u_r$$

7.27 $$\nu_{rs} v^s = -\kappa_2 v_r.$$

16. The curves which are tangential to the principal directions throughout their length are known as *lines of curvature*. If $\bar{\nu}_r$, ν_r are the unit surface normals at two points separated by a short distance ds along a line of curvature u^s, we have to a first order

$$\bar{\nu}_r = \nu_r + \nu_{rs} u^s ds \ . \ . \ . = \nu_r - \kappa_1 u_r ds \ . \ . \ .,$$

which shows that the three vectors $\bar{\nu}_r$, ν_r, and u_r are coplanar. Consequently, successive surface normals along a line of curvature intersect. In the case of any other curve, they would generally be skew.

CHAPTER 8

Further Extrinsic Properties of Curves and Surfaces

THE CONTRAVARIANT FUNDAMENTAL FORMS

1. We now consider a set of quantities $b^{\alpha\beta}$ defined as the cofactors of $b_{\alpha\beta}$ in the expansion of the determinant $|b_{\alpha\beta}|$ divided by the value b of the determinant, in the same way as the associated metric tensor $a^{\alpha\beta}$ is related to the determinant $|a_{\alpha\beta}|$. The $b^{\alpha\beta}$ can also be considered as constituting the inverse of the matrix $b_{\alpha\beta}$. We shall show that $b^{\alpha\beta}$ is a surface tensor, although it is *not* the tensor formed by raising the indices of $b_{\alpha\beta}$, that is,

$$b^{\alpha\beta} \neq a^{\alpha\gamma} a^{\beta\delta} b_{\gamma\delta}.$$

2. From the definition and Equation 2.43, we have

$$b b^{\alpha\beta} = e^{\alpha\gamma} e^{\beta\delta} b_{\gamma\delta}:$$

and dividing this by a, we have

8.01 $$K b^{\alpha\beta} = \epsilon^{\alpha\gamma} \epsilon^{\beta\delta} b_{\gamma\delta},$$

which shows at once that $b^{\alpha\beta}$ is a surface tensor because K is an absolute invariant. We can expand this last equation from Equations 2.32 and 7.12 as

8.02 $$K b^{\alpha\beta} = k^* l^\alpha l^\beta - t(l^\alpha j^\beta + j^\alpha l^\beta) + k j^\alpha j^\beta,$$

reducing, if we take l^α, j^α as the principal directions u^α, v^α, to

8.03 $$K b^{\alpha\beta} = \kappa_2 u^\alpha u^\beta + \kappa_1 v^\alpha v^\beta.$$

3. If we define $c^{\alpha\beta}$ in the same way as the cofactor of $c_{\alpha\beta}$ in the expansion of the determinant $|c_{\alpha\beta}|$ divided by c, or as the inverse of the matrix $c_{\alpha\beta}$, then we have similarly

8.04 $$K^2 c^{\alpha\beta} = \epsilon^{\alpha\gamma} \epsilon^{\beta\delta} c_{\gamma\delta},$$

which shows that $c^{\alpha\beta}$ is a tensor and, using Equation 7.14, expands to

$$K^2 c^{\alpha\beta} = (k^{*2} + t^2) l^\alpha l^\beta - 2Ht(l^\alpha j^\beta + j^\alpha l^\beta) + (k^2 + t^2) j^\alpha j^\beta$$

8.05 $$= \kappa_2^2 u^\alpha u^\beta + \kappa_1^2 v^\alpha v^\beta.$$

4. We have already found an expression in Equation 2.35 for the contravariant first fundamental form (the metric tensor) as

8.06 $$a^{\alpha\beta} = l^\alpha l^\beta + j^\alpha j^\beta = u^\alpha u^\beta + v^\alpha v^\beta$$

and can derive the contravariant form of Equation 7.20 by simple substitution as

8.07 $$a^{\alpha\beta} - 2H b^{\alpha\beta} + K c^{\alpha\beta} = 0.$$

5. From the definitions, we have, as for any matrix and its inverse,

8.08 $$b^{\alpha\beta} b_{\alpha\gamma} = \delta_\gamma^\beta \quad \text{and} \quad c^{\alpha\beta} c_{\alpha\gamma} = \delta_\gamma^\beta,$$

which enable us to switch between the fundamental forms. For instance, if we contract Equations 6.18 with $b^{\beta\epsilon}$ and rearrange indices, we have

8.09 $$b^{\alpha\beta} c_{\beta\gamma} = a^{\alpha\beta} b_{\beta\gamma}.$$

Thus, Weingarten's formula in Equation 6.17 can be written either as

8.10 $$b^{\alpha\beta} \nu_\beta^r = -a^{\alpha\beta} x_\beta^r$$

or as

8.11 $$c^{\alpha\beta} \nu_\beta^r = -b^{\alpha\beta} x_\beta^r.$$

If we contract this last equation with $g_{rs}x_\gamma^s$ and use Equations 6.18, we have

8.12 $$c^{\alpha\beta}b_{\beta\gamma} = b^{\alpha\beta}a_{\beta\gamma},$$

which is a reciprocal form of Equation 8.09.

6. Use of the above formulas, together with Equations 7.20 and 8.07, gives us without difficulty the following alternative formulas for the curvature invariants,

8.13 $$2H = a^{\alpha\beta}b_{\alpha\beta} = b^{\alpha\beta}c_{\alpha\beta} = Kc^{\alpha\beta}b_{\alpha\beta} = Kb^{\alpha\beta}a_{\alpha\beta}$$

8.14 $$a^{\alpha\beta}c_{\alpha\beta} = K^2c^{\alpha\beta}a_{\alpha\beta} = (4H^2 - 2K) = \kappa_1^2 + \kappa_2^2.$$

7. The main advantage of the formulas in this section is that one or the other of the forms may be simple in a particular coordinate system, or may be constant under some transformation, such as spherical representation, in which case we can often achieve a simple result quickly by switching into the favorable form.

COVARIANT DERIVATIVES OF THE FUNDAMENTAL FORMS

8. The covariant derivative of the first fundamental form (the metric tensor) is zero as we have seen in § 6–16. Consequently, by differentiating Equation 2.34, we have

8.15 $$(u_\alpha u_\beta)_\gamma = -(v_\alpha v_\beta)_\gamma$$

for any pair of perpendicular unit surface vectors, although we shall use this equation only for the principal directions (u_α, v_α) to simplify differentiation of the other fundamental forms.

9. We now differentiate Equation 7.24, use Equations 8.15 and 4.11, and obtain after some manipulation

$$b_{\alpha\beta\gamma} = (\kappa_1)_\gamma u_\alpha u_\beta + (\kappa_2)_\gamma v_\alpha v_\beta$$

8.16 $$+ (\kappa_1 - \kappa_2)(\sigma u_\gamma + \sigma^* v_\gamma)(u_\alpha v_\beta + v_\alpha u_\beta)$$

in which κ_1, σ (κ_2, σ^*) are, respectively, the principal curvature and geodesic curvature of the lines of curvature u_α, (v_α). We may note that the lines of curvature are defined at any point on the surface, other than at singular points (such as an *umbilic* where the normal curvature is the same in all directions and the principal directions are accordingly indeterminate) or on special surfaces (such as the sphere where all points are umbilics). Consequently, κ_1, κ_2 are functions whose values are, in general, defined at every point and may accordingly

be differentiated with respect to the surface coordinates; for example, in Equation 8.16, we have

$$(\kappa_1)_\gamma = \partial\kappa_1/\partial x^\gamma.$$

10. Differentiating Equation 7.25 in the same way, we have

$$c_{\alpha\beta\gamma} = (\kappa_1^2)_\gamma u_\alpha u_\beta + (\kappa_2^2)_\gamma v_\alpha v_\beta$$

8.17 $$+ (\kappa_1^2 - \kappa_2^2)(\sigma u_\gamma + \sigma^* v_\gamma)(u_\alpha v_\beta + v_\alpha u_\beta);$$

and similarly from Equations 8.03 and 8.05, we have

$$b^{\alpha\beta}_{\cdot\cdot\gamma} = (1/\kappa_1)_\gamma u^\alpha u^\beta + (1/\kappa_2)_\gamma v^\alpha v^\beta$$

8.18 $$+ (1/\kappa_1 - 1/\kappa_2)(\sigma u_\gamma + \sigma^* v_\gamma)(u^\alpha v^\beta + v^\alpha u^\beta)$$

$$c^{\alpha\beta}_{\cdot\cdot\gamma} = (1/\kappa_1^2)_\gamma u^\alpha u^\beta + (1/\kappa_2^2)_\gamma v^\alpha v^\beta$$

8.19 $$+ (1/\kappa_1^2 - 1/\kappa_2^2)(\sigma u_\gamma + \sigma^* v_\gamma)(u^\alpha v^\beta + v^\alpha u^\beta).$$

11. From the above formulas, we may easily derive contractions which are sometimes useful, such as

$$a^{\alpha\beta}b_{\alpha\beta\gamma} = (2H)_\gamma \qquad a^{\alpha\beta}c_{\alpha\beta\gamma} = (4H^2 - 2K)_\gamma$$

$$b^{\alpha\beta}b_{\alpha\beta\gamma} = (\ln K)_\gamma \qquad b^{\alpha\beta}c_{\alpha\beta\gamma} = (4H)_\gamma$$

$$c^{\alpha\beta}b_{\alpha\beta\gamma} = -(2H/K)_\gamma \qquad c^{\alpha\beta}c_{\alpha\beta\gamma} = 2(\ln K)_\gamma.$$

8.20

12. We can obtain more complicated expressions in terms of any pair of orthogonal vectors (l_α, j_α), defined in some way over the surface, by differentiating Equation 7.12, etc.; but we shall find it more convenient to obtain particular contractions, such as

$$b_{\alpha\beta\gamma}l^\alpha l^\beta,$$

when required.

13. The Codazzi equations for flat space (Equation 6.21) can be rewritten as

8.21 $$\epsilon^{\beta\gamma}b_{\alpha\beta\gamma} = b_{\alpha\beta\gamma}(u^\beta v^\gamma - v^\beta u^\gamma) = 0$$

because $b_{\alpha\beta\gamma}$ is symmetric in (β, γ). If we contract Equation 8.16 accordingly and separate the resulting vector equation, we have

$$(\kappa_1 - \kappa_2)\sigma = (\kappa_1)_\gamma v^\gamma$$

8.22 $$(\kappa_1 - \kappa_2)\sigma^* = (\kappa_2)_\gamma u^\gamma,$$

which are an alternative form of the Codazzi equations. We can obtain another form in terms of any two orthogonal unit vectors l_α, j_α by differentiating Equation 7.12, and shall do so later by a different method. The result,

$$\sigma(k - k^*) = (k)_\gamma j^\gamma - (t)_\gamma l^\gamma - 2t\sigma^*$$

8.23 $$\sigma^*(k - k^*) = (k^*)_\gamma l^\gamma - (t)_\gamma j^\gamma + 2t\sigma,$$

is merely stated at this place for the sake of completeness. In these formulas, k, t, σ are the normal curvature, geodesic torsion, and geodesic curvature of l_α, necessarily considered as belonging to a family of curves defined in some way over the surface, while k^*, σ^*, and minus t refer to j_α in the usual right-handed system (l_r, j_r, ν_r).

RELATION BETWEEN SURFACE AND SPACE TENSORS

14. We have seen in Equation 6.08 that if F_r is a surface vector, its space and surface components are related by the equation

8.24 $$F_r x_\alpha^r = F_\alpha.$$

The same equation holds true if F_r is the gradient of a scalar F because, by definition, we then have

$$\frac{\partial F}{\partial x^r} \frac{\partial x^r}{\partial x^\alpha} = \frac{\partial F}{\partial x^\alpha}.$$

It is also true if F_r is any space vector, as long as F_α is interpreted as the orthogonal projection of F_r on the surface. In that case, F_r is expressible in terms of any two orthogonal surface vectors and the unit normal as

$$F_r = A l_r + B j_r + C \nu_r;$$

and contracting this with x_α^r, we have

$$F_r x_\alpha^r = A l_\alpha + B j_\alpha,$$

which is clearly a surface vector having the same components on l_α, j_α as the space vector has.

15. Surface covariant differentiation of Equation 8.24, with respect to the x^β-coordinate (assuming as usual that F_r is defined over some finite region of the surface), and use of Equation 6.16 give

8.25 $$F_{rs} x_\alpha^r x_\beta^s = F_{\alpha\beta} - F_r x_{\alpha\beta}^r = F_{\alpha\beta} - (F_r \nu^r) b_{\alpha\beta}$$

in which F_{rs} is taken with respect to the space metric and $F_{\alpha\beta}$ with respect to the surface metric. If F_r is a surface vector, the last term is zero.

16. If we contract this result with the principal directions u^α, v^β (for which $t = b_{\alpha\beta} u^\alpha v^\beta = 0$), we have

8.26 $$F_{rs} u^r v^s = F_{\alpha\beta} u^\alpha v^\beta.$$

17. If we contract Equation 8.25 with $a^{\alpha\beta}$ and use Equations 6.10 and 7.15, we have

8.27 $$F_{\cdot r}^r = F_{\cdot \alpha}^\alpha - 2H(F_r \nu^r) + F_{rs} \nu^r \nu^s$$

connecting the space and surface divergences of the vector F_r. If F is a scalar, F_r^r and F_α^α are its space

and surface Laplacians. We can rewrite the last term as

8.28 $$F_{rs} \nu^r \nu^s = (F_r \nu^r)_s \nu^s - F_r (\nu_s^r \nu^s)$$

in which $\nu_s^r \nu^s$ is the vector curvature of the normal. The vector curvature must be a surface vector because its normal component $\nu_r \nu_s^r \nu^s$ is zero from Equation 3.19, so that we may write

$$\nu_s^r \nu^s = \chi w^r$$

in which χ is the curvature of the normal and w^r is a unit surface vector. If F is a scalar and ds is the arc element along the normal, Equation 8.28 becomes

$$F_{rs} \nu^r \nu^s = \partial^2 F / \partial s^2 - \chi (F_r w^r),$$

so that Equation 8.27 can be written as

8.29 $$\Delta F = \overline{\Delta F} - 2H(\partial F / \partial s) + \partial^2 F / \partial s^2 - \chi(F_r w^r)$$

where the surface Laplacian (taken with respect to the surface metric) is given an overbar. If F is constant over the surface, the last term is zero and the surface Laplacian is also zero.

18. We can connect the space and surface invariants of the type in Equation 3.14 by using Equation 6.10. We have

$$\nabla(F, G) = g^{rs} F_r G_s = a^{\alpha\beta} x_\alpha^r x_\beta^s F_r G_s + \nu^r \nu^s F_r G_s$$

8.30 $$= \overline{\nabla(F, G)} + \left(\frac{\partial F}{\partial s}\right)\left(\frac{\partial G}{\partial s}\right),$$

assuming in this case that both F and G are scalars.

EXTENSION TO CURVED SPACE

19. In Equation 6.28, we derived an equation connecting the intrinsic curvature K of a surface with the $b_{\alpha\beta}$'s and the curvature tensor of the surrounding space. We deferred further consideration of this equation until we had developed the connection between the $b_{\alpha\beta}$'s and the extrinsic curvature of the surface and of surface curves.

20. We take the usual pair of orthogonal surface vectors l^α, j^α, together with the normal curvatures k, k^* in those directions and the geodesic torsion t in the direction l^α, and contract Equation 6.28 with

$$l^\delta j^\alpha l^\beta j^\gamma.$$

Using Equations 2.31, 6.07, and 5.25, we then have

8.31 $$K = (kk^* - t^2) + C$$

in which C is the Riemannian curvature of the space

for the section (l^α, j^α). Because K and C are invariants which are independent of the particular surface directions, so also is $(kk^* - t^2)$. Indeed, we have already proved in Equations 7.16 and 7.18 that

8.32 $\qquad (kk^* - t^2) = b/a = (c/a)^{1/2}.$

The last two members of this equation are independent of direction and from §2–42 are also invariants. We are, however, no longer entitled to equate Equation 8.32 to the intrinsic curvature of the surface if C is not zero. *Nevertheless, it is clear from Equation 8.31 that all the equations containing* K, *which we have derived in Chapters 7 and 8, are still true provided that we write* $(K - C)$ *for* K.

21. From the definition of Riemannian curvature in §5–19, we know that C is the intrinsic or Gaussian curvature of the surface, formed by the space geodesics which are tangent to our surface at the point under consideration. Equation 8.31 then suggests that the normal curvatures of the surface are in some way connected with space geodesics tangential to the surface. We will investigate this suggestion.

22. We use a rectangular locally Cartesian coordinate system with an origin at the point P under consideration, x^3-axis in the direction of the surface normal ν^r, and x^1-axis tangential to the surface in the initial direction of a surface curve l^r. The unit tangent to a space geodesic, emanating from P initially in the same direction, is g^r. The situation is shown in figure 7 which represents the $(x^1\text{-}, x^3\text{-})$

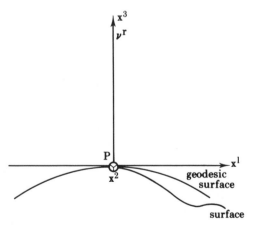

Figure 7.

coordinate surface. The l^r- and g^r-curves, initially in this surface, will not, however, remain in the coordinate surface. We shall determine now the coordinates of neighboring points to P on these

curves. For a small displacement ds along the l^r-curve, we have the Taylor expansion

8.33 $\qquad dx^r = l^r ds + \tfrac{1}{2}(l^r_{,s} l^s)(ds)^2$

in which it is understood that the coefficients are to have their values at P. In the Cartesian system, the coefficient of $\tfrac{1}{2}(ds)^2$ is, of course,

$$\frac{d^2 x^r}{ds^2},$$

but it will be simpler to retain the general tensor notation.

The change in coordinates along the space geodesic for an equal distance ds is to a second order

$$d\bar{x}^r = g^r ds \ \ldots \ +$$

because $g^r_{,s} g^s = 0$. Because we have made $g^r = l^r$ at P, the difference in coordinates to a second order is

$$dx^r - d\bar{x}^r = \tfrac{1}{2}(l^r_{,s} l^s)(ds)^2.$$

The difference in x^3-coordinates is then

$$\tfrac{1}{2}(\nu_r l^r_{,s} l^s)(ds)^2 = -\tfrac{1}{2}(\nu_{rs} l^r l^s)(ds)^2 = \tfrac{1}{2} k (ds)^2$$

where k is the normal curvature of the surface in the direction l^r as defined in Equation 7.03 and used throughout this book.

If j^r is as usual the surface vector perpendicular to l^r at P, then the difference in the x^2-coordinates is

$$\tfrac{1}{2}(j_r l^r_{,s} l^s)(ds)^2 = +\tfrac{1}{2}(l_{rs} j^r l^s)(ds)^2 = \tfrac{1}{2}\sigma(ds)^2$$

where σ is the geodesic curvature of l^r as defined in Equation 7.04 and used throughout this book. There is no second-order difference in the x^1-coordinates because

$$l_r l^r_{,s} l^s = 0.$$

If χ is the space curvature of the surface curve l^r from Equations 7.03 and 7.04, the total departure of the curve from the space geodesic is accordingly

$$\tfrac{1}{2}\chi(ds)^2,$$

which is evidently the same as the total departure of the curve from a straight line tangent in flat space.

23. All our notions about the curvature of surfaces and surface curves thus apply to curved space, as long as we consider departures from the tangent space geodesics. All we need do is to generalize the straight tangents and tangent planes of ordinary flat space to geodesic tangents and geodesic surfaces.

24. In the same way, we can easily show that the geodesic curvature of a surface curve in two dimensions is measurable as a linear departure from

the tangent geodesic. This is the same generalization applied to the ordinary notion of the curvature of plane curves.

25. We do not need to consider geodesic torsion in this context because we could replace $(kk^* - t^2)$ in Equation 8.31 by the product $(\kappa_1 \kappa_2)$ of the principal normal curvatures, without affecting either K or C in that equation.

26. Special forms of the Codazzi equations, which have been obtained from the flat space form in Equation 6.21, would need restatement to include the extra term in the full Equation 6.22. It does not seem, however, that any general conclusions can be drawn from Equation 6.22 without knowledge of the curvature tensor in particular cases. We shall provide an illustration in §10–29 of the use of a particular form of the curvature tensor.

CHAPTER 9

Areas and Volumes

ELEMENTS OF AREA AND VOLUME

1. We shall require an expression for the area of the small near-parallelogram formed by successive coordinate lines on a surface. For short lengths ds_1, ds_2 along the coordinate lines, the area is

$$(ds_1)(ds_2) \sin \theta$$

where θ is the angle between the coordinate lines as shown in figure 8. But, if the unit vectors in the

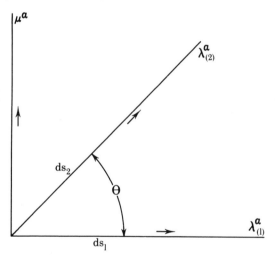

Figure 8.

coordinate directions are $\lambda_{(1)}^\alpha$, $\lambda_{(2)}^\alpha$ and if μ^α is a unit vector perpendicular to $\lambda_{(1)}^\alpha$, then we have

$$\sin \theta = \mu_\beta \lambda_{(2)}^\beta = \epsilon_{\alpha\beta} \lambda_{(1)}^\alpha \lambda_{(2)}^\beta$$
$$= \sqrt{a}\,(dx^1/ds_1)(dx^2/ds_2),$$

using Equations 2.37 and 2.30, so that finally the element of area is

9.01
$$dS = \sqrt{a}\,dx^1 dx^2.$$

2. For a similar element of volume in three dimensions, we have

$$(ds_1)(ds_2)(ds_3) \sin \theta \sin \phi$$

where ϕ is the angle which the $\lambda_{(3)}^r$-coordinate line makes with the plane of $\lambda_{(1)}^r$ and $\lambda_{(2)}^r$. But in this case, it is clear from the expression in Equation 2.25 for a scalar triple product that we have

$$\sin \theta \sin \phi = \epsilon_{rst} \lambda_{(1)}^r \lambda_{(2)}^s \lambda_{(3)}^t$$
$$= \sqrt{g}\,(dx^1/ds_1)(dx^2/ds_2)(dx^3/ds_3),$$

so that finally the required element of volume is

9.02
$$dV = \sqrt{g}\,dx^1 dx^2 dx^3.$$

SURFACE AND CONTOUR INTEGRALS

3. We shall use only one integral sign for contour, surface, and volume integrals, distinguishing them by the suffixes C, S, and V, respectively.
We state, without proof or consideration of its limitations,[1] a textbook formula attributable (in most English texts) to Green. If U_1, U_2 are two scalars, we have

9.03
$$\int_S \left(\frac{\partial U_2}{\partial x} - \frac{\partial U_1}{\partial y} \right) dx\,dy = \int_C (U_1 dx + U_2 dy)$$

in which the double integral on the left is taken

---

[1] The reader with no previous knowledge of this section should read Springer(1962), *Tensor and Vector Analysis*, 147–199, where the elementary theory is clearly explained. The treatment in this section generally follows Brand (1947), *Vector and Tensor Analysis* translated, with variations, into index notation.

306-962 O-69—5

over a closed region of the (x-, y-) plane and the line or contour integral on the right is taken around the closed boundary of the region. If ds is an element of the length of the contour, if dS is an element of area, and if we take U_1, U_2 to be the components of a vector F_α, then this formula can be written in the tensor form

9.04 $$\int_S \epsilon^{\alpha\beta} F_{\beta,\,\alpha}\, dS = \int_C F_\alpha l^\alpha ds$$

in which l^α is the unit tangent to the contour. It is clear that in this invariant form the equation holds true in any coordinates—not necessarily Cartesian. Moreover, because only the first covariant derivative of the vector is involved, it is immaterial whether the space is flat or curved, even though we derived the result from a plane formula in Cartesian coordinates. The formula accordingly holds for any curved surface, provided that F_α is defined and its covariant derivatives exist over the closed region S. The same conditions relating to connectivity (which are usually satisfied in the geodetic applications) must apply on the curved surface as on the plane.

4. To obtain the correct signs in either formula, we must describe the contour in such a direction that l^α generally rotates in the same sense as from the x- to the y-coordinate line (or, in general coordinates, from the u^1- to the u^2-coordinate line). The sense of description is as shown in figure 9, which

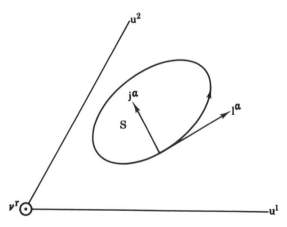

Figure 9.

also shows our usual convention for the perpendicular vector j^α. The normal to the surface (ν_r) is toward the reader.

5. If we expand Equation 9.04 in general surface coordinates u^1, u^2, we have, using Equation 9.01

and the symmetry of the Christoffel symbols,

9.05 $$\int_S \left(\frac{\partial F_2}{\partial u^1} - \frac{\partial F_1}{\partial u^2}\right) du^1 du^2 = \int_C (F_1 du^1 + F_2 du^2),$$

which is the same form as Equation 9.03.

6. To extend these results to three dimensions, we consider the following expression and use Equation 6.11. The tensor T_{ijk} can be of any order and type, but we shall assume Cartesian space coordinates so that covariant and ordinary derivatives are the same, and we then have

$$\epsilon^{lmn}\nu_l T_{ijk,\,m} = \epsilon^{\alpha\beta} x_\alpha^m x_\beta^n T_{ijk,\,m}$$

$$= (1/\sqrt{a}) e^{\alpha\beta} x_\beta^n \partial(T_{ijk})/\partial u^\alpha$$

$$= \frac{1}{\sqrt{a}}\left(\frac{\partial x^n}{\partial u^2}\frac{\partial T_{ijk}}{\partial u^1} - \frac{\partial x^n}{\partial u^1}\frac{\partial T_{ijk}}{\partial u^2}\right)$$

$$= \frac{1}{\sqrt{a}}\left\{\frac{\partial}{\partial u^1}\left(\frac{\partial x^n}{\partial u^2}T_{ijk}\right) - \frac{\partial}{\partial u^2}\left(\frac{\partial x^n}{\partial u^1}T_{ijk}\right)\right\}.$$

Next, we multiply by $dS = \sqrt{a}\, du^1 du^2$ and integrate over some region S of the surface bounded by a closed contour C. Using Equation 9.05, we have

$$\int_S \epsilon^{lmn}\nu_l T_{ijk,\,m}\, dS = \int_C T_{ijk}\left(\frac{\partial x^n}{\partial u^1} du^1 + \frac{\partial x^n}{\partial u^2} du^2\right)$$

9.06 $$= \int_C T_{ijk} l^n ds$$

in which l^n is the unit tangent vector to the contour. The boundary contour can be any closed curve in space spanned by any surface, subject to the usual conditions. We have proved this formula for Cartesian space coordinates and for the components of T_{ijk} in Cartesian coordinates, which means also that the space must be flat. If, however, we reduce the equation to an invariant form containing only first covariant derivatives, then both these limitations will disappear. For example, if T_{ijk} is a space vector F_n, we then have

9.07 $$\int_S \nu_l \epsilon^{lmn} F_{n,\,m}\, dS = \int_C F_n l^n ds$$

in which the two integrands are, respectively, the normal component of the curl (Equation 3.15) of the vector and its component along the boundary contour. This is the tensor form of Stokes' theorem, true in any coordinate system—in flat or curved three-dimensional space. Moreover, we can expect a similar formula to hold true in any number of dimensions. In four dimensions, we should need different forms of the permutation symbols, which we shall not discuss in this chapter.[2] However, in two dimensions, we should expect

$$\int_S \epsilon^{\alpha\beta} F_{\beta,\,\alpha}\, dS = \int_C F_\alpha l^\alpha\, ds$$

in which F_α is now a surface vector, and if we use Equations 6.11 and 8.25, we find at once that this is so. We have in fact recovered Equation 9.04.

7. If the surface is closed, it can be considered as divided into two parts by a closed contour. The contour integral will have the same value but opposite signs for the two parts of the surface, so that over the whole closed surface, we have

9.08
$$\int_S \nu_l \epsilon^{lmn} F_{n,\,m}\, dS = 0.$$

8. If we are prepared to continue working in Cartesian space coordinates, we can derive a number of other formulas from the basic Equation 9.06. We can, for instance, multiply by ϵ_{npq} which are constants in Cartesian coordinates and can therefore go under the integral signs. The surface integrand is then

$$\delta^{lm}_{pq} \nu_l T_{ijk,\,m} = \nu_p T_{ijk,\,q} - \nu_q T_{ijk,\,p},$$

and we have

9.09
$$\int_S (\nu_p T_{ijk,\,q} - \nu_q T_{ijk,\,p})\, dS = \int_C \epsilon_{npq} T_{ijk} l^n\, ds,$$

which is no less general than the basic Equation 9.06 and may be considered as an alternative.

9. If, for example, we take a contravariant vector G^q for the general tensor T_{ijk}, we have at once

9.10
$$\int_S (\nu_p G^q_{,q} - \nu_q G^q_{,p})\, dS = \int_C \epsilon_{npq} G^q l^n\, ds$$

for the contour integral of the vector product of a general vector with the unit tangent to the contour. Springer[3] uses this result to provide an interesting comparison, obtaining the result first in the old dot-and-cross notation and then deriving the same result in index notation in order to interpret the dot-and-cross result!

10. We can also use Equation 9.09 to introduce the perpendicular surface vector j_p (see fig. 9) by taking the general tensor T_{ijk} in the form $\nu^q U_{jk}$.

---

[2] See Synge and Schild (corrected reprint of 1964), *Tensor Calculus*, original ed. of 1949, 240–281.

[3] Springer, *op. cit. supra* note 1, 196.

Using Equation 3.19, we have for the surface integrand

$$\nu_p \nu^q_{,q} U_{jk} + \nu_p \nu^q U_{jk,\,q} - U_{jk,\,p}.$$

But from Equation 6.10, we have

$$\nu_p \nu^q = \delta^q_p - a^{\alpha\beta} g_{tp} x^q_\alpha x^t_\beta.$$

If we substitute this and Equation 7.19, the surface integrand becomes

$$-2H\nu_p U_{jk} - a^{\alpha\beta} g_{tp} x^q_\alpha x^t_\beta U_{jk,\,q}.$$

We now multiply this result by g^{pl} and can do the same to the contour integrand because the g^{pl} are constants in Cartesian space coordinates. The final result is

9.11
$$\int_S (2H\nu^l U_{jk} + a^{\alpha\beta} x^q_\alpha x^l_\beta U_{jk,\,q})\, dS = -\int_C j^l U_{jk}\, dS$$

which, because U_{jk} is a general tensor not necessarily of the second order, is just as general as either Equation 9.06 or 9.09.

11. As an example of the use of this last result, we take U_{jk} to be the gradient of a scalar ϕ_l and contract to

$$\int_S \{2H(\nu^l \phi_l) + a^{\alpha\beta} x^q_\alpha x^l_\beta \phi_{l,\,q}\}\, dS = -\int_C j^l \phi_l\, ds.$$

Using Equation 8.25, we can further reduce this to

9.12
$$\int_S \overline{\Delta\phi}\, dS = -\int_C \phi_l j^l\, ds$$

in which the Laplacian is taken with respect to the surface metric. In the same way as we obtained Equation 9.08, we conclude that over any closed surface

9.13
$$\int_S \overline{\Delta\phi}\, dS = 0.$$

VOLUME AND SURFACE INTEGRALS

12. We shall now consider the triple integration of a tensor $T_{ijk,\,m}$ over a closed region V of 3-space bounded by a closed surface S. Again, we assume Cartesian coordinates in flat space, and we suppose that an arbitrary field of parallel unit vectors A^m is defined over the region in much the same way as one of the Cartesian coordinate vectors would be defined. We suppose further that A^m is the axis of an elementary prism of constant cross-sectional area $d\sigma$ running through the region, and that dl is an element of length in the direction A^m. We then

have by integrating along the prism, all components of A^m being constant,

$$A^m \int T_{ijk,\,m}\,dV = \int T_{ijk,\,m} A^m dl\,d\sigma$$

$$= \int \frac{\partial T_{ijk}}{\partial x^m}\frac{\partial x^m}{\partial l}\,dl\,d\sigma$$

9.14 $$= \int [T_{ijk}]_1^2\,d\sigma$$

in which the integrand is now the difference in values of T_{ijk} on the boundary surface at the two ends of the prism. But, if an element of area of the boundary surface is dS and if the exterior or outward-drawn unit normal to the boundary surface is ν_m, we then have

$$d\sigma = \nu_m A^m dS$$

at the (2) end of the prism and

$$d\sigma = -\nu_m A^m dS$$

at the (1) end of the prism. By adding Equations 9.14 for all the elementary prisms required to fill the region, we can write

$$A^m \int_V T_{ijk,\,m}\,dV = \int_S T_{ijk}\nu_m A^m dS$$

$$= A^m \int_S T_{ijk}\nu_m dS$$

because the components of the parallel vectors A^m are constant over the whole region in Cartesian coordinates. But A^m is an arbitrary vector field, and so we have

9.15 $$\int_V T_{ijk,\,m}\,dV = \int_S T_{ijk}\nu_m dS.$$

Because we are working in Cartesian space coordinates, we can raise any of the indices of T_{ijk}, which can be of any order or type.

13. Again, we can remove the limitation to Cartesian coordinates in flat space if we form invariants containing only first covariant derivatives. For example, if we make the tensor T_{ijk} a contravariant vector F^m, then we have

9.16 $$\int_V F^m_{.,m}\,dV = \int_S F^m \nu_m dS = \int_S F_m \nu^m dS,$$

which is the tensor form of the *divergence theorem*. Or, if F^m are the contravariant components $g^{mr}\phi_r$ of the gradient of a scalar ϕ and if ds is an element of length along the surface normal, then the last

equation becomes

9.17 $$\int_V (\Delta\phi)\,dV = \int_S (\partial\phi/\partial s)\,dS,$$

which seems to have been given originally by Gauss.

14. Again, if we make

$$F^m = g^{mn}(\phi\psi_n)$$

where ϕ, ψ are any two scalars, then Equation 9.16 becomes

9.18 $$\int_V \{\nabla(\phi,\psi) + \phi\Delta\psi\}\,dV = \int_S \phi(\partial\psi/\partial s)\,dS,$$

which is usually attributed to Green. If we interchange ϕ and ψ and subtract, we have

9.19 $$\int_V \{\phi\Delta\psi - \psi\Delta\phi\}\,dV = \int_S \left(\phi\frac{\partial\psi}{\partial s} - \psi\frac{\partial\phi}{\partial s}\right)dS,$$

which is a form of Green much used in potential theory, where one of the scalars is often taken as the reciprocal of the radius vector.

15. The intrinsic invariance of the Gauss equation (Equation 9.17) suggests that we could also write in *two* dimensions

$$\int_S \overline{\Delta\phi}\,dS = \int_C \phi_\alpha \nu^\alpha ds$$

in which ν^α is now a *surface* vector, normal and outward-drawn to the contour, and the Laplacian is taken with respect to the surface metric. In fact, we have obtained this result as Equation 9.12 in which j^l or j^α is the inward-drawn normal to the contour (fig. 9) and is therefore the same as minus ν^α. The two-scalar forms of Equations 9.18 and 9.19 are similarly valid in two dimensions as between surface and contour integrals.

16. If we are prepared to continue working in Cartesian coordinates, then, as in the case of surface and contour integrals, we can obtain many other formulas by giving the basic tensor T_{ijk} in Equation 9.15 special forms. An instructive example is to give it the form

$$\epsilon^{mrs}F_{s,\,r},$$

in which case the closed surface integral vanishes because of Equation 9.08. The volume integral therefore vanishes over any arbitrary volume, which means that its integrand

$$\epsilon^{mrs}F_{s,\,rm}$$

must be zero. Although this is an invariant which allows us to use any coordinate system, we cannot generalize the result to curved space because it contains second covariant derivatives. We must therefore consider that the space is flat, in which case the tensor is symmetric in the two covariant indices. We then have

$$\epsilon^{mrs}F_{s,\,rm} = \epsilon^{mrs}F_{s,\,mr} = \epsilon^{rms}F_{s,\,rm} = -\epsilon^{mrs}F_{s,\,rm},$$

so that the volume integrand is zero, as it should be.

CHAPTER 10

Conformal Transformation of Space

METRICAL RELATIONS

1. We now consider the transformation of a space whose metric is ds^2 to another space whose metric is

10.01
$$d\bar{s}^2 = m^2 ds^2$$

in which m is a scalar function of position — continuous, single-valued, and differentiable over some finite region. The function m must also be an invariant because ds^2 and $d\bar{s}^2$ are invariants in Riemannian space. We shall call this function the *scale factor* because it multiplies infinitesimal lengths in the one space to obtain the corresponding lengths in the other.

2. We shall also assume that there is a one-to-one correspondence of points over some region of the two spaces. This relation means that the coordinates of points in one space are single-valued functions of the coordinates of corresponding points in the other; for instance, we have

$$\bar{x} = f(x, y, z),$$

which implies further that the x^r can be transformed to the $\bar{x}^r$ and are therefore possible coordinates in the overbarred space. We shall take the coordinates to be the same in both spaces. In that case, if Equation 10.01 is to hold true for all corresponding directions around a point, the two metric tensors will be related by

10.02
$$\bar{g}_{rs} = m^2 g_{rs}.$$

We then have the following relations between the determinants of the metric tensors and between the associated tensors,

10.03
$$|\bar{g}_{rs}| = m^6 |g_{rs}|$$

in three dimensions, and

10.04
$$\bar{g}^{rs} = m^{-2} g^{rs}.$$

3. We can also relate the Christoffel symbols straight from the definitions,

$$m^{-2} \overline{[ij,\,k]} = [ij,\,k] + g_{ik}(\ln m)_j + g_{jk}(\ln m)_i$$

10.05
$$- g_{ij}(\ln m)_k$$

$$\bar{\Gamma}^l_{ij} = \Gamma^l_{ij} + \delta^l_i(\ln m)_j + \delta^l_j(\ln m)_i - g_{ij}g^{lk}(\ln m)_k$$

10.06

in which δ^l_i, etc., are Kronecker deltas and $(\ln m)_j$ is the gradient of the natural logarithm of the scale factor.

4. Finally, we can relate the two curvature tensors straight from the definition in Equations 5.03 and 5.06, and after some manipulation, the result will be

$$m^{-2}\overline{R}_{qrst} - R_{qrst} = mg_{qs}(1/m)_{rt} - mg_{qt}(1/m)_{rs}$$

$$- mg_{rs}(1/m)_{qt} + mg_{rt}(1/m)_{qs}$$

10.07
$$+ m^2(g_{rs}g_{qt} - g_{rt}g_{qs})\nabla(1/m)$$

in which $\nabla(1/m)$ is the differential invariant from Equation 3.13, that is,

$$\nabla(1/m) = g^{rs}(1/m)_r(1/m)_s;$$

and the expressions $(1/m)_{rt}$, etc., are second covariant derivatives of $(1/m)$. The equations in Equation 10.07 are known as the Finzi equations.[1]

---

[1] Levi-Cività (1926), *The Absolute Differential Calculus*, 229–232.

55

THE CURVATURE TENSOR IN THREE DIMENSIONS

5. By contracting the curvature tensors in Equation 10.07 with g^{ql} or $m^2 \bar{g}^{ql}$, we obtain a relation between the Ricci tensors, which, as we have seen in §5–11, are sufficient to describe the curvature of 3-space. The result, introducing the Laplacian

$$\Delta m = g^{rs} m_{rs}$$

and using the identity

10.08 $\Delta m = 2m^3 \nabla (1/m) - m^2 \Delta (1/m),$

is

10.09 $\bar{R}_{rs} - R_{rs} = -m(1/m)_{rs} + (1/m)(\Delta m)g_{rs}.$

6. We can also relate the Lamé tensors in three dimensions by means of Equation 5.13. Using the identity

10.10 $\Delta (\ln m) = -m\Delta(1/m) + m^2 \nabla (1/m)$

and lowering indices, the result is

10.11 $\bar{S}_{rs} - S_{rs} = -m(1/m)_{rs} - (\Delta \ln m)g_{rs}.$

7. If both spaces are flat, then the left-hand side of the last equation is zero, and the scale factor must satisfy six second-order differential equations. Using rectangular Cartesian coordinates and substituting Equation 10.10, we see that three of these equations are of the form

$$\frac{\partial^2 (1/m)}{\partial x \partial y} = 0$$

and three are of the form

$$\frac{\partial^2 (1/m)}{\partial x^2} + \frac{\partial^2 (1/m)}{\partial y^2} = m \left\{ \left(\frac{\partial (1/m)}{\partial x} \right)^2 + \left(\frac{\partial (1/m)}{\partial y} \right)^2 + \left(\frac{\partial (1/m)}{\partial z} \right)^2 \right\}.$$

It can be shown[2] that the only nontrivial transformations which satisfy all six equations are inversions with respect to a sphere. If the curvatures of both spaces were to be specified without being zero, the scale factor similarly would have to satisfy six equations, and the choice of scale factor would similarly be restricted so that very few transformations would be available. We shall usually be compelled by the nature of the problem to make one

---

[2] See, for example, Forsyth (reprint of 1920), *Lectures on the Differential Geometry of Curves and Surfaces*, original ed. of 1912, 428.

space flat, but there is no need to make the other space flat or to specify its curvature. Nor do we have to attribute any physical significance to the other space; we can consider it simply as a mathematical device. We can then take the scale factor to be any continuous differentiable function and let it settle the curvature of the space in accordance with Equations 10.09 and 10.11. If, for instance, the unbarred space is flat, then we have $S_{rs} = 0$, and the metric tensor and covariant derivatives on the right of Equation 10.11 are all taken with respect to the metric of the flat space. For the present, however, we shall keep the discussion quite general and not assume that either space is flat.

TRANSFORMATION OF TENSORS

8. Unit contravariant vectors in corresponding directions can easily be related because we are using the same coordinates for both spaces. We have

10.12 $\bar{l}^r = \frac{\partial x^r}{\partial \bar{s}} = \frac{1}{m} \frac{\partial x^r}{\partial s} = m^{-1} l^r$

and, for the covariant components,

10.13 $\bar{l}_r = \bar{g}_{rs} \bar{l}^s = (m^2 g_{rs})(m^{-1} l^s) = m l_r.$

9. It is evident that the scalar product of any two unit vectors remains the same on transformation so that angles between corresponding directions are preserved. Small corresponding figures will be similar, differing only in scale, which, however, will vary from point to point. The transformation is called *conformal* for this reason.

10. In the case of a nonunit vector field, we could say that the magnitude is a function of the coordinates and remains the same on transformation so that nonunit vectors would transform in the same way as Equations 10.12 and 10.13. A tensor, which can be expressed as a sum of products of vectors, would also transform in the same way, but the power of m would, in accordance with Equations 10.12 and 10.13, be the number of covariant indices less the number of contravariant indices, for instance,

$$\bar{A}^q_{rst} = m^2 A^q_{rst}.$$

But it must be noted that all this refers only to tensor point functions. It does not apply to covariant derivatives which involve a difference in the values of a vector or tensor at two points where m may have different values. Covariant derivatives must accordingly contain derivatives of m and may also contain derivatives of the magnitudes of nonunit vectors.

11. We can relate the covariant derivatives of unit vectors by differentiating Equations 10.12 and 10.13 and by using the relation between the Christoffel symbols in Equation 10.06, the results being

10.14 $\quad m^{-1}\bar{l}_{r,s}=l_{r,s}-(\ln m)_r l_s+g_{rs}(\ln m)_t l^t$

10.15 $\quad m\bar{l}^r_{,s}=l^r_{,s}+\delta^r_s(\ln m)_t l^t-g^{rt}(\ln m)_t l_s.$

The second equation can be shown to be equivalent to the first by multiplying the equation by

$$(m^{-2}\bar{g}_{rq})=g_{rq}.$$

Higher derivatives can be related in the same way as required.

12. If ϕ is a scalar defined to have the same value at corresponding points, such as the scale factor or a common coordinate, then the second covariant derivative of the scalar will be

$$\bar{\phi}_{rs}=\frac{\partial^2\phi}{\partial x^r\partial x^s}-\bar{\Gamma}^t_{rs}\phi_t$$

$$=\phi_{rs}-\phi_r(\ln m)_s-\phi_s(\ln m)_r+g_{rs}\nabla(\ln m,\phi),$$

10.16

the differential invariant ∇ being as defined in Equation 3.14. We multiply by $m^2\bar{g}^{rs}=g^{rs}$ to obtain the Laplacian invariants

10.17 $\quad m^2\overline{\Delta\phi}=\Delta\phi+(\delta^r_r-2)\nabla(\ln m,\phi).$

Note that in two dimensions the last term is zero, whereas in three dimensions, we have

10.18 $\quad m^2\overline{\Delta\phi}=\Delta\phi+\nabla(\ln m,\phi).$

CURVATURE AND TORSION OF CORRESPONDING LINES

13. We shall now consider a curve whose unit tangent, normal, and binormal are l_r, p_r, q_r. In the transformed space, the unit tangent, normal, and binormal are $\bar{l}_r$, $\bar{n}_r$, $\bar{b}_r$. The two tangents l_r, $\bar{l}_r$ are corresponding directions because the two curves correspond. However, we cannot say that n_r, b_r, corresponding to $\bar{n}_r$, $\bar{b}_r$, will be the same as p_r, q_r because we have no reason to suppose that the normals and binormals are corresponding directions. From the conformal or angle-true properties of the transformation, we can, however, say that n_r, b_r will be perpendicular to each other and to l_r. The uncertainty in the correspondence is thereby

reduced to one angle θ between n_r and p_r, which we shall have to determine. The situation is as shown in figure 10, which represents a plane (or

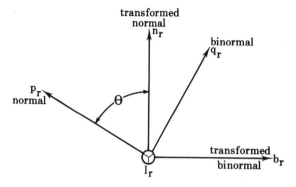

Figure 10.

"section" [3] in curved space) perpendicular to l_r.

14. The vector curvatures of the corresponding lines l_r, $\bar{l}_r$ are related by Equations 10.14 and 10.12 as

10.19 $\quad \bar{l}_{rs}\bar{l}^s=l_{rs}l^s-(\ln m)_r+\{(\ln m)_t l^t\}l_r.$

We can also write

$$(\ln m)_r=\{(\ln m)_t l^t\}l_r+\{(\ln m)_t p^t\}p_r$$
$$+\{(\ln m)_t q^t\}q_r,$$

and if χ, $\bar{\chi}$ are the two principal curvatures, we then have

$$\bar{\chi}\bar{n}_r=m\bar{\chi}n_r=\{\chi-(\ln m)_t p^t\}p_r-\{(\ln m)_t q^t\}q_r.$$

10.20

But from figure 10, we have

$$n_r=(\cos\theta)p_r+(\sin\theta)q_r$$

and so

$$m\bar{\chi}\cos\theta=\chi-(\ln m)_t p^t$$

10.21 $\quad m\bar{\chi}\sin\theta=-(\ln m)_t q^t,$

which determine both $\bar{\chi}$ and θ.

15. If the transformed curve is a geodesic, we then have $\bar{\chi}=0$. The first equation of Equations 10.21 then shows that the principal curvature χ

---

[3] A "section" in curved space is defined by a pair of vectors, p_r, q_r for instance, and is such that any other vector in the section can be expressed linearly in terms of p_r, q_r. If l_r is perpendicular to p_r, q_r, then all vectors in the section are perpendicular to l_r. See also §5–19.

of the curve in the unbarred space is the arc rate of change of (ln m) in the direction of the principal normal to the curve. The second equation of Equations 10.21 shows that the scale factor remains constant for a small displacement in the direction of the binormal to the curve.

16. In regard to the torsion of a general curve, we differentiate the equation

$$n_r p^r = \cos \theta$$

along the line and have, if ds is the arc element,

$$n_{rs} p^r l^s = -n_r p^r_{,s} l^s - \sin \theta (d\theta/ds)$$
$$= -n_r(-\chi l^r + \tau q^r) - \sin \theta (d\theta/ds)$$
$$= -\tau \sin \theta - \sin \theta (d\theta/ds),$$

using the Frenet equations in Equations 4.06 and introducing the torsion τ. Next, we transform the expression on the left to the barred space by means of Equations 10.14 and 10.12 to have

$$\{m^{-1}\bar{n}_{rs} + (\ln m)_r n_s - g_{rs}(\ln m)_t n^t\} p^r l^s$$
$$= m\bar{n}_{rs}\bar{p}^r \bar{l}^s$$
$$= m(-\bar{\chi}\bar{l}_r + \bar{\tau}\bar{b}_r)\bar{p}^r$$
$$= -m\bar{\tau} \sin \theta,$$

again using the second Frenet Equations 4.06 and introducing the torsion $\bar{\tau}$ of the transformed curve. We have finally

10.22 $$m\bar{\tau} = \tau + (d\theta/ds).$$

By differentiating Equations 10.21, we have after some manipulation

$$m\bar{\chi}(d\theta/ds) = -\sin \theta(\partial\chi/\partial s) + \tau(\ln m)_r n^r$$
10.23 $$+ m(1/m)_{rs} b^r l^s;$$

and by eliminating $(d\theta/ds)$ with Equation 10.22, we have

$$m^2\bar{\chi}\bar{\tau} = \chi\tau \cos \theta - \sin \theta(\partial\chi/\partial s) + m(1/m)_{rs} b^r l^s.$$
10.24

We have also the following equation connecting the arc rate of change of the two curvatures along the line,

$$m^2(\partial\bar{\chi}/\partial\bar{s}) = \cos \theta(\partial\chi/\partial s) - \tau(\ln m)_r b^r$$
10.25 $$+ m(1/m)_{rs} n^r l^s.$$

17. The curvature of space enters the equations for the torsion (but not for the curvature) because

$(\partial\chi/\partial s)$ involves second covariant derivatives. The second covariant derivative of the scale factor also involves the curvature of the two spaces. We have in fact from Equations 10.09 and 10.11

$$-m(1/m)_{rs} b^r l^s = (\bar{R}_{rs} - R_{rs}) b^r l^s$$
$$= (\bar{S}_{rs} - S_{rs}) b^r l^s.$$

18. A useful way of checking results in a correspondence between two spaces is to interchange the spaces. We can transfer the overbars in an equation, such as Equation 10.14, provided we write $(1/m)$ for m; and we then have

$$ml_{rs} = \bar{l}_{rs} + (\ln m)_r \bar{l}_s - \bar{g}_{rs}(\ln m)_t \bar{l}^t,$$

which is easily shown to be equivalent to the original equation. In the case of Equation 10.21, we shall also have to change the sign of θ because the rotation from the normal to the transformed normal has the opposite sense in the barred space. Moreover, instead of p^t, we must write the normal in the barred space, that is, $\bar{n}^t$; and instead of q^t, we must write the binormal in the barred space, that is, $\bar{b}^t$. We then have

$$(1/m)\chi \cos \theta = \bar{\chi} + (\ln m)_t \bar{n}^t$$
$$(1/m)\chi \sin \theta = -(\ln m)_t \bar{b}^t$$
or
$$m\bar{\chi} = \chi \cos \theta - (\ln m)_t n^t$$
10.26 $$\chi \sin \theta = -(\ln m)_t b^t,$$

which are equivalent to the original equations. A check on Equations 10.23 and 10.24 is more difficult, but can be applied using only results which have already been given—such as Equation 10.16.

TRANSFORMATION OF SURFACE NORMALS

19. A continuous differentiable scalar N in a space of three dimensions will define a family of surfaces, over each of which N is constant. For example,

$$N = f(x, y, z)$$

defines a surface containing all the points for which N has a particular constant value; different members of the family will be obtained by assigning different constant values to N. But N is constant in directions perpendicular to its gradient, so that the gradient of N must lie in the direction of the normal to that surface of the family which passes through the point under consideration. Excluding singular points where the gradient of N is a null vector, we can write

10.27 $$N_r = n\nu_r$$

in which ν_r is the unit surface normal and n is the magnitude of the gradient vector. We take the covariant derivative of Equation 10.27 and divide by n to give

$$(1/n)N_{rs} = \nu_{rs} + \nu_r(\ln n)_s.$$

Because N is a scalar, its second covariant derivative is a symmetric tensor; thus, we can interchange (r, s) and subtract to find that

10.28 $$\nu_{rs} = \nu_{sr} + \nu_s(\ln n)_r - \nu_r(\ln n)_s.$$

If we contract this equation with ν^s and use Equation 3.19, which makes $\nu_{sr}\nu^s$ zero, we have

10.29 $$\nu_{rs}\nu^s = (\ln n)_r - \nu_r(\ln n)_s\nu^s.$$

Finally, we compare this result with Equation 10.19 and conclude that *a scale factor of* n *will transform the space conformally to another space in which the surface normals become a family of geodesics.* Because of the conformal property of the transformation, these geodesics will be normal to the transformed N-surfaces. Moreover, an element of length along a transformed geodesic will be

$$d\bar{s} = n\,ds = (N_r\nu^r)\,ds = N_r\,dx^r = dN.$$

The length of a geodesic intercepted between two N-surfaces N_1 and N_2 will accordingly be $(N_2 - N_1)$ and will be the same for all geodesics between these two surfaces. For this reason, the transformed N-surfaces are known as *geodesic parallels.*

20. Conversely, if there exists a family of geodesics and geodesic parallels, expressible by a scalar N, in a conformal transformation with scale factor n, then we can say that the relation

$$N_r = n\nu_r$$

must hold true between the corresponding lines and surfaces in the untransformed space.

21. If we write

$$n = m \cdot f(N)$$

in which $f(N)$ is an arbitrary, continuous, differentiable, and nonvanishing function of N and if we substitute in Equation 10.29, we have

$$\nu_{rs}\nu^s = (\ln m)_r - \nu_r(\ln m)_s\nu^s$$
$$+ \frac{f'(N)}{f(N)}\,N_r - \frac{\nu_r f'(N)}{f(N)}\,(N_s\nu^s).$$

The last two terms cancel by virtue of Equation 10.27. Comparing this result with Equation 10.29, we conclude that the scale factor can well be n multiplied by an arbitrary function of N.

TRANSFORMATION OF SURFACES

22. It should be noted that we have nowhere assumed that either space is flat; the curvature of the space does not arise until we assign particular values to the curvature tensor or until we introduce the second covariant derivatives of vectors. Moreover, all the above properties are intrinsic to the space, being based solely on the metric tensor and its derivatives. We can accordingly use all the above tensor formulas with Greek indices for transformations between curved surfaces considered as two-dimensional spaces, provided we do not use results, such as Equation 10.09, which are valid only in three dimensions. We have, for instance,

$$\bar{a}_{\alpha\beta} = m^2 a_{\alpha\beta}$$
$$|\bar{a}_{\alpha\beta}| = m^4|a_{\alpha\beta}|$$

10.30 $$\bar{a}^{\alpha\beta} = m^{-2}a^{\alpha\beta},$$

and all of Equations 10.05, 10.06, 10.07, 10.12, 10.13, 10.14, 10.15, 10.16, and 10.17 are valid.

23. Because there is only one component of the curvature tensor in two dimensions, we can simplify the Finzi equations of Equation 10.07 which are, in two dimensions,

$$m^{-2}\bar{R}_{\alpha\beta\gamma\delta} - R_{\alpha\beta\gamma\delta} = ma_{\alpha\gamma}(1/m)_{\beta\delta} - ma_{\alpha\delta}(1/m)_{\beta\gamma}$$
$$- ma_{\beta\gamma}(1/m)_{\alpha\delta} + ma_{\beta\delta}(1/m)_{\alpha\gamma}$$
$$+ m^2(a_{\beta\gamma}a_{\alpha\delta} - a_{\beta\delta}a_{\alpha\gamma})\nabla(1/m)$$

where the invariant ∇ is now taken with respect to the surface metric $a_{\alpha\beta}$. We contract with $a^{\alpha\gamma} = m^2\bar{a}^{\alpha\gamma}$ and use Equations 5.19 and 2.45 to have

$$\bar{K}\bar{a}_{\beta\delta} - Ka_{\beta\delta} = ma_{\beta\delta}\Delta(1/m) - m^2 a_{\beta\delta}\nabla(1/m).$$

If we substitute

$$\bar{a}_{\beta\delta} = m^2 a_{\beta\delta}$$

and use the identity

$$\Delta(\ln m) = -m\Delta(1/m) + m^2\nabla(1/m),$$

we have finally as the sole curvature equation

10.31 $$\Delta(\ln m) = K - m^2\bar{K}$$

in which, of course, the Laplacian is taken with respect to the unbarred surface metric. This is a well-known formula in the theory of conformal map projections, attributed by Marussi[4] to Souslow (1898). If the Gaussian curvatures of the two surfaces are given, then this formula is a differential equation which the scale factor must satisfy. Alternatively, we could choose the scale factor and one surface, in which case the Gaussian curvature of the other surface is settled by Equation 10.31. If one surface is a plane, then we have

10.32 $\qquad \Delta(\ln m) = K$

in which the Laplacian and, of course, the Gaussian curvature refer to the curved surface.

GEODESIC CURVATURES

24. In two dimensions, Equation 10.19 becomes

$$\bar{\sigma}\bar{j}_\alpha = \sigma j_\alpha - (\ln m)_\alpha + \{(\ln m)_\beta l^\beta\} l_\alpha$$

in which σ, $\bar{\sigma}$ are, respectively, the geodesic curvatures of the curve l_α and of its transform; and j_α, $\bar{j}_\alpha$ are perpendicular to l_α and to its transform in the usual sense of figure 5 in § 6–13. But in this case, j_α, $\bar{j}_\alpha$, which are both surface vectors, must correspond because of the conformal property of the transformation. (Note that in three dimensions, we could not say that the two principal normals correspond.) So, from the two dimensional form of Equation 10.13, we have

$$\bar{j}_\alpha = m j_\alpha,$$

and the above equation reduces to

10.33 $\qquad \sigma - m\bar{\sigma} = (\ln m)_\alpha j^\alpha.$

If $\bar{\sigma} = 0$, this is equivalent to a well-known formula in the theory of map projections,[5] attributable to Schols.

All the properties of two-dimensional transformations naturally hold true for corresponding surfaces in a three-dimensional transformation. The Gaussian curvatures of the corresponding N-surfaces of the last section must, for example, satisfy Equation 10.31.

---

[4] Marussi (1957), "Sulle rappresentazioni fra superfici definite mediante la forma quadratica che ne determina il modulo di deformazione," *Festschrift zum 75. Geburtstag von Prof. Dr. C. F. Baeschlin*, 201–210. Reprint available from Istituto di Topografia e Geodesia dell' Universita di Trieste as Pubblicazione No. 33.

[5] See also Taucer (1954), "Alcune considerazioni sul teorema di Schols," *Bollettino di Geodesia e Scienze Affini*, v. 13, no. 2, 159–162. Reprint available from Istituto di Topografia e Geodesia dell' Universita di Trieste as Pubblicazione No. 16.

EXTRINSIC PROPERTIES OF CORRESPONDING SURFACES IN CONFORMAL SPACE

25. It is clear from the defining Equation 10.02 that conformal transformations are based solely on the metric tensor and its derivatives and therefore lead only to intrinsic properties. We cannot expect to derive any more conformal properties of surfaces from their extrinsic properties, even if the surfaces are embedded in conformal space. Nevertheless, this is a useful alternative approach, which, at the least, can serve as a check.

26. Because the coordinates are the same in both spaces, we can write

10.34 $\qquad \bar{x}^r_\alpha = x^r_\alpha.$

In order to relate the second and third fundamental forms, we need an expression for $\bar{\nu}^r_\alpha$. By expansion and use of Equations 10.06 and 10.12, we have

10.35 $\qquad m\bar{\nu}^r_\alpha = \nu^r_\alpha + n x^r_\alpha$

where we have used the special symbol

10.36 $\qquad n = (\ln m)_r \nu^r$

for the arc rate of change of $(\ln m)$ along the surface normal. This special symbol should not be confused with the "n" in the general gradient Equation 10.27 as used extensively elsewhere in this book.

27. The second and third fundamental forms follow as

10.37 $\qquad m^{-1}\bar{b}_{\alpha\beta} = -m^{-1}g_{rs}\bar{x}^r_\alpha\bar{\nu}^s_\beta = b_{\alpha\beta} - n a_{\alpha\beta}$

10.38 $\qquad \bar{c}_{\alpha\beta} = g_{rs}\bar{\nu}^r_\alpha\bar{\nu}^s_\beta = c_{\alpha\beta} - 2n b_{\alpha\beta} + n^2 a_{\alpha\beta},$

and the normal curvatures and geodesic torsion in the usual orthogonal directions are

10.39 $\qquad m\bar{k} = m\bar{b}_{\alpha\beta}\bar{l}^\alpha\bar{l}^\beta = k - n$

10.40 $\qquad m\bar{k}^* = m\bar{b}_{\alpha\beta}\bar{j}^\alpha\bar{j}^\beta = k^* - n$

10.41 $\qquad m\bar{t} = m\bar{b}_{\alpha\beta}\bar{l}^\alpha\bar{j}^\beta = t$

10.42 $\qquad m^2(\bar{k}\bar{k}^* - \bar{t}^2) = (kk^* - t^2) - 2Hn + n^2.$

28. But from Equation 10.31, we have

$$m^2\bar{K} = K - \Delta(\ln m),$$

all with respect to the surface metric; and subtracting Equation 10.42 from this expression and using Equation 8.31, we have

10.43 $\qquad m^2\bar{C} = C - \{\Delta(\ln m) - 2Hn + n^2\}$

for the Riemannian curvatures perpendicular to the surface normals.

We can verify this last equation by contracting Equation 10.11 with $\nu^r\nu^s$ as

$$m^2\bar{C} - C = -m(1/m)_{rs}\nu^r\nu^s - \Delta(\ln m),$$

all with respect to the space metric. With some manipulation and use of Equations 8.27 and 10.10, we can reduce this to Equation 10.43. However, we have added nothing new, but have confirmed a number of other results.

29. From Equation 10.41, we conclude that the principal directions correspond. Accordingly, we can write Equation 8.16 for the barred surface and transform the right-hand side to obtain a relation between the $b_{\alpha\beta}$'s. Or, we can take ordinary differentials of Equation 10.37, for example,

$$\frac{\partial \bar{b}_{\alpha\beta}}{\partial x^\gamma} = \bar{b}_{\alpha\beta\gamma} + \bar{\Gamma}^\delta_{\alpha\gamma}\bar{b}_{\delta\beta} + \bar{\Gamma}^\delta_{\beta\gamma}\bar{b}_{\alpha\delta},$$

and transform the Christoffel symbols by the two-dimensional form of Equation 10.06. The result in either case is

$$m^{-1}\bar{b}_{\alpha\beta\gamma} - b_{\alpha\beta\gamma} = a_{\alpha\beta}m(1/m)_{st}\nu^s x^t_\gamma$$
$$- \sum_{\alpha\beta\gamma}(\ln m)_\alpha b_{\beta\gamma}$$
10.44
$$+ a^{\delta\epsilon}(\ln m)_\epsilon \sum_{\alpha\beta\gamma} a_{\alpha\beta}b_{\gamma\delta}$$

in which we have used the summation symbol for the sum of terms with cyclic permutation of the indices (α, β, γ), for example,

$$\sum_{\alpha\beta\gamma}(\ln m)_\alpha b_{\beta\gamma} = (\ln m)_\alpha b_{\beta\gamma} + (\ln m)_\beta b_{\gamma\alpha} + (\ln m)_\gamma b_{\alpha\beta}.$$

The summation terms drop out if we interchange (β, γ) and subtract, as we shall do when we form the Codazzi equations.

Next, we contract the Finzi equations in Equation 10.07 with

$$\nu^q x^r_\alpha x^s_\beta x^t_\gamma$$

and have

$$m^{-1}\bar{R}_{qrst}\bar{\nu}^q \bar{x}^r_\alpha \bar{x}^s_\beta \bar{x}^t_\gamma - R_{qrst}\nu^q x^r_\alpha x^s_\beta x^t_\gamma$$
10.45
$$= -ma_{\alpha\beta}(1/m)_{qt}\nu^q x^t_\gamma + ma_{\alpha\gamma}(1/m)_{qs}\nu^q x^s_\beta.$$

By inspection, we can see that Equations 10.44 and 10.45 satisfy the full Codazzi equations of Equation 6.22 — another useful verification.

THE GAUSS–BONNET THEOREM

30. The properties of conformal transformations enable us, as one example, to establish easily an important result relating to the angles of closed figures drawn on a surface.

We suppose that one of the surfaces is a plane $(\bar{K}=0)$ so that Equation 10.32 holds true, and we then integrate Equation 10.33 around corresponding closed contours whose unit tangents are l_α, $\bar{l}_\alpha$. This amounts to multiplying Equation 10.33 by $ds = (1/m)d\bar{s}$ and integrating. We have

$$\int_C \sigma ds - \int_C \bar{\sigma} d\bar{s} = \int_C (\ln m)_\alpha j^\alpha ds$$
$$= -\int_S \Delta(\ln m)dS$$
10.46
$$= -\int_S K dS,$$

using Equation 9.12 in converting from the contour to the surface integral, which has to be taken over the whole area of the surface enclosed by the contour. In the plane, the geodesic curvature of the contour becomes the ordinary curvature of a plane curve, and the contour integral is the total angle swept out by the tangent to the contour in describing the contour. If the contour is continuous, this angle is 2π; for any continuous contour on the curved surface, we have accordingly

10.47
$$\int_C \sigma ds + \int_S K dS = 2\pi.$$

But if the contour in the plane has a corner enclosing an angle θ, then the tangent at that corner will turn $(\pi - \theta)$ without any contribution from the contour integral. If there are n such corners, then we have

$$\int_C \bar{\sigma} d\bar{s} = 2\pi - n\pi + \sum_n \theta_n.$$

The angles enclosed by the corners of the corresponding contour on the curved surface will be the same because of the conformal property of the transformation, and we have finally

10.48
$$\int_C \sigma ds + \int_S K dS = 2\pi - n\pi + \sum_n \theta_n.$$

In the case of a triangle with curved sides enclosing angles A, B, C, this is

10.49
$$\int_C \sigma ds + \int_S K dS = A + B + C - \pi;$$

and if the sides are geodesics, this is

10.50
$$\int_S K dS = A + B + C - \pi.$$

This last equation is the exact form of an approximate formula used in classical geodesy for calculating "spherical excess."

CHAPTER 11

Spherical Representation

DEFINITIONS

1. We can "represent" one surface on another by defining a correspondence between points on the two surfaces, so that to any figure drawn on the one surface, there corresponds a figure on the other surface. The conformal transformations between surfaces considered in the last chapter are a special class of such representation because they result in small corresponding figures being similar. The idea of representing a curved surface on a plane, as another example, is common in the theory of map projections; but whereas few map projections can be constructed by means of geometrical projection, they can all be defined by setting up a correspondence of points on the Earth and on the map, so that there is one and only one point on the map corresponding to or representing a given point on the Earth.

2. In this chapter, we shall consider the representation of a given surface on a sphere of unit radius, as first proposed by Gauss who defined the correspondence of points by making the normals to the two surfaces parallel at corresponding points. If the normals at two different points on the given surface are parallel and in the same sense, this means that both points would be represented by the same point on the sphere. To make the correspondence unique, we shall exclude regions of the given surface containing such points.

3. We shall assume that both surfaces are embedded in the same flat space, which means that we can choose Cartesian space coordinates and can use the same Cartesian axes for both surfaces. In later applications, we shall find this important. Without any loss of generality, we can, moreover,

take the origin of Cartesian coordinates as the center of the sphere; in which case, the following vector equation holds true in Cartesian coordinates between corresponding points on the two surfaces,

11.01 $$\nu^r = \bar{\rho}^r = \bar{\nu}^r$$

where ν^r is the unit normal to the given surface and $\bar{\rho}^r$ is the position vector of the corresponding point on the sphere. All quantities relating to the sphere will be denoted by overbars. We choose surface coordinates (x^α) to be the same for both surfaces at corresponding points; for instance, the latitude and longitude will be the same in relation to the same Cartesian axes because the two normals are parallel. Moreover, because any surface coordinates must be some single-valued functions of latitude and longitude, we can take the surface coordinates to be the same for both surfaces without specifying what they are. The ordinary derivatives of Equation 11.01 with respect to a surface coordinate will then be the same as the surface covariant derivative because the space coordinates are Cartesian and the space Christoffel symbols are accordingly zero. The following equations therefore hold true in space Cartesian coordinates,

11.02 $$\nu^r_\alpha = \bar{\rho}^r_\alpha = \bar{x}^r_\alpha = \bar{\nu}^r_\alpha,$$

provided that both surfaces are referred to the same surface coordinates x^α.

FUNDAMENTAL FORMS OF THE SURFACES

4. The metric tensor on the sphere is accordingly obtained from Equation 6.06 as

11.03 $$\bar{a}_{\alpha\beta} = \bar{g}_{rs}\bar{x}^r_\alpha \bar{x}^s_\beta = g_{rs}\nu^r_\alpha \nu^s_\beta = c_{\alpha\beta},$$

and the second and third forms for the sphere are given by Equations 6.18 as

11.04 $\bar{b}_{\alpha\beta} = -\bar{g}_{rs}\bar{x}^r_\alpha\bar{\nu}^s_\beta = -g_{rs}\nu^r_\alpha\nu^s_\beta = -c_{\alpha\beta} = -\bar{a}_{\alpha\beta}$

11.05 $\bar{c}_{\alpha\beta} = \bar{g}_{rs}\bar{\nu}^r_\alpha\bar{\nu}^s_\beta = g_{rs}\nu^r_\alpha\nu^s_\beta = c_{\alpha\beta} = \bar{a}_{\alpha\beta}.$

From Equation 7.18, we find that the determinant of the metric tensor is given by

11.06 $|\bar{a}_{\alpha\beta}| = |c_{\alpha\beta}| = K^2|a_{\alpha\beta}| = K|b_{\alpha\beta}|,$

and thus from Equations 11.04 and 11.05, we have

11.07 $\bar{a}^{\alpha\beta} = c^{\alpha\beta} = -\bar{b}^{\alpha\beta} = \bar{c}^{\alpha\beta}.$

5. The fact that the third fundamental form is the same for both surfaces is of considerable importance. For example, we have from Equation 6.17 (Weingarten's formula), using Equation 8.09,

$$\nu^r_\alpha = -a^{\beta\gamma}b_{\alpha\beta}x^r_\gamma = -b^{\beta\gamma}c_{\alpha\beta}x^r_\gamma$$

and so

11.08 $b^{\beta\gamma}x^r_\gamma = -c^{\beta\gamma}\nu^r_\gamma = \bar{b}^{\beta\gamma}\bar{x}^r_\gamma$

in which, it must be repeated, the space coordinates are Cartesian and the surface coordinates are the same for both surfaces. This means that all components of the tensor on the left are unaltered on spherical representation.

CORRESPONDING SURFACE VECTORS

6. Because the surface coordinates are the same for the two surfaces, a difference in coordinates between corresponding points will also be the same. The element of length (ds) between the two points will not, however, be the same; but to a first order, we can connect two *unit* vectors $(l^\alpha, \bar{l}^\alpha)$ as follows,

11.09 $dx^\alpha = l^\alpha ds = d\bar{x}^\alpha = \bar{l}^\alpha d\bar{s}.$

The covariant components will then be connected by

11.10 $\bar{l}_\alpha d\bar{s} = \bar{a}_{\alpha\beta}\bar{l}^\beta d\bar{s} = c_{\alpha\beta}l^\beta ds.$

By multiplying Equations 11.09 and 11.10, contracting, and using Equation 7.14, we have the square of the line element as

11.11 $d\bar{s}^2 = (c_{\alpha\beta}l^\alpha l^\beta)ds^2 = (k^2+t^2)ds^2$

where k and t are, respectively, the normal curvature and geodesic torsion of the given surface in the direction l^α. The spherical representation is not therefore, in general, conformal because the scale factor $(d\bar{s}/ds)$ is not the same for all directions at a point.

7. If the scale factor $(d\bar{s}/ds)$ in the direction l^α is m, then from Equation 11.09, we have

11.12 $l^\alpha = m\bar{l}^\alpha,$

always assuming that the same coordinates are used for the surface and for the spherical representation.

In regard to the covariant components, we have from Equations 11.10 and 7.14

11.13 $m\bar{l}_\beta = c_{\alpha\beta}l^\alpha = m^2l_\beta + 2Htj_\beta.$

Another formula connecting covariant components may be found as follows. From Equations 2.30, we have

11.14 $\epsilon_{\alpha\beta} = (a/c)^{1/2}\bar{\epsilon}_{\alpha\beta} = \bar{\epsilon}_{\alpha\beta}/K$

with the contravariant form

11.14A $\epsilon^{\alpha\beta} = K\bar{\epsilon}^{\alpha\beta}.$

If we multiply Equations 11.12 and 11.14 and use Equations 2.32, we have

11.15 $j_\beta = (m/K)\bar{\bar{j}}_\beta$

in which j_β, $\bar{\bar{j}}_\beta$ are unit vectors perpendicular to l^α, $\bar{l}^\alpha$, respectively. It should be noted, however, that $\bar{\bar{j}}_\beta$ is not, in general, the spherical representation of j_β because the representation is not conformal and a pair of perpendicular vectors will not necessarily remain perpendicular in the spherical representation.

THE PRINCIPAL DIRECTIONS

8. We shall now consider *two* directions at a point given by two small differences in surface coordinates dx^α and (dx^β), which, as before, will be the same for both surfaces. From Equation 7.20, we have

$$Ka_{\alpha\beta}dx^\alpha(dx^\beta) - 2Hb_{\alpha\beta}dx^\alpha(dx^\beta) + c_{\alpha\beta}dx^\alpha(dx^\beta) = 0.$$

11.16

If the two directions are orthogonal on the given surface, the first term is zero; and if the two directions are to remain orthogonal in the spherical representation $(\bar{a}_{\alpha\beta} = c_{\alpha\beta})$, then the third term must also be zero. The remaining term is, in general, zero only if

$$b_{\alpha\beta}dx^\alpha(dx^\beta) = 0,$$

in which case the orthogonal directions dx^α, (dx^β) must also be principal directions. On the sphere, any pair of orthogonal directions can be considered principal directions; and we conclude that the principal directions (or lines of curvature) are, in general, the only directions (or curves) which remain orthogonal on spherical representation.

Moreover, the normals at consecutive points on a line of curvature intersect, and the plane containing the normals must be parallel to the corresponding plane because the consecutive normals are parallel in the spherical representation. Consequently, a principal direction is parallel in space to its spherical representation.

9. We could satisfy Equation 7.20 without making dx^α, (dx^β) the principal directions if $2H$ were zero. In that case, the square of the scale factor in a direction l^α would be

$$c_{\alpha\beta} l^\alpha l^\beta = -K a_{\alpha\beta} l^\alpha l^\beta = -K,$$

which is the same for all directions at a point, so that the spherical representation would be conformal. But in this case, we are restricted to a special class of surfaces whose mean curvature H is zero. Such surfaces are known as minimal surfaces. They are of considerable importance in the physics of soap bubbles and in the minima of double integrals, but do not appear to have any present application in geodesy.

10. If the principal directions of the given surface are u^α, v^β (the principal curvatures are κ_1, κ_2, respectively), then $t = 0$ for these directions, and the scale factor for the u^α-direction reduces to

11.17 $$d\bar{s}/ds = \sqrt{\kappa_1^2}.$$

We shall consider that corresponding elements of length are in the same sense so that the scale factor is essentially positive. Throughout this book, we shall be dealing with convex surfaces whose radii of normal curvature run inward in the opposite sense to the outward-drawn normal and will therefore be numerically negative when computed in accordance with the usual sign conventions from formulas given in this book. Consequently, we must take the negative square root in Equation 11.17 and write

11.18 $$d\bar{s}/ds = -\kappa_1.$$

The scale factor in the v^α-direction will similarly be $-\kappa_2$. In this case, Equations 11.12 and 11.13 reduce to

11.19 $$u^\alpha = -\kappa_1 \bar{u}^\alpha; \qquad u_\beta = -\bar{u}_\beta/\kappa_1$$

11.20 $$v^\alpha = -\kappa_2 \bar{v}^\alpha; \qquad v_\beta = -\bar{v}_\beta/\kappa_2.$$

SCALE FACTOR AND DIRECTIONS REFERRED TO THE PRINCIPAL DIRECTIONS

11. If the unit surface vector l^α makes an angle ψ with the principal direction u^α, then an alternative expression for the square of the scale factor (m) in the direction l^α is from Equation 7.25

$$m^2 = (d\bar{s}/ds)^2 = c_{\alpha\beta} l^\alpha l^\beta = \kappa_1^2 \cos^2 \psi + \kappa_2^2 \sin^2 \psi.$$

11.21

From this equation and from Equations 11.12 and 11.19, we can obtain expressions for $\bar{\psi}$, the angle between the spherical representations of l^α, u^α, as follows,

$$\cos \bar{\psi} = \bar{l}^\alpha \bar{u}_\alpha = -\kappa_1 l^\alpha u_\alpha (ds/d\bar{s})$$

11.22 $$= \frac{-\kappa_1 \cos \psi}{(\kappa_1^2 \cos^2 \psi + \kappa_2^2 \sin^2 \psi)^{1/2}};$$

and similarly, we have

11.23 $$\sin \bar{\psi} = \bar{l}^\alpha \bar{v}_\alpha = \frac{-\kappa_2 \sin \psi}{(\kappa_1^2 \cos^2 \psi + \kappa_2^2 \sin^2 \psi)^{1/2}}$$

from which

11.24 $$\tan \bar{\psi} = (\kappa_2/\kappa_1) \tan \psi.$$

The sense of ψ is that of a positive rotation from u^α to l^α about the outward-drawn normal, as shown in figure 11.

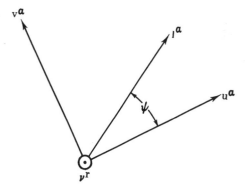

Figure 11.

CHRISTOFFEL SYMBOLS

12. We are now able to derive an important formula connecting the surface Christoffel symbols at corresponding points of the two surfaces. By taking ordinary derivatives with respect to a surface coordinate x^β of the Equation 11.02 and by remembering that the space coordinates are

Cartesian, we have

11.25　　　$\nu^r_{\alpha\beta} + \Gamma^\gamma_{\alpha\beta}\nu^r_\gamma = \bar{x}^r_{\alpha\beta} + \bar{\Gamma}^\gamma_{\alpha\beta}\bar{x}^r_\gamma .$

By surface covariant differentiation of the Weingarten formula (Equation 6.17), we have also

11.26　　　$\nu^r_{\alpha\beta} = -a^{\gamma\delta}b_{\alpha\beta\gamma}x^r_\delta - c_{\alpha\beta}\nu^r$

together with

11.27　　　$\bar{x}^r_{\alpha\beta} = \bar{b}_{\alpha\beta}\bar{\nu}^r = -c_{\alpha\beta}\nu^r$

in which we have used Equations 6.16, 11.04, and 11.01. Substitution in Equation 11.25 gives

11.28　　　$(\Gamma^\gamma_{\alpha\beta} - \bar{\Gamma}^\gamma_{\alpha\beta})\nu^r_\gamma = a^{\gamma\delta}b_{\alpha\beta\gamma}x^r_\delta .$

Contraction with $g_{rs}x^s_\epsilon$ gives

11.29　　$(\Gamma^\gamma_{\alpha\beta} - \bar{\Gamma}^\gamma_{\alpha\beta})b_{\gamma\epsilon} = -a^{\gamma\delta}b_{\alpha\beta\gamma}a_{\delta\epsilon} = -b_{\alpha\beta\epsilon}.$

Contraction with $b^{\epsilon\rho}$ and some rearrangement of indices give finally

11.30　　　$\Gamma^\gamma_{\alpha\beta} - \bar{\Gamma}^\gamma_{\alpha\beta} = -b^{\gamma\delta}b_{\alpha\beta\delta}.$

The Christoffel symbols in the spherical representation are usually very easy to evaluate in a given coordinate system, so that we have now a compact formula for the Christoffel symbols of any given surface, which we shall have frequent occasion to use. We note from Equation 11.04 that because $\bar{b}_{\alpha\beta} = -\bar{a}_{\alpha\beta}$, we must have $\bar{b}_{\alpha\beta\delta} = 0$, so that Equation 11.30 reduces further to the statement that the quantities

11.31　　　　$\Gamma^\gamma_{\alpha\beta} + b^{\gamma\delta}b_{\alpha\beta\delta}$

are unaltered on spherical representation.

REPRESENTATION OF A FAMILY OF SURFACES

13. If we have a family of surfaces defined over a certain region of space, for example, by assigning different values to a scalar N which is constant over each surface as discussed in §10–19, then the surface normals will also be defined over the region. In general, as we shall see in the next chapter, there will be a family of lines—to be known as the *isozenithals*—along any one of which the surface normals are parallel. The spherical representation of an isozenithal is accordingly a point. We can, moreover, draw a figure on any one of the N-surfaces and project it down the isozenithals onto the other surfaces of the family. The original figure and its isozenithal projections will all have the same spherical representation. Moreover, any set of quantities, such as those in Equation 11.31 which have the same values at corresponding points in the spherical representation, will also have the same value at isozenithally projected points. Their differentials along the isozenithals will be zero.

We shall carry the question of spherical representation further in the next two chapters by using a special coordinate system, which, nevertheless, produces quite general results.

CONTENTS

Part II

CHAPTER 12

The (ω, ϕ, N) Coordinate System

DEFINITIONS

1. We shall now consider a special, but quite general, coordinate system, generated by a continuous differentiable scalar function of position N in three-dimensional space. Points having a particular value of N, for instance C, will lie on a surface $N=C$; for different values of C, we shall have a family of surfaces. We take N as one coordinate of the system. But, if N is specified throughout some region of space, then so is the magnitude (n) and direction (ν_r) of its gradient (N_r) because, by definition, we have

12.001 $$N_r = n\nu_r.$$

The direction of ν_r in relation to three fixed Cartesian axes in flat space will define two independent scalars, which can take the form of longitude (ω) and latitude (ϕ). We shall take these as the other two coordinates. Each of these scalars generates a family of surfaces distinct from the N-surfaces and from one another. The position of a point in space can accordingly be defined as the intersection of three surfaces, one from each of the ω, ϕ, and N families over which each of the three coordinates has an assigned value, in much the same way as the position of a point in Cartesian coordinates (a, b, c) can be defined as the intersection of three planes $x=a$, $y=b$, $z=c$. In the more general case, the coordinate surfaces are curved; each coordinate line — that is, the line of intersection of two coordinate surfaces along which only the third coordinate varies — will also be curved. The three coordinate lines passing through a point will not, as a rule, be orthogonal, nor will they be parallel to the coordinate lines at any other point.

It will be assumed throughout this chapter that (ω, ϕ) are the N-surface coordinates as well as two of the space coordinates so that, with the notation of Equation 6.02, we have

$$x_\alpha^3 = 0; \qquad x_\alpha^\beta = \delta_\alpha^\beta.$$

In some cases, this leads to results which are clearly only true in this coordinate system because they relate only some of the components of tensors. In other cases, we shall derive relations connecting *all* the components of tensors. These will accordingly be tensor equations, true in any coordinates, which can be differentiated covariantly and manipulated generally as tensors even though they were derived in a special coordinate system.

SIGN CONVENTIONS

2. There is some advantage in making the (ω, ϕ, N) system right handed in the sense that (x, y, z) is conventionally right handed, as discussed in §1–22. If we look along the positive direction of an N-coordinate line, then the positive direction of the ϕ-line is to the right of the positive direction of the ω-line; a similar rule applies to the cyclic permutations $(\phi N\omega)$, $(N\omega\phi)$. A positive rotation about the N-coordinate line will be clockwise when we look outward along the positive direction of the N-coordinate line. We could say therefore that the ω-line can be rotated positively about the N-line toward the ϕ-line.

3. We shall later identify N with the gravitational potential, or geopotential, or some standard potential. The N-surfaces will be the level or equipotential surfaces; the n will be the gravitional force "g."

The positive direction of N, following the ordinary physical convention, will be toward the zenith even though this will make N negative in the geodetic applications. For Equation 12.001 to hold true—and in such applications as conformal transformation it is desirable that the equation should hold true in this positive form—we must also draw the positive direction of the normal to the N-surfaces toward the zenith; this accords with the usual mathematical convention of an outward-drawn normal to a closed surface. We have finally to make the (ω, ϕ, N) system right handed in that order; to do this, we must make longitude positive toward the east if we are to adopt the almost universal convention of making latitude positive toward the north. This accords with the European convention and with astronomical conventions for right ascension and local time (but not hour angle, which is reckoned positive toward the west). It also makes longitude a positive rotation in the mathematical sense about the northward axis of rotation of the Earth. It does not accord with geodetic practice in the United States where it is customary to make west longitudes positive, no doubt for reasons of historical development, although some Agencies in the United States adopt the more usual eastward convention. On the whole, the balance of advantage seems to lie with positive longitudes east. Any country using the opposite convention has merely to change the sign of longitude, or difference in longitude, wherever it occurs in any formula in this book; the same applies to south latitudes.

4. In the proposed convention, longitude will be the first coordinate, whereas the almost universal convention is to list latitude first. However, this should cause no confusion. We consider longitude to be the first coordinate in a right-handed system $(\omega, \phi, N = 1, 2, 3)$ in the derivation of mathematical formulas, but the results can, of course, be listed in any convenient order.

5. A positive rotation about the zenithal direction (ν_r) in the mathematical sense will be from north to west, whereas the almost universal geodetic convention for azimuth (α) is from north to east. The only way of reconciling the two would be to adopt an inward-drawn normal to the N-surfaces; this could lead to serious confusion in cases where formulas are taken straight from standard mathematical works. However, we can avoid confusion by giving azimuth its own convention and by remembering that azimuth is a negative mathematical rotation in cases where it is derived that way.

6. In another geodetic application, we shall need to identify N with "height." By universal convention, this is positive in the zenith direction; this then agrees with the proposed convention for N.

7. The conventions which will be adopted throughout this book are illustrated in the diagram (fig. 12);

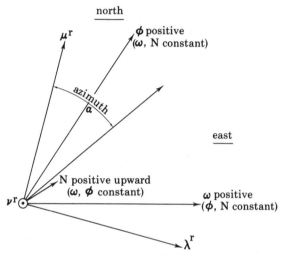

Figure 12.

the zenith direction (ν_r) or the gradient of N is toward the reader. In an unsymmetrical field, the ω- and ϕ-coordinate lines will not run exactly to the east and north, but they will, nevertheless, run in those general directions. In the same way, the N-coordinate line—that is, the direction in which ω, ϕ are constant—will not coincide, in general, with ν_r. The other two vectors λ_r, μ_r on the diagram lie in the plane of the paper and will now be defined.

THE BASE VECTORS

8. Next, we set up three mutually orthogonal unit parallel vector fields A^r, B^r, C^r to serve as the axes of a right-handed Cartesian coordinate system (x, y, z). This assumes that we are working in flat three-dimensional space because such a coordinate system would not otherwise be possible. In Cartesian coordinates, the components of these vectors would be

$$A^r = (1, 0, 0)$$

$$B^r = (0, 1, 0)$$

12.002 $\qquad C^r = (0, 0, 1),$

but we shall often require their components in other coordinate systems. The vectors are constant in the sense that their Cartesian components are the same throughout the region of space considered. Their components will not be the same at all points in other coordinate systems, but because they are parallel at all points, their covariant derivatives, from Equations 3.05 and 3.06, will be zero in all systems. We shall later identify these vectors physically—for example, in some applications C^r will be parallel to the axis of rotation of the Earth with its positive direction toward the north—but for the present, the vectors simply provide a fixed Cartesian reference system.

9. We also introduce a local system of mutually orthogonal unit vectors λ^r, μ^r, ν^r, right handed in that order. As before, ν^r is the zenith direction or the outward-drawn unit normal to the N-surface passing through the point under consideration. We define μ^r as coplanar with ν^r and a parallel to C^r, and call it the direction of the *meridian*; the positive direction of μ^r will be roughly in the direction of the ϕ-coordinate line, and because μ^r is perpendicular to ν^r, it will be tangential to the N-surface. The vector λ^r simply completes the orthogonal triad. It will also be an N-surface vector, roughly in the direction of the ω-coordinate line, and will be called the *parallel* direction to accord as nearly as possible with ordinary geographical terms. It is easy to see that λ^r will be parallel to a plane containing A^r and B^r because it is perpendicular to the plane of μ^r and ν^r, and is therefore perpendicular to C^r.

10. Next, we define longitude (ω) and latitude (ϕ) in terms of the direction cosines of the unit normal ν^r by means of the following scalar products,

12.003 $\qquad \cos \phi \cos \omega = \nu_r A^r$

12.004 $\qquad \cos \phi \sin \omega = \nu_r B^r$

12.005 $\qquad \sin \phi = \nu_r C^r$.

The arrangement is illustrated by figure 13 in which the meridian plane is the plane of the paper, except for the vectors A^r, B^r.

11. We define *azimuth* (α) as a rotation about ν^r from μ^r toward λ^r, as shown in figure 12. A unit N-surface vector l^r in azimuth α is accordingly given by

12.006 $\qquad l^r = \lambda^r \sin \alpha + \mu^r \cos \alpha$.

The use of the term azimuth suggests that the N-surfaces are level in the geodetic sense; in the main geodetic applications, this will be so. We do not yet, however, identify the N-surfaces with level

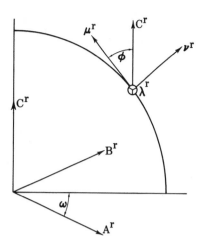

Figure 13.

or equipotential surfaces; and in this chapter, the term azimuth is to be understood in a wider sense. With the same object of avoiding multiplication of terms and on the same analogy, we shall sometimes refer to the direction of the normal ν_r as the *zenith* and to an angle measured from the zenith as a *zenith distance*. A unit vector in azimuth α and zenith distance β will be given by the vector equation

$$l^r = \lambda^r \sin \alpha \sin \beta + \mu^r \cos \alpha \sin \beta + \nu^r \cos \beta,$$

12.007

which can easily be verified from the direction cosines of l^r relative to the (λ^r, μ^r, ν^r) axes.

RELATIONS BETWEEN BASE VECTORS

12. We can now express one set of vectors in terms of the others, through their direction cosines, as follows,

$$\lambda_r = -A_r \sin \omega + B_r \cos \omega$$

$$\mu_r = -A_r \sin \phi \cos \omega - B_r \sin \phi \sin \omega + C_r \cos \phi$$

$$\nu_r = A_r \cos \phi \cos \omega + B_r \cos \phi \sin \omega + C_r \sin \phi.$$

12.008

In these vector equations, we can simply raise all the indices to obtain the contravariant components.

13. If we consider the Cartesian coordinate x to be a scalar function of position, then its gradient is

$$x_r = A_r,$$

a vector equation which is true in any coordinate system. We can solve the covariant form of the Equations 12.008 for A_r, etc., and obtain the reverse formulas

$$x_r = A_r = -\lambda_r \sin \omega - \mu_r \sin \phi \cos \omega$$
$$+ \nu_r \cos \phi \cos \omega$$

$$y_r = B_r = \lambda_r \cos \omega - \mu_r \sin \phi \sin \omega$$
$$+ \nu_r \cos \phi \sin \omega$$

12.009 $z_r = C_r = \mu_r \cos \phi + \nu_r \sin \phi.$

14. To obtain Cartesian coordinates in the $(\lambda^r, \mu^r, \nu^r)$ system, which we shall denote by overbars ($\bar{x}$, etc.) from (A^r, B^r, C^r) and vice versa, we need only contract with the position vector equation

$$\bar{\rho}_r = \rho_r - (\rho_0)_r$$

where $(\rho_0)_r$ is the position vector of the $(\lambda^r, \mu^r, \nu^r)$ origin. Thus, Equations 12.008 give

$$\bar{x} = -(x - x_0) \sin \omega + (y - y_0) \cos \omega$$

$$\bar{y} = -(x - x_0) \sin \phi \cos \omega$$
$$- (y - y_0) \sin \phi \sin \omega + (z - z_0) \cos \phi$$

$$\bar{z} = (x - x_0) \cos \phi \cos \omega$$

12.010 $+ (y - y_0) \cos \phi \sin \omega + (z - z_0) \sin \phi,$

and Equations 12.009 give

$$(x - x_0) = -\bar{x} \sin \omega - \bar{y} \sin \phi \cos \omega + \bar{z} \cos \phi \cos \omega$$

$$(y - y_0) = \bar{x} \cos \omega - \bar{y} \sin \phi \sin \omega + \bar{z} \cos \phi \sin \omega$$

$$(z - z_0) = \bar{y} \cos \phi + \bar{z} \sin \phi.$$

12.011

15. We may also note that the $(\lambda^r, \mu^r, \nu^r)$ system can be obtained from the (A^r, B^r, C^r) system by the following rotations:
First, $(\frac{1}{2}\pi + \omega)$ about the 3-axis C^r which brings A^r into parallelism with λ^r; and,
Second, $(\frac{1}{2}\pi - \phi)$ about the new 1-axis λ^r which brings C^r into parallelism with ν^r. Accordingly, we may substitute the following matrix equation for Equations 12.008,

$$\begin{pmatrix} \lambda_r \\ \mu_r \\ \nu_r \end{pmatrix} = \begin{pmatrix} 1 & 0 & 0 \\ 0 & \sin \phi & \cos \phi \\ 0 & -\cos \phi & \sin \phi \end{pmatrix} \begin{pmatrix} -\sin \omega & \cos \omega & 0 \\ -\cos \omega & -\sin \omega & 0 \\ 0 & 0 & 1 \end{pmatrix} \begin{pmatrix} A_r \\ B_r \\ C_r \end{pmatrix}.$$

12.012

In this equation, as in Equations 12.008, we may substitute components of the vectors in any one coordinate system. The same rotation matrices in the same order may be used on the position vectors to reproduce Equations 12.010.

The inverse transformation equivalent to Equations 12.009, which may also be used instead of Equations 12.011, is obtained by transposing the orthogonal rotation matrices as follows,

$$\begin{pmatrix} A_r \\ B_r \\ C_r \end{pmatrix} = \begin{pmatrix} -\sin \omega & -\cos \omega & 0 \\ \cos \omega & -\sin \omega & 0 \\ 0 & 0 & 1 \end{pmatrix} \begin{pmatrix} 1 & 0 & 0 \\ 0 & \sin \phi & -\cos \phi \\ 0 & \cos \phi & \sin \phi \end{pmatrix} \begin{pmatrix} \lambda_r \\ \mu_r \\ \nu_r \end{pmatrix}.$$

12.013

A very convenient, special notation for rotation matrices will often be found in the literature. A positive rotation of θ about each coordinate axis — positive in the usual mathematical sense illustrated in § 12–2 and § 12–5 — is denoted by

$$\mathbf{R}_1(\theta) = \begin{pmatrix} 1 & 0 & 0 \\ 0 & \cos \theta & \sin \theta \\ 0 & -\sin \theta & \cos \theta \end{pmatrix}$$

$$\mathbf{R}_2(\theta) = \begin{pmatrix} \cos \theta & 0 & -\sin \theta \\ 0 & 1 & 0 \\ \sin \theta & 0 & \cos \theta \end{pmatrix}$$

$$\mathbf{R}_3(\theta) = \begin{pmatrix} \cos \theta & \sin \theta & 0 \\ -\sin \theta & \cos \theta & 0 \\ 0 & 0 & 1 \end{pmatrix}$$

Using braces notation $\{A_r, B_r, C_r\}$ for column matrices, Equation 12.012 would then be written

$$\{\lambda_r, \mu_r, \nu_r\} = \mathbf{R}_1(\tfrac{1}{2}\pi - \phi)\mathbf{R}_3(\tfrac{1}{2}\pi + \omega)\{A_r, B_r, C_r\}.$$

12.012A

In these formulas, the *axes* are rotated and points in the space are held fixed; if the axes were fixed, the rotations would have opposite signs. To avoid any possible confusion, the few rotation matrices required in this book will be written in full.

DERIVATIVES OF THE BASE VECTORS

16. If we take the covariant derivative of the first equation of Equations 12.008 and remember that A_r, B_r, C_r are constant under covariant differentiation, we have

$$\lambda_{rs} = (-A_r \cos \omega - B_r \sin \omega)\omega_s$$

12.014 $= (\mu_r \sin \phi - \nu_r \cos \phi)\omega_s$

by substituting the other equations of Equations 12.008; in the same way, we have

12.015 $\qquad \mu_{rs} = -\sin \phi \; \lambda_r \omega_s - \nu_r \phi_s$

12.016 $\qquad \nu_{rs} = \cos \phi \; \lambda_r \omega_s + \mu_r \phi_s.$

In these expressions, ω_s, ϕ_s are the gradients of the coordinates considered as scalars. They are not necessarily surface vectors. But if we take (ω, ϕ) to be the N-surface coordinates as well as two of the space coordinates, then the (1, 2) components ω_α, ϕ_α will be the surface gradients. In the (ω, ϕ, N) system, we have

$$\omega_s = \delta_s^1 \; ; \qquad \phi_s = \delta_s^2,$$

but if we do not make this substitution, then the above tensor equations are true in any coordinate system.

17. By covariant differentiation of the basic gradient equation

$$N_r = n \nu_r,$$

we have

12.017 $\qquad N_{rs} = n_s \nu_r + n \nu_{sr}.$

But because N is a scalar, N_{rs} is a symmetrical tensor by Equation 3.11. Interchanging r, s and subtracting, we have

12.018 $\qquad n_s \nu_r + n \nu_{rs} = n_r \nu_s + n \nu_{sr}.$

Multiplying by ν_s and noting that $\nu_{sr}\nu^s = 0$ because ν_s is a unit vector (Equation 3.19), we have

12.019 $\qquad n \nu_{rs}\nu^s = n_r - (n_s \nu^s)\nu_r.$

But the vector n_r is expressible in terms of three orthogonal vectors as

$$n_r = (n_s \lambda^s)\lambda_r + (n_s \mu^s)\mu_r + (n_s \nu^s)\nu_r$$

so that Equation 12.019 reduces, after division by n, to

12.020 $\qquad \nu_{rs}\nu^s = \{(\ln n)_s \lambda^s\}\lambda_r + \{(\ln n)_s \mu^s\}\mu_r,$

showing that the principal normals to the ν_r are N- surface vectors. We shall write the arc rate of change of $(\ln n)$ in the parallel and meridian direction as γ_1, γ_2, respectively, so that this last equation can be written as

12.021 $\qquad \nu_{rs}\nu^s = \gamma_1 \lambda_r + \gamma_2 \mu_r,$

showing that the curvature of the normal is $(\gamma_1^2 + \gamma_2^2)^{1/2}$ The principal normal to the curve is in azimuth arctan (γ_1/γ_2); the binormal, along which n is constant, is a surface vector in azimuth arctan $(-\gamma_2/\gamma_1)$.

18. It should be noted that λ_{rs} is a space tensor taken in relation to the space metric. It will, nevertheless, have (1, 2) components which can be written as

$$\lambda_{\alpha\beta} = (\mu_\alpha \sin \phi - \nu_\alpha \cos \phi)\omega_\beta.$$

Again, if (ω, ϕ) are surface coordinates, we know from Equation 8.25 that $\lambda_{\alpha\beta}$ is also the corresponding surface tensor. We shall see later that $\nu_\alpha = 0$ in (ω, ϕ, N) coordinates so that we have

12.022 $\qquad \lambda_{\alpha\beta} = \mu_\alpha \omega_\beta \sin \phi,$

whether it is considered to be a surface tensor or the (1, 2) components of a space tensor.
In the same way,

12.023 $\qquad \mu_{\alpha\beta} = -\lambda_\alpha \omega_\beta \sin \phi$

is either a surface tensor or the (1, 2) components of a space tensor in (ω, ϕ, N) coordinates, provided (ω, ϕ) are taken as surface coordinates.

19. We can see from Equation 6.19 that the (1, 2) components of the space tensor ν_{rs}, again in the (ω, ϕ, N) system with (ω, ϕ) as surface coordinates, are given by

12.024 $\qquad \nu_{\alpha\beta} = -b_{\alpha\beta}$

where $b_{\alpha\beta}$ — the second fundamental form of the surface — is a surface tensor. Here again, we could say that $\nu_{\alpha\beta}$ is a surface tensor because $b_{\alpha\beta}$ is a surface tensor, and the $\nu_{\alpha\beta}$ are also the (1, 2) components of a space tensor.
Equations 12.022 and 12.023 are, however, surface tensor equations, but Equation 12.024 is merely a relation expressing some components of the space tensor ν_{rs}. If we want to manipulate Equation 12.024 further, we should have to generalize it first as

$$\nu_{rs}x_\alpha^r x_\beta^s = -b_{\alpha\beta}.$$

CONTRAVARIANT COMPONENTS OF THE BASE VECTORS

20. If we differentiate the defining Equation 12.005 covariantly and remember that C^r is a constant vector, we have

$$(\cos \phi)\phi_s = \nu_{rs}C^r$$
$$= \nu_{rs}(\mu^r \cos \phi + \nu^r \sin \phi \;)$$
$$= \omega_{rs}\mu^r \cos \phi,$$

in the derivation of which we have used Equations

12.009 and 3.19, with ν^r a unit vector, so that finally we have

12.025 $\phi_s = \nu_{rs}\mu^r = -\mu_{rs}\nu^r.$

21. In the same way, by covariant differentiation of Equations 12.003 or 12.004, we have

12.026 $(\cos \phi)\omega_s = \nu_{rs}\lambda^r = -\lambda_{rs}\nu^r;$

by repeating Equation 12.001 to complete the series, we have also

12.027 $N_s = n\nu_s.$

22. In addition, we have already found in Equation 12.021 a formula for the vector curvature of the normal to any family of N-surfaces,

$$\nu_{rs}\nu^s = \{(\ln n)_s\lambda^s\}\lambda_r + \{(\ln \nu)_s\mu^s\}\mu_r$$

12.028 $= \gamma_1\lambda_r + \gamma_2\mu_r.$

23. Now, if $(d\lambda)$ is an element of length in the λ^r-direction, then the contravariant components of λ^r in the (ω, ϕ, N) system are, by definition and by using Equations 12.026, 12.025, and 12.027,

$$\lambda^r = (\partial\omega/\partial\lambda,\ \partial\phi/\partial\lambda,\ \partial N/\partial\lambda)$$
$$= (\omega_s\lambda^s,\ \phi_s\lambda^s,\ N_s\lambda^s)$$
$$= (\sec \phi\ \nu_{rs}\lambda^r\lambda^s,\ \nu_{rs}\lambda^s\mu^r,\ 0)$$

12.029 $= (-k_1 \sec \phi,\ -t_1,\ 0)$

where k_1 is, from Equation 7.03, the normal curvature of the N-surface in the direction of the parallel, and where t_1 is, from Equation 7.08, the geodesic torsion of the N-surface in the same direction. (The geodesic torsion of the N-surface in the direction of the meridian is, of course, minus t_1.)

24. In the same way, we have

$$\mu^r = (\partial\omega/\partial\mu,\ \partial\phi/\partial\mu,\ \partial N/\partial\mu)$$
$$= (\sec \phi\ \nu_{rs}\lambda^r\mu^s,\ \nu_{rs}\mu^r\mu^s,\ 0)$$

12.030 $= (-t_1 \sec \phi,\ -k_2,\ 0)$

where k_2 is the normal curvature of the N-surface in the direction of the meridian.

25. To complete the triad, we need similarly to evaluate the components of ν^r. Writing (ds) for an element of length in the direction of the normal, we have from Equations 12.026, 12.025, 12.027, and 12.021

12.031 $\partial\phi/\partial s = \nu_{rs}\mu^r\nu^s = (\ln n)_s\mu^s = \gamma_2$

12.032 $\cos \phi\ \partial\omega/\partial s = \nu_{rs}\lambda^r\nu^s = (\ln n)_s\lambda^s = \gamma_1$

12.033 $\partial N/\partial s = N_s\nu^s = n$

so that we have finally

12.034 $\nu^r = (\gamma_1 \sec \phi,\ \gamma_2,\ n).$

26. Without any loss of generality, we can take (ω, ϕ) as coordinates in the N-surfaces as well as two of the space coordinates. We shall as usual use Greek indices restricted to the values (1, 2) for surface vectors and tensors; it is then evident from the definition that the components of λ^α, μ^α, considered as surface vectors, are

12.035 $\lambda^\alpha = (-k_1 \sec \phi,\ -t_1)$

12.036 $\mu^\alpha = (-t_1 \sec \phi,\ -k_2).$

27. Collecting results for easier reference, we have

$$\lambda^r = (-k_1 \sec \phi,\ -t_1,\ 0)$$
$$\mu^r = (-t_1 \sec \phi,\ -k_2,\ 0)$$

12.037 $\nu^r = (\gamma_1 \sec \phi,\ \gamma_2,\ n),$

with the same (1, 2) components for the surface vectors λ^α, μ^α in (ω, ϕ) coordinates.

28. All contravariant and, as we shall see, all covariant components of the base vectors can accordingly be written in terms of the five second-order quantities k_1, k_2, t_1, γ_1, γ_2, which we shall call the *curvature parameters* of the space or of the field. We have seen in Equation 12.021 that γ_1, γ_2 define the curvature of the normals; we shall see in the section commencing with § 12–36 that k_1, k_2, t_1 completely define the curvature properties of the N-surfaces.

COVARIANT COMPONENTS OF THE BASE VECTORS

29. Next, we find the covariant components from Equation 2.07

$$\lambda^r\lambda_s + \mu^r\mu_s + \nu^r\nu_s = \delta^r_s$$

in which δ^r_s is the Kronecker delta.
For $r = 3$, we have at once

$$n\nu_s = \delta^3_s,$$

which gives the components of the normal as

12.038 $\nu_s = (0,\ 0,\ 1/n).$

30. For $r = 1, 2$; $s = 1$, we have the two equations
$$-(k_1 \sec \phi)\lambda_1 - (t_1 \sec \phi)\mu_1 = 1$$
$$-t_1\lambda_1 - k_2\mu_1 = 0;$$

and writing K for $(k_1k_2 - t_1^2)$, which we have seen in Equation 7.17 is the Gaussian or specific curvature of the N-surface in flat space, we can solve these last equations to provide the 1-components as follows,

$$\lambda_1 = -k_2 \cos \phi/K$$
$$\mu_1 = +t_1 \cos \phi/K.$$

31. In the same way for $r = 1, 2 : s = 2$, we have the equations

$$-(k_1 \sec \phi)\lambda_2 - (t_1 \sec \phi)\mu_2 = 0$$
$$-t_1\lambda_2 - k_2\mu_2 = 1,$$

which can be solved for the 2-components

$$\lambda_2 = +t_1/K$$
$$\mu_2 = -k_1/K.$$

32. For $r = 1, 2 ; s = 3$, we have

$$-(k_1 \sec \phi)\lambda_3 - (t_1 \sec \phi)\mu_3 + \gamma_1 \sec \phi/n = 0,$$
$$-t_1\lambda_3 - k_2\mu_3 + \gamma_2/n = 0,$$

from which we have

$$K\lambda_3 = (k_2\gamma_1 - t_1\gamma_2)/n$$

12.039 $\qquad K\mu_3 = (k_1\gamma_2 - t_1\gamma_1)/n;$

or, substituting for γ_1, γ_2 from Equation 12.021, we have

$$K\lambda_3 = -(1/n)_s(k_2\lambda^s - t_1\mu^s)$$

12.040 $\qquad K\mu_3 = -(1/n)_s(-t_1\lambda^s + k_1\mu^s).$

Again, substituting the above values for λ_1, μ_1, etc., we have

$$\lambda_3 \cos \phi = (1/n)_s(\lambda_1\lambda^s + \mu_1\mu^s + \nu_1\nu^s)$$
$$= (1/n)_s\delta_1^s$$
$$= \partial(1/n)/\partial\omega$$

and

$$\mu_3 = (1/n)_s(\lambda_2\lambda^s + \mu_2\mu^s + \nu_2\nu^s)$$
$$= (1/n)_s\delta_2^s$$
$$= \partial(1/n)/\partial\phi.$$

33. Collecting results, we have

12.041 $\quad K\lambda_r = (-k_2 \cos \phi, +t_1, K \sec \phi \, \partial(1/n)/\partial\omega)$

12.042 $\quad K\mu_r = (+t_1 \cos \phi, -k_1, K\partial(1/n)/\partial\phi),$

with the alternative expressions in Equations 12.039 and 12.040 for the 3-components, and

12.043 $\qquad \nu_r = (0, 0, 1/n).$

34. We can similarly find the covariant components λ_α, μ_α, considered as surface vectors from the two-dimensional formula

$$\lambda^\alpha\lambda_\beta + \mu^\alpha\mu_\beta = \delta_\beta^\alpha,$$

and have finally

12.044 $\qquad K\lambda_\alpha = (-k_2 \cos \phi, +t_1)$

12.045 $\qquad K\mu_\alpha = (+t_1 \cos \phi, -k_1),$

which are the same as the (1, 2) components of the space vectors.

35. The gradients of the coordinates can now be expressed in terms of the base vectors λ_r, μ_r, ν_r by means of the following formulas,

12.046 $\qquad (\cos \phi)\omega_r = -k_1\lambda_r - t_1\mu_r + \gamma_1\nu_r$

12.047 $\qquad \phi_r = -t_1\lambda_r - k_2\mu_r + \gamma_2\nu_r,$

and we have also

12.048 $\qquad (\ln n)_r = \gamma_1\lambda_r + \gamma_2\mu_r + \{(\ln n)_s\nu^s\}\nu_r;$

because these gradients are vector equations, not merely relations between some components of vectors in a special coordinate system, they are true in any coordinates—provided ω, ϕ are considered to be scalars.

CURVATURES OF THE N-SURFACES

36. The three quantities k_1, k_2, and t_1—respectively, the normal curvatures of an N-surface in the direction of the parallel and the meridian, and the geodesic torsion in the direction of the parallel—enable us to determine the normal curvature and geodesic torsion in any azimuth (α). A unit surface vector in this azimuth will be

$$l_\beta = \lambda_\beta \sin \alpha + \mu_\beta \cos \alpha;$$

a unit vector in the perpendicular direction, obtained by a positive right-handed rotation of l_β about the normal, will be

$$j_\beta = -\lambda_\beta \cos \alpha + \mu_\beta \sin \alpha.$$

The normal curvature in the direction l_β, using space coordinates, will be

$$k = -\nu_{rs}l^rl^s$$
$$= -\nu_{rs}\lambda^r\lambda^s \sin^2 \alpha - 2\nu_{rs}\lambda^r\mu^s \sin \alpha \cos \alpha$$
$$\quad - \nu_{rs}\mu^r\mu^s \cos^2 \alpha$$
$$= k_1 \sin^2 \alpha + 2t_1 \sin \alpha \cos \alpha + k_2 \cos^2 \alpha;$$

12.049

the geodesic torsion in the direction l_β will be

$$t = -\nu_{rs}l^rj^s$$
$$= \nu_{rs}\lambda^r\lambda^s \sin \alpha \cos \alpha - \nu_{rs}\lambda^r\mu^s(\sin^2 \alpha - \cos^2 \alpha)$$
$$\quad - \nu_{rs}\mu^r\mu^s \sin \alpha \cos \alpha$$
$$= (k_2 - k_1) \sin \alpha \cos \alpha - t_1(\cos^2 \alpha - \sin^2 \alpha).$$

12.050

37. The geodesic torsion in a principal direction is zero so that the azimuth (A) of the principal directions is given by

12.051 $\tan 2A = +2t_1/(k_2 - k_1)$.

38. The principal curvatures (κ_1 in azimuth A and κ_2 in azimuth $(A - \frac{1}{2}\pi)$) are then given by Equation 12.049 as

$$\kappa_1 = k_1 \sin^2 A + 2t_1 \sin A \cos A + k_2 \cos^2 A$$

$$\kappa_2 = k_1 \cos^2 A - 2t_1 \sin A \cos A + k_2 \sin^2 A$$

12.052

so that the mean curvature is

12.053 $H = \frac{1}{2}(\kappa_1 + \kappa_2) = \frac{1}{2}(k_1 + k_2)$,

as we should expect, because it is the same for any two perpendicular directions.

39. We have also

$$(\kappa_1 - \kappa_2) = (k_2 - k_1) \cos 2A + 2t_1 \sin 2A$$

$$= (k_2 - k_1) \sec 2A$$

12.054 $= 2t_1 \csc 2A$,

using Equation 12.051.

40. The Gauss or specific curvature of the surface is then

$$K = \kappa_1 \kappa_2 = \frac{1}{4}(k_1 + k_2)^2 - \frac{1}{4}(k_1 - k_2)^2 \sec^2 2A$$

12.055 $= k_1 k_2 - t_1^2$,

as we should expect from Equation 7.17.

41. We can also recast Equation 12.049 to give the normal curvature in any azimuth (α) as

12.056 $k = \kappa_1 \cos^2 (A - \alpha) + \kappa_2 \sin^2 (A - \alpha)$

and the geodesic torsion in azimuth (α) as

12.057 $t = \frac{1}{2}(\kappa_1 - \kappa_2) \sin 2(A - \alpha)$.

By putting $\alpha = \frac{1}{2}\pi$, or zero, in these last two equations, we have also

$$k_1 = \kappa_1 \sin^2 A + \kappa_2 \cos^2 A$$

$$k_2 = \kappa_1 \cos^2 A + \kappa_2 \sin^2 A$$

12.058 $t_1 = (\kappa_1 - \kappa_2) \sin A \cos A$,

showing that, instead of the three curvature parameters k_1, k_2, t_1, we could equally well use κ_1, κ_2, A.

42. If k, t, α are the normal curvature, geodesic torsion, and azimuth in the direction of a general unit surface vector l^r and if k^*, $-t$, $(\alpha - \frac{1}{2}\pi)$ refer to a perpendicular unit surface vector j^r, then from

Equations 12.049 and 12.050, we have

$$k = k_1 \sin^2 \alpha + 2t_1 \sin \alpha \cos \alpha + k_2 \cos^2 \alpha$$

$$t = (k_2 - k_1) \sin \alpha \cos \alpha \ - t_1(\cos^2 \alpha - \sin^2 \alpha)$$

$$k^* = k_1 \cos^2 \alpha - 2t_1 \sin \alpha \cos \alpha + k_2 \sin^2 \alpha.$$

12.059

From these equations and Equations 12.046 and 12.047, if dl, dj are elements of length in the two directions, we easily derive

$$(\cos \phi)\partial\omega/\partial l = -k_1 \sin \alpha - t_1 \cos \alpha$$

$$= -k \sin \alpha + t \cos \alpha$$

$$\partial\phi/\partial l = -t_1 \sin \alpha - k_2 \cos \alpha$$

$$= -k \cos \alpha - t \sin \alpha$$

$$(\cos \phi)\partial\omega/\partial j = k_1 \cos \alpha - t_1 \sin \alpha$$

$$= k^* \cos \alpha - t \sin \alpha$$

$$\partial\phi/\partial j = t_1 \cos \alpha - k_2 \sin \alpha$$

12.060 $= -k^* \sin \alpha - t \cos \alpha$,

which enable us to rewrite Equations 12.046 and 12.047 as

$$(\cos \phi)\omega_r = (-k \sin \alpha + t \cos \alpha)l_r$$

12.061 $+ (k^* \cos \alpha - t \sin \alpha)j_r + \gamma_1 \nu_r$

$$\phi_r = -(k \cos \alpha + t \sin \alpha)l_r$$

12.062 $- (k^* \sin \alpha + t \cos \alpha)j_r + \gamma_2 \nu_r.$

GEODESIC CURVATURES

43. Because the geodesic curvature of a surface curve is intrinsic and does not depend on the surrounding space, we can use surface coordinates throughout to express it. We wish to determine the geodesic curvature (σ) of an N-surface curve in azimuth α whose unit tangent vector is

$$l_\beta = \lambda_\beta \sin \alpha + \mu_\beta \cos \alpha;$$

and, we shall also require the geodesic curvature (σ^*) of the usual orthogonal vector

$$j_\beta = -\lambda_\beta \cos \alpha + \mu_\beta \sin \alpha.$$

We shall assume as often before that l_β, j_β refer to a family of surface curves and their orthogonal trajectories.

By direct surface covariant differentiation, we have

$$l_{\beta\gamma} = \lambda_{\beta\gamma} \sin \alpha + \mu_{\beta\gamma} \cos \alpha - j_\beta \alpha_\gamma$$

12.063 $= j_\beta(\omega_\gamma \sin \phi - \alpha_\gamma)$,

using Equations 12.022 and 12.023. Equating this

to the first equation of Equations 4.11, we find that

12.064 $\qquad \sigma l_\gamma + \sigma^* j_\gamma = \omega_\gamma \sin \phi - \alpha_\gamma;$

if the arc element in the direction l_γ is dl, this reduces to

12.065 $\qquad \sigma = \sin \phi (\partial \omega / \partial l) - (\partial \alpha / \partial l).$

44. For the parallel trace, that is, for a surface curve whose tangent is throughout in the parallel direction, we have $\alpha = \frac{1}{2}\pi$ and $\partial \alpha / \partial l = 0$; while from Equation 12.029, we have $\partial \omega / \partial l = -k_1 \sec \phi$ so that the geodesic curvature of the parallel trace is given by

12.066 $\qquad \sigma_1 = -k_1 \tan \phi.$

45. Similarly for the meridian trace, we have $\alpha = 0$ and $\partial \alpha / \partial l = 0$; while from Equation 12.030, we have $\partial \omega / \partial l = -t_1 \sec \phi$ so that the geodesic curvature of the meridian trace is given by

12.067 $\qquad \sigma_2 = -t_1 \tan \phi.$

46. We can now express the geodesic curvature of any surface curve l_γ in azimuth α in terms of σ_1, σ_2 as

$$\sigma = (\sin \phi) \omega_\gamma (\lambda^\gamma \sin \alpha + \mu^\gamma \cos \alpha) - (\partial \alpha / \partial l)$$
$$= \sigma_1 \sin \alpha + \sigma_2 \cos \alpha - (\partial \alpha / \partial l)$$

12.068

in which dl is the arc element in the direction l_γ.

47. By equating Equation 12.065 or 12.068 to zero, we have the differential equation of the surface geodesics. It has usually been assumed in classical geodesy that the form of the equation derived from Equation 12.065, that is, $d\alpha = (\sin \phi) d\omega$, applies only to a surface of revolution; indeed, it has been stated that a reference spheroid was originally chosen for this purpose. Nevertheless, the equation is true for the geodesics on any surface.

48. In particular, Equation 12.067 enables us to say that the meridian trace is a geodesic if, and only if, $t_1 = 0$, and thus is also a line of curvature; it would then be also a plane curve because its space torsion (Equation 7.08) would be zero. The surface normals would also be plane curves because they are coplanar with the meridian and the fixed Cartesian axis C^r. Moreover, we can say by contracting Equations 12.046 and 12.047 that the meridian and parallel traces are then ϕ- and ω-coordinate lines. Finally, ω would not vary in the meridian plane, which contains the normal; and so, from Equation 12.032, we have $\gamma_1 = 0$. All these conditions occur when the field is symmetric about an axis parallel to C^r.

49. We may note now that the parallel trace is a plane curve anyway, even if t_1 is not zero; its vector curvature from Equation 12.014 is

$$\lambda_{rs}\lambda^s = (-A_r \cos \omega - B_r \sin \omega)\omega_s \lambda^s$$
$$= (k_1 \sec \phi)(A_r \cos \omega + B_r \sin \omega),$$

its principal normal is accordingly

$$- (A_r \cos \omega + B_r \sin \omega),$$

and its binormal is C_r which is a constant vector. The angle θ between the principal normal and the surface normal is given by Equations 12.009 as

$$\cos \theta = - \cos \phi$$

so that we have

$$\theta = \pi - \phi.$$

Finally, Equation 7.08 gives the space torsion as

$$t_1 - (\partial \theta / \partial \lambda) = t_1 + (\partial \phi / \partial \lambda) = 0,$$

using Equation 12.029. Again, we have proved that λ^r is a plane curve.

THE METRIC TENSOR

50. We can now obtain the covariant and contravariant components of the metric tensor from the formulas, Equations 2.08 and 2.09, as

$$g_{rs} = \lambda_r \lambda_s + \mu_r \mu_s + \nu_r \nu_s$$
$$g^{rs} = \lambda^r \lambda^s + \mu^r \mu^s + \nu^r \nu^s.$$

Components of the surface metric tensor are similarly given by Equations 2.34 and 2.35 as

$$a_{\alpha\beta} = \lambda_\alpha \lambda_\beta + \mu_\alpha \mu_\beta$$
$$a^{\alpha\beta} = \lambda^\alpha \lambda^\beta + \mu^\alpha \mu^\beta.$$

Using (ω, ϕ) as both surface and space coordinates and substituting the vector components from Equations 12.041, etc., we have

$$g_{11} = a_{11} = (k_2^2 + t_1^2) \cos^2 \phi / K^2$$

$$g_{12} = a_{12} = -2Ht_1 \cos \phi / K^2$$

$$g_{22} = a_{22} = (k_1^2 + t_1^2)/K^2$$

$$g_{13} = -\frac{k_2}{K}\frac{\partial(1/n)}{\partial\omega} + \frac{t_1 \cos \phi}{K}\frac{\partial(1/n)}{\partial\phi}$$
$$= -[\gamma_1(k_2^2 + t_1^2) - 2H\gamma_2 t_1]/(nK^2 \sec \phi)$$

$$g_{23} = \frac{t_1 \sec \phi}{K}\frac{\partial(1/n)}{\partial\omega} - \frac{k_1}{K}\frac{\partial(1/n)}{\partial\phi}$$
$$= -[\gamma_2(k_1^2 + t_1^2) - 2H\gamma_1 t_1]/nK^2$$

$$g_{33} = \sec^2 \phi \left(\frac{\partial(1/n)}{\partial\omega}\right)^2 + \left(\frac{\partial(1/n)}{\partial\phi}\right)^2 + \frac{1}{n^2}$$
$$= [\gamma_1^2(k_2^2 + t_1^2) + \gamma_2^2(k_1^2 + t_1^2)$$
$$- 4Ht_1\gamma_1\gamma_2 + K^2]/(n^2K^2)$$

12.069 $\qquad = \sec^2 \beta / n^2$

in which β is the zenith distance of the isozenithal. In this last result, we have anticipated Equation 12.098.

51. The determinants of the metric tensors by direct expansion are

12.070 $\qquad g = \cos^2 \phi / (n^2 K^2); \qquad a = \cos^2 \phi / K^2.$

52. Components of the contravariant space metric tensor are

$$g^{11} = (k_1^2 + t_1^2 + \gamma_1^2) \sec^2 \phi$$

$$g^{12} = (\gamma_1 \gamma_2 + 2Ht_1) \sec \phi$$

$$g^{22} = (k_2^2 + t_1^2 + \gamma_2^2)$$

$$g^{13} = n\gamma_1 \sec \phi$$

$$g^{23} = n\gamma_2$$

12.071 $\qquad g^{33} = n^2.$

53. Contravariant components of the surface metric tensor are

$$a^{11} = (k_1^2 + t_1^2) \sec^2 \phi$$

$$a^{12} = 2Ht_1 \sec \phi$$

12.072 $\qquad a^{22} = (k_2^2 + t_1^2).$

54. The determinants of the associated tensors are

12.073 $\qquad |g^{rs}| = n^2 K^2 \sec^2 \phi; \qquad |a^{\alpha\beta}| = K^2 \sec^2 \phi,$

which are, as they should be, the reciprocals of the covariant determinants.

SECOND FUNDAMENTAL FORM OF THE *N*-SURFACES

55. By contracting Equation 12.016 with $x_\alpha^r x_\beta^s$ and using Equation 6.19, we have

12.074 $\qquad -b_{\alpha\beta} = (\cos \phi)\lambda_\alpha \omega_\beta + \mu_\alpha \phi_\beta$

from which, assuming as usual that ω, ϕ are also surface coordinates, we have

$$b_{\alpha\beta} = -(\cos \phi\lambda_1, \mu_1, \mu_2)$$

12.075 $\qquad = (k_2 \cos^2 \phi / K, -t_1 \cos \phi / K, k_1 / K).$

56. The determinant of the form by direct calculation is

12.076 $\qquad b = \cos^2 \phi / K$

from which the contravariant form (from §8–1) is

12.077 $\qquad b^{\alpha\beta} = (k_1 \sec^2 \phi, t_1 \sec \phi, k_2).$

57. We have already seen in Equation 12.024 that

12.078 $\qquad b_{\alpha\beta} = -\nu_{\alpha\beta}$

in which it is understood that $\nu_{\alpha\beta}$ are components of the space tensor ν_{rs} taken in relation to the space metric.

58. By combining Equation 12.075 with Equations 12.044 and 12.045, we can write

12.079 $\qquad b_{1\alpha} = -(\cos \phi)\lambda_\alpha; \qquad b_{2\alpha} = -\mu_\alpha,$

which are frequently useful relations; also, we have

12.080 $\qquad b^{1\alpha} = -(\sec \phi)\lambda^\alpha; \qquad b^{2\alpha} = -\mu^\alpha.$

59. Yet, another useful formula can be obtained by noting from Equation 12.016 that in these co-ordinates we have $\nu_{r3} = 0$. We then have from Equations 12.020 and 12.024

$$(\ln n)_\alpha = \nu_{rs}\nu^s x_\alpha^r$$

12.081 $\qquad = -b_{\alpha\beta}\nu^\beta$

or

12.082 $\qquad \nu^\alpha = -b^{\alpha\beta}(\ln n)_\beta.$

THIRD FUNDAMENTAL FORM OF THE *N*-SURFACES

60. There are several ways of computing the third form $c_{\alpha\beta}$; perhaps the simplest being from the formula in Equation 7.20

$$c_{\alpha\beta} = 2Hb_{\alpha\beta} - Ka_{\alpha\beta}$$

so that we have

$$c_{11} = (k_1 + k_2)k_2 \cos^2 \phi / K - (k_2^2 + t_1^2) \cos^2 \phi / K$$

$$= \cos^2 \phi$$

$$c_{12} = -(k_1 + k_2)t_1 \cos \phi / K + 2Ht_1 \cos \phi / K$$

$$= 0$$

$$c_{22} = (k_1 + k_2)k_1 / K - (k_1^2 + t_1^2) / K$$

$$= 1,$$

and collecting results we have

12.083 $\qquad c_{\alpha\beta} = (\cos^2 \phi, 0, 1).$

The determinant is

12.084 $\qquad c = \cos^2 \phi,$

agreeing with Equations 7.18 and 12.076; the contravariant form is accordingly

12.085 $c^{\alpha\beta} = (\sec^2 \phi, 0, 1)$.

It may be noted that if we take the determinant of the defining Equations 6.18,

$$c_{\alpha\beta} = a^{\gamma\beta} b_{\alpha\gamma} b_{\beta\delta},$$

by the ordinary rule for multiplying determinants, we have

$$b^2 = ac,$$

a relation which is accordingly true in any coordinate system, as we may see also from Equation 7.18. It can easily be verified from the (ω, ϕ, N) values in Equations 12.070, 12.076, and 12.084.

THE COORDINATE DIRECTIONS

Longitude

61. From the metric, an element of length in the ω-coordinate direction ($d\phi$, dN zero) is $\sqrt{g_{11}}\,d\omega$. The contravariant components of a unit vector in this direction are accordingly

12.086 $i^r = (1/\sqrt{g_{11}}, 0, 0)$,

and its azimuth α_1 will be given by

$$\cos \alpha_1 = i^r \mu_r = t_1/(k_2^2 + t_1^2)^{1/2}$$

12.087 $\sin \alpha_1 = i^r \lambda_r = -k_2/(k_2^2 + t_1^2)^{1/2}$.

62. Using Equations 12.058 in which A is the azimuth of the κ_1-principal direction, we find without difficulty that

$$(k_2^2 + t_1^2)^{1/2} = (\kappa_2^2 \sin^2 A + \kappa_1^2 \cos^2 A)^{1/2}$$

$$= m_2, \text{ for instance,}$$

so that we have

$$\cos \alpha_1 = (\kappa_1 - \kappa_2) \sin A \cos A/m_2$$

12.088 $\sin \alpha_1 = -(\kappa_2 \sin^2 A + \kappa_1 \cos^2 A)/m_2$

$$\sin (A - \alpha_1) = \kappa_1 \cos A/m_2$$

12.089 $\cos (A - \alpha_1) = -\kappa_2 \sin A/m_2$.

Latitude

63. In the same way, the contravariant components of a unit vector in the ϕ-coordinate direction are

12.090 $j^r = (0, 1/\sqrt{g_{22}}, 0)$,

and its azimuth α_2 will be given by

$$\cos \alpha_2 = j^r \mu_r = -k_1/(k_1^2 + t_1^2)^{1/2}$$

12.091 $\sin \alpha_2 = j^r \lambda_r = t_1/(k_1^2 + t_1^2)^{1/2}$.

Again, using Equations 12.058, we have

$$(k_1^2 + t_1^2)^{1/2} = (\kappa_1^2 \sin^2 A + \kappa_2^2 \cos^2 A)^{1/2}$$

$$= m_1, \text{ for instance,}$$

$$\cos \alpha_2 = -(\kappa_1 \sin^2 A + \kappa_2 \cos^2 A)/m_1$$

12.092 $\sin \alpha_2 = (\kappa_1 - \kappa_2) \sin A \cos A/m_1$

$$\sin (A - \alpha_2) = -\kappa_1 \sin A/m_1$$

12.093 $\cos (A - \alpha_2) = -\kappa_2 \cos A/m_1$.

64. Now consider the spherical representation of the N-surface in which the surface coordinates (ω, ϕ) will be the same because the normals at corresponding points are parallel. It is evident that the ϕ-coordinate line is represented by the spherical meridian, which is parallel in space to the meridian direction μ^r on the surface. We have also seen in Chapter 11 that a principal direction and its spherical representation are parallel in space. Consequently, the angle ($A - \alpha_2$) on the surface corresponds to A on the sphere; from Equation 11.24, we have

$$\tan A = (\kappa_2/\kappa_1) \tan (A - \alpha_2),$$

which verifies Equations 12.093.

65. In the same way, the angle ($A - \alpha_1$) on the surface corresponds to ($A - \frac{1}{2}\pi$) on the sphere so that we have

$$-\cot A = (\kappa_2/\kappa_1) \tan (A - \alpha_1),$$

which verifies Equations 12.089.

66. The fact that the (ω, ϕ) coordinate lines are represented by the spherical meridians and parallels again shows that the representation is not as a rule conformal because the coordinate lines are not, in general, orthogonal. It is clear from Equations 12.087 and 12.091, or from a_{12} in Equations 12.069, that the coordinate lines will be orthogonal if, and only if, $t_1 = 0$, corresponding to the axially symmetrical case.

67. The metric of the spherical representation in these coordinates will be

12.094 $d\bar{s}^2 = \cos^2 \phi \, d\omega^2 + d\phi^2$,

so that the scale factor ($d\bar{s}/ds$) in the direction of the ω-coordinate line will be

$$\sqrt{(\cos^2 \phi / a_{11})} = K/(k_2^2 + t_1^2)^{1/2} = K/m_2$$

and in the direction of the ϕ-coordinate line will be

$$\sqrt{(1/a_{22})} = K/(k_1^2 + t_1^2)^{1/2} = K/m_1$$

in which m_1, m_2 have been defined in connection with Equations 12.092 and 12.088.

The Isozenithal

68. A unit vector in the N-coordinate direction (ω, ϕ constant) is similarly given by

12.095 $k^r = (0, 0, 1/\sqrt{g_{33}})$,

and its azimuth (α) and zenith distance (β) will be given by

$$\sin \alpha \sin \beta = k^r \lambda_r = \{\sec \phi \, \partial (1/n)/\partial \omega\}/\sqrt{g_{33}}$$

$$\cos \alpha \sin \beta = k^r \mu_r = \{\partial (1/n)/\partial \phi\}/\sqrt{g_{33}}$$

$$\cos \beta = k^r \nu_r = (1/n)/\sqrt{g_{33}}$$

12.096

or

$$\sin \alpha \tan \beta = -(\sec \phi) \partial (\ln n)/\partial \omega$$

12.097 $\cos \alpha \tan \beta = -\partial (\ln n)/\partial \phi$.

69. Because ω and ϕ are constant along this line, it is evident from Equations 12.008 that the λ^r at all points along the line are parallel; and so are the μ^r and ν^r. The whole triad of vectors can be transported parallel to itself along the line, which we shall call the *isozenithal* because the zenith direction ν^r is the same at all points along any one such line. Another way of expressing the parallel transport of these vectors is to state that there is no *intrinsic* change in their components along the line, or in tensor notation

12.098 $\lambda_{rs} k^s = \mu_{rs} k^s = \nu_{rs} k^s = 0$.

These tensor equations are, of course, true in any coordinates.

LAPLACIANS OF THE COORDINATES

70. For some applications, we need formulas for the Laplacian of each coordinate, particularly that of N and its derivatives. We start with the gradient equation

$$N_r = n \nu_r$$

and differentiate it covariantly as

12.099 $N_{rs} = n_s \nu_r + n \nu_{rs}$.

The Laplacian of N in space is then

$$\Delta N = g^{rs} N_{rs} = n_s \nu^s + n g^{rs} \nu_{rs}$$

and the last term from Equation 7.19 is equal to $(-2Hn)$, so that we have finally

12.100 $\Delta N = \partial n/\partial s - 2Hn$

in which ds is an element of length along the normal. This last equation will be recognized as an exact form of a formula usually attributed to Bruns in applications where N is the geopotential and n is gravity, but we see that it is simply a geometrical property of any family of surfaces.

71. From Equations 12.025 and 12.026, together with Equation 12.099, we have—without difficulty—the following generally useful relations,

12.101 $(\cos \phi)\omega_s = (1/n)N_{rs}\lambda^r$

12.102 $\phi_s = (1/n)N_{rs}\mu^r$

12.103 $n_s = N_{rs}\nu^r$;

differentiating the first covariantly, we have with some substitution

$$(\cos \phi)\omega_{st} = (\sin \phi)\omega_s \phi_t - (\ln n)_t (\cos \phi)\omega_s$$
$$+ (1/n)N_{rst}\lambda^r + (\sin \phi)\phi_s \omega_t$$
$$- (\ln n)_s (\cos \phi)\omega_t.$$

We note that because N is a scalar in flat space, its third covariant derivative is symmetrical in any two indices so that we have

$$g^{st}N_{rst} = (g^{st}N_{st})_r = (\Delta N)_r.$$

We also introduce the symbol ∇ for a differential invariant from Equation 3.14, such that we have

$$\nabla(\omega, \phi) = g^{rs}\omega_r \phi_s : \qquad \nabla(\omega) = g^{rs}\omega_r \omega_s, \quad \text{etc.,}$$

and finally obtain

$$(\cos \phi)\Delta\omega = 2 \sin \phi \, \nabla(\omega, \phi) - 2 \cos \phi \, \nabla(\omega, \ln n)$$

12.104 $+ (1/n)(\Delta N)_r \lambda^r$.

72. In the same way, we have

$$\Delta\phi = -2\nabla(\phi, \ln n) - \sin \phi \cos \phi \, \nabla(\omega)$$

12.105 $+ (1/n)(\Delta N)_r \mu^r$.

These last two equations are of particular value in this form in applications where ΔN is a constant because the last terms are then zero.

73. From Equations 12.103, 12.099, and 12.016, we have also

$$\Delta n = n\{\cos^2 \phi \nabla(\omega) + \nabla(\phi)\} + (\Delta N)_r \nu^r.$$

12.106

74. We can easily find the ∇ invariants from Equations 12.046, 12.047, and 12.048 in terms of the five parameters of the space, but first we need to find an alternative expression for the third component of $(\ln n)_r$, taking account of Equation 12.100. We have

12.107 $\qquad (\ln n)_r \nu^r = (1/n)\partial n/\partial s = 2H + (\Delta N)/n$

so that Equation 12.048 becomes

$$(\ln n)_r = \gamma_1 \lambda_r + \gamma_2 \mu_r + \{2H + (\Delta N)/n\}\nu_r.$$

12.108

We then have from Equations 12.046, etc.,

12.109 $\qquad \cos^2 \phi \nabla(\omega) = k_1^2 + t_1^2 + \gamma_1^2$

12.110 $\qquad \nabla(\phi) = k_2^2 + t_1^2 + \gamma_2^2$

12.111 $\qquad \cos \phi \nabla(\omega, \phi) = 2Ht_1 + \gamma_1\gamma_2$

$$\cos \phi \nabla(\omega, \ln n) = -k_1\gamma_1 - t_1\gamma_2 + 2H\gamma_1 + (\gamma_1\Delta N)/n$$

12.112 $\qquad = k_2\gamma_1 - t_1\gamma_2 + (\gamma_1\Delta N)/n$

$$\nabla(\phi, \ln n) = -t_1\gamma_1 - k_2\gamma_2 + 2H\gamma_2 + (\gamma_2\Delta N)/n$$

12.113 $\qquad = k_1\gamma_2 - t_1\gamma_1 + (\gamma_2\Delta N)/n.$

We have also

$$\cos^2 \phi \nabla(\omega) + \nabla(\phi) = (k_1 + k_2)^2 - 2(k_1k_2 - t_1^2)$$
$$+ \gamma_1^2 + \gamma_2^2$$
$$= 4H^2 - 2K + (\gamma_1^2 + \gamma_2^2)$$

12.114 $\qquad = \kappa_1^2 + \kappa_2^2 + (\gamma_1^2 + \gamma_2^2),$

which is the sum of the squares of the principal curvatures of the *N*-surface plus the square of the principal curvature of the normal, all at the point under consideration. An alternative expression for the Laplacian of *n* is accordingly

$$(1/n)\Delta n = 4H^2 - 2K + (\gamma_1^2 + \gamma_2^2)$$

12.115 $\qquad + (1/n)(\Delta N)_r \nu^r.$

75. All the previously mentioned formulas in this section refer to the space invariants. We can easily find the surface invariants of ω and ϕ (denoted by overbars) from the (1, 2) components of

Equations 12.026 and 12.025

12.116 $\qquad (\cos \phi)\omega_\alpha = -b_{\alpha\beta}\lambda^\beta$

12.117 $\qquad \phi_\alpha = -b_{\alpha\beta}\mu^\beta,$

which are surface tensor equations. By surface covariant differentiation of Equation 12.116, we have, using Equation 12.022,

$$(\cos \phi)\omega_{\alpha\gamma} = (\sin \phi)\omega_\alpha\phi_\gamma - b_{\alpha\beta\gamma}\lambda^\beta - b_{\alpha\beta}\mu^\beta\omega_\gamma \sin \phi$$

so that we have

$$(\cos \phi)\overline{\Delta\omega} = (\sin \phi)\overline{\nabla}(\omega, \phi) - a^{\alpha\gamma}b_{\alpha\beta\gamma}\lambda^\beta$$
$$+ (\sin \phi)\overline{\nabla}(\omega, \phi)$$

12.118 $\qquad = 2(\sin \phi)\overline{\nabla}(\omega, \phi) - (2H)_\alpha\lambda^\alpha$

with

12.119 $\qquad \overline{\nabla}(\omega, \phi) = 2Ht_1 \sec \phi;$

similarly, we have

12.120 $\qquad \overline{\Delta\phi} = -(\sin \phi \cos \phi)\overline{\nabla}(\omega) - (2H)_\alpha\mu^\alpha$

with

12.121 $\qquad \overline{\nabla}(\omega) = (k_1^2 + t_1^2) \sec^2 \phi.$

76. We cannot differentiate Equation 12.081,

$$(\ln n)_\alpha = -b_{\alpha\beta}\nu^\beta,$$

in the same way because this equation is simply a relation involving selected components of the space vector ν^r in a special coordinate system; it is not a surface tensor equation because ν^β is not a surface vector.

We shall, however, find in Equation 14.28 an expression for the surface Laplacian of *n*, which can easily be put into the following form, comparable with Equation 12.115, as

$$(1/n)\overline{\Delta n} = (4H^2 - 2K) + 2(\gamma_1^2 + \gamma_2^2) - \partial(2H)/\partial s$$

12.122

in which *s* is again the arc length of the normal. It should be noted that this, unlike the space invariant, does not depend on ΔN.

77. The surface Laplacian of *N* is, of course, zero because *N* is constant over the surface.

THE CHRISTOFFEL SYMBOLS

78. We can compute the Christoffel symbols straight from the definitions and the components of the metric tensor or from transformation formulas; but, because we know the components of the base

vectors and have formulas for the covariant derivatives of the coordinates, it is possible to take various shortcuts which are more instructive.

79. For example, we can express the tensor N_{rs} as

$$N_{rs} = -\Gamma_{rs}^t N_t = -\Gamma_{rs}^3;$$

by covariant differentiation of the gradient equation

$$N_r = n\nu_r,$$

we have

12.123 $\qquad N_{rs} = n_s\nu_r + n\nu_{rs}.$

We have also, from Equation 12.016, $\nu_{r3} = 0$; from Equation 12.024, we have $\nu_{\alpha\beta} = -b_{\alpha\beta}$. By simple substitution, we can then obtain all the distinct Christoffel symbols with superscript 3 as follows,

$$\Gamma_{\alpha\beta}^3 = nb_{\alpha\beta}\ ; \qquad \Gamma_{3\alpha}^3 = 0\ ; \qquad \Gamma_{33}^3 = -\partial(\ln n)/\partial N.$$

12.124

80. To evaluate the symbols which have a subscript 3 but no superscript 3, we shall make use of a device which is frequently useful in other directions. We can express a Christoffel symbol in terms of the components of any three mutually orthogonal vectors by means of the following formula, which can easily be verified by multiplying λ_j, μ_j, ν_j in turn,

$$\Gamma_{kl}^j = \frac{\partial\lambda_k}{\partial x^l}\lambda^j + \frac{\partial\mu_k}{\partial x^l}\mu^j + \frac{\partial\nu_k}{\partial x^l}\nu^j$$

12.125 $\qquad - (\lambda_{kl}\lambda^j + \mu_{kl}\mu^j + \nu_{kl}\nu^j).$

If $(\lambda_r,\ \mu_r,\ \nu_r)$ have their usual significance in this chapter and $l = 3$, then the whole term within parentheses vanishes because of Equations 12.014, 12.015, and 12.016; thus we have

$$\Gamma_{k3}^\alpha = \frac{\partial\lambda_k}{\partial N}\lambda^\alpha + \frac{\partial\mu_k}{\partial N}\mu^\alpha + \frac{\partial\nu_k}{\partial N}\nu^\alpha$$

12.126 $\qquad = -\frac{\partial\lambda^\alpha}{\partial N}\lambda_k - \frac{\partial\mu^\alpha}{\partial N}\mu_k - \frac{\partial\nu^\alpha}{\partial N}\nu_k,$

the last line being obtained by differentiating the identity

$$\lambda_k\lambda^\alpha + \mu_k\mu^\alpha + \nu_k\nu^\alpha = \delta_k^\alpha.$$

For $k = \beta(\neq 3)$ we have from Equations 12.079 and 12.080

$$\Gamma_{\beta3}^\alpha = \frac{\partial b_{1\beta}}{\partial N}b^{1\alpha} + \frac{\partial b_{2\beta}}{\partial N}b^{2\alpha}$$

$$= b^{\alpha\gamma}\frac{\partial b_{\beta\gamma}}{\partial N}$$

12.127 $\qquad = -b_{\beta\gamma}\frac{\partial b^{\alpha\gamma}}{\partial N}.$

We shall show in Equation 12.144 how this symbol can be expressed in terms of n and N-surface tensors.

81. For $k = 3$, using Equations 12.041, etc., we have

$$\Gamma_{33}^\alpha = -\frac{\partial^2(1/n)}{\partial\omega\partial N}b^{1\alpha} - \frac{\partial^2(1/n)}{\partial\phi\partial N}b^{2\alpha} - \frac{\partial(1/n)}{\partial N}b^{\alpha\beta}(\ln n)_\beta,$$

which simplifies without difficulty to

12.128 $\qquad \Gamma_{33}^\alpha = (1/n)b^{\alpha\beta}\frac{\partial^2(\ln n)}{\partial x^\beta\partial N}.$

82. The remaining symbols are all of the form

$$\Gamma_{\alpha\beta}^\gamma = \frac{\partial\lambda_\alpha}{\partial x^\beta}\lambda^\gamma + \frac{\partial\mu_\alpha}{\partial x^\beta}\mu^\gamma - \lambda_{\alpha\beta}\lambda^\gamma - \mu_{\alpha\beta}\mu^\gamma - \nu_{\alpha\beta}\nu^\gamma$$

$$= \frac{\partial\lambda_\alpha}{\partial x^\beta}\lambda^\gamma + \frac{\partial\mu_\alpha}{\partial x^\beta}\mu^\gamma - \omega_\beta\sin\phi(\mu_\alpha\lambda^\gamma - \lambda_\alpha\mu^\gamma) + b_{\alpha\beta}\nu^\gamma$$

12.129

on substituting Equations 12.022, 12.023, and 12.024. In evaluating this expression, we can make use of the symmetry of the Christoffel symbol in the subscripts. For example, if either α or $\beta = 2$, then we can eliminate the whole of the third term by taking $\beta = 2$. The expressions on the right, obtained by interchanging α and β, can be made identical by using the Mainardi-Codazzi equations of the N-surfaces, which we shall consider in the next section.

83. We can apply the general formula of Equation 12.125 in two dimensions and write

12.130 $\qquad \Gamma_{\alpha\beta}^\gamma = \frac{\partial\lambda_\alpha}{\partial x^\beta}\lambda^\gamma + \frac{\partial\mu_\alpha}{\partial x^\beta}\mu^\gamma - \lambda_{\alpha\beta}\lambda^\gamma - \mu_{\alpha\beta}\mu^\gamma$

in which the Christoffel symbol must now be taken in relation to the *surface* metric; $\lambda_{\alpha\beta}$, $\mu_{\alpha\beta}$ are surface tensors. By subtraction from Equation 12.129, we have

$$\Gamma_{\alpha\beta}^\gamma \quad \text{(space)} \quad - \Gamma_{\alpha\beta}^\gamma \quad \text{(surface)} \quad = -\nu_{\alpha\beta}\nu^\gamma$$

12.131 $\qquad\qquad\qquad\qquad\qquad = b_{\alpha\beta}\nu^\gamma$

because, as we have seen in Equations 12.022 and 12.023, the tensors $\lambda_{\alpha\beta}$, $\mu_{\alpha\beta}$ can be considered either as surface tensors or as components of space tensors in these coordinates. This last result is of frequent use.

THE MAINARDI-CODAZZI EQUATIONS

84. The two Mainardi-Codazzi equations of a

surface may be considered as conditions of integrability, or from § 6–27 as conditions for the surface to be embedded in flat space. In either case, use must be made of the fact that the Christoffel symbols are symmetrical in the two subscripts because this is a distinguishing mark of Riemannian geometry, arising from the nature of the metric tensor.

85. If we are given a set of functions $a_{\alpha\beta}$, $b_{\alpha\beta}$, does a surface exist for which these functions are the appropriate fundamental forms? To prove that a surface does exist in the neighborhood of a point where the $a_{\alpha\beta}$ and $b_{\alpha\beta}$ are given, we must be able to integrate the Weingarten and Gauss equations (Equations 6.17 and 6.16)

$$\nu_\alpha^r = -a^{\beta\gamma} b_{\alpha\gamma} x_\beta^r$$

$$x_{\alpha\beta}^r = b_{\alpha\beta} \nu^r;$$

it can be shown that the necessary conditions for this are the Mainardi-Codazzi equations. For our purposes, we shall always start with a family of surfaces—definable in nature over finite regions by other means—so that these equations may be considered as properties of the geometry or of the space.

86. If we take the surface covariant derivative of a surface vector λ_α, we have

$$\lambda_{\alpha\beta} = \partial\lambda_\alpha/\partial x^\beta - \lambda_\gamma \Gamma_{\alpha\beta}^\gamma;$$

then a necessary condition for the Christoffel symbol to be symmetrical in α, β is

12.132 $\quad \lambda_{\alpha\beta} - \lambda_{\beta\alpha} = \partial\lambda_\alpha/\partial x^\beta - \partial\lambda_\beta/\partial x^\alpha.$

For a given superscript, there is only one Christoffel symbol in two dimensions with dissimilar subscripts and therefore only two such symbols in all. It will accordingly be sufficient to satisfy Equation 12.132 for one other independent vector μ_α so that we have

12.133 $\quad \mu_{\alpha\beta} - \mu_{\beta\alpha} = \partial\mu_\alpha/\partial x^\beta - \partial\mu_\beta/\partial x^\alpha.$

Both equations are satisfied identically unless α and β are different; so it will be sufficient to make $\alpha = 1$, $\beta = 2$, and to substitute Equations 12.022 and 12.023 to obtain

$$-\mu_2 \sin \phi = \partial\lambda_1/\partial\phi - \partial\lambda_2/\partial\omega$$

$$\lambda_2 \sin \phi = \partial\mu_1/\partial\phi - \partial\mu_2/\partial\omega,$$

which reduce on substitution of Equations 12.079 to

$$\partial b_{11}/\partial\phi - \partial b_{12}/\partial\omega + b_{11} \tan \phi + b_{22} \sin \phi \cos \phi = 0$$

12.134

12.135 $\quad \partial b_{12}/\partial\phi - \partial b_{22}/\partial\omega - b_{12} \tan \phi = 0.$

It should be noted that in deriving these formulas, we have used Equations 12.022 and 12.023, which were themselves derived on the assumption that the space is flat through use of the Cartesian vectors A_r, B_r, C_r.

Equations 12.134 and 12.135 are the Mainardi-Codazzi equations of the N-surfaces in (ω, ϕ, N) coordinates. They can be expressed in several other equivalent forms, but for the present, we shall be content with them as they stand.

87. If, instead of the surface vectors λ_r, μ_r, we take the space Cartesian vectors A_r, B_r, C_r whose covariant derivatives are zero, then, so far as the N-surfaces are concerned, we have to satisfy the following equations to ensure that the appropriate Christoffel symbols are symmetrical,

$$\partial A_1/\partial\phi = \partial A_2/\partial\omega \; ; \qquad \partial B_1/\partial\phi = \partial B_2/\partial\omega \; ;$$

$$\partial C_1/\partial\phi = \partial C_2/\partial\omega$$

in which A_1, etc., are components in (ω, ϕ, N). If we obtain A_1, etc., from Equations 12.009 by substituting the (ω, ϕ, N) components of λ_r, etc., from Equation 12.041, then these conditions give exactly the same results as Equations 12.134 and 12.135—no more and no less. Moreover, it is evident from Equations 12.009, etc., that the above conditions are equivalent to

$$\frac{\partial^2 x}{\partial\phi\partial\omega} = \frac{\partial^2 x}{\partial\omega\partial\phi} \; ; \qquad \frac{\partial^2 y}{\partial\phi\partial\omega} = \frac{\partial^2 y}{\partial\omega\partial\phi} \; ; \qquad \frac{\partial^2 z}{\partial\phi\partial\omega} = \frac{\partial^2 z}{\partial\omega\partial\phi},$$

which are well-known integrability conditions for the existence of the Cartesian coordinates (x, y, z). This demonstration goes part of the way toward justifying the statement made in § 12–84 and § 6–27 that the Mainardi-Codazzi equations are conditions for a given surface to be embedded in flat space. If the surface is embedded in curved space, the Mainardi-Codazzi equations or integrability conditions take the different form of Equation 6.22.

88. We have so far considered only the N-surfaces, but there must similarly be two equations for each of the other coordinate surfaces. We need not, however, consider these surfaces specifically. We shall derive the same answer more easily if we form equations similar to Equation 12.132 for three independent space vectors and if we substitute such relations as Equations 12.014, 12.015, and 12.016 which apply only in flat space.

89. First, we consider the equation

12.136 $\quad \nu_{rs} - \nu_{sr} = \partial\nu_r/\partial x^s - \partial\nu_s/\partial x^r,$

and then substitute Equation 12.016 and the (ω, ϕ,

N) components of ν_r. For $r=1$, $s=2$, the equation is satisfied identically. For $r=1$, $s=3$ and $r=2$, $s=3$, we have

$$\lambda_3 \cos \phi = \partial(1/n)/\partial\omega \; ; \qquad \mu_3 = \partial(1/n)/\partial\phi,$$

obtained before in Equations 12.041 and 12.042.

90. The equation

12.137 $\qquad \lambda_{rs} - \lambda_{sr} = \partial\lambda_r/\partial x^s - \partial\lambda_s/\partial x^r$

for $r=1$, $s=2$ gives Equation 12.134, and for $r=1$, $s=3$ gives

$$-\mu_3 \sin \phi + \nu_3 \cos \phi = \partial\lambda_1/\partial N - \partial\lambda_3/\partial\omega,$$

which, on substitution of Equations 12.079, 12.042, and 12.043, reduces to

$$\frac{\partial b_{11}}{\partial N} = -\frac{\partial^2(1/n)}{\partial\omega^2} + \sin\phi \cos\phi \frac{\partial(1/n)}{\partial\phi} - \frac{\cos^2\phi}{n}.$$

12.138

For $r=2$, $s=3$, we have similarly

$$0 = \partial\lambda_2/\partial N - \partial\lambda_3/\partial\phi$$

or

12.139 $\qquad \dfrac{\partial b_{12}}{\partial N} = -\dfrac{\partial^2(1/n)}{\partial\omega\partial\phi} - \tan\phi \dfrac{\partial(1/n)}{\partial\omega},$

both of which are new.

91. The equation

$$\mu_{rs} - \mu_{sr} = \partial\mu_r/\partial x^s - \partial\mu_s/\partial x^r$$

for $r=1$, $s=2$ gives Equation 12.135, and for $r=1$, $s=3$ gives Equation 12.139. For $r=2$, $s=3$, we have

$$\nu_3 = \partial\mu_2/\partial N - \partial\mu_3/\partial\phi$$

or

12.140 $\qquad \dfrac{\partial b_{22}}{\partial N} = -\dfrac{\partial^2(1/n)}{\partial\phi^2} - \dfrac{1}{n}.$

92. There are accordingly only three independent Mainardi-Codazzi equations for the space in addition to the two for the N-surfaces—a total of five out of a maximum of six. The coordinate system is, nevertheless, perfectly general, except that the N-surfaces are generated by a scalar, which means that the equation

$$N_{rs} = n_s\nu_r + n\nu_{rs} = n_r\nu_s + n\nu_{sr}$$

must apply because N_{rs} is symmetrical in r and s. This symmetrical relation serves to satisfy Equation 12.136. We are not therefore missing one of the six equations; we have already included it.

93. Next, we shall put the Equations 12.138,

12.139, and 12.140 in tensor form. From Equation 11.03, the metric of the spherical representation of an N-surface in (ω, ϕ) coordinates is

12.141 $\qquad d\bar{s}^2 = c_{\alpha\beta}dx^\alpha dx^\beta = \cos^2\phi \, d\omega^2 + d\phi^2,$

using Equation 12.083. It is easy to show by direct calculation from the definitions that the only non-zero Christoffel symbols in this metric are

12.142 $\qquad \overline{\Gamma}^2_{11} = \sin\phi \cos\phi \; ; \qquad \overline{\Gamma}^1_{12} = -\tan\phi.$

By inspection, we can now write the Equations 12.138, 12.139, and 12.140 in the form

12.143 $\qquad \dfrac{\partial b_{\alpha\beta}}{\partial N} = -\dfrac{\partial^2(1/n)}{\partial x^\alpha \partial x^\beta} + \overline{\Gamma}^\gamma_{\alpha\beta} \dfrac{\partial(1/n)}{\partial x^\gamma} - \dfrac{c_{\alpha\beta}}{n};$

substituting Equation 11.30, we have

12.144 $\qquad \dfrac{\partial b_{\alpha\beta}}{\partial N} = -\left(\dfrac{1}{n}\right)_{\alpha\beta} + b^{\gamma\delta}b_{\alpha\beta\delta}\left(\dfrac{1}{n}\right)_\gamma - \dfrac{c_{\alpha\beta}}{n}$

in which the second covariant derivative of $(1/n)$ is taken with respect to the metric of the N-surface. *Each term of the right-hand side of this equation is a surface tensor; therefore, the left-hand side must be a surface tensor.*

94. The foregoing analysis has been given in some detail because it is important to ensure that we have not overlooked any essential relation in the differential geometry of the space, such as an omitted Mainardi-Codazzi equation. Moreover, we require Equation 12.144 to show how the Christoffel symbols of Equation 12.127,

$$\Gamma^\alpha_{\beta 3} = b^{\alpha\gamma}\frac{\partial b_{\beta\gamma}}{\partial N},$$

can be expressed in terms of n and surface tensors—as in the case of all other Christoffel symbols with a fixed 3-index.

ALTERNATIVE DERIVATION OF THE MAINARDI-CODAZZI EQUATIONS

95. In view of the fundamental importance of the three additional space equations in Equation 12.144, we shall now approach them from a different direction and, at the same time, shall derive some generally useful formulas.

We take one particular N-surface and draw the tangent plane at a point P (fig. 14). We drop a perpendicular OQ on the tangent plane from the Cartesian origin O, and denote the length of this perpendicular by p. The vector $\overrightarrow{OQ}$ is accordingly of magnitude p and of direction ν^r, while the vector $\overrightarrow{OP}$ is the position vector ρ^r. The coordinates (ω, ϕ, p) may be known as tangential coordinates.

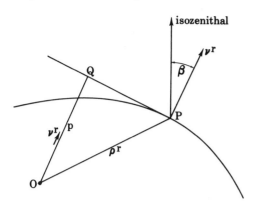

Figure 14.

We have at once

12.145
$$p = \rho_r \nu^r \; ;$$

taking the surface covariant derivative of this, we have also

$$p_\alpha = g_{rs} x_\alpha^s \nu^r + \rho_r \nu_\alpha^r$$

12.146
$$= \rho_r \nu_\alpha^r,$$

the remaining term being zero because of the orthogonality of x_α^s and ν^r as space vectors. We have also used the fact that the tensor equation $\rho_{rs} = g_{rs}$ is true in Cartesian, and therefore in any coordinates.

Again, taking the surface tensor derivative of Equation 12.146, we have

$$p_{\alpha\beta} = g_{rs} x_\beta^s \nu_\alpha^r + \rho_r \nu_{\alpha\beta}^r$$

$$= -b_{\alpha\beta} + \rho_r (b^{\gamma\delta} b_{\alpha\beta\delta} \nu_\gamma^r - c_{\alpha\beta} \nu^r)$$

in which we have used Equations 11.26 and 8.10. With some slight rearrangement and use of Equations 12.146 and 12.145, we have

$$b_{\alpha\beta} = -p_{\alpha\beta} + b^{\gamma\delta} b_{\alpha\beta\delta} p_\gamma - p c_{\alpha\beta}$$

12.147
$$= -\frac{\partial^2 p}{\partial x^\alpha \partial x^\beta} + \overline{\Gamma}_{\alpha\beta}^\gamma p_\gamma - p c_{\alpha\beta}$$

where we have used Equation 11.30; the (overbarred) Christoffel symbols of the spherical representation have values from Equations 12.142 in (ω, ϕ) coordinates.

96. Next, we differentiate this last expression along the isozenithal at P. The tangent plane moves parallel to itself because the direction of the normal is unaltered; for the same reason, the spherical representation remains unaltered. Consequently, the Christoffel symbols in Equation 12.147 remain constant, as is otherwise obvious from Equations 12.142, because they are functions of ϕ only. Again, the $c_{\alpha\beta}$ from Equation 12.083 are constant during

the differentiation. If the unit isozenithal vector is k^r and if the displacement along the isozenithal is ds, then we have

$$dN = N_r k^r ds = n \nu_r k^r ds = n \cos \beta \; ds = n dp$$

so that we may write

12.148
$$\frac{\partial p}{\partial N} = \frac{1}{n}.$$

This result also could have been obtained from the third component of the space covariant derivative of Equation 12.145 in (ω, ϕ, N).

Ordinary partial differentiation of Equation 12.147 accordingly gives us

12.149
$$\frac{\partial b_{\alpha\beta}}{\partial N} = -\frac{\partial^2 (1/n)}{\partial x^\alpha \partial x^\beta} + \overline{\Gamma}_{\alpha\beta}^\gamma \left(\frac{1}{n}\right)_\gamma - \frac{c_{\alpha\beta}}{n},$$

which is precisely the same as Equation 12.143 or 12.144. In deriving this equation, we have made use of the properties of the Cartesian position vector and of the constant components of Cartesian vectors during spherical representation. In other words, we have assumed that the space is flat, but have assumed nothing else; this again illustrates the two ways of considering the Mainardi-Codazzi equations.

97. We can also show by ordinary partial differentiation of Equation 12.147, with respect to surface coordinates, that we have

12.150
$$\frac{\partial b_{\alpha\beta}}{\partial x^\gamma} - \frac{\partial b_{\alpha\gamma}}{\partial x^\beta} = -\overline{\Gamma}_{\alpha\beta}^\delta b_{\gamma\delta} + \overline{\Gamma}_{\alpha\gamma}^\delta b_{\beta\delta},$$

which on expansion is easily shown to be equivalent to the Codazzi equations of the N-surface in Equations 12.134 and 12.135. Accordingly, we can say that Equation 12.147 is an integral of all five Codazzi equations, which are automatically satisfied every time we use Equation 12.147. A more compact form of Equation 12.147 is

12.151
$$-b_{\alpha\beta} = \bar{p}_{\alpha\beta} + p c_{\alpha\beta}$$

in which the overbar indicates that the second covariant derivative of p is taken with respect to the metric of the spherical representation of the N-surface.

HIGHER DERIVATIVES OF THE BASE VECTORS

98. Now that we have formulas for the Christoffel symbols and for the Mainardi-Codazzi equations, we can without difficulty find expressions for the higher derivatives of the base vectors in these coordinates. First, however, we shall collect some formulas for the first derivatives.

From Equations 12.014, etc., we have at once

12.152 $\lambda_{r3} = {}_,\mu_{r3} = \nu_{r3} = 0.$

The only nonzero components containing a 3-index are accordingly $\lambda_{3\alpha}$, etc.; by substitution in Equations 12.014, 12.041, etc., we have at once

12.153 $\lambda_{3\alpha} = \left(\sin\phi \, \dfrac{\partial(1/n)}{\partial\phi} - \dfrac{\cos\phi}{n} \right) \delta_\alpha^1$

12.154 $\mu_{3\alpha} = -\tan\phi \, \dfrac{\partial(1/n)}{\partial\omega} \, \delta_\alpha^1 - \dfrac{1}{n} \delta_\alpha^2$

12.155 $\nu_{3\alpha} = (1/n)_\alpha.$

99. The only other nonzero components have been obtained before in Equations 12.022, 12.023, and 12.024, but are collected for easy reference as follows,

12.156 $\lambda_{\alpha\beta} = \mu_\alpha \omega_\beta \sin\phi$

12.157 $\mu_{\alpha\beta} = -\lambda_\alpha \omega_\beta \sin\phi$

12.158 $\nu_{\alpha\beta} = -b_{\alpha\beta}.$

100. Components of the second covariant derivatives may now be obtained straight from the definition. For example, we have

$$\lambda_{\alpha\beta3} = \partial\lambda_{\alpha\beta}/\partial N - \Gamma_{\alpha3}^r \lambda_{r\beta} - \Gamma_{\beta3}^r \lambda_{\alpha r}$$
$$= (\omega_\beta \sin\phi)(\partial\mu_\alpha/\partial N) - \Gamma_{\alpha3}^\gamma \mu_\gamma \omega_\beta \sin\phi$$
$$- \Gamma_{\beta3}^\gamma \mu_\alpha \omega_\gamma \sin\phi$$

in which the first two terms cancel because $\mu_{\alpha3} = 0$. In the same way, using the fact that the second and third indices are interchangeable in flat space, we have

$$\lambda_{\alpha\beta3} = \lambda_{\alpha3\beta} = -(\sin\phi)\mu_\alpha b^{1\gamma}(\partial b_{\beta\gamma}/\partial N)$$
$$\mu_{\alpha\beta3} = \mu_{\alpha3\beta} = (\sin\phi)\lambda_\alpha b^{1\gamma}(\partial b_{\beta\gamma}/\partial N)$$

12.159 $\nu_{\alpha\beta3} = \nu_{\alpha3\beta} = \partial b_{\alpha\beta}/\partial N$

in which we can substitute Equation 12.143 or 12.144 for $\partial b_{\beta\gamma}/\partial N$.

In much the same way, we find

$$\lambda_{\alpha33} = -\Gamma_{33}^\gamma \lambda_{\alpha\gamma} = \mu_\alpha(1/n)\tan\phi \; \lambda^\delta\{\partial^2(\ln n)/\partial x^\delta \partial N\}$$
$$\mu_{\alpha33} = -\Gamma_{33}^\gamma \mu_{\alpha\gamma} = -\lambda_\alpha(1/n)\tan\phi \; \lambda^\delta\{\partial^2(\ln n)/\partial x^\delta \partial N\}$$
$$\nu_{\alpha33} = -\Gamma_{33}^\gamma \nu_{\alpha\gamma} = (1/n)\{\partial^2(\ln n)/\partial x^\alpha \partial N\}.$$

12.160

We can also find by direct covariant differentiation and by use of Equation 12.131 that

12.161 $\nu_{\alpha\beta\gamma} = -b_{\alpha\beta\gamma} - b_{\beta\gamma}(\ln n)_\alpha;$

other components can be found similarly when required.

THE MARUSSI TENSOR

101. It is now clear that the second and higher order metrical properties of the system can be written in terms of the five curvature parameters $(k_1, k_2, t_1, \gamma_1, \gamma_2)$ and their derivatives. But the entire system has been generated from a single scalar N whose covariant derivatives must be related to the curvature parameters. To show this, we have only to contract the tensor Equation 12.017,

$$N_{rs} = n_s \nu_r + n \nu_{rs},$$

with the base vectors to obtain

$$N_{rs}\lambda^r\lambda^s = -nk_1$$
$$N_{rs}\mu^r\mu^s = -nk_2$$
$$N_{rs}\lambda^r\mu^s = -nt_1$$
$$N_{rs}\lambda^r\nu^s = n\gamma_1$$
$$N_{rs}\mu^r\nu^s = n\gamma_2$$

12.162 $N_{rs}\nu^r\nu^s = n(\ln n)_s \nu^s$

in which we have used only definitions and Equation 12.028. Apart from the factor n, all the parameters on the right are accordingly the components of the symmetric tensor N_{rs}. This fact was first noticed by Marussi [1] in the case where N is a gravitational potential as well as a generalized coordinate.

102. As we shall see later, the case of a Newtonian gravitational field simply involves assigning a particular value to the Laplacian of N,

$$\Delta N = N_{rs}(\lambda^r\lambda^s + \mu^r\mu^s + \nu^r\nu^s)$$

12.163 $= -n(k_1 + k_2) + n(\ln n)_s \nu^s,$

so that the law of gravity eliminates one of the components of N_{rs}, leaving us with the other five. In a local Cartesian system (x, y, z) with axes $(\lambda^r, \mu^r, \nu^r)$, we have

$$N_{rs}\lambda^r\lambda^s = \partial^2 N/\partial x^2$$

12.164 $N_{rs}\lambda^r\mu^s = \partial^2 N/\partial x \partial y,$ etc.

The parameters are usually given in this particular form in the literature, except that the x-axis is sometimes μ^r.

THE POSITION VECTOR

103. We have seen in § 12–95 that the perpendicular p from the Cartesian origin to the tangent plane of an N-surface is of special significance in

[1] Marussi (1949), "Fondements de Géométrie Différentielle Absolue du Champ Potentiel Terrestre," *Bulletin Géodésique*, new series, no. 14, 411–439.

this coordinate system. Because p is the scalar product of the position vector ρ_r and the unit normal ν^r, the question naturally arises whether we can express the other components of the position vector in terms of p. We can express any vector in terms of the orthogonal triad λ_r, μ_r, ν_r, and so can write

12.165 $\rho_r = q\lambda_r + r\mu_r + p\nu_r$

in which the scalars q, r have to be determined.

104. In rectangular Cartesian coordinates, the components of ρ_r are (x, y, z); it is easy to verify from Equation 1.07 that in these coordinates

12.166 $g_{rs} = \rho_{rs},$

which is a tensor equation true in any coordinates. If we take the covariant derivative of Equation 12.165 and substitute Equations 12.014, 12.015, and 12.016, we have

$$g_{rs} = \{q_s - (r \sin \phi)\omega_s + (p \cos \phi)\omega_s\}\lambda_r$$
$$+ \{r_s + (q \sin \phi)\omega_s + p\phi_s\}\mu_r$$
$$+ \{p_s - (q \cos \phi)\omega_s - r\phi_s\}\nu_r;$$

contracting this in turn with λ^r, μ^r, ν^r, we have the equivalent three vector equations

$$\lambda_s = q_s - (r \sin \phi)\omega_s + (p \cos \phi)\omega_s$$
$$\mu_s = r_s + (q \sin \phi)\omega_s + p\phi_s$$

12.167 $\nu_s = p_s - (q \cos \phi)\omega_s - r\phi_s.$

105. Evaluation of the third of these equations in (ω, ϕ, N) coordinates gives at once

$$\partial p/\partial\omega = q \cos \phi \; ; \qquad \partial p/\partial\phi = r \; ; \qquad \partial p/\partial N = 1/n \; ;$$

12.168

substitution of these values in the first two equations of Equations 12.167, together with the (ω, ϕ, N) components of λ_s, μ_s, enables us to recover Equation 12.147, which, as we have seen in § 12–97, is an integral of the Codazzi equations.
We can finally rewrite Equation 12.165 as

12.169 $\rho_r = (\sec \phi) (\partial p/\partial\omega)\lambda_r + (\partial p/\partial\phi)\mu_r + p\nu_r.$

106. The same result could have been obtained from Equations 12.145 and 12.016, but it is of some interest to obtain the result by this alternative route, and at the same time to verify Equation 12.147.

107. If the equations of one of the N-surfaces are given in the Gaussian form of Equation 6.03 as

$$x^r = x^r(\omega, \phi)$$

where the x^r are Cartesian space coordinates

(x, y, z), then we can easily find p and its derivatives from the formulas

$$p = \rho_r\nu^r = x \cos \phi \cos \omega + y \cos \phi \sin \omega + z \sin \phi$$

12.170

$$\partial p/\partial\phi = \rho_r\mu^r = -x \sin \phi \cos \omega - y \sin \phi \sin \omega + z \cos \phi$$

12.171

$$(\sec \phi)\partial p/\partial\omega = \rho_r\lambda^r = -x \sin \omega + y \cos \omega$$

12.172

in which we have used Equations 12.008.

108. Otherwise, if a surface is given in the form

12.173 $N = f(x, y, z) = $ constant,

then by evaluating the gradient Equation 12.001 in Cartesian coordinates, we have

$$n \cos \phi \cos \omega = \partial f/\partial x$$
$$n \cos \phi \sin \omega = \partial f/\partial y$$

12.174 $n \sin \phi = \partial f/\partial z$

with

$$n^2 = (\partial f/\partial x)^2 + (\partial f/\partial y)^2 + (\partial f/\partial z)^2.$$

These equations are sufficient to express p and its derivatives in terms of (x, y, z); together with Equation 12.173, these equations may serve to express (x, y, z) in terms (ω, ϕ), that is, to recast the equation of the surface into the Gaussian form. By substitution in Equations 12.170, etc., we have

$$np = x(\partial f/\partial x) + y(\partial f/\partial y)$$
$$+ z(\partial f/\partial z)$$

$$n \frac{\partial p}{\partial\phi} \left\{\left(\frac{\partial f}{\partial x}\right)^2 + \left(\frac{\partial f}{\partial y}\right)^2\right\}^{1/2} = \left(\frac{\partial f}{\partial x}\right)\left(z \frac{\partial f}{\partial x} - x \frac{\partial f}{\partial z}\right)$$
$$+ \left(\frac{\partial f}{\partial y}\right)\left(z \frac{\partial f}{\partial y} - y \frac{\partial f}{\partial z}\right)$$

12.175 $n(\partial p/\partial\omega) = -x(\partial f/\partial y) + y(\partial f/\partial x).$

It should be noted, however, that n in these equations refers to the family in Equation 12.173 for different values of N. There are other families to which a given surface could belong, and the form of one given surface does not settle the value of n on that surface.

109. We have so far considered the position vectors of points in one particular N-surface. One of the basic operations of geodesy is, however, to determine the relative positions of the two ends of a line in space, which is equivalent to finding a relation between the position vectors at the two

ends. If one end of the line (of length s and unit tangent vector l^r) is distinguished by overbars, then the equation

$$\rho^r = \bar{\rho}^r + s\bar{l}^r + \tfrac{1}{2}s^2 \overline{(l^r_{,s}l^s)} + \tfrac{1}{6}s^3 \overline{(l^r_s l^s)_{,t}l^t} + \dots$$

12.176

is true in Cartesian coordinates where it reduces to a Taylor expansion for each Cartesian coordinate. If ρ^r is interpreted as drawn through the barred point parallel to its current direction and length so that its Cartesian components remain the same during the parallel transport, then Equation 12.176 can be considered as an equation between vectors all at the barred point. It is accordingly true between such parallel vectors in any coordinates, provided, of course, that the Taylor expansion is valid. We may also lower the r-index by contracting with $\bar{g}_{rk}$, in which case ρ_k become the covariant components of the parallel vector.

110. If the line is straight, then Equation 12.176 reduces to

12.177 $\rho^r = \bar{\rho}^r + s\bar{l}^r,$

which is an elementary vector equation either between the Cartesian components or between the components in any coordinates of vectors drawn equal and parallel to ρ^r, $\bar{\rho}^r$, $\bar{l}^r$ through any point in space.

111. The expression in Equation 12.169 of the position vector in terms of the base vectors is important because we are usually concerned with the terminal azimuths α and zenith distances β of the line. For example, if we contract Equation 12.177 with l_r and note that $l_r = \bar{l}_r$ for a straight line in Cartesian coordinates and in the invariant scalar products, we find that the length s is equal to the difference in the values of

$(\sec \phi)(\partial p/\partial \omega)\sin \alpha \sin \beta + (\partial p/\partial \phi)\cos \alpha \sin \beta + p \cos \beta$

at the two ends. This depends on knowing the value of p and its derivatives for the two N-surfaces. The problem then arises how to transfer such functions from one N-surface to another, usually along the isozenithals. We shall see how to do this in later chapters, both in a general (ω, ϕ, N) system and in simpler coordinate systems which can be used to linearize the problem.

CHAPTER 13

Spherical Representation in (ω, ϕ, N)

GENERAL

1. Some properties of the spherical representation of surfaces, over and above those derived in Chapter 11, can be obtained most simply in the special coordinate system of the last chapter; we are now able to do this.

CURVATURES AND AZIMUTHS

2. We have seen in § 11–8 that a principal direction of the surface is parallel in space to its spherical image. The meridian planes at corresponding points are parallel because they contain the parallel normals and parallels to the common C^r-axis. Accordingly, the meridian directions at corresponding points are parallel, and therefore the azimuth A of a principal direction is unaltered in the spherical representation.

3. If α, $\bar{\alpha}$ are, respectively, the azimuth of a line on the surface and the azimuth of the corresponding line on the sphere, and if ψ, $\bar{\psi}$ are the angles (in the sense of fig. 11, Chapter 11) between these corresponding directions and the principal direction whose azimuth is A, then we have

13.01 $\qquad (A-\alpha)=\psi\ ; \quad (A-\bar{\alpha})=\bar{\psi}.$

4. The normal curvature k in azimuth α is then from Equation 12.056

$$\begin{aligned} k&=\kappa_1 \cos \psi \sin (A-\alpha) + \kappa_2 \sin \psi \sin (A-\alpha)\\ &=-m \cos \bar{\psi} \cos (A-\alpha) - m \sin \bar{\psi} \sin (A-\alpha)\\ &=-m \cos (A-\bar{\alpha}) \cos (A-\alpha)\\ &\quad -m \sin (A-\bar{\alpha}) \sin (A-\alpha)\\ &=-m \cos (\alpha-\bar{\alpha}) \end{aligned}$$

13.02

in which m is the scale factor for the direction α, that is, $(k^2+t^2)^{1/2}$ from Equation 11.21, and we have used Equations 11.22 and 11.23.

5. Similarly, from Equation 12.057, the geodesic torsion in azimuth α is

13.03 $\qquad t=-m \sin (\alpha-\bar{\alpha}),$

which shows that the two azimuths are the same only if the direction considered is a principal direction.

6. Direct expressions for the azimuths are easily obtained from the last two equations as

$$\begin{aligned} m \cos \bar{\alpha}&=-k \cos \alpha - t \sin \alpha\\ &=-k_2 \cos \alpha - t_1 \sin \alpha \end{aligned}$$

13.04 $\qquad\qquad\quad =\partial\phi/\partial s,$

in the second line of which we have used Equations 12.060 while ds is the arc element in azimuth α; similarly, we have

$$\begin{aligned} m \sin \bar{\alpha}&=-k \sin \alpha + t \cos \alpha\\ &=-k_1 \sin \alpha - t_1 \cos \alpha \end{aligned}$$

13.05 $\qquad\qquad\quad =(\cos \phi)\partial\omega/\partial s.$

These equations give us the spherical azimuth and scale factor in terms of the three curvature parameters k_1, k_2, t_1 of the surface.

7. For the ϕ-coordinate direction, we have $\alpha = \alpha_2$ and $\bar{\alpha} = 0$ so that Equation 13.05 gives

13.06 $\tan \alpha_2 = -t_1/k_1 = t/k,$

agreeing with Equations 12.091, which, substituted in the Equations 13.02 and 13.03, give

$$k = Kk_1/(k_1^2 + t_1^2)$$
$$t = -Kt_1/(k_1^2 + t_1^2)$$
13.07 $m = K/(k_1^2 + t_1^2)^{1/2}.$

8. For the ω-coordinate direction, we have $\alpha = \alpha_1$ and $\bar{\alpha} = \frac{1}{2}\pi$ so that Equation 13.04 gives

13.08 $\tan \alpha_1 = -k_2/t_1 = -k/t,$

agreeing with Equations 12.087, which, substituted in the Equations 13.02 and 13.03, give

$$k = Kk_2/(k_2^2 + t_1^2)$$
$$t = Kt_1/(k_2^2 + t_1^2)$$
13.09 $m = K/(k_2^2 + t_1^2)^{1/2}.$

GEODESIC CURVATURES

9. The geodesic curvature of a surface curve whose unit tangent is l^α is derived from Equation 12.065 as

$$\sigma = (\omega_\beta \sin \phi - \alpha_\beta)l^\beta;$$

for the corresponding curve in the spherical representation, (ω, ϕ) remaining the same, we have

$$\bar{\sigma} = (\omega_\beta \sin \phi - \bar{\alpha}_\beta)\bar{l}^\beta.$$

But if m is the scale factor in the direction l^α, that is, $(k^2 + t^2)^{1/2}$, we have from Equation 11.12

$$l^\beta = m\bar{l}^\beta$$

and finally

$$m\bar{\sigma} - \sigma = (\alpha - \bar{\alpha})_\beta l^\beta$$
13.10 $= \left(\dfrac{k^2}{m^2}\right)\dfrac{\partial (t/k)}{\partial l}$

in which dl is an element of length in the direction l^α. The last line in this equation is obtained by differentiation of

$$\tan (\alpha - \bar{\alpha}) = t/k$$

from Equations 13.02 and 13.03.

10. We see at once that a geodesic of the surface ($\sigma = 0$) cannot correspond to a great circle ($\bar{\sigma} = 0$) unless (t/k) is constant along the curve. This would usually imply that $t = 0$ so that the curve would also have to be a line of curvature. Even in the symmetrical case when the meridian geodesics are lines of curvature, they would, in general, be the only geodesics to correspond with great circles.

11. If we multiply Equation 13.10 by the element of length $ds = (1/m)d\bar{s}$ of a closed continuous contour and then integrate Equation 13.10 around corresponding contours, we have

$$\int_C \bar{\sigma}\,d\bar{s} - \int_C \sigma\,ds = 0$$

because the total change in azimuth around each contour is 2π. We conclude from Equation 10.47 that

$$\int_S K\,dS$$

is the same over corresponding areas; we shall see in Equation 13.14 that this is true.

12. Equation 13.10 reduces in the case of the lines of curvature ($t = 0$) to

$$\sigma = m\bar{\sigma}.$$

If as usual the lines of curvature are

$$u^\alpha, \sigma', \kappa_1, A$$
$$v^\alpha, \sigma'', \kappa_2, (A - \tfrac{1}{2}\pi),$$

then we have

13.11 $\sigma' = \kappa_1\bar{\sigma}' \; ; \qquad \sigma'' = \kappa_2\bar{\sigma}''.$

COVARIANT DERIVATIVES

13. We suppose as usual that l_α are the unit tangents to a family of surface curves and that j_α are tangential to their orthogonal trajectories. This involves no loss of generality in dealing with one particular curve because any given curve can be considered a member of some family. For example, it is well known that any surface curve can generate a family of geodesic parallels, in which case the j_α would be tangential to a family of geodesics. From Equation 12.063, we have

$$l_{\alpha\beta} = j_\alpha(\omega_\beta \sin \phi - \alpha_\beta)$$

and the corresponding equation

$$\bar{l}_{\alpha\beta} = \bar{\bar{j}}_\alpha(\omega_\beta \sin \phi - \bar{\alpha}_\beta)$$

in which $\bar{\bar{j}}_\alpha$ is perpendicular to $\bar{l}_\alpha$ on the sphere, but does not necessarily correspond to j_α. Nevertheless, from Equation 11.15, we have

$$j_\alpha = (m/K)\,\bar{\bar{j}}_\alpha \; ;$$

the required relation follows at once as

$$(m/K)\bar{l}_{\alpha\beta} = l_{\alpha\beta} + j_\alpha(\alpha - \bar{\alpha})_\beta$$

13.12
$$= l_{\alpha\beta} + j_\alpha \left(\frac{k^2}{m^2}\right)\frac{\partial(t/k)}{\partial x^\beta}.$$

14. If F is a scalar defined over a region of the surface, it must be some function of (ω, ϕ) and can be regarded as having the same value at the corresponding point on the sphere. For its second covariant derivative, we have

$$F_{\alpha\beta} = \frac{\partial^2 F}{\partial x^\alpha \partial x^\beta} - \Gamma^\gamma_{\alpha\beta}F_\gamma$$

and

$$\bar{F}_{\alpha\beta} = \frac{\partial^2 F}{\partial x^\alpha \partial x^\beta} - \bar{\Gamma}^\gamma_{\alpha\beta}F_\gamma.$$

Using Equation 11.30, we then have

13.13
$$F_{\alpha\beta} - \bar{F}_{\alpha\beta} = b^{\gamma\delta}b_{\alpha\beta\delta}F_\gamma.$$

EXPANSION IN SPHERICAL HARMONICS

15. If K is the Gaussian curvature of an N-surface and if dS is an element of area of the surface, then in (ω, ϕ) coordinates, we have

13.14 $\quad KdS = K\sqrt{a}\,d\omega d\phi = (\cos \phi)d\omega d\phi = d\bar{S},$

using Equations 9.01 and 12.070 and writing $d\bar{S}$ for the corresponding element of area in the spherical representation. If we integrate over a closed area of the surface, then

$$\int_S KdS$$

is evidently the total corresponding area on the unit sphere, or is the solid angle enclosed by parallels to the surface normals around the boundary.

16. If F is a scalar defined over an N-surface as a function of (ω, ϕ), it can be considered as having the same value at corresponding points of the spherical representation where (ω, ϕ) are the same. It can accordingly be expanded in spherical harmonics u_n of (ω, ϕ) as

13.15
$$F = \sum a_n u_n$$

in which the coefficients a_n are constant over the

sphere or over the N-surface. Moreover, since all points on the same isozenithal will have the same spherical representation and the same (ω, ϕ), F can be a scalar defined over some region of space, in which case the a_n will be functions of N at most, always assuming that the resulting series is convergent.

17. We can also write

13.16
$$F/K = \sum b_n u_n$$

in which case the coefficients b_n for a particular N-surface can be obtained in the usual way by integrating over that surface and by using Equation 13.14. All the operations of spherical harmonic analysis, usually carried out in spherical polar coordinates over a sphere, can be generalized in this way for a family of N-surfaces. Ordinary spherical harmonic analysis is, in fact, a particular case ($K = 1$) of this generalization.

DOUBLE SPHERICAL REPRESENTATION

18. We shall now consider the case of two surfaces having a common spherical representation, which implies that the surface normals are parallel at corresponding points on the two surfaces. This definition would enable us to represent one surface directly on the other without a spherical intermediary; but if we retain the conception of a common spherical representation, we shall be able to use all the spherical results without having to rederive the geometry again. As in ordinary spherical representation, we use the same surface coordinates and the same Cartesian space system.

19. As an illustration, suppose we draw a figure on one of the N-surfaces of a (ω, ϕ, N) system and then project it down the isozenithals to another N-surface of the same family. The two figures will clearly have a common spherical representation, and are accordingly in this form of correspondence. We shall call this process *isozenithal projection*.

20. In the more general case, not restricted to two surfaces of the same family, we denote quantities related to the second surface with a star, and can then write equations corresponding to Equations 13.04 and 13.05 as

13.17 $\quad m^* \cos \bar{\alpha} = -k_2^* \cos \alpha^* - t_1^* \sin \alpha^*$

13.18 $\quad m^* \sin \bar{\alpha} = -k_1^* \sin \alpha^* - t_1^* \cos \alpha^*$

in which the same spherical azimuth $\bar{\alpha}$ is retained for the common corresponding direction on the sphere. Division of these equations into Equations 13.04 and 13.05 then gives

$$\frac{m}{m^*} = \frac{k_2 \cos \alpha + t_1 \sin \alpha}{k_2^* \cos \alpha^* + t_1^* \sin \alpha^*}$$

13.19
$$= \frac{k_1 \sin \alpha + t_1 \cos \alpha}{k_1^* \sin \alpha^* + t_1^* \cos \alpha^*}$$

in which m/m^* is the scale factor multiplying an element of length on the unstarred surface to obtain the corresponding length on the starred surface. Solution of these equations gives us

13.20
$$\tan \alpha = -\frac{a + b \tan \alpha^*}{c + d \tan \alpha^*}$$

13.21
$$\tan \alpha^* = -\frac{a + c \tan \alpha}{b + d \tan \alpha}$$

where

$$a = (k_2 t_1^* - t_1 k_2^*) ; \qquad b = (k_2 k_1^* - t_1 t_1^*)$$
$$c = (t_1 t_1^* - k_1 k_2^*) ; \qquad d = (t_1 k_1^* - k_1 t_1^*)$$

13.22
$$ad - bc = KK^*.$$

It is easy to verify from Equations 13.06 and 13.08 that the coordinate directions satisfy these formulas, and so are corresponding directions.

21. The unstarred surface will often be a reference surface which can be taken as symmetrical about the Cartesian z-axis, in which case $t_1 = 0$ and the remaining curvature parameters become the principal curvatures κ_1, κ_2. In that case, we have

13.23
$$\frac{\kappa_1}{\kappa_2} \tan \alpha = \frac{t_1^* + k_1^* \tan \alpha^*}{k_2^* + t_1^* \tan \alpha^*},$$

which is a simple generalization of the formula for the spherical azimuth $\bar{\alpha}$, obtainable directly from Equations 13.04 and 13.05 as

13.24
$$\tan \bar{\alpha} = \frac{t_1^* + k_1^* \tan \alpha^*}{k_2^* + t_1^* \tan \alpha^*}.$$

22. It should be noted that the functions a, b, c, d are the same for all directions at a point, but vary from point to point. Without a knowledge of the curvature parameters, either by calculation on a given surface or by measurement, the transformation cannot be effected. Once we have calculated the corresponding azimuth α^*, the scale factor follows from Equation 13.19, with the following alternative formulas connecting the scale factor and corresponding azimuths,

$$(m/m^*)K^* \sin \alpha^* = -(a \cos \alpha + c \sin \alpha)$$
$$(m/m^*)K^* \cos \alpha^* = (b \cos \alpha + d \sin \alpha)$$
$$(m^*/m)K \sin \alpha = (a \cos \alpha^* + b \sin \alpha^*)$$

13.25
$$(m^*/m)K \cos \alpha = -(c \cos \alpha^* + d \sin \alpha^*).$$

23. All the spherical formulas in Chapter 11, which depend on the scale factor or on direction, can now easily be modified for the more general case. Tensor point functions, such as Equations 11.08 and 11.31 which are unaltered on spherical representation, will also have the same value on a more general surface, provided, of course, that the metric of that surface is used in (ω, ϕ) coordinates.

CHAPTER 14

Isozenithal Differentiation

DEFINITION

1. Chapters 11 and 13 dealt only with integral relationships between two surfaces having a common spherical representation. In the case of isozenithal projection of N-surfaces, this meant that the two N-surfaces could be separated by any finite distance measured along the isozenithals. For example, the scale factor multiplying an element of length on the unstarred surface would be

$$\left(\frac{k^2 + t^2}{k^{*2} + t^{*2}}\right)^{1/2},$$

whatever the separation of the two surfaces. However, such formulas are not often of much practical use because we do not know the curvature parameters of both surfaces. We may know the curvature parameters on one surface and may have to derive them on another by means of a Taylor series; the same applies to any other metrical quantities defined or measured on one of the surfaces. For this purpose, we need to know the derivatives of these quantities along the isozenithals—or what amounts to the same thing, their ordinary partial derivatives with respect to N—because the other two coordinates (ω, ϕ) will be constant during the change.

2. In this chapter, we shall obtain such derivatives for most of the metrical quantities of the surfaces. The geodetic applications, such as projection from points on the topographic surface to the geoid, are not likely to be carried over considerable distances along the isozenithals; for this reason, we shall find first derivatives only. Higher derivatives could be obtained in much the same way, but would naturally be far more complicated.

3. Any quantities in the common spherical representation of the N-surfaces would, of course, be unchanged during the process, and their isozenithal derivatives are accordingly zero. For example, we have at once, from the definition of the representation or from Equation 11.01,

$$\partial(\nu^r)/\partial N = 0,$$

provided the space coordinates are Cartesian.

DIFFERENTIATION OF THE FUNDAMENTAL FORMS

4. We have already seen in Equations 12.143 and 12.144 that three of the five Mainardi-Codazzi equations of a system of N-surfaces can be written in the form of isozenithal derivatives of the second fundamental form

$$\frac{\partial b_{\alpha\beta}}{\partial N} = -\frac{\partial^2(1/n)}{\partial x^\alpha \partial x^\beta} + \overline{\Gamma}^\gamma_{\alpha\beta}\frac{\partial(1/n)}{\partial x^\gamma} - \frac{c_{\alpha\beta}}{n}$$

14.01
$$= -\left(\frac{1}{n}\right)_{\alpha\beta} + b^{\gamma\delta}b_{\alpha\beta\delta}\left(\frac{1}{n}\right)_\gamma - \frac{c_{\alpha\beta}}{n}$$

in which the overbarred Christoffel symbols are taken in the metric of the spherical representation; the only nonzero values from Equations 12.142 are

14.02 $\quad \overline{\Gamma}^2_{11} = \sin\phi\,\cos\phi\;; \qquad \overline{\Gamma}^1_{12} = -\tan\phi.$

We shall find that the isozenithal derivatives of most other metric quantities can be expressed in terms of $\partial b_{\alpha\beta}/\partial N$, and thus stem from the Codazzi equations.

5. We begin with the metric tensor of an N-surface whose components are seen from Equations 12.069 to be the same as the (1, 2) components of the space

metric tensor in (ω, ϕ, N) coordinates where the surface coordinates are (ω, ϕ). We then have

$$\partial a_{\alpha\beta}/\partial N = \partial g_{\alpha\beta}/\partial N$$
$$= g_{\alpha\beta3} + \Gamma^r_{\alpha3}g_{r\beta} + \Gamma^r_{\beta3}g_{\alpha r}.$$

Because all components of the covariant derivative of the metric tensor are zero and because $\Gamma^3_{\alpha3}$ is zero in these coordinates, this reduces to

$$\partial a_{\alpha\beta}/\partial N = \Gamma^\gamma_{\alpha3}a_{\beta\gamma} + \Gamma^\gamma_{\beta3}a_{\alpha\gamma}$$
14.03 $$= b^{\gamma\delta}a_{\beta\gamma}(\partial b_{\alpha\delta}/\partial N) + b^{\gamma\delta}a_{\alpha\gamma}(\partial b_{\beta\delta}/\partial N),$$

using Equation 12.127.

6. From the ordinary expression for the derivative of a determinant, we have also

$$\partial(\ln a)/\partial N = a^{\alpha\beta}(\partial a_{\alpha\beta}/\partial N)$$
$$\overset{\cdot}{=} 2b^{\alpha\beta}(\partial b_{\alpha\beta}/\partial N)$$
$$= 2\partial(\ln b)/\partial N.$$

But the specific curvature of the N-surface from Equation 7.18 is

$$K = b/a;$$

substituting the logarithmic differential of this, we have finally

14.04 $\partial(\ln a)/\partial N = 2\partial(\ln b)/\partial N = -2\partial(\ln K)/\partial N.$

We can verify this result by noting from Equation 12.070 that

$$Kb = K^2a = \cos^2\phi,$$

which is constant along an isozenithal.
As in Equation 9.01, an element of surface area is

$$dS = \sqrt{a}\, d\omega d\phi;$$

because the coordinates ω, ϕ are constant along the isozenithals, we have

14.05 $$\frac{\partial(dS)}{\partial N} = -\frac{\partial(\ln K)}{\partial N}dS,$$

using Equation 14.04.
This shows that KdS is constant under isozenithal differentiation, as we should expect from § 13–15.

7. By differentiating the identity

$$a^{\alpha\epsilon}a_{\alpha\beta} = \delta^\epsilon_\beta,$$

we find without difficulty that

$$\partial a^{\alpha\beta}/\partial N = -a^{\alpha\gamma}a^{\beta\delta}\partial a_{\gamma\delta}/\partial N$$
14.06 $$= -(a^{\alpha\gamma}b^{\beta\delta} + a^{\beta\gamma}b^{\alpha\delta})(\partial b_{\gamma\delta}/\partial N);$$

and, to complete the picture in regard to the second fundamental form, we have

14.07 $\partial b^{\alpha\beta}/\partial N = -b^{\alpha\gamma}b^{\beta\delta}(\partial b_{\gamma\delta}/\partial N).$

8. The third fundamental form is easy because all its components are, at most, functions of latitude only, and are constant along the isozenithals so that we have

14.08 $$\frac{\partial c_{\alpha\beta}}{\partial N} = 0 = \frac{\partial c^{\alpha\beta}}{\partial N}.$$

9. We shall also require derivatives of the surface permutation symbols

$$\epsilon_{\alpha\beta} = \sqrt{a}e_{\alpha\beta}; \qquad \epsilon^{\alpha\beta} = e^{\alpha\beta}/\sqrt{a}.$$

Using Equation 14.04, we have at once

14.09 $\partial\epsilon_{\alpha\beta}/\partial N = -\epsilon_{\alpha\beta}\partial(\ln K)/\partial N$

14.10 $\partial\epsilon^{\alpha\beta}/\partial N = +\epsilon^{\alpha\beta}\partial(\ln K)/\partial N.$

10. Note that $K\epsilon_{\alpha\beta}$ and $\epsilon^{\alpha\beta}/K$ behave as constants under isozenithal differentiation; because the specific curvature of a sphere is unity, the following relations hold true in spherical representation,

14.11 $\bar{\epsilon}_{\alpha\beta} = K\epsilon_{\alpha\beta}; \qquad \bar{\epsilon}^{\alpha\beta} = \epsilon^{\alpha\beta}/K$

where the overbars refer to the metric of the sphere.

DIFFERENTIATION OF SURFACE CHRISTOFFEL SYMBOLS

11. If we are working in flat space, the most direct way of obtaining derivatives of the Christoffel symbols is to equate to zero certain components of the Riemann-Christoffel space tensor. We have, for instance,

14.12 $$\frac{\partial}{\partial N}\Gamma^\alpha_{\beta\gamma} = \frac{\partial}{\partial x^\gamma}\Gamma^\alpha_{\beta3} - \Gamma^m_{\beta\gamma}\Gamma^\alpha_{m3} + \Gamma^\sigma_{\beta3}\Gamma^\alpha_{\sigma\gamma}$$

where we have dropped from the summation those symbols which are zero in (ω, ϕ, N) coordinates. All the symbols in this expression are space symbols; we need to replace those containing only Greek indices by surface symbols, denoted by an overbar, from the relation in Equation 12.131 so that we have

14.13 $\Gamma^\alpha_{\beta\gamma} = \bar{\Gamma}^\alpha_{\beta\gamma} + b_{\beta\gamma}\nu^\alpha.$

To differentiate this expression, we use

$$\partial(\nu^\alpha)/\partial N = \nu^\alpha_3 - \Gamma^\alpha_{r3}\nu^r$$
$$= -n\Gamma^\alpha_{33} - \Gamma^\alpha_{\sigma3}\nu^\sigma$$

because $\nu^\alpha_3 = 0$. Using Equations 12.124 and 12.127, we have

$$\frac{\partial(b_{\beta\gamma}\nu^\alpha)}{\partial N} = -\Gamma^3_{\beta\gamma}\Gamma^\alpha_{33} - \Gamma^\alpha_{\sigma3}(\Gamma^\sigma_{\beta\gamma} - \bar{\Gamma}^\sigma_{\beta\gamma}) + \Gamma^\sigma_{\beta3}(\Gamma^\alpha_{\sigma\gamma} - \bar{\Gamma}^\alpha_{\sigma\gamma}).$$

From this equation and Equations 14.13 and 14.12,

we then have

$$\frac{\partial}{\partial N} \overline{\Gamma}^{\alpha}_{\beta\gamma} = \frac{\partial}{\partial x^{\gamma}} \Gamma^{\alpha}_{\beta3} - \overline{\Gamma}^{\sigma}_{\beta\gamma}\Gamma^{\alpha}_{\sigma3} + \overline{\Gamma}^{\alpha}_{\sigma\gamma}\Gamma^{\sigma}_{\beta3}.$$

But we have already seen from Equations 12.127 and 12.144 that $\Gamma^{\alpha}_{\beta3}$ is a surface tensor, and the right-hand side of this last equation is its surface covariant derivative with respect to x^{γ}. We may accordingly write the last equation as

$$\frac{\partial}{\partial N} \Gamma^{\alpha}_{\beta\gamma} = (\Gamma^{\alpha}_{\beta3})_{\gamma}$$

$$= \left(b^{\alpha\delta} \frac{\partial b_{\beta\delta}}{\partial N} \right)_{\gamma}$$

14.14 $$= -\left(b_{\beta\delta} \frac{\partial b^{\alpha\delta}}{\partial N} \right)_{\gamma}.$$

12. This remarkable result shows that although the surface Christoffel symbols are not themselves surface tensors, their isozenithal derivatives are surface tensors. In the final result, we have dropped the overbar because there is no longer any confusion with the corresponding space symbols, but we must remember that we are differentiating the surface symbol in Equation 14.14.

It is evident that Equation 14.14 is symmetrical in (β, γ) so that we have

14.15 $$(\Gamma^{\alpha}_{\beta3})_{\gamma} = (\Gamma^{\alpha}_{\gamma3})_{\beta}.$$

DIFFERENTIATION OF $b_{\alpha\beta\gamma}$

13. We interpolate now, because it follows directly from the last section, a result which will be required later. We have seen in Equation 11.31 that the quantities

$$\Gamma^{\alpha}_{\beta\gamma} + b^{\alpha\delta}b_{\beta\gamma\delta}$$

have the same values at corresponding points on a surface and in its spherical representation, which imply that this expression is constant under isozenithal differentiation. Using Equations 14.14 and 14.07, we have

$$-b_{\beta\delta\gamma} \left(\frac{\partial b^{\alpha\delta}}{\partial N} \right) - b_{\beta\delta} \left(\frac{\partial b^{\alpha\delta}}{\partial N} \right)_{\gamma}$$

$$- b_{\beta\gamma\delta}b^{\alpha\rho}b^{\delta\sigma} \frac{\partial b_{\rho\sigma}}{\partial N} + b^{\alpha\delta} \frac{\partial b_{\beta\gamma\delta}}{\partial N} = 0.$$

The third term is

$$+ b_{\beta\gamma\delta}b^{\alpha\rho}b_{\rho\sigma} \frac{\partial b^{\delta\sigma}}{\partial N} = b_{\beta\gamma\delta} \frac{\partial b^{\alpha\delta}}{\partial N},$$

which cancels with the first term because $b_{\beta\gamma\delta}$ is

symmetrical in any two indices; we have finally, with some rearrangement of indices,

14.16 $$\frac{\partial b_{\alpha\beta\gamma}}{\partial N} = b_{\alpha\rho}b_{\beta\sigma} \left(\frac{\partial b^{\rho\sigma}}{\partial N} \right)_{\gamma}$$

in which the final index denotes surface covariant differentiation.

DIFFERENTIATION OF VECTORS DEFINED IN SPACE

14. We take a unit surface vector l^r in azimuth α which is defined in space, such as the meridian direction or a principal direction of the N-surface through the point under consideration. The usual perpendicular surface vector j^r in azimuth $(\alpha - \frac{1}{2}\pi)$ is defined as perpendicular to l^r, and must therefore remain perpendicular to l^r after differentiation. Because the space vector equations

$$l_r = \lambda_r \sin \alpha + \mu_r \cos \alpha$$

$$j_r = -\lambda_r \cos \alpha + \mu_r \sin \alpha$$

are to remain true after the process, we may differentiate them covariantly along the isozenithal, that is, with respect to N. Remembering from Equation 12.098 that $\lambda_{r3} = \mu_{r3} = 0$, we then have

$$l_{r3} = -j_r(\partial\alpha/\partial N)$$

14.17 $$j_{r3} = l_r(\partial\alpha/\partial N)$$

with similar contravariant equations. The change in azimuth in these equations refers to changes in the vectors as defined in space; it does not refer to the change of direction which would be obtained by projecting the two ends of the vector down the isozenithals. We shall consider this case in § 14–25.

15. We could expand Equations 14.17 with $r = \beta$ and substitute Equations 12.124, 12.127, and 12.128 for the Christoffel symbols, thus deriving expressions for the differentials of the components. However, in this case, we are able to use covariant differentiation; we shall find it simpler to do so as a means of obtaining changes in the normal curvatures k (of l_r) and k^* (of j_r), together with the change in the geodesic torsion t (of l_r). We have, for example,

$$\nu_{rs}l^rj^s = -t;$$

differentiating this covariantly along the isozenithal gives, with Equations 14.17,

$$\nu_{rs3}l^rj^s - \nu_{rs}j^rj^s(\partial\alpha/\partial N) + \nu_{rs}l^rl^s(\partial\alpha/\partial N) = -\partial t/\partial N.$$

In (ω, ϕ, N) coordinates and using Equations 12.159, the first term is $(\partial b_{\alpha\beta}/\partial N)l^{\alpha}j^{\beta}$ so that we have

14.18 $$(\partial b_{\alpha\beta}/\partial N)l^{\alpha}j^{\beta} = (k - k^*)(\partial\alpha/\partial N) - \partial t/\partial N;$$

in much the same way, we have

14.19 $(\partial b_{\alpha\beta}/\partial N)l^\alpha l^\beta = -2t(\partial\alpha/\partial N) - \partial k/\partial N$

14.20 $(\partial b_{\alpha\beta}/\partial N)j^\alpha j^\beta = +2t(\partial\alpha/\partial N) - \partial k^*/\partial N.$

16. Before substituting for $\partial b_{\alpha\beta}/\partial N$ from the Mainardi-Codazzi Equation 14.01, we need to work on the middle term of the latter, that is, on

$$b^{\gamma\delta}b_{\alpha\beta\delta}(1/n)_\gamma = (1/n)b_{\alpha\beta\delta}\nu^\delta,$$

using Equation 12.082. We have

$$b_{\alpha\beta\delta}l^\alpha j^\beta = (b_{\alpha\beta}l^\alpha j^\beta)_\delta - b_{\alpha\beta}l^\alpha_\delta j^\beta - b_{\alpha\beta}l^\alpha j^\beta_\delta$$

$$= \partial t/\partial x^\delta + (k-k^*)(\sigma l_\delta + \sigma^* j_\delta)$$

14.21 $= \partial t/\partial x^\delta + (k-k^*)(\omega_\delta \sin\phi - \alpha_\delta)$

in which σ, σ^* are the geodesic curvatures of l^α, j^β, respectively; in deriving the equation, we have used Equations 4.11, 7.08, and 12.064. Similarly, we have

14.22 $b_{\alpha\beta\delta}l^\alpha l^\beta = \partial k/\partial x^\delta - 2t(\sigma l_\delta + \sigma^* j_\delta)$

14.23 $b_{\alpha\beta\delta}j^\alpha j^\beta = \partial k^*/\partial x^\delta + 2t(\sigma l_\delta + \sigma^* j_\delta).$

17. Now, if F is any scalar or component of a tensor, we have

$$(\partial F/\partial x^\delta)\nu^\delta = (\partial F/\partial x^r)\nu^r - (\partial F/\partial N)\nu^3$$

14.24 $= (\partial F/\partial s) - n(\partial F/\partial N)$

in which ds is the arc element in the direction of the normal; so then we have from Equation 14.21, using Equation 12.032,

$$b^{\gamma\delta}b_{\alpha\beta\delta}l^\alpha j^\beta(1/n)_\gamma = (1/n)b_{\alpha\beta\delta}l^\alpha j^\beta\nu^\delta$$

$$= (1/n)(\partial t/\partial s - n\partial t/\partial N)$$

$$+ (1/n)(k-k^*)$$

$$\times (\gamma_1 \tan\phi - \partial\alpha/\partial s + n\partial\alpha/\partial N).$$

Substituting in Equations 14.01 and 14.18 and using Equation 7.14, we have finally

$$\partial t/\partial s = n\overline{(1/n)}_{\alpha\beta}l^\alpha j^\beta + 2Ht$$

14.25 $- (k-k^*)(\gamma_1 \tan\phi - \partial\alpha/\partial s);$

similarly from Equations 14.22 and 14.23, we have

$$\partial k/\partial s = n\overline{(1/n)}_{\alpha\beta}l^\alpha l^\beta + (k^2+t^2)$$

14.26 $+ 2t(\gamma_1 \tan\phi - \partial\alpha/\partial s)$

$$\partial k^*/\partial s = n\overline{(1/n)}_{\alpha\beta}j^\alpha j^\beta + (k^{*2}+t^2)$$

14.27 $- 2t(\gamma_1 \tan\phi - \partial\alpha/\partial s).$

In all three expressions, the covariant derivative $\overline{(1/n)}_{\alpha\beta}$ is taken with respect to the surface metric. Adding the last two equations gives

14.28 $\partial(2H)/\partial s = n\overline{\Delta(1/n)} + (4H^2 - 2K)$

in which $\overline{\Delta(1/n)}$ is the surface Laplacian. Multiplying the first equation by $(-2t)$, the second by k^*, and the third by k, using Equation 8.02 and adding, we have

14.29 $\partial(\ln K)/\partial s = nb^{\alpha\beta}\overline{(1/n)}_{\alpha\beta} + 2H.$

Multiplying the first equation by $(-4Ht)$, the second by $(k^{*2}+t^2)$, and the third by (k^2+t^2), using Equation 8.04 and adding, we have

14.30 $\partial(2H/K)/\partial s = -nc^{\alpha\beta}\overline{(1/n)}_{\alpha\beta} - 2.$

ISOZENITHAL AND NORMAL DIFFERENTIATION

18. The last six equations, giving variations along the normals, are somewhat simpler than the corresponding variations along the isozenithals.
We can, however, relate normal and isozenithal differentiation by Equation 14.24 or by means of the following formula. If F is any scalar or particular component of a tensor, defined in space and therefore also on the N-surfaces, we have

$$\partial F/\partial s = F_r\nu^r$$

$$= F_3\nu^3 + F_\alpha\nu^\alpha$$

$$= n(\partial F/\partial N) + \gamma_1 \sec\phi(\partial F/\partial\omega) + \gamma_2(\partial F/\partial\phi).$$

14.31

Or, if we use Equation 12.082, we have

14.32 $\partial F/\partial s = n(\partial F/\partial N) - b^{\alpha\beta}F_\alpha(\ln n)_\beta.$

In applying these formulas, it is important to realize that the N-surfaces must be the same for both operations. If we use Equation 14.31, then the (ω, ϕ) coordinates must also be the same; we are comparing the variation in F along two different lines (the isozenithal and the normal) in the same (ω, ϕ, N) system. If we use the second Equation 14.32, the N-surfaces must still be the same; but the surface coordinates need not be the same because the last term is a surface invariant, unless F is a component of a surface tensor, in which case we must use the same surface coordinates.
On this basis, for example, we have from Equation 14.28

$$\partial(2H)/\partial N = \overline{\Delta(1/n)} + (1/n)(4H^2 - 2K)$$

14.33 $- b^{\alpha\beta}(2H)_\alpha(1/n)_\beta.$

DIFFERENTIATION OF THE CURVATURE PARAMETERS

19. If we take l^α, j^β in Equations 14.18, etc., to be the parallel and meridian directions λ^α, μ^β, which are to remain the parallel and meridian directions after differentiation, then α is and remains either zero or $\frac{1}{2}\pi$; Equations 14.18 through 14.23 become

$$\partial t_1/\partial N = -(\partial b_{\alpha\beta}/\partial N)\lambda^\alpha\mu^\beta$$

$$\partial k_1/\partial N = -(\partial b_{\alpha\beta}/\partial N)\lambda^\alpha\lambda^\beta$$

14.34 $$\partial k_2/\partial N = -(\partial b_{\alpha\beta}/\partial N)\mu^\alpha\mu^\beta$$

$$b_{\alpha\beta\delta}\lambda^\alpha\mu^\beta = \partial t_1/\partial x^\delta + (k_1 - k_2)\omega_\delta \sin \phi$$

$$b_{\alpha\beta\delta}\lambda^\alpha\lambda^\beta = \partial k_1/\partial x^\delta - 2t_1\omega_\delta \sin \phi$$

14.35 $$b_{\alpha\beta\delta}\mu^\alpha\mu^\beta = \partial k_2/\partial x^\delta + 2t_1\omega_\delta \sin \phi,$$

giving the variations of the curvature parameters along the isozenithal and reducing, as in the last section, to the following variations along the normals,

$$\partial t_1/\partial s = n\overline{(1/n)}_{\alpha\beta}\lambda^\alpha\mu^\beta + 2Ht_1 - \gamma_1(k_1 - k_2) \tan \phi$$

$$\partial k_1/\partial s = n\overline{(1/n)}_{\alpha\beta}\lambda^\alpha\lambda^\beta + (k_1^2 + t_1^2) + 2\gamma_1 t_1 \tan \phi$$

$$\partial k_2/\partial s = n\overline{(1/n)}_{\alpha\beta}\mu^\alpha\mu^\beta + (k_2^2 + t_1^2) - 2\gamma_1 t_1 \tan \phi.$$

14.36

The equations for the invariants $2H$, K, $2H/K$ are, of course, the same as Equations 14.28 through 14.30.

20. We have seen that $\partial b_{\alpha\beta}/\partial N$ is a surface tensor so that we can express it as a sum of products of surface vectors. From Equations 14.34, we have at once

$$-\partial b_{\alpha\beta}/\partial N = (\partial k_1/\partial N)\lambda_\alpha\lambda_\beta + (\partial t_1/\partial N)(\lambda_\alpha\mu_\beta + \mu_\alpha\lambda_\beta)$$

14.37 $$+ (\partial k_2/\partial N)\mu_\alpha\mu_\beta.$$

Accordingly, for example, we have

$$\partial(2H)/\partial N = -a^{\alpha\beta}(\partial b_{\alpha\beta}/\partial N)$$
$$= \overline{\Delta(1/n)} - b^{\alpha\beta}(2H)_\alpha(1/n)_\beta$$
14.38 $$+ (1/n)(4H^2 - 2K),$$

using Equation 14.01 which requires the Laplacian to be taken in the surface metric. This agrees with Equation 14.33.

21. The remaining two parameters γ_1, γ_2 are best differentiated from

$$\gamma_1 = (\ln n)_r\lambda^r$$

$$\gamma_2 = (\ln n)_r\mu^r,$$

from which we have at once, because $\lambda_3^r = \mu_3^r = 0$,

$$\partial\gamma_1/\partial N = (\ln n)_{\alpha 3}\lambda^\alpha$$

14.39 $$\partial\gamma_2/\partial N = (\ln n)_{\alpha 3}\mu^\alpha.$$

Alternatively, we may take the covariant derivative of Equation 12.021,

$$\nu_{rs}\nu^s = \gamma_1\lambda_r + \gamma_2\mu_r,$$

to derive

$$\partial\gamma_1/\partial N = \nu_{rs3}\lambda^r\nu^s = \nu_{r3s}\lambda^r\nu^s;$$

using the fact that $\nu_{r3} = 0$, this formula reduces with the help of Equation 12.016 to

14.40 $$\partial\gamma_1/\partial N = -\Gamma^\alpha_{3s}\nu^s\nu_{r\alpha}\lambda^r = -\Gamma^1_{3s}\nu^s \cos \phi$$

and similarly to

14.41 $$\partial\gamma_2/\partial N = -\Gamma^2_{3s}\nu^s.$$

We could have obtained the same results by ordinary differentiation of the (1, 2) components of ν^r in Equation 12.034.

DIFFERENTIATION OF THE PRINCIPAL CURVATURES

22. If l^α, j^β in Equations 14.18, etc., are tangent to the lines of curvature u^α, v^β, then we have $t = 0$ throughout; Equations 14.18 through 14.23 become

$$(\kappa_1 - \kappa_2)(\partial A/\partial N) = (\partial b_{\alpha\beta}/\partial N)u^\alpha v^\beta$$

$$\partial\kappa_1/\partial N = -(\partial b_{\alpha\beta}/\partial N)u^\alpha u^\beta$$

14.42 $$\partial\kappa_2/\partial N = -(\partial b_{\alpha\beta}/\partial N)v^\alpha v^\beta$$

$$b_{\alpha\beta\delta}u^\alpha v^\beta = (\kappa_1 - \kappa_2)(\omega_\delta \sin \phi - A_\delta)$$

$$b_{\alpha\beta\delta}u^\alpha u^\beta = \partial\kappa_1/\partial x^\delta$$

14.43 $$b_{\alpha\beta\delta}v^\alpha v^\beta = \partial\kappa_2/\partial x^\delta,$$

leading to the following variations along the normals

14.44 $$(\kappa_1 - \kappa_2)(\gamma_1 \tan \phi - \partial A/\partial s) = n\overline{(1/n)}_{\alpha\beta}u^\alpha v^\beta$$

14.45 $$\partial\kappa_1/\partial s = n\overline{(1/n)}_{\alpha\beta}u^\alpha u^\beta + \kappa_1^2$$

14.46 $$\partial\kappa_2/\partial s = n\overline{(1/n)}_{\alpha\beta}v^\alpha v^\beta + \kappa_2^2$$

in which the covariant derivatives are taken in the surface metric. Equations 14.43 could have been obtained by contracting Equation 8.16 and by using Equation 12.064.

23. The surface tensor $\partial b_{\alpha\beta}/\partial N$ can be expressed as

$$\partial b_{\alpha\beta}/\partial N = -(\partial\kappa_1/\partial N)u_\alpha u_\beta$$
$$+ (\kappa_1 - \kappa_2)(\partial A/\partial N)(u_\alpha v_\beta + v_\alpha u_\beta)$$
14.47 $$- (\partial\kappa_2/\partial N)v_\alpha v_\beta;$$

the equations for the invariants can be obtained directly from this as

$$\partial(2H)/\partial N = -a^{\alpha\beta}(\partial b_{\alpha\beta}/\partial N)$$

$$\partial(\ln K)/\partial N = -b^{\alpha\beta}(\partial b_{\alpha\beta}/\partial N)$$

14.48 $\quad \partial(2H/K)/\partial N = c^{\alpha\beta}(\partial b_{\alpha\beta}/\partial N).$

PROJECTION OF SURFACE VECTORS

24. In the last few sections, we have considered vectors and the parameters associated with them, which can be considered as point functions in that the vectors are uniquely defined at all points of all the N-surfaces within a region of space; we have arranged for the vectors to retain their definition after isozenithal differentiation. For example, the principal directions are, in general, uniquely defined at points in space by the form of the N-surfaces, that is, by the form of the scalar point-function N and its derivatives. We have found expressions for the change in azimuth and curvature in the principal directions on the assumption that they remain principal directions during the change.

25. We now consider surface vectors which are not so defined; we shall obtain expressions for the changes associated with these vectors as they are projected an infinitesimal distance down the isozenithals. The two ends of a vector subjected to this process each move down isozenithals to a neighboring N-surface, the surface coordinates (ω, ϕ) of both ends remaining unchanged. The length of the vector will change as a rule, but we shall find it convenient to correct for this and to find expressions connecting unit vectors in the projected directions.

26. We must be careful not to differentiate such expressions as

$$t = b_{\alpha\beta}l^\alpha j^\beta,$$

containing two related vectors, because this would tend to hold the relation during the change with the result that neither would, in general, be projected in the sense we are considering. We should differentiate expressions containing only the one vector which we wish to project, together with point functions. For example, we could recast the preceding formula with the help of Equations 2.32 as

14.49 $\quad t = -b_{\alpha\beta}l^\alpha\epsilon^{\beta\gamma}l_\gamma$

before differentiating. We can, of course, restore the related (perpendicular) vector j^β after differentiation.

27. The process will involve ordinary partial differentiation with respect to N of various compo-

nents of tensor functions. We could use covariant differentiation only if it were possible to write the formula in terms of space components. For example, covariant differentiation of $a_{\alpha\beta}$ with respect to N is meaningless, but we can replace $a_{\alpha\beta}$ in these coordinates by $g_{\alpha\beta}$ and can take the covariant derivative $g_{\alpha\beta3}$, as indeed we did in deriving Equation 14.03. We must, of course, use one sort of differentiation throughout an operation.

28. Because the spherical representation is unchanged by this form of projection, we can take any formula connecting elements on an N-surface and on the unit sphere, and then can differentiate with the spherical elements fixed. We have had an example of this in § 14–3. As another example, we found in Equation 11.08 that if the space coordinates are Cartesian and the surface coordinates are the same for both surfaces, then

$$b^{\alpha\beta}x_\alpha^r$$

is unaltered on spherical representation. Differentiating with respect to N, we have

$$(\partial b^{\alpha\beta}/\partial N)x_\alpha^r + b^{\alpha\beta}(\partial x_\alpha^r/\partial N) = 0$$

from which we have

$$\partial x_\alpha^r/\partial N = -b_{\alpha\beta}(\partial b^{\beta\gamma}/\partial N)x_\gamma^r$$

$$= b^{\beta\gamma}(\partial b_{\alpha\beta}/\partial N)x_\gamma^r$$

14.50 $\quad = \Gamma_{\alpha3}^\gamma x_\gamma^r,$

using Equation 12.127.

Again, if the space coordinates are Cartesian, we know from Equation 11.02 that ν_α^r is unaltered on spherical representation, and therefore we have

14.51 $\quad \partial\nu_\alpha^r/\partial N = 0.$

We can also write

$$\nu_{\alpha\beta}^r = \partial\nu_\alpha^r/\partial x^\beta - \Gamma_{\alpha\beta}^\gamma\nu_\gamma^r$$

in space Cartesian coordinates because the space Christoffel symbols are then zero. Differentiating this and using Equation 14.14, we have

14.52 $\quad \partial\nu_{\alpha\beta}^r/\partial N = -(\Gamma_{\alpha3}^\gamma)_\beta\nu_\gamma^r.$

Length

29. If δs is the length of a small N-surface vector, the corresponding length in the spherical representation (scale factor m) is from Equation 11.11

$$\delta\bar{s} = (k^2 + t^2)^{1/2}\delta s = m\delta s$$

in which k, t are the normal curvature and geodesic torsion in the direction of the vector. Differentiating this isozenithally, $\delta\bar{s}$ remaining fixed, we have

$$\frac{\partial(\ln \delta s)}{\partial N} = -\frac{\partial(\ln m)}{\partial N} = -\frac{\partial\{\ln (k^2+t^2)^{1/2}\}}{\partial N}.$$

14.53

30. An alternative expression may be obtained as follows. If the element δs corresponds to a difference of surface coordinates δx^α in the direction of the unit vector l^α, we have

$$\delta s^2 = a_{\alpha\beta}\delta x^\alpha \delta x^\beta;$$

differentiating this, we have

$$\frac{\partial(\ln \delta s)}{\partial N} = \frac{1}{2}\frac{\partial a_{\alpha\beta}}{\partial N}\frac{\partial x^\alpha}{\partial s}\frac{\partial x^\beta}{\partial s}$$

$$= \frac{1}{2}\frac{\partial a_{\alpha\beta}}{\partial N}l^\alpha l^\beta$$

$$= l^\alpha b^{\beta\gamma}l_\gamma(\partial b_{\alpha\beta}/\partial N)$$

14.54 $$= l^\alpha l_\gamma \Gamma^\gamma_{\delta 3},$$

using Equations 14.03 and 12.127.

31. We have seen in Equations 14.48 that

$$-\partial(\ln K)/\partial N = b^{\alpha\beta}(\partial b_{\alpha\beta}/\partial N) = \Gamma^\alpha_{\alpha 3},$$

using the contraction of Equation 12.127. We may write further

$$-\partial(\ln K)/\partial N = \Gamma^\gamma_{\gamma 3}\delta^\alpha_\gamma = \Gamma^\gamma_{\gamma 3}(l^\alpha l_\gamma + j^\alpha j_\gamma),$$

if j^α is the usual surface vector perpendicular to l^α and if we remember that $\Gamma^\gamma_{\delta 3}$ is a surface tensor. If we add this last result to

14.55 $$\partial(\ln m)/\partial N = -\Gamma^\gamma_{\delta 3}(l^\alpha l_\gamma),$$

obtainable from Equations 14.53 and 14.54, we have

14.56 $$\partial\{\ln(m/K)\}/\partial N = \Gamma^\gamma_{\alpha 3}j^\alpha j_\gamma.$$

But if m^* is the scale factor in the j^α-direction, we have also

14.57 $$\partial(\ln m^*)/\partial N = -\Gamma^\gamma_{\alpha 3}j^\alpha j_\gamma$$

and so

14.58 $$\partial(\ln mm^*/K)/\partial N = 0.$$

But this last relation is true only to a first order. We cannot differentiate it again or assert that (mm^*/K) is constant over a finite length of the isozenithal because the two directions do not, in general, remain perpendicular when projected down the isozenithal.

Contravariant Components

32. If we use the same surface coordinates, for instance (ω, ϕ), for the N-surfaces and the sphere, we have found in Equation 11.12, relating the con-

travariant components of a unit surface vector and the corresponding unit vector in the spherical representation, that

$$(1/m)l^\alpha = \bar{l}^\alpha.$$

Differentiating this, we have at once

$$\partial l^\alpha/\partial N = l^\alpha(\partial \ln m/\partial N)$$

$$= l^\alpha\{\partial \ln (k^2+t^2)^{1/2}/\partial N\}$$

14.59 $$= -\Gamma^\beta_{\gamma 3}l^\gamma l_\beta l^\alpha$$

in which m is the scale factor of the representation, and we have used Equations 14.53 and 14.54.

Azimuth

33. The space components of a unit surface vector l^r in azimuth α and of its perpendicular j^r in azimuth $(\alpha - \frac{1}{2}\pi)$ are given by

$$l^r = \lambda^r \sin \alpha + \mu^r \cos \alpha$$

$$j^r = -\lambda^r \cos \alpha + \mu^r \sin \alpha.$$

If the space coordinates are Cartesian, then all components of λ^r, μ^r are functions of (ω, ϕ) only, and are therefore constant under isozenithal differentiation so that we have

$$\partial l^r/\partial N = (\lambda^r \cos \alpha - \mu^r \sin \alpha)(\partial\alpha/\partial N)$$

14.60 $$= -j^r(\partial\alpha/\partial N).$$

34. We now differentiate the equation

$$l^r = l^\alpha x^r_\alpha,$$

using Equations 14.59 and 14.50, and find that

$$-j^r(\partial\alpha/\partial N) = l^r(\partial \ln m/\partial N) + \Gamma^\gamma_{\alpha 3}l^\alpha x^r_\gamma.$$

Multiplication by l_r gives Equation 14.55 again, and multiplication by j_r gives

14.61 $$(\partial\alpha/\partial N) = -\Gamma^\gamma_{\alpha 3}l^\alpha j_\gamma.$$

Note that this is not the same as Equations 14.17. The change in azimuth in the perpendicular direction j^r is similarly

14.62 $$(\partial\alpha^*/\partial N) = \Gamma^\gamma_{\alpha 3}j^\alpha l_\gamma$$

and

$$\partial(\alpha + \alpha^*)/\partial N = \Gamma^\gamma_{\alpha 3}(\epsilon_{\gamma\delta}l^\alpha l^\delta + \epsilon_{\gamma\delta}j^\alpha j^\delta)$$

14.63 $$= \Gamma^\gamma_{\alpha 3}\epsilon_{\gamma\delta}a^{\alpha\delta}.$$

Note that this is a point function which is the same for all directions at a point. Consequently, the change in mean azimuth of a pair of perpendicular directions is the same for all pairs.

Covariant Components

35. If we differentiate the equation

$$l_r x_\alpha^r = l_\alpha$$

in which the space coordinates are Cartesian, in the same way we have

$$\partial l_\alpha / \partial N = -j_r(\partial \alpha / \partial N) x_\alpha^r + \Gamma_{\alpha 3}^\gamma x_\gamma^r l_r$$

14.64 $$= -j_\alpha(\partial \alpha / \partial N) + \Gamma_{\alpha 3}^\gamma l_\gamma$$

in which we can substitute Equations 14.61 and 12.127 and ultimately Equation 14.01 to show the result in terms of $(1/n)$ and surface tensors. However, we shall usually be content to leave the results in terms of the Christoffel symbols $\Gamma_{\beta 3}^\alpha$ or in a form which can readily be translated into these symbols.

Curvatures

36. The simplest way of differentiating the curvatures in the direction l^α is to differentiate Equations 13.02 and 13.03 in which $\bar\alpha$, the azimuth of the spherical representation of l^α, is held fixed. We have at once

14.65 $$\partial \dot{k} / \partial N = k\{\partial(\ln m)/\partial N\} - t(\partial \alpha / \partial N)$$

14.66 $$\partial t / \partial N = t\{\partial(\ln m)/\partial N\} + k(\partial \alpha / \partial N)$$

in which we can as usual substitute Equations 14.55 and 14.61. We have also an alternative expression for the variation in azimuth from these equations,

14.67 $$\frac{\partial \alpha}{\partial N} = \frac{k^2}{m^2} \frac{\partial(t/k)}{\partial N}.$$

37. It may be emphasized again that the expressions give the changes in k, t, etc., between a direction on an N-surface and the projected direction on the next surface. Suppose, for example, that we start with a principal direction ($t = 0$). Equations 14.65 and 14.66 then give the change in normal curvature and geodesic torsion resulting from projection of the principal direction down the isozenithals onto the neighboring surface. If the projected direction is to remain a principal direction, then we must also have $\partial t / \partial N = 0$, in which case we have $\partial \alpha / \partial N = 0$ from Equation 14.67. From Equation 14.61, we then have

$$\Gamma_{\alpha 3}^\gamma u^\alpha v_\gamma = 0$$

in which u^α, v^α are as usual the principal direc-

tions. With the help of Equations 12.127 and 8.03, we can show that this is equivalent to

14.68 $$(\partial b_{\alpha\beta} / \partial N) u^\alpha v^\beta = 0$$

as the condition for the principal directions to project as principal directions. It is clear from Equation 14.01 that this condition implies a special relationship between n and surface tensors which would restrict the form of N. We must conclude therefore that principal directions, in general, do not project isozenithally as principal directions.

38. To obtain the variation in geodesic curvature of isozenithally projected curves, we can differentiate Equation 13.10 in the form

$$\bar\sigma - (1/m)\sigma = (1/m)(\alpha - \bar\alpha)_\beta l^\beta,$$

holding the spherical elements $\bar\sigma$, $\bar\alpha$ constant. The result, after some simplification, is

14.69 $$\frac{\partial \sigma}{\partial N} = \sigma \frac{\partial(\ln m)}{\partial N} - \frac{\partial^2 \alpha}{\partial x^\beta \partial N} l^\beta$$

in which we should substitute Equation 14.55 and the differential of Equation 14.61 or 14.67. To verify this, the reader is invited to obtain the same result without spherical representation, but with greater labor, by differentiating

$$\sigma = -l_{\alpha\beta} \epsilon^{\alpha\gamma} l_\gamma l^\beta.$$

Covariant Derivatives

39. To find the variation in the surface covariant derivatives of isozenithally projected curves, we can similarly differentiate Equation 13.12. Alternatively, we can differentiate Equation 12.063 in the form

$$l_{\alpha\beta} = -\epsilon_{\alpha\gamma} l^\gamma (\omega_\beta \sin\phi - \alpha_\beta),$$

the result in either case being

14.70 $$\frac{\partial l_{\alpha\beta}}{\partial N} = l_{\alpha\beta} \frac{\partial\{\ln(m/K)\}}{\partial N} - j_\alpha \frac{\partial^2 \alpha}{\partial x^\beta \partial N}.$$

The reader may find it instructive to obtain this same result by straight differentiation of the ordinary formula for a covariant derivative, corresponding to Equation 3.08 in two dimensions, using Equations 14.14 and 14.64.

40. We have seen in Equations 12.127 and 12.144 that $\Gamma_{\alpha 3}^\gamma$ is a surface tensor; therefore, $\partial \alpha / \partial N$ in Equation 14.61 is a surface invariant. We conclude from Equation 14.70 that $\partial l_{\alpha\beta} / \partial N$ is a surface tensor; Equation 14.70 is a tensor equation, true in

any surface coordinates to the extent that these coordinates can be transformed while retaining N fixed.

41. If F is a scalar, defined in space and therefore over any N-surface, we can find the isozenithal variation of its second surface covariant derivative $F_{\alpha\beta}$ by differentiating either Equation 13.13 or the defining equation

$$F_{\alpha\beta} = \frac{\partial^2 F}{\partial x^\alpha \partial x^\beta} - \Gamma^\gamma_{\alpha\beta} F_\gamma.$$

The result in either case is

14.71 $$\frac{\partial F_{\alpha\beta}}{\partial N} = \left(\frac{\partial F}{\partial N}\right)_{\alpha\beta} - (\Gamma^\gamma_{\alpha3})_\beta F_\gamma.$$

CHAPTER 15

Normal Coordinate Systems

GENERAL

1. In the (ω, ϕ, N) system, the (ω, ϕ) surface coordinates are not, in general, constant along the normals to the N-surfaces so that the normals are not the N-coordinate lines. The gradients of (ω, ϕ), considered as space vectors, are not contained within the N-surfaces as is evident from Equations 12.046 and 12.047. We shall now consider how to overcome these complications by adopting surface coordinates, which are defined to be constant along a normal, so that the normals are the N-coordinate lines. The geometry of the system will be simpler and can often be used to derive quickly results in the form of invariants or tensor equations which are true in any coordinates. However, the surface coordinates are not directly measurable throughout a region of space; the system is accordingly of direct practical use only when we are interested in the immediate neighborhood of one particular surface.

2. As usual, we start with a scalar N, single-valued, continuous, and differentiable throughout some region of space, and make it one coordinate of the system. The family of N-surfaces, over each of which N is a constant, is accordingly one family of coordinate surfaces. The gradient of N is

$$\textbf{15.01} \qquad N_r = n\nu_r$$

in which ν_r are unit tangents to the normals or the orthogonal trajectories of the N-surfaces.

We have seen in § 10–19 that a scale factor of

n will transform the space conformally to a curved space in which the normals become a family of geodesics and the N-surfaces become a family of geodesic parallels. An element of length along the geodesic normals will be dN; it is well known [1] that the metric of the curved space can then be expressed in the quasi-Pythagorean form

$$d\bar{s}^2 = \bar{a}_{\alpha\beta}dx^\alpha dx^\beta + dN^2 \qquad (\alpha, \beta = 1, 2)$$

in which the dx^α are the other two coordinates. We transform this expression back to the original space with scale factor $(1/n)$ and have as the metric of the original space

$$\textbf{15.02} \qquad ds^2 = a_{\alpha\beta}dx^\alpha dx^\beta + (1/n)^2 dN^2$$

in which we have retained the same coordinates x^α, whatever they may be. This merely demonstrates the possibility of a metric in this form; we have now to examine it and to find all we can about the x^α.

THE METRIC TENSOR

3. We can write the metric tensor in the abbreviated form

$$\textbf{15.03} \qquad g_{rs} = (a_{\alpha\beta}, 1/n^2),$$

the determinant of which is

$$\textbf{15.04} \qquad g = (1/n^2)a,$$

---

[1] See, for instance, Eisenhart (1926), *Riemannian Geometry*, 57.

103

leading to the associated tensor

15.05 $g^{rs} = (a^{\alpha\beta}, n^2)$,

as we may easily verify from the definition in § 2–19.

4. The cosine of the angle between the gradients of x^1 and N is proportional to

$$g^{rs} x_r^1 N_s = g^{13} = 0.$$

Consequently, the gradient of x^1 is perpendicular to the gradient of N, that is, to ν_r, and must be therefore a surface vector. Similarly, the gradient of x^2 is a surface vector. Both x^α-coordinates are thus constant along the normals, which must therefore be the N-coordinate lines.

5. In much the same way, we can prove from the absence of $g_{\alpha 3}$-components in the metric tensor that the x^α-coordinate lines are perpendicular to the N-coordinate line, and must therefore lie in the N-surfaces.

6. As usual, we take the x^α as surface coordinates and as two of the space coordinates so that

15.06 $x_\alpha^r = \delta_\alpha^r$.

7. One possible way, and indeed so far as we know the only way, of defining the x^α-coordinates further is as follows. Through a point P in space, we draw a line or trajectory which is normal to all the N-surfaces. The intersection of this line with a particular N-surface, which we shall call the *base surface*, is Q. The coordinates of Q on the base surface are taken as the x^α-coordinates of P. Evidently, all points on the same normal have the same x^α, and the x^α can be used as surface coordinates on the other N-surfaces. In this way, we can meet all the preceding requirements of a metric in the form of Equation 15.02. We shall assume that coordinates have been chosen in this manner, but we shall leave open for the present the particular choice of coordinates on the base surface.

8. It should be noted that we have defined the x^α-coordinates as functions of position only on the base surface. We can transform them in two dimensions on the base surface, in which case their values will be settled at any point in space. We can also transform the x^α-coordinates at any point in space by taking the N-surface through the point as base surface. We cannot, in general, choose latitude and longitude, defined in §12–10, as coordinates in this system because they are not constant along the normals, unless the normals are straight. This would be a special case with which

we shall deal in Chapter 17. We could, however, choose latitude and longitude on one particular base surface, even if the normals are not straight.

9. Because we have not so far specified the actual surface coordinates, even on the base surface, we cannot specify the surface metric tensor $a_{\alpha\beta}$. Nor can we determine the second and third fundamental forms $b_{\alpha\beta}$, $c_{\alpha\beta}$ of the N-surfaces as we did in the (ω, ϕ, N) system where all three coordinates were completely specified in space. These three forms must vary between surfaces and must therefore be dependent on N. We shall derive expressions later for this which will enable us to calculate the $a_{\alpha\beta}$, $b_{\alpha\beta}$, and $c_{\alpha\beta}$ on any surface from the corresponding components on the base surface.

COMPONENTS OF THE NORMAL AND OF SURFACE VECTORS

10. From the basic gradient equation for N, that is,

$$N_r = n\nu_r,$$

we can find the covariant components of the unit normal at once because, whatever the $(1, 2)$ coordinates, N does not change when differentiated with respect to them. We then write

15.07 $\nu_r = (0, 0, 1/n)$.

The $(1, 2)$ contravariant components must also be zero because the $(1, 2)$ coordinates do not change along the normal. Also, we have $\nu_r \nu^r = 1$ because ν_r is a unit vector so that we can write

15.08 $\nu^r = (0, 0, n)$.

11. We shall also require expressions for the surface tensor derivative of the unit normal. Weingarten's formula in Equation 6.17 becomes

15.09 $\nu_\alpha^{\ r} = -a^{\beta\gamma} b_{\alpha\beta} x_\gamma^r = -a^{\beta\gamma} b_{\alpha\beta} \delta_\gamma^r$

so that we have

15.10 $\nu_\alpha^3 = 0$; $\nu_\beta^\alpha = -a^{\alpha\gamma} b_{\beta\gamma} = -b^{\alpha\gamma} c_{\beta\gamma}$,

using Equation 8.09.

12. Because any surface vector l_r is perpendicular to ν_r, we may write

$$l_r \nu^r = 0 \quad \text{and} \quad l^r \nu_r = 0;$$

expanding these formulas from Equations 15.07 and 15.08, we see at once that both the covariant and contravariant 3-components of any surface vector are zero in this system.

THE CHRISTOFFEL SYMBOLS

13. Because $g_{\alpha\beta} = a_{\alpha\beta}$ and the x^α-coordinates are the same on the surface and in space, it is evident that the Christoffel symbols of the first kind,

$$[\alpha\beta, \gamma],$$

are the same whether they are computed from the space metric or the surface metric. In regard to the Christoffel symbols of the second kind containing no 3-index, we consider the space symbols

$$\Gamma^\gamma_{\alpha\beta} = g^{r\gamma}[\alpha\beta, r] = g^{\gamma\delta}[\alpha\beta, \delta] = a^{\gamma\delta}[\alpha\beta, \delta] = \Gamma^\gamma_{\alpha\beta}$$

taken in relation to the surface metric. In deriving this result, we have used $g^{3\gamma} = 0$ and $g^{\gamma\delta} = a^{\gamma\delta}$. Consequently, all Christoffel symbols containing no 3-index are the same whether they refer to the space or to the surface metric, and we have no need to differentiate between the two. Their actual values, as in the case of the metric tensor from which they are derived, will depend on what coordinates are adopted for the base surface. Once the Christoffel symbols are settled for the base surface, we should be able to find them at other points in space; we shall later derive formulas for this.

14. Symbols containing a 3-index can be obtained by expanding Equations 15.10. We have

$$0 = \partial \nu^3 / \partial x^\alpha + \Gamma^3_{r\alpha}\nu^r = \partial n / \partial x^\alpha + n\Gamma^3_{3\alpha}$$

and

$$-a^{\alpha\gamma}b_{\beta\gamma} = \partial \nu^\alpha / \partial x^\beta + \Gamma^\alpha_{r\beta}\nu^r = n\Gamma^\alpha_{3\beta}.$$

Because the covariant derivatives of all components of the metric tensor are zero, we have

$$g_{\alpha 3\beta} = 0 = \partial g_{\alpha 3} / \partial x^\beta - \Gamma^r_{3\beta}g_{\alpha r} - \Gamma^r_{\alpha\beta}g_{r3}$$

$$= -\Gamma^\gamma_{3\beta}a_{\alpha\gamma} - \Gamma^3_{\alpha\beta}g_{33}$$

$$= (1/n)a^{\gamma\delta}b_{\beta\delta}a_{\alpha\gamma} - \Gamma^3_{\alpha\beta}(1/n^2),$$

using one of the preceding results and $g_{\alpha 3} = 0$, so that we have

$$\Gamma^3_{\alpha\beta} = nb_{\alpha\beta}.$$

In the same way from g_{333}, we obtain Γ^3_{33}; from $g_{\alpha 33}$, we obtain Γ^β_{33}. Collecting results, we can list all the symbols containing one or more 3-indices as

$$\Gamma^\alpha_{33} = (1/n^2)a^{\alpha\beta}(\ln n)_\beta ; \qquad \Gamma^\alpha_{\beta 3} = -(1/n)a^{\alpha\gamma}b_{\beta\gamma}$$

$$\Gamma^3_{\alpha\beta} = nb_{\alpha\beta} ; \qquad \Gamma^3_{3\alpha} = -(\ln n)_\alpha ; \qquad \Gamma^3_{33} = -\partial(\ln n)/\partial N .$$

15.11

15. In the last symbol, if ds is the arc element along the normal, we have

15.12
$$\frac{\partial}{\partial N} = \left(\frac{1}{n}\right)\frac{\partial}{\partial s}$$

because the other two coordinates are constant along the normal. This relation is, of course, true only in this particular coordinate system. To avoid confusion with results in Chapter 14 where $\partial/\partial N$ implied differentiation along the isozenithal and not along the normal, we shall usually express the results of normal differentiation in the form $\partial/\partial s$.

VARIATION OF THE METRIC TENSOR ALONG THE NORMAL

16. In the last section, we have not used the fact that the covariant derivatives of *all* components of the metric tensor are zero. To complete the picture in regard to derivatives containing one or more 3-indices, we need to evaluate $g_{\alpha\beta 3}$ which alone will provide a fresh result, although the others furnish useful checks. We have

$$g_{\alpha\beta 3} = 0 = \partial g_{\alpha\beta}/\partial N - \Gamma^r_{\alpha 3}g_{r\beta} - \Gamma^r_{\beta 3}g_{\alpha r}$$

$$= \partial a_{\alpha\beta}/\partial N - \Gamma^\gamma_{\alpha 3}a_{\beta\gamma} - \Gamma^\gamma_{\beta 3}a_{\alpha\gamma}$$

$$= \partial a_{\alpha\beta}/\partial N + (1/n)a^{\gamma\delta}b_{\alpha\delta}a_{\beta\gamma} + (1/n)a^{\gamma\delta}b_{\beta\delta}a_{\alpha\gamma}$$

$$= \partial a_{\alpha\beta}/\partial N + 2(1/n)b_{\alpha\beta}$$

so that

15.13
$$\partial a_{\alpha\beta}/\partial s = -2b_{\alpha\beta}.$$

Given the second fundamental form of the base surface, we can accordingly extend all components of the surface metric tensor along a normal by a Taylor expansion—at any rate to a first order. We shall show later how to obtain the higher derivatives.

17. By expanding $g^{\alpha\beta}_{\cdot\cdot 3}$ similarly or by differentiating

$$a^{\beta\gamma}a_{\alpha\beta} = \delta^\gamma_\alpha$$

along the normal, we find that

15.14
$$\frac{\partial a^{\alpha\beta}}{\partial s} = 2a^{\alpha\gamma}a^{\beta\delta}b_{\gamma\delta}.$$

Using Equations 8.07 and 8.09, the last equation can be written in the alternative form

15.15
$$\frac{\partial a^{\alpha\beta}}{\partial s} = 4Ha^{\alpha\beta} - 2Kb^{\alpha\beta}.$$

18. By the ordinary rules for differentiating a determinant, we have also

15.16 $\qquad \dfrac{\partial(\ln a)}{\partial s} = a^{\alpha\beta}\dfrac{\partial a_{\alpha\beta}}{\partial s} = -4H.$

19. We can now differentiate the permutation symbols

$$\epsilon_{\alpha\beta} = e_{\alpha\beta}\sqrt{a} \;; \qquad \epsilon^{\alpha\beta} = e^{\alpha\beta}/\sqrt{a}$$

to have

$$\dfrac{\partial\epsilon_{\alpha\beta}}{\partial s} = -2H\epsilon_{\alpha\beta}$$

15.17 $\qquad \dfrac{\partial\epsilon^{\alpha\beta}}{\partial s} = +2H\epsilon^{\alpha\beta},$

which should be compared with the results in Equations 14.09 and 14.10 for differentiation along the isozenithals.

SPACE DERIVATIVES OF THE NORMAL

20. In the (ω, ϕ, N) system, we found that the covariant derivatives of the meridian, parallel, and normal vectors were most useful. In this system, we have not yet defined any surface vectors in relation to the surrounding space, but we can now find the covariant derivatives of the normal by substitution of the preceding results in the defining formula

$$\nu_{rs} = \partial\nu_r/\partial x^s - (1/n)\Gamma^3_{rs}.$$

We find that

15.18 $\qquad \nu_{\alpha\beta} = -b_{\alpha\beta},$

as it should, because this result in Equation 6.19 depended only on making the surface coordinates x^α two of the space coordinates.
Also, we have

$$\nu_{\alpha 3} = -(1/n)_\alpha$$
$$\nu_{3\alpha} = 0$$

15.19 $\qquad \nu_{33} = 0.$

By substitution in Equation 11.26, we have in these coordinates

15.20 $\qquad \nu^3_{\alpha\beta} = -nc_{\alpha\beta}$

15.21 $\qquad \nu^\gamma_{\alpha\beta} = -a^{\gamma\delta}b_{\alpha\beta\delta}.$

THE MAINARDI-CODAZZI EQUATIONS

21. In the (ω, ϕ, N) system, we obtained all the Mainardi-Codazzi equations by considering the first covariant derivatives of three vectors in flat space. In this system, we have defined only one vector field, the normal; its first derivatives given in the last section do not include any condition that the space must be flat. We can, however, apply the alternative condition that the *second* covariant derivatives of an arbitrary vector must be symmetrical in the last two indices in flat space, as in Equation 5.01. In this case, we have

15.22 $\qquad \nu_{rst} = \nu_{rts}.$

At this stage, we use this formula as a necessary condition without asserting that it is sufficient to use only one vector field.

22. We consider first the components containing no 3-index,

$$\nu_{\alpha\beta\gamma} = \partial\nu_{\alpha\beta}/\partial x^\gamma - \Gamma^r_{\alpha\gamma}\nu_{r\beta} - \Gamma^r_{\beta\gamma}\nu_{\alpha r}$$
$$= -\partial b_{\alpha\beta}/\partial x^\gamma + \Gamma^\delta_{\alpha\gamma}b_{\delta\beta} + \Gamma^\delta_{\beta\gamma}b_{\alpha\delta} + \Gamma^3_{\beta\gamma}(1/n)_\alpha$$
$$= -b_{\alpha\beta\gamma} - b_{\beta\gamma}(\ln n)_\alpha.$$

15.23

We interchange (β, γ) and subtract in order to satisfy Equation 15.22 so that

15.24 $\qquad b_{\alpha\beta\gamma} = b_{\alpha\gamma\beta},$

which are the most general forms of the Codazzi equations for the N-surfaces in Equation 6.21.

23. Next, we evaluate

$$\nu_{\alpha\beta3} = \partial\nu_{\alpha\beta}/\partial N - \Gamma^r_{\alpha3}\nu_{r\beta} - \Gamma^r_{\beta3}\nu_{\alpha r}$$
$$= -\partial b_{\alpha\beta}/\partial N + \Gamma^\gamma_{\alpha3}b_{\gamma\beta} + \Gamma^\gamma_{\beta3}b_{\alpha\gamma} + \Gamma^3_{3\beta}(1/n)_\alpha$$
$$= -\partial b_{\alpha\beta}/\partial N - (1/n)a^{\gamma\delta}b_{\alpha\delta}b_{\gamma\beta} - (1/n)a^{\gamma\delta}b_{\beta\delta}b_{\alpha\gamma}$$
$$\quad - (\ln n)_\beta(1/n)_\alpha$$
$$= -\partial b_{\alpha\beta}/\partial N - 2c_{\alpha\beta}/n - (\ln n)_\beta(1/n)_\alpha$$

and also

$$\nu_{\alpha3\beta} = -\partial^2(1/n)/\partial x^\alpha\partial x^\beta - \Gamma^r_{\alpha\beta}\nu_{r3} - \Gamma^r_{3\beta}\nu_{\alpha r}$$
$$= -\partial^2(1/n)\,\partial x^\alpha\partial x^\beta + \Gamma^\gamma_{\alpha\beta}(1/n)_\gamma + \Gamma^3_{3\beta}(1/n)_\alpha$$
$$\quad + \Gamma^\gamma_{3\beta}b_{\alpha\gamma}$$
$$= -\overline{(1/n)}_{\alpha\beta} - c_{\alpha\beta}/n - (\ln n)_\beta(1/n)_\alpha$$

in which the overbar implies that the covariant derivative has been taken with respect to the surface metric. Applying Equation 15.22, we have finally

15.25 $\qquad \dfrac{\partial b_{\alpha\beta}}{\partial s} = n\overline{\left(\dfrac{1}{n}\right)}_{\alpha\beta} - c_{\alpha\beta},$

which should be compared with the corresponding Codazzi equations for the (ω, ϕ, N) system in

Equation 12.144. This gives us, in general, three independent equations, making a total of five with the Codazzi equations for the N-surfaces in Equation 15.24. As shown in the (ω, ϕ, N) system, five is all we can expect in the case of a family of coordinate surfaces derived from a given scalar N. Indeed, we can derive no fresh relations from Equation 15.22 for any other values of (r, s, t). We conclude therefore that the relation in Equation 15.22 is sufficient to ensure that the space is flat. We could directly ensure that the space is flat by equating to zero all the Riemann-Christoffel symbols of Equation 5.03 for the metric

$$ds^2 = a_{\alpha\beta}dx^\alpha dx^\beta + (1/n^2)dN^2;$$

or, what amounts to the same thing in three dimensions, we could equate to zero the six independent components of the contracted Ricci tensor of Equation 5.12. This gives us six equations, but we find that only five are independent in this metric and that they are the same as the five equations obtained far more simply above.

NORMAL DIFFERENTIATION

The Fundamental Forms

24. We have already shown how to differentiate $a_{\alpha\beta}$ and $b_{\alpha\beta}$ along the normals and incidentally how to obtain the second derivative of $a_{\alpha\beta}$. To carry the expansion further, we need to find an expression for $\partial c_{\alpha\beta}/\partial s$ in terms of the fundamental forms of the base surface and of n. If we differentiate the ordinary formula

$$c_{\alpha\beta} = a^{\gamma\delta}b_{\alpha\gamma}b_{\beta\delta}$$

and use Equations 15.14 and 15.25, we have

$$\partial c_{\alpha\beta}/\partial s = 2a^{\gamma\rho}a^{\delta\sigma}b_{\rho\sigma}b_{\alpha\gamma}b_{\beta\delta} - a^{\gamma\delta}c_{\alpha\gamma}b_{\beta\delta} - a^{\gamma\delta}b_{\alpha\gamma}c_{\beta\delta}$$
$$+ na^{\gamma\delta}b_{\beta\delta}\overline{(1/n)}_{\alpha\gamma} + na^{\gamma\delta}b_{\alpha\gamma}\overline{(1/n)}_{\beta\delta}.$$

If we make use of $a^{\gamma\delta}b_{\alpha\delta} = b^{\gamma\delta}c_{\alpha\delta}$ from Equation 8.09 and interchange some summation indices, we find that the first three terms on the right cancel and we have finally

15.26 $\qquad \dfrac{\partial c_{\alpha\beta}}{\partial s} = na^{\gamma\delta}b_{\alpha\gamma}\overline{\left(\dfrac{1}{n}\right)}_{\beta\delta} + na^{\gamma\delta}b_{\beta\gamma}\overline{\left(\dfrac{1}{n}\right)}_{\alpha\delta}.$

25. By differentiating

$$b^{\alpha\gamma}b_{\alpha\beta} = \delta^\gamma_\beta,$$

we have

$$\frac{\partial b^{\alpha\beta}}{\partial s} = -b^{\alpha\gamma}b^{\beta\delta}\frac{\partial b_{\gamma\delta}}{\partial s}$$

15.27 $\qquad = -nb^{\alpha\gamma}b^{\beta\delta}\overline{\left(\dfrac{1}{n}\right)}_{\gamma\delta} + a^{\alpha\beta};$

similarly, we have

15.28 $\qquad \dfrac{\partial c^{\alpha\beta}}{\partial s} = -nb^{\alpha\gamma}c^{\beta\delta}\overline{\left(\dfrac{1}{n}\right)}_{\gamma\delta} - nb^{\beta\gamma}c^{\alpha\delta}\overline{\left(\dfrac{1}{n}\right)}_{\gamma\delta},$

which completes the differentiation of all the fundamental forms.

26. The differentials of the surface invariants are now easily found. Using Equation 6.27, we have

$$\frac{\partial(\ln K)}{\partial s} = \frac{\partial(\ln b)}{\partial s} - \frac{\partial(\ln a)}{\partial s}$$

$$= b^{\alpha\beta}\frac{\partial b^{\alpha\beta}}{\partial s} + 4H$$

15.29 $\qquad = nb^{\alpha\beta}\overline{\left(\dfrac{1}{n}\right)}_{\alpha\beta} + 2H.$

Also, we have

$$\frac{\partial(2H)}{\partial s} = \frac{\partial(a^{\alpha\beta}b_{\alpha\beta})}{\partial s}$$

$$= b_{\alpha\beta}\frac{\partial a^{\alpha\beta}}{\partial s} + a^{\alpha\beta}\frac{\partial b_{\alpha\beta}}{\partial s}$$

$$= 2a^{\alpha\beta}c_{\alpha\beta} + n\overline{\Delta(1/n)} - a^{\alpha\beta}c_{\alpha\beta}$$

15.30 $\qquad = n\overline{\Delta(1/n)} + (4H^2 - 2K)$

in which the overbar implies that the Laplacian of $(1/n)$ is taken with respect to the surface metric. In addition, we have

$$\frac{\partial(2H/K)}{\partial s} = \frac{\partial(b^{\alpha\beta}a_{\alpha\beta})}{\partial s}$$

15.31 $\qquad = -nc^{\alpha\beta}\overline{\left(\dfrac{1}{n}\right)}_{\alpha\beta} - 2.$

27. These last three invariant equations are, of course, true in any surface coordinates, and can be evaluated, if we wish, by substituting (ω, ϕ) values of $a^{\alpha\beta}$, $b^{\alpha\beta}$, $c^{\alpha\beta}$, and $\overline{(1/n)}_{\alpha\beta}$. In fact, we have already obtained them from (ω, ϕ, N) coordinates as Equations 14.28, 14.29, and 14.30.

The Christoffel Symbols

28. Using Equation 15.13 for the normal derivative of the surface metric tensor, we can differentiate the equation which defines the surface

Christoffel symbols, that is,

$$a_{\alpha\delta}\Gamma^{\alpha}_{\beta\gamma}=[\beta\gamma,\delta]$$

$$=\tfrac{1}{2}\left(\frac{\partial a_{\beta\delta}}{\partial x^{\gamma}}+\frac{\partial a_{\gamma\delta}}{\partial x^{\beta}}-\frac{\partial a_{\beta\gamma}}{\partial x^{\delta}}\right).$$

Alternatively, as we did in the (ω,ϕ,N) system, we can equate the

$$R^{\alpha}_{\beta3\gamma}$$

components of the Riemann-Christoffel tensor of the flat space to zero and can use expressions appropriate to this (normal) system of coordinates for the Christoffel symbols. In either case, we obtain after some manipulation

$$\frac{\partial\Gamma^{\alpha}_{\beta\gamma}}{\partial s}=-a^{\alpha\delta}b_{\beta\gamma\delta}+a^{\alpha\delta}b_{\beta\delta}(\ln n)_{\gamma}$$

15.32 $+a^{\alpha\delta}b_{\gamma\delta}(\ln n)_{\beta}-a^{\alpha\delta}b_{\beta\gamma}(\ln n)_{\delta}.$

The more compact expression obtained in Equation 14.14 for (ω,ϕ,N) coordinates does not, however, hold in normal coordinates.

The $b_{\alpha\beta\gamma}$

29. Nor can we obtain

$$\partial(b_{\alpha\beta\gamma})/\partial s$$

in these coordinates by the shortcut used in (ω,ϕ,N) because points along the normals, as distinct from the isozenithals, do not have the same spherical representation. We can, however, differentiate the defining equation

$$b_{\alpha\beta\gamma}=\frac{\partial(b_{\alpha\beta})}{\partial x^{\gamma}}-\Gamma^{\delta}_{\alpha\gamma}b_{\delta\beta}-\Gamma^{\delta}_{\beta\gamma}b_{\delta\alpha};$$

after some manipulation and use of the identity

$$c_{\alpha\beta\gamma}=a^{\delta\epsilon}b_{\alpha\delta\gamma}b_{\beta\epsilon}+a^{\delta\epsilon}b_{\alpha\delta}b_{\beta\epsilon\gamma},$$

obtained by covariant differentiation of Equations 6.18, we find that

$$\partial(b_{\alpha\beta\gamma})/\partial s=n\,\overline{(1/n)}_{\alpha\beta\gamma}-c_{\alpha\beta}(\ln n)_{\gamma}$$

$$-c_{\beta\gamma}(\ln n)_{\alpha}-c_{\gamma\alpha}(\ln n)_{\beta}$$

15.33 $+a^{\delta\epsilon}(\ln n)_{\epsilon}(b_{\alpha\gamma}b_{\delta\beta}+b_{\beta\gamma}b_{\delta\alpha})$

in which the overbar denotes covariant differentiation with respect to the surface metric.

30. If we interchange β and γ and subtract the result from Equation 15.33, the left-hand side becomes zero by virtue of the Codazzi equations, and we have

$$n\,\overline{(1/n)}_{\alpha\beta\gamma}-n\,\overline{(1/n)}_{\alpha\gamma\beta}=a^{\delta\epsilon}(\ln n)_{\epsilon}(b_{\alpha\beta}b_{\gamma\delta}-b_{\alpha\gamma}b_{\beta\delta}).$$

At first sight, this shows a relation between n and surface tensors which is required in order to ensure that the Codazzi equations are satisfied on all the N-surfaces. However, we can see from Equations 5.22 and 6.26 that it is an identity true not only for n, but also for any scalar.

31. From Equation 15.33, we can derive

$$a^{\alpha\beta}\frac{\partial b_{\alpha\beta\gamma}}{\partial s}=n\,\frac{\partial\{\overline{\Delta(1/n)}\}}{\partial x^{\gamma}}-(4H^{2}-2K)(\ln n)_{\gamma}$$

$$b^{\alpha\beta}\frac{\partial b_{\alpha\beta\gamma}}{\partial s}=nb^{\alpha\beta}\overline{\left(\frac{1}{n}\right)}_{\alpha\beta\gamma}-2H(\ln n)_{\gamma}$$

$$c^{\alpha\beta}\frac{\partial b_{\alpha\beta\gamma}}{\partial s}=nc^{\alpha\beta}\overline{\left(\frac{1}{n}\right)}_{\alpha\beta\gamma}-2(\ln n)_{\gamma},$$

15.34

which can be verified by differentiating Equations 8.20 and by using formulas already given in this chapter.

Other Point Functions

32. There are no equations for the differentials of the point functions

$$x^{r}_{\alpha};\qquad \nu^{r}_{\alpha};\qquad \nu^{r}_{\alpha\beta}$$

in these coordinates corresponding to Equations 11.08, 14.50, 14.51, and 14.52 because the ν^{r} are not constant along the normals, even in Cartesian space coordinates. If required, differentials of these quantities should be obtained in normal space coordinates by differentiating Equations 15.06, 15.10, 15.20, and 15.21, using formulas which have now been given.

The differentials of any other functions which are defined in space, such as

$$\gamma_{1}=\nu_{rs}\lambda^{r}\nu^{s},$$

can be obtained by covariant differentiation along the normal and by evaluation either in these coordinates or in (ω,ϕ,N) because the result will be an invariant true in any coordinates.

Differentiation of Vectors Defined in Space

33. We take as usual a pair of unit orthogonal surface vectors l^{r}, j^{r} (l^{r}, j^{r}, ν^{r} right-handed) which are defined in space as vector functions of position. They could, for example, be the meridian and parallel directions defined in the usual way from the normal to the N-surface and from the Cartesian vectors; but in this case, the latitude and longitude

would be functions of position and not coordinates, except possibly on the base surface. The two vectors could also be the unit tangents to the lines of curvature of the N-surfaces, which similarly are uniquely defined at a point and, in consequence, constitute a vector field in space.

34. If α, k, t are the azimuth, normal curvature, and geodesic torsion in the direction l^r and if k^* is the normal curvature in the direction j^r, then all these quantities are point functions; Equations 14.25 through 14.27 hold equally well for changes in these functions along the normals, even though they were obtained in (ω, ϕ, N) coordinates. The only tensor functions in these equations are surface invariants which have the same value in any surface coordinates. We assume, of course, that the N-surfaces and the Cartesian vectors are the same in both cases, as we can do without any loss of generality.

35. In the same way, the formulas of Equations 14.36 apply as they stand in this system and give the normal variation of the curvature parameters k_1, k_2, t_1 of the meridians and parallels; Equations 14.44 through 14.46 give the normal variation of the principal curvatures and the azimuth of the principal directions.

36. We can obtain these results by a different route and, at the same time, can obtain some other formulas which we shall require later. We assume that the N-surfaces are the same in both the (ω, ϕ, N) system and in this normal system of coordinates, and that the Cartesian vectors of the two systems are the same. In that case, the meridian and parallel vectors μ^r, λ^r at any point in space are the same, although they will not, of course, have the same components. The vector equation

$$\mu_{rs}\nu^s = -\gamma_1 \tan \phi\, \lambda_r - \gamma_2 \nu_r,$$

obtainable from Equations 12.015 and 12.034 in (ω, ϕ, N) coordinates, is true in any coordinates. If we expand it in normal coordinates, we find that the equation for $r = 3$ is an identity; we are left then with

$$\frac{\partial \mu_\alpha}{\partial s} = -\gamma_1 \tan \phi\, \lambda_\alpha + n\Gamma^\gamma_{\alpha 3}\mu_\gamma$$

$$= -\gamma_1 \tan \phi\, \lambda_\alpha - b_{\alpha\beta}\mu^\beta$$

$$= -(\gamma_1 \tan \phi + t_1)\lambda_\alpha - k_2\mu_\alpha,$$

which gives us the ordinary differential of the meridian vector along the normal. The meridian vector remains the meridian vector and is not projected down the normals to the next N-surface.

In the same way and collecting the last equation, we have

$$\partial \mu^\alpha/\partial s = -(\gamma_1 \tan \phi - t_1)\lambda^\alpha + k_2\mu^\alpha$$

$$\partial \mu_\alpha/\partial s = -(\gamma_1 \tan \phi + t_1)\lambda_\alpha - k_2\mu_\alpha$$

$$\partial \lambda^\alpha/\partial s = (\gamma_1 \tan \phi + t_1)\mu^\alpha + k_1\lambda^\alpha$$

15.35 $\quad \partial \lambda_\alpha/\partial s = (\gamma_1 \tan \phi - t_1)\mu_\alpha - k_1\lambda_\alpha.$

We can now differentiate the equation

$$k_1 = b_{\alpha\beta}\lambda^\alpha\lambda^\beta,$$

using Equation 15.25 and the preceding formulas, and can obtain the second equation of Equations 14.36. The other two equations of Equations 14.36 follow similarly.

37. In general, if l_r (in azimuth α) and j_r (in azimuth $\alpha - \frac{1}{2}\pi$) are any pair of orthogonal unit surface vectors, we have

$$l_r = \lambda_r \sin \alpha + \mu_r \cos \alpha$$

$$j_r = -\lambda_r \cos \alpha + \mu_r \sin \alpha,$$

which are defined in space and have to preserve their identity under normal differentiation; or, if l_r is such a vector and if j_r is defined perpendicular to it, then we may write

$$l_{rs}\nu^s = \lambda_{rs}\nu^s \sin \alpha + \mu_{rs}\nu^s \cos \alpha - j_r(\partial\alpha/\partial s)$$

$$= j_r(\gamma_1 \tan \phi - \partial\alpha/\partial s) - \nu_r(\gamma_1 \sin \alpha + \gamma_2 \cos \alpha),$$

using Equations 12.014 and 12.015. Proceeding as for Equations 15.35, we find that

$$\partial l_\alpha/\partial s = -kl_\alpha + j_\alpha(\gamma_1 \tan \phi - t - \partial\alpha/\partial s)$$

15.36 $\quad \partial l^\alpha/\partial s = kl^\alpha + j^\alpha(\gamma_1 \tan \phi + t - \partial\alpha/\partial s)$

in which k, t are the normal curvature and geodesic torsion in the l^α-direction. These two equations cover all four equations of Equations 15.35 as the special case $\partial\alpha/\partial s = 0$.

38. For the principal directions $(t = 0)$, u^α (in azimuth A, principal curvature κ_1), and v^α (in azimuth $A - \frac{1}{2}\pi$, principal curvature κ_2), we have at once

$$\partial u_\alpha/\partial s = -\kappa_1 u_\alpha + v_\alpha(\gamma_1 \tan \phi - \partial A/\partial s)$$
$$\partial u^\alpha/\partial s = +\kappa_1 u^\alpha + v^\alpha(\gamma_1 \tan \phi - \partial A/\partial s)$$
$$\partial v_\alpha/\partial s = -\kappa_2 v_\alpha - u_\alpha(\gamma_1 \tan \phi - \partial A/\partial s)$$

15.37 $\quad \partial v^\alpha/\partial s = +\kappa_2 v^\alpha - u^\alpha(\gamma_1 \tan \phi - \partial A/\partial s).$

From these equations, we can derive Equations 14.44 through 14.46 by normal differentiation of

$$\kappa_1 = b_{\alpha\beta}u^\alpha u^\beta$$

$$\kappa_2 = b_{\alpha\beta}v^\alpha v^\beta$$

$$0 = b_{\alpha\beta}u^\alpha v^\beta.$$

NORMAL PROJECTION OF SURFACE VECTORS

39. We have now to consider, just as we did in isozenithal projection, the effect of projecting a surface vector from one N-surface to another down the normals. In this case, we shall not be able to derive any assistance from the spherical representation, unless the normals happen to be straight, because projected figures will not have the same spherical representation. Some of the formulas are, nevertheless, simpler. We shall not be able to obtain closed integral formulas any more than we could in isozenithal projection, and we shall again derive the first-order changes only. Changes of a higher order can be obtained when required by successive differentiation and substitution in a Taylor series.

Length

40. A first-order element of length δl on an N-surface is given by

$$(\delta l)^2 = a_{\alpha\beta} \delta x^\alpha \delta x^\beta$$

in which δx^α are changes in the surface coordinates over the element. Because the surface coordinates remain constant along the normals in this system, we may differentiate and use Equation 15.13 to obtain

$$\frac{\partial(\ln \delta l)}{\partial s} = -b_{\alpha\beta}\left(\frac{\delta x^\alpha}{\delta l}\right)\left(\frac{\delta x^\beta}{\delta l}\right)$$

15.38
$$= -k$$

in the limit when δl becomes infinitesimal. Of course, k is the normal curvature of the N-surface in the direction of the length element.

41. An element of area on an N-surface is given by

$$\delta S = \sqrt{a}\, \delta x^\alpha \delta x^\beta,$$

which can be differentiated with the help of Equation 15.16 to give

15.39
$$\frac{\partial(\ln \delta S)}{\partial s} = -2H.$$

Components

42. The change in surface coordinates over a small length δl of a unit surface vector l^α is given by

$$\delta x^\alpha = l^\alpha \delta l;$$

differentiating this with the aid of Equation 15.38,

we have

$$0 = \delta l(\partial l^\alpha/\partial s - kl^\alpha).$$

Because δl is not zero, we have

15.40
$$\frac{\partial l^\alpha}{\partial s} = kl^\alpha.$$

43. In regard to the covariant components, the simplest course in these coordinates is to differentiate

$$l_\alpha = a_{\alpha\beta} l^\beta$$

and to obtain

$$\frac{\partial l_\alpha}{\partial s} = -2b_{\alpha\beta}l^\beta + ka_{\alpha\beta}l^\beta$$
$$= -2(kl_\alpha + tj_\alpha) + kl_\alpha$$
15.41
$$= -kl_\alpha - 2tj_\alpha$$

in which t is the geodesic torsion of the surface in the direction l_α, and j_α is as usual a unit surface vector perpendicular to l_α. It should be noted that j_α will not, in general, project as a perpendicular vector. We cannot therefore differentiate Equation 15.41 again and use a formula corresponding to Equation 15.41 for the differential of j_α because to do so would require j_α to be defined as perpendicular to l_α, not only on one surface, but on projection to the next surface. As in the case of isozenithal projection, we need to recast Equation 15.41 in the form

15.42
$$\frac{\partial l_\alpha}{\partial s} = -kl_\alpha + 2t\epsilon_{\alpha\beta}l^\beta$$

before differentiating again. In this way, we retain j_α as an auxiliary perpendicular vector, but do not project it.

Azimuth

44. To obtain the change in azimuth α of the vector l^β on projection, we can differentiate

$$\cos \alpha = l^\beta \mu_\beta$$

in which μ_β is the meridian direction. We must not, however, project the meridian direction by using Equation 15.41, but must ensure that it remains the meridian direction by using Equations 15.35. With that proviso, we have

$$-\sin \alpha(\partial \alpha/\partial s) = k \cos \alpha - (\gamma_1 \tan \phi + t_1) \sin \alpha$$
$$- k_2 \cos \alpha,$$

which, with the help of the second equation of Equations 12.060, reduces to

15.43
$$\partial\alpha/\partial s = t + \gamma_1 \tan \phi$$

where as usual t is the geodesic torsion in the direction l_α.

This result may be obtained in a variety of other ways, for example, by differentiating

$$\sin \alpha = a_{\beta\gamma} l^\beta \lambda^\gamma.$$

45. If we project a principal direction ($t=0$ in Equation 15.43), the projected direction is not necessarily a principal direction of the new N surface. If it is, then we may write

$$\partial A/\partial s = \gamma_1 \tan \phi$$

in which A is the azimuth of a principal direction defined in space, that is, the azimuth of a principal direction not on one particular N-surface only, but on the neighboring N-surfaces as well. In that case, we see from Equation 14.44 that

$$\overline{\left(\frac{1}{n}\right)}_{\alpha\beta} u^\alpha v^\beta = 0,$$

which is a restriction on the form of the N-surfaces in order that their principal directions may project into principal directions. We shall see in the next chapter that this result has an important place in the theory of triply orthogonal coordinate systems.

Curvatures

46. Differentiation of

$$k = b_{\alpha\beta} l^\alpha l^\beta$$

leads directly to

$$\partial k/\partial s = n\overline{(1/n)}_{\alpha\beta} l^\alpha l^\beta - c_{\alpha\beta} l^\alpha l^\beta + 2k b_{\alpha\beta} l^\alpha l^\beta$$
15.44 $\quad = n\overline{(1/n)}_{\alpha\beta} l^\alpha l^\beta + (k^2 - t^2),$

using Equations 15.25, 15.40, and 7.14.

47. In order to differentiate

$$t = b_{\alpha\beta} j^\alpha l^\beta,$$

we must differentiate j^α, not as a direction which is to be projected, but as an auxiliary vector perpendicular to l^β as

$$\frac{\partial j^\alpha}{\partial s} = -\frac{\partial(\epsilon^{\alpha\beta} l_\beta)}{\partial s}$$

$$= 2Hj^\alpha + \epsilon^{\alpha\beta}(kl_\beta + 2tj_\beta)$$
15.45 $\quad = k^* j^\alpha + 2t l^\alpha,$

using Equations 15.17 and 15.41 and denoting the normal curvature in the direction of j^α by k^*. It can be seen that if we had projected j^α and used Equation 15.40, we should have the first term only, and

the result would be in error unless l^α is a principal direction ($t=0$). Using Equation 7.14, we now have

$$\partial t/\partial s = n\overline{(1/n)}_{\alpha\beta} j^\alpha l^\beta - 2Ht + k^* t + 2kt + kt$$
15.46 $\quad = n\overline{(1/n)}_{\alpha\beta} j^\alpha l^\beta + 2kt.$

Covariant Derivatives

48. As in the corresponding case of isozenithal projection, we now consider, but without any loss of generality, that l_α is the unit tangent to a *family* of curves defined in some way over a region of a particular N-surface. This enables us to consider the azimuth α as a differentiable function of position. We write the covariant derivative in the form used in isozenithal projection (see § 14–38) as

15.47 $\quad l_{\alpha\beta} = -\epsilon_{\alpha\gamma} l^\gamma (\omega_\beta \sin \phi - \alpha_\beta).$

Although this equation was obtained in (ω, ϕ, N) coordinates, it is, nevertheless, a surface tensor equation true in any coordinates, provided we treat ω, ϕ as scalar functions of position and not as coordinates. Because we are now dealing with the same N-surfaces and with the same Cartesian axes, it is evident that ω, ϕ, as originally defined in the (ω, ϕ, N) system, will have the same values; we can use Equations 12.032 and 12.031 and write

$$\partial\omega/\partial s = \gamma_1 \sec \phi \; ; \qquad \partial\phi/\partial s = \gamma_2.$$

49. We first differentiate the term within parentheses in Equation 15.47 and note that second derivatives, with respect to x^β and N, commute. Also in these coordinates, we have

$$\frac{\partial}{\partial s} = n\frac{\partial}{\partial N}$$

so that we have, for example,

$$\frac{\partial\omega_\beta}{\partial s} = n\frac{\partial}{\partial x^\beta}\left(\frac{1}{n}\frac{\partial\omega}{\partial s}\right) = n\frac{\partial}{\partial x^\beta}\left(\frac{\gamma_1 \sec \phi}{n}\right).$$

Using Equation 15.43, we then have

$$\frac{\partial(\omega_\beta \sin \phi - \alpha_\beta)}{\partial s} = n\sin\phi\frac{\partial}{\partial x^\beta}\left(\frac{\gamma_1 \sec \phi}{n}\right)$$

$$- n\frac{\partial}{\partial x^\beta}\left(\frac{t + \gamma_1 \tan \phi}{n}\right)$$

$$+ \gamma_2 \cos \phi \; \omega_\beta$$

$$= -\gamma_1\phi_\beta + \gamma_2 \cos \phi \; \omega_\beta$$
15.48 $\quad + t(\ln n)_\beta - t_\beta$

on expansion. Using Equations 12.061, 12.062, and

8.02, we can rewrite the first two terms as

$$-\gamma_1\phi_\beta + (\gamma_2\cos\phi)\omega_\beta = l_\beta(\ln n)_\gamma(tl^\gamma - kj^\gamma)$$
$$+ j_\beta(\ln n)_\gamma(k^*l^\gamma - tj^\gamma)$$
$$= Kb^{\gamma\delta}(\ln n)_\gamma\{l_\delta j_\beta - j_\delta l_\beta\}$$
$$= Kb^{\gamma\delta}(\ln n)_\gamma\epsilon_{\delta\beta}$$

15.49
$$= Q_\beta,$$

for instance, which shows that these two terms are a point function and that the only way a particular direction enters Equation 15.48 is through the geodesic torsion. Using Equation 8.01, we can also express the last relation as

15.50 $\quad Q_\beta = \epsilon^{\gamma\rho}\epsilon^{\delta\sigma}b_{\rho\sigma}(\ln n)_\gamma\epsilon_{\delta\beta} = \epsilon^{\gamma\alpha}(\ln n)_\gamma b_{\alpha\beta}.$

50. We can now differentiate Equation 15.47 without difficulty and find that

$$\frac{\partial l_{\alpha\beta}}{\partial s} = -2Hl_{\alpha\beta} + kl_{\alpha\beta} + j_\alpha\{Q_\beta + t(\ln n)_\beta - t_\beta\}$$

15.51 $\quad = -k^*l_{\alpha\beta} + j_\alpha\{Q_\beta + t(\ln n)_\beta - t_\beta\}.$

In addition to the expressions given previously for Q_β, we also find after some manipulation that

15.52 $\quad j_\alpha Q_\beta = b_{\alpha\beta}(\ln n)_\gamma l^\gamma - b_{\beta\delta}(\ln n)_\alpha l^\delta.$

It is instructive to obtain the same result, rather more laboriously, by direct differentiation of the defining equation

$$l_{\alpha\beta} = \partial l_\alpha/\partial x^\beta - \Gamma^\gamma_{\alpha\beta}l_\gamma,$$

using formulas which have already been given.

51. If l_α is the surface gradient of a scalar F defined in space, then, as in §14–40, we find

$$\frac{\partial F_{\alpha\beta}}{\partial s} = n\left(\frac{1}{n}\frac{\partial F}{\partial s}\right)_{\alpha\beta} + F^\gamma\{b_{\alpha\beta\gamma} - b_{\alpha\gamma}(\ln n)_\beta$$

15.53 $\qquad - b_{\beta\gamma}(\ln n)_\alpha + b_{\alpha\beta}(\ln n)_\gamma\}$

where $F^\gamma = a^{\gamma\delta}F_\delta$ and covariant derivatives are taken with respect to the surface metric.

Geodesic Curvature

52. To find the change in the geodesic curvature σ of l_α on projection, we differentiate the Equation 12.065,

$$\sigma = (\omega_\beta\sin\phi - \alpha_\beta)l^\beta,$$

which again is true in any surface coordinates for the same N-surfaces. Using Equation 15.48 and the first line of Equation 15.49, we find

$$\partial\sigma/\partial s = k\sigma + (\ln n)_\gamma(tl^\gamma - kj^\gamma) + t(\ln n)_\beta l^\beta - t_\beta l^\beta$$
$$= k\sigma + 2t(\ln n)_\beta l^\beta - k(\ln n)_\beta j^\beta - t_\beta l^\beta.$$

15.54

CHAPTER 16

Triply Orthogonal Systems

GENERAL

1. It is evident that the geometry of a normal coordinate system is simpler than the geometry of the general (ω, ϕ, N) system. As we shall see, the latter system has the advantage that all three coordinates are directly measurable quantities in many geodetic applications, whereas two of them in the normal system must be inferred from their values on a particular N-surface. Nevertheless, the normal system is of considerable theoretical value because it enables us to derive certain general results more simply than in other systems. We shall now inquire whether it is possible to achieve still greater simplification by adopting orthogonal surface coordinates in a normal system, in which case all three coordinate lines would be mutually perpendicular and, in addition, would have the same direction as the gradients of the scalar coordinates.

THE DARBOUX EQUATION

2. A small displacement on a surface can be written as δx^α where x^α are the surface coordinates because this displacement amounts to a small change in the coordinates x^α over the line considered. If it is a displacement along a coordinate line, then α is either 1 or 2, but we prefer to keep the notation general and still write it as δx^α. The displacement δx^α can be considered a small contravariant surface vector.

Now consider *two* small displacements δx^α, $\delta \bar{x}^\beta$ along the surface coordinate lines and choose orthogonal surface coordinates on the base surface so that, *on the base surface*, we have

16.01 $\qquad a_{\alpha\beta}\delta x^\alpha \delta \bar{x}^\beta = 0.$

If the coordinate lines are to remain orthogonal on the next N-surface, infinitesimally close to the base surface, then there must be no change in this relation as we proceed from one surface to the other. In other words, the differential of Equation 16.01 along the normal arc element ds must be zero. During this change, the δx^α, $\delta \bar{x}^\beta$ remain the same because, by definition, the surface coordinates are constant along the normals in a normal coordinate system. Accordingly, we may write

$$(\partial a_{\alpha\beta}/\partial s)\delta x^\alpha \delta \bar{x}^\beta = 0;$$

from Equation 15.13, this is equivalent to

16.02 $\qquad b_{\alpha\beta}\delta x^\alpha \delta \bar{x}^\beta = 0.$

In this equation, we can replace δx^α, $\delta \bar{x}^\beta$ by the unit vectors u^α, v^β in the coordinate directions simply by dividing by the lengths or magnitudes of the two displacements so that

$$b_{\alpha\beta}u^\alpha v^\beta = 0,$$

which shows that the geodesic torsion in the coordinate directions must be zero and therefore the coordinate lines *on the base surface* must be the lines of curvature. This is a well known, necessary condition, originally due to Dupin, for triply orthogonal systems. It is not, however, sufficient to ensure orthogonality throughout a finite region of space. For this to be possible, the coordinate lines must remain lines of curvature on the surface next to the base surface. The situation on this next surface will then be the same as on the base surface; we can repeat the process to build up the entire field. In other words, the differential of Equation 16.02 along

306–962 O–69—9

the normals must be zero; using Equation 15.25, we must have

$$n\overline{(1/n)}_{\alpha\beta}\delta x^\alpha\delta\bar{x}^\beta - c_{\alpha\beta}\delta x^\alpha\delta\bar{x}^\beta = 0.$$

But because the displacements δx^α, $\delta\bar{x}^\beta$ are in the principal directions, the second term is zero by Equation 7.25 so that we have finally

16.03 $\overline{(1/n)}_{\alpha\beta}u^\alpha v^\beta = 0.$

We can choose any one of the N-surfaces as the base surface so that this condition must apply to all of them. Moreover, it is evident from Equation 8.26 that the condition is equivalent to

16.04 $(1/n)_{rs}u^r v^s = 0$

in space, simply because $(1/n)$ is a scalar. The form of the scalar N settles not only n at any point in space, but also the principal directions of the N-surfaces. Accordingly, the condition of Equation 16.04 restricts the form of N, which must arise from a solution of Equation 16.04 in order to be one coordinate of a triply orthogonal system.

3. The Equation 16.03 or 16.04 is equivalent to what is usually known as the Darboux equation in classical differential geometry; it is given by such writers as Bianchi and Forsyth in several more complicated forms. Forsyth [1] gives a Cartesian version of the Darboux equation, which is equivalent to the invariant form of Equation 16.04, although he does not derive it in the same way.

4. Referring to Equation 14.44, we find that Equation 16.03 is equivalent to

$$(\kappa_1 - \kappa_2)(\gamma_1\tan\phi - \partial A/\partial s) = 0.$$

Unless $\kappa_1 = \kappa_2$, in which case the N-surfaces are spheres whose lines of curvature are indefinite, the Darboux equation can accordingly be expressed as

16.05 $\partial A/\partial s = \gamma_1\tan\phi.$

5. In the case of a field symmetrical about the Cartesian C^r-axis, we have seen in §12–48 that the meridians are principal directions ($A = 0$ everywhere) and $\gamma_1 = 0$ so that *each side* of this last equation is zero. Accordingly, the N-surfaces in such a symmetrical case are certainly possible triple orthogonals, but the Equation 16.05 then is oversatisfied; we may conclude that some non-symmetrical surfaces are also possible triple orthogonals. One such case is a family of confocal triaxial ellipsoids as is well known.

---

[1] Forsyth (reprint of 1920), *Lectures on the Differential Geometry of Curves and Surfaces*, original ed. of 1912, 437.

SOLUTIONS OF THE DARBOUX EQUATION

6. Because u^α, v^β must be the coordinate directions in a triply orthogonal coordinate system, Equation 16.03 can be written as

$$\overline{(1/n)}_{12} = 0$$

in the surface metric; this can be expanded as

16.06 $\dfrac{\partial^2(1/n)}{\partial x^1\partial x^2} = \Gamma_{12}^1\dfrac{\partial(1/n)}{\partial x^1} + \Gamma_{12}^2\dfrac{\partial(1/n)}{\partial x^2}.$

This is a second-order linear partial differential equation in the two independent variables x^1 and x^2, known usually in the theory of differential equations as Laplace's equation (not to be confused with the Laplace equation used in potential theory).

7. Equation 16.06 is also known as Laplace's equation in classical differential geometry [2] where it arises because three particular solutions of the equation are the Cartesian space coordinates (x, y, z). We can very easily show, for example, that x satisfies Equation 16.03 by using Equation 6.16 when we have

$$(x)_{\alpha\beta}u^\alpha v^\beta = \nu^1 b_{\alpha\beta}u^\alpha v^\beta = 0$$

in which ν^1 is the x-Cartesian component of the unit normal to the surface. In the same way, the equation is satisfied by y and z.

8. We can also show that Equation 16.06 is satisfied by $r^2 = g_{rs}\rho^r\rho^s$ in which r is the radius vector and ρ^r is the position vector of a current point on the surface. By surface covariant differentiation, we have

$$(r^2)_\alpha = 2g_{rs}x_\alpha^r\rho^s$$
$$(r^2)_{\alpha\beta} = 2g_{rs}x_{\alpha\beta}^r\rho^s + 2g_{rs}x_\alpha^r x_\beta^r$$
$$= 2(g_{rs}\nu^r\rho^s)b_{\alpha\beta} + 2a_{\alpha\beta};$$

and so we have

$$(r^2)_{\alpha\beta}u^\alpha v^\beta = 0,$$

provided only that u^α, v^β are the principal directions.

9. Moreover, because any function of N is constant under surface covariant differentiation, we can say at once that Equation 16.03 or 16.04 is satisfied by

16.07 $a + bx + cy + dz + er^2$

in which a, b, c, d, e are arbitrary functions of N. This is a very general solution of the equation, but

---

[2] *Ibid.*, 69.

still not the most general solution which would require two arbitrary functions, not of N only but of all three coordinates. This result, first obtained by Darboux, is also derived by Forsyth.[3] Anyone who doubts the value of the tensor calculus in such problems should compare the classical derivations with the derivation given here.

---

[3] *Ibid.*, 447.

10. It may help the reader to find his way through the considerable classical literature on the subject if he realizes that the surface tensor equation

$$F_{\alpha\beta}u^\alpha v^\beta = 0,$$

in which F is a scalar and the two vectors are the principal directions, is called Laplace's equation when F is x, y, or z and is called the Darboux equation when F is $(1/n)$.

The (ω, ϕ, h) Coordinate System

GENERAL DESCRIPTION OF THE SYSTEM

1. We have so far considered special coordinate systems in which a given family of N-surfaces are coordinate surfaces without applying any restriction on the form of the scalar N, other than continuity and differentiability. We now choose N to make the function n—the magnitude of the gradient of N—a constant which, without any real loss of generality, we can make unity. The form of the N-surfaces is then no longer as one chooses, but, as we shall see, one of the surfaces can still be chosen arbitrarily. This coordinate system is accordingly of value when we are concerned with space in the immediate vicinity of a given surface, which can be chosen to provide a close approximation to actual physical conditions. The geometry of the system is much simpler than that of the more general systems so far considered, and by suitable choice of surface can be made even more simple. We can also use the system to derive easily some valuable properties of surfaces in general.

2. In most current geodetic applications of this system, one of the surfaces is chosen to be a spheroid whose minor axis lies in the Cartesian C^r-direction and whose dimensions are chosen to make it a good approximation to an equipotential surface of the gravitational field. In such a system, it is possible to calculate finite distances and directions by means of closed formulas and so to linearize the observation equations for measures which are necessarily made in the less regular gravitational field. The problem usually involves a transformation of one N-system into another; a spheroidal $(\bar\omega, \bar\phi, h)$ system (known as the geodetic system) into a (ω, ϕ, N) system (known as the astronomical system) in which the N-surfaces are gravitational equipotential or level surfaces modified by the rotation of the Earth.

3. In the present chapter, however, we shall derive general formulas which do not involve the choice of a spheroid as a special case. The results can then be used for other applications, such as the choice of the geoid as a surface in this coordinate system. Modification of these more general results to the special choice of a spheroid as base surface is a very simple matter which will be treated in the next chapter.

4. The basic gradient equation for the coordinate N with $n = 1$ becomes

17.01 $$N_r = \nu_r,$$

which can be differentiated covariantly as

17.02 $$N_{rs} = \nu_{rs},$$

showing that the tensor ν_{rs}, like N_{rs}, must be symmetrical. The vector curvature of the normals is then

17.03 $$\nu_{rs}\nu^s = \nu_{sr}\nu^s = 0$$

because ν_s is a unit vector. See Equation 3.19. Consequently, we find from §4–2 that the normals are space geodesics, that is, straight lines in flat space. If h is a length measured along the normal, we have from Equation 17.01

$$\partial N/\partial h = N_r \nu^r = 1$$

so that we can take N as h—measured from one particular N-surface which we shall call the *base surface*. It is evident that equal lengths of the straight normals are intercepted by two particular N-surfaces which are, for this reason, known as parallel surfaces.

5. Because $n=1$, it follows at once from Equations 12.097 that the isozenithals are the same as the normals. The (ω, ϕ, N) and the normal coordinate systems become the same; we can derive the properties of this special system from either the (ω, ϕ, N) or the normal system, whichever is easier, simply by making $n=1$ and $N=h$. Because latitude and longitude, as defined in the (ω, ϕ, N) system, will be constant along the isozenithal-normals, we can use them as coordinates — not only on the base surface, but also in space.

6. It is evident that the Darboux equation of Equation 16.04 is satisfied if n is a constant so that we could choose triply orthogonal coordinates. In general, however, we could not use in that case latitude and longitude. We would have to refer the base surface to its lines of curvature and to define the resulting coordinates as constant along the normals, just as we did in the normal system. We have already seen from a_{12} in Equations 12.069 that the ω- and ϕ-coordinate lines are not orthogonal unless $t_1 = 0$, corresponding to the axially symmetrical system discussed in §12–48. In that case, but not otherwise, the ω- and ϕ-lines also would be the lines of curvature, and we could take latitude and longitude, together with h, as triply orthogonal coordinates.

7. For the present, however, we shall retain a general nonsymmetrical form for the base surface; unless otherwise stated, we shall assume that the surface coordinates are latitude and longitude. We can then use all the surface formulas in the (ω, ϕ, N) system, that is, any formula not containing N or n. In fact, the whole system becomes a special case of the (ω, ϕ, N) system or the normal system with $n=1$, $N=h$, and $ds=dh$. However, we shall find that some useful integral relationships can also be obtained in this special system which are not available in the general (ω, ϕ, N) system.

THE FUNDAMENTAL FORMS

8. The space metric in these coordinates, obtained by making $n=1$ in the normal system of Equations 15.03 and 15.05, is

17.04 $\qquad ds^2 = a_{\alpha\beta}dx^\alpha dx^\beta + dh^2,$

with the associated tensor

17.05 $\qquad\qquad g^{rs} = (a^{\alpha\beta}, 1).$

It is evident that $a^{\alpha\beta}$ and $a_{\alpha\beta}$ are also components of the h-surface metric, if as usual we make the surface coordinates two of the space coordinates. This will be done throughout this chapter in which also, as stated previously, the surface coordinates will be latitude and longitude.

9. The components of the metric tensor will depend on h. As in the normal system Equation 15.13, we have

17.06 $\qquad\qquad \partial a_{\alpha\beta}/\partial h = -2b_{\alpha\beta};$

from either Equation 15.25 or 14.01, we have

17.07 $\qquad\qquad \partial b_{\alpha\beta}/\partial h = -c_{\alpha\beta}.$

The third fundamental form, as in Equation 14.08, is constant along the isozenithal-normal so that we have

17.08 $\qquad\qquad \partial c_{\alpha\beta}/\partial h = 0.$

10. If overbars refer to the base surface where $h=0$, we have accordingly the following integral relations,

17.09 $\qquad a_{\alpha\beta} = \bar{a}_{\alpha\beta} - 2h\bar{b}_{\alpha\beta} + h^2\bar{c}_{\alpha\beta}$

17.10 $\qquad b_{\alpha\beta} = \bar{b}_{\alpha\beta} - h\bar{c}_{\alpha\beta}$

17.11 $\qquad\qquad c_{\alpha\beta} = \bar{c}_{\alpha\beta},$

enabling us to find all three fundamental forms at any point in space from values at the foot of the normal on the base surface — that is, from values at points on the base surface having the same latitude and longitude as the point in space.

11. The components of the three surface forms in terms of the three curvature parameters (k_1, k_2, t_1) *of the h-surfaces* are as given in the (ω, ϕ, N) system, namely,

$$a_{11} = (k_2^2 + t_1^2)\cos^2\phi/K^2 \qquad b_{11} = k_2\cos^2\phi/K$$

$$a_{12} = -2Ht_1\cos\phi/K^2 \qquad b_{12} = -t_1\cos\phi/K$$

$$a_{22} = (k_1^2 + t_1^2)/K^2 \qquad b_{22} = k_1/K$$

17.12 $\qquad c_{\alpha\beta} = (\cos^2\phi, 0, 1):$

12. If we denote the corresponding components on the base surface by overbars and substitute in Equation 17.10, we have

$$k_2/K = \bar{k}_2/\bar{K} - h$$

$$t_1/K = \bar{t}_1/\bar{K}$$

17.13 $\qquad k_1/K = \bar{k}_1/\bar{K} - h,$

which enable us to find the three curvature parameters at any point in space, given their values on the base surface. Multiplying the first and third equations and subtracting the square of the second, we have

17.14 $1/K = 1/\overline{K} - (2\overline{H}/\overline{K})h + h^2$

or

17.15 $\overline{K}/K = (1 - h\overline{\kappa}_1)(1 - h\overline{\kappa}_2),$

using the principal curvatures $\overline{\kappa}_1$, $\overline{\kappa}_2$. Also by adding the first and third equations of Equations 17.13, we have

17.16 $2H/K = 2\overline{H}/\overline{K} - 2h,$

which relate the curvature invariants of the *h*-surfaces.

13. We can also find without difficulty that

17.17 $a^{\alpha\beta}/K^2 = \overline{a}^{\alpha\beta}/\overline{K}^2 - 2h\overline{b}^{\alpha\beta}/\overline{K} + h^2\overline{c}^{\alpha\beta}$

17.18 $b^{\alpha\beta}/K = \overline{b}^{\alpha\beta}/\overline{K} - h\overline{c}^{\alpha\beta}$

17.19 $c^{\alpha\beta} = \overline{c}^{\alpha\beta}$

from the contravariant components

$$a^{11} = (k_1^2 + t_1^2)\sec^2\phi \qquad b^{11} = k_1 \sec^2\phi$$

$$a^{12} = 2Ht_1 \sec\phi \qquad b^{12} = t_1 \sec\phi$$

$$a^{22} = (k_2^2 + t_1^2) \qquad b^{22} = k_2$$

17.20 $c^{\alpha\beta} = (\sec^2\phi, 0, 1).$

14. In regard to the determinants of the three forms, we have from Equations 12.070, 12.076, and 12.084

$$\cos^2\phi = K^2 a = Kb = c,$$

and because ϕ is constant along a normal in these coordinates, we have

17.21 $\dfrac{a}{\overline{a}} = \dfrac{b^2}{\overline{b}^2} = \dfrac{\overline{K}^2}{K^2}.$

15. Because we can take any one of the *h*-surfaces as base surface, we can interchange the overbars in any of the preceding formulas, provided we also change the sign of *h*. For example,

$$\overline{a}^{\alpha\beta}/\overline{K}^2 = a^{\alpha\beta}/K^2 + 2hb^{\alpha\beta}/K + h^2 c^{\alpha\beta}$$

gives us the base metric tensor in terms of the three forms of the *h*-surface. This device is a useful check even when not required to generate new formulas.

16. We can differentiate any of these integral formulas along the normal. For example, Equation 17.14 becomes

$$-(1/\overline{K})(\partial\ln K/\partial h) = -2\overline{H}/\overline{K} + 2h;$$

in the neighborhood of the base surface $h = 0$, this is

$$\partial(\ln\overline{K})/\partial h = 2\overline{H}.$$

But because we may take any surface of the family as base surface, we can drop the overbars and write

17.22 $\partial(\ln K)/\partial h = 2H.$

THE BASE VECTORS

17. Components of the base vectors are given at once by making $n = 1$ in the (ω, ϕ, N) formulas, such as in Equations 12.037,

17.23 $\lambda^r = (-k_1 \sec\phi, -t_1, 0)$

17.24 $\mu^r = (-t_1 \sec\phi, -k_2, 0)$

17.25 $\nu^r = (0, 0, 1)$

17.26 $K\lambda_r = (-k_2 \cos\phi, +t_1, 0)$

17.27 $K\mu_r = (+t_1 \cos\phi, -k_1, 0)$

17.28 $\nu_r = (0, 0, 1).$

Because any surface vector can be expressed in terms of λ_r, μ_r, it follows that the 3-components, covariant and contravariant, of all surface vectors are zero. The surface components are the first two-space components.

We have also from Equations 12.046 and 12.047

17.29 $(\cos\phi)\omega_r = -k_1\lambda_r - t_1\mu_r$

17.30 $\phi_r = -t_1\lambda_r - k_2\mu_r.$

18. In regard to the derivatives of the base vectors, we have, as in Equations 12.022, 12.023, 12.024, and 12.074,

$$\lambda_{\alpha\beta} = \mu_\alpha\omega_\beta \sin\phi$$

$$\mu_{\alpha\beta} = -\lambda_\alpha\omega_\beta \sin\phi$$

17.31 $\nu_{\alpha\beta} = -b_{\alpha\beta} = (\cos\phi)\lambda_\alpha\omega_\beta + \mu_\alpha\phi_\beta,$

whether the components of $\lambda_{\alpha\beta}$, $\mu_{\alpha\beta}$ are taken in the space metric or in the surface metric. The only nonzero components containing a 3-index are from Equations 12.014, etc.,

17.32 $\lambda_{31} = -\cos\phi$; $\mu_{32} = -1.$

19. As in (ω, ϕ, N), all three base vectors remain parallel if translated along an isozenithal-normal.

20. Second derivatives of the base vectors can be found at once from Equations 12.159 and 12.160 or by direct calculation. For instance, we have

$$\lambda_{\alpha\beta 3} = \lambda_{\alpha 3\beta} = \sin\phi \; \mu_\alpha b^{1\gamma} c_{\beta\gamma}$$

17.33 $\nu_{\alpha 33} = 0.$

THE PRINCIPAL DIRECTIONS AND CURVATURES

21. It follows at once from Equations 17.13 that

$$t_1/(k_1 - k_2) = \bar{t}_1/(\bar{k}_1 - \bar{k}_2),$$

and therefore from Equation 12.051 we have

$$A = \bar{A}$$

so that the azimuth of a principal direction remains the same at all points along a normal. We could accordingly take the principal directions at a point as the meridian and parallel directions in a temporary coordinate system, in which case Equations 17.13 would apply to the principal curvatures κ_1, κ_2 as

$$\kappa_2/K = \bar{\kappa}_2/\bar{K} - h$$

17.34 $\kappa_1/K = \bar{\kappa}_1/\bar{K} - h$

or

$$(1/\kappa_1) = (1/\bar{\kappa}_1) - h$$

17.35 $(1/\kappa_2) = (1/\bar{\kappa}_2) - h.$

(The geodesic torsions are, of course, zero for the principal directions.) These last two equations reduce to a statement that the principal radii of curvature at points on the same normal differ by h. We must remember, however, that in the case of surfaces which are convex to the outward-drawn normal, such as we normally encounter in geodesy, the radii of curvature are negative, whereas h is positive along the outward-drawn normal.

22. Another way of viewing this matter is to consider the surface-normals at neighboring points along a line of curvature. We know that the normals then intersect in the center of curvature. Also, corresponding points on different h-surfaces will have the same straight normals. Consequently, the center of curvature will be the same at corresponding points on the lines of curvature of all the h-surfaces, which proves the previously mentioned statement about the principal radii of curvature. We can also say that the total angle swept out by the surface-normal along a line of curvature is the same between corresponding points on all the h-surfaces.

THE CHRISTOFFEL SYMBOLS

23. Because $\nu^\gamma = 0$ in these coordinates, we can see at once from Equation 12.131 that

$$\Gamma^\gamma_{\alpha\beta}$$

is the same for both the space and surface metrics, just as it is in normal coordinates.

24. Again, by making $n = 1$ in the (ω, ϕ, N) formulas, we find that the only nonzero symbols containing a 3-index are

$$\Gamma^3_{\alpha\beta} = b_{\alpha\beta}$$

17.36 $\Gamma^\alpha_{\beta 3} = -b^{\alpha\gamma}c_{\beta\gamma} = -a^{\alpha\gamma}b_{\beta\gamma} = \nu^\alpha_\beta.$

LAPLACIANS OF THE COORDINATES

25. Because $N = h$ and $n = 1$, we have at once from Equation 12.100

17.37 $\Delta h = -2H;$

from Equations 12.104 and 12.105, we have

17.38 $(\cos \phi)\Delta\omega = 2(\sin \phi)\nabla(\omega, \phi) - (2H)_\alpha \lambda^\alpha$

17.39 $\Delta\phi = -(\sin \phi \cos \phi)\nabla(\omega) - (2H)_\alpha \mu^\alpha$

with

17.40 $\nabla(\omega, \phi) = a^{12} = 2Ht_1 \sec \phi$

17.41 $\nabla(\omega) = a^{11} = (k_1^2 + t_1^2) \sec^2 \phi,$

using Equations 17.20.

It should be noted that the space Laplacians in Equations 17.38 and 17.39 are the same as the surface Laplacians, obtained in (ω, ϕ, N) coordinates as Equations 12.118 and 12.120. Although we have defined the coordinates (ω, ϕ) in the same way for both systems, they do not have the same values at any point in space because the two normals do not have the same direction. Consequently, the space Laplacians are different in the two systems. We can, however, choose any one of the N-surfaces as base surface in the (ω, ϕ, h) system; and on that surface, (ω, ϕ) will be the same. Consequently, the surface Laplacians will be the same in the two systems.

26. The general Equation 8.29, for converting the surface Laplacian of a scalar to the space Laplacian, becomes in these coordinates

17.42 $\Delta F = \overline{\Delta F} - 2H \dfrac{\partial F}{\partial h} + \dfrac{\partial^2 F}{\partial h^2}$

in which the surface Laplacian is denoted by an overbar. This equation shows again that the space and surface Laplacians of the coordinates (ω, ϕ) are the same in this system.

Using Equation 17.22, we may express Equation 17.42 in the alternative form

17.43 $\Delta F = \overline{\Delta F} + K \dfrac{\partial}{\partial h}\left(\dfrac{1}{K}\dfrac{\partial F}{\partial h}\right).$

CHANGE OF SCALE AND AZIMUTH IN NORMAL PROJECTION

27. Projection from one h-surface to the base surface down the isozenithal-normals requires the surface coordinates (ω, ϕ) to be the same for a point and its projection. We consider a displacement on the current surface given by a change dx^α in surface coordinates over an element of length ds in the direction of a unit vector l^α; the corresponding quantities, projected on the base surface, are denoted by overbars. Accordingly, we have

$$l^\alpha ds = dx^\alpha = d\bar{x}^\alpha = \bar{l}^\alpha d\bar{s}.$$

If now we multiply the three Equations 17.09, 17.10, and 17.11 by $(dx^\alpha dx^\beta)$, we have at once

$$(ds/d\bar{s})^2 = 1 - 2h\bar{k} + h^2(\bar{k}^2 + \bar{t}^2)$$

$$(ds/d\bar{s})^2 k = \bar{k} - h(\bar{k}^2 + \bar{t}^2)$$

17.44 $\qquad (ds/d\bar{s})^2(k^2 + t^2) = \bar{k}^2 + \bar{t}^2$

in which $\bar{k}, \bar{t}$ are the normal curvature and geodesic torsion of the base surface in the projected direction. The last of these formulas applies to isozenithal projection in the general coordinates (ω, ϕ, N) and could be obtained from the formula for spherical representation, but the other two formulas are peculiar to the (ω, ϕ, h) system.

28. Following Equations 13.04 and 13.05, we can also relate azimuths on the two surfaces as follows,

$$(ds/d\bar{s})(k \cos \alpha + t \sin \alpha) = -\partial\phi/\partial\bar{s}$$
$$= (\bar{k} \cos \bar{\alpha} + \bar{t} \sin \bar{\alpha})$$

$$(ds/d\bar{s})(k \sin \alpha - t \cos \alpha) = -\cos \phi \, \partial\omega/\partial\bar{s}$$
17.45 $\qquad = (\bar{k} \sin \bar{\alpha} - \bar{t} \cos \bar{\alpha});$

if the change in azimuth on projection is

$$\Delta\alpha = (\bar{\alpha} - \alpha),$$

we have the equivalent equations

$$(ds/d\bar{s})k = (\bar{k} \cos \Delta\alpha + \bar{t} \sin \Delta\alpha)$$
17.46 $\qquad (ds/d\bar{s})t = (-\bar{k} \sin \Delta\alpha + \bar{t} \cos \Delta\alpha).$

The only solution of the first of these equations which will also satisfy the first two equations of Equations 17.44 is

$$(ds/d\bar{s}) \sin \Delta\alpha = -h\bar{t}$$
17.47 $\qquad (ds/d\bar{s}) \cos \Delta\alpha = (1 - h\bar{k}),$

in which case the second equation of Equations 17.46 reduces to

17.48 $\qquad\qquad (ds/d\bar{s})^2 t = \bar{t}.$

Combined with the third equation of Equations 17.44, this shows that

17.49 $\qquad\qquad t/(k^2 + t^2)$

is unaltered on projection; we can verify this fact by differentiation, using formulas given in the Summary of Formulas.

29. In all the preceding equations, we can interchange the overbars; the interchange is equivalent to taking the unbarred surface as the base surface, provided we also change the sign of h and $\Delta\alpha$. For example, from Equations 17.47, we have

17.50 $\qquad \tan \Delta\alpha = \dfrac{-h\bar{t}}{(1 - h\bar{k})} = \dfrac{-ht}{(1 + hk)};$

from Equations 17.44, we have

17.51 $\qquad (d\bar{s}/ds)^2 = 1 + 2hk + h^2(k^2 + t^2).$

This device, applied to the first equation of Equations 17.47, enables us to verify Equation 17.48.

THE h-DIFFERENTIATION

30. Some formulas for differentiating the components of surface tensors, etc., along the straight normals have been given in previous sections of this chapter. Many more can be obtained from the collected formulas in the Summary of Formulas for Chapters 14 and 15, whichever is easier, simply by substituting $n = 1$, $N = h$, $ds = dh$. This fact results in drastic simplification. For example, from Equations 14.14, 17.07, and 8.09, we have

$$\frac{\partial}{\partial h} \Gamma^\alpha_{\beta\gamma} = -(b^{\alpha\delta}c_{\beta\delta})_\gamma = -(a^{\alpha\delta}b_{\beta\delta})_\gamma = -a^{\alpha\delta}b_{\beta\delta\gamma};$$

17.52

from Equations 14.16 and 14.07, we have

17.53 $\qquad \dfrac{\partial b_{\alpha\beta\gamma}}{\partial h} = b_{\alpha\rho}b_{\beta\sigma}(a^{\rho\sigma})_\gamma = 0,$

showing that $b_{\alpha\beta\gamma}$ has the same components at all points along a straight normal.

31. Again, from Equation 14.71 or 15.53, we have for the surface covariant derivatives of a scalar F

17.54 $\qquad \dfrac{\partial F_{\alpha\beta}}{\partial h} = \overline{\left(\dfrac{\partial F}{\partial h}\right)}_{\alpha\beta} + a^{\gamma\delta}F_\delta b_{\alpha\beta\gamma}.$

This last equation contracts to

17.55 $\qquad a^{\alpha\beta}\dfrac{\partial F_{\alpha\beta}}{\partial h} = \bar{\Delta}\left(\dfrac{\partial F}{\partial h}\right) + \bar{\nabla}(2H, F)$

in which the overbars indicate surface invariants. Using Equation 15.15, we then have after a little manipulation

$$\frac{\partial(\overline{\Delta}F)}{\partial h}=\overline{\Delta}\left(\frac{\partial F}{\partial h}\right)+\overline{\nabla}(2H,F)+4H\overline{\Delta}F-2Kb^{\alpha\beta}\overline{F}_{\alpha\beta}.$$

17.56

32. In some cases, we could obtain such results quickly and directly in (ω,ϕ,h) coordinates, but by deriving in this way, we have them as a byproduct of work already done in the more complicated coordinate systems.

Collected formulas obtained from those given in the Summary of Formulas for Chapters 14 and 15 are also included in the Summary of Formulas for this chapter under h-differentiation without further proof, together with some integral formulas which have either been obtained previously or can be verified easily. There are no corresponding integral formulas in the (ω,ϕ,N) or normal coordinate systems.

EXAMPLES OF h-DIFFERENTIATION

33. The process of differentiating a surface tensor equation along the normals is equivalent to asserting that a similar formula holds true between the projected quantities on the neighboring h-surface. We do not restrict the form of a surface by using it as a base surface in a (ω,ϕ,h) system, provided that adjacent normals do not intersect within the region of space considered; if they do, the (ω,ϕ) coordinates of the point of intersection then would not be single valued. We can usually avoid this, at any rate over some finite area of the surface, by choosing the positive h-direction in the direction of divergent normals.

34. Consequently, any surface tensor equation which is true on any regular surface can be differentiated along the normals by means of the formulas given in the Summary of Formulas under h-differentiation. The result, possibly with the help of the original equation, will either be an identity—in which case the original equation is verified—or will be some new relation between surface tensors or invariants. If any limits are imposed in the original equation, such as a closed contour, then it is assumed that these limits are projected onto the neighboring h-surface.

35. As an illustration of the process, we shall consider the two-dimensional tensor form of Stokes'

theorem in Equation 9.04,

$$\int_C l_\alpha\tau^\alpha ds=\int_S \epsilon^{\alpha\beta}l_{\beta\alpha}dS,$$

in which l_α is an arbitrary unit surface vector field defined on and within the contour and τ^α is the unit tangent vector to the contour. We note first, with the help of formulas given in the Summary of Formulas under h-differentiation, that we have

$$\partial(\epsilon^{\alpha\beta}dS)/\partial h=2H\epsilon^{\alpha\beta}dS-2H\epsilon^{\alpha\beta}dS=0$$

so that $(\epsilon^{\alpha\beta}dS)$ is constant under normal differentiation. So $(\tau^\alpha ds)$ also is constant because it is equal to a change in surface coordinates along the contours. Consequently, we have at once

$$\int_C (kl_\alpha+2tj_\alpha)\tau^\alpha ds=\int_S \epsilon^{\alpha\beta}\{k^*l_{\beta\alpha}+j_\beta(\partial t/\partial x^\beta)\}dS$$

in which k, t refer to the l^α-direction and k^* to the perpendicular j^α-field. Next, we transform each of the contour integrals to area integrals. For example, we have

$$\int_C kl_\alpha\tau^\alpha ds=\int_S \epsilon^{\alpha\beta}(kl_\beta)_\alpha dS$$

$$=\int_S \{k\epsilon^{\alpha\beta}l_{\beta\alpha}+\epsilon^{\alpha\beta}l_\beta(\partial k/\partial x^\alpha)\}dS.$$

The final area integrand, after some manipulation with Equations 2.32, 4.11, etc., becomes

17.57 $\sigma(k-k^*)+2t\sigma^*+t_\beta l^\beta-k_\beta j^\beta$

in which σ, σ^* are the geodesic curvatures of l^α, j^α and t_β, k_β are the differentials of t, k with respect to the x^β-coordinate. Because l^α is a surface vector field, t and k are point functions which can be differentiated in any direction. The area over which this integral is taken is quite arbitrary, and because the result is identically zero, then the integrand of Equation 17.57 must be zero. At first, this does not look likely, but reference to Equations 14.22 and 14.21 will show that the integrand is equivalent to

$$-b_{\alpha\beta\gamma}l^\alpha l^\beta j^\gamma+b_{\alpha\beta\gamma}l^\alpha j^\beta l^\gamma,$$

which vanishes because of the Codazzi Equation 6.21,

$$b_{\alpha\beta\gamma}=b_{\alpha\gamma\beta}.$$

36. The equation

17.58 $\sigma(k-k^*)+2t\sigma^*+t_\beta l^\beta-k_\beta j^\beta=0$

for an arbitrary orthogonal mesh l^α, j^α together with the corresponding equation for the j^α-direction

17.59 $\sigma^*(k^*-k)+2t\sigma-t_\beta j^\beta+k^*_\beta l^\beta=0$

are accordingly equivalent to the Codazzi equations of a surface. In deriving Equation 17.59 from Equation 17.58 for the j^α-curves, for which the geodesic curvature and torsion are σ^* and minus t and the normal curvature is k^*, we must remember that the new j^α-direction is *minus* l^α. In this direction of the l^α-curves, the geodesic curvature is *minus* σ, but the normal curvature is $+k$.

37. For the lines of curvature (u^α, v^α), $t = 0$ and Equations 17.58 and 17.59 reduce to

$$(\kappa_1 - \kappa_2)\sigma = (\kappa_1)_\alpha v^\alpha$$

17.60 $$(\kappa_1 - \kappa_2)\sigma^* = (\kappa_2)_\alpha u^\alpha,$$

which have been already given in Equations 8.22 as special forms of the Codazzi equations.

38. As another example, consider the two-dimensional divergence theorem in the form of Equation 9.12,

17.61 $$-\int_C F_\alpha j^\alpha ds = \int_C F_\alpha \epsilon^{\alpha\beta} l_\beta ds = \int_S \Delta F dS,$$

in which F is an arbitrary scalar defined on and in the immediate neighborhood of the surface. As before, to ensure that the unit surface vector normal to the contour stays that way after differentiation instead of becoming the projected direction, we have written it in the form ($\epsilon^{\beta\alpha}l_\beta$) where l_β is the unit vector *tangent* to the contour. After normal differentiation, the contour integrand becomes

$$(\partial F/\partial h)_\alpha \epsilon^{\alpha\beta} l_\beta + 2HF_\alpha \epsilon^{\alpha\beta} l_\beta$$
$$- F_\alpha \epsilon^{\alpha\beta}(kl_\beta + 2tj_\beta) - F_\alpha \epsilon^{\alpha\beta} l_\beta k$$

and the area integrand becomes

$$\Delta(\partial F/\partial h) + \nabla(2H, F) + 2H\Delta F - 2Kb^{\alpha\beta}F_{\alpha\beta}.$$

The first contour integral cancels the first area integral by the divergence theorem for the scalar $(\partial F/\partial h)$. The second contour integral, transformed to an area integral, becomes

$$\int_S a^{\alpha\beta}(2HF_\alpha)_\beta dS,$$

the integrand of which is

$$\nabla(2H, F) + 2H\Delta F.$$

This last formula cancels the second and third

terms of the main area integrand; we are left with

$$\int_S Kb^{\alpha\beta}F_{\alpha\beta}dS = \int_C F_\alpha \epsilon^{\alpha\beta}(kl_\beta + tj_\beta)ds$$

$$= \int_C F_\alpha \epsilon^{\alpha\beta} b_{\beta\gamma} l^\gamma ds$$

$$= \int_C (-kF_\alpha j^\alpha + tF_\alpha l^\alpha)ds$$

17.62 $$= -\int_C Kb^{\alpha\beta}F_\alpha j_\beta ds,$$

using Equations 7.12 and 8.02.

To verify this, we could differentiate again, using the second form of the contour integral, which does not contain j_β explicitly, and remembering that (KdS) is constant under normal differentiation. The result is an identity.

We cannot take the third form of the contour integral and transform this by the divergence and Stokes' theorems because k, t refer to the boundary curve only and are not defined over the area. We could, however, transform the second contour integral by Stokes' theorem. Or, we can transform the last form of the contour integral by the divergence theorem to an area integral whose integrand is

$$a^{\gamma\delta}(Kb^{\alpha\beta}F_\alpha a_{\beta\delta})_\gamma.$$

Because $a_{\beta\delta}$ is constant under covariant differentiation, this last expression is

$$(Kb^{\alpha\beta}F_\alpha)_\beta = Kb^{\alpha\beta}F_{\alpha\beta} + (Kb^{\alpha\beta})_\beta F_\alpha.$$

Combining this last equation with the original Equation 17.62 for an arbitrary area, we must have

$$(Kb^{\alpha\beta})_\beta F_\alpha = 0;$$

and because F is arbitrary, this means that

17.63 $$(Kb^{\alpha\beta})_\beta = 0.$$

Or, using Equation 8.01, we have

$$(\epsilon^{\alpha\gamma}\epsilon^{\beta\delta}b_{\gamma\delta})_\beta = 0 = \epsilon^{\alpha\gamma}\epsilon^{\beta\delta}b_{\gamma\delta\beta},$$

which is so because $b_{\gamma\delta\beta}$ is symmetrical in (δ, β) by virtue of the Codazzi equations of the surface. Again, we have verified the process and have checked a number of other results on the way. The form of the Codazzi equations in Equation 17.63 is sometimes useful and, although easy to verify, might otherwise have escaped notice.

If we differentiate Equation 8.02 covariantly, use Equation 4.11, and substitute in Equation 17.63, we obtain the Codazzi equations in the form of Equations 17.58 and 17.59.

THE POSITION VECTOR

39. If ρ^r is the position vector at a point in space and $\bar{\rho}^r$ is the position vector of the projected point on the base surface, then

17.64 $$\rho^r = \bar{\rho}^r + h\nu^r$$

is evidently true in Cartesian coordinates or between parallel vectors at a single point in space. Equation 12.169, written for the projected point on the base surface, is

17.65 $$\bar{\rho}^r = (\sec \phi \ \partial\bar{p}/\partial\omega)\bar{\lambda}^r + (\partial\bar{p}/\partial\phi)\bar{\mu}^r + \bar{p}\bar{\nu}^r$$

in which $\bar{p}$ is the perpendicular from the origin onto the tangent plane to the base surface at the projected point. The base vectors $\bar{\lambda}^r$, $\bar{\mu}^r$, $\bar{\nu}^r$ are parallel to λ^r, μ^r, ν^r (see § 17–19) so that we may drop the overbars on these vectors in Cartesian coordinates. Substituting in Equation 17.64, we have

$$\rho^r = (\sec \phi \ \partial\bar{p}/\partial\omega)\lambda^r + (\partial\bar{p}/\partial\phi)\mu^r + (\bar{p} + h)\nu^r,$$

17.66

an equation between vectors at the same point in space which, although derived in Cartesian coordinates, is true in any coordinates.

Contracting Equation 17.64 with $\nu_r = \bar{\nu}_r$, we have also

17.67 $$p = \bar{p} + h.$$

CHAPTER 18

Symmetrical (ω, ϕ, h) Systems

DEFINITION

1. We shall now introduce a minimum simplification into the general (ω, ϕ, h) system by making the parameter t_1 zero at all points of the base surface, in which case it is clear from Equations 17.13 that t_1 will be zero at all points in the region of space covered by the coordinate system. As we have seen in § 12–48, the meridian and parallel traces on any h-surface are then the latitude- and longitude-coordinate lines which are accordingly orthogonal; it is clear from § 17–6 that the (ω, ϕ, h) system is triply orthogonal. The ω, ϕ coordinate lines are lines of curvature, and the parameters k_1, k_2 are the principal curvatures κ_1, κ_2 of the h-surfaces. In addition to being the ϕ-coordinate lines, the meridian traces are h-surface geodesics and plane curves (see § 12–48).

2. Later, we shall introduce an extra condition, requiring the h-surfaces to be surfaces of revolution about a C^r-axis passing through the Cartesian origin. This does not affect the differential geometry of the field; the condition arises through the choice of constants of integration of the Codazzi equations.

PRINCIPAL RADII OF CURVATURE

3. We shall find it simpler at this stage to introduce the principal *radii* of curvature R_1, R_2 in the parallel and meridian directions in place of the principal curvatures $\kappa_1 = k_1$ and $\kappa_2 = k_2$. The closed surfaces, which mostly concern us, will have negative curvature in the usual conventions because the centers of curvature will lie in the opposite

direction to the outward-drawn normal. Accordingly, we make R_1, R_2 positive by writing

$$R_1 = -1/k_1 = -1/\kappa_1$$

18.01 $$R_2 = -1/k_2 = -1/\kappa_2,$$

in which case we have from Equations 17.13

$$R_1 = \bar{R}_1 + h$$

18.02 $$R_2 = \bar{R}_2 + h.$$

These equations enable us to express the radii of curvature of the h-surfaces at any point in space in terms of their values on the base surface at a point having the same latitude and longitude. See also § 17–22.

COLLECTED FORMULAS

4. Most of the formulas for this coordinate system can be obtained simply by making $t_1 = 0$ in the formulas of Chapter 17 or by making $t_1 = 0$, $n = 1$, $N = h$, $\gamma_1 = \gamma_2 = 0$ in the formulas of Chapter 12. Nevertheless, we shall list for easy reference certain formulas relating to this system and shall give a reference on the right to the original formula.

The Fundamental Forms

5. Components of the metric tensor and of the three fundamental forms are given by

18.03 $$g^{rs} = (a^{\alpha\beta}, 1) \; ; \qquad g_{rs} = (a_{\alpha\beta}, 1)$$

$$\textbf{17.04; 17.05}$$

18.04 $$a_{\alpha\beta} = \{(\bar{R}_1 + h)^2 \cos^2 \phi, 0, (\bar{R}_2 + h)^2\}$$

18.05 $b_{\alpha\beta} = \{-(\bar{R}_1 + h)\cos^2\phi,\ 0,\ -(\bar{R}_2 + h)\}$

17.12

18.06 $c_{\alpha\beta} = \{\cos^2\phi,\ 0,\ 1\}$

18.07 $a^{\alpha\beta} = \{\sec^2\phi/(\bar{R}_1 + h)^2,\ 0,\ 1/(\bar{R}_2 + h)^2\}$

18.08 $b^{\alpha\beta} = \{-\sec^2\phi/(\bar{R}_1 + h),\ 0,\ -1/(\bar{R}_2 + h)\}$

17.20

18.09 $c^{\alpha\beta} = \{\sec^2\phi,\ 0,\ 1\}.$

The Base Vectors

6. Components of the base vectors and principal directions are

$$\lambda^r = u^r = \{\sec\phi/(\bar{R}_1 + h),\ 0,\ 0\}$$
$$\mu^r = v^r = \{0,\ 1/(\bar{R}_2 + h),\ 0\}$$

18.10 $\nu^r = \qquad \{0,\ 0,\ 1\}$ **17.23**, etc.

$$\lambda_r = u_r = \{(\bar{R}_1 + h)\cos\phi,\ 0,\ 0\}$$
$$\mu_r = v_r = \{0,\ (\bar{R}_2 + h),\ 0\}$$

18.11 $\nu_r = \qquad \{0,\ 0,\ 1\}.$

The surface components of λ^r, μ^r, λ_r, μ_r are the same as the first two space components.

7. For the gradients of the coordinates, we have

18.12 $(\cos\phi)\omega_r = \lambda_r/(\bar{R}_1 + h)$ **17.29**

18.13 $\phi_r = \mu_r/(\bar{R}_2 + h).$ **17.30**

8. A unit vector l^r in azimuth α and zenith distance β is

$$l^r = \lambda^r \sin\alpha \sin\beta + \mu^r \cos\alpha \sin\beta + \nu^r \cos\beta;$$

its components are

$$l^r = \left\{ \frac{\sec\phi \sin\alpha \sin\beta}{(\bar{R}_1 + h)},\ \frac{\cos\alpha \sin\beta}{(\bar{R}_2 + h)},\ \cos\beta \right\}$$

$$l_r = \{(\bar{R}_1 + h)\cos\phi \sin\alpha \sin\beta,$$

18.14 $(\bar{R}_2 + h)\cos\alpha \sin\beta,\ \cos\beta\}.$

Derivatives of Base Vectors

9. The only nonzero components are

18.15 $\lambda_{21} = (\bar{R}_2 + h)\sin\phi\ ;\qquad \lambda_{31} = -\cos\phi$

17.31

18.16 $\mu_{11} = -(\bar{R}_1 + h)\sin\phi \cos\phi\ ;\qquad \mu_{32} = -1$

17.32

18.17 $\nu_{11} = (\bar{R}_1 + h)\cos^2\phi\ ;\qquad \nu_{22} = \bar{R}_2 + h.$

The components λ_{21}, μ_{11} have the same values in the surface and space metrics.

Surface Curvatures

10. Normal curvature and geodesic torsion in azimuth α are

$$-k = 1/R$$

18.18 $= \sin^2\alpha/(\bar{R}_1 + h) + \cos^2\alpha/(\bar{R}_2 + h)$

12.049

18.19 $t = \dfrac{(\bar{R}_2 - \bar{R}_1)\sin\alpha \cos\alpha}{(\bar{R}_1 + h)(\bar{R}_2 + h)}.$ **12.050**

The meridians μ^r or v^r are geodesics.   **12.067**

Geodesic curvature of the parallels λ^r or u^r is

18.20 $\sigma_1 = \tan\phi/(\bar{R}_1 + h).$ **12.067**

Geodesic curvature in azimuth α, arc element dl is

18.21 $\sigma = \tan\phi \sin\alpha/(\bar{R}_1 + h) - \partial\alpha/\partial l.$

12.068

Codazzi Equations

11. The Codazzi equations for all the h-surfaces reduce to these two,

18.22 $\dfrac{\partial \bar{R}_1}{\partial \phi} = (\bar{R}_1 - \bar{R}_2)\tan\phi$ **12.134**

18.23 $\dfrac{\partial \bar{R}_2}{\partial \omega} = 0,$ **12.135**

because h cancels on substitution in Equations 12.134 and 12.135, and we can accordingly drop the overbars. The remaining Codazzi equations of the space are

18.24 $\dfrac{\partial b_{\alpha\beta}}{\partial h} = -c_{\alpha\beta},$ **12.143**

which are satisfied by expressing the fundamental forms as in Equations 18.05 and 18.06.

12. Over a particular surface, Equation 18.23 shows that R_2 is a function of latitude only. This implies that all the meridians of the surface, which we have seen are plane curves, must be superimposable in much the same way as two circles of the same radius can be superimposed. This condition is met if we take the h-surfaces as surfaces of revolution about the C^r-axis passing through the Cartesian origin; it will be sufficient for our purposes to do so, although this restriction is not required by the differential relations. If the h-surfaces

are surfaces of revolution, then the parallels are circles of radius $R_1 \cos \phi$ (§ 12–49); R_1 over a particular surface is also a function of latitude only.

Again, this condition is not necessary to satisfy the differential relations. The other Codazzi Equation 18.22 would be satisfied if

$$R_1 = g(\phi) + \sec \phi \, j(\omega)$$

where $g(\phi)$ is some function of latitude and $j(\omega)$ is an arbitrary function of longitude. If the h-surfaces are of revolution, then the arbitrary function of longitude resulting from the integration of the Codazzi Equation 18.22 is zero. The integral of this equation is then

18.25 $\qquad R_1 \cos \phi = - \int R_2 \sin \phi \, d\phi.$

The Position Vector

13. In Equation 12.169, we found an equation for the position vector in terms of the perpendicular p from the Cartesian origin to the tangent plane of an N-surface. If the N-surfaces are of revolution about the C^r-axis through the Cartesian origin, then from considerations of symmetry, we have

$$\partial p / \partial \omega = 0;$$

thus we obtain from Equation 12.172

18.26 $\qquad x \sin \omega = y \cos \omega.$

In this case, we find from § 12–49 that the radius of the parallel is

18.27 $\qquad (x^2 + y^2)^{1/2} = -1/(k_1 \sec \phi) = R_1 \cos \phi$

so that from Equations 18.26 and 18.27 we can write

$$x = R_1 \cos \phi \cos \omega$$

18.28 $\qquad y = R_1 \cos \phi \sin \omega.$

14. As we proceed northward along a meridian over the closed surface, we have

18.29 $\qquad dz = -(\cot \phi) d(R_1 \cos \phi).$

Using Equation 18.25 or integrating by parts, we can then express the z-coordinate with a suitable choice of limits in any of the three following forms,

$$z = \int R_2 \cos \phi \, d\phi$$

$$= -R_1 \cos \phi \cot \phi - \int R_1 \cos \phi \operatorname{cosec}^2 \phi \, d\phi$$

$$= R_1 \sin \phi - \int (R_1 - R_2) \sec \phi \, d\phi.$$

18.30

Substituting these forms and Equations 18.28 in 12.170 and 12.171, we have

$$p = R_1 \cos^2 \phi + \sin \phi \int R_2 \cos \phi \, d\phi$$

$$= -\sin \phi \int R_1 \cos \phi \operatorname{cosec}^2 \phi \, d\phi$$

18.31 $\quad = R_1 - \sin \phi \int (R_1 - R_2) \sec \phi \, d\phi$

$$dp/d\phi = -R_1 \sin \phi \cos \phi + \cos \phi \int R_2 \cos \phi \, d\phi$$

$$= -R_1 \cot \phi - \cos \phi \int R_1 \cos \phi \operatorname{cosec}^2 \phi \, d\phi$$

$$= -\cos \phi \int (R_1 - R_2) \sec \phi \, d\phi.$$

18.32

15. The last four sets of equations apply to any surface of revolution and therefore to the h-surfaces of any axially symmetrical system. If we distinguish these equations by overbars on R_1, R_2, and p, they apply to the base surface in a symmetrical (ω, ϕ, h) system. The position vector of any point in space in this system is then given by Equation 17.66 as

18.33 $\qquad \rho^r = (d\bar{p}/d\phi) \mu^r (\bar{p} + h) \nu^r.$

Christoffel Symbols

16. The only nonzero symbols are

$$\Gamma_{11}^2 = (\bar{R}_1 + h) \sin \phi \cos \phi / (\bar{R}_2 + h)$$

$$\Gamma_{12}^1 = -(\bar{R}_2 + h) \tan \phi / (\bar{R}_1 + h)$$

18.34 $\quad \Gamma_{22}^2 = \dfrac{\partial \ln (\bar{R}_2 + h)}{\partial \phi},$ $\qquad$ **12.129**

all in the surface or space metric, and

$$\Gamma_{11}^3 = -(\bar{R}_1 + h) \cos^2 \phi$$

$$\Gamma_{22}^3 = -(\bar{R}_2 + h)$$

$$\Gamma_{13}^1 = 1/(\bar{R}_1 + h)$$

18.35 $\quad \Gamma_{23}^2 = 1/(\bar{R}_2 + h).$ $\qquad$ **17.36**

Higher Derivatives of Base Vectors

17. Second derivatives of the base vectors can be found direct from Equations 18.15, 18.16, 18.17, together with the Christoffel symbols in Equations 18.34 and 18.35, or by substitution in previous

formulas. For example, we have

18.36 $\quad \lambda_{213} = -(\bar{R}_2 + h) \sin \phi / (\bar{R}_1 + h),$

$$\qquad\qquad\qquad\qquad\qquad\qquad \textbf{12.159}$$

with all other $\lambda_{\alpha\beta3}$ zero; we have

18.37 $\quad\quad\quad \mu_{113} = \sin \phi \cos \phi,$ $\quad$ **12.159**

with all other $\mu_{\alpha\beta3}$ zero; and we have

18.38 $\quad\quad\quad \nu_{\beta\beta3} = -c_{\alpha\beta}$ $\quad\quad$ **12.159**

18.39 $\quad\quad \lambda_{\alpha33} = \mu_{\alpha33} = \nu_{\alpha33} = 0$ $\quad$ **12.160**

18.40 $\quad\quad\quad \nu_{\alpha\beta\gamma} = -b_{\alpha\beta\gamma}$ $\quad\quad$ **12.161**

$$\nu_{\alpha\beta\gamma} = \delta_\alpha^1 \delta_\beta^1 (\bar{R}_1)_\gamma \cos^2 \phi + \delta_\alpha^2 \delta_\beta^2 (\bar{R}_2)_\gamma$$

18.41 $\quad + (\bar{R}_1 - \bar{R}_2) \sin \phi \cos \phi (\delta_\alpha^1 \delta_\beta^2 + \delta_\alpha^2 \delta_\beta^1) \delta_\gamma^1.$

$$\qquad\qquad\qquad\qquad\qquad\qquad \textbf{8.16}$$

Laplacians of the Coordinates

18. As in Equation 17.37, we have

18.42 $\quad\quad\quad\quad \Delta h = -2H;$

also in the symmetrical (ω, ϕ, h) system, we have

18.43 $\quad\quad\quad \nabla(\omega, \phi) = 0$ $\quad\quad$ **17.40**

18.44 $\quad (\cos^2 \phi) \nabla(\omega) = 1/(\bar{R}_1 + h)^2,$ $\quad$ **17.41**

leading to

18.45 $\quad\quad\quad\quad \Delta\omega = 0$ $\quad\quad\quad$ **17.38**

because both principal curvatures and thus $(2H)$ are independent of ω, and therefore constant in the λ^r-direction. We have also

$$\Delta\phi = -\tan \phi / (\bar{R}_1 + h)^2 - (2H)_\alpha \mu^\alpha$$

18.46 $\quad = -\dfrac{\tan \phi}{(\bar{R}_1 + h)(\bar{R}_2 + h)} - \dfrac{1}{(\bar{R}_2 + h)^3} \dfrac{d\bar{R}_2}{d\phi}.$

$$\qquad\qquad\qquad\qquad\qquad\qquad \textbf{17.39}$$

The second (alternative) expression may be obtained either by manipulating the first, or direct from the defining equation

$$\Delta\phi = -g^{rs}\Gamma_{rs}^2,$$

using components of the metric tensor and the Christoffel symbols already given.

The surface and space Laplacians of ω and ϕ are the same.

SURFACE GEODESICS

19. If $\bar{\alpha}$ is the azimuth of its spherical representation, the differential equation of any curve on

any surface is obtained at once from Equations 13.04 and 13.05 as

$$\frac{\cos \phi \, d\omega}{d\phi} = \tan \bar{\alpha} = \frac{k_1 \sin \alpha + t_1 \cos \alpha}{k_2 \cos \alpha + t_1 \sin \alpha}$$

18.47 $\quad\quad\quad = \dfrac{k \sin \alpha - t \cos \alpha}{k \cos \alpha + t \sin \alpha}.$

If the curve is a geodesic of the surface, we have also from § 12–47

18.48 $\quad\quad\quad\quad d\alpha = \sin \phi \, d\omega$

along the curve so that

$$\cot \phi \frac{\partial \alpha}{\partial \phi} = \frac{k_1 \sin \alpha + t_1 \cos \alpha}{k_2 \cos \alpha + t_1 \sin \alpha}$$

18.49 $\quad\quad\quad = \dfrac{k \sin \alpha - t \cos \alpha}{k \cos \alpha + t \sin \alpha}.$

If k_1, k_2, t_1 are specified as functions of ω, ϕ and if we then assume that the curve belongs to some family of geodesics defined over some region of the surface, we can integrate this equation numerically.

20. In the case we are considering $(t_1 = 0$; k_1, k_2 functions of ϕ only), the equation becomes the ordinary differential equation

$$\cot \alpha \, d\alpha = (R_2/R_1) \tan \phi \, d\phi$$

$$= -\{(R_1 - R_2)/R_1\} \tan \phi \, d\phi + \tan \phi \, d\phi$$

$$= -(1/R_1)(dR_1/d\phi) d\phi + \tan \phi \, d\phi,$$

using the Codazzi Equation 18.22.

This integrates to

18.50 $\quad\quad R_1 \cos \phi \sin \alpha = \text{constant}$

or

18.51 $\quad (\bar{R}_1 + h) \cos \phi \sin \alpha = \text{constant}$

as the general equation of geodesics on an axially symmetrical h-surface. It is a generalization of the result usually known as Clairaut's theorem in classical geodesy.

21. The normal projection of a geodesic, even in an axially symmetrical system, is not, in general, a geodesic on any other h-surface. For this to be true, it is clear from Equation 15.54 that the geodesic torsion would have to be constant along the curve.

22. The general equation of a surface geodesic whose unit tangent is l_α is, from Equation 4.07,

18.52 $\quad\quad\quad\quad l_{\alpha\beta} l^\beta = 0.$

If we evaluate this equation in the symmetrical

(ω, ϕ, h) system of this chapter and use the Christoffel symbols given in the last section, we can show that the equation for $\alpha=1$ leads to the Clairaut Equation 18.51, while the equation for $\alpha=2$ reduces to

$$\frac{d\alpha}{ds}=\sin\phi\,\frac{d\omega}{ds},$$

with ds as the arc element of the curve, which is equivalent to Equation 18.48. The Clairaut equation is accordingly a complete first integral of both Equations 18.52.

THE SPHEROIDAL BASE

23. We now suppose, as a special case, that the base surface of a symmetrical (ω, ϕ, h) system is a spheroid so that the meridian section is an ellipse of semimajor axis a and eccentricity e. The semiminor axis b is the Cartesian z-axis; we define the complementary eccentricity $\bar{e}$ as

18.53 $\qquad \bar{e}=b/a=+(1-e^2)^{1/2}.$

24. The principal radii of curvature in and perpendicular to the meridian (variously known in the literature as M, N or ρ, ν, respectively) are well known as

$$\bar{R}_2(=M=\rho)=a\bar{e}^2(1-e^2\sin^2\phi)^{-3/2}$$
18.54 $\qquad\qquad =\bar{e}^2\bar{R}_1^3/a^2$
18.55 $\quad \bar{R}_1(=N=\nu)=a(1-e^2\sin^2\phi)^{-1/2},$

which are compatible with Equation 18.22. Indeed,

we could have defined $\bar{R}_2$ as Equation 18.54, or any other required function of ϕ, and have determined $\bar{R}_1$ from Equation 18.25.

25. From any of the Equations 18.30, 18.31, and 18.32, we now find

18.56 $\qquad \bar{z}=\bar{e}^2\bar{R}_1\sin\phi$
18.57 $\qquad \bar{p}=a^2/\bar{R}_1$
18.58 $\qquad d\bar{p}/d\phi=-e^2\bar{R}_1\sin\phi\cos\phi.$

26. By evaluating Equation 17.64 in Cartesian coordinates and using Equations 18.28, we can express the Cartesian coordinates of any point in space as

$$x=\bar{x}+h\cos\phi\cos\omega=(\bar{R}_1+h)\cos\phi\cos\omega$$
$$y=\bar{y}+h\cos\phi\sin\omega=(\bar{R}_1+h)\cos\phi\sin\omega$$
$$z=\bar{z}+h\sin\phi\qquad =(\bar{e}^2\bar{R}_1+h)\sin\phi,$$
18.59

while from Equation 18.33, the position vector is

$$\rho^r=-(e^2\bar{R}_1\sin\phi\cos\phi)\mu^r+(a^2/\bar{R}_1+h)\nu^r.$$
18.60

These last two equations enable us to express the whole field in terms of one of the principal radii of curvature of the base surface. We can use any of the formulas of Chapter 17 by making $t_1=0$, $\bar{k}_1=-1/\bar{R}_1$, $\bar{k}_2=-1/\bar{R}_2$ and by using the spheroidal values of $\bar{R}_1$, $\bar{R}_2$ from Equations 18.54 and 18.55; or, we can use any of the formulas of this chapter simply by using the appropriate values of $\bar{R}_1$ (or $\bar{R}_2$).

CHAPTER 19

Transformations Between N-Systems

GENERAL REMARKS

1. Transformations between coordinate systems arise in geodesy mainly from the practical necessity to linearize computations. The general (ω, ϕ, N) system, in which N is interpreted as the gravitational potential and the effect of the Earth's rotation is included, is most useful for theoretical investigations and is closely related to most systems of measurement; for example, the ν^r in this system are then the directions of the astronomical zenith or plumbline and so enter directly into astronomical observations and into the measurement of horizontal and vertical angles. Nevertheless, we have little numerical knowledge as yet of the curvature parameters in this system; ultimately, if they become known in sufficient detail, the curvature parameters will probably be too irregular to provide a practical basis for calculation over finite distances. It is usual therefore to work in the simpler (ω, ϕ, h) system $(N = h)$ with a regular base surface and to transform the observations accordingly. Moreover, we usually make the base surface a spheroid, which is a close approximation to an actual equipotential surface, so as to ensure that first-order transformation—leading to linear observational equations—shall be sufficient.

2. An alternative would be to use a regular (ω, ϕ, N) system, representing a standard gravitational field in which one of the equipotential N-surfaces is a spheroid—approximating closely to a selected equipotential surface in nature. Calculations over finite distances in such a system, although possible, are not as simple as in the (ω, ϕ, h) system. For certain purposes, we need a standard or model gravitational field, but there seems to be no advantage in making all of the field's equipotentials the coordinate surfaces of the geometric system. Instead, we can calculate the standard gravitational elements at positions given in (ω, ϕ, h) coordinates, an operation which again amounts to coordinate transformation.

3. We shall continue to assume, as we have done throughout this book, that the N-systems share a common Cartesian system whose C^r-axis is parallel to the physical axis of rotation of the Earth at a particular epoch; we shall derive conditions which ensure this arrangement. It may be thought that an unnecessary and an arbitrary restriction thereby is introduced, but this is not so. We cannot transform from one system to another without completely relating the two in some way; the adoption of a third system, common to the two, introduces no more conditions than are necessary and sufficient for this purpose. The adoption of a common *Cartesian* system can also be used to ensure that the space remains flat during the transformation.

4. In addition to specifying the n's (the magnitudes of the scalar gradients N_r), we shall relate the base vectors in the two systems. We do this by means of vector equations, true in either coordinate system. The same vector equations will then hold between *parallel* vectors at other points in space because, in that case, the equations will be true in Cartesian coordinates at the new point—and thus in any coordinates at the new point. The same equations will accordingly serve to relate the base vectors and other vectors associated with them, *either*

(a) at the same point in space after a coordinate transformation, *or*,

(b) at a different point in space in the same coordinate system, in which case the relation will hold true between parallel vectors.

The changes in coordinates in case (a) will usually be small in practice; whereas, in case (b), they may be large. To take advantage of both possibilities, we shall accordingly derive quite general transformation formulas not confined to first-order changes. Quantities in the second N-system (or at the second point in space in the same N-system) will be denoted by overbars.

DIRECTIONS

5. We shall first deal with transformation of directions; for this purpose, it will be convenient to define a few auxiliary angles on the spherical diagram in figure 15. A radius vector of the sphere

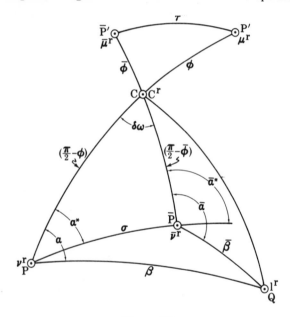

Figure 15.

is drawn parallel to a direction in space (such as one of the normals ν^r); the point P where the radius cuts the sphere can accordingly be said to represent the direction (ν^r). The normal at the other point in space or in the other coordinate system is represented by $\bar{P}$. The Q represents a fixed direction l^r during transformation or a parallel direction at the overbarred point. The C represents the common Cartesian axis so that the latitudes ϕ, $\bar{\phi}$ and the difference in longitude $\delta\omega = (\bar{\omega} - \omega)$ are as shown in the diagram. The great circle $P\bar{P}$ or arc-length

$\sigma = \text{arc cos } (\nu^r \bar{\nu}_r)$ is simply an auxiliary, and so are the angles α^*, $\bar{\alpha}^*$. The azimuths $(\alpha, \bar{\alpha})$ and zenith distances $(\beta, \bar{\beta})$ of the fixed direction Q (or of the parallel directions Q) are as shown.

6. The PP' and $\bar{P}\bar{P}'$ are quadrants so that the vectors represented by P', $\bar{P}'$ are N-surface vectors in the plane containing the normal and C^r; these vectors are accordingly by definition μ^r, $\bar{\mu}^r$. The $P'\bar{P}'$ defines another auxiliary angle τ. The remaining base vectors λ^r, λ^r (not shown in the diagram) are, respectively, the poles (to the right in the diagram) of great circles PCP' and $\bar{P}C\bar{P}'$.

7. The following formulas, collected for easy reference, are obtainable from scalar and vector products or by ordinary spherical trigonometry from the triangles $CP\bar{P}$, $CP'\bar{P}'$,

$$\cos \sigma = \sin \phi \sin \bar{\phi} + \cos \phi \cos \bar{\phi} \cos \delta\omega$$

19.01

$$\cos \tau = \cos \phi \cos \bar{\phi} + \sin \phi \sin \bar{\phi} \cos \delta\omega$$

19.02 $\quad = \sin \alpha^* \sin \bar{\alpha}^* + \cos \alpha^* \cos \bar{\alpha}^* \cos \sigma$

$$\cos \delta\omega = \cos \alpha^* \cos \bar{\alpha}^*$$

19.03 $\qquad + \sin \alpha^* \sin \bar{\alpha}^* \cos \sigma$

$$\sin \phi \sin \delta\omega = -\sin \alpha^* \cos \bar{\alpha}^*$$

19.04 $\qquad + \cos \alpha^* \sin \bar{\alpha}^* \cos \sigma$

$$\sin \bar{\phi} \sin \delta\omega = \cos \alpha^* \sin \bar{\alpha}^*$$

19.05 $\qquad - \sin \alpha^* \cos \bar{\alpha}^* \cos \sigma$

$$\sin \sigma \cos \alpha^* = \cos \phi \sin \bar{\phi}$$

19.06 $\qquad - \sin \phi \cos \bar{\phi} \cos \delta\omega$

$$\sin \sigma \cos \bar{\alpha}^* = -\sin \phi \cos \bar{\phi}$$

19.07 $\qquad + \cos \phi \sin \bar{\phi} \cos \delta\omega$

19.08 $\quad \sin \sigma \sin \bar{\alpha}^* = \cos \phi \sin \delta\omega$

19.09 $\quad \sin \sigma \sin \alpha^* = \cos \bar{\phi} \sin \delta\omega$

$$\cos \bar{\phi} \cos \bar{\alpha}^* = -\sin \phi \sin \sigma$$

19.10 $\qquad + \cos \phi \cos \sigma \cos \alpha^*$

$$\cos \phi \cos \alpha^* = \sin \bar{\phi} \sin \sigma$$

19.11 $\qquad + \cos \bar{\phi} \cos \sigma \cos \bar{\alpha}^*$

$$\cos \bar{\phi} \cos \delta\omega = \cos \phi \cos \sigma$$

19.12 $\qquad - \sin \phi \sin \sigma \cos \alpha^*$

$$\cos \phi \cos \delta\omega = \cos \bar{\phi} \cos \sigma$$

19.13 $$+ \sin \bar{\phi} \sin \sigma \cos \bar{\alpha}^*$$

$$\cot \alpha^* \sin \delta\omega = \cos \phi \tan \bar{\phi}$$

19.14 $$- \sin \phi \cos \delta\omega$$

$$\cot \bar{\alpha}^* \sin \delta\omega = - \cos \bar{\phi} \tan \phi$$

19.15 $$+ \sin \bar{\phi} \cos \delta\omega,$$

together with the following differential relations,

$$\sin \sigma \, d\alpha^* = \sin \alpha^* \cos \sigma \, d\phi + \cos \bar{\phi} \cos \bar{\alpha}^* \, d(\delta\omega)$$

19.16 $$- \cos \phi \sec \bar{\phi} \sin \alpha^* \, d\bar{\phi}$$

$$\sin \sigma \, d\bar{\alpha}^* = \sin \bar{\alpha}^* \sec \phi \cos \bar{\phi} \, d\phi$$

19.17 $$+ \cos \phi \cos \alpha^* d(\delta\omega) - \sin \bar{\alpha}^* \cos \sigma \, d\bar{\phi}$$

$$d\sigma = - \cos \alpha^* \, d\phi$$

19.18 $$+ \cos \phi \sin \alpha^* \, d(\delta\omega) + \cos \bar{\alpha}^* \, d\bar{\phi}.$$

Several of the preceding formulas may be obtained or verified by changing the symbolism between the two ends of the line or between the two co-ordinate systems, that is, by interchanging the overbars and by changing the signs of $\delta\omega$ and σ.

BASE VECTORS

8. We can obtain scalar products of the base vectors from the spherical diagram in figure 15. For example, $\lambda_r \bar{\lambda}^r$ is the cosine of the angle between the great circles PCP' and $\bar{P}C\bar{P}'$, that is, $\cos \delta\omega$. Again, $\bar{\nu}_r \lambda^r$ is the sine of the perpendicular from $\bar{P}$ to the great circle PCP', that is, $\sin \alpha^* \sin \sigma$ or $\sin \delta\omega \cos \bar{\phi}$. Proceeding in this way, we obtain one set of base vectors in terms of the other set as

$$\begin{pmatrix} \bar{\lambda}^r \\ \bar{\mu}^r \\ \bar{\nu}^r \end{pmatrix} =$$

$$\begin{pmatrix} \cos \delta\omega & \sin \phi \sin \delta\omega & -\cos \phi \sin \delta\omega \\ -\sin \bar{\phi} \sin \delta\omega & \cos \tau & -\sin \sigma \cos \bar{\alpha}^* \\ \cos \bar{\phi} \sin \delta\omega & \sin \sigma \cos \alpha^* & \cos \sigma \end{pmatrix} \begin{pmatrix} \lambda^r \\ \mu^r \\ \nu^r \end{pmatrix}.$$

19.19

9. Next, we shall derive this same result in terms of the rotation matrices of § 12–15. Writing

19.20 $$\mathbf{\Phi} = \begin{pmatrix} 1 & 0 & 0 \\ 0 & \sin \phi & \cos \phi \\ 0 & -\cos \phi & \sin \phi \end{pmatrix}$$

19.21 $$\mathbf{\Omega} = \begin{pmatrix} -\sin \omega & \cos \omega & 0 \\ -\cos \omega & -\sin \omega & 0 \\ 0 & 0 & 1 \end{pmatrix}$$

19.22 $$\mathbf{Q} = \mathbf{\Phi\Omega},$$

all of which are orthogonal matrices, together with the transpose

19.23 $$\mathbf{Q}^T = \mathbf{\Omega}^T \mathbf{\Phi}^T,$$

and using Equations 12.012 and 12.013, we have at once

$$\{\bar{\lambda}_r, \bar{\mu}_r, \bar{\nu}_r\} = \bar{\mathbf{Q}}\{A_r, B_r, C_r\}$$

19.24 $$= \bar{\mathbf{Q}}\mathbf{Q}^T\{\lambda_r, \mu_r, \nu_r\}$$

in which the braces signify as usual a column "vector" in the matrix sense. This vector equation holds true for each of the components of the base vectors, covariant or contravariant, in any one coordinate system. Comparing this result with Equation 19.19, we have

$$\bar{\mathbf{Q}}\mathbf{Q}^T = \begin{pmatrix} \cos \delta\omega & \sin \phi \sin \delta\omega & -\cos \phi \sin \delta\omega \\ -\sin \bar{\phi} \sin \delta\omega & \cos \tau & -\sin \sigma \cos \bar{\alpha}^* \\ \cos \bar{\phi} \sin \delta\omega & \sin \sigma \cos \alpha^* & \cos \sigma \end{pmatrix};$$

19.25

we can easily verify this equation by multiplying out the $\mathbf{Q}$-matrices. For easy reference, we add the full expression for $\mathbf{Q}$,

$$\mathbf{Q} = \begin{pmatrix} -\sin \omega & \cos \omega & 0 \\ -\sin \phi \cos \omega & -\sin \phi \sin \omega & \cos \phi \\ \cos \phi \cos \omega & \cos \phi \sin \omega & \sin \phi \end{pmatrix}.$$

19.26

AZIMUTHS AND ZENITH DISTANCES

10. The arbitrary unit vector l^r in figure 15 can be expressed in the following alternative forms

$$l^r = \lambda^r \sin \alpha \sin \beta + \mu^r \cos \alpha \sin \beta + \nu^r \cos \beta$$

$$= \bar{\lambda}^r \sin \bar{\alpha} \sin \bar{\beta} + \bar{\mu}^r \cos \bar{\alpha} \sin \bar{\beta} + \bar{\nu}^r \cos \bar{\beta};$$

using these forms to contract the vector Equation 19.24, we have

$$\{\sin \bar{\alpha} \sin \bar{\beta}, \cos \bar{\alpha} \sin \bar{\beta}, \cos \bar{\beta}\}$$

19.27 $$= \bar{\mathbf{Q}}\mathbf{Q}^T\{\sin \alpha \sin \beta, \cos \alpha \sin \beta, \cos \beta\}.$$

Only two of these three equations for $\bar{\alpha}, \bar{\beta}$ are independent because each term is equivalent to the component of a unit vector so that an identity would result from squaring and adding the equations.

11. Equation 19.27 gives the azimuth and zenith distance of a vector in the transformed (barred) coordinates. The equations also relate the azimuths and zenith distances of two parallel vectors in the same coordinate system at two different points in space so that it is immaterial whether the changes result from coordinate transformation or from parallel transport—or both.

12. In particular, Equation 19.27 can refer to the straight line joining two points in space in any (ω, ϕ, N) coordinate system. The equation would enable us to determine any two of the seven quantities $\alpha, \beta, \bar{\alpha}, \bar{\beta}, \phi, \bar{\phi}, \delta\omega$ from the other five. For example, if $\alpha, \beta, \bar{\alpha}, \bar{\beta}, \phi$ are measured or given, we can determine $\bar{\phi}$ and $\delta\omega$ and so can build up a latitude and azimuth traverse without measuring any more latitudes, although error would be likely to accumulate through the effect of residual (uncorrected) atmospheric refraction on $\beta, \bar{\beta}$. At the other extreme, if $\alpha, \bar{\alpha}, \phi, \bar{\phi}, \delta\omega$ are measured, then we could determine $\beta, \bar{\beta}$ and so could evaluate the refraction. Whatever we do, we must take account of the fact that these seven quantities are related.

ORIENTATION CONDITIONS

13. If we transform from one N-system to another, the seven quantities in the last section cannot be independently chosen, but they must satisfy two conditions—equivalent to the two independent equations in Equation 19.27—to ensure parallelism of the Cartesian axes.
The most common case in practice arises when the changes in (ω, ϕ) coordinates are small. If we write $\bar{\phi} = \phi + \delta\phi$ as we have already written $\bar{\omega} = \omega + \delta\omega$, then it is easy to show to a first order that Equation 19.25 or 19.26 gives

$$\bar{\mathbf{Q}}\mathbf{Q}^T = \mathbf{I} + \begin{pmatrix} 0 & \sin\phi\,\delta\omega & -\cos\phi\,\delta\omega \\ -\sin\phi\,\delta\omega & 0 & -\delta\phi \\ \cos\phi\,\delta\omega & \delta\phi & 0 \end{pmatrix}$$

19.28

where $\mathbf{I}$ as usual is the unit matrix, and Equation 19.27 then reduces to the following two independent equations, connecting the first-order changes in latitude, longitude, azimuth, and zenith distance,

$$\delta\alpha = \sin\phi\,\delta\omega + \cot\beta\,(\sin\alpha\,\delta\phi - \cos\alpha\,\cos\phi\,\delta\omega)$$

$$\delta\beta = -\cos\phi\,\sin\alpha\,\delta\omega - \cos\alpha\,\delta\phi.$$

19.29

14. If β is nearly $90°$ so that the line is almost horizontal, the first equation reduces to

19.30 $\delta\alpha = \sin\phi\,\delta\omega$,

which is independent of the direction chosen as a fixed line in the two coordinate systems and is simply a difference in the azimuths of all nearly horizontal lines emanating from the same point. This is the so-called Laplace equation of classical geodesy, which alone is used in the hope of preserving orientation of the Cartesian axes. But even if $\beta = 90°$ is on all observed lines emanating from a point, this fact does nothing to satisfy the second condition of Equations 19.29, which does not depend on β at all and cannot therefore be satisfied by choosing favorable values of β. Satisfaction of the equations of Equations 19.29 for a particular (α, β) ensures that the Cartesian components of the corresponding direction are the same in both coordinate systems; but this fact is not sufficient to ensure parallelism of the Cartesian axes because it would still be possible to rotate either system about the (α, β) direction without any effect on its Cartesian components. To ensure parallelism of the Cartesian axes, we need to satisfy both Equations 19.29 for two different directions.

15. It is clear therefore that the simple Laplace azimuth Equation 19.30 does not preserve orientation at a single point during a change of N-coordinate systems, such as the change from an astronomical (ω, ϕ, N) system to a standard gravitational field or to a geodetic (ω, ϕ, h) system. It is sometimes claimed that the repeated application of Equation 19.30 at different points connected by triangulation would not only ensure correct initial orientation, but would also preserve orientation throughout the network, even though the second necessary condition in Equation 19.29 is ignored everywhere. No doubt, it would be sufficient to satisfy one of the conditions of Equations 19.29 at two or more widely separated points instead of both at one point, provided the points are rigidly connected by error-free triangulation; but it is difficult to see how this procedure can initiate and preserve correct orientation as well as serve to adjust the intervening triangulation. The most that can reasonably be said is that if the one condition of Equation 19.30 is applied at a number of points during the adjustment of a triangulation, the condition will tend to be satisfied at intermediate points; but that fact does not imply that the adjusted triangulation is also properly oriented everywhere. It should be said, however, that, until recently, no other course has been open to the triangulator.

Owing to the effect of atmospheric refraction on zenith distances, the triangulator could not satisfy both conditions of Equations 19.29 to the same degree of accuracy; the satisfaction of one condition may have some beneficial effect.

THE R AND S MATRICES

16. We now introduce the matrices of (ω, ϕ, N) components of the base vectors from §12–27 and §12–33,

$$\mathbf{R} = \begin{pmatrix} \lambda^1 \ \lambda^2 \ \lambda^3 \\ \mu^1 \ \mu^2 \ \mu^3 \\ \nu^1 \ \nu^2 \ \nu^3 \end{pmatrix} = \begin{pmatrix} -k_1 \sec \phi & -t_1 & 0 \\ -t_1 \sec \phi & -k_2 & 0 \\ \gamma_1 \sec \phi & \gamma_2 & n \end{pmatrix}$$

19.31

$$\mathbf{S} = \begin{pmatrix} \lambda_1 \ \lambda_2 \ \lambda_3 \\ \mu_1 \ \mu_2 \ \mu_3 \\ \nu_1 \ \nu_2 \ \nu_3 \end{pmatrix}$$

$$= \begin{pmatrix} -k_2 \cos \phi / K & t_1 / K & \sec \phi \ \partial(1/n)/\partial\omega \\ t_1 \cos \phi / K & -k_1 / K & \partial(1/n)/\partial\phi \\ 0 & 0 & (1/n) \end{pmatrix}.$$

19.32

Because the base vectors are unit orthogonal vectors so that, for example, $\lambda^r \lambda_r = 1$, $\lambda^r \mu_r = 0$, etc., we have also

19.33 $$\mathbf{R}\mathbf{S}^T = \mathbf{S}\mathbf{R}^T = \mathbf{I}$$

in which **I** as usual is the unit matrix; thus, we have

$$\mathbf{R}^{-1} = \mathbf{S}^T$$

19.34 $$\mathbf{S}^{-1} = \mathbf{R}^T.$$

17. We also define

$$\bar{\mathbf{R}} = (\bar{\lambda}^1, \ldots) = (-\bar{k}_1 \sec \bar{\phi}, \ldots)$$

and $\bar{\mathbf{S}}$ similarly as the corresponding matrices in the $(\bar{\omega}, \bar{\phi}, \bar{N})$ system, that is, the matrices of the $(\bar{\omega}, \bar{\phi}, \bar{N})$ components of the base vectors *of the barred system*. It should be noted from Equation 19.24 that

$$\bar{\mathbf{Q}}\mathbf{Q}^T\mathbf{R}$$

does *not* give $\bar{\mathbf{R}}$; it gives the (ω, ϕ, N) components of the base vectors of the barred system. To transform these components to $(\bar{\omega}, \bar{\phi}, \bar{N})$ components, we use the vector transformation formula of Equation 1.18, equivalent to postmultiplying by the transpose of the transformation matrix of Equa-

tion 19.37 in §19–21. To verify this, we have

$$\bar{\mathbf{R}} = \bar{\mathbf{Q}}\mathbf{Q}^T\mathbf{R}(\bar{\mathbf{R}}^T\bar{\mathbf{Q}}\mathbf{Q}^T\mathbf{S})^T = \bar{\mathbf{Q}}\mathbf{Q}^T\mathbf{R}\mathbf{S}^T\mathbf{Q}\bar{\mathbf{Q}}^T\bar{\mathbf{R}} = \bar{\mathbf{R}},$$

using Equation 19.33 and the fact that the **Q**'s are orthogonal matrices.

18. If one of the systems is a symmetric (ω, ϕ, h) system, the corresponding **R** and **S** matrices become diagonal; this introduces a considerable simplification into all matrix equations containing **R** and **S**. The necessary modifications can be made at sight, using the results of Chapter 18.

TENSOR TRANSFORMATION MATRICES

19. To transform vectors and tensors between Cartesian and (ω, ϕ, N) coordinate systems, we need the partial differentials $\partial x/\partial\omega$, $\partial N/\partial y$, etc. These are all components of the Cartesian vectors A_r, etc., in the (ω, ϕ, N) system. For example, we have from Equations 12.009

$$A_r = (\partial x/\partial\omega, \partial x/\partial\phi, \partial x/\partial N),$$

while the contravariant components give

$$A^r = (\partial\omega/\partial x, \partial\phi/\partial x, \partial N/\partial x).$$

If we use Equation 12.013 and substitute the (ω, ϕ, N) components of the base vectors, we then have the complete matrix of transformation factors as

$$\begin{pmatrix} \partial x/\partial\omega & \partial x/\partial\phi & \partial x/\partial N \\ \partial y/\partial\omega & \partial y/\partial\phi & \partial y/\partial N \\ \partial z/\partial\omega & \partial z/\partial\phi & \partial z/\partial N \end{pmatrix} = \begin{pmatrix} A_1 \ A_2 \ A_3 \\ B_1 \ B_2 \ B_3 \\ C_1 \ C_2 \ C_3 \end{pmatrix} = \mathbf{Q}^T\mathbf{S}.$$

19.35

The Jacobian of the transformation is

$$|\mathbf{Q}^T||\mathbf{S}| = |\mathbf{S}| = e^{ijk}\lambda_i\mu_j\nu_k = \sqrt{|g_{rs}|} = \cos \phi/(nK).$$

20. In the same way, the inverse transformation is

$$\begin{pmatrix} \partial\omega/\partial x & \partial\phi/\partial x & \partial N/\partial x \\ \partial\omega/\partial y & \partial\phi/\partial y & \partial N/\partial y \\ \partial\omega/\partial z & \partial\phi/\partial z & \partial N/\partial z \end{pmatrix} = \begin{pmatrix} A^1 \ A^2 \ A^3 \\ B^1 \ B^2 \ B^3 \\ C^1 \ C^2 \ C^3 \end{pmatrix} = \mathbf{Q}^T\mathbf{R}$$

19.36

with the Jacobian $(nK \sec \phi)$.

21. To transform between (ω, ϕ, N) systems, we have, for example,

$$\frac{\partial\bar{\omega}}{\partial\omega} = \frac{\partial\bar{\omega}}{\partial x}\frac{\partial x}{\partial\omega} + \frac{\partial\bar{\omega}}{\partial y}\frac{\partial y}{\partial\omega} + \frac{\partial\bar{\omega}}{\partial z}\frac{\partial z}{\partial\omega}$$

so that

$$\begin{pmatrix} \partial\bar\omega/\partial\omega & \partial\bar\omega/\partial\phi & \partial\bar\omega/\partial N \\ \partial\bar\phi/\partial\omega & \partial\bar\phi/\partial\phi & \partial\bar\phi/\partial N \\ \partial\bar N/\partial\omega & \partial\bar N/\partial\phi & \partial\bar N/\partial N \end{pmatrix} = \overline{(\mathbf{Q}^T\mathbf{R})}^T\mathbf{Q}^T\mathbf{S}$$

19.37 $$= \bar{\mathbf{R}}^T\bar{\mathbf{Q}}\mathbf{Q}^T\mathbf{S}.$$

PARALLEL TRANSPORT OF VECTORS

22. To obtain the (ω, ϕ, N) components of parallel vectors $(l^r, \bar l^r)$ at two different points in space (one point overbarred), we can use the vector equation at the barred point

$$\bar l^r = \bar A^r(A_s l^s) + \bar B^r(B_s l^s) + \bar C^r(C_s l^s),$$

which expresses the equality of Cartesian components at the two points. We have

$$\begin{pmatrix} \bar l^1 \\ \bar l^2 \\ \bar l^3 \end{pmatrix} = \begin{pmatrix} \bar A^1 & \bar B^1 & \bar C^1 \\ \bar A^2 & \bar B^2 & \bar C^2 \\ \bar A^3 & \bar B^3 & \bar C^3 \end{pmatrix} \begin{pmatrix} A_1 & A_2 & A_3 \\ B_1 & B_2 & B_3 \\ C_1 & C_2 & C_3 \end{pmatrix} \begin{pmatrix} l^1 \\ l^2 \\ l^3 \end{pmatrix}$$

$$= \overline{(\mathbf{Q}^T\mathbf{R})}^T\mathbf{Q}^T\mathbf{S}\{l^1, l^2, l^3\}$$

$$= \bar{\mathbf{R}}^T\bar{\mathbf{Q}}\mathbf{Q}^T\mathbf{S}\{l^1, l^2, l^3\}$$

19.38 $$= \bar{\mathbf{R}}^T\bar{\mathbf{Q}}\mathbf{Q}^T\{\sin\alpha\sin\beta, \cos\alpha\sin\beta, \cos\beta\}$$

if α, β are the azimuth and zenith distance of l^r. This equation is easily verified from Equation 19.27. The covariant components are similarly given by

$$\{\bar l_1, \bar l_2, \bar l_3\} = \bar{\mathbf{S}}^T\bar{\mathbf{Q}}\mathbf{Q}^T\mathbf{R}\{l_1, l_2, l_3\}$$

19.39 $$= \bar{\mathbf{S}}^T\bar{\mathbf{Q}}\mathbf{Q}^T\{\sin\alpha\sin\beta, \cos\alpha\sin\beta, \cos\beta\}.$$

THE DEFLECTION VECTOR

23. We define the deflection vector Δ^r as the change in the ν^r on transformation between N-systems so that we have

19.40 $$\Delta^r = \bar\nu^r - \nu^r.$$

In the usual geodetic application, the overbarred vector will refer to the astronomical (ω, ϕ, N) system with N interpreted as the geopotential, that is, the gravitational potential with allowance for the Earth's rotation. The unbarred vector will refer to the geodetic system, usually an (ω, ϕ, h) system with a spheroidal base.

24. The definition does not require the change of coordinates to be small. For example, if l_r is a unit vector which remains fixed during the trans-

formation, such as the direction between two ground stations, then the component of deflection in that direction is

19.41 $$\Delta^r l_r = \cos\bar\beta - \cos\beta$$

where $\bar\beta$, β are the astronomical and geodetic zenith distances, respectively. This relation is rigorously true even for large deflections.

25. The definition does, however, agree with the usual first-order conventions in classical geodesy. For small changes in coordinates, we have at once from Equations 19.24 and 19.28

19.42 $$\Delta^r = \bar\nu^r - \nu^r = (\cos\phi\,\delta\omega)\lambda^r + (\delta\phi)\mu^r$$

in which $\delta\phi = \bar\phi - \phi$ is the astronomical minus the geodetic latitude; similarly, $\delta\omega = \bar\omega - \omega$ is the astronomical minus the geodetic longitude of the point under consideration. To a first order, the meridian and parallel components of the deflection vector are accordingly $\delta\phi$ and $\cos\phi\,\delta\omega$ as in the classical conception.

26. We can express the deflection vector rigorously from Equations 19.24 and 19.25 as

$$\Delta^r = (\cos\bar\phi\sin\delta\omega)\lambda^r$$

19.43 $$+ (\sin\sigma\cos\alpha^*)\mu^r - 2\sin^2(\sigma/2)\nu^r,$$

which holds true also for the change in the ν^r between two widely separated points, if we use Cartesian coordinates or if we interpret $\bar\nu^r$ in the usual way as a parallel vector at the unbarred point.

CHANGE IN COORDINATES

27. Another way of viewing this question is to consider the differences in the coordinates themselves,

$$\delta\omega = \bar\omega - \omega$$
$$\delta\phi = \bar\phi - \phi$$
$$\delta N = \bar N - N,$$

as a measure of "deflection," with an appropriate choice of unit for the N's. This method is sometimes useful in considering changes in the "deflections" between two points in the field; and for this purpose, we require their gradients.

28. Using Equation 19.31, Equations 12.046, 12.047, and 12.001 can be put in the matrix form

$$\{\bar{\omega}_r, \bar{\phi}_r, \bar{N}_r\} = \bar{\mathbf{R}}^T\{\bar{\lambda}_r, \bar{\mu}_r, \bar{\nu}_r\}$$

$$= \bar{\mathbf{R}}^T\bar{\mathbf{Q}}\mathbf{Q}^T\{\lambda_r, \mu_r, \nu_r\}$$

$$= \bar{\mathbf{R}}^T\bar{\mathbf{Q}}\mathbf{Q}^T\mathbf{S}\{\omega_r, \phi_r, N_r\}$$

19.44 $$= \bar{\mathbf{S}}^{-1}\bar{\mathbf{Q}}\mathbf{Q}^T\mathbf{S}\{\omega_r, \phi_r, N_r\}$$

in which we have used Equations 19.24 and 19.34 so that

$$\{(\delta\omega)_r, (\delta\phi)_r, (\delta N)_r\} = (\bar{\mathbf{S}}^{-1}\bar{\mathbf{Q}}\mathbf{Q}^T\mathbf{S} - \mathbf{I})\{\omega_r, \phi_r, N_r\}$$

19.45 $$= (\bar{\mathbf{R}}^T\bar{\mathbf{Q}}\mathbf{Q}^T - \mathbf{R}^T)\{\lambda_r, \mu_r, \nu_r\}.$$

29. In evaluating Equation 19.45 for small $\delta\omega$, $\delta\phi$, we can use Equation 19.28; but there is no guarantee that the changes in the curvatures in the **R** or **S** matrices will also be small.

30. If we complete the three vector equations in Equation 19.45 and contract in turn with λ^r, μ^r, ν^r, then, if elements of length in the direction of the base vectors are $d\lambda$, $d\mu$, $d\nu$, we have

$$\mathbf{M} = \begin{pmatrix} \dfrac{\partial(\delta\omega)}{\partial\lambda} & \dfrac{\partial(\delta\omega)}{\partial\mu} & \dfrac{\partial(\delta\omega)}{\partial\nu} \\[2mm] \dfrac{\partial(\delta\phi)}{\partial\lambda} & \dfrac{\partial(\delta\phi)}{\partial\mu} & \dfrac{\partial(\delta\phi)}{\partial\nu} \\[2mm] \dfrac{\partial(\delta N)}{\partial\lambda} & \dfrac{\partial(\delta N)}{\partial\mu} & \dfrac{\partial(\delta N)}{\partial\nu} \end{pmatrix} = \bar{\mathbf{R}}^T\bar{\mathbf{Q}}\mathbf{Q}^T - \mathbf{R}^T,$$

19.46

giving components of the "deflections" in the directions of the base vectors.

31. By transposing the equation

$$\mathbf{M} = \bar{\mathbf{R}}^T\bar{\mathbf{Q}}\mathbf{Q}^T - \mathbf{R}^T,$$

we have

19.47 $$\mathbf{R} + \mathbf{M}^T = \mathbf{Q}\bar{\mathbf{Q}}^T\bar{\mathbf{R}} = (\bar{\mathbf{Q}}\mathbf{Q}^T)^T\bar{\mathbf{R}},$$

which gives us a relation between the **R**'s; from this, we have a relation between the parameters k_1, k_2, t_1, γ_1, γ_2 and the components of the "deflections."

32. We may also require the components of the "deflections" in the direction of a unit vector

$$l^r = \lambda^r \sin\alpha \sin\beta + \mu^r \cos\alpha \sin\beta + \nu^r \cos\beta$$

in azimuth α, zenith distance β, and arc element dl. Contracting Equation 19.45 with l^r, we have at once

$$\left\{\frac{\partial(\delta\omega)}{\partial l}, \frac{\partial(\delta\phi)}{\partial l}, \frac{\partial(\delta N)}{\partial l}\right\}$$

$$= (\bar{\mathbf{R}}^T\bar{\mathbf{Q}}\mathbf{Q}^T - \mathbf{R}^T)\{\sin\alpha \sin\beta, \cos\alpha \sin\beta, \cos\beta\}\cdot$$

19.48

33. It is clear from Equation 19.44 that

$$\mathbf{Q}^T\mathbf{S}\{\omega_r, \phi_r, N_r\} = \bar{\mathbf{Q}}^T\bar{\mathbf{S}}\{\bar{\omega}_r, \bar{\phi}_r, \bar{N}_r\}$$

is an invariant which has the same value in any (ω, ϕ, N) system; it is useful to inquire what this invariant may be. Using Equation 19.35, we have

$$\mathbf{Q}^T\mathbf{S}\{\omega_r, \phi_r, N_r\} = \begin{pmatrix} A_1 A_2 A_3 \\ B_1 B_2 B_3 \\ C_1 C_2 C_3 \end{pmatrix}\begin{pmatrix} \omega_r \\ \phi_r \\ N_r \end{pmatrix}$$

$$= \begin{pmatrix} \omega_r(\partial x/\partial\omega) + \phi_r(\partial x/\partial\phi) + N_r(\partial x/\partial N) \\ \cdots \qquad \cdots \qquad \cdots \\ \cdots \qquad \cdots \qquad \cdots \end{pmatrix}$$

$$= \{x_r, y_r, z_r\}$$

19.49 $$= \{A_r, B_r, C_r\},$$

using Equations 12.009. The invariant is accordingly the common Cartesian system.

CONTENTS

Part III

CHAPTER 20

The Newtonian Gravitational Field

SUMMARY OF MECHANICAL PRINCIPLES

1. In this chapter, we shall show that the geometry of the Newtonian gravitational field can be treated as a special case of a (ω, ϕ, N) coordinate system in which N is the potential, the N-surfaces are equipotentials, and the form of N is restricted by the Newtonian law of gravitation.

The Central Field

2. In a gravitational field set up by a single particle of mass m, the *force of attraction* on another particle of unit mass at a distance r from the first particle is, by Newton's law,

$$Gm/r^2$$

in which G is the gravitational constant. The direction of the force is toward the massive particle along the line joining the two particles. The particle of unit mass is usually known as a *test particle* because the notion of such a particle serves to materialize the gravitational force and so helps us to explore the field; there must be at least two particles in the field for Newtonian gravitation to have any meaning.

3. The *potential* is usually defined physically as the negative of the work done by the force of attraction on a test particle of unit mass in moving the test particle from an infinite distance to the distance r from the massive particle or the positive work which must somehow be done against the force of attraction to remove the test particle to an infinite distance. The potential in a field set up by a single particle of mass m is accordingly

20.01 $$-\int_{\infty}^{r} \frac{Gm}{r^2} \times (-dr) = -\frac{Gm}{r},$$

which is opposite in sign to the usual geodetic convention. We shall, however, use the physical convention, which accords better with mathematical conventions. The work done by the force of attraction in moving the test particle from infinity is considered to be stored as available energy, known as *potential energy*, which is accordingly the negative of the potential.

4. The equipotential surfaces in a central field set up by a single massive particle are evidently spheres centered on the attracting particle; the outward-drawn unit normal to the equipotential surfaces is the gradient of r, that is, r_s. If we take N as the potential, then by covariant differentiation of Equation 20.01, we have

20.02 $$N_s = n\nu_s = (Gm/r^2)r_s$$

in which n, the "distance function" of the family of N-surfaces obtained from Equation 12.001, is seen to be the magnitude of the attracting force whose direction is $-\nu_s$. Differentiating Equation 20.02 again, we have

$$N_{st} = -\frac{2Gm}{r^3} r_s r_t + \frac{Gm}{r^2} r_{st}$$

$$= -\frac{2Gm}{r^3} \nu_s \nu_t + \frac{Gm}{r^2} \nu_{st}.$$

If we contract this equation with the metric tensor g^{st} and use Equation 7.19, together with the fact that the mean curvature H of the spherical N-surfaces is $(-1/r)$, we find that the potential satisfies the Laplace equation

20.03 $$\Delta N = g^{rs}N_{rs} = 0$$

which, expanded in Cartesian coordinates, is

20.04 $$\frac{\partial^2 N}{\partial x^2} + \frac{\partial^2 N}{\partial y^2} + \frac{\partial^2 N}{\partial z^2} = 0.$$

It is an essential part of the Newtonian system that the space should be flat and unbounded because the expressions of force and potential require r to be a finite radial distance measured in a straight line; the field must extend to infinity to satisfy Equation 20.01. Accordingly, we can use simple Euclidean geometry and can choose Cartesian coordinates.

5. If F_s is the force vector of magnitude Gm/r^2 and direction $-r_s$ or $-\nu_s$, then Equation 20.02 is equivalent to

20.05 $$F_s = -N_s = -n\nu_s,$$

which means that the force vector is the negative gradient of the potential. Accordingly, the field is completely specified if we know the scalar potential N at each point of the field; we shall find that this statement applies also to more complicated fields.

Superposition of Fields

6. In dealing with the geometrical properties of more complicated fields, we shall continue to use the symbols N and n, respectively, for the potential and the magnitude of the gravitational force—in place of the more usual symbols V (or W) and g—because this will enable us to use all of the more general formulas of Part II as they stand. However, we shall also use V (or W) and g in expressing final results or when the physical properties of the field predominate.

7. We can generalize the simple central field set up by a single massive particle to the more complicated field set up by any number of massive particles in an attracting body of finite dimensions by invoking the *principle of superposition*, which simply states that the total effect on the test particle will be the sum of the effects arising from each individual massive particle. The total potential will be the sum of the individual potentials

$$\sum -Gm/r;$$

the total potential will satisfy the Laplace equation

because each term in the summation satisfies the invariant form of the Laplace Equation 20.03, regardless of the coordinate system. We do not, for example, require the origin of Cartesian coordinates to be at an attracting particle as in § 20–4; the origin could be at the test particle or anywhere else, and the Laplacian property would still hold true.

8. The forces of attraction, unlike the scalar potentials, have direction as well as magnitude and would have to be added vectorially. But it is evident that the vector Equation 20.05 still holds true (and holds in any coordinates) between the gradient of the total potential and the vector sum—or resultant—of the individual force vectors, even though the potential no longer has the simple form $-Gm/r$ and the magnitude n of the resultant force is no longer Gm/r^2. The direction ν_r of the gradient of the potential N is no longer the radial direction from a Cartesian origin, but is the unit normal to the equipotential surface or N-surface passing through the test particle, as in Equation 1.21. If the attracting body is the Earth, ν_r is the direction of the zenith at the test particle or at the point under consideration, and $-\nu_s$ is the direction of the plumbline or the direction of the resultant force.

The Effect of Rotation

9. All the previously mentioned conclusions apply to the attraction of a static body. The Earth, however, rotates, which means that particles attached to it, or resting on it, are subject to centrifugal force acting generally against the gravitational attraction. Because the effects of the two forces are, for the most part, indistinguishable, it is usual to combine them into a single force called "gravity." The scalar whose gradient is equivalent to the resultant force of gravity, including the centrifugal force, is known as the *geopotential*.

10. We shall consider the rotation of the Earth in more detail in § 21–55 through § 21–59; for the present, it will be sufficient to assume rotation with uniform angular velocity $\tilde{\omega}$ about a physical axis which we shall suppose is fixed in the Earth. The direction of this physical axis is not fixed in relation to the stars, but that does not at present concern us. It will be shown in § 21–56 that the center of mass, which we shall choose as Cartesian origin, must lie on the physical axis of rotation, which we shall choose as z-axis of coordinates, unit vector C_r. The other Cartesian vectors $\bar{A}_r$, $\bar{B}_r$ (fig. 16) are

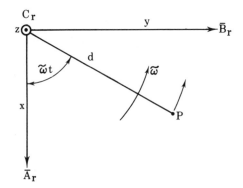

Figure 16.

fixed in space, not in the Earth, in the sense that they do not rotate with the Earth. The linear velocity vector of a point P at a distance d from the z-axis is then

20.06 $\tilde{\omega}d(\bar{B}_r \cos \tilde{\omega}t - \bar{A}_r \sin \tilde{\omega}t)$

in which t is the time which has elapsed since the point P crossed the xz-plane. The acceleration vector is the intrinsic time derivative of the velocity vector, that is,

$$-\tilde{\omega}^2 d(\bar{B}_r \sin \tilde{\omega}t + \bar{A}_r \cos \tilde{\omega}t) = -\tilde{\omega}^2(x\bar{A}_r + y\bar{B}_r)$$
$$= -\tilde{\omega}^2(xx_r + yy_r)$$
20.07 $$= -\tfrac{1}{2}\tilde{\omega}^2(x^2 + y^2)_r.$$

We can consider this expression to be the force, acting on a test particle of unit mass required to maintain the particle on the Earth's surface. The force is directed inward and must come from the force of attraction whose inward sense is

$$-n\nu_r = -N_r.$$

If we assume that the residual force is derived from a geopotential M with the same conventions as for N, then we must have

$$-M_r = -N_r + \tfrac{1}{2}\tilde{\omega}^2(x^2 + y^2)_r.$$

Integrating this equation, subject to the condition that there is no rotational effect on the axis $(x = y = 0)$, we have

$$M = N - \tfrac{1}{2}\tilde{\omega}^2(x^2 + y^2)$$
20.08 $$= N - \tfrac{1}{2}\tilde{\omega}^2 d^2.$$

The geopotential at P of a particle of mass m at the origin is, for example,

$$-Gm/r - \tfrac{1}{2}\tilde{\omega}^2 d^2.$$

The Laplacian of Equation 20.08 is

20.09 $$\Delta M = -2\tilde{\omega}^2$$

because $\Delta N = 0$ so that the geopotential is not a harmonic function whose Laplacian would be zero. We may note, however, that the Laplacian of the geopotential, in addition to being independent of the coordinate system, is also independent of the location of the rotation axis.

11. Reverting to the original notation, we can say that the basic gradient equation

$$N_r = n\nu_r$$

represents the Newtonian gravitational field of the rotating Earth if N is the geopotential, as defined in §20–9, if n is "gravity," and if ν_r is the outward-drawn normal to the N-surfaces, that is, the level surfaces of the combined attraction and rotation. The unit normal ν_r is accordingly the direction of the astronomical zenith as revealed by instrumental spirit levels. The remaining coordinates (ω, ϕ) of a (ω, ϕ, N) system are the astronomical longitude and latitude in relation to the physical axis of rotation, which we have assumed is fixed in the Earth, and in relation to an initial meridian plane defined by the physical axis and by the zenith at some fixed point on the Earth's surface. The Newtonian law of gravity is expressed by the condition

$$\Delta N = -2\tilde{\omega}^2,$$

and this alone distinguishes the system from any other (ω, ϕ, N) system. Subject to this condition, the general geometry of a (ω, ϕ, N) system, as developed in Part II, applies in its entirety.

12. In the basic geometry of the (ω, ϕ, N) system, we consider the Cartesian axes A_r, B_r to be fixed in relation to all points belonging to the system, that is, fixed in the Earth and rotating with the Earth. We can derive from figure 16 the following relations between the A_r, B_r axes, revolving like the point P, and the inertial $\bar{A}_r$, $\bar{B}_r$ axes, which are fixed in space,

$$A_r = \bar{A}_r \cos \tilde{\omega}t + \bar{B}_r \sin \tilde{\omega}t$$
20.10 $$B_r = -\bar{A}_r \sin \tilde{\omega}t + \bar{B}_r \cos \tilde{\omega}t.$$

In these equations, t is the time which has elapsed since the two sets of axes coincided. So far as the condition

$$\Delta N = -2\tilde{\omega}^2$$

is concerned, it does not matter whether we consider the point P as moving in relation to the fixed axes $\bar{A}_r$, $\bar{B}_r$ or the axes A_r, B_r as moving in relation to $\bar{A}_r$, $\bar{B}_r$ because the condition is invariant and is therefore unaffected by the choice of coordinate system. We could say that substitution of the geopotential for the static attraction has had the effect of reducing the whole system to rest.

13. If we are dealing with an object such as an artificial satellite, which is not attached to the rotating Earth, then, in the absence of any other impressed force, the only force acting on the satellite would be the gradient of the attraction potential $-V_r$, and the Newtonian condition would be $\Delta V = 0$. In accordance with Newton's second law, the equations of motion of a satellite of unit mass *relative to fixed axes* $\bar{A}_r$, $\bar{B}_r$, C_r would be

20.11 $\dfrac{\delta^2 \rho_r}{\delta t^2} = \dfrac{\delta v_r}{\delta t} = -V_r,$

the left-hand member of which is the acceleration vector—that is, the second intrinsic time derivative of the position vector ρ_r. The second member of Equation 20.11 is the intrinsic time derivative of the velocity vector of the satellite relative to the fixed axes $\bar{A}_r$, $\bar{B}_r$, C_r. The attraction potential at a fixed point in space would not be constant, but would generally vary with time as the unsymmetrical field rotates with the Earth. The coordinates of terrestrial observation stations or tracking stations would also change with time.

14. If we refer the motion of the satellite to rotating axes, A_r, B_r, C_r fixed in the Earth, the equations of motion will include three forces: The force of attraction $-V_r$; the centrifugal or centripetal force in Equation 20.07 which, being the gradient of a scalar, can be combined with $-V_r$ as the force of "gravity" arising from the geopotential; and the *Coriolis force* which is twice the vector product of the angular rotation vector ($\omega^s = \tilde{\omega} C^s$) and the apparent velocity vector $\bar{v}_r$ of the satellite relative to the moving axes A_r, B_r, C_r. We have

20.12 $\dfrac{\delta \bar{v}_r}{\delta t} = -W_r - 2\epsilon_{rst}(\tilde{\omega}C^s)\bar{v}^t$

in which W is the geopotential. To offset the extra complication in the equations of motion, the geopotential would be a function of coordinates in the (A_r, B_r, C_r) system only and would not vary with time. The coordinates of tracking stations in the same system would also be independent of time. The equations of satellite motion referred to rotating axes are considered more fully in Chapter 28.

THE POISSON EQUATION

15. If the test particle or the point P at which the potential is required were to coincide with a massive

particle, then the potential arising from the massive particle would be infinite and could no longer be added to the potential set up by other particles. Therefore, all the preceding argument would break down. In particular, we could not say that the Laplacian of the total potential at points inside or on matter is zero. The difficulty can be overcome by some limiting process involving the temporary removal of matter to form a cavity whose dimensions are finally reduced indefinitely. However, we shall approach the problem by a different route more in line with modern geodetic applications. This route indicates more clearly what assumptions are being made.

16. We consider first the field set up by a single particle of mass m at a point O (fig. 17) and suppose

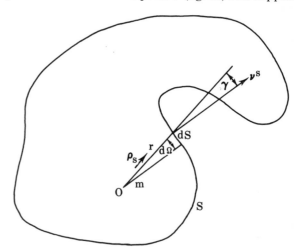

Figure 17.

that O is surrounded by an arbitrary closed surface S. At a point on the surface whose position vector from O is ρ_s, the force vector is

$$F_s = (-G_m/r^2)(\rho_s/r),$$

directed toward O. We shall apply the divergence theorem (§ 9–13) to this vector. If ν^s is the outward-drawn unit normal to the closed surface, then the surface integral in the divergence theorem will be

$$\int F_r \nu^r dS = -\int (Gm/r^2) \cos \gamma \, dS$$

$$= -\int Gm d\Omega = -4\pi Gm$$

where $d\Omega$ is the element of solid angle subtended at O by the element of surface area dS. If the elementary cone ($d\Omega$) is extended and cuts the surface again, it would have to do so twice more as we can see from figure 17; the corresponding extra contributions to the surface integral would cancel so that the form of the surface is immaterial as long as it is closed. If the mass m is outside the surface, then the elementary cone would cut the surface twice (or an even number of times); again, the contributions to the integral would cancel, although the force F_r on the surface arising from this external mass would not be zero. Applying the principle of superposition to all the masses inside and outside the surface, we can accordingly say that

20.13 $$\int F_r \nu^r dS = -4\pi GM.$$

In this result, due to Gauss, F_r is the vector sum of all forces at a point on the surface arising from all masses *inside and outside* the surface S; M is the sum of all masses *inside* the surface. If, instead of a number of discrete masses, we have a continuous distribution of matter, we can write

$$M = \int \rho \, dv$$

where ρ is the density of a volume element dv and the integral is taken over the whole volume enclosed by the surface S. Transforming the first member of Equation 20.13 by the divergence theorem and using Equation 20.05, we have

$$\int g^{rs} F_{rs} dv = -\int \Delta N dv = -4\pi G \int \rho \, dv$$

or

$$\int (\Delta N - 4\pi G\rho) dv = 0.$$

But the initial closed surface S (and therefore its enclosed volume) is quite arbitrary, so the integrand of this last integral must be zero at all points of the volume; we then have

20.14 $$\Delta N = 4\pi G\rho$$

in which ρ is the density at the point where the Laplacian of the potential is taken. In deriving this result, which is known as Poisson's equation, we use only the inverse square law of force and the principle of superposition and make no other assumptions at all.

17. Also, we verify that at any point in empty space ($\rho = 0$), we have

$$\Delta N = 0.$$

The potential at points attached to a body rotating with constant angular velocity $\bar{\omega}$ about the z-axis was modified in Equation 20.08 by subtracting

$$\tfrac{1}{2}\bar{\omega}^2(x^2 + y^2)$$

from the static potential; we must do the same for points within the rotating body. The full Poisson equation modified for rotation is accordingly

20.15 $$\Delta M = 4\pi G\rho - 2\bar{\omega}^2$$

in which M represents the geopotential.

18. If we cross from a region of empty space into a region occupied by matter, the potential must satisfy Laplace's equation on one side of the surface—separating the two regions—and Poisson's equation on the other side. We conclude that some of the second derivatives of the potential at least are discontinuous across such a surface. A similar conclusion applies to a surface within the attracting body, if the density is discontinuous across the surface. In that case, we can form Equation 20.15 for two points close to and on opposite sides of the surface and subtract; the discontinuities in the second derivatives are then equal to $4\pi G\bar{\rho}$ where $\bar{\rho}$ is the difference in density across the surface.

The Newtonian System—General Remarks

19. The Newtonian system has received massive support from observations on the outer planets in the solar system, which indicates that the inverse square law at least is true to within the precision of modern observations. The system does not account for the observed advance in the perihelion of Mercury, the nearest planet to the Sun. However, this discrepancy has been accounted for by high-velocity relativistic effects, which are not at present (1968) measurable and are unlikely ever to be significant in the case of near-Earth satellites. In short, the system has been amply verified in the case of a few near-spherical attracting bodies whose dimensions are small compared with their distances apart, in which case the principle of superposition is involved to a limited extent only. But it has never been demonstrated to the degree of accuracy now attainable that this principle of superposition applies close to, or actually on, a large unsymmetrical mass such as the Earth. An opportunity to do so may arise in reconciling results from satellites with those from ground observations. There are already indications, through the consistency obtained in results from satellites at different heights, that the effect of any departure from the principle becomes inappreciable at satellite distances from the Earth.

GEOMETRY OF THE FIELD

20. It is clear from Equations 20.05 and 12.001 that the field can be represented by the coordinate system of Chapter 12. In this coordinate system, N is the potential, the N-surfaces are equipotentials, n is the magnitude of the resultant force, and ν_r is the unit normal to the N-surfaces—the negative direction of the resultant force—and the unit tangent to the lines of force. The unit normal ν_r is also the apparent vertical and defines the (ω, ϕ) coordinates, that is, the longitude and latitude of the apparent vertical in relation to Cartesian axes fixed in the Earth in accordance with Equations 12.003, 12.004, and 12.005. The Cartesian z-axis coincides with, or is at least parallel to, the axis of rotation.

21. The Newtonian law of gravity is necessarily and sufficiently expressed by making ΔN

(a) zero in a static field at points not occupied by matter; or

(b) $-2\tilde\omega^2$ in a field rotating with constant angular velocity $\tilde\omega$; or

(c) $4\pi G\rho$ at points in a static field occupied by matter of density ρ, G being the gravitational constant; or

(d) $(4\pi G\rho - 2\tilde\omega^2)$ in the rotating field at points occupied by matter.

Subject to whichever of these restrictions is appropriate in a particular region of space and with the connotation of symbols given in the preceding section, all the geometrical relations in Chapters 12 and 13 apply to the gravitational field; these relations give us at once, for example, the curvature properties of the equipotential surfaces and of the lines of force, together with the properties of lines traced on the equipotential surfaces and in space. There is no need to repeat all the formulas of Chapters 12 and 13; indeed, it will be found that most of the formulas do not contain ΔN, and so do not need any modification at all.

22. We shall be concerned mostly with a rotating field in regions of space not occupied by matter, in which case the formula

20.16 $\Delta N = -2\tilde\omega^2$

will apply. The only formulas in Chapters 12 and 13 which contain ΔN are Equations 12.100, 12.104, 12.105, 12.106, 12.112, 12.113, and 12.115. Assuming that $\tilde\omega$ and therefore ΔN are constant, these equations reduce to

20.17 $-2\tilde\omega^2 = (\partial n/\partial s) - 2Hn$

20.18 $\Delta\omega = 2\tan\phi\ \nabla(\omega, \phi) - 2\nabla(\omega, \ln n)$

20.19 $\Delta\phi = -\sin\phi\cos\phi\ \nabla(\omega) - 2\nabla(\phi, \ln n)$

$(1/n)\Delta n = \cos^2\phi\ \nabla(\omega) + \nabla(\phi)$

20.20 $= \kappa_1^2 + \kappa_2^2 + (\gamma_1^2 + \gamma_2^2)$

20.21 $\cos\phi\nabla(\omega, \ln n) = k_2\gamma_1 - t_1\gamma_2 - 2\tilde\omega^2\gamma_1/n$

20.22 $\nabla(\phi, \ln n) = k_1\gamma_2 - t_1\gamma_1 - 2\tilde\omega^2\gamma_2/n.$

However, the last five of these equations, although useful, are not independent, but can all be derived from Equation 20.17 with the help of other relations given in Chapter 12. For example, by differentiating the logarithmic form of Equation 20.17, that is,

20.23 $\partial(\ln n)/\partial s = (\ln n)_r\nu^r = 2H - 2\tilde\omega^2/n$

in the parallel direction λ^s, we obtain after some manipulation

$$\partial\gamma_1/\partial s = (2H)_a\lambda^a + 4\tilde\omega^2\gamma_1/n$$

20.24 $+ \gamma_1\gamma_2\tan\phi + \gamma_2 t_1 - \gamma_1 k_2,$

which can be shown to be equivalent to Equation 20.18, using nothing but relations given in Chapter 12. In the same way, by differentiating Equation 20.23 in the meridian direction μ^s, we find that

$$\partial\gamma_2/\partial s = (2H)_a\mu^a + 4\tilde\omega^2\gamma_2/n$$

20.25 $- \gamma_1^2\tan\phi + \gamma_1 t_1 - \gamma_2 k_1,$

which can be proved equivalent to Equation 20.19. Differentiation in the normal direction ν^r leads to Equation 20.20, although we do not obtain any relation in this case which has not already been given in Chapter 12. The remaining Equations 20.21 and 20.22 follow directly from Equation 20.17 without differentiation. Equation 20.17 or 20.23 is usually known as Bruns' equation if n is interpreted as gravity at a point in a rotating field and if H is the mean curvature of the equipotential surface passing through the same point.

23. We conclude that no independent geometrical relations other than Equation 20.17 have been introduced by applying the law of gravity, and that Equations 20.16 and 20.17 must therefore be equivalent. Indeed, we can write

$-2\tilde\omega^2 = \Delta N = (n\nu^r)_r = n_r\nu^r + n\nu_r^r = (\partial n/\partial s) - 2Hn$

20.26

in which we have used Equation 7.19. We can say that either Equation 20.16 or 20.17 is a sufficient expression of the law of gravity. We may note that Equation 20.17 gives us an expression for the variation of gravity along the lines of force; the law of gravity tells us nothing in general about the variation of gravity over an equipotential surface, although we may be able to deduce this geometrically in special cases.

24. For example, if the equipotential surfaces are all concentric spheres of radius $r(H=-1/r)$, the gravitational equation becomes

$$\frac{\partial n}{\partial r}+\frac{2n}{r}=-2\tilde{\omega}^2$$

or

$$\frac{\partial(nr^2)}{\partial r}=-2\tilde{\omega}^2 r^2,$$

which can be integrated to

$$nr^2=-\tfrac{2}{3}\tilde{\omega}^2 r^3+f(\omega,\phi)$$

or

$$\frac{\partial N}{\partial r}=-\tfrac{2}{3}\tilde{\omega}^2 r+\frac{f(\omega,\phi)}{r^2},$$

and can be integrated again to

$$N=-\tfrac{1}{3}\tilde{\omega}^2 r^2-f(\omega,\phi)/r+g(\omega,\phi).$$

But N is constant over the spheres and must therefore be a function of r only so that the arbitrary functions $f(\omega,\phi)$, $g(\omega,\phi)$ are at most constants. Gravity (n) is accordingly constant over an equipotential surface, as it would be in the case of a nonrotating field with spherical equipotentials, although the magnitude of gravity is different in the rotating field.

25. If we know the form of one equipotential surface and the variation of gravity over that surface, we can build the whole field along either the normals or the isozenithals. If we work along the isozenithals, we shall need to recast the gravitational equation, with the help of Equation 14.32, into the form

$$\frac{\partial(1/n)}{\partial N}=-2H\left(\frac{1}{n}\right)^2+2\tilde{\omega}^2\left(\frac{1}{n}\right)^3-b^{\alpha\beta}\left(\frac{1}{n}\right)_\alpha\left(\frac{1}{n}\right)_\beta.$$

20.27

Next, we differentiate the Codazzi equations in the form of Equation 12.143 with respect to N, using the fact that all the coefficients in Equation 12.143 are constant during the differentiation. Substitution of the gravitational equation in the result of this last operation gives us the second isozenithal derivative of $b_{\alpha\beta}$ in terms solely of surface functions or surface derivatives of $(1/n)$, which are presumed known or calculable on the starting surface. Repetition of the process gives us higher isozenithal derivatives of $b_{\alpha\beta}$ in the neighborhood of the starting surface and leads to a Taylor expansion for $b_{\alpha\beta}$ along the isozenithals.

The other fundamental forms and metrical properties of the equipotential surfaces can be expanded similarly from formulas for isozenithal differentiation given in Chapter 14. For example, we could obtain successive differentials of $b^{\alpha\beta}$ from Equation 14.07 and then of $a_{\alpha\beta}$ from Equation 14.03. The formulas soon become very complicated in the case of a general starting surface, but in practice, it would not be necessary to carry the process very far. The first differentials can be obtained from the Codazzi Equation 12.143 simply by knowing the variation of gravity over the starting surface; the law of gravity enters only in the second and higher differentials.

26. We could similarly expand the elements of the starting surface along the normals instead of along the isozenithals. In that case, we should work in the normal coordinates of Chapter 15. The Codazzi Equations 15.25 now contain covariant derivatives which would have to be differentiated by Equation 15.53; the $c_{\alpha\beta}$ are no longer constants, but would have to be differentiated by Equation 15.26. Otherwise, the procedure is much the same as expansion along the isozenithals, remembering that in these coordinates

$$\frac{\partial}{\partial N}=\frac{1}{n}\frac{\partial}{\partial s};$$

differentials with respect to N, not with respect to s, commute with differentials with respect to the surface coordinates.

FLUX OF GRAVITATIONAL FORCE

27. The common normals, or orthogonal trajectories, of the equipotential surfaces are also known as lines of force because the tangent to such a line indicates the direction of the resultant force in accordance with the generalized form of Equation 20.05. A volume of small cross-sectional area δS, bounded by lines of force, is called a *tube of force*. The cross-sectional areas of a tube of force, where the tube crosses different equipotential surfaces, are evidently related by the normal projection system of § 15–39; and from Equation 15.39, we have

20.28
$$\frac{\partial(\ln \delta S)}{\partial s}=-2H$$

in which as usual ds is an element of length along the normal and H is the mean curvature of the equipotential surface. Substitution of this last equation in the gravitational Equation 20.26 gives

$$\frac{\partial\{\ln(n\delta S)\}}{\partial s}=\frac{\Delta N}{n}$$

or

20.29 $$\frac{\partial(n\delta S)}{\partial s}=(\Delta N)\delta S.$$

We now introduce a quantity known as the *flux of force* across the area δS, and define this quantity as

$$F_r \nu^r \delta S$$

in which F_r is the force vector and ν^r is the unit normal to the element of area δS. In the case we are now considering, the generalized form of Equation 20.05 shows that the flux is

$$f=-n\delta S;$$

we can rewrite Equation 20.29 as

20.30 $$\partial f/\partial s=-(\Delta N)\delta S.$$

In this equation, the positive direction of ∂s is that of ν_s in Equation 20.05, that is, against the direction of the force. Consequently, the rate of change of flux along a tube of force in the direction of the force is $+(\Delta N)\delta S$ in which ΔN takes one of the Newtonian values given in § 20–21, depending on whether the field is rotating and on whether the tube contains matter in the small area under consideration. All of the preceding is simply an alternative statement of the Newtonian law of gravity. In particular, we may note that the flux is constant along a tube not containing matter in a static field; because this is true for any number of adjacent tubes, there is no need for the tube to be of small cross-sectional area. Again, if the tube does not contain matter in a static field, the cross-sectional area of the tube is inversely proportional to the magnitude or intensity n of the force.

28. Another and more usual way of considering the flux is to apply the divergence theorem to a finite length of a tube of force between equipotential surfaces. From Equation 9.16, we have

20.31 $$\int_S F_r \nu^r \delta S=-\int_V \Delta N dV$$

in which ν^r is now the unit normal to the surface of the tube. The contributions of the sides of the tube to the surface integral are zero because ν^r at points on the sides is perpendicular to the force vector; we are left with the contributions of the ends. Now suppose that one end of the tube is held fixed and that the other end is extended a short length ds, ending on another equipotential surface. The resulting increase in the area integral is evidently

$$\frac{\partial(F_r\nu^r\delta S)}{\partial s}\,ds=-\frac{\partial(n\delta S)}{\partial s}\,ds=\frac{\partial f}{\partial s}\,ds,$$

and the increase in the volume integral is

$$-(\Delta N)\delta S ds.$$

Because the divergence theorem still holds true for the extended tube, we may equate these two increases to have

$$(\partial f/\partial s)\,ds=-(\Delta N)\delta S ds;$$

and because ds, although small, is arbitrary, we have

$$\partial f/\partial s=-(\Delta N)\delta S,$$

which is the same as Equation 20.30, obtained solely by differential methods.

MEASUREMENT OF THE PARAMETERS

29. We have seen in Chapter 12 how the geometry of the field depends on the curvature parameters $(k_1, k_2, t_1, \gamma_1, \gamma_2)$ and on $(\ln n)_r\nu^r$, which are directly related to the six components of the symmetric Marussi tensor N_{rs} by Equations 12.162. The law of gravity expressed by Equation 20.23, which can be written as

20.32 $$(\ln n)_r\nu^r=(k_1+k_2)-2\tilde{\omega}^2/n,$$

provides one relation between the six parameters; the question naturally arises whether we can obtain other relations by direct measurement. One possibility is the Eötvös torsion balance, which consists essentially of two masses A, B (fig. 18) suspended

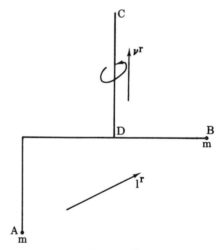

Figure 18.

at different levels from a horizontal bar. The bar itself is suspended by a wire whose torsion, arising from the unequal effects of gravity on the two masses, can be accurately measured.

30. We suppose that the line AB is of length $2l$ in azimuth α and zenith distance β and that the two masses (m) are equal. The unit vector in the direction AB is from Equation 12.007

$$l^r = \lambda^r \sin \alpha \sin \beta + \mu^r \cos \alpha \sin \beta + \nu^r \cos \beta.$$

20.33

A unit equipotential surface vector perpendicular to the plane of l^r and ν^r is, with the usual right-handed convention,

20.34 $\quad j^r = -\lambda^r \cos \alpha + \mu^r \sin \alpha.$

If N is the geopotential at B, the force on B is $-mN_r$; the turning moment of this force about CD is

$$-mN_r j^r \times DB = -(ml \sin \beta) N_r j^r.$$

Similarly, the turning moment about CD in the same sense arising from the force on A is

$$+ (ml \sin \beta)\bar{N}_r j^r$$

in which $\bar{N}$ is the geopotential at A, so that the resultant torque is

$$(ml \sin \beta)(\bar{N}_r - N_r)j^r = -(2ml^2 \sin \beta)N_{rs}j^r l^s$$

20.35

because $(\bar{N}_r - N_r)$ can be considered the intrinsic change in N_r in the direction $(-l^r)$ over a distance $(2l)$. Expanding Equation 20.35 with Equations 20.33 and 20.34 and using Equations 12.162, we have finally the resultant torque as

$$-(2ml^2 \sin^2 \beta)n\{(k_1 - k_2) \sin \alpha \cos \alpha$$
$$+ t_1(\cos^2 \alpha - \sin^2 \alpha)$$
20.36 $\qquad -\gamma_1 \cos \alpha \cot \beta + \gamma_2 \sin \alpha \cot \beta\}.$

31. Measurement in several azimuths will accordingly determine $(k_1 - k_2)$, t_1, γ_1, γ_2 and some instrumental constants, but will not separate k_1 and k_2. To do this, we need an additional form of measurement. As one possibility, Marussi in 1947 suggested measurement of the torsion about the horizontal axis j^r, but no instrument has yet (1968) been constructed on these lines. In principle, Marussi's suggestion is equivalent to the classical method of an inclined balance. The Haalck horizontal pendulum is still another possibility which has not yet materialized as a field instrument. The only practicable method at present seems to be a direct measure of the vertical gradient of gravity with a gravimeter, leading to evaluation of $(k_1 + k_2)$ from Equation 20.32, but this has not so far produced results comparable in accuracy with the torsion balance. No doubt, the problem will not remain unsolved much longer.

32. An alternative expression for the torque can be obtained from Equations 20.35 and 12.017 as

$$-(2ml^2 \sin \beta)(n_s \nu^r + n\nu_{rs})j^r l^s$$
20.37 $\qquad = -(2mnl^2 \sin \beta)(\nu_{rs}j^r l^s)$

because ν^r and j^r are perpendicular. By using Equations 7.08, 10.29, and 20.34, we can express the torque as

20.38 $\quad = (2mnl^2 \sin \beta)\{t \sin \beta - (\ln n)_r j^r \cos \beta\}$

$$= (2mnl^2 \sin \beta)\{t \sin \beta + \gamma_1 \cos \alpha \cos \beta$$
20.39 $\qquad\qquad -\gamma_2 \sin \alpha \cos \beta\}$

in which t is the geodesic torsion of the equipotential surface in the azimuth of the line joining the masses. We can eliminate the term containing t, leaving only the horizontal gradients of gravity γ_1, γ_2 to be determined, by adding an observation in azimuth $(\frac{1}{2}\pi + \alpha)$.

33. Eötvös himself introduced a double torsion balance with parallel beams and hanging weights at opposite ends, while modern instruments have incorporated photographic recording and automatic azimuth-change. However, the principles remain the same.

34. The torsion balance has been used extensively in geophysical prospecting to determine differences in gravity from measured (γ_1, γ_2) and standard values of the vertical gradient, but the instrument has been superseded for this purpose by sensitive gravimeters which are easier to use. Geodesists, other than Eötvös himself who experimented on the Hungarian plains, have never used the torsion balance extensively because the instrument is extremely sensitive to the attraction of masses in the immediate neighborhood, and is accordingly not considered to give sufficiently representative values for the locality. Recent work [1] [2] on the interpolation of deflections of the vertical with the torsion balance has, for example, involved all-round leveling of the sites within 100 meters of the instrument. In addition, due precautions have to be taken to exclude the effect of such temporary masses as wandering cattle; the effect of the observer's mass is usually eliminated by photographic recording and automatic operation.

---

[1] Mueller (1963), "Geodesy and the Torsion Balance," *Proceedings of the American Society of Civil Engineers, Journal of the Surveying and Mapping Division*, v. 89, no. SU3, 123–155.

[2] Mueller (1966), "Interpolation of Deflections of the Vertical by Means of a Torsion Balance," *Bulletin Géodésique*, new series, no. 80, 171–174.

CHAPTER 21

The Potential in Spherical Harmonics

GENERALIZED HARMONIC FUNCTIONS

1. Suppose that H is any continuous, differentiable scalar function of position and that the nth-order tensor

21.001 $H_{rst \ldots (n)}$

is formed by n successive covariant differentiations of H; the notation indicating that there are n-indices $r, s, t \ldots$. The tensor equation

$$H_{rts \ldots (n)} = H_{rst \ldots (n)},$$

in which any two indices have been interchanged, is clearly true in Cartesian coordinates when the covariant derivatives become ordinary commutable derivatives, and is therefore true in any coordinate system in flat space. The nth-order tensor Equation 21.001 is accordingly symmetrical in any two indices and has therefore

$$\tfrac{1}{2}(n+1)(n+2)$$

distinct components at most.

2. Next, suppose that H is a harmonic function. The Laplacian of the tensor Equation 21.001 is then

$$g^{jk}H_{rst \ldots (n)jk} = (g^{jk}H_{jk})_{rst \ldots (n)} = 0$$

so that all components of the tensor Equation 21.001 are harmonic functions.

3. We may similarly write

21.002 $g^{rs}H_{rst \ldots (n)} = (g^{rs}H_{rs})_{t \ldots (n)} = 0.$

The contracted tensor in this equation is of order $(n-2)$ and has at most

$$\tfrac{1}{2}\{(n-2)+1\}\{(n-2)+2\} = \tfrac{1}{2}n(n-1)$$

distinct components. When H is harmonic, there are accordingly

$$\tfrac{1}{2}n(n-1)$$

relations, such as Equation 21.002, between the components of the original tensor in Equation 21.001, which can therefore have

$$\tfrac{1}{2}(n+1)(n+2) - \tfrac{1}{2}n(n-1) = (2n+1)$$

independent components at most.

4. We now form an invariant

21.003 $A^{rst \ldots (n)}H_{rst \ldots (n)}$

in which the contracting tensor is constant under covariant differentiation; that is, all components of the contracting tensor are absolute constants in Cartesian coordinates, and are the transforms of Cartesian constants in other coordinate systems. The resulting summation will contain at most $(2n+1)$ independent harmonic functions, so that the contracting tensor should be chosen to introduce no more than $(2n+1)$ Cartesian constants, and may therefore be chosen in the form

21.004 $CL^r M^s N^t \ldots Q^{(n)}H_{rst \ldots (n)}$

in which C is an arbitrary constant and the L^r are n arbitrary *fixed* unit vectors, each contributing two independent constant Cartesian components. This last result, as an invariant, is true in any coordinate system provided the vectors L^r are fixed—that is, provided their covariant derivatives are zero.

5. If the elements of length in the direction of the fixed vectors L^r, M^s are dl, dm, etc., we can rewrite Equation 21.004 as

$$CM^sN^t \ . \ . \ . \ Q^{(n)}(H_rL^r)_{st \ . \ . \ . \ (n)}$$

$$= CM^sN^t \ . \ . \ . \ Q^{(n)}\left(\frac{\partial H}{\partial l}\right)_{st \ . \ . \ . \ (n-1)}$$

21.005 $$= C\frac{d}{dq} \ . \ . \ . \ \frac{d}{dn}\frac{d}{dm}\frac{d}{dl}(H),$$

which shows that the same result would be obtained by successive differentiation of H along each of the arbitrary fixed vectors in turn.

6. We have now succeeded in generating $(2n + 1)$ independent harmonic functions from a single initial function H, all of the same order n. The result of adding these functions with $(2n + 1)$ arbitrary constants is to provide a more generalized harmonic function; we can obviously express a still more general harmonic function K by adding similar groups of higher and lower order as

21.006 $$K = \sum_n A^{rst \ . \ . \ . \ (n)}H_{rst \ . \ . \ . \ (n)},$$

with corresponding expressions for the alternative forms, Equations 21.004 and 21.005, of the constants. We can extend this result into an infinite series, provided H and the components of the contracting tensors are chosen to make the resulting series convergent. The question then arises whether *any* harmonic function K can be expressed in terms of another harmonic function H. This is true in the special case where $H = 1/r$ and where the coordinate system is Cartesian, in which case we shall see that the derivatives of H are solid spherical harmonics; we could reasonably suppose, without formal proof, that it would be true in the more general case when fewer restrictions are applied.

7. If K in Equation 21.006 is to be a Newtonian potential, then we can reasonably expect that the leading, or absolute, undifferentiated term in Equation 21.006 would be of the form $(1/r)$ because this is the simplest form of Newtonian potential. In that case, H would be $(1/r)$. This fact was first noticed by James Clerk Maxwell,[1] who showed that n-differentiations of $1/r$, as in Equation 21.005, generated all the nth-degree spherical harmonics. We shall derive this result more simply for a New-

---

[1] Maxwell (1881), *A Treatise on Electricity and Magnetism*, 2d ed., v. I, 179–214.

tonian gravitational potential, and at the same time shall provide a physical interpretation of the contracting tensors in Equation 21.006.

8. We shall find that a convergent series for the Newtonian potential in the form of Equation 21.006 with $H = 1/r$ may not always be possible; we are led to consider an alternative expansion in homogeneous polynomials in the tensor form

21.007 $$J = \sum_n B_{rst \ . \ . \ . \ (n)}\rho^r\rho^s\rho^t \ . \ . \ . \ \rho^{(n)}$$

in which ρ^r is the position vector, whose Cartesian components are (x, y, z), and $B_{rst \ . \ . \ .}$ is a contracting tensor symmetrical in any two indices and with constant Cartesian components. We notice that the covariant derivative of the position vector is given by the Kronecker delta (§ 1–21), that is,

$$\rho^r_{\ k} = \delta^r_k$$

in Cartesian coordinates; and because this result is a tensor equation, it is true in any coordinates. Covariant differentiation of Equation 21.007 then gives

$$J_k = \sum nB_{rst \ . \ . \ . \ (n)}\delta^r_k\rho^s\rho^t \ . \ . \ . \ \rho^{(n)}$$

$$= \sum nB_{kst \ . \ . \ . \ (n)}\rho^s\rho^t \ . \ . \ . \ \rho^{(n-1)};$$

and the second derivative is

$$J_{kl} = \sum n(n-1)B_{klt \ . \ . \ . \ (n)}\rho^t \ . \ . \ . \ \rho^{(n-2)}$$

so that the Laplacian is given by

$$\Delta J = g^{kl}J_{kl} = \sum n(n-1)g^{kl}B_{klt \ . \ . \ . \ (n)}\rho^t \ . \ . \ . \ \rho^{(n-2)}.$$

21.008

Accordingly, if J is to be harmonic for all components of the position vectors at all points of some finite domain, then we must have

21.009 $$g^{kl}B_{klt \ . \ . \ . \ (n)} = 0$$

for the coefficients of each polynomial in Equation 21.007 of degree two and higher. As in § 21–3, these harmonic conditions, together with the symmetricality in any two indices, restrict the number of independent polynomials of the nth-degree in Equation 21.007 to $(2n + 1)$. We have then merely to substitute spherical polar coordinates for the (x, y, z) Cartesian components of the position vectors in Equation 21.007 to obtain after some manipulation an expansion in spherical harmonics. It is well known that all the nth-degree spherical harmonics can be represented in this way by homogeneous polynomials of the nth-degree.

THE NEWTONIAN POTENTIAL AT DISTANT POINTS

9. We shall now find the Newtonian potential at a point P (fig. 19) in empty space (often described

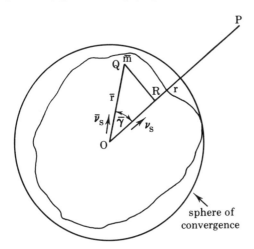

Figure 19.

as "free air") outside an attracting body of irregular shape and irregular mass distribution such as the Earth. Two cases are of particular importance:

(a) When P is farther from the origin O of the coordinate system than all points of the attracting body, and

(b) when P is nearer to the origin than some or all points of the attracting body.

We shall deal with the first case now, and second case later.

10. We shall suppose first that the attracting body consists of discrete particles, and shall then show that results in the same form would be obtained for a continuous distribution of matter.

11. The potential at P, arising from an elementary particle of mass $\bar{m}$ at Q (omitting for the present the gravitational constant G), is

$$-\bar{m}/PQ = -\bar{m}(r^2 - 2r\bar{r}\cos\bar{\gamma} + \bar{r}^2)^{-1/2}$$

$$= -\frac{\bar{m}}{r}\left\{1 + \frac{\bar{r}}{r}\cos\gamma + \ldots \left(\frac{\bar{r}}{r}\right)^n P_n(\cos\bar{\gamma}) \ldots\right\}$$

21.010

by definition of the Legendre functions or zonal harmonics $P_n(\cos\bar{\gamma})$. This series, like the geometric

power series which dominates it, is absolutely and uniformly convergent if $r > \bar{r}$; and, in that case, we may add to it term-by-term the similar series representing the contribution to the potential at P which arises from the other particles of the attracting body. If $r > \bar{r}$ for *all* particles of the body, it is evident that P must lie outside a sphere centered on the origin which just contains all the particles; and we shall accordingly call this the *sphere of convergence* for this case. Otherwise, some particles may set up divergent series which cannot be added term-by-term to the other series. In special cases, the final series might be convergent inside the sphere, which just encloses all the matter, because the elementary divergent series cancels in the sum or is otherwise insignificant, but this would have to be proved by considering the convergence of the final series. In any case, we have not said that the final series is necessarily divergent on or inside the sphere of convergence, but only that it is certainly convergent outside this sphere. Because r is the same for all particles, the total potential V at P, after replacing the gravitational constant G, would then be given by

$$-\frac{V}{G} = \frac{M}{r} + \frac{\Sigma\bar{m}\bar{r}\cos\bar{\gamma}}{r^2} + \ldots \frac{\Sigma\bar{m}\bar{r}^n P_n(\cos\bar{\gamma})}{r^{n+1}} + \ldots$$

21.011

in which M is the total mass of the attracting body and the summations are carried out over all particles.

The Potential in Maxwell's Form

12. We shall first recast Equation 21.011 in the tensor form involving successive differentials of $(1/r)$, and shall relate the coefficients in this expansion to the mass distribution. Later, we shall obtain the more usual expansion in spherical harmonics related to a fixed Cartesian coordinate system. For some purposes, one form is more convenient than the other, and we need both.

13. If we take OQ (fig. 19) as a temporary axis of z and use the well-known formula [2]

$$\frac{\partial^n}{\partial z^n}\left(\frac{1}{r}\right) = \frac{(-)^n n!}{r^{n+1}} P_n(\cos\bar{\gamma}),$$

we find from Equation 21.011 that the nth-degree term in the potential *arising from a single particle $\bar{m}$*

[2] Hobson (1931), *The Theory of Spherical and Ellipsoidal Harmonics*, 15–16.

is

$$\frac{(-)^n \bar{m} \bar{r}^n}{n!} \frac{\partial^n}{\partial z^n} \left(\frac{1}{r}\right).$$

Because the unit vector $\bar{\nu}_s$ toward the particle and in the direction of the temporary z-axis is constant during differentiation at P of $(1/r)$, we can rewrite this last expression in the tensor form

$$\frac{(-)^n \bar{m} \bar{r}^n}{n!} \left(\frac{1}{r}\right)_{stu \,\ldots\, (n)} \bar{\nu}^s \bar{\nu}^t \bar{\nu}^u \,\ldots\, \bar{\nu}^{(n)},$$

which is no longer dependent on a particular coordinate system involving a single particle, so that we can sum this expression over all particles. We have also

$$\bar{\nu}^s = \bar{x}^s / \bar{r},$$

if $\bar{x}^s$ are rectangular Cartesian coordinates of the particle $\bar{m}$ in any fixed system with origin O, so that the nth-degree term in the total potential at P is finally

$$\frac{(-)^n}{n!} I^{stu \,\ldots\, (n)} \left(\frac{1}{r}\right)_{stu \,\ldots\, (n)}$$

where

21.012 $\qquad I^{stu \,\ldots\, (n)} = \sum \bar{m} \bar{x}^s \bar{x}^t \bar{x}^u \,\ldots\, \bar{x}^{(n)}.$

This last expression is evidently a tensor because it is formed by the multiplication and addition of of position vectors $\bar{x}^s$. We shall call this tensor *the nth-order inertia tensor* because its value depends solely on the mass distribution within the attracting body and on the position within the body of the point O chosen as origin. We can similarly define inertia tensors of the first, second, third, etc., orders as

21.013 $\qquad I^s = \sum \bar{m} \bar{x}^s$

21.014 $\qquad I^{st} = \sum \bar{m} \bar{x}^s \bar{x}^t$

21.015 $\qquad I^{stu} = \sum \bar{m} \bar{x}^s \bar{x}^t \bar{x}^u$

in which, of course, the summation is carried out over all particles. The *inertia tensor of zero order* is simply the total mass (M) of the body

21.016 $\qquad \sum \bar{m} = M.$

With these conventions, we can finally rewrite Equation 21.011 as

$$-\frac{V}{G} = \sum_{n=0}^{\infty} \frac{(-)^n}{n!} I^{stu \,\ldots\, (n)} \left(\frac{1}{r}\right)_{stu \,\ldots\, (n)}.$$

21.017

It is understood that when $n=0$, the inertia tensor is M and $(1/r)$ is undifferentiated; in addition, as

usual $n!$ is interpreted as unity when $n=0$. The expression

$$\left(\frac{1}{r}\right)_{stu \,\ldots\, (n)}$$

signifies the nth-covariant derivative of $(1/r)$ successively with respect to the coordinates x^s, x^t, x^u .... In Cartesian coordinates, the covariant derivatives become, of course, ordinary derivatives, and are then combined with the Cartesian form (Equation 21.012) of the inertia tensors.

14. So far, the inertia tensors have been defined only at, and in relation to, a particular origin, although we shall later derive expressions for their components at a different origin where $(1/r)$ and its derivatives would also be different. When the inertia tensors are contracted with other tensors, as in Equation 21.017, we should use values of the contracting tensors at the origin, or else express the contracting tensors as sums and products of vectors and use parallel vectors through the origin. We should also use values of the metric tensor at the origin in conjunction with the inertia tensors. No difficulty arises if we use Cartesian coordinates because the components of parallel vectors and of the metric tensor are then the same at all points in space.

Continuous Distribution of Matter

15. We can consider that the attracting body consists of a continuous distribution of matter of density ρ per unit volume instead of a system of discrete particles. In that case, we have only to write

21.018 $\qquad \bar{m} = \rho \, dv$

for the mass contained in an element of volume dv and replace the summation sign by a volume or triple integral taken over the whole body, so that, for example, we have

21.019 $\qquad I^{rst \,\ldots\, (n)} = \int_V \rho \bar{\rho}^r \bar{\rho}^s \bar{\rho}^t \,\ldots\, \bar{\rho}^{(n)} dv$

in which $\bar{\rho}^r$ is the position vector of the element of volume—that is, in Cartesian coordinates

$$\bar{\rho}^r = \bar{x}^r.$$

The density ρ can, of course, vary from point to point, but because it is supposed to have a definite value at a point, the density can be considered a function of position, that is, of (x, y, z). The density need not, however, be a continuous function in the mathematical sense because we could integrate over subvolumes bounded by discontinuities and add the results; this result will be clear if we consider the original distribution of an aggregate of particles, which need not have been all of the same mass and indeed could have been separated by empty space. In some cases, we shall find it more convenient to deal with a system of particles, and in other cases with a continuous distribution. There is, however, no essential difference between the two cases, which are quite simply related by use of Equation 21.018 and by integration instead of summation, whether we are dealing with inertia tensors or with any other formulas in this chapter that relate to the mass distribution.

Successive Derivatives of $(1/r)$

16. In order to use the basic Equation 21.017 for the potential, we shall require formulas for the successive derivatives of $(1/r)$ which are intimately connected with the unit position vector ν_s of the point P where the formula gives the potential (fig. 19). The vector ν_s is in fact the gradient of the radius vector r, so that we have

21.020 $$\nu_s = r_s$$

and

21.021 $$\left(\frac{1}{r}\right)_s = -\left(\frac{1}{r^2}\right)\nu_s,$$

giving the first derivatives of $(1/r)$.

17. Throughout this chapter, (ω, ϕ) will be the longitude and latitude of the radius vector OP, that is, the *geocentric* longitude and latitude, unless otherwise stated. We can accordingly consider ν_s to be the unit normal to the r-surfaces (spheres) in a symmetrical (ω, ϕ, r) coordinate system. From Equations 18.12 and 18.13, we then have

$$(\cos\phi)\omega_s = \lambda_s/r$$

$$\phi_s = \mu_s/r;$$

and from Equations 12.016 and 2.08, we have

$$\nu_{st} = (\lambda_s\lambda_t + \mu_s\mu_t)/r$$
21.022 $$= (g_{st} - \nu_s\nu_t)/r,$$

so that the second covariant derivative of $(1/r)$ is from Equation 21.021

$$(1/r)_{st} = (2/r^3)\nu_s\nu_t - (1/r^2)\nu_{st}$$
21.023 $$= (3\nu_s\nu_t - g_{st})/r^3.$$

The third derivative, using the last two equations, is

$$(1/r)_{stu} = (-3/r^4)(3\nu_s\nu_t - g_{st})\nu_u$$
$$+ (1/r^4)(3g_{su}\nu_t + 3g_{tu}\nu_s - 6\nu_s\nu_t\nu_u)$$
21.024 $$= (3/r^4)(g_{st}\nu_u + g_{tu}\nu_s + g_{us}\nu_t - 5\nu_s\nu_t\nu_u);$$

proceeding in this manner, we find without difficulty that the nth-derivative is given by

$$\frac{(-)^n(1/r)_{pqrst\ldots(n)}r^{n+1}}{1\cdot3\cdot5\ldots(2n-1)} = \nu_p\nu_q\nu_r\nu_s\nu_t\ldots\nu_{(n)}$$

$$-\frac{\{g_{pq}\nu_r\nu_s\nu_t\ldots\nu_{(n)}\}}{(2n-1)}$$

$$+\frac{\{g_{pq}g_{rs}\nu_t\ldots\nu_{(n)}\}}{(2n-1)(2n-3)}$$

21.025 $$-\ldots$$

in which the symbol

$$\{g_{pq}\nu_r\nu_s\nu_t\ldots\nu_{(n)}\}$$

implies that the indices are permuted cyclically in all different ways, allowing for the symmetry of the metric tensor g_{pq}, and the results are summed as in Equation 21.024. At each successive term in the expansion, we drop two "ν's" which we replace by one "g." The final term contains one "ν" if n is odd, but otherwise all "g's."

18. Equation 21.025 can also be obtained by successive covariant differentiation of the identity

$$x^2 + y^2 + z^2 = r^2,$$

remembering that all components of the tensors $x_{pq}\ldots, y_{pq}\ldots, z_{pq}\ldots$ are zero in any coordinate system because the components are zero in Cartesian coordinates. For example, we have

$$xx_p + yy_p + zz_p = \rho_p = r\nu_p = -r^3(1/r)_p,$$

which is equivalent to Equation 21.021. Also, we have

$$x_qx_p + y_qy_p + z_qz_p = g_{pq} = 3r^4(1/r)_p(1/r)_q - r^3(1/r)_{pq},$$

which is equivalent to Equation 21.023, and

$$0 = -12r^5(1/r)_p(1/r)_q(1/r)_s + 3r^4\{(1/r)_{pq}(1/r)_s$$
$$+ (1/r)_{qs}(1/r)_p + (1/r)_{sp}(1/r)_q\} - r^3(1/r)_{pqs},$$

which is equivalent to Equation 21.024.

19. The number of terms in the symbol

$$\{g_{pq}\nu_r\nu_s\nu_t\ldots\nu_{(n)}\}$$

is $n(n-1)/2$, obtained by taking two indices at a time from n, regardless of order. The same operation, applied to the remaining $(n-2)$ indices in each term, gives

$$\{(n-2)(n-3)/2\} \times n(n-1)/2$$

as the number of terms in the second symbol

$$\{g_{pq}g_{rs}\nu_t \ldots \nu_{(n)}\}.$$

But half of these terms are the same as the other half, for example,

$$g_{pq}g_{rs}\nu_t \ldots \nu_{(n)} = g_{rs}g_{pq}\nu_t \ldots \nu_{(n)},$$

so that finally the number of dissimilar terms in the second symbol is

$$n(n-1)(n-2)(n-3)/(2 \cdot 4),$$

and in the third symbol is

$$n(n-1)(n-2)(n-3)(n-4)(n-5)/(2 \cdot 4 \cdot 6),$$

and so on.

20. We shall usually contract Equation 21.025 with an nth-order contravariant tensor which is symmetric in any two indices. Each term in a particular braces symbol will make the same contribution to the resulting invariant, so that *in such cases* we can rewrite Equation 21.025 as

$$\frac{(-)^n(1/r)_{pqrst \ldots (n)}r^{n+1}}{1 \cdot 3 \cdot 5 \ldots (2n-1)}$$
$$= \nu_p\nu_q\nu_r\nu_s\nu_t \ldots \nu_{(n)}$$
$$- \frac{n(n-1)}{2(2n-1)}g_{pq}\nu_r\nu_s\nu_t \ldots \nu_{(n)}$$
$$+ \frac{n(n-1)(n-2)(n-3)}{2 \cdot 4(2n-1)(2n-3)}g_{pq}g_{rs}\nu_t \ldots \nu_{(n)}$$
$$- \ldots .$$

21.026

21. As some verification of this last formula, we take the latitude and longitude of the direction OP as (ϕ, ω) with respect to rectangular Cartesian axes and take O as origin. Then the Cartesian components of the unit vector ν_p are as usual

$$(\cos \phi \cos \omega, \cos \phi \sin \omega, \sin \phi),$$

and we have also

$$g_{pq} = 1\,(p=q) \; ; \qquad g_{pq} = 0\,(p \neq q).$$

Substitution in Equation 21.026 and use of the usual expansion for $P_n(x)$ in powers of x then give us at once

$$\left(\frac{1}{r}\right)_{333 \ldots (n)} = \frac{\partial^n}{\partial z^n}\left(\frac{1}{r}\right) = \frac{(-)^n n\,!}{r^{n+1}}P_n(\sin \phi).$$

21.027

This equation recovers our starting point in § 21–13. In the same way, we have

$$\left(\frac{1}{r}\right)_{111 \ldots (n)} = \frac{\partial^n}{\partial x^n}\left(\frac{1}{r}\right) = \frac{(-)^n n\,!}{r^{n+1}}P_n(\cos \phi \cos \omega)$$

21.028

$$\left(\frac{1}{r}\right)_{222 \ldots (n)} = \frac{\partial^n}{\partial y^n}\left(\frac{1}{r}\right) = \frac{(-)^n n\,!}{r^{n+1}}P_n(\cos \phi \sin \omega).$$

21.029

Corresponding formulas for mixed derivatives are, however, less simple as we shall see.

22. Equation 21.026 is a purely geometrical relation. If we multiply by r^n and note that $r\nu_p = \rho_p$, the position vector of P whose distance from the origin is r in the direction ν_p, and if we also contract with an arbitrary constant tensor $A^{pqr \cdots (n)}$ symmetric in any two indices, then the first term on the right becomes a homogeneous polynomial of the nth-degree

21.030 $$f_n(x, y, z) = A^{pqr \cdots (n)}\rho_p\rho_q\rho_r \ldots \rho_{(n)}.$$

The Laplacian of this last equation, as we have already seen in Equation 21.008, is

$$\Delta f_n = n(n-1)A^{pqr \cdots (n)}g_{pq}\rho_r \ldots \rho_{(n-2)};$$

again taking the Laplacian, we have

$$\Delta^2 f_n = n(n-1)(n-2)(n-3)$$
$$\times A^{pqrst \cdots (n)}g_{pq}g_{rs}\rho_t \ldots \rho_{(n-4)}$$

so that the right-hand side of Equation 21.026 can be written as

$$\left[1 - \frac{r^2\Delta}{2(2n-1)}\right.$$
$$\left. + \frac{r^4\Delta^2}{2 \cdot 4(2n-1)(2n-3)} - \ldots\right]f_n(x, y, z)$$

while the left-hand side is

$$\frac{(-)^n A^{pqrst \cdots (n)}(1/r)_{pqrst \ldots (n)}r^{2n+1}}{1 \cdot 3 \ldots (2n-1)}.$$

We can also write

$$A^{pqrst \cdots (n)}(1/r)_{pqrst \ldots (n)} = f_n\left(\frac{\partial}{\partial x}, \frac{\partial}{\partial y}, \frac{\partial}{\partial z}\right)\left(\frac{1}{r}\right)$$

in which f_n is the same function of the operators $\partial/\partial x$, etc., as $f_n(x, y, z)$ is of the Cartesian coordinates of P in Equation 21.030. The final result is a classical theorem of very general application due to Hobson,[3]

---

[3] Hobson, *op. cit. supra* note 2, 127–129.

$$\frac{(-)^n r^{2n+1}}{1 \cdot 3 \ldots (2n-1)} f_n\left(\frac{\partial}{\partial x}, \frac{\partial}{\partial y}, \frac{\partial}{\partial z}\right)\left(\frac{1}{r}\right)$$

$$= \left[1 - \frac{r^2 \Delta}{2(2n-1)} + \frac{r^4 \Delta^2}{2 \cdot 4(2n-1)(2n-3)}\right.$$

21.031 $$\left. - \ldots \right] f_n(x, y, z).$$

23. Hobson's formula is frequently useful as a means of expressing the successive derivatives of $(1/r)$ in spherical harmonics. Suppose, for example, we want to express $(1/r)_{112}$, then the corresponding polynomial is

$$f_3(x, y, z) = x^2 y;$$

and we have

$$\frac{-r^7}{1 \cdot 3 \cdot 5} \cdot \left(\frac{1}{r}\right)_{112} = x^2 y - (\tfrac{1}{5}) r^2 y$$

$$= (r^3/5)(5 \cos^3 \phi \cos^2 \omega \sin \omega$$
$$\qquad - \cos \phi \sin \omega)$$

$$= (r^3/5)\{\cos \phi \sin \omega (5 \cos^2 \phi - 1)$$
$$\qquad - 5 \cos^3 \phi \sin^3 \omega\}$$

$$= (r^3/5)\{\tfrac{1}{4} \cos \phi \sin \omega (1 - 5 \sin^2 \phi)$$
$$\qquad + \tfrac{5}{4} \cos^3 \phi \sin 3\omega\}$$

$$= (r^3/5)\{-\tfrac{1}{6} P_3^1(\sin \phi) \sin \omega$$
$$\qquad + \tfrac{1}{12} P_3^3(\sin \phi) \sin 3\omega\}$$

so that finally

$$r^4(1/r)_{112} = \tfrac{1}{2} P_3^1(\sin \phi) \sin \omega - \tfrac{1}{4} P_3^3(\sin \phi) \sin 3\omega.$$

21.032

We can be certain that the result must be in terms of harmonic functions. The process is assisted if we first convert powers of the sine or cosine of the longitude into multiple angles.

The Potential in Spherical Harmonics

24. If we return to the basic Equation 21.011 and figure 19, we see that the coefficient of $(1/r^{n+1})$, that is,

$$\sum \bar{m} \bar{r}^n P_n(\cos \bar{\gamma}),$$

is a function of the position of the mass point Q in relation to a temporarily fixed direction OP and of the distribution of mass, and so must be expressible in terms of the inertia tensors for a particular origin. We now seek to express this function alternatively in terms of spherical harmonics.

25. If the latitude and longitude of the mass point are overbarred and of the point P are unbarred, we have

$$\cos \bar{\gamma} = \sin \phi \sin \bar{\phi} + \cos \phi \cos \bar{\phi} \cos (\bar{\omega} - \omega)$$

21.033

and by the ordinary addition formula

$$P_n(\cos \bar{\gamma}) = P_n(\sin \phi) P_n(\sin \bar{\phi})$$

$$+ 2 \sum_{m=1}^{m=n} \left[\frac{(n-m)!}{(n+m)!} P_n^m(\sin \phi) P_n^m(\sin \bar{\phi})\right.$$

21.034 $$\left. \times \{\cos m\omega \cos m\bar{\omega} + \sin m\omega \sin m\bar{\omega}\}\right].$$

We can accordingly rewrite Equation 21.011 to give the potential in the form

$$-\frac{V}{G} = \sum_{n=0}^{\infty} \sum_{m=0}^{n} P_n^m(\sin \phi)\{C_{nm} \cos m\omega$$

21.035 $$+ S_{nm} \sin m\omega\}/r^{n+1}$$

in which the term independent of longitude is

21.036 $$C_{n0} P_n^0(\sin \phi) = C_{n0} P_n(\sin \phi),$$

provided that

$$C_{n0} = \sum \bar{m} \bar{r}^n P_n(\sin \bar{\phi})$$

$$C_{nm} = 2 \sum \bar{m} \bar{r}^n \frac{(n-m)!}{(n+m)!} P_n^m(\sin \bar{\phi}) \cos m\bar{\omega}$$

21.037 $$S_{nm} = 2 \sum \bar{m} \bar{r}^n \frac{(n-m)!}{(n+m)!} P_n^m(\sin \bar{\phi}) \sin m\bar{\omega}$$

in which m can be any integer between unity and n inclusive, and $(n-m)!$ is interpreted as unity if $m=n$. The summation in these expressions is not, however, taken over these values of m as in Equation 21.034, but is taken over all mass points in the attracting body. Accordingly, the C's and S's are constants for a particular body and depend only on the mass distribution. Like the inertia tensors, to which we shall relate them later, the C's and S's can be calculated if we know or postulate the mass distribution. Conversely, a knowledge of the C's and S's or of the components of the inertia tensors, obtained by observation or measurement, will provide information about the mass distribution, although the C's and S's and the inertia tensors do not determine the mass distribution uniquely.

26. If a is a constant, such as the radius of a sphere centered on the origin and enclosing all the matter, we can multiply Equation 21.035 by a^n without affecting the convergence of the series, provided we also divide the C's and S's by a^n. This

device will also ensure the convergence of the series in Equations 21.037, and of the corresponding integrals in the case of continuous distributions. The size of the C's and S's will depend largely on m, and to render them more readily comparable, it is usual to adopt *normalized* functions instead; one such scheme, due to Kaula,[4] is to use the following overbarred coefficients

$$\bar{C}_{n0} = C_{n0}/(2n+1)^{1/2}$$

$$\begin{pmatrix} \bar{C}_{nm} \\ \bar{S}_{nm} \end{pmatrix} = \left[\frac{(n+m)!}{2(2n+1)(n-m)!} \right]^{1/2} \begin{pmatrix} C_{nm} \\ S_{nm} \end{pmatrix}$$

21.038 $m \neq 0,$

which in effect reduce the coefficients to about the same comparable size as their root mean square values over a sphere. The dimensions of the constants need some consideration. The dimensions of the potential, defined as work done on a particle of unit mass, are L^2T^{-2}. From the formula Gm/r for the potential, the dimensions of the gravitational constant G are $L^3M^{-1}T^{-2}$ and the dimensions of V/G are $L^{-1}M$. Consequently, the dimensions of the C_{nm}, S_{nm} in Equation 21.035 must be L^nM, which is verified by Equations 21.037. If, however, we multiply Equation 21.035 by G and alter the constants accordingly, the dimensions of the constants would be $L^{n+1}(L^2T^{-2})$.

Relations Between the Constants

27. It will be clear from Equation 21.026 that the nth-degree term in the inertial form of the potential, Equation 21.017, consists of $1/r^{n+1}$ multiplied by quantities which are independent of r; similarly, so does the nth-degree term of the spherical harmonic form of the potential, Equation 21.035. Both forms of the potential must hold for all values of r outside the sphere of convergence; we may accordingly equate the nth-degree terms in the two Equations 21.017 and 21.035. That is not to say, however, that individual terms within the nth-degree are equal; only the sums of these individual terms, comprising the whole of the nth-degree terms, are the same. We conclude that the C's and S's in Equations 21.037 are expressible in terms of inertia tensors of the same nth-degree.

28. The simplest way of expressing this result is to expand the C's and S's as Cartesian polynomials

[4] Kaula (1959), "Statistical and Harmonic Analysis of Gravity," *Journal of Geophysical Research*, v. 64, 2410.

from the usual formulas

$$P_n(\sin \bar{\phi}) = \frac{1 \cdot 3 \cdot 5 \ldots (2n-1)}{n!}$$

$$\times \left[\sin^n \bar{\phi} - \frac{n(n-1)}{2(2n-1)} \sin^{(n-2)}\bar{\phi} \right.$$

$$+ \frac{n(n-1)(n-2)(n-3)}{2 \cdot 4(2n-1)(2n-3)} \sin^{(n-4)}\bar{\phi}$$

21.039 $\left. - \ldots \right]$

$$P_n^m(\sin \bar{\phi}) = \frac{(2n)! \cos^m \bar{\phi}}{2^n n!(n-m)!}$$

$$\times \left[\sin^{(n-m)}\bar{\phi} - \frac{(n-m)(n-m-1)}{2(2n-1)} \sin^{(n-m-2)}\bar{\phi} \right.$$

$$+ \frac{(n-m)(n-m-1)(n-m-2)(n-m-3)}{2 \cdot 4(2n-1)(2n-3)}$$

$$\left. \times \sin^{(n-m-4)}\bar{\phi} - \ldots \right]$$

21.040

$$\cos m\bar{\omega} = \cos^m \bar{\omega} - \frac{m(m-1)}{2!} \cos^{(m-2)}\bar{\omega} \sin^2 \bar{\omega} + \ldots$$

21.041

$$\sin m\bar{\omega} = m \cos^{(m-1)}\bar{\omega} \sin \bar{\omega}$$

$$- \frac{m(m-1)(m-2)}{3!} \cos^{(m-3)} \bar{\omega} \sin^3 \bar{\omega} + \ldots,$$

21.042

and to substitute the relations

$$\bar{x} = \bar{r} \cos \bar{\phi} \cos \bar{\omega}$$

$$\bar{y} = \bar{r} \cos \bar{\phi} \sin \bar{\omega}$$

$$\bar{z} = \bar{r} \sin \bar{\phi}$$

$$\bar{x}^2 + \bar{y}^2 + \bar{z}^2 = \bar{r}^2.$$

For example, we have

$$C_{33} = 2 \sum \bar{m}\bar{r}^3 \times (1/6!)$$

$$\times \left(\frac{6! \cos^3 \bar{\phi}}{2^3 3!} \right) [1][\cos^3 \bar{\omega} - 3 \cos \bar{\omega} \sin^2 \bar{\omega}]$$

$$= \tfrac{1}{24} \sum \bar{m}(\bar{x}^3 - 3\bar{x}\bar{y}^2)$$

$$= \tfrac{1}{24}(I^{111} - 3I^{122}).$$

29. In this way, we find that the complete sets of relations for the second and third orders are

$$C_{20} = I^{33} - \tfrac{1}{2}(I^{11} + I^{22})$$

$$C_{21} = I^{13}$$

$$S_{21} = I^{23}$$

$$C_{22} = \tfrac{1}{4}(I^{11} - I^{22})$$

21.043 $S_{22} = \tfrac{1}{2}I^{12}$

and

$$C_{30} = I^{333} - \tfrac{3}{2}(I^{113} + I^{223})$$

$$C_{31} = I^{133} - \tfrac{1}{4}(I^{111} + I^{122})$$

$$S_{31} = I^{233} - \tfrac{1}{4}(I^{112} + I^{222})$$

$$C_{32} = \tfrac{1}{4}(I^{113} - I^{223})$$

$$S_{32} = \tfrac{1}{2}I^{123}$$

$$C_{33} = \tfrac{1}{24}(I^{111} - 3I^{122})$$

21.044 $\qquad S_{33} = \tfrac{1}{24}(3I^{112} - I^{222}).$

30. To find more general relations, we rewrite the last two equations of Equations 21.037 in the complex form

$$C_{nm} + iS_{nm} = 2\,\frac{(n-m)!}{(n+m)!}\sum \bar m\bar r^{(n-m)}\,P_n^m(\sin\overline\phi)\,(re^{i\omega})^m$$

$$= \frac{(2n)!}{2^{(n-1)}n!(n+m)!}\sum \bar m(\bar x + i\bar y)^m\Bigg[\,\bar z^{(n-m)}$$

$$-\frac{(n-m)(n-m-1)}{2(2n-1)}\,\bar r^2\bar z^{(n-m-2)}$$

$$+\frac{(n-m)(n-m-1)(n-m-2)(n-m-3)}{2\cdot 4\,(2n-1)(2n-3)}$$

21.045 $\qquad \times \bar r^4\bar z^{(n-m-4)} - \ldots\Bigg]$

on substituting Equation 21.040. The result is a combination of components of the nth-order inertia tensor which can be written down at once after expanding $(\bar x + i\bar y)^m$. Terms containing $\bar r^2$ will appear as

$$g_{rs}I^{rspqk\ldots(n)} = I^{11pq\ldots(n)} + I^{22pq\ldots(n)} + I^{33pq\ldots(n)},$$

and terms containing $\bar r^4$ will appear as

$$g_{rs}g_{tu}I^{rstuk\ldots(n)},$$

and so on. For example, we have

$$C_{41} + iS_{41} = \frac{8!}{8\cdot 4!5!}\sum \bar m(\bar x + i\bar y)\left[\bar z^3 - \frac{3\cdot 2}{2\cdot 7}\bar r^2\bar z\right]$$

$$= \tfrac{7}{4}\{I^{1333} - \tfrac{3}{7}(I^{1113} + I^{2213} + I^{3313})$$

$$+ iI^{2333} - \tfrac{3}{7}i(I^{1123} + I^{2223} + I^{3323})\}$$

leading to

$$C_{41} = I^{3313} - \tfrac{3}{4}(I^{1113} + I^{2213})$$

21.046 $\qquad S_{41} = I^{3323} - \tfrac{3}{4}(I^{1123} + I^{2223}).$

Apart from the factor of 2 in Equations 21.037, the zonal terms C_{n0} can also be obtained from the general Equation 21.045 simply by making $m = 0$.

Otherwise, we can use Equation 21.039 and write

$$C_{no} = \sum \bar m\,\frac{1\cdot 3\cdot 5\,\ldots\,(2n-1)}{n!}\Bigg[\bar z^n$$

21.047 $\qquad -\frac{n(n-1)}{2(2n-1)}\bar r^2\bar z^{(n-2)} + \ldots\Bigg].$

31. We have seen in § 21–4 that the number of independent terms of the nth-degree is $(2n+1)$ at most, and there are indeed $(2n+1)$ of the C_{nm} and S_{nm}. The inertia tensor of the nth-degree, nevertheless, has $\tfrac{1}{2}(n+1)(n+2)$ distinct components, and we might expect to find

$$\tfrac{1}{2}(n+1)(n+2) - (2n+1) = \tfrac{1}{2}n(n-1)$$

relations between these components. There are no such relations. The explanation is that the number of independent functions

$$(1/r)_{rst\ldots(n)}$$

is restricted by the Laplace equation to $(2n+1)$; the number of components of the inertia tensor is not so restricted. For example, the Laplace equation in Cartesian coordinates applied to terms of the second degree is

$$(1/r)_{11} + (1/r)_{22} + (1/r)_{33} = 0,$$

and we can write the sum of the corresponding terms in the potential as

$$I^{11}(1/r)_{11} + I^{22}(1/r)_{22} + I^{33}(1/r)_{33}$$

$$= (I^{11} - I^{33})(1/r)_{11} + (I^{22} - I^{33})(1/r)_{22}.$$

Consequently, we shall obtain the same result for the sum of the second-degree terms in the potential if we take as coefficients

$$(I^{11}) = I^{11} - I^{33}$$

$$(I^{22}) = I^{22} - I^{33}$$

$$(I^{33}) = 0$$

$$(I^{12}) = I^{12}$$

$$(I^{23}) = I^{23}$$

$$(I^{13}) = I^{13}.$$

We do not reduce the number of components of the inertia tensor by this device, but we do reduce the number of separate terms to the requisite five. The same derivation applies to the nth-order terms where the $\tfrac{1}{2}n(n-1)$ relations

$$(1/r)_{11tu\ldots(n)} + (1/r)_{22tu\ldots(n)} + (1/r)_{33tu\ldots(n)} = 0$$

are introduced by differentiating the Laplace equation $(n-2)$ times. As we shall see later, the number of components of the inertia tensor can be reduced by a suitable choice of coordinate axes, but in that case, the number of C's and S's is also reduced.

32. For these reasons, it is not possible to express each component of the inertia tensor explicitly in terms of the C's and S's. We can see from Equations 21.037 that the C's and S's are linear combinations of harmonic functions; therefore, any linear combination of these terms must also be a harmonic function. Each component of the inertia tensor is, however, a homogeneous polynomial by definition in Equation 21.012, and not all polynomials are harmonic functions. The most we can do is to express certain combinations of the components of an nth-order inertia tensor, which happen to be harmonic functions, in terms of C_{n0}, C_{nm}, and S_{nm}. This procedure will reduce the number of independent relations to $(2n+1)$.

33. For example, the third-degree polynomial $(y^3 - 3yz^2)$ is harmonic and can therefore be expressed in terms of solid spherical harmonics as

$$(y^3 - 3yz^2) = r^3 \, (\cos^3 \phi \sin^3 \omega$$
$$- 3 \cos \phi \sin^2 \phi \sin \omega)$$
$$= - r^3 \{ \tfrac{1}{60} P_3^3 \, (\sin \phi) \sin 3\omega$$
$$+ \tfrac{1}{2} P_3^1 (\sin \phi) \sin \omega \};$$

multiplying this equation by the mass of the particle at (x, y, z) and summing with the aid of Equations 21.037, we have

$$I^{222} - 3I^{233} = - 6S_{33} - 3S_{31}.$$

Proceeding in this way for the other six basic third-degree harmonic polynomials

$$(xy^2 - xz^2), \ (yz^2 - yx^2), \ (zx^2 - zy^2),$$
$$(x^3 - 3xy^2), \ (z^3 - 3zx^2), \ xyz,$$

we have for the complete third-order set

$$I^{122} - I^{133} = - 6C_{33} - C_{31}$$
$$I^{233} - I^{112} = - 6S_{33} + S_{31}$$
$$I^{113} - I^{223} = 4C_{23}$$
$$I^{111} - 3I^{122} = 24C_{33}$$
$$I^{222} - 3I^{233} = - 6S_{33} - 3S_{31}$$
$$I^{333} - 3I^{113} = C_{30} - 6C_{32}$$

21.048 $\qquad\qquad I^{123} = 2S_{32},$

agreeing with the reverse set in Equations 21.044. The harmonic polynomials are suggested by Equations 21.044. For example,

$$C_{32} = \tfrac{1}{4}(I^{113} - I^{223})$$

shows that $(x^2z - y^2z)$ is harmonic, and we obtain

two others by permuting x, y, z. In the same way,

$$C_{33} = \tfrac{1}{24}(I^{111} - 3I^{122})$$

shows that $(x^3 - 3xy^2)$ is harmonic with two others by permutation, and finally

$$S_{32} = \tfrac{1}{2}I^{123}$$

gives the remaining basic harmonic as xyz. The remaining harmonics in Equations 21.044 are linear combinations of the basic set of seven. For example,

$$C_{30} = I^{333} - \tfrac{3}{2}(I^{113} + I^{223})$$

shows that

$$z^3 - \tfrac{3}{2}(x^2z + y^2z)$$

is harmonic, but this can be expressed as

$$(z^3 - 3zx^2) + \tfrac{3}{2}(zx^2 - zy^2).$$

34 For the sake of completeness, we give the reverse second-order set as

$$I^{11} - I^{22} = 4C_{22}$$
$$I^{22} - I^{33} = - C_{20} - 2C_{22}$$
$$I^{12} = 2S_{22}$$
$$I^{13} = C_{21}$$

21.049 $\qquad\qquad I^{23} = S_{21}.$

Again, the basic harmonics are suggested by Equations 21.043 as $(x^2 - y^2)$ and xy with permutations.

Invariance

35. If we define the Newtonian potential at a point as the negative of the work done by the force of attraction in moving a particle from an infinite distance to the point P, then it is clear that the potential depends only on the position of P in relation to the attracting body, not on the choice of a particular coordinate system. In other words, the potential must be a scalar invariant. We arrive at the same conclusion if we define the potential as a scalar whose gradient is the resultant force of attraction; the attraction vector at P must also be independent of the coordinate system, although its *components* will, of course, depend on the coordinate system. Again, we can define the potential as a scalar whose Laplacian is zero outside matter and which behaves like $(1/r)$ at great distances from the attracting body; we have seen that the Laplacian is invariant, and if it is required to have a defined (zero) value—independent of the coordinate system—at all points in free space, then the original scalar potential must also be an invariant.

That is not to say, however, that every mathematical expression for the potential is necessarily invariant; we should test the expression for invariance and so ensure that it is a valid representation of the physical definitions. For example, we have added the principle of superposition to the physical definition of the potential which arises from a particle in deriving Equation 21.011, and if this were to result in noninvariance, then the principle could not possibly be true. Some of the mathematical processes could also introduce noninvariance, especially when we work in a particular coordinate system. Accordingly, we shall now test the basic Equation 21.017 for invariance.

36. From the tensor form of the potential in Equation 21.017, we can see at once that each group of terms of the same order is invariant under coordinate transformations which do not change the Cartesian origin because, in that case, $(1/r)$ does not change and the inertia tensors remain the same even though their components change. Accordingly, Equation 21.017 is invariant for rotations of the coordinate axes.

37. Next, we consider the effect on the potential at P (fig. 20) of shifting the origin from O to O_0. The

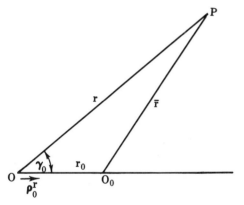

Figure 20.

position vector of O_0 in the old system is ρ_0^r in a direction making an angle γ_0 with OP, and the magnitude OO_0 of the change is r_0. Quantities related to the new system are denoted by overbars, for example, $O_0P = \bar{r}$; an overbarred inertia tensor signifies that its values are to be taken at the point O_0. We must show that we have

$$\sum_{n=0}^{\infty} \frac{(-)^n}{n!} I^{stu\ldots(n)} \left(\frac{1}{r}\right)_{stu\ldots(n)}$$

21.050
$$= \sum_{n=0}^{\infty} \frac{(-)^n}{n!} \bar{I}^{stu\ldots(n)} \left(\frac{1}{\bar{r}}\right)_{stu\ldots(n)}$$

for arbitrary values of the vector ρ_0^r.

38. As in Equation 21.010, we have

$$\bar{r} = r\{1 - 2(r_0/r)\cos\gamma_0 + (r_0/r)^2\}^{1/2}$$

$$\frac{1}{\bar{r}} = \frac{1}{r}\left\{1 + \frac{r_0}{r}P(\cos\gamma_0)\right.$$

21.051
$$\left. + \ldots \left(\frac{r_0}{r}\right)^m P_m(\cos\gamma_0) + \ldots \right\},$$

provided that $r_0 < r$. We have also to ensure that P lies outside the new sphere of convergence (fig. 19), centered on O_0, so that both series in Equation 21.050 may be convergent. Because terms of the same order in either series are invariant for rotations of the coordinate axes, we can take OO_0 as the old z-axis without any loss of generality. We then follow § 21–13 and rewrite Equations 21.051 as

$$\frac{1}{\bar{r}} = \frac{1}{r} - r_0\frac{\partial}{\partial z}\left(\frac{1}{r}\right) + \ldots \frac{(-)^m r_0^m}{m!}\frac{\partial^m}{\partial z^m}\left(\frac{1}{r}\right)\ldots$$

21.052

in which the derivatives refer to virtual displacements of the point P. This expression is similar, apart from signs, to a Taylor expansion for $(1/\bar{r})$ along OO_0. However, it should not be confused with a Taylor expansion, which would require $(1/r)$ to be defined along OO_0 and would require values of the derivatives at O. If the unit vector along the z-axis, OO_0, is σ^p, then we have

$$r_0\frac{\partial}{\partial z}\left(\frac{1}{r}\right) = r_0\sigma^p\left(\frac{1}{r}\right)_p = \rho_0^p\left(\frac{1}{r}\right)_p;$$

and because ρ_0^p and σ^p are fixed during displacements of P, we may similarly write

$$r_0^m\frac{\partial^m}{\partial z^m}\left(\frac{1}{r}\right) = \rho_0^p\rho_0^q \ldots \rho_0^{(m)}\left(\frac{1}{r}\right)_{pq\ldots(m)}$$

so that Equation 21.052 may be rewritten in tensor form as

$$\frac{1}{\bar{r}} = \frac{1}{r} + \sum_{m=1}^{\infty}\frac{(-)^m}{m!}\rho_0^p\rho_0^q \ldots \rho_0^{(m)}\left(\frac{1}{r}\right)_{pq\ldots(m)}$$

21.053

in which the mth-order term has m vectors, ρ_0^p, and m successive covariant derivatives of $(1/r)$. These covariant derivatives still refer to displacements of P with O, O_0 fixed. We can accordingly differentiate Equation 21.053 further for displacements of P, with ρ_0^p a fixed vector, and obtain

$$\left(\frac{1}{\bar{r}}\right)_{stu\ldots(n)} = \left(\frac{1}{r}\right)_{stu\ldots(n)}$$

$$+ \sum_{m=1}^{\infty} \frac{(-)^m}{m!}\rho_0^p\rho_0^q\,\cdots\,\rho_0^{(m)}\left(\frac{1}{r}\right)_{pq\ldots(m)stu\ldots(n)}.$$

21.054

39. We have now to evaluate the inertia tensors at O_0. If ρ^r, $\bar{\rho}^r$ are the position vectors from O and O_0, respectively, to a particle of mass m, then we have

$$\bar{\rho}^s = \rho^s - \rho_0^s$$

in which ρ_0^s is, as before, the vector $\overrightarrow{OO_0}$. The second-order inertia tensor at O_0 is then

$$\bar{I}^{st} = \sum m\bar{\rho}^s\bar{\rho}^t$$
$$= \sum m(\rho^s - \rho_0^s)(\rho^t - \rho_0^t)$$
21.055 $\quad = I^{st} - \rho_0^s I^t - \rho_0^t I^s + M\rho_0^s\rho_0^t$

in which M is the total mass. If later we contract with a covariant symmetric tensor such as $(1/\bar{r})_{st}$, then this last expression may be written as

21.056 $\qquad \bar{I}^{st} = I^{st} - 2\rho_0^s I^t + M\rho_0^s\rho_0^t.$

In the same way, the nth-order inertia tensor is

$$\bar{I}^{stu\ldots(n)} = \sum m(\rho^s - \rho_0^s)(\rho^t - \rho_0^t)(\rho^u - \rho_0^u)$$
21.057 $\qquad\qquad\qquad \ldots (\rho^{(n)} - \rho_0^{(n)}),$

and if this last equation is to be contracted with a covariant tensor symmetrical in any two indices, it can be written as

$$\bar{I}^{stu\ldots(n)} = I^{stu\ldots(n)} - n\rho_0^s I^{tu\ldots(n-1)}$$
$$+ \tfrac{1}{2}n(n-1)\rho_0^s\rho_0^t I^{u\ldots(n-2)}$$
21.058 $\qquad \ldots (-)^n M\rho_0^s\rho_0^t\rho_0^u\,\cdots\,\rho_0^{(n)}.$

40. Multiplication and contraction of the two Equations 21.054 and 21.058 now show that we have

$$\bar{I}^{stu\ldots(n)}\left(\frac{1}{\bar{r}}\right)_{stu\ldots(n)} = I^{stu\ldots(n)}\left(\frac{1}{r}\right)_{stu\ldots(n)} + \ldots;$$
21.059

the remaining terms on the right all contain the arbitrary vector ρ_0^p. The term containing one vector ρ_0^p is

$$-I^{stu\ldots(n)}\rho_0^p\left(\frac{1}{r}\right)_{pstu\ldots(n)} - nI^{tu\ldots(n-1)}\rho_0^s\left(\frac{1}{r}\right)_{stu\ldots(n)},$$

which becomes on exchanging dummy indices

$$-\rho_0^p\frac{\partial}{\partial x^p}\left[I^{stu\ldots(n)}\left(\frac{1}{r}\right)_{stu\ldots(n)}\right.$$
$$\left. + nI^{tu\ldots(n-1)}\left(\frac{1}{r}\right)_{tu\ldots(n)}\right]$$

21.060 $\quad = \rho_0^p\dfrac{\partial}{\partial x^p}\left[\dfrac{n!}{(-)^n}\left\{\left(\dfrac{V}{G}\right)_{(n)} - \left(\dfrac{V}{G}\right)_{(n-1)}\right\}\right]$

where $-(V/G)_{(n)}$ signifies the nth-term in the expansion of Equation 21.017. If the term in Equation 21.060 is to be invariant for arbitrary ρ_0^p, then the term within brackets in the last expression must be constant or zero, which, in general, is not the case. If, however, we multiply Equation 21.059 by $(-)^n/n!$ and sum from $n=0$ to $n=\infty$, then the term containing ρ_0^p becomes zero, provided that $-(V/G)_\infty$ is zero as it must be because the series for $-(V/G)$ is convergent. The potential given by Equation 21.017 is then invariant, at least to a first order, although each term or group of terms is not invariant. In the same way, the term in Equation 21.059 containing two vectors is

$$\rho_0^p\rho_0^q\frac{\partial^2}{\partial x^p\partial x^q}\left[\frac{n!}{(-)^n}\left\{\tfrac{1}{2}\left(\frac{V}{G}\right)_{(n)} - \left(\frac{V}{G}\right)_{(n-1)} + \tfrac{1}{2}\left(\frac{V}{G}\right)_{(n-2)}\right\}\right],$$

21.061

which again becomes zero if, and only if, we multiply by $(-)^n/n!$ and sum. The same result is obtained for terms of higher degree, and we conclude therefore that the potential as given by Equation 21.017 is invariant although each sum of terms of the same order is not invariant under change of origin as is the case for rotations. We may note also that the proof depends on summing the complete series; if we omit any numerically significant term, the truncated series would not necessarily be invariant. We conclude also that the expression of the potential in spherical harmonics is invariant to the same extent because groups of terms of the same degree in $(1/r)$ are equivalent in the two expressions.

The First-Order Inertia Tensor

41. We have seen in Equation 21.016 that the inertia tensor of zero order is the total (scalar) mass (M) of the attracting body, and we shall now investigate some properties of the higher order inertia tensors.

42. If x_0^s are the Cartesian coordinates of the center of mass of the body, then by definition of the

center of mass, we have from Equation 21.013

21.062A $$I^s = \sum \bar{m}\bar{x}^s = Mx_0^s,$$

or, in terms of position vectors,

21.062B $$I^s = \sum \bar{m}\bar{\rho}^s = M\rho_0^s.$$

If the origin O of Cartesian coordinates is at the center of mass, then ρ_0^s is a null vector and all components of the first-order inertia tensor are zero. In that case, the first-order terms ($n = 1$),

$$-I^s(1/r)_s,$$

in the Equation 21.017 for the potential are all zero. Conversely, if all these three terms are absent in the expression for the potential, then all components of ρ_0^s must be zero because the derivatives of $(1/r)$ are not, in general, zero. In that case, the origin of the coordinate system is at the center of mass.

The Second-Order Inertia Tensor

43. We shall next consider some properties of the second-order inertia tensor

21.063 $$I^{rs} = \sum \bar{m}\bar{x}^r\bar{x}^s = \sum \bar{m}\bar{\rho}^r\bar{\rho}^s,$$

and of the corresponding terms in the potential. We shall also relate this tensor to the moments and products of inertia as usually defined.

44. Returning to figure 19, we note first that the invariant $g_{rs}I^{rs}$, evaluated in Cartesian coordinates (g_{rs} is the same at the origin as at all other points), is

21.064 $$I = g_{rs}I^{rs} = \sum \bar{m}g_{rs}\bar{\rho}^r\bar{\rho}^s = \sum \bar{m}\bar{r}^2$$

and is also

$$I^{rs}\nu_r\nu_s = \sum \bar{m}\bar{\rho}^r\bar{\rho}^s\nu_r\nu_s = \sum \bar{m}\bar{r}^2 \cos^2 \bar{\gamma}.$$

Therefore, the moment of inertia about the axis OP (unit vector ν_r) as usually defined is

$$I_{OP} = \sum \bar{m}(QR)^2 = \sum \bar{m}\bar{r}^2 \sin^2 \bar{\gamma} = I^{rs}(g_{rs} - \nu_r\nu_s)$$

21.065 $$= I^{rs}(\lambda_r\lambda_s + \mu_r\mu_s)$$

where λ_r, μ_r are any orthogonal unit vectors perpendicular to ν_r, and we have used Equation 2.08. It follows that the sum of the moments of inertia about *any* three mutually orthogonal axes through the origin is

$$I^{rs}(\lambda_r\lambda_s + \mu_r\mu_s) + I^{rs}(\mu_r\mu_s + \nu_r\nu_s)$$
$$+ I^{rs}(\nu_r\nu_s + \lambda_r\lambda_s) = 2g_{rs}I^{rs} = 2I,$$

which is another way of considering the invariant

I.[5] If the latitude and longitude of ν_r, with the direction OP, are (ϕ, ω), we can at once expand Equation 21.065 as

$$I_{OP} = I - I^{11} \cos^2 \phi \cos^2 \omega - I^{22} \cos^2 \phi \sin^2 \omega$$
$$- I^{33} \sin^2 \phi - 2I^{12} \cos^2 \phi \sin \omega \cos \omega$$
$$- 2I^{13} \sin \phi \cos \phi \cos \omega$$
$$- 2I^{23} \sin \phi \cos \phi \sin \omega.$$

21.066

45. The off-diagonal components of the inertia tensor

$$I^{12} = \sum \bar{m}\bar{x}\bar{y}$$

$$I^{13} = \sum \bar{m}\bar{x}\bar{z}$$

21.067 $$I^{23} = \sum \bar{m}\bar{y}\bar{z}$$

are usually known as products of inertia.[6]

46. The moment of inertia about an axis depends on the position and direction of the axis. In deriving Equations 21.065 and 21.066, we have in fact assumed that the axis passes through the origin because we have used values of the inertia tensor appropriate to the origin. If we transfer the origin to the center of mass, whose position vector is ρ_0^r, and use Equation 21.055 with $I^t = M\rho_0^t$, we have for the moment of inertia about a parallel axis through

---

[5] There is some confusion in the literature as to the definition of the "inertia tensor." Our second-order inertia tensor is the same as McConnell's inertia tensor (see McConnell (Blackie ed. of 1931, corrected 1936), *Applications of the Absolute Differential Calculus*, or (Dover ed. of 1957), *Applications of Tensor Analysis*, 233). On the other hand, what Goldstein calls the inertia tensor (see Goldstein (1950), *Classical Mechanics*, 149) is equivalent in our notation to

$$(Ig^{rs} - I^{rs}),$$

which, as we can see from Equation 21.065, gives the *moment* of inertia about an axis whose unit vector is ν_r by direct contraction with $\nu_r\nu_s$. If $\tilde{\omega}_r$ is the angular velocity vector, then the angular momentum vector in our notation is

$$(Ig^{rs} - I^{rs})\tilde{\omega}_r,$$

relative to an origin at the center of mass; the kinetic energy of rotation is

$$\tfrac{1}{2}(Ig^{rs} - I^{rs})\tilde{\omega}_r\tilde{\omega}_s.$$

Accordingly, the Goldstein convention suits these dynamical operations slightly better, but the McConnell convention is almost mandatory for our present purposes, particularly in connection with the higher order tensors.

[6] Goldstein's definition of products of inertia (Goldstein, *op. cit. supra* note 5, 145) is the negative of ours because of the difference in definition of the inertia tensor. The Goldstein convention is, however, unusual.

the center of mass

$$\bar{I}^{rs}(g_{rs}-\nu_r\nu_s)=I^{rs}(g_{rs}-\nu_r\nu_s)-M\rho_0^r\rho_0^s(g_{rs}-\nu_r\nu_s)$$

21.068 $$=I_{OP}-Md^2$$

where d is the perpendicular distance of the center of mass from the original axis OP, a result that is well known. Because Md^2 is positive, it follows that the moment of inertia about an axis through the center of mass is less than the moment of inertia about any parallel axis.

47. In much the same way as we investigated the maximum and minimum curvatures of a surface in § 7–14, we now consider the directions of axes about which the moments of inertia are a maximum or a minimum, or at least have stationary values. To obtain these directions, we differentiate Equation 21.065 for a change in the *unit* vector ν_r, keeping the origin and therefore I and I^{rs} fixed. The condition for I_{OP} to have a stationary value about the axis ν_r then is

$$I^{rs}A_r\nu_s=0$$

in which A_r is a unit vector perpendicular to ν_s. But if the moment of inertia is to be stationary about the axis ν_s, regardless of the direction in which we shift ν_s, then A_r must be an *arbitrary* unit vector perpendicular to ν_s. We may express A_r by means of a single parameter θ in relation to two fixed vectors λ_r, μ_r, both perpendicular to ν_s, as

$$A_r=\lambda_r\cos\theta+\mu_r\sin\theta$$

so that the stationary condition becomes

$$I^{rs}\lambda_r\nu_s\cos\theta+I^{rs}\mu_r\nu_s\sin\theta=0$$

for all values of θ; this condition requires both

$$I^{rs}\lambda_r\nu_s=0$$

21.069 $$I^{rs}\mu_r\nu_s=0.$$

48. If the moment of inertia about λ_r is also to be stationary, we must have also

$$I^{rs}\nu_r\lambda_s=0$$

21.070 $$I^{rs}\mu_r\lambda_s=0,$$

the first of which is automatically satisfied by the previous condition $I^{rs}\lambda_r\nu_s=0$ because I^{rs} is symmetrical. From Equations 21.069 and 21.070, we then have

$$I^{rs}\lambda_r\mu_s=0$$

$$I^{rs}\nu_r\mu_s=0,$$

which show that the moment of inertia about the third axis μ_s is also stationary. The three perpendicular axes about which the moments of inertia are stationary are known as *principal axes of inertia*,

and the corresponding moments are *principal moments of inertia*. If the principal axes are taken as rectangular Cartesian coordinate axes, then the condition Equations 21.069 and 21.070 are equivalent to stating that the products of inertia are zero, that is,

$$I^{12}=\sum\bar{m}\bar{x}\bar{y}=0$$

$$I^{23}=\sum\bar{m}\bar{y}\bar{z}=0$$

21.071 $$I^{13}=\sum\bar{m}\bar{x}\bar{z}=0.$$

In other words, the matrix I^{rs} has been diagonalized by taking the principal axes as coordinate lines. We know that a symmetric tensor I^{rs} in three dimensions can always be diagonalized, and we may therefore reasonably infer the general existence of principal axes of inertia. There are in fact three principal axes passing through any point. If the z-axis is a principal axis, but the other two coordinate axes are not, then we still have from Equations 21.069

$$I^{13}=0$$

21.072 $$I^{23}=0;$$

conversely, if these two equations are satisfied, then the z-axis is a principal axis of inertia.

49. We have seen in §21–45 that the moment of inertia about an axis through the center of mass is less than about any parallel axis; we shall now consider this question further. We can see from Equation 21.055 that the change in the inertia tensor for a small displacement dr in the direction of a unit vector λ^s is

$$\frac{dI^{st}}{dr}=-\lambda^sI^t-\lambda^tI^s,$$

which is zero at the center of mass because all components of I^t are zero at that point; therefore, all components of the second-order inertia tensor are stationary at the center of mass. At the center of mass, we have also from Equation 21.055

$$\frac{d^2I^{st}}{dr^2}=M\lambda^s\lambda^t,$$

which is essentially positive when $s=t$, making these components a minimum, but which can be negative in certain directions for the nondiagonal components $s\neq t$. Next, we take the principal axes of inertia at the center of mass as coordinate axes A_r, B_r, C_r so that we have

$$I^{st}A_sB_t=I^{st}A_sC_t=I^{st}B_sC_t=0$$

at the center of mass. These relations must also

hold at points near the center of mass because the inertia tensor is stationary and A_r, B_r, C_r are constant vectors. We conclude that for small displacements from the center of mass, the principal axes of inertia remain parallel to their directions at the center of mass. Moreover, there are now no nondiagonal components at or near the center of mass; we conclude that the remaining three components of the inertia tensor are all a minimum at the center of mass, compared with their values at neighboring points.

50. We shall now express the second-order term in the potential Equation 21.017 in terms of moments of inertia. Using Equation 21.023, we have

$$\tfrac{1}{2}I^{st}(1/r)_{st} = I^{st}(3\nu_s\nu_t - g_{st})/(2r^3)$$

$$= -I^{st}(3g_{st} - 3\nu_s\nu_t - 2g_{st})/(2r^3)$$

21.073 $$= (2I - 3I_{OP})/(2r^3)$$

from Equation 21.065. The OP is the radius vector from the origin to the point P at which the potential is taken, and I_{OP} is the moment of inertia of the attracting body about OP as axis. The same result can be obtained less simply by using the second-degree term in spherical harmonics in Equation 21.035 and by substituting Equations 21.043 and 21.066.

51. Equation 21.073 is a generalization of a formula due to MacCullagh. The equation is usually obtained in the special case when the origin is at the center of mass; but it will be clear from our method of derivation, which does not introduce the center of mass, that the same result is true for any origin, provided the moments of inertia are taken with respect to axes passing through that origin.

52. Next, we shall suppose that the z-axis is a principal axis of inertia without requiring the other coordinate axes also to be principal axes, and we shall consider what difference this makes to the second-order term in the potential. We have at once from Equations 21.072 and 21.043

$$I^{13} = C_{21} = 0$$

21.074 $$I^{23} = S_{21} = 0.$$

Expressed in spherical harmonics from Equation 21.035, for example, the second-degree term multiplied by r^3 is reduced to

$$C_{20}P_2(\sin\phi) + C_{22}P_2^2(\sin\phi)\cos 2\omega$$

21.075 $$+ S_{22}P_2^2(\sin\phi)\sin 2\omega;$$

we can readily verify this result from Equations

21.066 and 21.043. The C_{21}- and S_{21}-terms are simply missing, and this is true for any origin.

53. If all three coordinate axes are principal axes of inertia, then, *in addition*, we have from Equations 21.071 and 21.043

$$I^{12} = 2S_{22} = 0;$$

the second-degree term in the potential (multiplied by r^3) further reduces to

21.076 $$C_{20}P_2(\sin\phi) + C_{22}P_2^2(\sin\phi)\cos 2\omega.$$

In this case, if A, B, C are the three principal moments of inertia, we have from Equation 21.065

$$A = I_x = I - I^{11} = I^{22} + I^{33}$$

$$B = I_y = I - I^{22} = I^{33} + I^{11}$$

$$C = I_z = I - I^{33} = I^{11} + I^{22}$$

21.077 $$I = \tfrac{1}{2}(A + B + C);$$

therefore, from Equations 21.043 we have

$$C_{20} = (I - C) - \tfrac{1}{2}C = \tfrac{1}{2}(A + B) - C$$

21.078 $$C_{22} = \tfrac{1}{4}(I - A - I + B) = \tfrac{1}{4}(B - A),$$

and the second-degree term can be written as

$$\{\tfrac{1}{2}(A + B) - C\}P_2(\sin\phi)$$

21.079 $$+ \tfrac{1}{4}(B - A)P_2^2(\sin\phi)\cos 2\omega.$$

54. If the body itself and the distribution of mass in it are symmetrical about the z-axis, then $I^{11} = \sum \bar{m}\bar{x}^2$, which is equivalent to the moment of inertia about the yz-plane, is obviously the same wherever we take the y-axis; the same applies to $I^{22} = \sum \bar{m}\bar{y}^2$. We could interchange the x- and y-axes without effect on I^{11} and I^{22}, and we conclude that in this symmetrical case

$$I^{11} = I^{22}.$$

If, in addition, the z-axis is a principal axis, then it is evident from Equations 21.077 that

$$A = B.$$

The moment of inertia is the same about any axis in the xy-plane, and any pair of perpendicular axes in the xy-plane are principal axes of inertia. In this case, we have also from Equations 21.078

$$C_{20} = A - C$$

$$C_{22} = 0,$$

and the second-degree term in the potential (multiplied by r^3) reduces further to the single zonal harmonic

21.080 $$(A - C)P_2(\sin\phi),$$

which is the form generally used for the attraction of planets on their satellites when the satellites are distant enough for the planet to be considered rotationally symmetrical and for the higher order terms in the potential to be neglected. These assumptions are, of course, too drastic in the case of near-Earth satellites and for the general expression of the Earth's gravitational field to the degree of accuracy now attainable.

ROTATION OF THE EARTH

55. It can be shown that the rotation of a rigid body is stable about a principal axis of greatest moment of inertia; if the motion is slightly disturbed, the axis of rotation will describe a cone about the principal axis.[7] The same is true of an elastic body, except that the period of disturbed oscillation will be different.[8] In the case of the Earth, the period of this oscillation (the Eulerian free nutation or the Chandler wobble) can be computed theoretically at about 14 months; this oscillation is confirmed by measurements of variation of latitude over long periods. The amplitude, which has similarly been observed, depends on the nature and duration of the disturbance and on damping effects, but does not seem to exceed one- or two-tenths of a second of arc. In addition, there are small annual variations of about the same magnitude caused by shifts of mass resulting, for example, from seasonal weather changes.[9] The conclusion seems to be that the instantaneous axis of rotation coincides with a principal axis (of greatest inertia) to within a few tenths of a second of arc. It may eventually be possible to provide worthwhile corrections for this variation from data provided by the International Polar Motion Service (prior to 1962, known as the International Latitude Service), but meanwhile the effect seems to be negligible for our present purposes. We have seen that the whole group of terms of the same degree in the potential is invariant under rotations of the coordinate system; the only effect of such errors in orientation (these errors are, in any case, small) is to change the magnitude of some terms at the expense of others of the same degree.

56. We can easily show that the center of mass

---

[7] Routh (Dover ed. of 1955), *The Advanced Part of a Treatise on the Dynamics of a System of Rigid Bodies*, original 6th ed. of 1905, 86–130 (especially § 155, 101–102).

[8] Jeffreys (1959), *The Earth; Its Origin, History, and Physical Constitution*, 4th ed., 211–229 (especially § 7.04, 216–218).

[9] For a complete discussion of this entire question, see Munk and MacDonald (1960), *The Rotation of the Earth, A Geophysical Discussion*.

must lie on the axis of rotation of a freely rotating body. If we take the axis of rotation as z-axis, then we have seen in § 20–10 that the Cartesian components of centrifugal force on a particle of mass $\bar{m}$ at $(\bar{x}, \bar{y}, \bar{z})$ for uniform angular velocity $\bar{\omega}$ would be

$$(\bar{m}\bar{\omega}^2\bar{x}, \ \bar{m}\bar{\omega}^2\bar{y}, \ 0).$$

Because the rotation is free, there is no force acting on the axis to balance any resultant of these centrifugal forces, and we must therefore have

$$\sum \bar{m}\bar{x} = \sum \bar{m}\bar{y} = 0$$

summed over all masses. We find from Equation 21.061 that the center of mass must lie on the axis of rotation.

57. In § 19–13, we considered means of setting up a coordinate system whose z-axis is *parallel* to the axis of rotation. This can be done, and it is of fundamental importance that it should be done, although all major survey systems are not oriented in this way as yet. Satellite triangulation using stellar photography automatically ensures and preserves such an orientation for a worldwide coordinate system, but we have no geometrical means of setting up a coordinate system whose z-axis *coincides* with the axis of rotation. If the z-axis is parallel to the axis of rotation but does not coincide with it, then the first-degree terms are not absent in the harmonic series for the potential because the center of mass does not lie on the z-axis and is not therefore the origin of coordinates. We have seen, nevertheless, in § 21–48 that if the z-axis is reasonably close to the axis of rotation, then it is also a principal axis of inertia within the limits of the Chandler wobble and seasonal variations. In accordance with § 21–51, therefore the C_{21}- and S_{21}-terms *must* be omitted from the potential series even though first-degree terms are present.

58. If the z-axis *coincides* with the axis of rotation, then all three first-degree terms and the C_{21}- and S_{21}-terms must be omitted from the potential series. Conversely, if we set up a series in which these terms are omitted, then § 21–41 and § 21–47, together with the dynamical considerations in § 21–54, allow us to assert that the z-axis and the axis of rotation coincide. If we use this form of the potential series in the equations of motion of a satellite, we must ensure that the tracking stations are located in the same coordinate system. If the coordinates of the tracking stations are in the "parallel" system of § 21–57, then we must include origin corrections in the observation equations which, provided the observations are sufficiently

widespread, will accordingly determine the position of the center of mass in the tracking system. In short, angular measurements, which must include astronomical observations, will enable us to set up the *z*-axis parallel to the axis of rotation. Coincidence of the two axes, through location of the center of mass, can be assured only by global measures of gravity or potential.

59. We have seen in Equation 20.08 that the total potential or geopotential is obtained by adding

$$-\tfrac{1}{2}\tilde{\omega}^2(x^2+y^2)$$

to the attraction potential, that is, to

$$-\frac{MG}{r}-\ldots,$$

to allow for the centrifugal force on points attached to the rotating Earth. In deriving this result, we assumed that we have $x=y=0$ on the axis of rotation—or, in other words, that the *z*-axis *coincides* with the axis of rotation—so that the rotation term in the form $-\tfrac{1}{2}\tilde{\omega}^2(x^2+y^2)$ is valid only in such a coordinate system. If the attraction potential is expressed as a harmonic series with no first-order terms and no C_{21}, S_{21} terms, then this condition is satisfied; the rotation term in the form $-\tfrac{1}{2}\tilde{\omega}^2(x^2+y^2)$ is the correct form to use with such a series.

THE NEWTONIAN POTENTIAL AT NEAR POINTS

60. We have now to consider the case, illustrated in figure 21, when the point P at which the potential

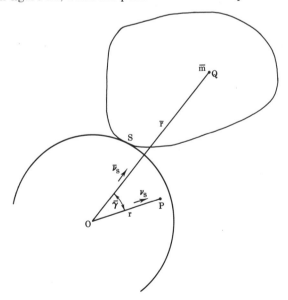

Figure 21.

is required is nearer to the origin of coordinates than any point of the attracting body. We shall for the present choose an origin O outside the body.

61. As before, the potential at P arising from an elementary particle of mass $\bar{m}$ at Q (omitting for the present the gravitational constant G) is

$$-\bar{m}/PQ = -\bar{m}(\bar{r}^2 - 2r\bar{r}\cos\bar{\gamma} + r^2)^{-1/2}$$

$$= -\frac{\bar{m}}{\bar{r}}\left\{1 + \frac{r}{\bar{r}}\cos\bar{\gamma}\right.$$

21.081 $$\left. + \ldots \left(\frac{r}{\bar{r}}\right)^n P_n(\cos\bar{\gamma})\ldots\right\}.$$

This series is absolutely and uniformly convergent if $r < \bar{r}$; for this to hold true for all particles in the body, P must lie within a *sphere of convergence* centered on the origin and just touching the attracting body at S. In that case, we may add series corresponding to Equation 21.081 for all particles and obtain the potential V arising from the whole body in the form

$$-\frac{V}{G} = \sum\frac{\bar{m}}{\bar{r}} + \sum\frac{\bar{m}r\cos\bar{\gamma}}{\bar{r}^2}\ldots + \sum\frac{\bar{m}r^n}{\bar{r}^{n+1}}P_n(\cos\bar{\gamma})\ldots.$$

21.082

We notice at once that the first term is $-V_0/G$ where V_0 is the total potential at the origin, and we proceed to evaluate the remaining terms. For the second term, we have

$$\sum\frac{m\bar{r}\cos\bar{\gamma}}{\bar{r}^2} = \sum\frac{\bar{m}\bar{\nu}_s(r\nu^s)}{\bar{r}^2} = \left(\sum\frac{\bar{m}\bar{\nu}_s}{\bar{r}^2}\right)\rho^s$$

in which ρ^s is the position vector $\overrightarrow{OP}$ of P, and the coefficient of ρ^s (when multiplied by G) is evidently the resultant vector force exerted by the whole body on a particle of unit mass at the origin O. The whole term is accordingly r multiplied by the resolved part of this total force in the direction OP. Alternatively, we can write this second term in the form

$$-(V_s)_0\rho^s/G$$

in which $(V_s)_0$ is the gradient of the potential at O.

62. Now the potential at the point O arising from $\bar{m}$ is $-G\bar{m}/\bar{r}$. If we consider for the moment that Q is fixed and O variable, we can take covariant derivatives of this element of potential at O as

$$-(G\bar{m}/\bar{r})_{stu}\ldots = -G\bar{m}(1/\bar{r})_{stu}\ldots,$$

and we can add these elementary tensors to have

21.083 $$(V_{stu}\ldots)_0 = -\sum G\bar{m}(1/\bar{r})_{stu}\ldots.$$

It is understood that the covariant derivatives of $(1/\bar{r})$ refer to virtual displacements of O relative to a temporary fixed origin Q, and in that case Equation 21.025 applies with overbars. For example, considering the second covariant derivatives and using Equation 21.023, we have

21.084 $\qquad -(V_{st})_0/G = \sum \bar{m}(3\bar{\nu}_s\bar{\nu}_t - \bar{g}_{st})/\bar{r}^3$

and

$$(V_{st})_0 \rho^s \rho^t / G = \sum \bar{m}(3\bar{\nu}_s\bar{\nu}_t - \bar{g}_{st}) r^2 \nu^s \nu^t / \bar{r}^3$$
$$= \sum \bar{m} r^2 (3\cos^2\bar{\gamma} - 1)/\bar{r}^3$$
$$= 2\sum \bar{m} r^2 P_2(\cos\bar{\gamma})/\bar{r}^3$$

so that the third term in the series of Equation 21.082 is

$$-\tfrac{1}{2}(V_{st})_0 \rho^s \rho^t / G;$$

proceeding in this manner, we may verify that Equation 21.082 can be rewritten in the form

$$V_P = V_0 + (V_s)_0 \rho^s + \tfrac{1}{2}(V_{st})_0 \rho^s \rho^t + \ldots$$

21.085 $\qquad + \dfrac{1}{n!}(V_{st\ldots(n)})_0 \rho^s \rho^t \ldots \rho^{(n)} + \ldots$

But this is simply the Taylor expansion of the potential function over a distance r in the direction OP. Equation 21.085 is convergent within the same domain as the equivalent series in Equation 21.082, and we conclude that the potential can be expressed by means of a convergent Taylor series within the sphere of convergence specified in connection with figure 21.

Expression in Spherical Harmonics

63. Returning to Equation 21.082 and using the Addition theorem Equation 21.034 for the Legendre functions, we find as before that the potential can be expressed in the form

$$-\frac{V}{G} = \sum_{n=0}^{\infty} \sum_{m=0}^{n} r^n P_n^m(\sin\phi)\{[C_{nm}]\cos m\omega$$

21.086 $\qquad\qquad\qquad + [S_{nm}]\sin m\omega\},$

provided that

$$[C_{n0}] = \sum \frac{\bar{m}}{\bar{r}^{(n+1)}} P_n(\sin\bar{\phi})$$

$$[C_{nm}] = 2\sum \frac{\bar{m}}{\bar{r}^{(n+1)}}\frac{(n-m)!}{(n+m)!} P_n^m(\sin\bar{\phi})\cos m\bar{\omega}$$

$$[S_{nm}] = 2\sum \frac{\bar{m}}{\bar{r}^{(n+1)}}\frac{(n-m)!}{(n+m)!} P_n^m(\sin\bar{\phi})\sin m\bar{\omega}$$

21.087

in which the summations are carried out over all particles $\bar{m}(\bar{\phi}, \bar{\omega})$ in the attracting body. To distinguish these coefficients from those obtained in Equations 21.037, we have enclosed the coefficients of Equations 21.086 and 21.087 in brackets.

64. If a is a constant, such as the radius of the sphere of convergence, we can divide Equation 21.086 by a^n, provided that we multiply the C's and S's by a^n. This device ensures the convergence of the series in Equations 21.087 and of the corresponding integrals in the case of continuous distributions. The coefficients can be normalized in accordance with Equations 21.038.

65. To express the C's and S's in terms of the coefficients of the Taylor series (Equation 21.085), that is, in terms of successive differentials of the potential at the origin, we use Equation 21.083 and convert the differentials of $(1/r)$ to spherical harmonics as explained in §21–22. For example, using Equation 21.032, we have

$$-(V_{112})_0/G = \sum \bar{m}(1/\bar{r})_{112}$$
$$= \sum \frac{\bar{m}}{\bar{r}^4}\left\{\tfrac{1}{2}P_3^1(\sin\bar{\phi})\sin\bar{\omega}\right.$$
$$\left. -\tfrac{1}{4}P_3^3(\sin\bar{\phi})\sin 3\bar{\omega}\right\}$$

21.088 $\qquad = 3[S_{31}] - 90[S_{33}].$

The zonal coefficients can be found at once from Equation 21.027 as

$$-(V_{333\ldots(n)})_0/G = \sum \bar{m}(1/\bar{r})_{333\ldots(n)}$$
$$= \sum \frac{(-)^n n!}{\bar{r}^{(n+1)}}\bar{m}P_n(\sin\bar{\phi})$$

21.089 $\qquad = (-)^n n![C_{n0}].$

66. Proceeding in this way, we find that

$$-V_0/G = [C_{00}]$$
$$-(V_1)_0/G = -[C_{11}]$$
$$-(V_2)_0/G = -[S_{11}]$$

21.090 $\qquad -(V_3)_0/G = -[C_{10}]$

$$-(V_{11})_0/G = -[C_{20}] + 6[C_{22}]$$
$$-(V_{22})_0/G = -[C_{20}] - 6[C_{22}]$$
$$-(V_{33})_0/G = 2[C_{20}]$$
$$-(V_{12})_0/G = 6[S_{22}]$$
$$-(V_{13})_0/G = 3[C_{21}]$$

21.091 $\qquad -(V_{23})_0/G = 3[S_{21}]$

$$- (V_{111})_0/G = 9[C_{31}] - 90[C_{33}]$$

$$- (V_{221})_0/G = 3[C_{31}] + 90[C_{33}]$$

$$- (V_{331})_0/G = -12[C_{31}]$$

$$- (V_{112})_0/G = 3[S_{31}] - 90[S_{33}]$$

$$- (V_{222})_0/G = 9[S_{31}] + 90[S_{33}]$$

$$- (V_{332})_0/G = -12[S_{31}]$$

$$- (V_{113})_0/G = 3[C_{30}] - 30[C_{32}]$$

$$- (V_{223})_0/G = 3[C_{30}] + 30[C_{32}]$$

$$- (V_{333})_0/G = -6[C_{30}]$$

21.092 $- (V_{123})_0/G = -30[S_{32}].$

Only five of the second-order terms and seven of the third-order terms are independent because of the relations provided by the Laplace equation and its derivatives

$$(V_{11})_0 + (V_{22})_0 + (V_{33})_0 = 0$$

$$(V_{11r})_0 + (V_{22r})_0 + (V_{33r})_0 = 0 \qquad (r = 1, 2, 3).$$

67. The reverse formulas can be found by expressing the C's and S's as (necessarily harmonic) homogeneous polynomials and by substituting the homogeneous polynomial as $f(x, y, z)$ in Hobson's formula (Equation 21.031) in which all the Laplacian terms will be zero. For example, we have

$$[C_{32}] = \tfrac{1}{60} \sum \frac{\bar{m}}{\bar{r}^4} P_3^2(\sin \bar{\phi}) \cos 2\bar{\omega}$$

$$= \tfrac{1}{4} \sum \frac{\bar{m}}{\bar{r}^4} \sin \bar{\phi} \cos^2 \bar{\phi} (\cos^2 \bar{\omega} - \sin^2 \bar{\omega})$$

$$= \tfrac{1}{4} \sum \frac{\bar{m}}{\bar{r}^7} (\bar{x}^2 \bar{z} - \bar{y}^2 \bar{z})$$

$$= - \tfrac{1}{60} \sum \bar{m} \{(1/\bar{r})_{113} - (1/\bar{r})_{223}\}$$

$$= + \tfrac{1}{60} \{(V_{113})_0/G - (V_{223})_0/G\}.$$

The second- and third-order reversals are easy enough to obtain directly from Equations 21.091 and 21.092, and so are not written down, but this more general method may be necessary for the higher orders. A general formula has been given in Equation 21.089 for the zonal terms, and we can readily obtain a general formula for the tesseral terms on the same lines as Equation 21.045, using

$$[C_{nm}] + i[S_{nm}] = 2\sum \frac{\bar{m}}{\bar{r}^{(n+1)}} \frac{(n-m)!}{(n+m)!} P_n^m(\sin \bar{\phi}) e^{im\bar{\omega}}$$

$$= \frac{(2n)!}{2^{n-1}n!(n+m)!} \sum \frac{\bar{m}}{\bar{r}^{(2n+1)}} (\bar{x} + i\bar{y})^m$$

$$\times \left[\bar{z}^{(n-m)} - \frac{(n-m)(n-m-1)}{2(2n-1)} \bar{z}^{(n-m-2)} + \ldots \right].$$

After expanding $(\bar{x} + i\bar{y})^m$, we can substitute for each polynomial

$$\sum \frac{\bar{m}}{\bar{r}^{(2n+1)}} (i) \bar{x}^p \bar{y}^q \bar{z}^r \qquad (p + q + r = n)$$

the corresponding term derived from Hobson's formula (Equation 21.031), that is,

$$(i) \frac{(-)^n}{1 \cdot 3 \ldots (2n-1)} (V_{111 \ldots (p)222 \ldots (q)333 \ldots (r)})_0/G,$$

and finally separate the real and imaginary parts.

68. Powers of $\bar{r}$ cancel in relating the two sets of constants, just as they did in relating the I's with the C's and S's in the formulas for the potential at distant points. We cannot, however, relate the constants in the two formulas for the potential at near and distant points, even if both series were convergent over the same region, because the $\bar{r}$'s appear in different places and vary during summation over the entire mass. A comparison of Equations 21.037 and 21.087, in which the C's and S's have different meanings, will make this statement clear.

Invariance

69. It is evident from the tensor form of Equation 21.085 that each group of terms

$$\frac{1}{n!} (V_{st \ldots (n)})_0 \rho^s \rho^t \ldots \rho^{(n)}$$

is invariant under rotation of the coordinate axes, provided the origin does not change. If the origin changes and the point P remains within the new sphere of convergence, then the new Taylor expansion from the new origin remains convergent. The values of $(V_{st \ldots (n)})$ at the new origin and the position vector of P will become different tensors so that the group of terms is no longer invariant on change of origin. However, we can show, almost exactly as in the section on invariance of the potential at distant points (§ 21–35), that the sum of all terms in the new series remains the same, provided the term of infinite order in the original series is zero, which must be so if the series is convergent. The situation on invariance is accordingly exactly the same as for the potential at distant points.

ANALYTIC CONTINUATION

70. We have seen that Equation 21.017 or its spherical harmonic equivalent may be divergent at points inside a sphere centered on the origin, which just encloses all the matter, and so may not represent the potential at most points on the Earth's surface. This would mean that values of the coefficients C_{nm}, etc., obtained from observations on artificial satellites—the most convenient and accurate method for evaluating at least the lower harmonics—could not properly be used in conjunction with observations on the ground. We might expect to overcome the difficulty by using Equation 21.017 to evaluate all the successive differentials of the potential at a point P outside the sphere of convergence of Equation 21.017 (fig. 22). These

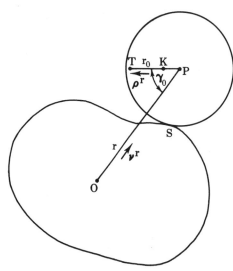

Figure 22.

successive differentials of the potential are then substituted in the Taylor series (Equation 21.085), which we have seen is the same by groups of terms of the same degree as the series derived from the law of Newtonian attraction. This latter series is convergent within a sphere centered on P which just touches the attracting body at S, and the equivalent Taylor series is accordingly convergent within the same sphere PS. The whole process is equivalent to the standard operation of analytic continuation within this sphere.

71. Symbolically, the process leads to the following expression for the potential at a point T (fig. 22), within the sphere of convergence PS, whose posi-

tion vector $\overrightarrow{PT}$ relative to P as origin is ρ^p,

$$-\frac{V_T}{G} = \sum_{m=0}^{\infty} \sum_{n=0}^{\infty} \frac{1}{m!} \frac{(-)^n}{n!} I^{stu \ldots (n)} \left(\frac{1}{r}\right)_{stu \ldots (n)pqr \ldots (m)}$$

21.093 $\times \rho^p \rho^q \rho^r \ldots \rho^{(m)}.$

In this formula, inertia tensors are taken with respect to the origin O from which Equation 21.017 for the potential at P was evaluated; all the $(m+n)$ derivatives of $(1/r)$ refer to changes in $(1/OP)$ for virtual displacements of P or for changes in the coordinates of P, with O fixed.

72. Equation 21.093 can be written as an infinite matrix

$$M(1/r) \qquad -I^s(1/r)_s \qquad +\tfrac{1}{2}I^{st}(1/r)_{st} \quad \ldots$$
$$M(1/r)_p\rho^p \qquad -I^s(1/r)_{sp}\rho^p \qquad +\tfrac{1}{2}I^{st}(1/r)_{stp}\rho^p \quad \ldots$$
$$\tfrac{1}{2}M(1/r)_{pq}\rho^p\rho^q \ -\tfrac{1}{2}I^s(1/r)_{spq}\rho^p\rho^q \ +\tfrac{1}{4}I^{st}(1/r)_{stpq}\rho^p\rho^q \ \ldots$$
$$\cdot \ \cdot \ \cdot \ \cdot \ \cdot \ \cdot \ \cdot \ \cdot \ \cdot \ \cdot \ \cdot \ \cdot \ \cdot$$
$$\cdot \ \cdot \ \cdot \ \cdot \ \cdot \ \cdot \ \cdot \ \cdot \ \cdot \ \cdot \ \cdot \ \cdot \ \cdot$$

21.094

in which the inertia tensor of zero order is the total mass M. The first row summed represents the potential at P. The second row summed is the first derivative of the potential at P contracted with the fixed bounded vector ρ^p, and so on. The fact that the series in Equation 21.093 is convergent implies that the matrix is convergent if the rows are summed first. On the other hand, if we sum the columns first (and this process is not necessarily valid), then it can be shown that the final result would be

21.095 $-\dfrac{V_T}{G} = \displaystyle\sum_{n=0}^{\infty} \dfrac{(-)^n}{n!} I^{stu \ldots (n)} \left(\dfrac{1}{OT}\right)_{stu \ldots (n)}$

in which the derivatives are now evaluated at T. But this last Equation 21.095 is the same as Equation 21.017 evaluated at T; if Equation 21.095 correctly represents the potential at T, then Equation 21.017 must be convergent at T even though T lies inside the sphere of convergence of Equation 21.017 (fig. 19). The convergence of Equation 21.017 at T accordingly depends on whether interchanging the order of summation in Equation 21.093 is valid. The necessary and sufficient conditions for the interchange to be valid do not yet appear to have been established rigorously, but the question may be considered in general terms by taking Equation 21.093 for a point K on PT (fig. 22), which lies outside the sphere of convergence of Equation 21.017. In that case, Equation 21.017 certainly represents the potential at K, and the summation interchange in Equation 21.093 is valid at K. But the two continuation series (Equation 21.093) for K and for T — both of which are convergent — must also have the same properties of absolute and uniform convergence because the coefficients of the vectors are the potential at P and derivatives of the potential at P, and are therefore the same for both series. The only difference between the two series is the magnitude, not the direction, of the contracting vector ρ^ν; this does not affect the convergence of either series. Accordingly, if the necessary and sufficient conditions for the summation interchange depend solely on convergence properties, then these conditions would seem to be satisfied at T as well as at K. However, this demonstration is a long way from a formal proof, and there is another factor which we shall now consider.

73. Proof of convergence of Equation 21.093, obtained in § 21–62, depends on absence of matter within the sphere PS. This proof would not necessarily be valid if there is an alternative distribution of matter, which is nearer to P than the actual distribution and gives the same potential and derivatives of the potential at P as the actual distribution. According to Kellogg,[10] there is always such an alternative distribution which could invalidate the whole process of analytical continuation in this case. The question has been considered from a different angle by Moritz,[11] who concludes that the series is divergent, but his demonstration is also a long way from a formal proof. More research is needed on this controversial question of convergence, which cannot yet be considered as definitely settled. In particular, it may be that the series at points on the topographic surface, although divergent, can be truncated at a certain number of terms to give a better answer than a formally convergent series would give for the same number of terms.

THE POTENTIAL AT INTERNAL POINTS

74. For some purposes, it is desirable to have formulas for the potential at points inside the Earth, developed from the same geometrical definition of a Newtonian potential, although the physical meaning of the result may be doubted. We have no means of inserting a test particle or of making any measurements at such points; therefore, we have

[10] Kellogg (1929), *Foundations of Potential Theory*, 197.
[11] Moritz (1961), "Über die Konvergenz der Kugelfunktionsentwicklung für das Aussenraumpotential an der Erdoberfläche," *Österreichischen Zeitschrift für Vermessungswesen*, v. 49, no. 1, 1–5.

no experimental verification of the law of Newtonian attraction so close to the attracting matter.

75. We draw a sphere, centered on the origin O, which passes through the point P (fig. 23) where we

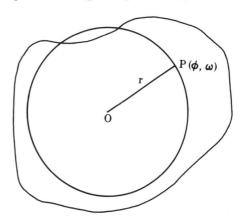

Figure 23.

require the potential. There will be matter outside this sphere, where we shall add a subscript E, as well as inside, where we shall add a subscript I. The contribution to the potential at P arising from the *internal* matter can be expressed as a convergent series in the form of Equation 21.035 in which the summations or integrations in the C's and S's are carried out over all the *internal* matter. We write the resulting coefficients as

$$(C_{n0})_I, \ (C_{nm})_I, \ (S_{nm})_I.$$

The contribution to the potential at P arising from the *external* matter can be expressed as a convergent series in the form of Equation 21.086 in which the summations or integrations in the C's and S's are now carried out over all the *external* matter. We write the resulting coefficients as

$$[C_{n0}]_E, \ [C_{nm}]_E, \ [S_{nm}]_E$$

in which the brackets indicate that Equations 21.087 are to be used.
The potential at P is then

$$-\frac{V}{G} = \sum_{n=0}^{\infty} \sum_{m=0}^{n} P_n^m (\sin \phi) \{\bar{C}_{nm} \cos m\omega + \bar{S}_{nm} \sin m\omega\}$$

where we have

21.096 $\qquad \bar{C}_{nm} = (C_{nm})_I / r^{(n+1)} + r^n [C_{nm}]_E$

and a similar formula for S_{nm}.

76. We can rewrite this last formula as

$$\bar{C}_{nm} = (C_{nm})_{I+E} / r^{(n+1)} - (C_{nm})_E / r^{(n+1)} + r^n [C_{nm}]_E$$

21.097

in which $(C_{nm})_{I+E}$ are the result of summing or integrating over the entire mass in Equations 21.037. The $(C_{nm})_{I+E}$ are also the coefficients of a spherical harmonic series which would be obtained by observation on distant points such as artificial satellites. We may consider the remaining terms in Equation 21.097, that is,

21.098 $\qquad - (C_{nm})_E/r^{(n+1)} + r^n [C_{nm}]_E,$

as a correction [12] which must be added to the first term, obtained from satellites, in order to give the corresponding coefficient in the potential at the internal point. If we proceed in this manner, we do not need to know or to assume the mass distribution or densities at points inside the sphere passing through P in figure 23.

77. In deriving the preceding formulas, we have assumed that both series for the internal and external contributions to the potential at P are convergent actually on their respective spheres of convergence, an assumption which is not necessarily true. Moreover, the contribution to the potential at P becomes infinite for masses infinitesimally close to P, and we have no right to add the corresponding elementary series to the others. We can overcome this difficulty by the usual device of supposing that a thin spherical shell of matter of radii $(r + \epsilon)$ and $(r - \epsilon)$ is removed. We can then show that the contribution of the removed matter to $(C_{nm})/r^{(n+1)}$ and $r^n [C_{nm}]$ for all n is negligible when ϵ is reduced indefinitely.

ALTERNATIVE EXPRESSION OF THE EXTERNAL POTENTIAL

78. We have seen that all the harmonics of the external potential can be obtained by repeated differentiation of the primitive $(1/r)$, that is, the potential of degree zero among the resulting harmonics. Another form of the primitive potential is, however, indicated in a formula by Hobson [13]

21.099 $\qquad \dfrac{P_n^m(\sin \phi)}{r^{(n+1)}} = \dfrac{(-)^n}{(n-m)!} \dfrac{\partial^n}{\partial z^n} \left[\dfrac{1}{r} \left\{ \dfrac{r-z}{r+z} \right\}^{m/2} \right],$

---

[12] Equivalent formulas for the correction have been obtained in 1966 by A. H. Cook (see Cook (1967) "The Determination of the External Gravity Field of the Earth From Observations of Artificial Satellites," *The Geophysical Journal of the Royal Astronomical Society*, v. 13, 297–312) and by F. Foster Morrison (*Validity of the Expansion for the Potential Near the Surface of the Earth*, paper not yet published). The latter paper was read at the 6th Western National Meeting of the American Geophysical Union, Los Angeles, Calif., September 7, 1966.

[13] Hobson, *op. cit. supra* note 2, 106–107. Note, however, that Hobson's P_n^m is $(-)^m$ times our P_n^m, which is the more usual convention.

which degenerates to Equation 21.027 for $m = 0$ and has the advantage that it can generate all the required harmonics by differentiation with respect to z only. We may note that any function of the longitude ω is constant under differentiation with respect to z because $\tan \omega = y/x$, so that we have

$$\dfrac{P_n^m(\sin \phi)}{r^{(n+1)}} \begin{pmatrix} \cos m\omega \\ \sin m\omega \end{pmatrix}$$

21.100 $\qquad = \dfrac{(-)^n}{(n-m)!} \dfrac{\partial^n}{\partial z^n} \left[\dfrac{1}{r} \left\{ \dfrac{r-z}{r+z} \right\}^{m/2} \begin{pmatrix} \cos m\omega \\ \sin m\omega \end{pmatrix} \right].$

This last formula shows that the Newtonian attraction potential, which we have seen is expressible as a sum of the Legendre functions on the left (Equation 21.035), is equally well expressed by a sum of the derivatives on the right. The resulting series will converge in the same way as the spherical harmonic series; the two series are in fact equivalent term-by-term.

79. At this stage, we introduce the spherical *isometric latitude* ψ, defined by the following expressions which are easily shown to be equivalent

$$e^\psi = \cosh \psi + \sinh \psi = \sec \phi + \tan \phi = \tan (\tfrac{1}{4}\pi + \tfrac{1}{2}\phi)$$

$$= \dfrac{1 + \sin \phi}{\cos \phi} = \left(\dfrac{1 + \sin \phi}{1 - \sin \phi} \right)^{1/2}$$

21.101

We can also verify by differentiation that

21.102 $\qquad \psi = \displaystyle\int_0^\phi \sec \phi \, d\phi,$

from which the isometric latitude or Mercator latitude derives its name in the theory of map projections. Equation 21.100 can now easily be cast into the form

$$\dfrac{P_n^m(\sin \phi)}{r^{(n+1)}} e^{im\omega} = \dfrac{(-)^n}{(n-m)!} \dfrac{\partial^n}{\partial z^n} \left[\left(\dfrac{1}{r} \right) e^{-m(\psi - i\omega)} \right]$$

21.103

in which we can change the sign of ω independently of the latitude functions to have also

$$\dfrac{P_n^m(\sin \phi)}{r^{(n+1)}} e^{-im\omega} = \dfrac{(-)^n}{(n-m)!} \dfrac{\partial^n}{\partial z^n} \left[\left(\dfrac{1}{r} \right) e^{-m(\psi + i\omega)} \right].$

21.104

80. The appearance of the complex variable $(\psi + i\omega)$ in these equations suggests an analogy with the theory of orthomorphic or conformal map projections, which arises in the following way. The Laplace equation

$$g^{rs}V_{rs} = \dfrac{\partial^2 V}{\partial x^r \partial x^s} g^{rs} - g^{rs} \Gamma_{rs}^k V_k = 0$$

in spherical polar coordinates can easily be written from formulas in Chapter 18 by substituting $(\bar{R}_1 + h) = (\bar{R}_2 + h) = r$. The metric tensor is given by Equations 18.03, etc., the Christoffel symbols are given by Equations 18.34, etc., and the final equation expands to

$$\frac{\sec^2 \phi}{r^2} \frac{\partial^2 V}{\partial \omega^2} + \frac{1}{r^2} \frac{\partial^2 V}{\partial \phi^2} + \frac{\partial^2 V}{\partial r^2} - \frac{\tan \phi}{r^2} \frac{\partial V}{\partial \phi} + \frac{2}{r} \frac{\partial V}{\partial r} = 0,$$

which for r constant reduces to

$$\cos \phi \frac{\partial}{\partial \phi} \left(\cos \phi \frac{\partial V}{\partial \phi} \right) + \frac{\partial^2 V}{\partial \omega^2} = 0$$

or

21.105
$$\frac{\partial^2 V}{\partial \psi^2} + \frac{\partial^2 V}{\partial \omega^2} = 0.$$

Equation 21.105 is a well-known equation, satisfied by either coordinate $(\bar{x}, \bar{y})$ of any conformal projection of the sphere or by the complex variable $(\bar{x} + i\bar{y})$. The general solution of Equation 21.105 — that is, all solutions of the Laplace equation not containing r — is well known to be

21.106
$$V = f(\psi + i\omega) + g(\psi - i\omega)$$

in which f, g are arbitrary functions. Instead of $1/r$, we could take

21.107
$$V_0 = \frac{1}{r} \{ f(\psi + i\omega) + g(\psi - i\omega) \},$$

which is easily verified to be harmonic, as the primitive potential; we differentiate this expression successively by any or all of (x, y, z) to obtain more general harmonic functions. We should, nevertheless, have to choose f and g to contain a parameter (such as m in Equation 21.103), one value of which would reduce the functions f and g to constants so that Equation 21.107 can contain the primitive *Newtonian* potential $(1/r)$. This alternative form of the primitive potential is sometimes [14] given as

21.107A
$$V_0 = \left(\frac{1}{r} \right) F \left(\frac{x + iy}{r + z} \right) + \left(\frac{1}{r} \right) G \left(\frac{x - iy}{r + z} \right),$$

which is easily shown to be equivalent to Equation 21.107.

The (ξ, η, z) System

81. In manipulating these alternative forms of the potential, it is sometimes advisable to transform

the coordinates to (ξ, η, z) where

$$\xi = x + iy = r \cos \phi e^{i\omega}$$
$$\eta = x - iy = r \cos \phi e^{-i\omega}.$$

The following relations are easily verified,

$$r^2 = \xi \eta + z^2$$
$$e^{i\omega} = (\xi/\eta)^{1/2}$$

21.108
$$e^{\psi} = (r + z)/(\xi \eta)^{1/2}$$
$$e^{\psi + i\omega} = (r + z)/\eta = \xi/(r - z)$$

21.109
$$e^{\psi - i\omega} = (r + z)/\xi = \eta/(r - z)$$

$$\frac{\partial r}{\partial \xi} = \frac{1}{2} \frac{\eta}{r}$$

$$\frac{\partial r}{\partial \eta} = \frac{1}{2} \frac{\xi}{r}$$

21.110
$$\frac{\partial r}{\partial z} = \frac{z}{r}$$

$$\frac{\partial (\psi + i\omega)}{\partial \xi} = \frac{1}{2r} e^{-(\psi + i\omega)}; \qquad \frac{\partial (\psi - i\omega)}{\partial \xi} = -\frac{1}{2r} e^{(\psi - i\omega)}$$

$$\frac{\partial (\psi + i\omega)}{\partial \eta} = -\frac{1}{2r} e^{(\psi + i\omega)}; \qquad \frac{\partial (\psi - i\omega)}{\partial \eta} = \frac{1}{2r} e^{-(\psi - i\omega)}$$

$$\frac{\partial (\psi + i\omega)}{\partial z} = \frac{1}{r}; \qquad \frac{\partial (\psi - i\omega)}{\partial z} = \frac{1}{r}$$

21.111

$$2 \frac{\partial}{\partial \xi} = \frac{\partial}{\partial x} - i \frac{\partial}{\partial y}$$

21.112
$$2 \frac{\partial}{\partial \eta} = \frac{\partial}{\partial x} + i \frac{\partial}{\partial y}.$$

82. The metric in these coordinates is

$$ds^2 = dx^2 + dy^2 + dz^2$$
$$= (dx + idy)(dx - idy) + dz^2$$

21.113
$$= d\xi d\eta + dz^2$$

so that the only nonzero components of the metric tensor are

$$g_{12} = \tfrac{1}{2}; \qquad g_{33} = 1; \qquad |g| = -\tfrac{1}{4};$$
$$g^{12} = 2; \qquad g^{33} = 1.$$

All Christoffel symbols are zero, and the Laplacian is accordingly

21.114
$$\Delta = 4 \frac{\partial^2}{\partial \xi \partial \eta} + \frac{\partial^2}{\partial z^2},$$

which shows that any function of ξ only, or of η only, is harmonic. This property introduces some simplification in the use of Hobson's formula (Equa-

---

[14] See, for example, Bateman (Dover ed. of 1944), *Partial Differential Equations of Mathematical Physics*, original ed. of 1932, 357.

tion 21.031) in these variables because any function of ξ or η can be treated as a constant on the right-hand side of this equation. A corresponding simplification is also introduced into Equations 21.025 and 21.026, which are tensor equations true in these or in any other coordinates, because there are only two nonzero components of the metric tensor. Using Equations 21.111, etc., we can also show that ψ, ω and any function of $(\psi + i\omega)$ or $(\psi - i\omega)$ are harmonic, as is clear from Equation 21.106.

83. Using the relations in § 21–81, we can obtain the following formulas

21.115 $2\dfrac{\partial}{\partial \xi}\left(\dfrac{1}{r}\,e^{-m(\psi - i\omega)}\right) = -\dfrac{\partial}{\partial z}\left(\dfrac{1}{r}\,e^{-(m-1)(\psi - i\omega)}\right)$

21.116 $2\dfrac{\partial}{\partial \xi}\left(\dfrac{1}{r}\,e^{-m(\psi + i\omega)}\right) = \dfrac{\partial}{\partial z}\left(\dfrac{1}{r}\,e^{-(m+1)(\psi + i\omega)}\right)$

21.117 $2\dfrac{\partial}{\partial \eta}\left(\dfrac{1}{r}\,e^{-m(\psi - i\omega)}\right) = \dfrac{\partial}{\partial z}\left(\dfrac{1}{r}\,e^{-(m+1)(\psi - i\omega)}\right)$

21.118 $2\dfrac{\partial}{\partial \eta}\left(\dfrac{1}{r}\,e^{-m(\psi + i\omega)}\right) = -\dfrac{\partial}{\partial z}\left(\dfrac{1}{r}\,e^{-(m-1)(\psi + i\omega)}\right)$

which enable us to differentiate Equations 21.103 and 21.104 with respect to ξ and η, to switch into a higher differential with respect to z, and then to move into a Legendre polynomial of higher degree. For example, we have

$$2\frac{\partial}{\partial \xi}\left\{\frac{P_n^m(\sin\phi)}{r^{(n+1)}}\,e^{im\omega}\right\}$$
$$= \frac{(-)^{n+1}}{(n-m)!}\frac{\partial^{n+1}}{\partial z^{n+1}}\left(\frac{1}{r}\,e^{-(m-1)(\psi - i\omega)}\right),$$

and by rewriting Equation 21.103 for the $(n+1)$th-degree and $(m-1)$th-order, we have also

$$\frac{P_{n+1}^{m-1}(\sin\phi)}{r^{(n+2)}}\,e^{im\omega}$$
$$= \frac{(-)^{n+1}}{(n-m+2)!}\frac{\partial^{n+1}}{\partial z^{n+1}}\left(\frac{1}{r}\,e^{-(m-1)(\psi - i\omega)}\right);$$

therefore, together with three other similarly derived equations, we have finally

$$2\frac{\partial}{\partial \xi}\left\{\frac{P_n^m(\sin\phi)}{r^{(n+1)}}\,e^{im\omega}\right\}$$
$$= (n-m+2)(n-m+1)\frac{P_{n+1}^{m-1}(\sin\phi)}{r^{(n+2)}}\,e^{i(m-1)\omega}$$

21.119

$$2\frac{\partial}{\partial \xi}\left\{\frac{P_n^m(\sin\phi)}{r^{(n+1)}}\,e^{-im\omega}\right\} = -\frac{P_{n+1}^{m+1}(\sin\phi)}{r^{(n+2)}}\,e^{-i(m+1)\omega}$$

21.120

$$2\frac{\partial}{\partial \eta}\left\{\frac{P_n^m(\sin\phi)}{r^{(n+1)}}\,e^{-im\omega}\right\}$$
$$= (n-m+2)(n-m+1)\frac{P_{n+1}^{m-1}(\sin\phi)}{r^{(n+2)}}\,e^{-i(m-1)\omega}$$

21.121

$$2\frac{\partial}{\partial \eta}\left\{\frac{P_n^m(\sin\phi)}{r^{(n+1)}}\,e^{im\omega}\right\} = -\frac{P_{n+1}^{m+1}(\sin\phi)}{r^{(n+2)}}\,e^{i(m+1)\omega}.$$

21.122

Formulas corresponding to Equations 21.119 and 21.122 have been given by Bateman,[15] and the other two formulas can be obtained from them by changing the signs of ω and y. If we separate real and imaginary parts, it will be found that Equations 21.119 and 21.121 are equivalent as are Equations 21.120 and 21.122 also.

By differentiating Equations 21.103 and 21.104 with respect to z, we have in much the same way

$$\frac{\partial}{\partial z}\left\{\frac{P_n^m(\sin\phi)}{r^{(n+1)}}\,e^{\pm im\omega}\right\} = -(n-m+1)\frac{P_{n+1}^m(\sin\phi)}{r^{(n+2)}}\,e^{\pm im\omega}.$$

21.123

We shall require these equations for later use in order to express the gravitational force. They could, of course, be obtained by direct differentiation with some considerable manipulation.

MAXWELL'S THEORY OF POLES

84. We have seen in § 21–4 that any given nth-degree spherical harmonic can be expressed as

21.124 $CL^pM^qN^r \ldots (1/r)_{pqr \ldots (n)}$

where L^p, etc., are n unit vectors and C is a scalar. The unit vectors are known as the *axes* of the harmonic; parallels to the unit vectors through the origin cut the sphere of radius r in the *poles* of the harmonic. If we know the poles, then the harmonic is obtained by simply contracting Equation 21.025 with $CL^pM^q \ldots$; the result will contain the cosines $(L^p\nu_p)$ of the angles between the axes (L^p) and the unit position vector (ν_p) of the point where the harmonic is to be evaluated, as well as the cosines $(g_{pq}L^pM^q)$ of the angles between pairs of axes. This is equivalent to Maxwell's own result.[16] For example, the third-degree harmonic at P with poles L, M, N is

$$r^4L^pM^qN^r(1/r)_{pqr} = 3(\cos LM \cos NP$$
$$+ \cos MN \cos LP$$
$$+ \cos LN \cos MP$$
$$- 5\cos LP \cos MP \cos NP).$$

[15] Bateman, *op. cit. supra* note 14, ex. 2, 361.

[16] Hobson, *op. cit. supra* note 2, 131.

85. The axes are known [17] for the Legendre harmonics of degree n and order m,

$$\frac{P_n^m(\sin \phi)}{r^{(n+1)}} \begin{pmatrix} \cos m\omega \\ \sin m\omega \end{pmatrix}.$$

There are $(n-m)$ axes coincident with the axis of z, and the remaining m-axes are equally spaced in the xy-plane at intervals of π/m. If A^r, B^r, C^r are as usual the (x, y, z) coordinate axes, then the axes of

$$\frac{P_n^m(\sin \phi)}{r^{(n+1)}} \cos m\omega$$

are

(a) $C^p C^q C^r \ldots C^{(n-m)}$ and

(b) (m odd) $A^j\{A^k \cos(\pi/m) + B^k \sin(\pi/M)\} \ldots$

$$\ldots \left\{ A^{(m)} \cos \frac{(m-1)\pi}{m} \right.$$

$$\left. + B^{(m)} \sin \frac{(m-1)\pi}{m} \right\}, \quad \text{or}$$

(c) (m even) $\left\{ A^j \cos \frac{\pi}{2m} + B^j \sin \frac{\pi}{2m} \right\}$

$$\times \left\{ A^k \cos \frac{3\pi}{2m} + B^k \sin \frac{3\pi}{2m} \right\} \ldots$$

$$\ldots \left\{ A^{(m)} \cos \frac{(2m-1)\pi}{2m} \right.$$

21.125 $\left. \qquad + B^{(m)} \sin \frac{(2m-1)\pi}{2m} \right\}.$

The axes of

$$\frac{P_n^m(\sin \phi)}{r^{(n+1)}} \sin m\omega$$

are the same with (m odd) and (m even) interchanged, that is,

$$(m \text{ even}) \quad (a) + (b)$$

21.126 $\qquad (m \text{ odd}) \quad (a) + (c).$

The scalar C in Equation 21.124 is

(m odd: $\cos m\omega$, $\sin m\omega$) $\dfrac{(-)^n 2^{m-1}}{(n-m)!} (-)^{(m-1)/2}$

(m even: $\cos m\omega$) $\dfrac{(-)^n 2^{m-1}}{(n-m)!} (-)^{m/2}$

(m even: $\sin m\omega$) $\dfrac{(-)^n 2^{m-1}}{(n-m)!} (-)^{(m-2)/2}.$

21.127

---

[17] *Ibid.*, 132–135. An interesting derivation is also given by Hilbert and Courant (Interscience ed. of 1953), *Methods of Mathematical Physics*, original ed. of 1924, v. I, 510–521.

The axes of the zonal harmonic

$$\frac{P_n(\sin \phi)}{r^{(n+1)}}$$

can be seen from Equation 21.027 to be all C^r, and the scalar is $(-)^n/n!$.

86. The determination of the n poles or axes of a general harmonic of the nth-degree with arbitrary coefficients C_{nm}, S_{nm} for the Legendre harmonics is a matter of considerable difficulty, and the authorities seem to be content with proving the existence of a unique solution if all the poles are to be real.[18] The standard method converts the spherical harmonic to a homogeneous polynomial $f_n(x, y, z)$, as explained in § 21–27 and § 21–29. The polynomial, which is, of course, a harmonic function, is then substituted in Equation 21.031 to give

$$\frac{(-)^n r^{(2n+1)}}{1 \cdot 3 \ldots (2n-1)} f_n\left(\frac{\partial}{\partial x}, \frac{\partial}{\partial y}, \frac{\partial}{\partial z}\right)\left(\frac{1}{r}\right) = f_n(x, y, z).$$

21.128

If $f_{(n-2)}(x, y, z)$ is an arbitrary homogeneous polynomial of degree $(n-2)$, we note that

$$(x^2 + y^2 + z^2) f_{(n-2)}(x, y, z)$$

can be added to the right-hand side of Equation 21.128 without affecting the left side because the resulting additional term on the left would be in the form of

$$\left(\frac{\partial^2}{\partial x^2} + \frac{\partial^2}{\partial y^2} + \frac{\partial^2}{\partial z^2}\right) f_{(n-2)}\left(\frac{\partial}{\partial x}, \frac{\partial}{\partial y}, \frac{\partial}{\partial z}\right)\left(\frac{1}{r}\right),$$

which is zero by virtue of the Laplace equation

$$\left(\frac{\partial^2}{\partial x^2} + \frac{\partial^2}{\partial y^2} + \frac{\partial^2}{\partial z^2}\right)\left(\frac{1}{r}\right) = 0.$$

The next step is to factorize

21.129 $\qquad f_n(x, y, z) + (x^2 + y^2 + z^2) f_{(n-2)}(x, y, z)$

into

$$(a_1 x + b_1 y + c_1 z)(a_2 x + b_2 y + c_2 z) \ldots,$$

in which case the left-hand side of Equation 21.128 can be put into the form

$$\left(a_1 \frac{\partial}{\partial x} + b_1 \frac{\partial}{\partial y} + c_1 \frac{\partial}{\partial z}\right) \ldots \left(\frac{1}{r}\right)$$

$$= CL^p M^q \ldots \left(\frac{1}{r}\right)_{pq \ldots (n)}$$

---

[18] Hobson, *op. cit. supra* note 2, 135–136.

where (a_1, b_1, c_1) are proportional to the Cartesian components of the axis L^p, etc. The scalar C is the product of all the moduli $(a_1^2 + b_1^2 + c_1^2)^{1/2}$. The difficulty lies in factorizing Equation 21.129 when each separate term in the expression has an arbitrary coefficient.

87. It is sometimes better to work in terms of the inertia tensors, which should be easier to break down into vectors. For example, we can see at once from Equation 21.062 that the single axis of the first-degree harmonics is in the direction of the center of mass (distant r_0 from the origin), and the scalar is Mr_0. In regard to the second-degree harmonics, we can, without any loss of generality, take the principal axes of inertia as coordinate axes (A^r, B^r, C^r), in which case we have seen in Equations 21.071 and 21.077 that the inertia tensor can be written as

$$I^{pq} = (I-A)A^pA^q + (I-B)B^pB^q + (I-C)C^pC^q$$

where A, B, C are the principal moments of inertia and $I = \frac{1}{2}(A+B+C)$. The total second-degree potential is then given by

$$\frac{1}{2}I^{pq}(1/r)_{pq} = \frac{1}{2}\{(I-A)A^pA^q$$

21.130 $\qquad + (I-B)B^pB^q + (I-C)C^pC^q\}(1/r)_{pq};$

this result is unaffected if we add any multiple of

$$A^pA^q + B^pB^q + C^pC^q$$

to the inertia tensor because

$$(A^pA^q + B^pB^q + C^pC^q)(1/r)_{pq} = 0$$

by virtue of the Laplace equation. We can use this fact to eliminate one term from Equation 21.130, but if the remainder is to be split into real factors, the two remaining terms must be opposite in sign. If $C > B > A$, we accordingly subtract

$$0 = \frac{1}{2}(I-B)(A^pA^q + B^pB^q + C^pC^q)(1/r)_{pq}$$

from Equation 21.130 and have

$$\frac{1}{2}I^{pq}(1/r)_{pq} = \frac{1}{2}\{(B-A)A^pA^q - (C-B)C^pC^q\}(1/r)_{pq}.$$

21.131

This last equation factorizes to

$$\frac{1}{2}\{(B-A)^{1/2}A^p + (C-B)^{1/2}C^p\}\{(B-A)^{1/2}A^q - (C-B)^{1/2}C^q\}(1/r)_{pq}$$

so that the two axes are parallel to

21.132 $\qquad (B-A)^{1/2}A^p \pm (C-B)^{1/2}C^p,$

which can be verified from results previously

given—such as Equations 21.023, 21.073, and 21.066. This result (Equation 21.132) does not require the principal axes of inertia to be the coordinate axes. The expression for the potential in Equation 21.131 is an invariant which has the same value in any coordinate system having the same origin. If the attracting body is symmetrical about the C-axis, we have seen in § 21–53 that $A = B$, so that both axes coincide with C^p.

88. If the mass distribution is known, then all components of all the inertia tensors can be calculated, but only in this sense is there any dependence between inertia tensors of different order. The only known "recursion" formula connecting the inertia tensors is a differential relation for change of origin obtainable from Equation 21.057, the symmetric form of which is Equation 21.058. We could, nevertheless, use the methods of § 21–87 to find the axes of the higher order tensors. Proceeding as in § 21–46, we might look for three preferred orthogonal directions, which would not necessarily be the principal axes of inertia related to the second-order tensor but would contract the tensor to zero as in Equation 21.069. The expression of the potential in terms of these preferred vectors, and of certain components associated with these preferred vectors, corresponding to Equation 21.130, would then contain fewer terms; these terms could be still further reduced by adding multiples of differentials of the Laplace equation, such as

$$(A^rA^s X^t + B^rB^s X^t + C^rC^s X^t)(1/r)_{rst} = 0$$

in which X^t is an arbitrary vector, until finally the result can be split into linear factors, of which there would be n in the case of the nth-order tensor. We can be assured that such a result exists, if only we can find it, and the result containing real axes would be unique. Further research is needed on this question, which might also result in more knowledge of the nature and properties of the inertia tensors.

89. An apparent advantage of expressing the potential in the polar form of Equation 21.124 instead of in Legendre harmonics is that we obtain expressions of the same form by differentiation. For example, the component of the gravitational force, arising from the potential in Equation 21.124, in the direction of a fixed unit vector λ^w is

$$CL^pM^qN^r \ldots \lambda^w \ldots (1/r)_{pqr\ldots w \ldots (n+1)},$$

21.133

which is evidently a harmonic of degree $(n+1)$

with the same scalar C and the same axes as the corresponding nth-degree term in the potential *plus* the additional axis λ^w. This facility is, however, mainly of theoretical use as indicating the nature of the harmonics in the gravitational force because of the difficulty in locating the poles of the general harmonics in the potential. Much the same theoretical advantage is obtained by using the inertial form of the potential in Equation 21.017, as we have done in investigating invariance and analytic continuation. For practical purposes, however, we require formulas in Legendre harmonics at least for the first differentials.

REPRESENTATION OF GRAVITY

90. Attempts, which have been made to express gravity (g) in Legendre harmonics, have not met with much success because g is not a harmonic function. Like most other functions, g can be expressed over a sphere in surface spherical harmonics of the geocentric latitude and longitude. For that matter, g can be expressed in spherical harmonics of the latitude and longitude of the normal to any surface, as we can see at once if we consider the spherical representation of the surface in § 13–16. For example, we can express g over an equipotential surface in terms of spherical harmonics of the astronomical latitude and longitude. We cannot express g as a series of solid harmonic functions of any sort. However, we can express the component of the gravitational force in any *fixed* direction, such as a Cartesian coordinate axis, in solid harmonics; and if we do so in three fixed directions, we shall have expressions which give us the direction as well as the magnitude of the gravitational force.

91. Addition and subtraction of Equations 21.119 and 21.120 and use of Equations 21.112, followed by separation into real and imaginary parts, give

$$2\frac{\partial}{\partial x}\left\{\frac{P_n^m(\sin\phi)}{r^{(n+1)}}\binom{\cos m\omega}{\sin m\omega}\right\}$$

$$=\frac{(n-m+2)(n-m+1)P_{n+1}^{m-1}(\sin\phi)}{r^{(n+2)}}$$

$$\times\binom{\cos(m-1)\omega}{\sin(m-1)\omega}$$

$$-\frac{P_{n+1}^{m+1}(\sin\phi)}{r^{(n+2)}}\binom{\cos(m+1)\omega}{\sin(m+1)\omega}$$

$$2\frac{\partial}{\partial y}\left\{\frac{P_n^m(\sin\phi)}{r^{(n+1)}}\binom{\cos m\omega}{\sin m\omega}\right\}$$

$$=\frac{(n-m+2)(n-m+1)P_{n+1}^{m-1}(\sin\phi)}{r^{(n+2)}}$$

$$\times\binom{-\sin(m-1)\omega}{\cos(m-1)\omega}$$

21.134 $$+\frac{P_{n+1}^{m+1}(\sin\phi)}{r^{(n+2)}}\binom{-\sin(m+1)\omega}{\cos(m+1)\omega},$$

which are to be multiplied by the appropriate constants C_{nm}, S_{nm} in the potential formula and summed to give the differentials of the total potential $(-V/G)$. But if $(\bar{\omega}, \bar{\phi})$ are the *astronomical* longitude and latitude, we have

$$\frac{\partial}{\partial x}\left(-\frac{V}{G}\right)=\frac{g\cos\bar{\phi}\cos\bar{\omega}}{G}$$

21.135 $$\frac{\partial}{\partial y}\left(-\frac{V}{G}\right)=\frac{g\cos\bar{\phi}\sin\bar{\omega}}{G};$$

we can write finally

$$\frac{g\cos\bar{\phi}\cos\bar{\omega}}{G}=\sum_{n=0}^{\infty}\sum_{m=0}^{n+1}\frac{P_{n+1}^m(\sin\phi)}{r^{(n+2)}}$$

$$\times(\bar{C}_{(n+1),m}\cos m\omega$$

21.136 $$+\bar{S}_{(n+1),m}\sin m\omega)$$

where

$$\bar{C}_{(n+1),0}=\tfrac{1}{2}n(n+1)C_{n1}$$

$$\bar{C}_{(n+1),1}=-C_{n0}+\tfrac{1}{2}n(n-1)C_{n2}$$

$$\bar{S}_{(n+1),1}=\tfrac{1}{2}n(n-1)S_{n2}$$

$$\cdot\ \cdot\ \cdot\ \cdot\ \cdot\ \cdot\ \cdot\ \cdot\ \cdot\ \cdot\ \cdot\ \cdot\ \cdot\ \cdot\ \cdot$$

$$\left\{\begin{array}{l}\bar{C}_{(n+1),m}=-\tfrac{1}{2}C_{n,(m-1)}\\[4pt]\qquad+\tfrac{1}{2}(n-m+1)(n-m)C_{n,(m+1)}\\[6pt]\bar{S}_{(n+1),m}=-\tfrac{1}{2}S_{n,(m-1)}\\[4pt]\qquad+\tfrac{1}{2}(n-m+1)(n-m)S_{n,(m+1)}\end{array}\right\}$$

$$(m=2,3,\ldots(n-1))$$

$$\cdot\ \cdot\ \cdot\ \cdot\ \cdot\ \cdot\ \cdot\ \cdot\ \cdot\ \cdot\ \cdot\ \cdot\ \cdot\ \cdot\ \cdot$$

$$\bar{C}_{(n+1),n}=-\tfrac{1}{2}C_{n,(n-1)}$$

$$\bar{S}_{(n+1),n}=-\tfrac{1}{2}S_{n,(n-1)}$$

$$\bar{C}_{(n+1),(n+1)}=-\tfrac{1}{2}C_{n,n}$$

$$\bar{S}_{(n+1),(n+1)}=-\tfrac{1}{2}S_{n,n}.$$

21.137

In deriving this result, the Legendre functions on the right of Equations 21.134 for $m=0$ contain

$$(n+1)(n+2)P_{n+1}^{-1}(\sin \phi),$$

which must be transformed to

$$-P_{n+1}^1(\sin \phi)$$

in accordance with the usual formula. Alternatively, we could obtain the term $m=0$ in Equations 21.134 by direct differentiation as

$$2\frac{\partial}{\partial x}\left(\frac{P_n(\sin \phi)}{r^{(n+1)}}\right)=-2\frac{P_{n+1}^1(\sin \phi)\,\cos \omega}{r^{(n+2)}}.$$

92. In the same way, we have

$$\frac{g\cos \bar{\phi}\sin \bar{\omega}}{G}=\sum_{n=0}^{\infty}\sum_{m=0}^{n+1}\frac{P_{n+1}^m(\sin \phi)}{r^{(n+2)}}$$
$$\times(\bar{C}_{(n+1),\,m}\cos m\omega$$

21.138
$$+\bar{S}_{(n+1),\,m}\sin m\omega)$$

where

$$\bar{C}_{(n+1),\,0}=\tfrac{1}{2}n(n+1)S_{n1}$$

$$\bar{C}_{(n+1),\,1}=\tfrac{1}{2}n(n-1)S_{n2}$$

$$\bar{S}_{(n+1),\,1}=-C_{n0}-\tfrac{1}{2}n(n-1)C_{n2}$$

· ·

$$\left\{\begin{array}{l}\bar{C}_{(n+1),\,m}=\tfrac{1}{2}S_{n,\,(m-1)}\\[4pt] \qquad+\tfrac{1}{2}(n-m+1)(n-m)S_{n,\,(m+1)}\end{array}\right.$$

$$\left.\begin{array}{l}\bar{S}_{(n+1),\,m}=-\tfrac{1}{2}C_{n,\,(m-1)}\\[4pt] \qquad-\tfrac{1}{2}(n-m+1)(n-m)C_{n,\,(m+1)}\end{array}\right\}$$
$$(m=2,\,3,\,\ldots\,(n-1))$$

· ·

$$\bar{C}_{(n+1),\,n}=\tfrac{1}{2}S_{n,\,(n-1)}$$

$$\bar{S}_{(n+1),\,n}=-\tfrac{1}{2}C_{n,\,(n-1)}$$

$$\bar{C}_{(n+1),\,(n+1)}=\tfrac{1}{2}S_{n,\,n}$$

$$\bar{S}_{(n+1),\,(n+1)}=-\tfrac{1}{2}C_{n,\,n}.$$

21.139

93. Derived in the same way from Equation 21.123, the third component of the gravitational force is

$$\frac{\partial}{\partial z}\left(-\frac{V}{G}\right)=\frac{g\sin \bar{\phi}}{G}$$
$$=\sum_{n=0}^{\infty}\sum_{m=0}^{n+1}\frac{P_{n+1}^m(\sin \phi)}{r^{(n+2)}}$$

21.140
$$\times(\bar{C}_{(n+1),\,m}\cos m\omega+\bar{S}_{(n+1),\,m}\sin m\omega)$$

where

$$\bar{C}_{(n+1),\,m}=-(n-m+1)C_{nm}$$

21.141
$$\bar{S}_{(n+1),\,m}=-(n-m+1)S_{nm}.$$

Equations 21.136, 21.138, and 21.140 give the components of the gravitational force in the positive direction of the coordinate axes, that is, outward, whereas the positive direction of the gravitational force according to Equation 20.05 is inward. We should therefore change the sign of g in order to obtain values in accordance with our normal conventions. Also, the equations apply only to an external potential in the form

$$\sum_{n=0}^{\infty}\sum_{m=0}^{n}\frac{P_n^m(\sin \phi)}{r^{(n+1)}}(C_{nm}\cos m\omega+S_{nm}\sin m\omega),$$

although corresponding formulas for potential in the interior form

$$\sum_{n=0}^{\infty}\sum_{m=0}^{n}r^nP_n^m(\sin \phi)(C_{nm}\cos m\omega+S_{nm}\sin m\omega)$$

can be found.

Rotating Field

94. If the field is rotating about the z-axis with angular velocity $\tilde{\omega}$ and if $(\bar{\phi},\,\bar{\omega})$ are to refer to the direction of the total gravitational force, then instead of $(-V/G)$ in Equations 21.135 and 21.140, we should have

$$-V/G+\tfrac{1}{2}\tilde{\omega}^2(x^2+y^2)/G.$$

To the right-hand side of Equation 21.136 we should add

21.142
$$\frac{\tilde{\omega}^2 x}{G}=\frac{\tilde{\omega}^2 rP_1^1(\sin \phi)\,\cos \omega}{G},$$

and to the right-hand side of Equation 21.138 we should add

21.143
$$\frac{\tilde{\omega}^2 y}{G}=\frac{\tilde{\omega}^2 rP_1^1(\sin \phi)\,\sin \omega}{G}.$$

Equation 21.140 is unaffected.

CURVATURES OF THE FIELD

95. The second Cartesian differentials of the potential in spherical harmonics are easily found by a second application of Equations 21.137, 21.139, and 21.141. Each differentiation results in harmonics which are one degree higher and may contain tesseral harmonics of greater or lesser order. For this reason, it is desirable to list the zonal and first-order tesseral harmonics separately instead

of attempting to include them in a general formula; in the case of the second differentials, we shall, for the same reason, list the first- and second-order harmonics separately. There is no need, however, to list separately the harmonics of highest order, such as $\bar{C}_{(n+1),\,n}$, $\bar{C}_{(n+1),\,(n+1)}$ in Equations 21.137, because these harmonics can be derived from the general formula for $\bar{C}_{(n+1),\,m}$; we must remember that the order of a harmonic cannot exceed its degree so that the term containing $C_{n,\,(m+1)}$ must be omitted if $(m+1)$ exceeds n. In any case, the coefficient $\frac{1}{2}(n-m+1)(n-m)$ becomes zero for $m=n$ or $m=n+1$. We shall find that similar considerations apply to the second differentials.

96. The second Cartesian differentials of the potential are, of course, harmonic functions which can be written, for example, in the form

$$-\frac{\partial^2}{\partial x^2}\left(\frac{V}{G}\right)=\sum_{n=0}^{\infty}\sum_{m=0}^{n+2}\frac{P_{n+2}^m(\sin\phi)}{r^{(n+3)}}\left(\bar{\bar{C}}_{(n+2),\,m}\cos m\omega+\bar{\bar{S}}_{(n+2),\,m}\sin m\omega\right).$$

If this result is obtained by differentiating Equation 21.136, then Equations 21.137 tell us that

$$\bar{\bar{C}}_{(n+2),\,m}=-\tfrac{1}{2}\bar{C}_{(n+1),\,(m-1)}+\tfrac{1}{2}(n-m+2)(n-m+1)\bar{C}_{(n+1),\,(m+1)},$$

and substituting Equations 21.137 for the coefficients of the first differential with respect to x, we have for $m>2$,

$$\bar{\bar{C}}_{(n+2),\,m}=\tfrac{1}{4}C_{n,\,(m-2)}-\tfrac{1}{4}(n-m+2)(n-m+1)C_{nm}$$
$$+\tfrac{1}{2}(n-m+2)(n-m+1)\{-\tfrac{1}{2}C_{nm}+\tfrac{1}{2}(n-m)(n-m-1)C_{n,\,(m+2)}\}$$
$$=\tfrac{1}{4}C_{n,\,(m-2)}-\tfrac{1}{2}(n-m+1)(n-m+2)C_{nm}$$

21.144
$$+\tfrac{1}{4}(n-m-1)(n-m)(n-m+1)(n-m+2)C_{n,\,(m+2)}.$$

If m were 1 or 2, we should have substituted instead the zonal or first-order harmonics given earlier in Equations 21.137. A complete list of all the harmonics in all six second differentials are given as follows:

$\dfrac{\partial^2}{\partial x^2}\left(-\dfrac{V}{G}\right)$: $\bar{\bar{C}}_{(n+2),\,0}=-\tfrac{1}{2}(n+1)(n+2)C_{n0}+\tfrac{1}{2}(n-1)n(n+1)(n+2)C_{n2}$

$\bar{\bar{C}}_{(n+2),\,1}=-\tfrac{3}{4}n(n+1)C_{n1}+\tfrac{1}{4}(n-2)(n-1)n(n+1)C_{n3}$

$\bar{\bar{S}}_{(n+2),\,1}=-\tfrac{1}{4}n(n+1)S_{n1}+\tfrac{1}{4}(n-2)(n-1)n(n+1)S_{n3}$

$\bar{\bar{C}}_{(n+2),\,2}=\tfrac{1}{2}C_{n0}-\tfrac{1}{2}n(n-1)C_{n2}+\tfrac{1}{4}(n-3)(n-2)(n-1)nC_{n4}$

$\bar{\bar{S}}_{(n+2),\,2}=-\tfrac{1}{2}n(n-1)S_{n2}+\tfrac{1}{4}(n-3)(n-2)(n-1)nS_{n4}$

$\bar{\bar{C}}_{(n+2),\,m}=\tfrac{1}{4}C_{n,\,(m-2)}-\tfrac{1}{2}(n-m+1)(n-m+2)C_{nm}+\tfrac{1}{4}(n-m-1)(n-m)(n-m+1)(n-m+2)C_{n,\,(m+2)}$

$\bar{\bar{S}}_{(n+2),\,m}=\tfrac{1}{4}S_{n,\,(m-2)}-\tfrac{1}{2}(n-m+1)(n-m+2)S_{nm}+\tfrac{1}{4}(n-m-1)(n-m)(n-m+1)(n-m+2)S_{n,\,(m+2)}$

21.145 $(m>2)$

$\dfrac{\partial^2}{\partial y^2}\left(-\dfrac{V}{G}\right)$: $\bar{\bar{C}}_{(n+2),\,0}=-\tfrac{1}{2}(n+1)(n+2)C_{n0}-\tfrac{1}{2}(n-1)n(n+1)(n+2)C_{n2}$

$\bar{\bar{C}}_{(n+2),\,1}=-\tfrac{1}{4}n(n+1)C_{n1}-\tfrac{1}{4}(n-2)(n-1)n(n+1)C_{n3}$

$\bar{\bar{S}}_{(n+2),\,1}=-\tfrac{3}{4}n(n+1)S_{n1}-\tfrac{1}{4}(n-2)(n-1)n(n+1)S_{n3}$

$\bar{\bar{C}}_{(n+2),\,2}=-\tfrac{1}{2}C_{n0}-\tfrac{1}{2}n(n-1)C_{n2}-\tfrac{1}{4}(n-3)(n-2)(n-1)nC_{n4}$

$\bar{\bar{S}}_{(n+2),\,2}=-\tfrac{1}{2}n(n-1)S_{n2}-\tfrac{1}{4}(n-3)(n-2)(n-1)nS_{n4}$

$\bar{\bar{C}}_{(n+2),\,m}=-\tfrac{1}{4}C_{n,\,(m-2)}-\tfrac{1}{2}(n-m+1)(n-m+2)C_{nm}-\tfrac{1}{4}(n-m-1)(n-m)(n-m+1)(n-m+2)C_{n,\,(m+2)}$

$\bar{\bar{S}}_{(n+2),\,m}=-\tfrac{1}{4}S_{n,\,(m-2)}-\tfrac{1}{2}(n-m+1)(n-m+2)S_{nm}-\tfrac{1}{4}(n-m-1)(n-m)(n-m+1)(n-m+2)S_{n,\,(m+2)}$

21.146 $(m>2)$

$\dfrac{\partial^2}{\partial z^2}\left(-\dfrac{V}{G}\right):$ $\qquad \bar{\bar{C}}_{(n+2),\,0}=(n+1)(n+2)C_{n0}$

$$\bar{\bar{C}}_{(n+2),\,1}=n(n+1)C_{n1}$$

$$\bar{\bar{S}}_{(n+2),\,1}=n(n+1)S_{n1}$$

$$\bar{\bar{C}}_{(n+2),\,2}=n(n-1)C_{n2}$$

$$\bar{\bar{S}}_{(n+2),\,2}=n(n-1)S_{n2}$$

$$\bar{\bar{C}}_{(n+2),\,m}=(n-m+1)(n-m+2)C_{nm}$$

$$\bar{\bar{S}}_{(n+2),\,m}=(n-m+1)(n-m+2)S_{nm}$$

21.147

$$(m>2)$$

$\dfrac{\partial^2}{\partial x\partial y}\left(-\dfrac{V}{G}\right):$ $\qquad \bar{\bar{C}}_{(n+2),\,0}=\tfrac14(n-1)n(n+1)(n+2)S_{n2}$

$$\bar{\bar{C}}_{(n+2),\,1}=-\tfrac14 n(n+1)S_{n1}+\tfrac14(n-2)(n-1)n(n+1)S_{n3}$$

$$\bar{\bar{S}}_{(n+2),\,1}=-\tfrac14 n(n+1)C_{n1}-\tfrac14(n-2)(n-1)n(n+1)C_{n3}$$

$$\bar{\bar{C}}_{(n+2),\,2}=\tfrac14(n-3)(n-2)(n-1)nS_{n4}$$

$$\bar{\bar{S}}_{(n+2),\,2}=\tfrac12 C_{n0}-\tfrac14(n-3)(n-2)(n-1)nC_{n4}$$

$$\bar{\bar{C}}_{(n+2),\,m}=-\tfrac14 S_{n,\,(m-2)}+\tfrac14(n-m-1)(n-m)(n-m+1)(n-m+2)S_{n,\,(m+2)}$$

$$\bar{\bar{S}}_{(n+2),\,m}=\tfrac14 C_{n,\,(m-2)}-\tfrac14(n-m-1)(n-m)(n-m+1)(n-m+2)C_{n,\,(m+2)}$$

21.148

$$(m>2)$$

$\dfrac{\partial^2}{\partial y\partial z}\left(-\dfrac{V}{G}\right):$ $\qquad \bar{\bar{C}}_{(n+2),\,0}=-\tfrac12 n(n+1)(n+2)S_{n1}$

$$\bar{\bar{C}}_{(n+2),\,1}=-\tfrac12(n-1)n(n+1)S_{n2}$$

$$\bar{\bar{S}}_{(n+2),\,1}=(n+1)C_{n0}+\tfrac12(n-1)n(n+1)C_{n2}$$

$$\bar{\bar{C}}_{(n+2),\,2}=-\tfrac12 nS_{n1}-\tfrac12(n-2)(n-1)nS_{n3}$$

$$\bar{\bar{S}}_{(n+2),\,2}=\tfrac12 nC_{n1}+\tfrac12(n-2)(n-1)nC_{n3}$$

$$\bar{\bar{C}}_{(n+2),\,m}=-\tfrac12(n-m+2)S_{n,\,(m-1)}-\tfrac12(n-m)(n-m+1)(n-m+2)S_{n,\,(m+1)}$$

$$\bar{\bar{S}}_{(n+2),\,m}=\tfrac12(n-m+2)C_{n,\,(m-1)}+\tfrac12(n-m)(n-m+1)(n-m+2)C_{n,\,(m+1)}$$

21.149

$$(m>2)$$

$$\frac{\partial^2}{\partial z \partial x}\left(-\frac{V}{G}\right): \qquad \bar{\bar{C}}_{(n+2),\,0} = -\tfrac{1}{2}n(n+1)(n+2)C_{n1}$$

$$\bar{\bar{C}}_{(n+2),\,1} = (n+1)C_{n0} - \tfrac{1}{2}(n-1)n(n+1)C_{n2}$$

$$\bar{\bar{S}}_{(n+2),\,1} = -\tfrac{1}{2}(n-1)n(n+1)S_{n2}$$

$$\bar{\bar{C}}_{(n+2),\,2} = \tfrac{1}{2}nC_{n1} - \tfrac{1}{2}(n-2)(n-1)nC_{n3}$$

$$\bar{\bar{S}}_{(n+2),\,2} = \tfrac{1}{2}nS_{n1} - \tfrac{1}{2}(n-2)(n-1)nS_{n3}$$

$$\bar{\bar{C}}_{(n+2),\,m} = \tfrac{1}{2}(n-m+2)C_{n,(m-1)} - \tfrac{1}{2}(n-m)(n-m+1)(n-m+2)C_{n,(m+1)}$$

$$\bar{\bar{S}}_{(n+2),\,m} = \tfrac{1}{2}(n-m+2)S_{n,(m-1)} - \tfrac{1}{2}(n-m)(n-m+1)(n-m+2)S_{n,(m+1)}$$

21.150 $\hspace{9cm} (m > 2).$

The Laplace equation

$$-\frac{\partial^2}{\partial x^2}\left(\frac{V}{G}\right) - \frac{\partial^2}{\partial y^2}\left(\frac{V}{G}\right) - \frac{\partial^2}{\partial z^2}\left(\frac{V}{G}\right) = 0$$

is satisfied by each harmonic of the same degree and order; also, the mixed derivatives $\partial^2/\partial x \partial y$ or $\partial^2/\partial y \partial x$ give the same result, although the first differential is not the same in both cases.

97. Second differentials of the geopotential W are given by

$$-\frac{\partial^2}{\partial x^2}\left(\frac{W}{G}\right) = -\frac{\partial^2}{\partial x^2}\left(\frac{V}{G}\right) + \frac{\tilde{\omega}^2}{G}$$

21.151
$$-\frac{\partial^2}{\partial y^2}\left(\frac{W}{G}\right) = -\frac{\partial^2}{\partial y^2}\left(\frac{V}{G}\right) + \frac{\tilde{\omega}^2}{G}$$

from Equation 20.08. There is no difference between the other second differentials of W and V.

98. We have finally the six Cartesian components of the Marussi tensor W_{rs}, which can be contracted with the base vectors λ^r, μ^r, ν^r of the equipotential surfaces to give us the six curvature parameters of the field, as in Equations 12.162. The Cartesian components of the base vectors are given by Equations 12.008 in which ϕ, ω are the latitude and longitude of the line of force, obtainable together with gravity g from Equations 21.136, 21.138, and 21.140. To avoid confusion with the geocentric latitude and longitude in the spherical harmonics, we shall overbar the latitude and longitude of the line of force—that is, the astronomical latitude and longitude—from Equations 12.008. For example, the median curvature k_2 is given by

$$\frac{gk_2}{G} = -\left(\frac{W}{G}\right)_{rs}\mu^r\mu^s$$

$$= -\sin^2\bar{\phi}\,\cos^2\bar{\omega}\,\frac{\partial^2}{\partial x^2}\left(\frac{W}{G}\right)$$

$$- \sin^2\bar{\phi}\,\sin^2\bar{\omega}\,\frac{\partial^2}{\partial y^2}\left(\frac{W}{G}\right)$$

$$- \cos^2\bar{\phi}\,\frac{\partial^2}{\partial z^2}\left(\frac{W}{G}\right)$$

$$- 2\sin^2\bar{\phi}\,\sin\bar{\omega}\cos\bar{\omega}\,\frac{\partial^2}{\partial x\partial y}\left(\frac{W}{G}\right)$$

$$+ 2\sin\bar{\phi}\,\cos\bar{\phi}\sin\bar{\omega}\,\frac{\partial^2}{\partial y\partial z}\left(\frac{W}{G}\right)$$

21.152
$$+ 2\sin\bar{\phi}\,\cos\bar{\phi}\cos\bar{\omega}\,\frac{\partial^2}{\partial z\partial x}\left(\frac{W}{G}\right),$$

with similar equations which can be written at once for the other parameters.

DETERMINATION OF THE POTENTIAL IN SPHERICAL HARMONICS

99. The advantage of using Equations 21.136, 21.138, and 21.140 for $g \cos \bar\phi \cos \bar\omega$, $g \cos \bar\phi \sin \bar\omega$, $g \sin \bar\phi$, compared with expressions for g, is that these equations are spherical harmonic series in the usual form and are linear in the C_{nm}, S_{nm} of the potential. Accordingly, we may use these three equations as linear observation equations to determine the C_{nm}, S_{nm} to the limit of computer capacity from sufficient and widespread measurements of g, $\bar\phi$, $\bar\omega$; time will be saved in the computation of the coefficients of the C_{nm}, S_{nm} from the positions of the observing stations. In these equation, $\bar\phi$ and $\bar\omega$ are astronomical latitude and longitude, but it would not usually be necessary to make astronomical measurements at every gravity station in an intensive local survey; it would be sufficient to apply regional deflections to geodetic values. The lower harmonics could not be determined in this way from regional surveys, but are already well determined from satellites. The satellite values should be substituted in the equations, leaving the higher harmonics to be determined from regional surveys.

100. The same considerations apply to Equation 21.152 and to similar expressions for the other curvature parameters. These equations are also linear in the coefficients C_{nm}, S_{nm} of the potential and could be used as observation equations in conjunction with Equations 21.136, 21.138, and 21.140. The curvature parameters, other than the vertical gradient of gravity, can already be measured to a high degree of accuracy and might be of value in the determination of the higher harmonics in local or regional surveys. This has not yet been done, and further research is required to explore the practical possibilities.

MAGNETIC ANALOGY

101. If we take a small magnet QQ' (fig. 24) of pole strength p situated inside the Earth, then in accordance with the usual geophysical convention, the negative pole will be at Q nearest the north and the positive direction of the axis (unit vector L^s) will be $\overrightarrow{QQ'}$. The magnetic potential at an external point P, writing $\mu = p \times QQ'$ for the mag-

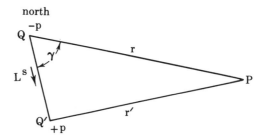

Figure 24.

nitude of the magnetic moment, will be

$$-\frac{cp}{r'}+\frac{cp}{r}=-\frac{c\mu}{QQ'}\left(\frac{1}{r'}-\frac{1}{r}\right)=-c\mu\left(\frac{1}{r}\right)_s L^s$$

21.153

in the limit when $QQ' \to 0$, and the magnet becomes a dipole. In this expression, c is a constant depending on the units employed. The differentiation of $(1/r)$ refers to displacement of Q relative to a fixed origin at P so that the gradient of r is in the direction $\overrightarrow{PQ}$. The magnetic potential at P can then be written as

$$\frac{c\mu}{r^2}\, r_s L^s = -\frac{c\mu}{r^2}\cos\gamma.$$

102. In deriving this formula, we have assumed unit permeability of the medium between the dipole and P. We are not proposing to determine the actual external magnetic field of a dipole buried in the Earth; all we want to do is to set up a mathematical model analogous to the gravitational field, and in doing so we can make any stated assumptions, such as a completely permeable medium. The reason for this assumption is that we shall later superimpose the fields of dipoles in different locations, and the analogy would break down if the permeability changed.

103. Instead of the dipole, we shall now suppose that we have a particle of mass m at Q. The gravitational potential at P will be $(-Gm/r)$, and the component of force at P in a direction parallel to QQ' will be

$$-(-Gm/r)_s L^s$$

in which the gradient of r is now in the direction $\overrightarrow{QP}$ because the differentiation must be carried out by displacement of P relative to a fixed origin at Q. The component of force at P parallel to QQ' is accordingly

$$-\frac{Gm}{r^2}\, r_s L^s = -\frac{Gm}{r^2}\cos\gamma,$$

which is exactly the same as the potential of the dipole if we make $c\mu = Gm$. Subject to this relation and to the assumption of unit permeability, the component of the gravitational force in a given direction is the same as the potential of a dipole situated at the mass point and oriented in the same direction.

104. If we set up dipoles at all other mass points with the same proportion of mass to magnitude of magnetic moment and with the same orientation, the total magnetic potential at P will be the same as the component in the same direction of the total gravitational force exerted by the whole body at P. Moreover, the same conclusion will evidently apply to a continuous dipole distribution and to a continuous mass distribution, provided the dipoles are oriented in the same direction. Finally, we could set up at each mass point a cluster of three dipoles of equal moment, oriented in the direction of the coordinate axes, and so obtain all three components of the gravitational force. The scalar magnetic potential of such an arrangement could not, however, represent the vector gravitational force field, and there would be no physical correspondence.

105. Nevertheless, the correspondence between magnetic potential and the component of gravitational force in a fixed direction of magnetization is established, and a similar correspondence clearly exists between successive differentials of these scalar quantities in fixed directions—such as the coordinate axes. Thus, components of magnetic force correspond generally to second differentials of the gravitational potential so that magnetometer and torsion balance measurements correspond. This is not to say that the actual magnetic field of the Earth can be used to derive the gravitational field, or vice versa, but merely that methods applied to the one field can often be applied to the other. Torsion balance interpretation formulas are, for example, used in the calculation of magnetic anomalies.[19] We might also expect that frequencies in harmonic analysis of the magnetic field would generally be one higher than the harmonics of the gravitational field in relation to the noise level, although the amplitudes might differ widely.

Multipole Representation

106. We note that the magnetic potential in Equation 21.153 of a dipole situated at the origin

[19] Heiland (1940), *Geophysical Exploration*, 393.

is proportional to the first-degree terms in the polar form of the gravitational potential (Equation 21.124). We shall now show that the higher degree terms can be represented by *multipoles* at the origin. We reverse the direction of the axis of the original dipole at Q in figure 24, transfer it to figure 25, and add another dipole at R in the direction of the unit vector M^t. This second dipole has the same magnetic moment in magnitude (μ) and direction (L^s) as the original dipole at Q. The magnetic potential at P, arising from the whole arrangement, is then

$$-c\mu(1/\bar{r})_s L^s + c\mu(1/r)_s L^s.$$

We now define a quantity $\nu = \mu \times QR$ in much the same way as we have defined $\mu = p \times QQ'$, and suppose that ν remains finite (because μ increases) when QR is decreased indefinitely. The limiting arrangement is known as a *quadrupole*

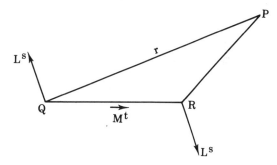

Figure 25.

of moment ν, and its potential at p is

$$-\frac{c\nu}{QR}\left\{\left(\frac{1}{\bar{r}}\right)_s - \left(\frac{1}{r}\right)_s\right\}L^s = -c\nu\left(\frac{1}{r}\right)_{st} L^s M^t.$$

If L^s, M^t are the axes and $(c\nu)$ is the scalar of the second harmonics of the gravitational potential $(-V/G)$, then the latter is represented by the potential of the quadrupole. In the same way, we can set up another quadrupole at a point S in the direction $\overrightarrow{QS} = N^u$. The limiting potential of this arrangement, when QS decreases indefinitely while $\nu \times QS$ remains finite, will be proportional to

$$(1/r)_{stu} L^s M^t N^u,$$

that is, to the third harmonics of the gravitational field if L^s, M^t, N^u are chosen as the axes of these harmonics, and so on.

107. The multipole analogy is mostly of theoretical use for indicating possible applications of electromagnetic methods in the gravitational field, and vice versa. For example, Maxwell introduced

his theory of poles in connection with electro-magnetic problems, but we have, nevertheless, found his theory of use, not only in itself, but also because it has suggested representation of the gravitational field in the inertial form of Equation 21.017.

CHAPTER 22

The Potential in Spheroidal Harmonics

THE COORDINATE SYSTEM

1. In this chapter, we shall first develop a special coordinate system; the N-surfaces of this system are all oblate spheroids formed by rotating a family of confocal ellipses about their common minor axis, which we shall choose as the Cartesian C^r-axis. Later, we shall obtain by standard methods a general solution in these coordinates of the Laplace equation which can represent a general attraction potential, and we shall investigate the corresponding mass distribution.

2. There are currently two main gravimetric uses of this spheroidal coordinate system: The expression of the potential in spheroidal coordinates has less restrictive properties of formal convergence than the corresponding expression in spherical harmonics, and leads also to an exact formulation of the standard gravitational field to be considered in Chapter 23. The coordinate system itself and the properties of the meridian ellipse on which it is based, nevertheless, have other uses, and the system will be considered in more detail than is necessary for the immediate gravimetric purposes.

THE MERIDIAN ELLIPSE

3. Any meridian plane containing the axis of rotation cuts each spheroid of the family in an ellipse as shown in figure 26. We begin by collecting,

without proof, some well-known properties of this ellipse. We denote the equatorial radius or semi-major axis $CA = CA'$ by a, and the polar radius or semiminor axis $CP = CP'$ by b. The two foci S, S' are located on the major axis at $CS = CS' = ae$ where e is the eccentricity of the ellipse. If O is any point on the ellipse, then we have

22.01 $$SO + S'O = 2a$$

so that $S'P = SP = a$. It is usual in classical geodesy to define a complementary eccentricity as b/a or $(1 - e^2)^{1/2}$, and yet another eccentricity as ae/b. Instead, we shall introduce the auxiliary angle $\alpha = S'PC$, in which case the three eccentricities become $\sin \alpha$, $\cos \alpha$, and $\tan \alpha$, respectively.

4. A circle on $A'A$ as diameter is known as the *auxiliary circle*. We can consider the ellipse as formed from this circle by shortening all ordinates parallel to the minor axis in the ratio b/a so that we have

22.02 $$ON/O'N = b/a = \cos \alpha.$$

The tangents to the ellipse and to the auxiliary circle meet on the major axis at T. The angle $O'CT$ is known as the *reduced latitude u*.

5. The normal OGH to the ellipse at O makes an angle ϕ with the major axis, which is evidently the latitude of the spheroidal normal as usually defined throughout this book. We shall call this latitude the *spheroidal latitude* and shall use the same symbol for it as we used in Chapters 12 and 21

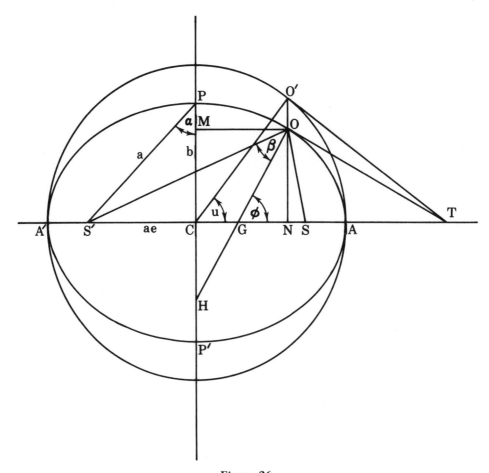

Figure 26.

for different but similar quantities. The context serves to avoid confusion. The spheroidal longitude is, in the same way, denoted by ω and is the angle between the meridian plane of figure 26 and the meridian plane through an origin such as Greenwich, with the same conventions as in § 12–7. We have not yet identified the spheroid with an equipotential surface, in which case the spheroidal latitude would be also the latitude of the line of force at points on the spheroid; or, with the base surface of the coordinate system of § 18–23 used for the description of geodetic positions, in which case the spheroidal latitude would be the geodetic latitude of points in space. For the present, we are dealing with the spheroid solely in its ordinary mathematical sense as an ellipsoid of revolution.

6. It can be shown that the normal bisects the angle SOS', and the half-angle β is given by

22.03 $\qquad \sin \beta = \sin \alpha \sin \phi$

or

$\qquad \tan \beta = \tan \alpha \sin u.$

From the fact that the tangents at O, O' intersect at T on the major axis, we infer that

22.04 $\qquad \tan u = \cos \alpha \tan \phi,$

leading to other formulas connecting the reduced and spheroidal latitudes as follows,

$\qquad \sin u = \cos \alpha \sec \beta \sin \phi$

22.05 $\qquad = \cos \alpha \sin \phi / (1 - \sin^2 \alpha \sin^2 \phi)^{1/2}$

$\qquad \cos u = \sec \beta \cos \phi$

22.06 $\qquad = \cos \phi / (1 - \sin^2 \alpha \sin^2 \phi)^{1/2}$

22.07 $\quad (1 - \sin^2 \alpha \sin^2 \phi)(1 - \sin^2 \alpha \cos^2 u) = \cos^2 \alpha$

22.08 $\qquad (1 - \sin^2 \alpha \cos^2 u)^{1/2} = \cos \alpha \sec \beta.$

7. In this chapter, we shall denote the principal radii of curvature of the spheroid by ρ (the radius of curvature of the plane elliptic meridian) and ν (the principal radius of curvature perpendicular to the meridian). We found in §12–49 that the radius of curvature of the parallel of latitude is $-1/(k_1 \sec \phi)$, which in this case is $\nu \cos \phi$ and is

evidently OM in figure 26, for any surface of revolution. Consequently, we have $\nu = OH$ in figure 26 and

22.09 $\qquad \nu \cos \phi = a \cos u = OM = CN$

so that we have

$$\nu = a \cos u \sec \phi = a \sec \beta$$
$$= a \sec \alpha / (1 + \tan^2 \alpha \cos^2 \phi)^{1/2}$$
$$= a / (1 - \sin^2 \alpha \sin^2 \phi)^{1/2}$$
$$= a \sec \alpha (1 - \sin^2 \alpha \cos^2 u)^{1/2}$$

22.10 $\qquad = a^2 / (a^2 \cos^2 \phi + b^2 \sin^2 \phi)^{1/2}.$

If dm is an element of length of the meridian ellipse, then by projecting small corresponding arcs of the auxiliary circle (a, du) and of the ellipse (dm) on the major axis, we have

$$\sin \phi \, dm = \rho \sin \phi \, d\phi = a \sin u \, du;$$

by differentiating Equation 22.04, we have

22.11 $\qquad \sec^2 u \, du = \cos \alpha \sec^2 \phi \, d\phi$

so that

$$\rho = a \cos^2 \alpha \sec^3 \beta$$
$$= a \sec \alpha / (1 + \tan^2 \alpha \cos^2 \phi)^{3/2}$$
$$= a \cos^2 \alpha / (1 - \sin^2 \alpha \sin^2 \phi)^{3/2}$$

22.12 $\qquad = a \sec \alpha (1 - \sin^2 \alpha \cos^2 u)^{3/2},$

together with the following differential relations which are often useful,

22.13 $\qquad d\beta / d\phi = \sin \alpha \cos u$

22.14 $\qquad d\beta / du = \tan \alpha \cos^2 \beta \cos u$

22.15 $\qquad d(\ln \rho) / d\phi = 3 \sin \alpha \tan \alpha \sin u \cos u$

22.16 $\qquad d(\nu \cos \phi) / d\phi = -\rho \sin \phi$

22.17 $\qquad d(\nu \sin \phi) / d\phi = \rho \sec^2 \alpha \cos \phi$

22.18 $\qquad d\nu / d\phi = (\nu - \rho) \tan \phi.$

The last equation is equivalent to the sole Codazzi equation of the spheroid as derived in Equation 18.22.

8. The principal curvatures k_1, k_2 are $-1/\nu$ and $-1/\rho$ so that the curvature invariants are

$$K = 1 / (\rho \nu)$$

22.19 $\qquad 2H = -(1/\rho + 1/\nu).$

9. In the case of the Kepler ellipse used in orbital geometry, the origin of rectangular coordi-

nates (q_1, q_2) is taken as a focus S (fig. 26), and the angle TSO is known as the *true anomaly f*. The reduced latitude u is known as the *eccentric anomaly E*. By relating rectangular coordinates in the two systems—origin S and origin C—we have at once

$$q_1 = OS \sin f = b \sin E = a(1 - e^2)^{1/2} \sin E$$
$$q_2 = OS \cos f = (a \cos E - ae) = a(\cos E - e);$$

22.20

by squaring and adding, we have

$$r = OS = a(1 - e \cos E).$$

From the last two equations, we have

$$(1 + e \cos f) = \frac{(1 - e^2)}{(1 - e \cos E)}$$

so that

22.21 $\qquad r = OS = a(1 - e \cos E) = \dfrac{a(1 - e^2)}{(1 + e \cos f)}.$

These equations are sometimes useful in branches of geodesy other than satellite geodesy.

10. The three-dimensional Cartesian coordinates of O—considered as a point on the meridian ellipse whose longitude is ω—with respect to the usual axes are

$$x = CN \cos \omega = a \cos u \cos \omega$$
$$= (ae) \operatorname{cosec} \alpha \cos u \cos \omega$$
$$y = CN \sin \omega = a \cos u \sin \omega$$
$$= (ae) \operatorname{cosec} \alpha \cos u \sin \omega$$
$$z = ON = (b/a)O'N = b \sin u = (ae) \cot \alpha \sin u,$$

22.22

from which we may obtain the *radius vector CO* as

$$r = (ae)(\cos^2 u + \cot^2 \alpha)^{1/2}$$
$$= (ae)(\cos u + i \cot \alpha)^{1/2}(\cos u - i \cot \alpha)^{1/2}.$$

22.23

The tangent of the *geocentric latitude OCS* is given by

22.24 $\qquad \dfrac{z}{(x^2 + y^2)^{1/2}} = \cos \alpha \tan u.$

SPHEROIDAL COORDINATES

11. It is evident that α is a constant over the one spheroid we have been considering, and would be

a different constant over any other spheroid. We now consider a family of confocal spheroids for which $CS = CS' = ae$ (fig. 26) is the same for all, so that (ae) is an absolute constant in space. It is then clear from Equations 22.22 that, instead of (x, y, z), we could equally well take (ω, u, α) as space coordinates, in which case the confocal spheroids will be the constant α coordinate surfaces. The other two space coordinates, which as usual we shall also use as surface coordinates on the spheroids, will be the longitude and reduced latitude with reference to the particular spheroid passing through the point in space under consideration.

12. By differentiating Equations 22.22, we find after some manipulation that the metric of the space in the coordinates (ω, u, α) is

$$ds^2 = dx^2 + dy^2 + dz^2$$
$$= (a^2 \cos^2 u) d\omega^2 + (\nu^2 \cos^2 \alpha) du^2$$
22.25 $$+ (\nu^2 \cot^2 \alpha) d\alpha^2;$$

the only nonzero components of the associated metric tensor are

$$g^{11} = 1/(a^2 \cos^2 u) ; \qquad g^{22} = 1/(\nu^2 \cos^2 \alpha) ;$$
22.26 $$g^{33} = 1/(\nu^2 \cot^2 \alpha).$$

The coordinate system is accordingly triply orthogonal, and the surface coordinates (ω, u) are constant along the spheroidal normals. Consequently, the coordinate system is a *normal* system with a spheroidal base, and all formulas of Chapter 15 apply with $N = \alpha$ and with the spheroidal latitude ϕ converted to the reduced latitude u by means of the formulas given in the last section. We can, however, retain the spheroidal latitude and the principal radii of curvature, etc., as functions, which are defined in relation to the spheroid passing through a point in space, as long as we remember that they are now functions of the *two* variables (u, α).

13. We shall require the differentials of some of the spheroidal quantities—in particular a and ν—along the normals before we can substitute in the formulas of Chapter 15. The basic gradient Equation 15.01 is now

22.27 $$\alpha_r = n\nu_r$$

where n has its usual geometric significance and ν_r is the unit outward-drawn normal to the spheroids, not to be confused with the gradient, which we shall not require, of the radius of curvature ν. If ds is an element of length along the outward-drawn

normal, we have

$$d\alpha = n\,ds,$$

while differentiations along the normal and with respect to α are related by

22.28 $$\frac{\partial}{\partial \alpha} = \frac{1}{n} \frac{\partial}{\partial s}.$$

From Equations 15.03 and 22.25, we have at once

22.29 $$n = -\frac{\tan \alpha}{\nu}.$$

We have taken the negative sign for n, which appears in the metric only as $1/n^2$, in order to make the positive direction of the α-coordinate outward in spite of the fact that α decreases numerically outward, and so we preserve the right-handed system used throughout this book in the order $(\omega, u, \alpha) = (1, 2, 3)$. This device enables us to use all formulas in Chapter 15 as they stand.

14. By differentiating

$$\sin \alpha = (ae)/a$$

with, of course, (ae) constant, we have

22.30 $$\frac{\partial (\ln a)}{\partial \alpha} = -\cot \alpha ; \qquad \frac{\partial (\ln a)}{\partial s} = \frac{1}{\nu}$$

in which a is the semimajor axis of the coordinate spheroid, not to be confused with the determinant of the surface metric. By differentiating Equations 22.03 and 22.04 with u constant and simplifying, we have also

22.31 $$\frac{\partial \beta}{\partial \alpha} = \sec \alpha \cos \beta \sin \phi$$

22.32 $$\frac{\partial \phi}{\partial \alpha} = \tan \alpha \sin \phi \cos \phi;$$

then by differentiating other relations in the last section, we have

22.33 $$\frac{\partial \ln (\nu \cos \phi)}{\partial \alpha} = \frac{\partial \ln (a \cos u)}{\partial \alpha} = -\cot \alpha$$

22.34 $$\frac{\partial \ln \nu}{\partial \alpha} = -\cot \alpha + \tan \alpha \sin^2 \phi$$

22.35 $$\frac{\partial \ln \rho}{\partial \alpha} = -\cot \alpha - 2 \tan \alpha + 3 \tan \alpha \sin^2 \phi.$$

By differentiating the metric tensor in accordance with Equation 15.13, we have the components of the second fundamental form of the spheroids as

22.36 $$b_{\alpha\beta} = (-\nu \cos^2 \phi, 0, -a^2/\nu).$$

From Equation 7.20, we have after some manipulation

22.37 $\qquad c_{\alpha\beta} = (\cos^2\phi,\, 0,\, a^2 K).$

15. The nonzero Christoffel symbols containing a 3-index follow at once from Equations 15.11 as

$$\Gamma^1_{13} = -\cot\alpha$$

$$\Gamma^2_{23} = -a^2/(\nu^2\sin\alpha\cos\alpha) = -1/(n\rho)$$

$$\Gamma^2_{33} = -\sec\alpha\sin\phi\cos\phi$$

$$\Gamma^3_{11} = \tan\alpha\cos^2\phi$$

$$\Gamma^3_{22} = (a^2\tan\alpha)/\nu^2$$

$$\Gamma^3_{33} = -\frac{\partial\ln n}{\partial\alpha} = \frac{1}{n}\frac{\partial\ln n}{\partial s} = -\cot\alpha - \frac{a^2}{\nu^2\sin\alpha\cos\alpha}$$

$$\qquad = -\frac{1}{n}\left(\frac{1}{\rho}+\frac{1}{\nu}\right) = \frac{2H}{n}$$

$$\Gamma^3_{32} = -\frac{\partial\ln n}{\partial u} = \sin\alpha\tan\alpha\sin\phi\cos\phi.$$

22.38

The remaining space symbols, which are the same as the surface symbols, are obtained directly from the surface metric as

$$\Gamma^1_{12} = -\tan u$$

$$\Gamma^2_{11} = \sec\alpha\sin\phi\cos\phi$$

$$\Gamma^2_{22} = \sin\alpha\tan\alpha\sin\phi\cos\phi = -\frac{\partial\ln n}{\partial u} = \frac{\partial\ln\nu}{\partial u}.$$

22.39

16. The components of the surface tensor

$$n\overline{\left(\frac{1}{n}\right)}_{\alpha\beta}$$

are required in many of the formulas of Chapter 15 to compute variation along the normals. We can easily obtain these components either from the Codazzi Equation 15.25 or by direct covariant differentiation, using the values of the Christoffel symbols given in Equations 22.38 and 22.39, as

$$n\overline{(1/n)}_{11} = -\tan^2\alpha\sin^2\phi\cos^2\phi$$

$$n\overline{(1/n)}_{12} = 0$$

$$n\overline{(1/n)}_{22} = \tan^2\alpha\cos 2\phi(1-\sin^2\alpha\sin^2\phi)$$

22.40 $\qquad = \tan^2\alpha\cos^2\beta\cos 2\phi.$

THE POTENTIAL IN SPHEROIDAL COORDINATES

17. We can readily expand the Laplacian of a scalar V,

$$\Delta V = g^{rs}V_{rs},$$

in spheroidal coordinates either by using Equation 3.18 or by expanding the covariant derivative and using values of the Christoffel symbols given in Equations 22.38 and 22.39. The result in either case is

$$(\nu^2\cos^2\phi)\Delta V = \frac{\partial^2 V}{\partial\omega^2}$$

$$+ \sec^2\alpha\cos^2\phi\sec u\,\frac{\partial}{\partial u}\left\{\cos u\,\frac{\partial V}{\partial u}\right\}$$

22.41 $\qquad + \tan^2\alpha\cos^2\phi\,\dfrac{\partial^2 V}{\partial\alpha^2}$

in which we must make $\Delta V = 0$, if V is to be harmonic and so to represent a Newtonian potential. For reasons which will become apparent later, we change the independent variables in the resulting partial differential equation to

$$p = \sin u$$

22.42 $\qquad q = i\cot\alpha$

so that we have

$$\frac{\partial}{\partial u} = \cos u\,\frac{\partial}{\partial p}$$

$$\frac{\partial}{\partial\alpha} = -i\,\operatorname{cosec}^2\alpha\,\frac{\partial}{\partial q};$$

the differential equation becomes then

$$0 = \frac{\partial^2 V}{\partial\omega^2} + \sec^2\alpha\cos^2\phi\,\frac{\partial}{\partial p}\left\{(1-p^2)\,\frac{\partial V}{\partial p}\right\}$$

$$- \sec^2\alpha\cos^2\phi\,\frac{\partial}{\partial q}\left\{(1-q^2)\,\frac{\partial V}{\partial q}\right\}.$$

We propose to obtain solutions analogous to the expression for the attraction potential in spherical harmonics, that is, in the so-called "normal" form

22.43 $\qquad V = \Omega P Q$

in which Ω, P, Q are, respectively, functions of ω, p, q only. If we substitute Equation 22.43 in the differential equation and divide by $\Omega P Q$, we have

$$0 = \frac{1}{\Omega}\frac{d^2\Omega}{d\omega^2} + \frac{\sec^2\alpha\cos^2\phi}{P}\frac{d}{dp}\left\{(1-p^2)\frac{dP}{dp}\right\}$$

22.44 $\qquad - \dfrac{\sec^2\alpha\cos^2\phi}{Q}\dfrac{d}{dq}\left\{(1-q^2)\dfrac{dQ}{dq}\right\}.$

The last two terms in this equation are independent of longitude ω and the first term is a function of ω only, so that if the equation is to hold for all values of ω, we must have

22.45
$$\frac{1}{\Omega}\frac{d^2\Omega}{d\omega^2}=-m^2$$

in which m is an arbitrary constant. If A and B are constants of integration, the general solution of Equation 22.45 is

22.46 $\Omega = A\cos m\omega + B\sin m\omega.$

Combining Equations 22.44 and 22.45, we have

$$\frac{1}{P}\frac{d}{dp}\left\{(1-p^2)\frac{dP}{dp}\right\}-\frac{1}{Q}\frac{d}{dq}\left\{(1-q^2)\frac{dQ}{dq}\right\}$$
$$=m^2\cos^2\alpha\sec^2\phi$$
$$=m^2(1-\sin^2\alpha\cos^2 u)\sec^2 u$$
$$=\frac{m^2}{(1-p^2)}-\frac{m^2}{(1-q^2)},$$

using Equations 22.06, 22.07, and 22.42. The variables in this last equation are now completely separated, and we can write

$$\frac{1}{P}\frac{d}{dp}\left\{(1-p^2)\frac{dP}{dp}\right\}-\frac{m^2}{(1-p^2)}$$
$$=\frac{1}{Q}\frac{d}{dq}\left\{(1-q^2)\frac{dQ}{dq}\right\}-\frac{m^2}{(1-q^2)}$$
$$=-n(n+1)$$

in which n is an arbitrary constant because the first member is at most a function of p only, and because the second member is at most a function of q only; the two members cannot be the same for all values of p and q unless they are constant. The P and Q must now satisfy similar ordinary differential equations of the form

$$\frac{d}{dx}\left\{(1-x^2)\frac{dy}{dx}\right\}+\left\{n(n+1)-\frac{m^2}{(1-x^2)}\right\}y=0;$$

if C, D, E, F are constants of integration, the general solutions [1] are

$$P=CP_n^m(p)+DQ_n^m(p)$$
22.47 $Q=EP_n^m(q)+FQ_n^m(q)$

where P_n^m, Q_n^m are the associated Legendre functions of the first and second kinds. The expansions of the Q_n^m's in the usual forms, which we shall often need

[1] Hobson (1931), *The Theory of Spherical and Ellipsoidal Harmonics*, 89.

to use, are

$$Q_n(q)=\frac{2^n n!\,n!}{(2n+1)!}\left\{\frac{1}{q^{n+1}}+\frac{(n+1)(n+2)}{2(2n+3)}\frac{1}{q^{n+3}}\right.$$
$$\left.+\frac{(n+1)(n+2)(n+3)(n+4)}{2\cdot4\cdot(2n+3)(2n+5)}\frac{1}{q^{n+5}}\cdots\right\}$$

22.48

and

$$Q_n^m(q)=(-)^m\frac{2^n n!(n+m)!}{(2n+1)!}(1-q^2)^{m/2}\left\{\frac{1}{q^{n+m+1}}\right.$$
$$+\frac{(n+m+1)(n+m+2)}{2(2n+3)}\frac{1}{q^{n+m+3}}$$
$$+\frac{(n+m+1)(n+m+2)(n+m+3)(n+m+4)}{2\cdot4\cdot(2n+3)(2n+5)}$$
22.49 $\left.\times\frac{1}{q^{n+m+5}}+\cdots\right\};$

these series are convergent only if we have $|q|>1$. Consequently, it is advisable to include $Q_n^m(q)=Q_n^m(i\cot\alpha)$ in our solution only when we have $\cot\alpha>1$, that is, when we have $b>ae$ for the coordinate spheroid through the point under consideration.[2] For the same reason, we cannot include $Q_n^m(\sin u)$ if we require u to be zero. For the *external potential* (at great distances from the Cartesian origin), we take $D=E=0$ in the general solution, Equations 22.47, to give the potential in the form

$$-\frac{V}{G}=\sum_{n=0}^{\infty}\sum_{m=0}^{n}Q_n^m(i\cot\alpha)P_n^m(\sin u)(A_{nm}\cos m\omega$$
$$+B_{nm}\sin m\omega)$$

22.50

in which we have amalgamated the constants in Equations 22.47 with those in Equation 22.46, and we have included the gravitational constant G. Equation 22.50 corresponds to Equation 21.035, which we know to be sufficiently general. On the other hand, if we require an expression for the *internal potential* which has to be valid at and near

[2] No matter how we express $Q_n^m(i\cot\alpha)$, we cannot include it in the potential if $\cot\alpha$ is small. If we differentiate this function in the direction of the normal to a coordinate spheroid and use Equations 22.28 and 22.29, we have

$$\frac{\partial Q_n^m(i\cot\alpha)}{\partial s}=-\frac{n+1}{\nu}Q_n^m(i\cot\alpha)$$
$$-\frac{i(n-m+1)\tan\alpha}{\nu}Q_{n+1}^m(i\cot\alpha)$$

which becomes infinite for $\cot\alpha=0$, that is, for points on the limiting "spheroid" formed by rotating the interfocal line. The function will not therefore serve as part of a Newtonian potential in such a region.

the Cartesian origin, we must make $D=F=0$ in Equations 22.47 to give

$$-\frac{V}{G}=\sum_{n=0}^{\infty}\sum_{m=0}^{n}P_n^m(i\cot\alpha)P_n^m(\sin u)([A_{nm}]\cos m\omega +[B_{nm}]\sin m\omega),$$

22.51

which corresponds to Equation 21.086. All quantities in these last two equations are dimensionless except V, A_{nm}, B_{nm}; we conclude that the dimensions of A_{nm}, B_{nm} are the same as those of V/G, that is, $L^{-1}M$.

18. The first three Legendre functions of the second kind in our notation are

$$Q_0(i\cot\alpha)=-i\alpha$$
$$Q_1(i\cot\alpha)=\alpha\cot\alpha-1$$
$$Q_2(i\cot\alpha)=\tfrac{1}{2}i(\alpha+3\alpha\cot^2\alpha-3\cot\alpha);$$

22.52

the remainder can be found from the recursion formula

$$(n+1)Q_{n+1}-(2n+1)i\cot\alpha\,Q_n+nQ_{n-1}=0.$$

22.53

To derive the associated functions, we use Ferrers' definition, even though the argument is imaginary, so that we have

$$Q_n^m(i\cot\alpha)=\operatorname{cosec}^m\alpha\,\frac{d^mQ_n(i\cot\alpha)}{d(i\cot\alpha)^m}.$$

22.54

19. In most of the literature on spheroidal harmonics, the third coordinate is η where we have

$$\sinh\eta=\cot\alpha$$

with other relations which can easily be derived from Equation 21.101. This alternative, however, loses the advantage of the simple geometrical interpretation of α given by figure 26.

THE MASS DISTRIBUTION

20. To relate the A_{nm}, B_{nm} in the general formula for the potential to the mass distribution, we require an expression in spheroidal coordinates for the elementary potential at (ω, u, α) arising from a single particle of mass $\bar{m}$ at $(\bar{\omega}, \bar{u}, \bar{\alpha})$: in short, we require an expression for the reciprocal of the distance between the two points. We shall deal with the case illustrated by figure 19, Chapter 21, to find the ex-

ternal potential when the origin is inside the body, and for this purpose Equation 22.50 is appropriate. The case illustrated by figure 21, Chapter 21, can be dealt with similarly by using Equation 22.51.

21. The reciprocal of the distance $(1/r_0)$ between two points in spheroidal coordinates is itself a potential function, and must therefore be expressible in the form of Equation 22.50 in which the constants A_{nm}, B_{nm} will be functions of the coordinates of the overbarred point. Moreover, if we interchange the overbars, we can expect the formula to change to the form of Equation 22.51. By taking a temporary origin for longitude at the barred point, we see that the longitude term must take the form

$$A_{nm}\cos m(\omega-\bar{\omega})+B_{nm}\sin m(\omega-\bar{\omega}):$$

and because the field is symmetrical in longitude so that $1/r_0$ does not change if the signs of both ω and $\bar{\omega}$ are changed, the B_{nm} must be zero. These considerations are satisfied by the form

$$\frac{1}{r_0}=\sum_{n=0}^{\infty}\sum_{m=0}^{n}Q_n^m(i\cot\alpha)P_n^m(i\cot\bar{\alpha})P_n^m(\sin u)P_n^m(\sin\bar{u})$$
$$\times A_{nm}\cos m(\omega-\bar{\omega}),$$

and in fact the final formula, due to Heine, is

$$\frac{ae}{r_0}=i\sum_{n=0}^{\infty}(2n+1)\left[Q_n(i\cot\alpha)P_n(i\cot\bar{\alpha})P_n(\sin u)\right.$$
$$\times P_n(\sin\bar{u})+2\sum_{m=1}^{n}(-)^m\left(\frac{(n-m)!}{(n+m)!}\right)^2$$
$$\times Q_n^m(i\cot\alpha)P_n^m(i\cot\bar{\alpha})P_n^m(\sin u)$$

22.55 $$\left.\times P_n^m(\sin\bar{u})\cos m(\omega-\bar{\omega})\right].$$

A rigorous proof is given by Hobson.[3]

22. If we multiply Equation 22.55 by the mass $\bar{m}$ of the particle at the overbarred point and sum over the whole mass of the attracting body, we find that the constants in Equation 22.50 are given by

$$A_{n0}=\sum\frac{i(2n+1)}{ae}\bar{m}P_n(i\cot\bar{\alpha})P_n(\sin\bar{u})$$

$$\binom{A_{nm}}{B_{nm}}=\sum\frac{2i(2n+1)}{ae}(-)^m\left(\frac{(n-m)!}{(n+m)!}\right)^2\bar{m}P_n^m(i\cot\bar{\alpha})$$

22.56 $$\times P_n^m(\sin\bar{u})\binom{\cos m\bar{\omega}}{\sin m\bar{\omega}}$$

---

[3] Hobson, *op. cit. supra* note 1, 430. Hobson's conventions for the associated Legendre functions are different, but make no difference in this case. Hobson omits the overall factor i necessary to give real values of r_0.

in which m can be any integer between unity and n inclusive, and $(n-m)!$ is to be interpreted as unity if we have $m=n$. These equations correspond to Equations 21.037 in spherical harmonics. As in § 21–15, we can replace $\bar{m}$ by ρdv where ρ is the density at the overbarred point and dv is an element of volume. The summation is then replaced, in the case of a continuous distribution of matter, by a volume integral taken over the whole attracting body.

CONVERGENCE

23. The series in Equation 22.55 converges [4] if we have $\bar{\alpha} > \alpha$, which implies that the overbarred mass point must lie within the coordinate spheroid passing through the unbarred point (ω, u, α) where the potential is sought. If this condition is to apply to all mass points, then the point where the potential is sought must lie outside the coordinate spheroid which just encloses all the matter. Moreover, the spheroid enclosing all the matter must have $b > ae$ so that we have $\cot \alpha > 1$, if the external potential is to be expressed by Equation 22.50. In that case, all the individual particle series can be multiplied by the particle mass and added term-by-term, and the resulting series for the total potential will converge. As in § 21–11, we cannot say, however, that convergence of all the individual particle series is necessary, although it is certainly sufficient.

24. The sphere of convergence of § 21–11 and figure 19, Chapter 21, is accordingly replaced by a *spheroid of convergence* if we express the potential in spheroidal coordinates, and the conditions are otherwise exactly the same. In the case of the actual Earth, it is possible to choose a coordinate spheroid which just encloses all the matter and is generally much nearer to the topographic surface than any sphere that also encloses all the matter. Accordingly, we can say that the expression of the potential of the Earth in spheroidal harmonics can be made certainly convergent much nearer to the topographic surface than the potential expressed in spherical harmonics.

RELATIONS BETWEEN SPHERICAL AND SPHEROIDAL COEFFICIENTS

25. For the same mass distribution, Equations 21.035 and 22.50 for the potential in spherical and spheroidal harmonics, respectively, must give the same answer at all points in space where both series are convergent. Accordingly, there must be some

relation between the C_{nm}, S_{nm} and the A_{nm}, B_{nm}. To obtain this relation, we make use of a formula, due to Blades,[5] which, in our present notation and with a slight modification arising from changing the sign z and therefore of u also, is

$$\frac{1}{2\pi} \int_{-\pi}^{\pi} P_n\left(\frac{x \cos t + y \sin t - iz}{ae}\right) \binom{\cos mt}{\sin mt} dt$$

$$= \frac{(n-m)!}{(n+m)!} (-)^{n+m} P_n^m(i \cot \alpha) P_n^m(\sin u) \binom{\cos m\omega}{\sin m\omega}.$$

22.57

The corresponding formula [6] for the spherical harmonics of the geocentric latitude (ϕ) and longitude (ω), as used throughout Chapter 21, is

$$\frac{1}{2\pi} \int_{-\pi}^{\pi} (x \cos t + y \sin t - iz)^n \binom{\cos mt}{\sin mt}^{dt}$$

22.58 $\qquad = \dfrac{n!}{(n+m)!} i^{(m-n)} r^n P_n^m(\sin \phi) \binom{\cos m\omega}{\sin m\omega}.$

The spherical and spheroidal longitudes (ω) are the same in these last two equations because both systems are symmetrical about the same axis—the axis of rotation of the Earth—and have the same Cartesian axes. We consider that (ω, ϕ, r) and (ω, u, α) represent the same point where a mass $\bar{m}$ is situated. We can expand

$$P_n\left(\frac{x \cos t + y \sin t - iz}{ae}\right)$$

in Equation 22.57 in powers of

$$(x \cos t + y \sin t - iz),$$

and substitute Equation 22.58. The result is multiplied by $\bar{m}$, summed over the whole attracting body, and Equations 21.037 and 22.56 for the coefficients C_{nm}, S_{nm} and A_{nm}, B_{nm} are substituted. The final result after some simplification is

$$\binom{A_{nm}}{B_{nm}} = \frac{1 \cdot 3 \cdot 5 \ldots (2n+1)}{(n+m)!} i^{(m+n+1)} \left[\frac{1}{(ae)^{n+1}} \binom{C_{nm}}{S_{nm}} \right.$$

$$+ \frac{(n-m)(n-m-1)}{2 \cdot (2n-1)} \frac{1}{(ae)^{n-1}} \binom{C_{(n-2),\, m}}{S_{(n-2),\, m}}$$

$$+ \frac{(n-m)(n-m-1)(n-m-2)(n-m-3)}{2 \cdot 4(2n-1)(2n-3)}$$

$$\times \frac{1}{(ae)^{n-3}} \binom{C_{(n-4),\, m}}{S_{(n-4),\, m}} + \ldots \left. \right].$$

22.59

[4] *Ibid.*, 430.

[5] Whittaker and Watson (reprint of 1963), *A Course of Modern Analysis*, 4th ed. of 1927, 403. A simple proof of the formula with the usual difference in conventions is given by Hobson, *op. cit. supra* note 1, 423.

[6] Whittaker and Watson, *op. cit. supra* note 5, 392. In this case, a change in the sign of z is not required.

The same formula gives the zonal coefficients A_{n0} in terms of C_{n0}, $C_{(n-2), 0}$ ... simply by making $m=0$.

26. The reverse formula for C_{nm}, S_{nm} in terms of A_{nm}, B_{nm} is obtained by expanding

$$\left(\frac{x \cos t + y \sin t - iz}{ae}\right)^n$$

in Equation 22.58 in terms of the Legendre functions

$$P_n\left(\frac{x \cos t + y \sin t - iz}{ae}\right)$$

$$P_{n-2}\left(\frac{x \cos t + y \sin t - iz}{ae}\right),$$

etc., for substitution in Equation 22.57. The result after simplification is

$$i^{(m+n+1)}\binom{C_{nm}}{S_{nm}} = \frac{(ae)^{n+1}(n-m)!}{1 \cdot 3 \cdot 5 \ldots (2n+1)}\left[\frac{(n+m)!}{(n-m)!}\binom{A_{nm}}{B_{nm}}\right.$$

$$+ \frac{2n+1}{2}\frac{(n+m-2)!}{(n-m-2)!}\binom{A_{(n-2), m}}{B_{(n-2), m}}$$

$$+ \frac{(2n+1)(2n-1)}{2 \cdot 4}\frac{(n+m-4)!}{(n-m-4)!}\binom{A_{(n-4), m}}{B_{(n-4), m}}$$

$$+ \frac{(2n+1)(2n-1)(2n-3)}{2 \cdot 4 \cdot 6}\frac{(n+m-6)!}{(n-m-6)!}\binom{A_{(n-6), m}}{B_{(n-6), m}}$$

22.60
$$\left. + \ldots \right].$$

The same formula gives the zonal coefficients C_{n0} simply by making $m=0$.

Equations 22.59 and 22.60 enable us, for example, to transform rapidly an expression for the potential in an area where this expression is certainly convergent. The corresponding expression in spheroidal harmonics is then certainly convergent almost to the topographic surface.

27. We are now able to relate the spheroidal A_{nm}, B_{nm} to components of the inertia tensors by means of formulas given for the C_{nm}, S_{nm} in § 21–28 through § 21–34, and, in particular, to the total mass, to the center of mass, and to the moments of inertia of the attracting body.

Zero-Order Inertia Tensor

28. From Equations 21.016, 21.037, and 22.60, we have the inertia tensor of zero order as the total mass M where

22.61 $$M = C_{00} = -i(ae)A_{00},$$

which shows that the coefficient A_{00} is imaginary.

29. The leading term $(m=0, n=0)$ in Equation 22.50 for the potential is

22.62 $$A_{00}Q_0(i \cot \alpha) = -i\alpha A_{00} = M\alpha/(ae),$$

which is not the same as the leading term in the spherical harmonic expression (M/r). However, the two terms become nearly the same at great distances from the attracting body where the coordinate spheroids become nearly spheres of radius r and $\alpha \sim (ae)/r$.

First-Order Inertia Tensor

30. From Equations 21.06J, 21.037, and 22.60, the Cartesian coordinates of the center of mass are

$$I^s/M = (C_{11}/M, S_{11}/M, C_{10}/M)$$

22.63 $$= \left(\tfrac{2}{3}i(ae)^2\frac{A_{11}}{M}, \tfrac{2}{3}i(ae)^2\frac{B_{11}}{M}, -\tfrac{1}{3}(ae)^2\frac{A_{10}}{M}\right).$$

Consequently, if the origin of spheroidal coordinates — that is, the common center of the coordinate spheroids — is at the center of mass, then we have

$$A_{11} = B_{11} = A_{10} = 0,$$

and all the first-degree harmonics are absent from the expression of the potential in spheroidal harmonics. Conversely, if these harmonics are missing, the origin is at the center of mass as shown in § 21–42.

Second-Order Inertia Tensor

31. From Equations 21.043 and 22.60, we have

$$C_{20} = I^{33} - \tfrac{1}{2}(I^{11} + I^{22}) = \tfrac{1}{3}i(ae)^3(\tfrac{2}{5}A_{20} + A_{00})$$

$$C_{21} = I^{13} = \tfrac{2}{5}(ae)^3 A_{21}$$

$$S_{21} = I^{23} = \tfrac{2}{5}(ae)^3 B_{21}$$

$$C_{22} = \tfrac{1}{4}(I^{11} - I^{22}) = -\tfrac{8}{5}i(ae)^3 A_{22}$$

$$S_{22} = \tfrac{1}{2}I^{12} = -\tfrac{8}{5}i(ae)^3 B_{22}$$

22.64

from which we can draw much the same conclusions as in § 21–52 and § 21–53. For example, if the z-axis — the minor axis of the coordinate spheroids — is a principal axis of inertia, then we have

$$A_{21} = B_{21} = 0.$$

If all three Cartesian axes are principal axes, then, in addition, we have

$$B_{22} = 0;$$

certain relations between the three principal moments of inertia are then given by Equations 21.078 and 22.64. If the distribution of mass is symmetrical about the z-axis, then we have

$$A_{22} = 0.$$

The same conclusions, as were drawn in § 21–57 and § 21–58 regarding the omission of certain terms in the spherical harmonic expression of the potential, apply similarly to the expression in spheroidal harmonics.

THE POTENTIAL AT NEAR AND INTERNAL POINTS

32. If the point P at which the potential is required is nearer to the origin of coordinates than any point of the attracting body, we consider that P is at the overbarred point in Equation 22.55 and the particle of mass $\bar{m}$ is situated at the unbarred point. In that case, the series will remain convergent because $\bar{\alpha}$ is still greater than α. We must also take the potential in the form of Equation 22.51, in which we now suppose that the coordinates (ω, u, α) are overbarred. Proceeding as in § 22–22, we then find that

$$[A_{n0}] = \sum \frac{i(2n+1)}{ae} \bar{m} Q_n(i \cot \bar{\alpha}) P_n(\sin \bar{u})$$

$$\begin{pmatrix} [A_{nm}] \\ [B_{nm}] \end{pmatrix} = \sum \frac{2i(2n+1)}{ae} (-)^m \left(\frac{(n-m)!}{(n+m)!} \right)^2 \bar{m}$$

22.65 $\times Q_n^m(i \cot \bar{\alpha}) P_n^m(\sin \bar{u}) \begin{pmatrix} \cos m\bar{\omega} \\ \sin m\bar{\omega} \end{pmatrix}$

in which we have finally overbarred the mass point to correspond with Equations 22.56, so that Equation 22.51 may be used as it stands for the potential. As usual, the summations are taken over the whole mass of the attracting body and can be replaced by volume integrals in the case of continuous density distributions. The equations for the potential and the mass distribution correspond to Equations 21.086 and 21.087 in spherical harmonics. We may note that the only difference from the formulas for the potential at distant points in Equations 22.56 consists of an interchange between Legendre functions of the first and second kinds in much the same way as the corresponding difference in spherical harmonics consists of an interchange between r^n and $1/r^{n+1}$.

33. The spheroidal harmonics

$$P_n^m(i \cot \alpha) P_n^m(\sin u) \begin{pmatrix} \cos m\omega \\ \sin m\omega \end{pmatrix}$$

in Equation 22.51, for the potential at points near the origin, can be transformed to spherical harmonics in the form

$$r^n P_n^m(\sin \phi) \begin{pmatrix} \cos m\omega \\ \sin m\omega \end{pmatrix}$$

by the method of § 22–25, without assuming that the mass distribution remains the same. This transformation illustrates the fact that the potential given by either Equation 22.50 or 22.51, or by either of the corresponding series in spherical harmonics, does not uniquely settle the mass distribution; the same external or internal potential can arise from a variety of mass distributions. To settle the mass distribution, we require knowledge of the potential at all points throughout space which cannot be provided by a single series divergent in some areas.

34. In the same way, it must be possible to transform the spheroidal harmonics

$$Q_n^m(i \cot \alpha) P_n^m(\sin u) \begin{pmatrix} \cos m\omega \\ \sin m\omega \end{pmatrix}$$

in Equation 22.50, for the potential at distant points, to spherical harmonics in the form

$$\frac{1}{r^{n+1}} P_n^m(\sin \phi) \begin{pmatrix} \cos m\omega \\ \sin m\omega \end{pmatrix}.$$

We have so far achieved this transformation only by assuming the same mass distribution. It is more difficult to effect the transformation without making any assumption about the mass distribution, although Jeffery [7] has given a formula corresponding to Blades' Equation 22.57 which could be used for the purpose. However, there is no need in any current geodetic application to suppose that the mass distribution changes during the transformation.

DIFFERENTIAL FORM OF THE POTENTIAL

35. It is evident from Equation 22.41 that α is a harmonic function. Also, we have seen in § 22–29 that α behaves like $(ae)/r$ at great distances and is accordingly proportional to the Newtonian potential of some finite mass distribution. Accordingly, we infer from § 21–6 and § 21–7 that

22.66 $-\dfrac{V}{G} = \sum\limits_{n=0}^{\infty} J^{rst \ldots (n)} (\alpha)_{rst \ldots (n)}$

---

[7] Whittaker and Watson, *op. cit. supra* note 5, 403, and Hobson, *op. cit. supra* note 1, 424.

represents the Newtonian potential of a general mass distribution, provided the J's are arbitrary and are constant under covariant differentiation. Equation 22.66 corresponds to Maxwell's form of the potential as expressed in Equation 21.017.

36. We have seen in § 21–27 that the sum of all terms of the same degree is the same whether the potential is expressed in general spherical harmonics or in Maxwell's form. For example, the three first differentials of $(1/r)$ are the first-degree spherical harmonics. There is no such simple relation between even the first differentials of (α) and first-degree spheroidal harmonics.

For example, it can be shown that we have

$$(ae)\partial\alpha/\partial z = \sum_{n=0}^{\infty} (2n+1)Q_n(i \cot \alpha)P_n(\sin u)$$

22.67   (n odd only),

which is a spheroidal harmonic although not solely of the first degree. The other differentials must similarly be expressible in spheroidal harmonics because they are harmonic functions, but the expressions become progressively more complicated. Equation 22.66 is not therefore of much use for deriving spheroidal harmonic properties of the potential, but the expression of the potential in this compact form can be of use in theoretical investigations.

CHAPTER 23

The Standard Gravity Field

FIELD MODELS

1. To facilitate calculation of directions and distances between widely separated points in the gravity field, we require a mathematical model of the field which shall be near enough to the actual field for us to form first-order or linear observation equations. In much the same way, it is useful to have a model or standard field in which it is easy to compute the potential and derivatives of the potential, so that we can confine our attention to the small departures from the model encountered in actual measurement. Departures from the mathematical model are known as *anomalies*, *disturbances*, and *deflections*; the smaller we can make these departures, without sacrificing the simplicity and regularity of the mathematical model, the better. The model field is often called the normal field in the literature; however, the word "standard" describes the situation at least as well, and the word "normal" is already overworked in a book which also deals with the differential geometry of families of surfaces whose normals define a vector field. Standard gravity is usually denoted by γ in the literature; we shall use this convention later when actual gravity appears in the same formulas. In this chapter, we shall be dealing entirely with standard gravity; we shall use the ordinary symbol "g" to avoid confusion with the curvature parameters γ_1, γ_2, which appear later in the chapter. Standard potential is usually denoted by U in the literature, either for the attraction potential or the geopotential, and we shall follow this convention in later chapters when the actual potential is used in the same formula; in this chapter, there is no ambiguity in continuing to use V or W for the potential of the particular standard field.

SYMMETRICAL MODELS

2. An obvious simplification of the general expression for the potential would be to suppose that the field is symmetrical about the z-axis of rotation, thereby making all the tesseral harmonics anomalous. In that case, the model potential is independent of longitude and is given in spherical harmonics as

23.01 $$-\frac{W}{G} = \sum_{n=0}^{\infty} \frac{C_{n0}P_n(\sin\phi)}{r^{n+1}} + \frac{\frac{1}{2}\tilde{\omega}^2(x^2+y^2)}{G}$$

in which, as always in spherical harmonic expressions in this book, ϕ is the geocentric latitude or latitude of the radius vector. Moreover, the longitude of the line of force in the model ($\bar{\omega}$ in Equations 21.136 and 21.138) is the same as the geocentric longitude. There will be no zonal harmonics in Equations 21.136 and 21.138, and the only tesseral harmonics will be of the first order so that Equations 21.136 and 21.138, corrected for rotation, reduce to the single equation

$$g\cos\bar{\phi} = \sum_{n=0}^{\infty} \frac{GC_{n0}}{r^{n+2}}P_{n+1}^1(\sin\phi) - \tilde{\omega}^2 r P_1^1(\sin\phi).$$

23.02

There will be no tesseral harmonics in Equation 21.140, which is unaffected by rotation and becomes

23.03 $$g\sin\bar{\phi} = \sum_{n=0}^{\infty} \frac{(n+1)GC_{n0}}{r^{n+2}}P_{n+1}(\sin\phi).$$

As noted in § 21–93, Equations 21.136, 21.138, and

21.140 give the outward components of the gravitational force, which is, nevertheless, positive inward. We have accordingly introduced an overall change of sign in Equations 23.02 and 23.03 in order that g may be positive.

3. Alternative gravity formulas can be given in terms of $(\bar\phi - \phi)$, which might be termed the deflection in latitude with respect to a central field, by combining the last two equations. After some manipulation involving well-known properties of the Legendre functions, we have

$$g \sin (\bar\phi - \phi) = - \sum_{n=1}^{\infty} \frac{GC_{n0}}{r^{n+2}} P_n^1(\sin \phi)$$

23.04 $\qquad\qquad + \tilde\omega^2 r \sin \phi \cos \phi$

$$g \cos (\bar\phi - \phi) = \sum_{n=0}^{\infty} \frac{(n+1)GC_{n0}}{r^{n+2}} P_n(\sin \phi)$$

23.05 $\qquad\qquad - \tilde\omega^2 r \cos^2 \phi.$

At any point where the direction of the line of force is radial, the first of these equations is zero and the second gives g direct. For example, this situation would occur at the poles in a symmetrical field. In that case, the first equation is identically zero because we have $P_n^1(1) = 0$, and the second could be obtained by radial differentiation of the potential in Equation 23.01.

4. A further simplification would be to make the model also symmetrical about the equatorial plane, in which case the C_{n0} in Equations 23.01, 23.02, 23.03, 23.04, and 23.05 would become zero for n odd. After omitting all the tesseral harmonics and the zonal harmonics of odd degree, we might as well omit all the zonal harmonics beyond the fourth or even the second degree. However, the most convenient coordinate system for geometrical purposes is a (ω, ϕ, h) system with a spheroidal base. We must be able to relate the geometric and gravimetric systems and, the simplest way of doing this is to make the base spheroid of the geometrical system the same as an equipotential surface of the gravimetric system. We shall accordingly investigate this type of model next, instead of an arbitrarily truncated spherical harmonic model.

THE SPHEROIDAL MODEL

5. The model most often used for gravimetric purposes consists of an axially symmetrical field in which *one* equipotential surface is an oblate spheroid. This spheroidal equipotential of the model field is chosen as nearly as possible to fit the *geoid*, that is, the actual equipotential surface nearest to Mean Sea Level. The minor axis of the spheroid is oriented parallel to the axis of rotation of the Earth. Ideally, the minor axis should coincide with the axis of rotation, and the center of the spheroid should coincide with the center of mass of the Earth so as to provide also a unique worldwide geometric reference system, as discussed in § 21–57 and § 21–58.

6. The model field rotates with the same angular velocity $\tilde\omega$ as the actual Earth. Whenever we need to consider the mass distribution which gives rise to the model or standard potential, we suppose that the total mass in the model is the same as the total mass M of the actual Earth, although the mass cannot, of course, be distributed in the same way.

7. The problem of developing such a model field would already have been solved if the field were static. We have seen in § 22–33 that the spheroidal coordinate α is proportional to a Newtonian potential and is constant over each of the coordinate spheroids, one of which can be chosen to approximate the geoid. The potential would be given by Equation 22.62 as

23.06 $\qquad\qquad -\dfrac{V}{G} = \dfrac{M\alpha}{ae},$

and gravity by Equations 22.28 and 22.29 as

23.07 $\qquad\qquad g = \dfrac{GM \tan \alpha}{(ae)\nu}$

so that $g\nu$ would be constant over any one equipotential surface.

8. However, we are not concerned with a static field; the case we have to consider is a field rotating with uniform angular velocity $\tilde\omega$. In that case, it is still possible to arrange for the geopotential to be constant over *one* of the coordinate surfaces of a spheroidal coordinate system. The other coordinate spheroids will not, however, be equipotential surfaces.

THE STANDARD POTENTIAL IN SPHEROIDAL HARMONICS

9. The geopotential W in a field rotating with constant angular velocity $\tilde\omega$ is obtained from Equations 20.08 and 22.22 as

$$-W = -V + \tfrac{1}{2}\tilde{\omega}^2(x^2 + y^2)$$

$$= -V + \tfrac{1}{3}\tilde{\omega}^2 a^2 \cos^2 u$$

23.08 $\qquad = -V + \tfrac{1}{3}\tilde{\omega}^2 a^2 - \tfrac{1}{3}\tilde{\omega}^2 a^2 P_2(\sin u),$

assuming that the axis of rotation coincides with the minor axes of the coordinate spheroids. If we assume also that the standard or model field is axially symmetric so that the potential is independent of longitude, then we have $m = 0$ in Equation 22.50 for the attraction potential V, and we have

$$-W = \sum_{n=0}^{\infty} GA_{n0}Q_n(i \cot \alpha)P_n(\sin u) + \tfrac{1}{3}\tilde{\omega}^2 a^2$$

23.09 $\qquad -\tfrac{1}{3}\tilde{\omega}^2 a^2 P_2(\sin u).$

The geopotential on one particular coordinate spheroid, for which we have $\alpha = \alpha_0$, $a = a_0$, is

$$-W_0 = GA_{00}Q_0(i \cot \alpha_0) + \tfrac{1}{3}\tilde{\omega}^2 a_0^2$$

$$+ GA_{10}Q_1(i \cot \alpha_0)P_1(\sin u)$$

$$+ \{GA_{20}Q_2(i \cot \alpha_0) - \tfrac{1}{3}\tilde{\omega}^2 a_0^2\}P_2(\sin u)$$

$$+ GA_{30}Q_3(i \cot \alpha_0)P_3(\sin u)$$

$$+ \ldots;$$

if the geopotential is to be a constant over this spheroid for all values of u, we must have

$$-W_0 = GA_{00}Q_0(i \cot \alpha_0) + \tfrac{1}{3}\tilde{\omega}^2 a_0^2$$

$$A_{10} = 0$$

$$GA_{20}Q_2(i \cot \alpha_0) = \tfrac{1}{3}\tilde{\omega}^2 a_0^2$$

23.10 $\qquad A_{n0} = 0 \qquad\qquad (n > 2).$

The first of these results, combined with Equation 22.62, gives the potential on the base spheroid $(\alpha = \alpha_0)$ in terms of the dimensions of that spheroid and the total mass M as

23.11 $\qquad -W_0 = GM\alpha_0/(a_0 \sin \alpha_0) + \tfrac{1}{3}\tilde{\omega}^2 a_0^2.$

It is usually supposed that the total mass is contained within the base spheroid, so that the potential on and outside the base spheroid may be represented by a convergent series in Equation 23.09, in accordance with §22-23. If this series was not convergent, we could not have proceeded beyond Equation 23.09.

10. From Equations 23.10, we have also

$$GA_{20} = \tfrac{1}{3}\tilde{\omega}^2 a_0^2 / Q_2(i \cot \alpha_0)$$

23.12 $\qquad = \dfrac{\tfrac{2}{3}i\tilde{\omega}^2 a_0^2}{3 \cot \alpha_0 - \alpha_0(1 + 3 \cot^2 \alpha_0)},$

using Equations 22.52. The coefficient iA_{20} can accordingly be computed definitely for a particular base spheroid. Finally, the geopotential can be written in the spheroidal coordinates (u, α) as

$$-W = GM\alpha/(ae) + GA_{20}Q_2(i \cot \alpha)P_2(\sin u)$$

23.13 $\qquad + \{\tfrac{1}{3}\tilde{\omega}^2 a^2 - \tfrac{1}{3}\tilde{\omega}^2 a^2 P_2(\sin u)\}$

in which $(ae) = a_0 \sin \alpha_0$ is an absolute constant, while we have

23.14 $\qquad a = a_0 \sin \alpha_0 \csc \alpha.$

The term within braces in Equation 23.13 arises from rotation, and is equally well expressed by

$$\tfrac{1}{2}\tilde{\omega}^2(x^2 + y^2).$$

We may note that if we have $\tilde{\omega} = 0$, the potential is the same as we obtained for the static case in Equation 23.06.

THE STANDARD POTENTIAL IN SPHERICAL HARMONICS

11. For the same mass distribution, whatever that may be, the spherical and spheroidal coefficients are related by Equation 22.60, which in the symmetrical case $(m = 0)$ takes the form

$$i^{n+1}C_{n0} = \frac{(ae)^{n+1}n!}{1 \cdot 3 \cdot 5 \ldots (2n+1)}$$

$$\times \left[A_{n0} + \frac{2n+1}{2}A_{(n-2),\,0} \right.$$

23.15 $\qquad \left. + \frac{(2n+1)(2n-1)}{2 \cdot 4}A_{(n-4),\,0} + \ldots \right].$

Because the only nonzero spheroidal coefficients are A_{20} and A_{00}, the C_{n0} are zero if n is odd, as we should expect from the equatorial symmetry of the model. We can rewrite the last equation, after considering the terms of lowest degree in the A's, as

23.16 $\qquad C_{n0} = \frac{(-)^{(n/2)+1}(ae)^{n+1}}{(n+1)}\left[iA_{00} + \frac{niA_{20}}{(n+3)} \right]$

in which n is to have only even values. To reflect this restriction to even values, we may write $(2n - 2)$ for n so that

$$C_{(2n-2),\,0} = \frac{(-)^n(ae)^{2n-1}}{(2n-1)}\left[iA_{00} + \frac{(2n-2)iA_{20}}{(2n+1)} \right]$$

23.17

in which the range of n is from unity to infinity. The geopotential, including the rotation term, can now be written in the form

$$-\frac{W}{G} = \sum_{n=1}^{\infty} (-)^n \frac{(2n+1)iA_{00}+(2n-2)iA_{20}}{(2n-1)(2n+1)}$$

23.18 $\qquad \times \frac{(ae)^{2n-1}}{r^{2n-1}} P_{2n-2}(\sin \phi) + \frac{\frac{1}{2}\tilde{\omega}^2(x^2+y^2)}{G}$

in which ϕ is the geocentric latitude. For substitution in this equation, we have A_{20} from Equation 23.12 and

23.19 $\qquad A_{00}=iM/(ae)$

from Equation 22.61.

12. We can check this result by considering the potential along the z-axis where figure 26, Chapter 22, shows that we have $\cot \alpha = z/(ae)$ and $\sin u = 1$. In that case, we have from Equation 23.13

$$-\frac{W}{G} = \frac{M}{ae}\tan^{-1}\left(\frac{ae}{z}\right) + A_{20}Q_2\left(\frac{iz}{ae}\right),$$

which can easily be expanded as

$$-\frac{W}{G} = \sum_{n=1}^{\infty} (-)^n \frac{(2n+1)iA_{00}+(2n-2)iA_{20}}{(2n-1)(2n+1)}\left(\frac{ae}{z}\right)^{2n-1}.$$

From this last formula, the expansion in spherical harmonics, given in Equation 23.18, follows after restoring the rotation term.

STANDARD GRAVITY ON THE EQUIPOTENTIAL SPHEROID

13. From Equations 20.05, 22.28, and 22.29, the magnitude of the component of gravity in the direction of the inward-drawn normal to a coordinate spheroid will be

$$g_n = -\frac{\tan \alpha}{\nu}\frac{\partial W}{\partial \alpha} \qquad (u \text{ constant})$$

where α and ν are evaluated with respect to the coordinate spheroid in question. Differentiating Equation 23.13 and using Equations 22.30, we have

23.20 $\qquad g_n = \frac{\tan \alpha}{\nu}\{J+LP_2(\sin u)\}$

where J, L are constant over the coordinate spheroid and are given by

$$J = GM/(ae) - \tfrac{2}{3}\tilde{\omega}^2 a^2 \cot \alpha$$

$$L = -iGA_{20}\operatorname{cosec} \alpha\, Q_2^1(i \cot \alpha) + \tfrac{2}{3}\tilde{\omega}^2 a^2 \cot \alpha$$

23.21

in which we have introduced the Legendre functions defined by Equation 22.54. At the pole of the

coordinate spheroid, we have $\nu = a^2/b$ and $\sin u = 1$ so that

23.22 $\qquad g_p = (b \tan \alpha/a^2)\{J+L\}.$

On the equator of the coordinate spheroid, we have $\nu = a$ and $\sin u = 0$ so that

23.23 $\qquad g_e = (\tan \alpha/a)\{J-\tfrac{1}{2}L\}.$

Considerations of symmetry show that the normal component of gravity at the poles and on the equator is the same as the total gravity at such points.

Somigliana's Formula

14. From the last two equations, we have

$$(g_p/b) \sin^2 u + (g_e/a) \cos^2 u = (\tan \alpha/a^2)$$

$$\times \{J+LP_2(\sin u)\}$$

$$= g_n \nu/a^2$$

on substituting Equation 23.20. Using Equations 22.05, 22.06, and 22.10, this last equation is easily put into the form

23.24 $\qquad g_n = \dfrac{ag_e \cos^2 \phi + bg_p \sin^2 \phi}{(a^2 \cos^2 \phi + b^2 \sin^2 \phi)^{1/2}}$

in which ϕ is the latitude of the normal to the coordinate spheroid; a, b are the semiaxes of the coordinate spheroid; and g_e, g_p are the values of gravity on the equator and at the poles of the coordinate spheroid. The formula, due originally to Somigliana, gives the component of gravity normal to the coordinate spheroid in latitude ϕ. If the coordinate spheroid is the base equipotential surface of the standard field, then g_n is the total force of gravity, but the formula is of more general application and gives one component of gravity normal to the coordinate spheroid at any point in space.

Clairaut's Formula

15. With some manipulation and use of Equation 23.12, we may rewrite L in Equations 23.21 as

$$\frac{3L}{2} = \frac{(\tilde{\omega}^2 \cot \alpha)\{a^2 Q_2(i \cot \alpha_0)-a_0^2 Q_2(i \cot \alpha)\}}{Q_2(i \cot \alpha_0)}$$

23.25 $\qquad - \dfrac{i\tilde{\omega}^2 a_0^2 Q_1(i \cos \alpha)}{Q_2(i \cot \alpha_0)}.$

From Equations 23.22 and 23.23, we have also

23.26 $\qquad \dfrac{g_p}{b}-\dfrac{g_e}{a}=\dfrac{\tan \alpha}{a^2}\times\dfrac{3L}{2};$

on the base (equipotential) spheroid ($\alpha = \alpha_0$), this is

23.27 $$\frac{g_p}{b} - \frac{g_e}{a} = \frac{\tilde{\omega}^2 Q_1(i \cot \alpha_0)}{(i \cot \alpha_0)Q_2(i \cot \alpha_0)}$$

which, if we use the expansion in Equation 22.48, reduces to

$$\frac{g_p}{b} - \frac{g_e}{a} = \frac{5\tilde{\omega}^2}{2}\left(1 + \tfrac{9}{35}\tan^2 \alpha_0 - \tfrac{16}{245}\tan^4 \alpha_0 + \ldots\right).$$

23.28

If we omit the small terms in tan α_0, this equation reduces to the classical Clairaut equation. It should be noted that Equation 23.28 applies only on the equipotential spheroid. The corresponding equation at other points in space is Equation 23.26 with Equation 23.25.

Pizetti's Formula

16. From the metric in spheroidal coordinates in Equation 22.25, an element of area dS of a coordinate spheroid is

$$dS = a\nu \cos \alpha \cos u \, du \, d\omega = a\nu \cos \alpha \, d(\sin u)d\omega.$$

Integrating Equation 23.20 over the spheroid, we have

$$\int_S g_n dS = \int_S ae\{J + LP_2(\sin u)\}d(\sin u)d\omega$$

23.29 $= 4\pi aeJ.$

Next, we eliminate L between Equations 23.22 and 23.23 in much the same way as we eliminated J to obtain Clairaut's formula. We have

23.30 $$\left(\frac{2g_e}{a} + \frac{g_p}{b}\right) = \frac{3J \tan \alpha}{a^2} = \frac{3aeJ}{a^2 b} = \frac{4\pi aeJ}{\nu}$$

where ν is the volume of the coordinate spheroid. Also, from Equations 23.21, we have

23.31 $$4\pi aeJ = 4\pi GM - 2\tilde{\omega}^2\nu$$

so that

23.32 $$\left(\frac{2g_e}{a} + \frac{g_p}{b}\right)\nu = \int_S g_n dS = 4\pi GM - 2\tilde{\omega}^2\nu.$$

This last equation applies to any of the coordinate spheroids, provided g_n is the component of gravity in the direction of the inward-drawn normal to the spheroid. From Equation 20.05, we have

$$g_n = +\,\partial W/\partial s$$

where ds is an element of length along the *outward*-drawn normal and W is the potential given by Equation 23.13. The divergence theorem of Equation 9.17 gives

$$\int_S g_n dS = \int_S \frac{\partial W}{\partial s}\,dS = \int_V \Delta W\,dV = 4\pi GM - 2\tilde{\omega}^2 v,$$

using Equation 20.15. In this equation, M is the total mass contained within the coordinate spheroid over whose surface we have integrated. The last two members of Equation 23.32 are compatible therefore if, and only if, the coordinate spheroid we have been considering contains all the mass. In that case, we can rewrite Equation 23.32 as

23.33 $$\frac{2g_e}{a} + \frac{g_p}{b} = 4\pi G\rho - 2\tilde{\omega}^2$$

in which ρ is the average density obtained by dividing the total mass by the volume of the coordinate spheroid. This result is due to Pizetti; it holds true, not only for the equipotential spheroid, but also for any coordinate spheroid enclosing all the mass.

General Remarks on Gravity

17. If we know the dimensions of the equipotential spheroid, then g_e and g_p are directly related by the Clairaut Equation 23.28; we need to know only one of these quantities, for example, g_e. The Somigliana Equation 23.24 then gives us gravity at any point of the equipotential spheroid in terms of this one constant g_e, which is directly related to the average density or total mass by means of the Pizetti Equation 23.33. Provided $\tilde{\omega}$ is known, the three Equations 23.28, 23.24, and 23.33 accordingly allow us to express gravity on the equipotential spheroid—of known a and b—in terms of a single constant: either the total mass, or gravity on the equator, or gravity at any point. Several approximate formulas are given in the literature, all of which can be derived from these three exact equations; the degree of approximation involved appears in the derivation. The exact equations are not, however, more difficult to compute. Some formulas are given in terms of the *flattening* of the spheroid, $f = (a - b)/a$; of the *gravitational flattening*, $(g_p - g_e)/g_e$; and of the ratio of centrifugal force on the equator to standard gravity on the equator, $q = \tilde{\omega}^2 a/g_e$. For example, the Somigliana Equation 23.24 can easily be expanded in the form

23.34 $g = g_e(1 + B_2 \sin^2 \phi + B_4 \sin^2 2\phi + \ldots).$

If we omit $\tan^4 \alpha_0$ and higher powers in Equation

23.28, the coefficients become

$$B_2 = -f + \tfrac{5}{2}q - \tfrac{17}{14}qf + \tfrac{15}{4}q^2$$

23.35 $$B_4 = \tfrac{1}{8}f^2 - \tfrac{5}{8}qf,$$

omitting f^3, qf^2, and higher powers.

18. The international gravity formula, adopted in 1930, is in the form of Equation 23.34. However, g_e and B_2 do not have their theoretical values for a spheroid of given dimensions, enclosing a given mass, but were obtained empirically from gravity measurements. The B_4-term was obtained theoretically, but is not in line with modern ideas of the flattening. The 1966 international values of the constants were

$$g_e = 978.049 \text{ cm./sec.}^2$$

$$B_2 = 0.0052884$$

23.36 $$B_4 = -0.0000059.$$

Values recommended by the International Association of Geodesy in 1967, and also by the International Astronomical Union, are

$$g_e = 978.031 \text{ cm./sec.}^2$$

$$B_2 = 0.0053024$$

$$B_4 = -0.0000059.$$

19. In the same way, there are many classical formulas expressing the coefficients of the second- and fourth-spherical harmonics of the standard potential in terms of e or f and q (which usually appears as m) to various degrees of accuracy; the usual line of development is to add second- and third-order terms to Clairaut's first-order result. However, it is as easy, if not easier, to compute the coefficients of the second, fourth, or any harmonic from the exact formula given as Equation 23.18.

STANDARD GRAVITY IN SPACE

20. Because the standard geopotential is independent of longitude, there is no component of gravity in the direction of the parallels of latitude of the coordinate spheroids. To find the meridian component, we note that the metric in Equation 22.25 gives an element of length along the meridian of the coordinate spheroid as

$$(\nu \cos \alpha)\,du.$$

Accordingly, the magnitude of the northward component of gravity in the direction of the meridian is

$$g_m = -\frac{1}{\nu \cos \alpha}\frac{\partial W}{\partial u}$$

$$= \frac{3 \sin u \cos u}{\nu \cos \alpha}\left[GA_{20}Q_2(i\cot\alpha) - \tfrac{1}{3}\tilde{\omega}^2 a^2\right],$$

23.37

which is zero (as it should be) on the equipotential spheroid, where the terms in brackets become zero by Equation 23.12. The meridian component is also zero at the poles and on the equators of the coordinate spheroids where u is $\tfrac{1}{2}\pi$ or zero.

21. At other points in space, we can combine normal gravity g_n, given by the Somigliana Equation 23.24, with the meridian component g_m, given by Equation 23.37, to give both the magnitude and direction of the total gravitational force. If ϕ is the latitude of the spheroidal normal, then the latitude of the line of force is

23.38 $$\phi - \tan^{-1}(g_m/g_n);$$

and the magnitude of the total force is

23.39 $$g = (g_m^2 + g_n^2)^{1/2}.$$

STANDARD GRAVITY IN SPHERICAL HARMONICS

22. It is necessary for some purposes and convenient for others to have standard gravity expressed in spherical harmonics. Because the field is axially symmetric, Equations 23.02 and 23.03 apply; and because the field is equatorially symmetric, the n-odd terms are zero. Accordingly, we write $(2n-2)$ for n and substitute for the C's from Equation 23.17 to obtain

$$g\cos\bar{\phi} = \sum_{n=1}^{\infty} G(-)^n \frac{(2n+1)iA_{00} + (2n-2)iA_{20}}{(2n-1)(2n+1)}$$

23.40 $$\times \frac{(ae)^{2n-1}}{r^{2n}}P^1_{2n-1}(\sin\phi) - \bar{\omega}^2 r\cos\phi$$

$$g\sin\bar{\phi} = \sum_{n=1}^{\infty} G(-)^n \frac{(2n+1)iA_{00} + (2n-2)iA_{20}}{(2n+1)}$$

23.41 $$\times \frac{(ae)^{2n-1}}{r^{2n}}P_{2n-1}(\sin\phi)$$

in which ϕ is the geocentric latitude and $\bar{\phi}$ is the latitude of the line of force.

23. From Equations 23.04 and 23.05, we have similarly

$$g \sin (\bar{\phi} - \phi) = \sum_{n=2}^{\infty} G(-)^{n+1} \frac{(2n+1)iA_{00} + (2n-2)iA_{20}}{(2n-1)(2n+1)}$$

$$\times \frac{(ae)^{2n-1}}{r^{2n}} P_{2n-2}^1 (\sin \phi)$$

23.42 $\qquad + \tilde{\omega}^2 r \sin \phi \cos \phi$

$$g \cos (\bar{\phi} - \phi) = \sum_{n=1}^{\infty} G(-)^n \frac{(2n+1)iA_{00} + (2n-2)iA_{20}}{(2n+1)}$$

23.43 $\qquad \times \frac{(ae)^{2n-1}}{r^{2n}} P_{2n-2} (\sin \phi) - \tilde{\omega}^2 r \cos^2 \phi.$

The difference in the two latitudes $(\bar{\phi} - \phi)$ can be considered the "deflection" in latitude of the standard field relative to a centrally symmetrical gravitational field. There is, of course, no corresponding deflection in longitude.

24. On the equator of the base spheroid, for example, we have $\bar{\phi} = \phi = 0$, and either Equation 23.40 or 23.43 reduces to

$$g_e = -\tilde{\omega}^2 a - \sum_{n=1}^{\infty} G \frac{(2n+1)iA_{00} + (2n-2)iA_{20}}{(2n+1)} \frac{(ae)^{2n-1}}{a^{2n}}$$

23.44 $\qquad \times \frac{1 \cdot 3 \cdot 5 \ldots (2n-3)}{2 \cdot 4 \cdot 6 \ldots (2n-2)}.$

CURVATURES OF THE FIELD

25. The curvature parameters of the field can be evaluated in any coordinate system from Equations 12.162 by contracting the Marussi tensor, in this case W_{rs} where W is the standard geopotential. However, evaluation of the parameters in spheroidal coordinates is not simple, even though the potential in spheroidal coordinates includes only two terms. The covariant derivatives of the potential are found by successive differentiation of Equation 23.13 and by use of the Christoffel symbols in Equations 22.38 and 22.39. The covariant derivatives are then contracted with the base vectors of the equipotential surfaces, which can be found from the matrix equation

$$\begin{pmatrix} \lambda^r \\ \mu^r \\ \nu^r \end{pmatrix} = \begin{pmatrix} 1 & 0 & 0 \\ 0 & \cos(\bar{\phi} - \phi) & -\sin(\bar{\phi} - \phi) \\ 0 & \sin(\bar{\phi} - \phi) & \cos(\bar{\phi} - \phi) \end{pmatrix}$$

$$\times \begin{pmatrix} 1/(\nu \cos \phi) & 0 & 0 \\ 0 & 1/(\nu \cos \alpha) & 0 \\ 0 & 0 & -\tan \alpha / \nu \end{pmatrix}$$

23.45

where $\bar{\phi}$ is the latitude of the line of force obtained from Equations 23.40 and 23.41, ϕ is the latitude of the normal to the coordinate spheroid, and the other quantities ν, α also refer to the coordinate spheroid.

Curvatures in Spherical Harmonics

26. An alternative method is to evaluate the Marussi invariants of Equations 12.162 in the fixed Cartesian system, as explained in general in § 21–95 through § 21–98. Components of the tensor N_{rs} or W_{rs} become ordinary differentials of the geopotential with respect to Cartesian coordinates; these components are easily obtained from Equations 21.145 through 21.150.

27. In the case we are considering, the only nonzero harmonic coefficients in the attraction potential V are C_{n0}, and the only nonzero harmonic coefficients in the first differentials are obtained from Equations 21.137, 21.139, and 21.141 as

$$-\frac{\partial}{\partial x}\left(\frac{V}{G}\right): \qquad \bar{C}_{(n+1),1} = -C_{n0}$$

$$-\frac{\partial}{\partial y}\left(\frac{V}{G}\right): \qquad \bar{S}_{(n+1),1} = -C_{n0}$$

23.46 $\qquad -\frac{\partial}{\partial z}\left(\frac{V}{G}\right): \qquad \bar{C}_{(n+1),0} = -(n+1)C_{n0}.$

The only nonzero harmonic coefficients in the second differentials are given by Equations 21.145 through 21.150 as

$$-\frac{\partial^2}{\partial x^2}\left(\frac{V}{G}\right): \qquad \bar{\bar{C}}_{(n+2),0} = -\tfrac{1}{2}(n+1)(n+2)C_{n0}$$

$$\bar{\bar{C}}_{(n+2),2} = \tfrac{1}{2}C_{n0}$$

$$-\frac{\partial^2}{\partial y^2}\left(\frac{V}{G}\right): \qquad \bar{\bar{C}}_{(n+2),0} = -\tfrac{1}{2}(n+1)(n+2)C_{n0}$$

$$\bar{\bar{C}}_{(n+2),2} = -\tfrac{1}{2}C_{n0}$$

$$-\frac{\partial^2}{\partial z^2}\left(\frac{V}{G}\right): \qquad \bar{\bar{C}}_{(n+2),0} = (n+1)(n+2)C_{n0}$$

$$-\frac{\partial^2}{\partial x \partial y}\left(\frac{V}{G}\right): \qquad \bar{\bar{S}}_{(n+2),2} = \tfrac{1}{2}C_{n0}$$

$$-\frac{\partial^2}{\partial y \partial z}\left(\frac{V}{G}\right): \qquad \bar{\bar{S}}_{(n+2),1} = (n+1)C_{n0}$$

$$-\frac{\partial^2}{\partial z \partial x}\left(\frac{V}{G}\right): \qquad \bar{\bar{C}}_{(n+2),1} = (n+1)C_{n0}.$$

23.47

28. Allowing for the rotation term in the geopotential from Equations 21.151 and substituting in Equations 21.152 for $\bar{\omega} = \omega$, we have

$$gk_2 = A + G \sum_{n=0}^{\infty} \frac{C_{n0}}{r^{n+3}} \{ BP_{n+2}(\sin\phi)$$

23.48
$$+ CP_{n+2}^1(\sin\phi) + DP_{n+2}^2(\sin\phi)\}$$

where

$$A = \tilde{\omega}^2 \sin^2 \bar{\phi}$$

$$B = (n+1)(n+2)(\cos^2\bar{\phi} - \tfrac{1}{2}\sin^2\bar{\phi})$$

$$C = -(n+1)\sin 2\bar{\phi}$$

23.49 $D = \tfrac{1}{2}\sin^2\bar{\phi},$

and the C_{n0} are given by Equation 23.16. To reflect the fact that the only nonzero values of C_{n0} occur when n is even, we can substitute $(2n-2)$ for n in Equation 23.48 and in the coefficients B, C, and can use Equation 23.17 for the $C_{(2n-2),0}$. As always in spherical harmonic expressions, ϕ is the geocentric latitude in Equation 23.48 and $\bar{\phi}$ is the latitude of the line of force, computed, together with g, from Equations 23.40 and 23.41.

29. The remaining nonzero parameters are given by formulas similar to Equation 23.48, but with the following coefficients

for gk_1: $A = \tilde{\omega}^2$

$$B = -\tfrac{1}{2}(n+1)(n+2)$$

$$C = 0$$

23.50 $D = -\tfrac{1}{2}$

for $g\gamma_2$: $A = \tfrac{1}{2}\tilde{\omega}^2 \sin 2\bar{\phi}$

$$B = -\tfrac{3}{4}(n+1)(n+2)\sin 2\bar{\phi}$$

$$C = -(n+1)\cos 2\bar{\phi}$$

23.51 $D = \tfrac{1}{4}\sin 2\bar{\phi}$

for $\dfrac{\partial g}{\partial s}$: $A = -\tilde{\omega}^2 \cos^2\bar{\phi}$

$$B = -(n+1)(n+2)(\sin^2\bar{\phi} - \tfrac{1}{2}\cos^2\bar{\phi})$$

$$C = -(n+1)\sin 2\bar{\phi}$$

23.52 $D = -\tfrac{1}{2}\cos^2\bar{\phi}.$

From Equation 12.021, the curvature of the lines of force is γ_2 because we have $\gamma_1 = 0$ in this case. Equations 23.52, giving the variation in gravity along the lines of force, provide a rigorous form of the "free air" or height correction to the value of gravity on the equipotential spheroid. At points close to the equipotential spheroid, the correction would be given with sufficient accuracy by Equation

20.17, which in this case reduces to

23.53 $\dfrac{\partial g}{\partial s} = -g\left(\dfrac{1}{\rho} + \dfrac{1}{\nu}\right) - 2\tilde{\omega}^2$

at points near the spheroidal equipotential; the correction is often still further simplified by taking ρ and ν as a mean radius of the Earth.

30. As a check, we find that the law of gravity in the form of Equation 20.17, that is,

$$\partial g/\partial s - g(k_1 + k_2) = -2\tilde{\omega}^2,$$

is satisfied by each harmonic in Equation 23.48 formed for each of the appropriate parameters. The remaining parameters t_1, γ_1 are found to be zero, as they should be in the symmetrical field we are considering. We can also use these results to determine gravity at points where the curvature is known. For example, on the equator of the equipotential spheroid, $k_1 = -1/a$, and we then have

$$-\frac{g_e}{a} = \tilde{\omega}^2 + G \sum_{n=0}^{\infty} \frac{C_{n0}}{a^{n+3}} \{ -\tfrac{1}{2}(n+1)(n+2)P_{n+2}(0)$$

$$- \tfrac{1}{2}P_{n+2}^2(0)\}$$

$$= \tilde{\omega}^2 + G \sum_{n=0}^{\infty} (-)^{(n+2)/2} \frac{C_{n0}}{a^{n+3}} \times \frac{1\cdot3\cdot5 \,\ldots\, (n+1)}{2\cdot4\cdot6 \,\ldots\, n}$$

with n even. Because n is even, we can rewrite this equation with $(2n-2)$ instead of n as

$$-\frac{g_e}{a} = \tilde{\omega}^2 + G \sum_{n=1}^{\infty} (-)^n \frac{C_{(2n-2),0}}{a^{2n+1}} \times \frac{1\cdot3\cdot5 \,\ldots\, (2n-1)}{2\cdot4\cdot6 \,\ldots\, (2n-2)},$$

which agrees with Equation 23.44 if $C_{(2n-2),0}$ is substituted from Equation 23.17.

31. Another interesting comparison arises from the fact that $-1/k_1$ for any surface of revolution is the length of the normal intercepted by the axis of rotation. Consequently, $-(1/k_1)\cos\bar{\phi}$ for the equipotential surface is the perpendicular distance between the point under consideration and the axis of rotation; this distance is $r\cos\phi$ where ϕ is the geocentric latitude. Substitution in Equation 23.48 for gk_1 and use of Equations 23.50 give

$$g\cos\bar{\phi} = -\tilde{\omega}^2 r\cos\phi$$

$$+ G \sum_{n=0}^{\infty} \frac{C_{n0}}{r^{n+2}} [\tfrac{1}{2}(n+1)(n+2)\cos\phi\, P_{n+2}(\sin\phi)$$

$$+ \tfrac{1}{2}\cos\phi\, P_{n+2}^2(\sin\phi)]$$

$$= -\tilde{\omega}^2 r\cos\phi + G \sum_{n=0}^{\infty} \frac{C_{n0}}{r^{n+2}} P_{n+1}^1(\sin\phi),$$

applying some well-known properties of the Legendre functions. If we write $(2n-2)$ for n and substitute for $C_{(2n-2),0}$ from Equation 23.17, this last result becomes Equation 23.40.

32. This method of determining the curvature parameters is rigorous and can be applied at any distance from the equipotential spheroid to any required degree of accuracy. However, for many purposes, it will be sufficient to use first-order formulas close to the spheroidal equipotential; we shall now investigate this third method, due originally to Marussi.

Curvatures in the Neighborhood of the Equipotential Spheroid

33. The curvature parameters at points in the neighborhood of the equipotential spheroid can also be found by Taylor expansions along the normals or isozenithals.[1] For example, in this symmetrical case, we have from Equations 12.075 and 12.143, with N or W as the standard geopotential,

$$\frac{\partial}{\partial W}\left(\frac{1}{k_1}\right) = \sec^2\phi\,\frac{\partial b_{11}}{\partial N} = \tan\phi\,\frac{\partial(1/g)}{\partial\phi} - \frac{1}{g}$$

$$\frac{\partial}{\partial W}\left(\frac{1}{k_2}\right) = \frac{\partial b_{22}}{\partial N} = -\frac{\partial^2(1/g)}{\partial\phi^2} - \frac{1}{g};$$

or, if the principal radii of curvature of the equipotential surface are ν, ρ, we have

$$\frac{\partial\nu}{\partial W} = -\tan\phi\,\frac{\partial(1/g)}{\partial\phi} + \frac{1}{g}$$

23.54
$$\frac{\partial\rho}{\partial W} = \frac{\partial^2(1/g)}{\partial\phi^2} + \frac{1}{g},$$

which can be evaluated on the base spheroid from Equation 23.24 or 23.34. The expansions to a first order along the isozenithals follow from the initial spheroidal values of ρ, ν.

34. We can expand along the normals by using Equation 14.32, which in this case becomes

---

[1] See also Marussi (1950), "Sulla variazione con l'altezza dei raggi di curvatura principali nella teoria di Somigliana," *Bollettino di Geodesia e Scienze Affini*, v. 9, 3–9. Marussi does not use the physical convention for the sign of the potential.

$$\frac{\partial}{\partial s} = g\frac{\partial}{\partial N} - b^{22}\frac{\partial(\ln g)}{\partial\phi}\frac{\partial}{\partial\phi}$$

23.55
$$= g\frac{\partial}{\partial W} + \frac{1}{\rho}\frac{\partial(\ln g)}{\partial\phi}\frac{\partial}{\partial\phi}.$$

35. The variation along the normal of the other nonzero parameter γ_2 can most easily be found by direct substitution in Equation 20.25; in this case, that equation becomes, for points on the equipotential spheroid,

23.56
$$\frac{\partial\gamma_2}{\partial s} = -\frac{1}{\rho}\frac{\partial}{\partial\phi}\left(\frac{1}{\rho}+\frac{1}{\nu}\right) + \frac{4\tilde{\omega}^2\gamma_2}{g} + \frac{\gamma_2}{\nu}$$

with

$$\gamma_2 = \frac{\partial(\ln g)}{\rho\partial\phi}$$

where ϕ is the latitude of the normal to the spheroid.

THE GRAVITY FIELD IN GEODETIC COORDINATES

36. If we are given the position of a point in geodetic coordinates $(\bar{\bar{\omega}}, \bar{\bar{\phi}}, h)$ and if we require the potential or its derivatives at the point, the simplest procedure is to convert the geodetic to geocentric coordinates and then to use spherical harmonic expressions for the potential or its derivatives. The geodetic and Cartesian coordinates are related by Equations 18.59, which in our present notation become

$$x = (\nu+h)\cos\bar{\bar{\phi}}\cos\bar{\bar{\omega}}$$
$$y = (\nu+h)\cos\bar{\bar{\phi}}\sin\bar{\bar{\omega}}$$
23.57
$$z = (\nu\cos^2\alpha+h)\sin\bar{\bar{\phi}}$$

where ν, α refer to the base spheroid of the geodetic system. The geodetic and geocentric longitudes are the same; if ϕ, r are the geocentric latitude and radius vector, we have

$$r\cos\phi = (\nu+h)\cos\bar{\bar{\phi}}$$
23.58
$$r\sin\phi = (\nu\cos^2\alpha+h)\sin\bar{\bar{\phi}}.$$

The same procedure applies to both a general field and the standard field; the only difference is in the formulas for the potential and its derivatives, whether for those formulas given in Chapter 21 or for those given in this chapter.

CHAPTER 24

Atmospheric Refraction

GENERAL REMARKS

1. Almost all geodetic measurements of direction and distance are necessarily made through the Earth's atmosphere, which refracts the line of observation into a complicated space curve. The universal practice is to remove the effect of refraction by applying corrections to the observations, the effect of which is to replace the curved line of observation by the straight chord joining the end points of the line. In following this procedure, we shall begin with a rigorous treatment, which may become necessary in future developments, and then introduce progressive approximations that are justified by our present inability to measure completely the refractive index and its gradient, even at the two end points.
Atmospheric refraction is particularly important in the three-dimensional methods used throughout this book, although no method of reducing the observations can overcome uncertainty in the refraction; three-dimensional methods are no better and no worse in this respect than any other. Accordingly, we shall treat the subject fully and, in addition to the rigorous theoretical treatment, we shall give some account of the empirical methods in current use.

2. The geometrical corrections depend on the curvature and torsion of the refracted ray, which in turn depend on the first and second covariant derivatives of the index of refraction. The first approximation will accordingly be to choose a geodetic model atmosphere, which, in most cases, allows us to ignore the torsion of the ray and fixes the direction of the gradient of the index, leaving us with the problem of measuring the magnitude of the gradient. The index of refraction itself can be found from measurements of temperature, pressure, and humidity, but in the present state-of-the-art some further assumptions are necessary to establish the magnitude of the gradient of the index. However, the meteorologists may before long be able to supply, in addition to such field measurements as may be possible, a sufficiently accurate model of the actual atmosphere at the time and in the locality of the observations. In that case, the method of reduction may switch to numerical integration of the rigorous equations of the ray. Moritz,[1] for example, proposes a direct solution of the eikonal Equation 24.05. In addition, programs are well advanced to measure by two-wavelength techniques the total effect of refraction over the observed line at the time of observation; the theoretical basis of these methods also will be examined in this chapter.

THE LAWS OF REFRACTION

3. The basic physical law for studying the propagation of light or other electromagnetic waves in a refracting medium is known as *Fermat's principle* which states that light, for example, will follow that path between two fixed points involving the least traveltime t. Moreover, the *refractive index* μ of the medium is related to the velocity v of light in the medium by the equation

24.01 $$\mu = c/v$$

[1] Moritz (1967), "Application of the Conformal Theory of Refraction," *Proceedings of the International Symposium Figure of the Earth and Refraction*, Vienna, Austria, March 14–17, 1967, 323–334.

in which c is the constant velocity of light *in a vacuum*. Accordingly, if ds is an element of length along the path, we have

24.02 $\mu ds = (c/v)ds = cdt$.

The *optical path length* or *eikonal* is defined as (ct) and denoted by S so that we have

24.03 $S = ct = \int \mu ds$.

This integral has to be a minimum along the actual path, compared with any other path joining two fixed terminals. The integral in Equation 24.03 is taken along the actual path.

4. We may also consider a family of light rays emitted in all directions from a point source at the same instant. After a given time t, the light will arrive at a surface known as a *geometrical wave front*; for different values of t, we shall have a family of surfaces $S = ct = $ constant. The integral

$$\int \mu ds$$

will have the same value over the actual path between the source and a given S-surface.

5. We suppose that the medium is isotropic, but not necessarily homogeneous, so that μ is a point function, having a definite value at each point of the space considered. In that case, we can transform the space conformally to a curved space with scale factor μ as in § 10–19. Because of the minimum principle in Equation 24.03, the rays become geodesics of the curved space and S becomes the length of any of these geodesics between the source and the transform of the S-surface. The geometrical wave fronts accordingly transform to geodesic parallels, and the rays are normal to the wave fronts in both the transformed and untransformed spaces because of the conformal properties of the transformation. As in § 10–20, we can say that the basic gradient equation

24.04 $S_r = \mu l_r$

holds true in the untransformed space. In this equation, l_r is the unit tangent to a light ray, or the unit normal to the wave front. Equation 24.04 is fundamental in geometrical optics, and can be reconciled with wave theory even though it has been derived geometrically. Born and Wolf, for example, derive the equation for short wavelengths both from the Maxwell equations and from the electromagnetic wave equations, and then use the equation

to prove Fermat's principle.[2] The expression of the space in Equation 24.04 by means of a single scalar S and the direction of its gradient, which we have seen in Chapter 12 can be made the basis of a general coordinate system, is equivalent to Fermat's principle and to other physical laws based on a similar minimum or variational principle, simply by giving the symbols an appropriate connotation.

6. Contraction of Equation 24.04 with $g^{rs}S_s = \mu g^{rs}l_s$ gives

24.05 $\nabla S = g^{rs}S_r S_s = \mu^2$.

This equation is generally known as the *eikonal equation*.

7. Instead of a point source, we could equally well have considered a family of rays perpendicular to any given surface, whose transform could initiate a family of geodesic parallels in the curved conformal space. In either case, the gradient Equation 24.04 holds true, and we have already developed completely the geometry of the rays and of the wave fronts in Chapters 12, 13, and 14. To use any of the results in these chapters, all we need do is to change the notation from (N, n, ν_r) to (S, μ, l_r).

8. In particular, Equation 12.020 tells us at once that the principal normal to a ray is an S-surface vector, the principal curvature of the ray is the arc rate of change of $(\ln \mu)$ in the direction of the principal normal, and there is no change of $(\ln \mu)$ in the direction of the binormal. These results agree with § 10–15. If the principal normal, binormal, and curvature of the ray are m^r, n^r, χ, we have

$$(\ln \mu)_r m^r = \chi$$

24.06 $(\ln \mu)_r n^r = 0$.

DIFFERENTIAL EQUATION OF THE REFRACTED RAY

9. We can eliminate the scalar S from Equation 24.04 by covariant differentiation along the ray. Using the fact that $S_{rs} = S_{sr}$, we have

$$(\mu l_r)_s l^s = S_{rs}l^s = S_{sr}l^s = (\mu l_s)_r l^s = \mu_r + \mu l_{sr}l^s.$$

The last term is zero by Equation 3.19 because l_s is a unit vector, so that the intrinsic derivative of (μl_r) along the ray is

24.07 $\dfrac{\delta(\mu l_r)}{\delta s} = \mu_r$

[2] Born and Wolf (1964), *Principles of Optics; Electromagnetic Theory of Propagation, Interference and Diffraction of Light*, 2d rev. ed., 110–115, 128.

in which μ_r is the gradient of the refractive index. This equation is equivalent to either Equation 24.03 or 24.04. For example, if we expand the intrinsic derivative, we have

$$(\mu_s l^s)\,l_r + \mu l_{rs} l^s = \mu_r.$$

This equation contains the same information as Equations 24.06, obtained by transforming the basic gradient Equation 24.04 which we have seen is equivalent to Fermat's principle.

THE SPHERICALLY SYMMETRICAL MEDIUM

10. An important particular solution of Equation 24.07 is obtained by considering the variation along the ray of the vector product

$$\epsilon^{rst}(\mu l_s)\rho_t$$

in which ρ_t is the position vector. We have

$$\frac{\delta(\epsilon^{rst}\mu l_s \rho_t)}{\delta s} = \epsilon^{rst}\frac{\delta(\mu l_s)}{\delta s}\rho_t + \epsilon^{rst}\mu l_s \rho_{tk} l^k$$

24.08 $$= \epsilon^{rst}\mu_s \rho_t + \epsilon^{rst}\mu l_s l_t,$$

if we remember that ρ_{tk} is the metric tensor g_{tk}. The last term is the vector product of two parallel vectors and is therefore zero. For the same reason, the preceding term also is zero if μ_s is parallel to the position vector, that is, if μ is a function of the radius vector r only. But the left side of the equation is a tensor, all of whose components are now shown to be zero. We can say therefore that if μ is a function of r only, we have

24.09 $$\frac{\delta(\epsilon^{rst}\mu l_s \rho_t)}{\delta s} = 0$$

in Cartesian coordinates. The Christoffel symbols are zero, and the equation can be immediately integrated along the ray to show that

24.10 $$\mu\epsilon^{rst}l_s \rho_t = (\mu r \sin \beta)q^r$$

is constant along the ray where β is the angle between the ray and the radius vector whose length is r. The vector q^r is a unit vector perpendicular to both l_r and ρ_r so that q^r is perpendicular to the plane — containing l_r and ρ_r — which passes through the origin. Because q^r is a constant vector, this plane must remain fixed, and the ray must be a plane curve lying wholly within the plane containing the source, the origin, and the initial direction of the ray. The origin must be the center of symmetry for μ, which could not otherwise be a

function of r only; the refractive index μ can, however, be any continuous function of r. The constant μ-surfaces are spheres centered on the origin. It is clear also from Equation 24.10 that along any ray in this medium we have

24.11 $$\mu r \sin \beta = \text{constant}.$$

GEOMETRY OF FLAT CURVES

11. A refracted ray in the actual atmosphere will approximate to a straight line, and is best treated as a Taylor expansion from one end. Quantities at the other end of the line will be denoted by over-bars. If F is any continuous, differentiable scalar and if s is the arc length of the ray from the unbarred end, then the Taylor expansion is

$$\bar{F} = F + \left(\frac{\partial F}{\partial s}\right)s + \tfrac{1}{2}\left(\frac{\partial^2 F}{\partial s^2}\right)s^2 + \tfrac{1}{6}\left(\frac{\partial^3 F}{\partial s^3}\right)s^3 + \; \ldots\ldots$$

24.12

If the unit tangent, normal, and binormal of the ray are l^r, m^r, n^r, if the curvature and torsion of the ray are χ, τ, and if we use the Frenet Equations 4.06, we have

$$\partial F/\partial s = F_r l^r$$
$$\partial^2 F/\partial s^2 = (F_r l^r)_s l^s = F_{rs}l^r l^s + \chi F_r m^r$$
$$\partial^3 F/\partial s^3 = F_{rst}l^r l^s l^t + 3\chi F_{rs}m^r l^s$$
24.13 $$+ (\partial\chi/\partial s)F_r m^r + \chi F_r(\tau n^r - \chi l^r).$$

These successive differentials are evaluated at the unbarred end of the line.

12. Next, we suppose that F is any one of the Cartesian coordinates (x, y, z). All components of the tensors F_{rs}, F_{rst}, etc., are then zero in Cartesian coordinates, and are therefore zero in any coordinate system. The invariant $F_r m^r$ becomes, for example $x_r m^r = A_r m^r$, which is the x-component of the vector m^r. If ρ^r is the position vector, Equations 24.12 and 24.13 in Cartesian coordinates become

$$\bar{\rho}^r = \rho^r + sl^r + \tfrac{1}{2}s^2\chi m^r$$
24.14 $$+ \tfrac{1}{6}s^3\{-\chi^2 l^r + (\partial\chi/\partial s)m^r + \chi\tau n^r\} + \; \ldots,$$

which as a vector equation is true at the unbarred point in any coordinates if we consider a parallel to $\bar{\rho}^r$ through the unbarred point. Also, the equation is true for any curve which is sufficiently flat (χ, τ small) for the Taylor series to be convergent. It should be noted that χ, τ, $(\partial\chi/\partial s)$ and all the vectors except $\bar{\rho}^r$ have their values at the unbarred point.

13. The difference of the two position vectors $\bar{\rho}^r$ and ρ^r is the chord vector whose magnitude and unit vector will be denoted by (s), k^r so that we have

$$
\begin{aligned}
(\bar{\rho}^r - \rho^r)/s &= \{(s)/s\}k^r \\
&= l^r(1 - \tfrac{1}{6}\chi^2 s^2) \\
&\quad + m^r\{\tfrac{1}{2}\chi s + \tfrac{1}{6}(\partial\chi/\partial s)s^2\} \\
\textbf{24.15} \qquad &\quad + n^r(\tfrac{1}{6}\chi\tau s^2),
\end{aligned}
$$

correct to a second order in the small quantities χ, τ. Taking the modulus of this last vector equation to the same degree of accuracy, we have

$$
\{(s)/s\}^2 = 1 - \tfrac{1}{3}\chi^2 s^2 + \tfrac{1}{4}\chi^2 s^2 = 1 - \tfrac{1}{12}\chi^2 s^2
$$

$$
\textbf{24.16} \qquad (s)/s = 1 - \tfrac{1}{24}\chi^2 s^2
$$

so that the correction to the arc length s to obtain the chord length (s) is

$$
\textbf{24.17} \qquad\qquad -\tfrac{1}{24}\chi^2 s^3.
$$

14. The angle δ between the chord and the principal normal is given by

$$
\frac{(s)}{s}\cos\delta = \tfrac{1}{2}s\{\chi + \tfrac{1}{3}\frac{\partial\chi}{\partial s}s\}
$$

$$
\textbf{24.18} \qquad\qquad = \tfrac{1}{2}s\chi_3,
$$

omitting second derivatives of the curvature, if χ_3 is the curvature at a point one-third the way along the ray. Equation 24.17 shows that the factor $(s)/s$ can be dropped without affecting the result to a second order. The simple "one-third" rule in this subject seems to have been introduced first by de Graaff-Hunter. Equation 24.14 shows clearly that it holds true, for both plane and twisted curves, as far as the third-order terms in s^3 in the Taylor expansion along the line; this is the highest degree of accuracy we can attain without introducing second derivatives of the curvature. The validity of the Taylor expansion depends on the existence of successive derivatives of χ. For example, Equation 24.18 would not give the correct answer at a point well outside the effective atmosphere ($\chi=0$; $\partial\chi/\partial s=0$) over a line extending to the surface of the Earth.

15. Dufour[3] obtains a different formula for the angle $(\tfrac{1}{2}\pi - \delta)$ between the chord and the tangent at the starting point of a plane curve. In our present notation, his formula is

[3] Dufour (1952), "Etude Générale de la Correction Angulaire Finie (Reduction à la Corde) Pour une Courbe Quelconque Tracée sur le Plan ou sur la Sphère," *Bulletin Géodésique*, new series, no. 25, 359–374.

$$
\textbf{24.19} \qquad \tfrac{1}{2}\pi - \delta = \frac{1}{(s)}\int \{(s) - s\}\chi\,ds.
$$

The integral is taken over the whole curve from the unbarred to the overbarred end, and the chord length (s) is considered a constant during the integration. It will be shown in § 25–16 that, if F is any scalar, the expansion

$$
\textbf{24.20} \qquad (\bar{F} - F) = \tfrac{1}{2}s(F' + \bar{F}') + \tfrac{1}{12}s^2(F'' - \bar{F}'')
$$

is correct to a fourth order where the superscripts refer to successive derivatives of F with respect to the arc length s. If we take F as the *indefinite integral*

$$
\frac{1}{(s)}\int \{(s) - s\}\chi\,ds
$$

and substitute in Equation 24.20, Dufour's formula becomes

$$
\tfrac{1}{2}\pi - \delta = \tfrac{1}{2}s\chi + \tfrac{1}{12}s^2\left\{\frac{\partial\chi}{\partial s} + \frac{\bar{\chi}}{(s)} - \frac{\chi}{(s)}\right\}.
$$

To compare this with Equation 24.18, we shall have to introduce the approximations

$$
\bar{\chi} = \chi + \frac{\partial\chi}{\partial s}(s)
$$

$$
\cos\delta = \tfrac{1}{2}\pi - \delta
$$

when Dufour's formula becomes the same as Equation 24.18 with the factor $(s)/s$ dropped. The approximations involve only terms of the third order in s^3. Accordingly, we may say that to a second order the two formulas are equivalent, and either may be used as more convenient. There is no reason to suppose that Dufour's formula is any more accurate than the simple "one-third" rule, which holds true for twisted as well as plane curves.

16. The angle ϵ between the chord and the binormal is given by

$$
\textbf{24.21} \qquad \{(s)/s\}\cos\epsilon = \tfrac{1}{6}\chi\tau s^2
$$

in which the factor $\{(s)/s\}$ can be ignored. But $s\chi$ and $s\tau$ are of the same order as the radian measure of the angles swept out in the whole course of the ray by the normal and the binormal, respectively; in the case of a flat curve, $s\chi$ and $s\tau$ are small quantities so that δ and ϵ must be nearly 90°. Compared with $\cos\delta$, which is a first-order quantity, $\cos\epsilon$ is a second-order quantity and can often be ignored.

ARC-TO-CHORD CORRECTIONS

17. The basic physical law of refraction as expressed by Equations 24.06 does not directly introduce the torsion, which must, nevertheless, be expressible in terms of derivatives of $(\ln \mu)$ and in the direction of the ray if the law is to be sufficient to settle the course of the ray. To investigate this matter further, we set up a (ω, ϕ, N) coordinate system in which we have $N = \ln \mu$, as we can do if the field is to be defined uniquely at all points by $(\ln \mu)$ and its derivatives. In this system, the binormal n^r to any ray must be an N-surface vector to satisfy Equations 24.06, and is therefore perpendicular to both the ray l^r and to the N-surface normal ν^r. Any other vector perpendicular to the binormal, such as the principal normal m^r, must accordingly lie in the plane of l^r and ν^r. If α, β are the azimuth and zenith distance of the ray in this coordinate system, the azimuth and zenith distance of the principal normal will be $\alpha, \beta + \frac{1}{2}\pi$; we can write then

$$l^r = \lambda^r \sin \alpha \sin \beta + \mu^r \cos \alpha \sin \beta$$
$$+ \nu^r \cos \beta$$
$$m^r = \lambda^r \sin \alpha \cos \beta + \mu^r \cos \alpha \cos \beta$$
$$- \nu^r \sin \beta$$

24.22 $\qquad n^r = -\lambda^r \cos \alpha + \mu^r \sin \alpha$

in which the base vectors λ^r, μ^r, ν^r have their usual significance in a (ω, ϕ, N) coordinate system.

18. To determine the torsion of the ray, we contract the third of the Frenet equations in Equations 4.06 with ν^r to obtain

$$\tau = n_{rs}\nu^r l^s \csc \beta$$
$$= -\nu_{rs}n^r l^s \csc \beta, \qquad \text{using Equation 3.20}$$
$$= (k_2 - k_1) \sin \alpha \cos \alpha - t_1(\cos^2 \alpha - \sin^2 \alpha)$$
$$+ (\gamma_1 \cos \alpha - \gamma_2 \sin \alpha) \cot \beta$$

24.23

in which the parameters have their usual significance in a (ω, ϕ, N) system, and we have substituted Equations 24.22, 12.016, 12.046, etc. We may note from Equation 12.050 that the first two terms in Equation 24.23 are the geodesic torsion of the $\mu = $ constant surface in the azimuth of the ray. In the third term, $(-\gamma_1 \cos \alpha + \gamma_2 \sin \alpha)$ is the component—in the direction of the binormal—of the vector curvature of the normal to the $\mu = $ constant surface. We can therefore rewrite Equation 24.23

in the alternative form

24.24 $\qquad \tau = t - \nu_{rs}n^r\nu^s \cot \beta.$

The basic gradient equation of the coordinate system is

24.25 $\qquad (\ln \mu)_r = -q\nu_r$

in which q, corresponding to n in a general (ω, ϕ, N) system, is the magnitude of the gradient vector $(\ln \mu)_r$. We can therefore express the curvature of the ray in the form

24.26 $\qquad \chi = (\ln \mu)_r m^r = q \sin \beta \cdot$

If we specify the initial direction of the ray, the $(\ln \mu)$ field settles the initial curvature and torsion of the ray and will enable us to trace the course of the ray throughout.

19. If we differentiate $(\ln \mu)_r n^r = 0$ covariantly along the ray and use the third of the Frenet equations in Equations 4.06, we have

24.27 $\qquad \chi\tau = (\ln \mu)_{rs}n^r l^s$

as an alternative expression for the torsion.

20. If $(\alpha), (\beta)$ are the azimuth and zenith distance of the *chord* in the $(\omega, \phi, \ln \mu)$ system, we can combine Equations 24.15 and 24.22 to give

$$\{(s)/s\} \sin (\alpha) \sin (\beta) = A \sin \alpha \sin \beta$$
$$+ B \sin \alpha \cos \beta - C \cos \alpha$$
$$\{(s)/s\} \cos (\alpha) \sin (\beta) = A \cos \alpha \sin \beta$$
$$+ B \cos \alpha \cos \beta + C \sin \alpha$$

24.28 $\qquad \{(s)/s\} \cos (\beta) = A \cos \beta - B \sin \beta$

in which

$$A = 1 - \tfrac{1}{6}\chi^2 s^2$$
$$B = \tfrac{1}{2}s\left\{\chi + \tfrac{1}{3}\left(\frac{\partial \chi}{\partial s}\right)s\right\} = \tfrac{1}{2}s\chi_3$$
$$C = \tfrac{1}{6}\chi\tau s^2$$

24.29 $\quad (s)/s = 1 - \tfrac{1}{24}\chi^2 s^2$

where χ_3 is the curvature at a point one-third the way along the ray. An alternative expression obtained from the first two equations of Equations 24.28 is

24.30 $\qquad \tan \{(\alpha) - \alpha\} = -\dfrac{C}{A \sin \beta + B \cos \beta},$

which gives us a direct arc-to-chord correction for azimuth. If we can neglect C, there is no azimuth correction, and the arc-to-chord correction for zenith distance would be given by

24.31 $\{(s)/s\} \sin \{(\beta) - \beta\} = B.$

Otherwise, we can compute the zenith distance correction from the third equation of Equations 24.28.

THE GEODETIC MODEL ATMOSPHERE

21. Investigation of the form of the refracted ray could be carried without any difficulty to terms of higher order on the same lines, but we should then be involved with higher differentials of the curvature and torsion which we have no hope of measuring. Moreover, the $(\ln \mu)$ pattern may change rapidly with time. For these reasons, we require an atmospheric model, which makes as few assumptions as possible and leaves room for such measurements as we can make, such as measurements of temperature, pressure, and humidity at the two ends of the line.

22. One possible assumption is that the model atmosphere is in static equilibrium, which might be approximately so in settled weather conditions during the afternoon. This would mean that the *isopycnics*—or surfaces of equal density—which are nearly the same as the surfaces of equal refractive index, are gravitational equipotentials: the gradient of $(\ln \mu)$ is accordingly in the direction of the astronomical nadir. In that case, ν_r in Equation 24.25 is the unit normal to the equipotential surfaces: the torsion of the ray can be calculated from Equation 24.24, which now contains nothing but gravitational parameters and the astronomical azimuth and zenith distance of the ray. Equations 24.28 and 24.29 give arc-to-chord corrections as corrections to the observed astronomical azimuth and zenith distance of the ray, provided that we also assume or can measure q, the magnitude of the gradient of $(\ln \mu)$, for substitution in Equation 24.26.

23. However, the present state of measurement of the gravitational parameters and of q hardly justifies the use of an exact gravitational model, which itself rests on the unreal assumption of static equilibrium. We shall accordingly use a simpler model in which the isopycnics are h-surfaces in the geodetic (ω, ϕ, h) coordinate system, so that the gradient of $(\ln \mu)$ is everywhere in the direction of the geodetic nadir. The normals to the

h-surfaces in this system are straight so that the zenith directions are unrefracted. We do not as yet make any assumptions about the magnitude q of the gradient of $(\ln \mu)$. The only assumption we have made so far relates to the direction of the gradient of $(\ln \mu)$, which will not usually differ from an exact gravitational model by more than a few minutes of arc.

ARC-TO-CHORD CORRECTIONS— GEODETIC MODEL

24. If the refractive index is to be considered constant over the geodetic h-surfaces, then it follows from Equation 24.24 that the torsion τ of the refracted ray is simply the geodesic torsion of the h-surface through the point under consideration in the geodetic azimuth α of the ray. From Equation 18.19, we have

24.32 $\tau = \dfrac{(\rho - \nu) \sin \alpha \cos \alpha}{(\rho + h)(\nu + h)}$

in which we have written ρ, ν for the principal curvatures of the base spheroid in the meridian and parallel directions, respectively. We shall know, or can infer, the curvature χ of the ray from measurements to be described later, and we shall also know, at least roughly, the length s of the ray. We can therefore compute the quantities A, B, C, $(s)/s$ from Equations 24.29. Next, we compute the arc-to-chord azimuth correction from Equation 24.30, using the zenith distance β of the ray at the end where we are correcting the azimuth. If the azimuth correction is significant, we determine the zenith distance of the chord from the third equation of Equations 24.28. If the azimuth correction is not significant, and it will seldom be significant, we obtain the arc-to-chord zenith distance correction from Equation 24.31. Finally, the geometrical arc-to-chord distance correction is obtained from Equation 24.17 as

$$-\tfrac{1}{24} \chi^2 s^3.$$

To the degree of accuracy we are working, this last correction should be the same if computed from simultaneous observations for the curvature at either end of the line; if not, the two corrections can be meaned. This is not to say, however, that the curvature χ is assumed the same at both ends.

25. The system can be simplified if we make some further assumptions. For example, we can assume that τ can be neglected compared with χ; this assumption can easily be justified for a whole

series of observations by rough computation of τ from Equation 24.32 compared with an average value of χ. The ray is then a plane curve; there is no azimuth correction. Equation 24.21 shows that the chord is perpendicular to the binormal. The arc-to-chord correction for zenith distance $\Delta\beta$, known as the *angle of refraction*, is obtained from Equation 24.31, dropping the factor $(s)/s$, as

24.33 $$\Delta\beta = \tfrac{1}{2}s\chi_3$$

where χ_3 is the curvature at a point one-third the way along the ray.

26. If we make the further assumption that χ is the same at all points of the ray, then the angle of refraction is the same at both ends of the ray and is given by

24.34 $$\Delta\beta = \tfrac{1}{2}s\chi,$$

as we should expect, because the ray is now a circular arc and $s\chi$ is the angle in radian measure, subtended at the center of the circle by the ray. The ratio of χ, assumed constant over the ray, to a mean curvature of the Earth, expressed as the reciprocal of a constant radius R, is defined as the *coefficient of refraction* [4] f so that we have

24.35 $$f = \chi R.$$

However, this notion is merely a matter of nomenclature and does not introduce any new approximation. If χ is constant over the ray, so is f. Indeed, it is frequently assumed that f is a constant for all rays at a given time, and even for all rays at all times within the afternoon period of minimum refraction. For optical wavelengths, f varies at different times and places between about 0.10 and 0.15; for microwaves, f is more likely to be 0.25, depending much more on the humidity.

27. If we merely assume that χ (or f) is constant along a particular line and that simultaneous measurements are made of zenith distances β, $\bar\beta$, then Equation 25.39 shows that, to a fourth order, the error in height difference arising from refraction is

$$\tfrac{1}{12}s^2\chi(\sin\bar\beta - \sin\beta) \doteqdot \tfrac{1}{12}s^3\chi\cos\beta(k\sin\beta + \chi)$$

24.36

where k is the normal curvature of the h-surface in the azimuth of the line, and we have anticipated

---

[4] In the literature of surveying, the coefficient of refraction is usually denoted by k, which in this book is mainly used for the normal curvature of a surface. Sometimes the coefficient is defined as $\tfrac{1}{2}\alpha R$.

from Equations 24.40 that

24.37 $$d\beta/ds = (k\sin\beta + \chi).$$

For most rays between terrestrial stations, β is nearly 90° and the effect of refraction in Equation 24.36 can be entirely neglected. In fact, the assumption of uniform curvature, combined with simultaneous reciprocal measurement of zenith distances at the two ends of the line, provides surprisingly accurate results, especially during the afternoon period of minimum refraction. We can, moreover, use the reciprocal observations of β and $\bar\beta$ to determine χ (or f). We have

$$\bar\beta - \beta \doteqdot s(d\beta/ds) = s(k\sin\beta + \chi).$$

If we assume that β is nearly 90° and write $k = -1/R$ where R is a mean radius of the Earth, we have

$$\bar\beta - \beta = (s/R)(f-1)$$

24.38 $$f = 1 + (R/s)(\bar\beta - \beta)$$

in which $\bar\beta$, β are, of course, in radian measure. The sum of the measured vertical angles at the two ends of the line (elevations positive) equals $(\bar\beta - \beta)$.

28. For the methods of adjustment to be described in later chapters, only arc-to-chord corrections (as described in this chapter) should be applied, together with the velocity correction in electronic distance measurement (considered in the following section). We do not require any other corrections, such as "reductions to sea level" or to any supposed equivalent curve on the base spheroid.

VELOCITY CORRECTION

29. All electronic distance measurement systems in current use measure the time taken by either light waves or microwaves to travel in air over the distance to be measured and back. If t is one-half this measured time, then we have from Equation 24.03

$$ct = \int_P^{\bar P} \mu\,ds$$

in which c is the constant velocity of propagation in a vacuum and the integral is taken over the actual path from the emitting point P to the distant point $\bar P$.

30. If we return to Equation 24.20 and substitute for F the indefinite integral

$$\int \mu\,ds,$$

then $(\bar{F}-F)$ is the definite integral

$$\int_P^{\bar{P}} \mu\, ds.$$

Also, we have $\bar{F}'=\bar{\mu}$, $F'=\mu$ and

$$F''=\frac{\partial\mu}{\partial s}=\mu(\ln\mu)_r l^{\,r}=\mu(\ln\mu)_r\nu^r\cos\beta$$

$$=-\mu(\ln\mu)_r m^r\cot\beta=-\mu\chi\cot\beta$$

in which we have used Equations 24.22 and 24.06 and the fact that there is no change in the refractive index in the λ^r- and μ^r-directions, which lie in the constant h-surface and therefore in the constant μ-surface of the geodetic model. In the last equation, β is the geodetic zenith distance of the refracted ray and χ is the curvature of the ray. We have finally

24.39 $ct=\tfrac{1}{2}s(\bar{\mu}+\mu)+\tfrac{1}{12}s^2(\bar{\mu}\bar{\chi}\cot\bar{\beta}-\mu\chi\cot\beta).$

This equation is very easily solved for s from a preliminary value, obtained by dividing ct by the mean index. The preliminary value is then used to evaluate the second-order term, which under various disguises is usually known as the "second velocity correction" or as the "velocity component of the curvature correction."

31. For example, we have

$$\cos\beta=\nu_r l^r$$

$$-\sin\beta(d\beta/ds)=\nu_{rs}l^r l^s+\nu_r l_s^r l^s$$

24.40 $=-k\sin^2\beta-\chi\sin\beta$

in which k is the normal curvature of the h-surface, so that to a first order, we have

$$(\cot\bar{\beta}-\cot\beta)=-s\,\mathrm{cosec}^2\,\beta\,(d\beta/ds)$$

$$=-s\,(k\cos\mathrm{ec}\,\beta+\chi\,\mathrm{cosec}^2\,\beta).$$

If, in evaluating this small correction, we consider that we have $\mu=\bar{\mu}=1$ and that χ is constant along the line, then the velocity correction, considered as an additive correction to the preliminary value of s, is

$$\tfrac{1}{12}s^3\chi\,(k\cos\mathrm{ec}\,\beta+\chi\,\mathrm{cosec}^2\,\beta).$$

If there is no considerable difference in height over the line, $\mathrm{cosec}\,\beta$ is nearly unity; if we confuse $-1/k$ with a mean radius R of the Earth and write $f=\chi R$ for the coefficient of refraction, the correction becomes finally

24.41 $-\tfrac{1}{12}\dfrac{s^3}{R^2}f(1-f),$

which is the form given by Saastamoinen[5] or Höpcke.[6] The correction can further be combined with the geometrical curvature correction (Equation 24.17) as

24.41A $-\tfrac{1}{12}\dfrac{s^3}{R^2}f(2-f).$

Saastamoinen[7] combines this result with a further chord correction to sea level, which we do not require.

32. In microwave measurements, it is usual to assume $f=0.25$. For precise Geodimeter measurements, Saastamoinen recommends evaluating the coefficient of refraction by Equations 24.38 from reciprocal zenith distances or from vertical angles measured at the same time as the Geodimeter observations. But if any such special measurements are to be made, the reciprocal zenith distances β, $180°-\bar{\beta}$ can enter the precise Equation 24.39 without any of the mass assumptions made in deriving Equations 24.40 or 24.41. For substitution in the precise formula, μ and $\bar{\mu}$ will be known from temperature and pressure measurements at the two ends. The end curvatures are obtained by differentiation, as we shall see, and will depend on lapse rates of temperature and humidity.

THE EQUATION OF STATE

33. We have next to consider how the refractive index and its gradient may be measured or otherwise determined in order that the curvature of the ray may be deduced and substituted in formulas for the arc-to-chord and velocity corrections. This is always necessary in the case of electronic distance measurements, and may be necessary in the case of zenith distance measurements when there is a considerable difference in height over the line and the assumption of constant curvature no longer holds. For this purpose, we shall require certain physical laws affecting the behavior of gases; these laws are collected here for easy reference.

34. At low pressures p and high temperatures T on the Kelvin (°K.) or absolute scale, p and T are related to the density ρ of a gas by the perfect,

[5] Saastamoinen (1964), "Curvature Correction in Electronic Distance Measurements," *Bulletin Géodésique*, new series, no. 73, 265–269.

[6] Höpcke (1964), Über die Bahnkrümmung Elektromagnetischer Wellen und Ihren Einfluss auf die Streckenmessungen," *Zeitschrift für Vermessungswesen*, no. 89, 183–200.

[7] Saastamoinen, *loc. cit. supra* note 5.

or ideal, gas law as

24.42 $$p = c\rho T$$

in which c is a constant for a particular gas.

35. Another required physical law, which is very nearly in agreement with the latest ideas on the subject if μ is nearly unity, is that the *refractivity*, defined as $(\mu - 1)$, is proportional to the density ρ of the medium for a particular wavelength of radiation so that we have

24.43 $$(\mu - 1)/\rho = \text{constant},$$

although the value of the "constant" will depend to some extent on the wavelength, as we shall see later.

36. Because of the difficulty of measuring densities in the field, we need to replace ρ by other quantities, such as the pressure and temperature, which can more easily be measured. If there is to be no vertical movement of the atmosphere, and this, of course, is an assumption, then the change in pressure (dp) between the top and bottom of a column of air of unit cross-sectional area must equal the weight of air in the column so that we have

24.44 $$dp = -\rho g dh$$

in which dh is the height of the column and g is gravity.

Equations for Moist Air

37. We shall see later that dry air behaves very nearly as a perfect gas, whose equation of state is Equation 24.42, in which the gas constant is

24.45 $$c = 2.8704 \times 10^6 \text{c.g.s. units.}[8]$$

If we suppose that moist air also behaves as a perfect gas and that both dry and moist air obey Dalton's law of partial pressures, then the equation of state for moist air [9] is

24.46 $$p = \left(\frac{1 + r/\epsilon}{1 + r}\right) c\rho T$$

in which p, T, ρ are the pressure, absolute temperature, and density of the moist air, and where
c is the gas constant for dry air,
$\epsilon = 0.62197$ is the ratio [10] of the molecular weight of water vapor to that of dry air, and

r is the mixing ratio (grams of water vapor per gram of dry air).

38. In terms of the vapor pressure [11] e, we have

$$\frac{e}{p} = \frac{r}{r + \epsilon};$$

Equation 24.46, after we eliminate r, becomes

24.47 $$p = \frac{c\rho T}{1 - (1 - \epsilon)(e/p)} = \frac{c\rho T}{1 - 0.37803(e/p)}.$$

39. If it is necessary to consider departures of moist air, and of the dry air in a mixture, from a perfect gas, the *Smithsonian Meteorological Tables* [12] provide the necessary modifications to the formulas and tables, but this refinement is not necessary in current geodetic practice.

Integration of Equation of State

40. Combining Equations 24.44 and 24.47, we have

24.48 $$\frac{dp}{p} = -\frac{\{1 - 0.37803(e/p)\}gdh}{cT},$$

which gives, on approximate integration between limits denoted by subscripts 1 to 2,

$$\ln\left(\frac{p_1}{p_2}\right) = \frac{g_m}{cT_m}\{1 - 0.37803(e/p)_m\}(h_2 - h_1)$$

24.49

where the subscript m refers to a mean value over the interval. For routine use, the natural logarithm is converted to base 10 by means of the relation

$$\log_{10}\left(\frac{p_1}{p_2}\right) = 0.43429 \ln\left(\frac{p_1}{p_2}\right).$$

41. Equation 24.49 is usually known as the hypsometric formula, which is normally used to obtain a difference in height from simultaneous measurements of p, e, and T at the two ends of a line and by substitution of a mean of the two end values for $(e/p)_m$ and T_m. Mean gravity g_m is obtained sufficiently and accurately by application of the free-air height correction to the international gravity formula at an initially estimated halfway point. Saastamoinen [13] proposes the use of the

[8] Smithsonian Institution (1951), *Smithsonian Meteorological Tables*, 6th rev. ed., 280.
[9] *Ibid.*, 295.
[10] *Ibid.*, 332.
[11] *Ibid.*, 347.
[12] *Ibid.*, 295–317.
[13] Saastamoinen (1965), "On the Determination of the Refractive Index of Electromagnetic Waves in Mountainous Terrain," *Survey Review*, no. 135, 11–13.

hypsometric formula to obtain, from a large known difference of height in mountainous country, a value of T_m, which he claims is better than the mean of measured temperatures at the two ends. This value of T_m is used to obtain a mean value of the index of refraction over the line from Equations 24.54 and 24.57 for use in the reduction of precise Geodimeter measurements. In the case of optical wavelengths, uncertainty in e and $(e/p)_m$ is of little importance.

42. An alternative integral of Equation 24.48 in terms of the temperature *lapse rate*

$$l = - dT/dh$$

is frequently useful in the form

$$\ln \left(\frac{p_2}{p_1}\right) = \{1 - 0.37803 (e/p)_m\} \frac{g_m}{cl_m} \ln \left(\frac{T_2}{T_1}\right).$$

24.50

A knowledge of the actual mean lapse rate is of particular importance in the case of lines covering a considerable difference in altitude, and thus a considerable range of temperature and pressure.[14] This formula should give a better answer than

$$(T_2 - T_1)/h,$$

even when the difference in height h is accurately known.

INDEX OF REFRACTION – OPTICAL WAVELENGTHS

43. The refractivity for a gas, defined as $(\mu - 1)$, depends not only on the density and composition of the gas, but also on the wavelength of the light. The dependence on the wavelength λ is expressed by an experimentally determined *dispersion formula*, which is naturally subject to continual minor improvements, such as those recently summarized by Edlén.[15] The formula adopted by the International Association of Geodesy in 1960 is in the Cauchy form of

$$(\mu_s - 1) \times 10^7 = 2876.04 + 16.288\lambda^{-2} + 0.136\lambda^{-4}$$

24.51

in which λ is the wavelength in microns (10^{-6} meters) of monochromatic light in a vacuum. The constants in the formula are due to Barrell and

Sears.[16] The formula applies to "standard air" at a temperature of 0 °C., with a pressure of 760 mm., Hg., and with a carbon dioxide content of 0.03 percent. More recent determinations, which are usually expressed in terms of the *wave number* (defined as the reciprocal of the wavelength in microns) and in a different form, suggest that the Barrell and Sears result is correct to better than one part in 10^7.

44. The Barrell and Sears formula gives the refractivity in terms of the wavelength of monochromatic light. However, the measurement of distances in such instruments as the Geodimeter implies the use of a *group* of waves of slightly different wavelengths, which have slightly different velocities of propagation in a refracting medium. In such cases, it is appropriate to use a group velocity, compounded from the individual waves, or, what is equivalent, a group index of refraction given by the formula [17]

24.52 $$\mu_G = \mu_s - \left(\frac{d\mu_s}{d\lambda}\right) \lambda$$

so that we have

$$(\mu_G - 1) \times 10^7 = 2876.04 + (3 \times 16.288)\lambda^{-2}$$
24.53 $$+ (5 \times 0.136)\lambda^{-4}$$

from Equation 24.51. This formula should be used in preference to Equation 24.51, even for lasers in a refracting medium. If a true monochromatic source ever becomes available, the formula should still be used if the light is modulated.

45. Measurements are not, of course, made in a "standard atmosphere," and we have to allow for the effect of different temperatures and pressures and for a different composition of the air, particularly the inclusion of water vapor. The formula [18]

---

[14] See, for example, Rainsford (1955), "Trigonometric Heights and Refraction," *Empire Survey Review*, no. 98, 164–177.

[15] Edlén (1966), "The Refractive Index of Air," *Metrologia*, v. 2, 71–80.

[16] Barrell and Sears (1939), "The Refraction and Dispersion of Air for the Visible Spectrum," *Philosophical Transactions of the Royal Society of London*, Series A, v. 238, 1–64. The constants in the international formula, Equation 24.51, have been derived by substituting $t = 0°C$. and $p = 760$ mm., in Barrell and Sears' Equation (7.7), 52.

[17] See Born and Wolf, *op. cit. supra* note 2, 19–21.

[18] International Association of Geodesy (1963), *Report of I.A.G. Special Study Group No. 19 on Electronic Distance Measurement 1960–1963*, 2–3. This is the second report of the SSG19; the first report, delivered at the 1960 XIIth General Assembly in Helsinki, Finland, has been incorporated in the proceedings of that Assembly (Secretariat of the International Association of Geodesy (1962), *Travaux de l'Association Internationale de Geodesie*, Tome 21, 62–64). The finally adopted formulas are given in Resolution 9 of the 1963 XIIIth General Assembly in Berkeley, Calif. (see Secretary General of the International Union of Geodesy and Geophysics (1965), *Comptes Rendus de la XIIIe Assemblée Générales de l'U.G.G.I.*, 159–160).

adopted by the International Association of Geodesy in 1960 is a slightly simplified version of a formula due to Barrell and Sears [19] and is

$$24.54 \qquad (\mu - 1) = \frac{(\mu_G - 1)}{(1 + \alpha t)} \left(\frac{p}{760}\right) - \frac{55 \times 10^{-9} e}{(1 + \alpha t)}$$

where

μ = actual refractive index,

μ_G = group refractive index calculated from Equation 24.53,

t = temperature of the air in °C.,

p = total atmospheric pressure in mm., Hg.,

e = partial pressure of water vapor content in mm., Hg.,

α = temperature coefficient of refractivity of air (or the coefficient of thermal expansion), (0.003661).

46. The full 1938 Barrell and Sears formula in the notation and units of the International Association of Geodesy formula, Equations 24.51 and 24.54, is

$$(\mu - 1)10^6 = [\, 0.378125 + 0.0021414\lambda^{-2}$$
$$+ 0.00001793\lambda^{-4}\,]$$
$$\times \frac{p\{1 + (1.049 - 0.0157t)p \times 10^{-6}\}}{(1 + \alpha t)}$$

$$24.55 \qquad - [0.0624 - 0.000680\lambda^{-2}] \times \frac{e}{(1 + \alpha t)}.$$

Barrell and Sears themselves suggest simplification of the vapor pressure (last) term to the form given in the international formula, except that their recommended value of the constant is 55.6 instead of 55. The constants in the dispersion formula—the content of the first brackets—become the same as in the international formula for $p = 760$mm., $t = 0$, and $e = 0$. After making this adjustment, the international formula drops the term $(1.049 - 0.0157t)p \times 10^{-6}$, which indicates a slight departure of dry air from the ideal gas law Equation 24.42. Dry air in the international formula, as thus modified, obeys the ideal gas law, provided Equation 24.43 takes the form

$$24.56 \qquad \frac{(\mu - 1)}{\rho} = \frac{c(\mu_G - 1)}{760\alpha},$$

which, together with Equation 24.53, exhibits the dependence on the wavelength of the "constant" in Equation 24.43. In deriving this result, we have used the fact that

$$24.57 \qquad (1 + \alpha t) = \alpha T$$

where T is in °K. According to the latest determination, °K. equal °C. plus 273.16, which exactly fit this last formula if $\alpha = 0.003661$. Equation 24.57 can be said to define the Kelvin scale.

INDEX OF REFRACTION— MICROWAVES

47. Although a number of slightly simpler formulas have been extensively used for the refraction of radio waves employed in such instruments as the Tellurometer, the formula adopted by the International Association of Geodesy in 1960 is due to Essen and Froome[20] and is

$$(\mu - 1) \times 10^6 = \frac{103.49}{T}(p - e) + \frac{86.26}{T}\left(1 + \frac{5748}{T}\right)e$$

24.58

where

T = temperature in °K. (°C. plus 273.16),

p = atmospheric pressure in mm., Hg.,

e = partial pressure of water vapor in mm., Hg.

48. In place of the first term on the right, the original Essen and Froome formula contains the two terms

$$\frac{103.49}{T}p_1 + \frac{177.4}{T}p_2$$

in which p_1, p_2 are, respectively, the partial pressures of dry air and carbon dioxide, so that the international formula assumes no carbon dioxide content. In view of the very small proportion of carbon dioxide generally present in the atmosphere, Essen and Froome themselves consider that the effect can be neglected. We can therefore make p_2 zero, and substitute $(p - e)$ for p_1 if p is the total measured pressure.

49. Interestingly, the first term in the Essen and Froome formula is simply an expression of the ideal gas law for dry air, if the density is assumed to be proportional to $(\mu - 1)$ and if the electrically determined experimental value of 288.15×10^{-6} is substituted for $(\mu - 1)$ at 0° C., with a pressure of one atmosphere. The formula also reflects the fact that water vapor behaves as an ideal gas at any one temperature. The effect of water vapor on the refraction of microwaves is much greater than on the refraction

[19] Barrell and Sears, *op. cit. supra* note 16, Equation (7.7), 52.

[20] Essen and Froome (1951), "The Refractive Indices and Dielectric Constants of Air and its Principal Constituents at 24,000 Mc/s," *Proceedings of the Physical Society of London*, Series B, v. 64, 862–875.

of optical waves, and the vapor pressure needs to be measured about as accurately as the total pressure.

50. Although short by radio standards, the microwaves in common use for distance measurement are much longer than optical wavelengths. The effect of different wavelengths in a dispersion formula, which, on theoretical grounds, could not differ much from Equation 24.51, would be very small; there is no sensible effect of group velocity. It is interesting to note that the dispersion Equation 24.51 for a wavelength of 1.25 cm., which is too long to have any appreciable effect, gives $(\mu - 1) = 0.00028760$ for standard air. The experimentally determined figure of Essen and Froome is 0.00028815. Essen and Froome performed their measurements at a frequency of 24,000 Mc/s. [MHz] (wavelength 1.25 cm.), and they estimated that their results held true for all wavelengths above 7 mm.

MEASUREMENT OF REFRACTIVE INDEX

51. Determination of μ from Equation 24.54 or 24.58 depends on measurements of temperature, pressure, and humidity, which can normally be made only at the two ends of the line. Sufficiently accurate measures of pressure and humidity can be made without difficulty, even if this is not always done in current practice. Humidity is usually obtained from wet-and-dry-bulb temperatures, from which the vapor pressure can be derived from formulas and tables given in the *Smithsonian Meteorological Tables*.[21] Sometimes data may be in the form of *relative humidity*, considered equal to

$$100e/e_w$$

where e_w is the saturation vapor pressure over water at the dry-bulb temperature.[22]

52. The accurate measurement of air temperature requires fairly elaborate precautions [23] which are not always employed. Angus-Leppan [24] has found that radiation intensity, as measured by "black-bulb" thermometers placed on the ground at the observing station, is a more reliable indicator

of refraction than air temperature measured by ordinary thermometers; but more work is required before the appropriate modifications can be made to Equations 24.54 and 24.58, which in their present form require the actual air temperature.

CURVATURE

53. The curvature of the ray is found by simply differentiating Equation 24.54 or 24.58 and using Equation 24.26. For example, if we differentiate Equation 24.54 with respect to geodetic height h in the geodetic model atmosphere, we have

$$\chi = -\frac{\sin \beta}{\mu}\frac{d\mu}{dh}$$

$$= \frac{\sin \beta}{\mu(1+\alpha t)}\left[(\mu-1)\alpha\frac{dt}{dh} - \frac{\mu_G - 1}{760}\frac{dp}{dh}\right.$$

24.59 $$\left. + 55 \times 10^{-9}\frac{de}{dh}\right],$$

with a similar equation for microwaves from Equation 24.58. We can substitute

24.60 $$\frac{dp}{dh} = -\rho g = -\left(\frac{g}{c}\right)\left(\frac{p}{T}\right)$$

from Equations 24.44 and 24.42 on the assumption that the moist air behaves as a perfect gas. The determination of curvature then depends on a knowledge of the *lapse rates* $-dt/dh$, $-de/dh$, which we shall consider more fully in the next section.

Approximate Formula—Optical Waves

54. An approximate formula for curvature of optical paths, based on the assumption that we have $e = 0$, is often used. In that case, Equations 24.59 and 24.60 reduce to

24.61 $$\chi = \frac{(\mu-1)\sin\beta}{\mu T}\left[\frac{dT}{dh} + \frac{g}{c}\right]$$

in which T is the absolute temperature; here, we have used Equations 24.57 and 24.54 for $e = 0$. In most cases, we shall already have computed μ, and there will be no need to introduce any more approximations. Bomford [25] derives a formula in this form without using the international Equation 24.54 for μ. However, we have seen in § 24–46 that the international formula for $e = 0$ is simply an expression with appropriate constants of the perfect

[21] Smithsonian Institution, *op. cit. supra* note 8, 365–369.

[22] *Ibid.*, 350–359.

[23] See Angus-Leppan (1961), "A Study of Refraction in the Lower Atmosphere," *Empire Survey Review*, no. 120, 62–69; no. 121, 107–119; and no. 122, 166–177. In addition to experimental results, these three papers provide a useful summary of the subject.

[24] *Ibid.*

[25] Bomford (1962), *Geodesy*, 2d ed., 212.

gas law, which Bomford does use, so that Bomford's result must be equivalent to Equation 24.61 with some further assumptions. We can combine Equations 24.61 and 24.54 for $e = 0$ as

24.62 $\quad \chi = \dfrac{(\mu_G - 1) \sin \beta}{760 \mu \alpha} \dfrac{p}{T^2} \left[\dfrac{dT}{dh} + \dfrac{g}{c} \right],$

which should be equivalent to Bomford's

24.63 $\quad \chi = 16.5 \dfrac{p}{T^2} \left[\dfrac{dT}{dh} + 0.0334 \right]$

where p is in millibars, T is in °K., h is in meters, and χ is in seconds per meter. To reconcile the two formulas, we can use the definition

1 millibar = 0.750062 mm., Hg. (standard).[26]

Bomford makes the additional assumption that $\beta = 90°$ and also makes reasonable assumptions for μ_G, μ, and g. Such assumptions are not necessary if we use Equation 24.61 in which c is the gas constant for dry air (2.8704×10^6 in c.g.s. units). We can use any realistic value for g, such as the international formula with a free-air height correction.

55. The question arises whether neglect of humidity in these approximate formulas is justified or whether it has been too readily assumed that, because humidity has little effect on the refractive index for optical waves, the effect is equally small on the curvature—that is, on the first differential of the index. As an example, we take e as the saturation vapor pressure over water at 15° C., which is about 13 mm., Hg.; p is 760 mm., Hg.; and $(\mu_G - 1)$ is 0.00028. The humidity term in Equation 24.54 is then about 0.25 percent of the pressure term and can certainly be neglected. For substitution in the curvature Equation 24.59, we calculate de/dh from Equation 24.64 as $-1/210$ mm. of pressure per meter of height. The omitted humidity term within the brackets of Equation 24.61 is then

$$- \frac{55 \times 10^{-9}}{210} \times \frac{760T}{0.00028p},$$

which is about (-0.25×10^{-3})°K. per meter. If the temperature lapse rate is 0.0055 °K. per meter, which is an average figure, the omitted humidity term is accordingly equivalent to an error of about 5 percent in the temperature lapse rate. At present, we are unlikely to know the lapse rate within 5 percent, but humidity may become more significant in the future.

[26] Smithsonian Institution, *op. cit. supra* note 8, 13.

LAPSE RATES

56. We have seen that the curvature and thus the arc-to-chord and velocity corrections depend on the vertical gradients of temperature and vapor pressure. Sufficiently representative values of these quantities cannot at present be obtained by direct measurement near the ground. We shall now fill in the present state of our knowledge of these quantities.

Humidity

57. All that seems to be known at present about the lapse rate of vapor pressure ($-de/dh$) is an empirical formula by Hann,[27] determined in 1915 as

$$e/e_0 = 10^{-h/6300}$$

where e is the vapor pressure at a height of h-meters above sea level and e_0 is the vapor pressure at sea level. Differentiating logarithmically, we have

24.64 $\quad \dfrac{de}{dh} = - \dfrac{e}{6300 \times 0.43429}.$

Temperature

58. Some idea of the possible values of the temperature lapse rate can be obtained from Equation 24.63. If we have $dT/dh = -0.0334$ °C. per meter, then the ray is straight. If dT/dh has an even greater negative value than that figure, the ray will curve upward; we know from the common observation of mirage conditions, which do not by any means occur only in deserts, that this condition is possible close to superheated ground. Also, we know that temperature inversions are frequent, especially on clear nights, and, in that case, dT/dh would be positive and the ray would be very strongly curved. We cannot expect to obtain accurate results by assuming that dT/dh is constant at all times and at all places. Accordingly, we shall consider first whether the lapse rate can be assumed constant at certain times, such as the afternoon period of minimum refraction.

The Adiabatic Lapse Rate

59. Much consideration has been given to the lapse rate associated with the adiabatic expansion of air.[28] The theory assumes that a given volume of

[27] *Ibid.*, 204.

[28] For example, de Graaff-Hunter (1913), "Formulae for Atmospheric Refraction and Their Application to Terrestrial Refraction and Geodesy," *Survey of India Professional Paper No. 14*, 1–114.

air is heated mainly by radiation from the ground, not by direct solar radiation, and then rises, *without acquiring or losing any more heat*, to an equilibrium height where its temperature is settled by the outside pressure. We may expect the process to be complete during the afternoon, that is, around the period of observed minimum refraction.

60. Absolute temperature (T) and pressure (p) in an adiabatic expansion of dry air are related to some initial temperature (T_0) and pressure (p_0) by the equation [29]

24.65 $$T_0/T = (p_0/p)^\delta$$

where δ is the ratio of the gas constant for dry air to the specific heat of dry air at constant pressure. We can take δ as 2/7. If we differentiate this equation logarithmically with respect to height and use Equations 24.44 and 24.42, we have

$$\frac{1}{T}\frac{dT}{dh} = \frac{2}{7}\frac{1}{p}\frac{dp}{dh} = -\frac{2}{7}\frac{1}{T}\frac{g}{c}$$

so that the adiabatic lapse rate, in a very suitable form for substitution in Equation 24.61, is given by

$$\frac{dT}{dh} = -\frac{2}{7}\frac{g}{c}.$$

Using the value for g/c in Equation 24.63, the lapse rate $(-dT/dh)$ is very nearly 0.01° C. per meter. Unfortunately, this is almost double what is usually found during the period of minimum refraction from reciprocal vertical angle measurements. The reason for this condition may be that there is some delay in reaching adiabatic equilibrium, if indeed it is ever reached. Also, the adiabatic assumption may be invalidated by acquisition of latent heat through condensation. Whatever the reason, this value of the lapse rate is no longer used.

Other Constant Lapse Rates

61. Either of the two standard atmospheres in common use [30] employs a lapse rate of 0.0065° C. per meter, which seems too high to fit geodetic observations at minimum refraction. For such purposes, a rate of 0.0055° C. is usually assumed, but there are considerable departures from this figure at different seasons and heights, especially near the ground. Attempts to measure the local lapse rate at a ground station by taking temperatures over a known height difference have seldom given

satisfactory results, partly because of the difficulty of accurately measuring the small difference of air temperatures without elaborate precautions and partly because such local measurements would not be sufficiently representative of the air actually traversed by the ray.

Recent Work

62. Because the assumption of a constant temperature lapse rate appears too drastic, even at restricted times, various attempts have been made to find formulas, other than the simple adiabatic formula, for the variation of temperature with height (h) and time (t). One such formula,[31] based on eddy conductivity K of the atmosphere, is

$$T = T_0 - lh + Ae^{-bh}\sin(qt - bh)$$
$$b^2 = q/(2K)$$

in which l is a mean lapse rate and e^{-bh} is an exponential damping factor. Other formulas containing more harmonics have been proposed on much the same basis. Unfortunately, the eddy conductivity K, which was expected to be constant, is known now to be even more erratic than the lapse rate.

63. More recently, Levallois and de Masson d'Autume [32] have proposed a formula in the form

$$T = T_0 - lh + e^{-bh}f(t - h/V) + \phi(t)$$

in which V is a velocity of upward transfer of heat; these geodesists obtained the form of the periodic functions and the constants from large numbers of meteorological observations covering a considerable range of altitude and time.

64. Angus-Leppan [33] finds that formulas of the same type fit the observations within a restricted range of heights in other localities, but the constants vary considerably with locality; the practical use of the method seems to be restricted until more work has been done in a particular area.

65. Meanwhile, the more developed meteorological services could no doubt provide a reasonable estimate of lapse rate at given heights and times within a particular locality—for example, by

[29] Smithsonian Institution, *op. cit. supra* note 8, 308.

[30] *Ibid.*, 265–268.

[31] Sutton (1949), *Atmospheric Turbulence*, 1st ed., 33, 40.

[32] Levallois and de Masson d'Autume (1953), "Étude sur la Refraction Géodésique et le Nivellement Barométrique," *Institut Géographique National*, 1–112.

[33] Angus-Leppan, *loc. cit. supra* note 23.

interpolation from radiosonde records — particularly where the observed rays cover a considerable range in height; undoubtedly, such facilities will increase. For rays between points at about the same height, it is very doubtful if our present knowledge has progressed much beyond the simple assumption of constant curvature over the path, and the determination of that curvature from reciprocal vertical angles. The lapse rate, used in conjunction with Equation 24.61, is mainly required for rays covering a considerable difference of height when the assumption of constant curvature is no longer valid; but for that purpose, we require representative values of the lapse rate at the two ends of the ray. If this information is not available, then the simple assumption of constant curvature would have to be made also in this case.

ASTRONOMICAL REFRACTION

66. We have so far considered terrestrial observations where measurements of temperature, pressure, and humidity can be made at the ends of the line and used to sample the actual refractive index. The gradient of the index, necessary to establish the curvature of the ray, cannot in the present state-of-the-art be directly measured, and we have to rely on more-or-less plausible atmospherical models to provide the necessary lapse rates. In the case of observations to stars or satellites, the ray passes through the effective atmosphere, and it becomes necessary to develop a more complete atmospheric model based on measurements at one end only of the ray.

67. In all investigations of astronomical refraction so far made, a spherically symmetrical model is assumed leading to Equation 24.11; the various investigations which have been made differ only in the assumed radial variation of the index of refraction, or of density, or of temperature, and in the methods used for the further integration of Equation 24.11. A good historical summary is given by Newcomb.[34] The latest investigation, using a discontinuous radial variation of temperature in line with modern meteorology, is due to Garfinkel,[35] but even so the values of the atmospheric param-

eters are subject to continual revision as more data become available.

68. In the spherically symmetrical case, we have from Equation 24.11

24.66 $$\sin \beta = \frac{\mu_0 r_0 \sin \beta_0}{\mu^r}$$

where β is the angle between the ray and the radius vector, and the zero subscripts refer to the ground station. Because the gradient of $(\ln \mu)$ is radial and because the ray is a plane curve, the curvature is

24.67 $$\chi = (\ln \mu)_r m^r = \{\nabla (\ln \mu)\}^{1/2} \sin \beta;$$

we have the variation of refraction along the ray as

24.68 $$\partial (\ln \mu)/\partial s = (\ln \mu)_r l^r = -\{\nabla (\ln \mu)\}^{1/2} \cos \beta.$$

The total angle of refraction is

$$\int \chi ds = -\int \tan \beta \left(\frac{\partial (\ln \mu)}{\partial s} \right) ds$$

24.69 $$= -\int_{\mu_0}^{1} \left\{ \left(\frac{\mu^r}{\mu_0 r_0 \sin \beta_0} \right)^2 - 1 \right\}^{-1/2} d(\ln \mu)$$

on substitution of the last three equations. In the case of astronomical refraction, the limits of integration are between the ground station and the end of the effective atmosphere, that is, between μ_0 and 1. The assumed model atmosphere gives μ as a function of r, directly or indirectly, and the final integration can always be carried out numerically no matter how complicated the model.

69. An important case arises in satellite triangulation when the satellite (S in fig. 27) is photographed against a background of stars. The apparent direction of the satellite from the ground station P is PS'. If the satellite is outside the effective atmosphere, the outward continuation ST' of the ray to the satellite is straight, and a parallel PT to ST' gives the total astronomical refraction as $S'PT$. To simplify the argument, we can assume that T' is a star whose true direction is PT. If the satellite is assumed to have the same direction as the star, its true position would lie on PT, whereas in fact, the true position is at S. Accordingly, the zenith distance of the satellite, as calculated from the true position of the background star T', must be corrected by the angle σ.

70. If we assume that the satellite is *at* the effective limit of the atmosphere so that SP is curved and ST' is straight, then Equation 24.33 applies,

[34] Newcomb (Dover ed. of 1960), *A Compendium of Spherical Astronomy With its Applications to the Determination and Reduction of Positions of the Fixed Stars*, original ed. of 1906, 173–224.

[35] Garfinkel (1944), "An Investigation in the Theory of Astronomical Refraction," *The Astronomical Journal*, v. 50, 169–179. Also, Garfinkel (1967), "Astronomical Refraction in a Polytropic Atmosphere," *The Astronomical Journal*, v. 72, 235–254.

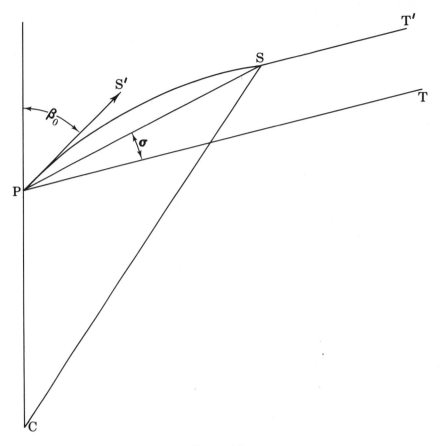

Figure 27.

and we have

24.70 $$\sigma = \tfrac{1}{2}(SP)\chi_2$$

where χ_2 is the curvature of the ray at two-thirds the way along PS. The total atmospheric refraction is

24.71 $$\sigma + \tfrac{1}{2}(SP)\chi_1$$

where χ_1 is the curvature of the ray at one-third the way along PS at which point the air is much denser. The correction angle σ is accordingly much less than the astronomical refraction. We can obtain σ direct from Equation 24.70, if we first calculate the radius vector from the center C of an assumed spherical Earth to the "two-thirds" point of PS, and then use appropriate model values in Equations 24.66 and 24.67. However, we have assumed that the satellite is at the effective limit of the atmosphere; a further correction, to be obtained from the geometry of the figure, would be required if the satellite is well outside the effective atmosphere at some point on ST'.

71. As an alternative, we can calculate the total atmospheric refraction and use Equation 24.71 to obtain σ. In that case, we should calculate χ_1 at one-third the distance to the limit of the effective atmosphere in the direction PS, even if the satellite lies well outside this limit. In effect, as we have seen in § 24–15, Dufour[36] uses this method to establish quite simple formulas both for the atmospheric refraction and for the satellite correction, using an exponential atmospheric model.

72. Hellmut Schmid[37] obtains an extremely simple formula that can be translated into our present notation in radian measure as

24.72 $$\sigma = \frac{2.33}{(SP)}\frac{\tan\beta_0}{\cos\beta_0}\times W$$

where

$$W = \frac{p}{760}\times\frac{273.16}{T}$$

[36] Dufour (1964), "Choix de Formules de la Réfraction Atmosphérique Pour les Observations par Chambres Balistiques," *Bulletin Géodésique*, new series, no. 73, 217–229.

[37] Schmid (1963), "The Influence of Atmospheric Refraction on Directions Measured to and from a Satellite," *GIMRADA Research Note No. 10*, 1–17.

in which p in mm., Hg. and T in °K. are the pressure and temperature at the ground station. In deriving this formula, Schmid finds that σ is insensitive to changes in both the astronomical refraction and the distance to the satellite, unless β_0 is larger than would be tolerated in practice.

MEASUREMENT OF REFRACTION

Distance Measurement

73. Bender and Owens [38] have described the use of a two-wavelength method for eliminating the effect of refraction in electronic distance measurements with optical wavelengths. The theory of the method is simple. From Equation 24.03, the one-way [39] optical path length is given by

$$S = ct = \int \mu \, ds$$

in which μ is the actual refractive index from Equation 24.54, using a standard group index μ_G where applicable, and the integral is taken over the actual path. The measured time of travel is t, so that we may consider S as the measured distance, if the velocity of light in a vacuum C is used in conjunction with the measured time. The geometrical path length is, however,

$$\int ds$$

so that

$$\Delta = \int (\mu - 1) \, ds$$

represents a correction which must be subtracted from the measured distance S to obtain the geometrical distance, both distances being measured along the curved path. If measurements are made with two wavelengths denoted by subscripts R and B, we have two equations

$$\Delta_R = \int (\mu_R - 1) \, ds$$

$$\Delta_B = \int (\mu_B - 1) \, ds,$$

which can be subtracted to give

24.73 $$\Delta_B - \Delta_R = \int A(\mu_R - 1) \, ds,$$

where

$$A = (\mu_B - \mu_R) / (\mu_R - 1).$$

Bender and Owens quote Erickson as having shown experimentally that A is independent of atmospheric density and is only weakly dependent on atmospheric composition, so that A may be evaluated for the particular wavelengths and for approximate actual atmospheric conditions in the Barrell and Sears Equations 24.53 and 24.54. The A is then considered constant during the path integration so that we have

24.74 $$\Delta_B - \Delta_R = A \int (\mu_R - 1) \, ds = A \Delta_R.$$

The difference $(\Delta_B - \Delta_R)$ is measured; Δ_R is calculated from Equation 24.74 and subtracted from the measured distance with wavelength R to give the geometrical path length.

74. The assumption that A is only weakly dependent on atmospheric composition, particularly the water vapor content, is justified by Barrell and Sears as well as by Erickson, but only in the case of optical wavelengths. The effect of water vapor on microwaves can be seen from the Essen and Froome formula to be much greater. Nevertheless, Thompson and Wood [40] have shown that, to the accuracy now being sought, the neglect of water vapor pressure can be serious, even in the case of optical wavelengths, and should be corrected. Moreover, the correction can be seen from the full Barrell and Sears formula, Equation 24.55, to be partly dependent on the wavelength and should therefore be evaluated from this full formula for two-wavelength techniques. Thompson [41] has also suggested measurement at three wavelengths (two optical and one microwave) to account more completely for the water vapor effect.

75. The method corrects only for the effect of

[38] Bender and Owens (1965), "Correction of Optical Distance Measurements for the Fluctuating Atmospheric Index of Refraction," *Journal of Geophysical Research*, v. 70, 2461–2462. See also, Owens (1967), "Recent Progress in Optical Distance Measurements: Lasers and Atmospheric Dispersion," *Proceedings of the International Symposium Figure of the Earth and Refraction*, Vienna, Austria, March 14–17, 1967, 153–161.

[39] The measured time in such instruments as the Geodimeter refers to the two-way path, and would have to be halved.

[40] Thompson, M. C., Jr., and Wood, L. E. (1967), "The Use of Atmospheric Dispersion for the Refractive Index Correction of Optical Distance Measurements," *Electromagnetic Distance Measurement*, 165–172. A symposium held in Oxford, England, under the auspices of IAG Special Study Group No. 19, September 6–11, 1965.

[41] Thompson, M. C., Jr. (1967), "A Radio-Optical Dispersion Technique for Higher-Order Correction of Optical Distance Measurements," *Proceedings of the International Symposium Figure of the Earth and Refraction*, Vienna, Austria, March 14–17, 1967, 161–163.

refraction on the velocity of light. A correction for the curvature of the geometrical path must be applied separately to derive the chord distance.

Angle of Refraction

76. It is possible to measure the difference in angles of refraction for two known wavelengths and thus to determine the angle of refraction for any other wavelength. The method seems to have been proposed originally by Näbauer some decades ago, but is now becoming a practical possibility through the introduction, mainly by Tengström,[42] of modern interferometer measurements.

77. A general formula for the dependence of the refractive index on atmospheric conditions is

24.75 $\qquad \mu = 1 + A(\mu_G - 1) + B$

where A is a function of temperature and pressure and B is a function of temperature and water vapor pressure. The Barrell and Sears formula is, for example, in this form with values of A and B given by Equation 24.54. If m is an element of length along the normal to the ray, the curvature is then given by

$$\chi = \frac{(\mu_G - 1)(dA/dm) + (dB/dm)}{1 + A(\mu_G - 1) + B};$$

the total angle of refraction swept out by the tangent to the ray is

24.76 $\qquad \Delta\beta = (\mu_G - 1)P + Q$

where

$$P = \int \frac{(dA/dm)}{1 + A(\mu_G - 1) + B}\, ds$$

$$Q = \int \frac{(dB/dm)}{1 + A(\mu_G - 1) + B}\, ds,$$

integrated over the whole length of the ray. The denominator of the integrands is μ, which differs very little from unity, and is assumed not to change significantly when the standard refractive index μ_G is changed for a different wavelength in accordance with Equation 24.53. The other terms of the integrands are atmospheric parameters, which are justifiably assumed constant because the measurements at different wavelengths are made simul-

taneously and because the two paths cannot be very different. Accordingly, for two different wavelengths denoted by subscripts R and B, we shall have two equations

$$(\Delta\beta)_R = (\mu_{GR} - 1)P + Q$$

24.77 $\qquad (\Delta\beta)_B = (\mu_{GB} - 1)P + Q$

in which μ_{GR}, μ_{GB} are obtained for the actual wavelengths from either Equation 24.51 or 24.53, depending on whether a phase or group velocity is appropriate in the circumstances of measurement. By subtraction, we have

24.78 $\qquad (\Delta\beta)_B - (\Delta\beta)_R = (\mu_{GB} - \mu_{GR})P,$

which determines P if $(\Delta\beta)_B - (\Delta\beta)_R$ is known by simultaneous measurements at both ends of the line. We cannot, however, determine the humidity term Q, the effect of which is fortunately small in the case of optical wavelengths and must either be ignored or estimated. A similar situation must arise in the Bender-Owens proposal, probably in the assumption that A of Equation 24.73 is constant.

78. For any other wavelength, such as a mean wavelength of daylight or of a luminous beacon, we can obtain the total angle of refraction from an equation similar to Equation 24.76. The result will be between one and two orders of magnitude larger than the difference $(\Delta\beta)_B - (\Delta\beta)_R$, which must accordingly be measured to a very high degree of accuracy.

79. Tengström proposes to obtain the separate angles of refraction at each end, instead of the total angle of refraction, by a slight extension of the method. He considers that the tangent to the ray must be parallel to the chord at one intermediate point at least, which is certainly the case if the ray is assumed to be a continuous plane curve: he forms Equation 24.76 between the nearest such point R and the observing station O. The two integrals P and Q must now be taken over the path OR, and $\Delta\beta$ will be the angle of refraction at O. If it is assumed that the point R is the same for both wavelengths, which is no more drastic than the earlier assumption that the two paths are approximately the same, then two equations similar to Equation 24.77 can be formed, the integral P can be eliminated, and the integral Q can be estimated from conditions nearer to the observing station O. The angle of refraction at O for any wavelength is in this way determined solely from measurements at O.

---

[42] Tengström (1967), "Elimination of Refraction at Vertical Angle Measurements, Using Lasers of Different Wavelengths," *Proceedings of the International Symposium Figure of the Earth and Refraction*, Vienna, Austria, March 14–17, 1967, 292–303.

CHAPTER 25

The Line of Observation

GENERAL REMARKS

1. Apart from the effects of atmospheric refraction, geodetic measurements of angles, distances, and directions are invariably made along straight lines in three-dimensional flat space. For example, the path in electronic distance measurements, which have replaced direct measurements by Invar tapes or wires, is necessarily curved slightly by refraction, but the universal practice is to reduce the measurement to the straight-line distance on the best available refraction data before using the resulting straight-line distance for the determination of positions. In the same way, an optical instrument, which is used for the measurement of angles or directions, such as a theodolite, is necessarily sighted along the tangent to an optical path curved by refraction. Here again, it is necessary to correct the measurement to the straight-chord direction before proceeding further or else to ignore the effects of refraction altogether. The final results will be vitiated by the extent to which refraction has been ignored or imperfectly corrected. There is no preferred method of computation which will overcome this defect, although unfounded claims are still occasionally made that classical or two-dimensional methods have an advantage in this respect.

2. For example, it is usual in classical geodesy to assume that the tangent to the refracted ray lies in the *plane of normal section*, that is, the plane containing the spheroidal normal of the geodetic coordinate system at the observing station and the position of the station sighted. But this plane also contains the straight line joining the two stations, and so far as subsequent methods of reduction utilizing only such planes are concerned, the line of observation might have been assumed to be straight. This fact is even more obvious when we consider that the two planes of normal section at the two stations are, in general, not the same, and the only line common to them is the straight line in space joining the two stations. The remaining operations of classical geodesy — corrections of observed directions for "geoidal tilt" and elevation of the station sighted, replacement of the two curves of normal section by a spheroidal geodesic, and solution of geodesic triangles on the spheroid of reference — are purely geometrical. Exactly the same positions on the spheroid of reference would be obtained more simply and directly by considering the line of observation to be a straight line in three-dimensional space.

3. The effect of refraction on the determination of relative elevations is, of course, much greater; as we have seen in Chapter 24, more drastic assumptions have to be made until it becomes possible to make more complete measurements of refraction effects. For this reason, calculations for differences in height are made separately in classical geodesy in the belief that positions on the reference spheroid would be vitiated in a three-dimensional computation. This question will become clearer when we come to the adjustment of space networks in Chapter 26. Meanwhile, it is sufficient to say that a similar separation can be effected, if required, in a three-dimensional adjustment by using appropriate coordinates.

GENERAL EQUATIONS OF THE LINE

4. We have seen in § 4–2 that the contravariant equation of a geodesic in three-dimensional space,

that is, of a straight line in three-dimensional flat space, is

25.01 $$l^r_{,s}l^s = 0 \qquad (r = 1, 2, 3)$$

or

25.02 $$\frac{\partial l^r}{\partial s} + \Gamma^r_{st}l^s l^t = 0$$

where l^r is the unit tangent to the line. These three equations can be integrated, numerically or otherwise, in any coordinate system for which the Christoffel symbols are given to provide the three contravariant components of the unit tangent, which can be further integrated to provide the changes in coordinates along the line.

5. In Cartesian coordinates, for example, the Christoffel symbols are all zero, and Equation 25.02 tells us that all three Cartesian components of the unit tangent are constant along the line so that changes in coordinates are proportional to the length s of the line. The constant components of the unit tangent are the direction cosines of the line (a, b, c); the changes in Cartesian coordinates are given by

$$\bar{x} - x = sa$$
$$\bar{y} - y = sb$$

25.03 $$\bar{z} - z = sc,$$

or, expressed in terms of the position vectors ρ^r, $\bar{\rho}^r$ at the two ends of the line as

25.04 $$\bar{\rho}^r - \rho^r = sl^r,$$

a vector equation which holds true in any coordinates — provided it is applied to parallel vectors at the same point in space.

6. The fact that a solution of the problem exists in Cartesian coordinates shows that a first integral in any coordinates of the tensor Equation 25.01 can be obtained simply by transforming the Cartesian tangent vector (a, b, c). If Cartesian coordinates and components are overbarred, then the covariant components of the unit tangent in a general (ω, ϕ, N) coordinate system are given by

$$l_r = (\partial \bar{x}^s / \partial x^r)\bar{l}_s$$
$$= ax_r + by_r + cz_r$$
$$= \lambda_r(-a \sin \omega + b \cos \omega)$$
$$+ \mu_r(-a \sin \phi \cos \omega - b \sin \phi \sin \omega + c \cos \phi)$$
$$+ \nu_r(+a \cos \phi \cos \omega + b \cos \phi \sin \omega + c \sin \phi),$$

25.05

using Equations 12.009. If the azimuth and zenith distance of the line in relation to the N-surface normal are α, β, we then have from Equation 12.007

$$\sin \alpha \sin \beta = -a \sin \omega + b \cos \omega$$
$$\cos \alpha \sin \beta = -a \sin \phi \cos \omega - b \sin \phi \sin \omega$$
$$+ c \cos \phi$$
$$\cos \beta = +a \cos \phi \cos \omega + b \cos \phi \sin \omega$$

25.06 $$+ c \sin \phi$$

in which a, b, c can be considered as constants of integration. Only two of these equations are independent because l_r is a unit vector and $a^2 + b^2 + c^2 = 1$. We obtain an identity by squaring and adding the three equations.

7. The (ω, ϕ, N) components of the unit tangent are now given by substitution of the appropriate components of the base vectors λ^r, λ_r, etc., from Equations 12.037, 12.041, etc., in Equation 25.05. We have

$$(\sec \phi)l_1 = -(k_2/K) \sin \alpha \sin \beta$$
$$+ (t_1/K) \cos \alpha \sin \beta$$
$$l_2 = (t_1/K) \sin \alpha \sin \beta$$
$$- (k_1/K) \cos \alpha \sin \beta$$
$$l_3 = \frac{\partial(1/n)}{\partial \omega} \sec \phi \sin \alpha \sin \beta$$

25.07 $$+ \frac{\partial(1/n)}{\partial \phi} \cos \alpha \sin \beta + \frac{\cos \beta}{n}$$

and

$$(\cos \phi)l^1 = -k_1 \sin \alpha \sin \beta$$
$$- t_1 \cos \alpha \sin \beta + \gamma_1 \cos \beta$$
$$l^2 = -t_1 \sin \alpha \sin \beta$$
$$- k_2 \cos \alpha \sin \beta + \gamma_2 \cos \beta$$

25.08 $$l^3 = n \cos \beta$$

in which, of course, α, β have the values given by Equations 25.06. An alternative expression for the third covariant component is obtained from Equations 12.097 as

25.09 $$l_3 = (1/n) \sec \bar{\beta} \cos \bar{\sigma}$$

in which $\bar{\beta}$ is the zenith distance of the isozenithal k^r and $\cos \bar{\sigma} = l_r k^r$.

8. In terms of the **Q**-matrix of Equation 19.26, we can rewrite Equations 25.06 in the form

$$\{\sin \alpha \sin \beta, \cos \alpha \sin \beta, \cos \beta\} = \mathbf{Q}\{a, b, c\},$$

25.10

which implies that

$$\mathbf{Q}^T\{\sin\alpha\sin\beta, \cos\alpha\sin\beta, \cos\beta\} = \{a, b, c\}$$

25.11

is constant along the line and verifies Equation 19.27. The last matrix equation expanded for reference is

$$a = -\sin\omega\sin\alpha\sin\beta$$
$$-\sin\phi\cos\omega\cos\alpha\sin\beta$$
$$+\cos\phi\cos\omega\cos\beta$$
$$b = \cos\omega\sin\alpha\sin\beta$$
$$-\sin\phi\sin\omega\cos\alpha\sin\beta$$
$$+\cos\phi\sin\omega\cos\beta$$

25.12 $c = \cos\phi\cos\alpha\sin\beta + \sin\phi\cos\beta.$

THE LINE IN GEODETIC COORDINATES

9. Using Equations 25.03, we can also write

$$\{s\sin\alpha\sin\beta, s\cos\alpha\sin\beta, s\cos\beta\}$$

25.13 $= \mathbf{Q}\{(\bar{x}-x), (\bar{y}-y), (\bar{z}-z)\},$

which enables us to calculate azimuth, zenith distance, and length of the line if we are given the latitude and longitude of one end of the line and the Cartesian coordinates of both ends. This equation holds true in any (ω, ϕ, N) coordinate system, provided $\alpha, \beta, \omega, \phi$ all refer to the same system. We cannot, however, proceed further unless we know the relationship between the Cartesian and (ω, ϕ, N) coordinates, that is, unless we specify the particular (ω, ϕ, N) system. The simplest results will be obtained if we can express (x, y, z) directly in terms of (ω, ϕ, N) because, in that case, Equation 25.13 would lead to closed formulas for (s, α, β) in terms of (ω, ϕ, N). To provide such formulas, we should integrate Equations 12.009, having first substituted the components of the base vectors from Equations 12.041, etc., and this would hardly be possible in the case of a general (ω, ϕ, N) system. However, reference to Equation 17.64 shows that we can do so in a (ω, ϕ, h) system, provided the equation of the base surface is expressible in the Gaussian form of Equation 6.03. We could then rewrite Equation 17.64 in Cartesian coordinates as

$$x = x_0(\omega, \phi) + h\cos\phi\cos\omega$$
$$y = y_0(\omega, \phi) + h\cos\phi\sin\omega$$

25.14 $z = z_0(\omega, \phi) + h\sin\phi,$

substitute in Equation 25.13, and so obtain closed formulas for s, α, β. In Equations 25.14, x_0, y_0, z_0 are the Cartesian coordinates at the foot of the normal to the base surface ($h = 0$), and are functions of (ω, ϕ) only.

10. Greater simplicity can be achieved if we use a symmetrical (ω, ϕ, h) system, as discussed in Chapter 18, leading to the Cartesian Equations 18.28 and 18.30. Still greater simplicity results from the use of a spheroid as base surface because Equation 18.30 is then integrable and the Cartesian coordinates are given explicitly by Equations 18.59. To avoid confusion with the overbars, which in this chapter we shall reserve for quantities at the far end of the line, we rewrite Equations 18.59 in terms of ν—the principal radius of curvature of the base spheroid perpendicular to the meridian—as

$$x = (\nu + h)\cos\phi\cos\omega$$
$$y = (\nu + h)\cos\phi\sin\omega$$
$$z = (\bar{e}^2\nu + h)\sin\phi = (\nu + h)\sin\phi - e^2\nu\sin\phi$$

25.15

in which e is the eccentricity of the base spheroid and $\bar{e}^2 = (1 - e^2)$. Latitude and longitude (ϕ, ω) in these formulas refer to the straight normals to the base spheroid. It is apparent from the first two equations of Equations 25.15, or from Equations 18.28 in the case of a more general symmetrical system, that ν is also the length of the normal, intercepted between the base surface and the z-axis of symmetry. We shall in the future refer to the (ω, ϕ, h) system, defined by Equations 25.15, as the *geodetic coordinate system*.

11. In the geodetic system, ρ (the radius of curvature of the meridian) and ν are principal radii of curvature of the base spheroid because the parameter t_1 is zero in a symmetrical system, and the principal radii of an h-surface are given by Equations 18.02 and 18.01 as

$$(\nu + h) = -1/k_1$$
$$(\rho + h) = -1/k_2$$

25.16 $(\nu + h)(\rho + h) = 1/K.$

In any (ω, ϕ, h) system, we also have $n = 1$ so that components of the unit vector of the straight line in the geodetic system are obtained from Equations 25.07 and 25.08 as

$$l_r = \{(\nu + h)\cos\phi\sin\alpha\sin\beta,$$
$$(\rho + h)\cos\alpha\sin\beta, \cos\beta\}$$

25.17 $l^r = \left\{\dfrac{\sin\alpha\sin\beta\sec\phi}{(\nu + h)}, \dfrac{\cos\alpha\sin\beta}{(\rho + h)}, \cos\beta\right\}$

in which α, β have the values given by Equations 25.06. These results agree with Equations 18.14.

Reverse Problem

12. Substitution of Equations 25.15 in Equation 25.13 gives

$$\{s \sin \alpha \sin \beta, s \cos \alpha \sin \beta, s \cos \beta\}$$
$$= \mathbf{Q}\{\bar{x}, \bar{y}, \bar{z}\} - \mathbf{Q}\{x, y, z\}$$
$$= (\bar{\nu} + \bar{h})\mathbf{Q}\{\cos \bar{\phi} \cos \bar{\omega}, \cos \bar{\phi} \sin \bar{\omega}, \sin \bar{\phi}\}$$
$$- e^2\bar{\nu} \sin \bar{\phi}\mathbf{Q}\{0, 0, 1\}$$
$$- (\nu + h)\mathbf{Q}\{\cos \phi \cos \omega, \cos \phi \sin \omega, \sin \phi\}$$
$$+ e^2\nu \sin \phi\mathbf{Q}\{0, 0, 1\}$$
$$= (\bar{\nu} + \bar{h})\{\sin \sigma \sin \alpha^*, \sin \sigma \cos \alpha^*, \cos \sigma\}$$
$$- (\nu + h)\{0, 0, 1\}$$
$$- e^2(\bar{\nu} \sin \bar{\phi} - \nu \sin \phi)\{0, \cos \phi, \sin \phi\},$$

25.18

using the auxiliary angles defined in the same notation in Equations 19.01, etc. These equations solve what is usually known as the "reverse problem" by enabling us to compute (s, α, β) directly from the geodetic coordinates of the two ends of the line. If preferred, we could, of course, have computed Cartesian coordinates of the two ends from Equations 25.15 for substitution in Equation 25.13.

13. The azimuth and zenith distance at the far or barred end of the line (produced) are very easily obtained by interchanging overbars and changing the sign of s and σ so that we have

$$\{s \sin \bar{\alpha} \sin \bar{\beta}, s \cos \bar{\alpha} \sin \bar{\beta}, s \cos \bar{\beta}\}$$
$$= \bar{\mathbf{Q}}\{\bar{x}, \bar{y}, \bar{z}\} - \bar{\mathbf{Q}}\{x, y, z\}$$
$$= (\nu + h)\{\sin \sigma \sin \bar{\alpha}^*, \sin \sigma \cos \bar{\alpha}^*, -\cos \sigma\}$$
$$+ (\bar{\nu} + \bar{h})\{0, 0, 1\}$$
$$- e^2(\bar{\nu} \sin \bar{\phi} - \nu \sin \phi)\{0, \cos \bar{\phi}, \sin \bar{\phi}\}.$$

25.19

In particular, we notice that we have

$$s \sin \bar{\alpha} \sin \bar{\beta} = (\nu + h)\sin \sigma \sin \bar{\alpha}^*$$
$$= (\nu + h)\cos \phi \sin (\bar{\omega} - \omega),$$

and from Equation 25.18, we have

$$s \sin \alpha \sin \beta = (\bar{\nu} + \bar{h})\sin \sigma \sin \alpha^*$$
$$= (\bar{\nu} + \bar{h}) \cos \bar{\phi} \sin (\bar{\omega} - \omega)$$

so that

25.20 $\qquad (\nu + h)\cos \phi \sin \alpha \sin \beta$

has the same value at the two ends of the line, and is therefore constant along the line. It is of some interest to compare this last equation with the generalized Clairaut Equation 18.51 for geodesics on the h-surfaces, which in this notation is

$$(\nu + h) \cos \phi \sin \alpha = \text{constant}.$$

This relation between the straight line in space and the surface geodesic could be used as a link with classical methods. Also, we may note from Equations 25.17 that

$$(\nu + h)\cos \phi \sin \alpha \sin \beta$$

is the covariant component l_1 of the line in the geodetic system. The fact that this component is constant along the line may be verified from the covariant form of Equation 25.01, using the Christoffel symbols in Equations 18.34 and 18.35.

Direct Problem

14. If we are given s, ω, ϕ, h, α, β and we require $\bar{\omega}$, $\bar{\phi}$, $\bar{h}$, $\bar{\alpha}$, $\bar{\beta}$—which is usually known as the "direct" problem—then we can rewrite Equation 25.13 as

$$\{\bar{x}, \bar{y}, \bar{z}\} = \{x, y, z\}$$
$$+ \mathbf{Q}^T\{s \sin \alpha \sin \beta, s \cos \alpha \sin \beta, s \cos \beta\}$$
$$= \{x, y, z\} + s\{a, b, c\},$$

25.21

which enables us to compute $\bar{x}$, $\bar{y}$, $\bar{z}$ directly. From Equations 25.15, we then have at once

25.22 $\qquad \tan \bar{\omega} = \bar{y}/\bar{x},$

but some process of iteration is necessary to determine $\bar{\phi}$, $\bar{h}$ from

$$(\bar{\nu} + \bar{h})\cos \bar{\phi} = (\bar{x}^2 + \bar{y}^2)^{1/2}$$

and

25.23 $\qquad (\bar{e}^2\bar{\nu} + \bar{h})\sin \bar{\phi} = \bar{z},$

starting with an approximate value

$$\tan \bar{\phi} = \bar{z}/\{\bar{e}^2(\bar{x}^2 + \bar{y}^2)^{1/2}\}.$$

Azimuth and zenith distance then follow from Equation 19.27. Chovitz[1] has shown that iteration will not always converge if we have $e^2 \geq \frac{1}{2}$, but this case does not arise in the present context.

15. Alternatively, we can use one of the differ-

[1] Chovitz (1967), *On the Use of Iterative Procedures in Geodetic Applications* (unpublished manuscript). The paper was read at the 48th Annual Meeting of the American Geophysical Union, Washington, D.C., April 17, 1967.

ential methods developed in the next two chapters. From Equations 27.19 and 27.20, we have, for example,

$$\{(\bar{\nu}+\bar{h})\cos\bar{\phi}\,d\bar{\omega},\ (\bar{\rho}+\bar{h})d\bar{\phi},\ d\bar{h}\}$$

25.24 $$=\bar{\mathbf{A}}\{ds,\ sd\beta_0,\ -s\sin\beta\,d\alpha_0\}$$

in which the overbars refer to the far end of the line and ds, $d\beta_0$, $d\alpha_0$ are corrections to length, zenith distance, and azimuth at the near end of the line associated with changes $d\bar{\omega}$, $d\bar{\phi}$, $d\bar{h}$ in the coordinates of the far end. The matrix $\bar{\mathbf{A}}$ is obtained from the azimuth $\bar{\alpha}$ and from the zenith distance $\bar{\beta}$ of the line produced at the far end as

$$\bar{\mathbf{A}}=\begin{pmatrix} \sin\bar{\alpha}\sin\bar{\beta} & \sin\bar{\alpha}\cos\bar{\beta} & -\cos\bar{\alpha} \\ \cos\bar{\alpha}\sin\bar{\beta} & \cos\bar{\alpha}\cos\bar{\beta} & \sin\bar{\alpha} \\ \cos\bar{\beta} & -\sin\bar{\beta} & 0 \end{pmatrix}.$$

25.25

To apply this method, we start with assumed approximate coordinates $\bar{\omega}$, $\bar{\phi}$, $\bar{h}$ at the far end, and compute s, α, β, $\bar{\alpha}$, $\bar{\beta}$ from Equations 25.18 and 25.19. We are given "observed" values of s, α, β, and we substitute observed minus computed values as ds, $d\alpha_0$, $d\beta_0$ in Equation 25.24, which directly gives corrections $d\bar{\omega}$, $d\bar{\phi}$, $d\bar{h}$ to the initial approximate values. The whole process is then repeated as necessary to obtain results of the desired accuracy.

TAYLOR EXPANSION ALONG THE LINE

16. Subject to the usual conditions of differentiability and convergence, which we shall assume are satisfied by intuitive physical considerations in the cases we are going to discuss, or at least are justified by results, we can expand a scalar function of position F along a line of finite length s as

$$(\bar{F}-F)=sF'+\tfrac{1}{2}s^2F''+\tfrac{1}{6}s^3F'''+\tfrac{1}{24}s^4F''''\ \ldots$$

25.26

in which the overbar refers to the value of the function at the far end of the line, and the superscripts mean successive derivatives with respect to s. Quantities without overbars, F and its successive derivatives, are supposed to be evaluated at the near end of the line. If the derivatives are measured in the same sense of the line at the far end, that is, in the direction of the line produced, then the corresponding expansion from the far end of the line is obtained by interchanging overbars and changing the sign of s as

$$(\bar{F}-F)=s\bar{F}'-\tfrac{1}{2}s^2\bar{F}''+\tfrac{1}{6}s^3\bar{F}'''-\tfrac{1}{24}s^4\bar{F}''''+\ \cdots\ \cdot$$

25.27

In the mean, we have

$$(\bar{F}-F)=\tfrac{1}{2}s(F'+\bar{F}')+\tfrac{1}{4}s^2(F''-\bar{F}'')$$
$$+\tfrac{1}{12}s^3(F'''+\bar{F}''')$$

25.28 $$+\tfrac{1}{48}s^4(F''''-\bar{F}'''')+\ \ldots$$

The derivatives can be considered as functions of position, defined at all points along the line, and can similarly be expanded as

$$(\bar{F}'-F')=sF''+\tfrac{1}{2}s^2F'''+\tfrac{1}{6}s^3F''''+\ \ldots$$
$$=s\bar{F}''-\tfrac{1}{2}s^2\bar{F}'''+\tfrac{1}{6}s^3\bar{F}''''-\ \ldots$$

so that we have

$$0=s(F''-\bar{F}'')+\tfrac{1}{2}s^2(F'''+\bar{F}''')$$

25.29 $$+\tfrac{1}{6}s^3(F''''-\bar{F}'''')+\ \ldots;$$

while by direct expansion, as in Equation 25.28, we have

$$0=(F''-\bar{F}'')+\tfrac{1}{2}s(F'''+\bar{F}''')$$

25.30 $$+\tfrac{1}{4}s^2(F''''-\bar{F}'''')+\ \ldots\ .$$

Multiplying Equations 25.29 and 25.30 by $-\tfrac{1}{4}s$ and $\tfrac{1}{12}s^2$, respectively, and adding to Equation 25.28, we can eliminate the third- and fourth-order terms and can say that

25.31 $$(\bar{F}-F)=\tfrac{1}{2}s(F'+\bar{F}')+\tfrac{1}{12}s^2(F''-\bar{F}'')$$

is correct to a fourth order. We could, of course, have eliminated the second-order term instead of the third to the same degree of accuracy, but did not do so because it will usually be possible to measure the second order, but not the third-order terms. Also, we could have eliminated the third- and fifth-order terms instead of the third and fourth, but this would have no effect on the second-order term. We could continue the process by adding equations similar to Equations 25.29 and 25.30, starting with fourth-order terms, and so could eliminate more terms of still higher order, but this also would have no effect on the second-order terms. We may conclude that Equation 25.31 gives us the best possible second-order approximation in cases where we have values of the derivatives at both ends of the line.

EXPANSION OF THE GRAVITATIONAL POTENTIAL

17. For the sake of greater generality, we shall assume in this case that the line is curved and that its binormal is an equipotential surface vector. In the case of a refracted ray, this relation is equivalent to the assumption that the isopycnics are level

equipotential surfaces. The principal normal (m^r) to the curved line then lies in the plane of normal section, as shown in figure 28, where we have also

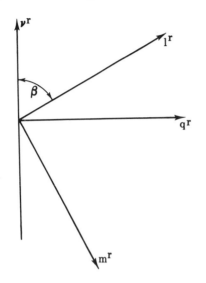

Figure 28.

shown a unit equipotential surface vector q^r in the same azimuth as the line l^r. We then have

$$l^r = q^r \sin \beta + \nu^r \cos \beta$$
$$m^r = q^r \cos \beta - \nu^r \sin \beta.$$

The first differential of the potential along the line is

$$\partial N/\partial s = N_r l^r = n\nu_r l^r = n \cos \beta$$

in which we identify N with the geopotential and n with gravity. The second differential is

$$\partial^2 N/\partial s^2 = (N_r l^r)_s l^s$$
$$= N_{rs} l^r l^s + N_r l^r_s l^s$$
$$= (n_s \nu_r + n\nu_{rs}) l^r l^s + \chi n\nu_r m^r$$

in which χ is the principal curvature of the line so that we have

$$(1/n)\partial^2 N/\partial s^2 = (\ln n)_s l^s \cos \beta$$
$$+ \nu_{rs}(q^r \sin \beta)(q^s \sin \beta + \nu^s \cos \beta)$$
$$- \chi \sin \beta$$
$$= -k \sin^2 \beta - \chi \sin \beta$$
$$+ 2(\ln n)_s q^s \sin \beta \cos \beta$$
25.32 $$+ (\ln n)_s \nu^s \cos^2 \beta$$

where k is the normal curvature of the equipotential surface in the azimuth of the line and where the zenith distance β of the line is measured from the

plumbline to the refracted ray. While k is always negative,[2] χ is usually positive, so that curvature and refraction have opposite effects in the determination of the second-order terms of the potential. The final Taylor expansion is

$$(\bar{N} - N)/n = s \cos \beta + \tfrac{1}{2}s^2\{-k \sin^2 \beta - \chi \sin \beta$$
$$+ 2(\ln n)_s q^s \sin \beta \cos \beta$$
25.33 $$+ (\ln n)_s \nu^s \cos^2 \beta\}.$$

18. We have seen in § 20–31 that $(\ln n)_s \nu^s$, the vertical gradient of gravity, is not at present measurable to a high degree of accuracy. However, from Equation 20.17, we have

25.34 $$(\ln n)_s \nu^s = 2H - 2\tilde{\omega}^2/n,$$

which shows that the vertical gradient is of the same order as the normal curvatures of the equipotential surface. The zenith distance β will normally be near $\tfrac{1}{2}\pi$, so that the last term on the right of Equation 25.32 will usually be small compared with the first term. Even so, we should require a knowledge of the vertical gradient in order to determine k from torsion balance measurements. Subject to these considerations, everything in Equation 25.33, except the refraction curvatures, can be measured at both ends of the line; by substitution in Equation 25.31, we can determine either the difference in potential or a relation between the refraction curvatures. It is noteworthy that the effect of refraction cancels if $n\chi \sin \beta$ is the same at both ends of the line. Because $n \sin \beta$ is usually nearly the same at the two ends, this fact means that to a fourth order in the expansion of the potential, the effect of refraction depends solely on the difference in curvature of the ray at the two ends.

19. The difference of potential to a *first order* is
25.35 $$\bar{N} - N = \tfrac{1}{2}s(n \cos \beta + \bar{n} \cos \bar{\beta}).$$

If gravity n at the two ends is assumed to be the same, then we have

25.36 $$\frac{\bar{N} - N}{n} = \tfrac{1}{2}s(\cos \beta + \cos \bar{\beta});$$

this equation is the difference in "height" which would be obtained by the ordinary surveying process of calculating "trigonometric heights" from reciprocal vertical angles measured from the plumbline. This process accordingly gives heights related to the first-order difference of potential, comparable with results which would be obtained from spirit

---

[2] Otherwise, two adjacent plumblines could intersect in air at points which would have double values of astronomic latitude and longitude. This is contrary to experience.

leveling, within the limits of approximation and of the observing procedure. This first-order result is unaffected by refraction, which is a second-order effect, provided that β, $\bar{\beta}$ refer to the same ray, that is, to observations taken at the same time.

EXPANSION OF GEODETIC HEIGHTS

20. Equations 25.32 and 25.33, before the introduction of Equation 25.34, hold true in any (ω, ϕ, N) system. In the geodetic (ω, ϕ, h) system, we have $n = 1$ so that

$$\partial h / \partial s = \cos \beta$$

25.37
$$\frac{\partial^2 h}{\partial s^2} = -k \sin^2 \beta - \chi \sin \beta$$

in which β is now the zenith distance of the refracted line from the geodetic (spheroidal) normal and k is the normal curvature of the h-surface in the azimuth of the line. From Equation 18.18, we have

25.38
$$-k = \frac{\sin^2 \alpha}{(\nu + h)} + \frac{\cos^2 \alpha}{(\rho + h)}.$$

21. Including the effect of refraction, the difference in geodetic heights is given by Equation 25.31 as

$$\bar{h} - h = \tfrac{1}{2} s (\cos \bar{\beta} + \cos \beta)$$
$$+ \tfrac{1}{12} s^2 (\bar{k} \sin^2 \bar{\beta} + \bar{\chi} \sin \bar{\beta}$$
25.39
$$- k \sin^2 \beta - \chi \sin \beta),$$

correct to a fourth order. It should be noted that β, $\bar{\beta}$ must be measured simultaneously because the changing refraction would alter the curvature of the line between observations; the formula has been derived on the assumption that β, $\bar{\beta}$ refer to a single state of the line. In accordance with the convention adopted throughout this book, $\bar{\beta}$ is the zenith distance of the line produced. The observed zenith distance at the overbarred end will be $(180° - \bar{\beta})$.

22. As in the case of the potential, we find that the effect of refraction cancels if $\chi \sin \beta$ is the same at the two ends of the line. Apart from the effects of refraction, the formula obtained from Equation 25.31 for the difference in geodetic heights is extremely accurate. For example, over a line 80 kilometers long in the worst azimuth, the error in height is no more than 3 mm. in 2,700 meters, that is, about one part in a million, compared with exact calculation from formulas given earlier in this chapter. The second-order terms in this example amount to 138 mm.

EXPANSION OF LATITUDE AND LONGITUDE

23. Geodetic latitude and longitude may be expanded along the line in much the same way as geodetic heights. For example, the expansion of longitude in radian measure to a second-order along a straight line is

25.40
$$\bar{\omega} - \omega = s l^1 + \tfrac{1}{2} s^2 \omega_{rs} l^r l^s$$

in which we have

25.41
$$l^1 = \frac{\partial \omega}{\partial s} = \frac{\sin \alpha \sin \beta}{(\nu + h) \cos \phi}$$

and

$$\tfrac{1}{2} \omega_{rs} l^r l^s = -\tfrac{1}{2} \Gamma^1_{rs} l^r l^s$$
$$= \frac{\sin \alpha \sin \beta (\sin \phi \cos \alpha \sin \beta - \cos \phi \cos \beta)}{(\nu + h)^2 \cos^2 \phi},$$
25.42

using values of the Christoffel symbols given in Equations 18.34 and 18.35. Calculation of the terminal coordinates in this way seldom is justified in comparison with the exact methods given in § 25–14 and § 25–15, but the first-order expansions are sometimes useful to give preliminary values. Equations 25.41 and 25.42 are, of course, evaluated at the unbarred end of the line.

ASTRO-GEODETIC LEVELING

24. In this section, we shall enclose quantities related to the astronomical system in parentheses, while quantities not in parentheses are related to the geodetic system. Quantities at the far end of a line, whose unit vector is l^r and length is s, will as usual be overbarred. In § 19–23, we defined the vector deflection as

$$\Delta^r = (\nu^r) - \nu^r$$

and showed that, to a first order, this definition is equivalent to the classical first-order notions of deflection. The component of deflection in the direction l^r is accordingly

$$\Delta = \Delta^r l_r = (\cos \beta) - \cos \beta.$$

At the far end of the line, the component is

$$\bar{\Delta} = \bar{\Delta}^r l_r = (\cos \bar{\beta}) - \cos \bar{\beta}$$

so that, using Equations 25.36 and 25.39, we have

$$\tfrac{1}{2} s (\Delta + \bar{\Delta}) = \tfrac{1}{2} s \{ (\cos \beta) + (\cos \bar{\beta}) \}$$
$$- \tfrac{1}{2} s \{ \cos \beta + \cos \bar{\beta} \}$$
$$= (1/n) \{ \bar{N} - N \} - \{ \bar{h} - h \}$$

25.43
= rise in "trigonometric heights" minus the rise in geodetic height along the line, all to a first order.

25. The components of deflection Δ are obtained to a first order from Equation 19.42 as

25.44
$$\Delta = \Delta^r l_r = (\cos \phi \; \delta\omega) \, \sin \alpha \, \sin \beta + (\delta\phi) \cos \alpha \, \sin \beta$$

in which $\delta\omega$, for example, is the astronomic minus the geodetic longitude. The astronomic coordinate is directly measured, and the geodetic coordinate is carried forward by calculation along the sides of a triangulation or traverse. Starting from known or assumed values of $(N/n - h)$, we can accordingly derive values of $(N/\bar{n} - h)$ at all other points. If N is the potential relative to the potential of the geoid, then N/n is roughly the depth of the geoid below the observing station, and $(N/n - h)$ is roughly the local separation of geoid and spheroid. The approximations involved are, however, equivalent to the assumption that the deflections are the same at a point on the topographic surface as the deflections would be if measurable at a point "vertically" below on the geoid or spheroid. This assumption would require the actual plumblines to have the same curvature as the geodetic normals. At points not much above the geoid (or spheroid) in gravitationally undisturbed country, the approximation might be justified; but in other circumstances, the accumulation of error could be serious, and the results should be accepted with reservation until such time as they can be checked by other methods.

DEFLECTIONS BY TORSION BALANCE MEASUREMENTS

26. We have seen that deflections of the vertical, relating the normals to the third coordinate surfaces of two (ω, ϕ, N) systems, usually the astronomic system and a geodetic (ω, ϕ, h) system with a spheroidal base, can be obtained by direct astronomical measurement of latitude and longitude (or azimuth) and by comparison with the geodetic coordinates extended from an origin by triangulation or traverse. The results are, of course, affected by accumulation of error in the triangulation or traverse. Relative deflections can also be obtained, or at least interpolated, from measurement of zenith distances, but the results in this case may be vitiated by uncertainty in atmospheric refraction. The two methods may be combined in the adjustment of a space network, as we shall see in Chapter 26.

27. A third method is to integrate gravity anomalies over large areas surrounding the point where the deflection is required. For accurate results, gravity measurements should be made over the entire globe; even so, the results would be vitiated by smoothing the actual measures of gravity.

28. A fourth method, which we shall now consider, uses the torsion balance as originally proposed by Eötvös—the inventor of the balance—and since used by Mueller and a few others. Some of the disadvantages of this method, mentioned in §20–34, restrict its use to rather flat terrain where the deflections are of least interest and where simplified formulas are justifiable. With a view to the possibility of a more extended future use of the instrument or of a much improved modern gravity sensor, we shall consider the basic theory rigorously so that the nature of any approximations made may be fully understood.

29. We shall adopt exactly the same notation as in the spherical figure 15, Chapter 19. The normals to the equipotential surfaces at the two observing stations P, $\bar{P}$ will be ν^r and $\bar{\nu}^r$; the fixed vector l^r, represented in the spherical diagram by Q, will be the unit vector of the straight line $P\bar{P}$. In addition, we shall require a unit vector m^r normal to the plane containing ν^r and l^r, that is, perpendicular to the plane of normal section at P. This vector m^r is shown in the spherical figure 29 as the pole of the great circle PQ. In the same way, the unit vector $\bar{m}^r$ is perpendicular to the plane of normal section at $\bar{P}$ and is shown as the pole of the great circle $\bar{P}Q$ in figure 29. The angle between the two planes of normal section is shown as λ in figure 29. All other quantities shown in figure 15, Chapter 19, will be required and are connected by Equations 19.01 through 19.18.

30. We shall now consider the integral

25.45
$$\int_P^{\bar{P}} \bar{\nu}_{rs} (m^r \csc \bar{\beta} - \bar{m}^r \csc \beta) l^s ds$$

along the line $P\bar{P}$. The reason for considering an integral in this form will appear later. In this integral, $\bar{\nu}_r$ is the normal to the equipotential surface at the current point and ds is an element of length of $P\bar{P}$ so that we have

$$l^s ds = dx^s.$$

The vector in parentheses is evidently constant during the integration, so that we have the value of the integral as

$$\int_P^{\bar{P}} \{\bar{\nu}_r (m^r \csc \bar{\beta} - \bar{m}^r \csc \beta)\}_s dx^s$$
$$= [\bar{\nu}_r (m_r \csc \bar{\beta} - \bar{m}^r \csc \beta)]_P^{\bar{P}}$$
$$= \sin \bar{\theta} \csc \bar{\beta} + \sin \theta \csc \beta$$

25.46
$$= 2 \sin \lambda$$

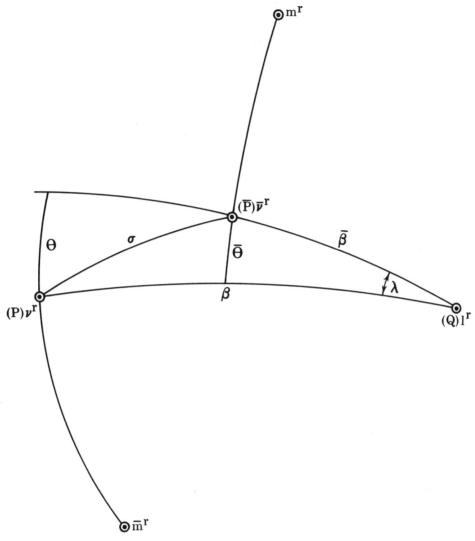

Figure 29.

where θ, $\bar{\theta}$ are as shown in figure 29.

31. The next step is to obtain an approximate value of the integral in Equation 25.45 — in terms of the gravitational parameters at the two ends of the line — by evaluating the integrand at P and $\bar{P}$ and by meaning the results on the assumption that the integrand varies uniformly along the line. Less approximate methods of integration, such as the use of Equation 25.31 with F equal to the indefinite integral of Equation 25.45, would require measurement of the gradients of the gravitational parameters which is not at present possible. For our immediate purpose, it will be easier to evaluate the integrand in the alternative form

$$(\operatorname{cosec} \beta \; \operatorname{cosec} \bar{\beta}) \, \bar{\nu}_{rs} \, \epsilon^{rpq} (\nu_p + \bar{\nu}_p) l_q l^s,$$

obtained by using the relations

$$\epsilon^{rpq} \nu_p l_q = (\sin \beta) m^r$$

$$\epsilon^{rpq} l_p \bar{\nu}_q = (\sin \bar{\beta}) \bar{m}^r.$$

The value of the integrand at P is accordingly

$$(\operatorname{cosec} \beta \; \operatorname{cosec} \bar{\beta}) \nu_{rs} \epsilon^{rpq} (\nu_p + \bar{\nu}_p) l_q l^s$$

in which $\bar{\nu}_p$ is taken as translated to P by parallel displacement whose components are accordingly given by Equation 19.19, so that we have

$$(\nu_p + \bar{\nu}_p) = (\cos \bar{\phi} \, \sin \delta\omega) \lambda_p + (\sin \sigma \, \cos \alpha^*) \mu_p$$
$$+ (1 + \cos \sigma) \nu_p$$
$$= (\sin \sigma \, \sin \alpha^*) \lambda_p + (\sin \sigma \, \cos \alpha^*) \mu_p$$
$$+ (1 + \cos \sigma) \nu_p,$$

using Equation 19.09. We have also

$$l_q = \lambda_q \sin \alpha \sin \beta + \mu_q \cos \alpha \sin \beta + \nu_q \cos \beta.$$

Some labor may be saved by evaluating

$$\epsilon^{rpq}(\nu_p + \bar\nu_p) l_q$$

first and ignoring terms in ν^r because we have

$$\nu_{rs}\nu^r = 0.$$

The curvature parameters are introduced from Equations 12.016, 12.046, and 12.047 as

$$k_1 = -\nu_{rs}\lambda^r\lambda^s$$
$$k_2 = -\nu_{rs}\mu^r\mu^s$$
$$t_1 = -\nu_{rs}\lambda^r\mu^s = -\nu_{rs}\mu^r\lambda^s$$
$$\gamma_1 = \nu_{rs}\lambda^r\nu^s$$

25.47 $\qquad \gamma_2 = \nu_{rs}\mu^r\nu^s;$

we have finally for the value of the integrand at P,

$$I_P = +k_1 \sin\beta \,\mathrm{cosec}\,\bar\beta \,\{\sin\alpha\cos\alpha(1+\cos\sigma)$$
$$- \sin\alpha\cot\beta\sin\sigma\cos\alpha^*\}$$
$$- k_2 \sin\beta \,\mathrm{cosec}\,\bar\beta \,\{\sin\alpha\cos\alpha(1+\cos\sigma)$$
$$- \cos\alpha\cot\beta\sin\sigma\sin\alpha^*\}$$
$$+ t_1 \sin\beta \,\mathrm{cosec}\,\bar\beta \,\{(\cos^2\alpha - \sin^2\alpha)(1+\cos\sigma)$$
$$- \cot\beta\sin\sigma\cos(\alpha+\alpha^*)\}$$
$$- \gamma_1 \cos\beta \,\mathrm{cosec}\,\bar\beta \,\{\cos\alpha(1+\cos\sigma)$$
$$- \cot\beta\sin\sigma\cos\alpha^*\}$$
$$+ \gamma_2 \cos\beta \,\mathrm{cosec}\,\bar\beta \,\{\sin\alpha(1+\cos\sigma)$$

25.48 $\qquad - \cot\beta\sin\sigma\sin\alpha^*\}.$

The value of the integrand at $\bar P$ is very easily obtained by interchanging overbars in this formula and changing the sign of σ so that we have

$$I_{\bar P} = \bar k_1 \sin\bar\beta \,\mathrm{cosec}\,\beta \,\{\sin\bar\alpha\cos\bar\alpha(1+\cos\sigma)$$
$$+ \sin\bar\alpha\cot\bar\beta\sin\sigma\cos\bar\alpha^*\},$$

$$\text{etc.}$$

From Equation 25.46, we then have

25.49 $\qquad s(I_P + I_{\bar P}) = 4\sin\lambda$

where s is the length $P\bar P$ of the line. The sole assumption made in the derivation of this result is that the integrand varies uniformly along the line. Otherwise, all the formulas are exact and, in addition to the five parameters, require five of the seven observable quantities ϕ, $\bar\phi$, $\delta\omega$, α, β, $\bar\alpha$, $\bar\beta$ from which all other required quantities can be calculated from Equations 19.01, etc., in accordance with § 19–12.

32. In practice, β will be somewhere near $90°$ and $\sin\sigma$ will be small so that the second terms within the braces of Equation 25.48 will be very small compared with the first terms, and we may usually write

$$I_P \simeq \sin\beta \,\mathrm{cosec}\,\bar\beta \,(1+\cos\sigma)$$
$$\times \{(k_1 - k_2)\sin\alpha\cos\alpha + t_1(\cos^2\alpha - \sin^2\alpha)$$
25.50 $\qquad - \gamma_1\cos\alpha\cot\beta + \gamma_2\sin\alpha\cot\beta\}.$

In this form, the curvature parameters $(k_1 - k_2)$, t_1, γ_1, γ_2 may be obtained from torsion balance measurements. In fact, reference to Equation 20.36 will show that the expression within braces could be obtained by a single torsion balance reading if it were possible to set the line joining the weights in the azimuth and zenith distance of $P\bar P$. Similar results for measurements at $\bar P$ are obtained by interchanging overbars in Equation 25.50, if we remember that, in accordance with our usual convention, $\bar\alpha$, $\bar\beta$ refer to the line $P\bar P$ produced through $\bar P$, and not to the back direction $\bar P P$.

33. A further approximation may often be made in cases where β and $\bar\beta$ are nearly $\frac{1}{2}\pi$ by writing

$$I_P \simeq (1+\cos\sigma)\{(k_1 - k_2)\sin\alpha\cos\alpha$$
25.51 $\qquad + t_1(\cos^2\alpha - \sin^2\alpha)\}.$

Moreover, in these approximate formulas, it will usually be sufficient to evaluate α, β, σ, s from geodetic coordinates without making astronomical observations. From Equation 12.050, we can see that I_P in this last result is directly proportional to the geodesic torsion of the equipotential surface in the azimuth of the line.

34. If the equipotential surfaces were spheres, then $P\bar P$ and the normals at P and $\bar P$ would be coplanar, so that l^r, ν^r, $\bar\nu^r$ in figure 29 would lie on the same great circle and λ would be zero. The magnitude of λ, obtained from Equation 25.49, is accordingly an indication of the departure of the field from spherical symmetry.

35. So far, we have been working entirely in astronomical coordinates, but the formulas apply equally well in any other (ω, ϕ, N) coordinate system, provided we substitute appropriate values of the curvature parameters. We shall normally work in the geodetic (ω, ϕ, h) system with a spheroidal base, as discussed in § 18–20. In that case, we can evaluate the integrand I_P from whichever equation of Equation 25.48, 25.50, or 25.51 is appropriate simply by substituting $k_1 = -1/\nu$, $k_2 = -1/\rho$, $t_1 = 0$,

$\gamma_1 = \gamma_2 = 0$. The azimuths and zenith distances, etc., should now properly be computed from the geodetic coordinates of P and $\bar{P}$, but in practice, the coefficients of the curvature parameters will be sufficiently accurate if computed in either system of coordinates. We can similarly evaluate $I_{\bar{P}}$ in geodetic coordinates; by substitution in Equation 25.49, we have a geodetic value for λ which we shall write as λ_G. We shall write λ_A for the value of λ, obtained in the astronomical system from torsion balance measures of the gravitational parameters. The geodetic value λ_G is the angle between two planes, one containing the line $P\bar{P}$ and the geodetic normal at P and the other containing $P\bar{P}$ and the geodetic normal at $\bar{P}$; we have, of course, assumed throughout that the positions of P and $\bar{P}$ remain fixed in space, whatever coordinate system is used to describe these positions.

36. We can now obtain a first-order relation between $(\lambda_A - \lambda_G)$ and the deflections at P and $\bar{P}$. For this purpose, we consider changes $d\phi$, $d\omega$ in the latitude and longitude of P in the triangle CPQ of figure 15, Chapter 19. We have seen in § 19–4 that $d\phi$, $d\omega$ can arise from either a change in the coordinate system or a change in the position of P. In this case, we consider that $d\phi$, $d\omega$ arise from a change in the coordinate system, with P and $\bar{P}$ fixed, so that the vector $l^r(Q)$ as well as the axis of rotation C^r are fixed. In the spherical triangle PCQ, we have

$$\sin Q = \cos \phi \sin \alpha \operatorname{cosec} CQ.$$

Logarithmic differentiation of this equation with CQ fixed gives

$$\cot Q \, dQ = -\tan \phi \, d\phi + \cot \alpha \, d\alpha$$
$$= d\omega(\cot \alpha \sin \phi - \cot \alpha \cos \alpha \cot \beta \cos \phi)$$
$$+ d\phi(\cos \alpha \cot \beta - \tan \phi)$$

on substitution of Equations 19.29. Division by

$$\cot Q = \operatorname{cosec} \alpha \sin \beta \tan \phi - \cot \alpha \cos \beta$$

gives us finally

$$dQ = (\cos \alpha \operatorname{cosec} \beta \cos \phi)d\omega - (\sin \alpha \operatorname{cosec} \beta)d\phi.$$

If we start with geodetic coordinates ω_G, ϕ_G, the changes $d\omega$, $d\phi$ to the astronomical system ω_A, ϕ_A are $(\omega_A - \omega_G)$, $(\phi_A - \phi_G)$ and

$$dQ = (\omega_A - \omega_G) \cos \alpha \operatorname{cosec} \beta \cos \phi$$
$$- (\phi_A - \phi_G) \sin \alpha \operatorname{cosec} \beta,$$

with a similar equation

$$d\bar{Q} = (\bar{\omega}_A - \bar{\omega}_G) \cos \bar{\alpha} \operatorname{cosec} \bar{\beta} \cos \bar{\phi}$$
$$- (\bar{\phi}_A - \bar{\phi}_G) \sin \bar{\alpha} \operatorname{cosec} \bar{\beta}$$

arising from a change in the coordinates of $\bar{P}$. In this equation, $\bar{\alpha}$, $\bar{\beta}$ refer as usual to $P\bar{P}$ produced, and $(\bar{\omega}_A - \bar{\omega}_G)$, $(\bar{\phi}_A - \bar{\phi}_G)$ are the deflections at $\bar{P}$. The difference is

$$dQ - d\bar{Q} = Q_A - Q_G - (\bar{Q}_A - \bar{Q}_G)$$
$$= (Q_A - \bar{Q}_A) - (Q_G - \bar{Q}_G)$$
$$= \lambda_A - \lambda_G$$

so that we have finally

$$(\lambda_A - \lambda_G) = -\cos \bar{\alpha} \operatorname{cosec} \bar{\beta} \cos \bar{\phi} \, (\bar{\omega}_A - \bar{\omega}_G)$$
$$+ \sin \bar{\alpha} \operatorname{cosec} \bar{\beta} \, (\bar{\phi}_A - \bar{\phi}_G)$$
$$+ \cos \alpha \operatorname{cosec} \beta \cos \phi \, (\omega_A - \omega_G)$$
25.52 $$- \sin \alpha \operatorname{cosec} \beta \, (\phi_A - \phi_G).$$

This single relation, which is in the nature of an observation equation, does not, of course, determine the four deflections at both ends of the line. Observations at the three vertices of a triangle would give us three equations connecting six unknown deflections. A fourth point would add two more equations and two extra unknowns, while a crossed quadrilateral would provide six equations for eight unknowns. In theory, a strong network would eventually provide sufficient and even redundant equations to determine the deflections at all points. Nevertheless, the main application of the method is likely to be the interpolation of deflections between known values, which could be substituted in the observation equations, such as Equation 25.52, before solution.

CHAPTER 26

Internal Adjustment of Networks

GENERAL REMARKS

1. In this chapter, we shall consider the formation of differential observation equations for most of the usual systems of geodetic measurement, including, in some cases, the derivation of finite formulas that may be necessary to provide computed values. Differentiation of such formulas leads to the observation equations. Instrumentation and observation procedures will be considered only to the very limited extent necessary to understand the nature of the resulting measurements insofar as this affects the formation of the observation equations. We shall not deal with the formation and solution of normal equations from the observation equations; these matters are not peculiar to geodesy and are best studied in the standard literature. The old distinction between adjustment by observation and condition equations is ignored; any fixed condition can always be turned into an observation equation by differentiation and given a very large weight in the solution. The order in which various systems are treated and the amount of space devoted to each system have nothing to do with relative importance, but have been decided partly by history and mainly by simplicity and continuity of explanation. Line-crossing techniques are given last, for example, because they introduce a minimum principle not required in any of the other systems. Lunar methods are discussed after stellar triangulation and satellite triangulation, not because lunar methods are later and more sophisticated, but simply because they require less explanation in that order. In every case, only enough detail is given to provide a full understanding of the method in the general context of this book. Satellite triangulation, for example, which grows

in sophistication every week, will eventually need to be presented in a separate book when the rate of growth slows down enough for a detailed description to remain in date long enough to justify publication in print.

THE TRIANGLE IN SPACE

2. If we are given the geodetic coordinates (ω, ϕ, h) of a Point 1 (fig. 30) and have also the

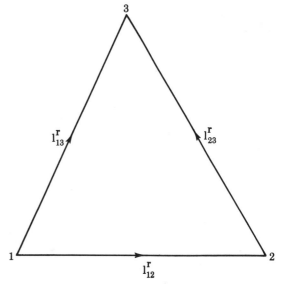

Figure 30.

geodetic azimuth, zenith distance, and distance $(\alpha_{12}, \beta_{12}, s_{12})$ of Point 2 from Point 1, we can compute $(\bar{\omega}, \bar{\phi}, \bar{h}, \bar{\alpha}_{12}, \bar{\beta}_{12})$ at Point 2 from formulas given in this chapter. If we are also given $(\alpha_{13}, \beta_{13})$

at Point 1 and $(\alpha_{23}, \beta_{23})$ at Point 2, then the position of Point 3 can be found by intersection, but in order to compute the position of Point 3, we have to solve the triangle 123 for the two sides (s_{13}, s_{23}). We can always do this by computing the angles 312 and 123 from azimuths and zenith distances, by deducing the third angle 231, and then by applying the rule of sines. For example, we have

$$\cos 312 = \cos \beta_{12} \cos \beta_{13}$$

26.01 $+ \sin \beta_{12} \sin \beta_{13} \cos (\alpha_{12} - \alpha_{13}).$

We are here dealing with computations in geodetic coordinates; the α's and β's are referred to the geodetic or spheroidal normal and are assumed to be free of error. Later in this chapter, we shall relate the geodetic quantities to actual measurements, necessarily referred to the astronomical zenith and subjected to atmospheric refraction and observational error; but for the present, we are merely discussing operations in the geodetic coordinate system on the assumption that we are given a consistent set of quantities in that system. In that case, the two lines in space, 13 and 23, will intersect in a unique Point 3, whose position will be the same whether it is computed from Point 1 or from Point 2.

3. Alternatively, we obtain direct expressions for the sides (s_{13}, s_{23}) in a convenient matrix form. The basic vector equation of the triangle is

26.02 $s_{12}l_{12}^r + s_{23}l_{23}^r - s_{13}l_{13}^r = 0,$

which expresses the condition that there shall be no change in the Cartesian coordinates of the Point 1 on proceeding around the triangle. As a relation between vectors, Equation 26.02 is true in any coordinates, provided that parallels to the vectors are considered at a single point in space. If we substitute the Cartesian components of the three vectors in Equation 26.02 and use Equation 25.11, we have

$s_{12}\mathbf{Q}^T\{\sin \alpha_{12} \sin \beta_{12}, \cos \alpha_{12} \sin \beta_{12}, \cos \beta_{12}\}$

$+ s_{23}\overline{\mathbf{Q}}^T\{\sin \bar{\alpha}_{23} \sin \bar{\beta}_{23}, \cos \bar{\alpha}_{23} \sin \bar{\beta}_{23}, \cos \bar{\beta}_{23}\}$

$- s_{13}\mathbf{Q}^T\{\sin \alpha_{13} \sin \beta_{13}, \cos \alpha_{13} \sin \beta_{13}, \cos \beta_{13}\} = 0$

26.03

in which overbarred quantities refer to Point 2 and all other quantities refer to Point 1. We thus have two independent equations to determine s_{13} and s_{23}. We can eliminate s_{13} and so directly determine s_{23} if we first premultiply Equation 26.03 by $\mathbf{Q}$ and

then by $(\cos \alpha_{13}, -\sin \alpha_{13}, 0)$, which gives us

$s_{12} (\cos \alpha_{13}, -\sin \alpha_{13}, 0)$

   $\times \{\sin \alpha_{12} \sin \beta_{12}, \cos \alpha_{12} \sin \beta_{12}, \cos \beta_{12}\}$

$= - s_{23} (\cos \alpha_{13}, -\sin \alpha_{13}, 0)$

   $\times \mathbf{Q}\overline{\mathbf{Q}}^T\{\sin \bar{\alpha}_{23} \sin \bar{\beta}_{23}, \cos \bar{\alpha}_{23} \sin \bar{\beta}_{23}, \cos \bar{\beta}_{23}\}.$

26.04

This entire operation is equivalent to contraction of Equation 26.02 with m_r, a unit h-surface vector at Point 1 perpendicular to l_{13}^r, so that we have

$$m_r = \lambda_r \cos \alpha_{13} - \mu_r \sin \alpha_{13}.$$

In the same way, if we premultiply Equation 26.03 by $\overline{\mathbf{Q}}$ and then by $(\cos \bar{\alpha}_{23}, -\sin \bar{\alpha}_{23}, 0)$, we have

$s_{12} (\cos \bar{\alpha}_{23}, -\sin \bar{\alpha}_{23}, 0)$

   $\times \overline{\mathbf{Q}}\mathbf{Q}^T\{\sin \alpha_{12} \sin \beta_{12}, \cos \alpha_{12} \sin \beta_{12}, \cos \beta_{12}\}$

$= s_{13} (\cos \bar{\alpha}_{23}, -\sin \bar{\alpha}_{23}, 0)$

   $\times \overline{\mathbf{Q}}\mathbf{Q}^T\{\sin \alpha_{13} \sin \beta_{13}, \cos \alpha_{13} \sin \beta_{13}, \cos \beta_{13}\}.$

26.05

The matrix $\overline{\mathbf{Q}}\mathbf{Q}^T$ is given by Equation 19.25, with auxiliary angles as in Equations 19.01, etc., and contains only latitudes and longitudes of Points 2 (overbarred) and 1.

4. The triangle can also be solved by the differential method given in § 25–15 from initial approximate values of the geodetic coordinates of Point 3, but in this case, the correction to length ds would be unknown. Thus, for the line 13, we have three equations connecting four unknowns: three corrections to the coordinates of Point 3 and one correction to the length 13. The line 23 adds three equations and only one more unknown: the correction to the length 23. Accordingly, we have six equations connecting five unknowns, and the problem is soluble with a complete check if the data are consistent. If the data are inconsistent or refer to a different coordinate system, we must treat the triangle as part of a network by methods described in the following sections.

VARIATION OF POSITION

5. We shall now consider first-order changes in the components of the straight-line unit vector l^r arising from changes dx^r, $d\bar{x}^r$ in the coordinates of the two ends of the line. If we suppose that we

are working in Cartesian coordinates, then we have from Equation 25.04

26.06 $$sl^r = \bar{x}^r - x^r,$$

which can be differentiated as

26.07 $$sd(l^r) + l^r ds = d\bar{x}^r - dx^r.$$

We know from Equation 3.19 that the differential of a unit vector, which remains a unit vector after the change is a small vector perpendicular to the original vector so that $d(l^r)$ is perpendicular to l^r; if we contract Equation 26.07 with l_r (or $\bar{l}_r$, which has the same Cartesian components at the far end of the line), we have

26.08 $$ds = \bar{l}_r d\bar{x}^r - l_r dx^r,$$

giving us the change in the length of the line arising from dx^r and $d\bar{x}^r$. But dx^r, $d\bar{x}^r$ are small vectors at the two ends of the line, and this last equation is accordingly an invariant equation which is true in any coordinates, even though we derived the equation in Cartesian coordinates. We can substitute the changes in any coordinates for dx^r, $d\bar{x}^r$, provided that we substitute the covariant components of $\bar{l}_r$, l_r in the same coordinate system.

6. Elimination of ds between Equations 26.07 and 26.08 gives

$$sd(l^r) = d\bar{x}^r - dx^r - (\bar{l}_s d\bar{x}^s - l_s dx^s) l^r$$
$$= (d\bar{x}^s - dx^s)(\delta^r_s - l^r l_s)$$

26.09 $$= (d\bar{x}^s - dx^s)(m_s m^r + n_s n^r),$$

using Equation 2.07 and denoting by m^r, n^r *any* perpendicular vectors which form a right-handed orthogonal triad with l^r. If $\bar{m}_s$, $\bar{n}_s$ are parallel vectors at the overbarred end of the line, we can re-write this last equation as

$$sd(l^r) = (\bar{m}_s d\bar{x}^s - m_s dx^s) m^r + (\bar{n}_s d\bar{x}^s - n_s dx^s) n^r,$$

26.10

which again shows that $d(l^r)$ is perpendicular to l^r because it is in the plane of m^r and n^r. Moreover, Equation 26.10 is a vector equation with invariant coefficients, holding true in any coordinate system.

VARIATION OF POSITION IN GEODETIC COORDINATES

7. If the azimuth and zenith distance of l^r are α, β, we have from Equation 12.007

$$l^r = \lambda^r \sin \alpha \sin \beta + \mu^r \cos \alpha \sin \beta + \nu^r \cos \beta.$$
26.11

Differentiation of this equation for changes in ω, ϕ, α, β and use of Equations 12.008 or 12.014, etc., give

$$d(l^r) = (\mu^r \sin \phi \, d\omega - \nu^r \cos \phi \, d\omega) \sin \alpha \sin \beta$$
$$- (\lambda^r \sin \phi \, d\omega + \nu^r d\phi) \cos \alpha \sin \beta$$
$$+ (\lambda^r \cos \phi \, d\omega + \mu^r d\phi) \cos \beta$$
$$+ m^r d\beta - n^r \sin \beta \, d\alpha$$

26.12

in which we have written

$$m^r = \lambda^r \sin \alpha \cos \beta + \mu^r \cos \alpha \cos \beta - \nu^r \sin \beta$$
$$n^r = -\lambda^r \cos \alpha + \mu^r \sin \alpha$$

26.13

so that the azimuth and zenith distance of m^r are $(\alpha, \frac{1}{2}\pi + \beta)$ and of n^r are $(\frac{3}{2}\pi + \alpha, \frac{1}{2}\pi)$. It is evident that (l^r, m^r, n^r) form a right-handed orthogonal triad and that m^r, n^r can accordingly be used in Equation 26.10. Also, it must be possible to express $d(l^r)$ in Equation 26.12 completely in terms of m^r, n^r because $d(l^r)$, being perpendicular to l^r, must lie in the plane of m^r and n^r. Indeed, we find after some manipulation

$$d(l^r) = m^r \{ d\beta + \cos \phi \sin \alpha \, d\omega + \cos \alpha \, d\phi \}$$
$$+ n^r \{ -\sin \beta \, d\alpha + (\sin \phi \sin \beta$$
$$- \cos \phi \cos \alpha \cos \beta) d\omega$$
26.14 $$+ \sin \alpha \cos \beta \, d\phi \}.$$

Equating coefficients of m^r and n^r in this last equation with the corresponding coefficients in Equation 26.10, we have

$$sd\beta = \bar{m}_s d\bar{x}^s - m_s dx^s - s \cos \phi \sin \alpha \, d\omega - s \cos \alpha \, d\phi$$
26.15

$$s \sin \beta \, d\alpha = -\bar{n}_s d\bar{x}^s + n_s dx^s$$
$$+ s(\sin \phi \sin \beta - \cos \phi \cos \alpha \cos \beta) d\omega$$
26.16 $$+ s \sin \alpha \cos \beta \, d\phi,$$

giving the changes in azimuth and zenith distance at the unbarred end of the line that arise from changes of $d\omega$, $d\phi$, dh and $d\bar{\omega}$, $d\bar{\phi}$, $d\bar{h}$ at the two ends, provided that we use the (ω, ϕ, h) components of m_s and n_s as given by Equations 26.13 and provided $\bar{m}_s$, $\bar{n}_s$ are the (ω, ϕ, h) components of parallel vectors at the overbarred end of the line.

8. From Equations 19.32 and 26.13, we have

$$\{m_1, m_2, m_3\} = \mathbf{S}^T\{\sin \alpha \cos \beta, \cos \alpha \cos \beta,$$
$$-\sin \beta\}$$
$$\{n_1, n_2, n_3\} = \mathbf{S}^T\{-\cos \alpha, \sin \alpha, 0\};$$

26.17

and from Equation 19.39, we have

$$\{\bar{m}_1, \bar{m}_2, \bar{m}_3\} = \bar{\mathbf{S}}^T\mathbf{Q}\bar{\mathbf{Q}}^T\{\sin \alpha \cos \beta, \cos \alpha \cos \beta,$$
$$-\sin \beta\}$$
$$\{\bar{n}_1, \bar{n}_2, \bar{n}_3\} = \bar{\mathbf{S}}^T\mathbf{Q}\bar{\mathbf{Q}}^T\{-\cos \alpha, \sin \alpha, 0\} \cdot$$

26.18

These equations hold true in any (ω, ϕ, N) system. In the geodetic system, substitution of $-k_1 = 1/(\nu + h)$, $-k_2 = 1/(\rho + h)$, $t_1 = 0$, $n = 1$ in Equations 19.31 and 19.32 and use of Equations 19.34 give

$$\mathbf{R} = (\mathbf{S}^T)^{-1} = \begin{pmatrix} \sec \phi/(\nu + h) & 0 & 0 \\ 0 & 1/(\rho + h) & 0 \\ 0 & 0 & 1 \end{pmatrix}$$

26.19 $\quad \mathbf{S} = \begin{pmatrix} (\nu + h) \cos \phi & 0 & 0 \\ 0 & (\rho + h) & 0 \\ 0 & 0 & 1 \end{pmatrix}$

so that we may write

$$\left\{\frac{m_1}{(\nu + h) \cos \phi}, \frac{m_2}{(\rho + h)}, m_3\right\}$$
$$= \{\sin \alpha \cos \beta, \cos \alpha \cos \beta, -\sin \beta\}$$

$$\left\{\frac{n_1}{(\nu + h) \cos \phi}, \frac{n_2}{(\rho + h)}, n_3\right\}$$

26.20 $\quad = \{-\cos \alpha, \sin \alpha, 0\}$

and

$$\left\{\frac{\bar{m}_1}{(\bar{\nu} + \bar{h}) \cos \bar{\phi}}, \frac{\bar{m}_2}{(\bar{\rho} + \bar{h})}, \bar{m}_3\right\}$$
$$= \mathbf{Q}\bar{\mathbf{Q}}^T\{\sin \alpha \cos \beta, \cos \alpha \cos \beta, -\sin \beta\}$$

$$\left\{\frac{\bar{n}_1}{(\bar{\nu} + \bar{h}) \cos \bar{\phi}}, \frac{\bar{n}_2}{(\bar{\rho} + \bar{h})}, \bar{n}_3\right\}$$
$$= \mathbf{Q}\bar{\mathbf{Q}}^T\{-\cos \alpha, \sin \alpha, 0\} \cdot$$

26.21

The matrix $\mathbf{Q}\bar{\mathbf{Q}}^T$, set forth in Equation 19.25, depends solely on the terminal latitudes and longitudes.

9. Some checks may be applied at this stage. Because the right-hand sides of Equations 26.21 consist of orthogonal matrices and a unit vector, we can premultiply each side by its transpose and obtain

$$\frac{\bar{m}_1^2}{(\bar{\nu} + \bar{h})^2 \cos^2 \bar{\phi}} + \frac{\bar{m}_2^2}{(\bar{\rho} + \bar{h})^2} + \bar{m}_3^2 = 1,$$

26.22

with a similar equation for the components of $\bar{n}_r$, together with comparable equations without the overbars for the components of m_r and n_r. In Equations 26.15 and 26.16, we may note that an alteration in the origin of longitudes could have no effect on these equations because of the longitudinal symmetry of the geodetic coordinate system. The longitude terms must accordingly reduce to some multiple of $(d\bar{\omega} - d\omega)$, or, in other words, the coefficients of $d\bar{\omega}$ and $d\omega$ must be equal in Equations 26.15 and 26.16. Extracting the $d\bar{\omega}$, $d\omega$ terms from these equations, we have

$$\bar{m}_1 = m_1 + s \cos \phi \sin \alpha$$

$$\bar{n}_1 = n_1 + s (\sin \phi \sin \beta - \cos \phi \cos \alpha \cos \beta),$$

26.23

which can be verified algebraically from Equations 19.27, 25.18, and 25.21. For reasons which will appear in the next section, we do not, however, use these relations to simplify Equations 26.15 and 26.16 at this time.

OBSERVATION EQUATIONS IN GEODETIC COORDINATES

Horizontal and Vertical Angles

10. We start with approximate geodetic positions (ω, ϕ, h), computed roughly from formulas given in Chapter 25. In the case of a triangulation, we may first have to compute the unmeasured side-lengths from Equations 26.04 and 26.05. If the position of a point is computed from more than one other point, the mean can be accepted. The approximate coordinates are then used to compute *accurately* s, α, β, $\bar{\alpha}$, $\bar{\beta}$ from Equations 25.18 and and 25.19, and thus to compute the components of the vectors m_r, n_r, $\bar{m}_r$, $\bar{n}_r$ from Equations 26.20 and 26.21. If we could measure geodetic azimuths and zenith distances, Equations 26.15 and 26.16 would become the observation equations by substituting "observed minus computed" values for $d\alpha$ and $d\beta$,

and could be solved in the usual way to provide corrections dx^s, $d\bar{x}^s$ to the initial geodetic coordinates. However, observations for azimuth and zenith distance are necessarily made in relation to the physical plumbline or astronomical zenith, and we must, *in addition*, correct the geodetic α, β by adding Equations 19.29 to effect a transformation to the astronomical system. In Equations 19.29, $\delta\omega$, $\delta\phi$ will accordingly be the astronomical minus the corrected geodetic coordinates, with longitude positive eastward and latitude positive northward as in figure 12, Chapter 12. In Equations 26.15 and 26.16, $d\omega$, $d\phi$ will be the corrected minus the initially computed geodetic coordinates. Consequently, $(\delta\omega + dw)$, $(\delta\phi + d\phi)$ will be the astronomical minus the initially computed geodetic coordinates.

11. Two further corrections are necessary. If no astronomical azimuth has been measured, an initial direction for the astronomical meridian must be assumed, and we must add a *station correction* $\Delta\alpha$ to the assumed astronomical azimuth (or subtract $\Delta\alpha$ from the calculated azimuth). To reduce the observed zenith distance to the straight line on which Equation 26.15 is based, we must also add the *angle of refraction* $\Delta\beta$ to the observed zenith distance (or subtract $\Delta\beta$ from the calculated zenith distance).

12. Application of Equations 19.29 and the corrections $\Delta\alpha$, $\Delta\beta$ to Equations 26.15 and 26.16 give us the following observation equations,

(Observed Minus Computed) Zenith Distance

$$= -\Delta\beta + \bar{m}_1 d\bar{\omega}/s + \bar{m}_2 d\bar{\phi}/s + \bar{m}_3 d\bar{h}/s$$
$$- m_1 d\omega/s - m_2 d\phi/s - m_3 dh/s$$
$$- (d\omega + \delta\omega)\cos\phi\sin\alpha - (d\phi + \delta\phi)\cos\alpha$$

26.24

(Observed Minus Computed) Azimuth

$$= -\Delta\alpha - \bar{n}_1 d\bar{\omega}\,(\operatorname{cosec}\beta)/s - \bar{n}_2 d\bar{\phi}\,(\operatorname{cosec}\beta)/s$$
$$- \bar{n}_3 d\bar{h}\,(\operatorname{cosec}\beta)/s$$
$$+ n_1 d\omega\,(\operatorname{cosec}\beta)/s + n_2 d\phi\,(\operatorname{cosec}\beta)/s$$
$$+ n_3 dh\,(\operatorname{cosec}\beta)/s$$
$$+ (d\omega + \delta\omega)(\sin\phi - \cos\phi\cos\alpha\cot\beta)$$
$$+ (d\phi + \delta\phi)\sin\alpha\cot\beta.$$

26.25

Reverse Equations

13. If measurements have been made at the other end of the line, as will almost always be the case, we must form observation equations for the reverse direction for which the vectors m_r, n_r, $\bar{m}_r$, $\bar{n}_r$ are not the same. The same equations, nevertheless, hold true if we remember that the initial azimuth and zenith distance are now $(180° + \bar{\alpha})$ and $(180° - \bar{\beta})$ and will already have been computed. If we retain the same overbarred notation for what is now the initial point, the matrix $\bar{\mathbf{Q}}\mathbf{Q}^T$ remains unaltered; the vector components at the new initial point are given by Equations 26.20 as

$$\left\{ \frac{\bar{m}_1}{(\bar{\nu} + \bar{h})\cos\bar{\phi}},\ \frac{\bar{m}_2}{(\bar{\rho} + \bar{h})},\ \bar{m}_3 \right\}$$
$$= \{\sin\bar{\alpha}\cos\bar{\beta},\ \cos\bar{\alpha}\cos\bar{\beta},\ -\sin\bar{\beta}\}$$

$$\left\{ \frac{\bar{n}_1}{(\bar{\nu} + \bar{h})\cos\bar{\phi}},\ \frac{\bar{n}_2}{(\bar{\rho} + \bar{h})},\ \bar{n}_3 \right\}$$
26.26$\qquad = \{\cos\bar{\alpha},\ -\sin\bar{\alpha},\ 0\},$

while the components at the new far point are given by Equations 26.21 as

$$\left\{ \frac{m_1}{(\nu + h)\cos\phi},\ \frac{m_2}{(\rho + h)},\ m_3 \right\}$$
$$= \mathbf{Q}\bar{\mathbf{Q}}^T\{\sin\bar{\alpha}\cos\bar{\beta},\ \cos\bar{\alpha}\cos\bar{\beta},\ -\sin\bar{\beta}\}$$

$$\left\{ \frac{n_1}{(\nu + h)\cos\phi},\ \frac{n_2}{(\rho + h)},\ n_3 \right\}$$
$$= \mathbf{Q}\bar{\mathbf{Q}}^T\{\cos\bar{\alpha},\ -\sin\bar{\alpha},\ 0\}$$
26.27

in which we may substitute for $\mathbf{Q}\bar{\mathbf{Q}}^T$ the transpose of the original matrix $\mathbf{Q}\bar{\mathbf{Q}}^T$. The advantage of proceeding in this manner is that the vectors for the reverse direction are easy to compute and refer to the same points as for the forward direction. We must make the same substitutions for azimuth and zenith distance in the remaining terms and remember that the *initial* point is now overbarred. The full observation equations for the reverse direction are then

(Observed Minus Computed) Zenith Distance

$$= -\overline{\Delta\beta} - \bar{m}_1 d\bar{\omega}/s - \bar{m}_2 d\bar{\phi}/s - \bar{m}_3 d\bar{h}/s$$
$$+ m_1 d\omega/s + m_2 d\phi/s + m_3 dh/s$$
$$+ (d\bar{\omega} + \overline{\delta\omega})\cos\bar{\phi}\sin\bar{\alpha}$$
$$+ (d\bar{\phi} + \overline{\delta\phi})\cos\bar{\alpha}$$

26.28

(Observed Minus Computed) Azimuth

$$= -\overline{\Delta\alpha} + \bar{n}_1 d\bar{\omega} \,(\operatorname{cosec} \bar{\beta})/s + \bar{n}_2 d\bar{\phi} \,(\operatorname{cosec} \bar{\beta})/s$$
$$+ \bar{n}_3 d\bar{h} \,(\operatorname{cosec} \bar{\beta})/s$$
$$- n_1 d\omega \,(\operatorname{cosec} \bar{\beta})/s - n_2 d\phi \,(\operatorname{cosec} \bar{\beta})/s$$
$$- n_3 dh \,(\operatorname{cosec} \bar{\beta})/s$$
$$+ (d\bar{\omega} + \overline{\delta\omega}) \,(\sin \bar{\phi} - \cos \bar{\phi} \cos \bar{\alpha} \cot \bar{\beta})$$
$$+ (d\bar{\phi} + \overline{\delta\phi}) \sin \bar{\alpha} \cot \bar{\beta}$$

26.29

in which the components of $\bar{m}_r$, m_r, $\bar{n}_r$, n_r are now given by Equations 26.26 and 26.27. The angle of refraction $\overline{\Delta\beta}$, the station correction to azimuths $\overline{\Delta\alpha}$, and the deflections $\overline{\delta\omega}$, $\overline{\delta\phi}$ at the barred point are new unknowns which are not related to $\Delta\beta$, $\Delta\alpha$, $\delta\omega$, $\delta\phi$.

General Considerations Affecting the Angular Equations

14. If an astronomical longitude has been measured, then $(d\omega + \delta\omega)$, which is the astronomical minus the initial approximate geodetic longitude, is known. The corresponding terms in the observation equations can be computed and added to the absolute terms. This procedure does not ignore the possibility of random error in the measured astronomical longitude, which would appear in the residuals. If an astronomical longitude has not been measured, it may be advisable to assume one from the general values of deflections in the area. In that case, the corresponding terms in the observation equations can be computed with the assumed value and added to the absolute terms. We should, however, retain terms $-d\omega_1 \cos \phi \sin \alpha$ and $d\omega_1 (\sin \phi - \cos \phi \cos \alpha \cot \beta)$ in which $d\omega_1$ is a correction to the assumed astronomical longitude to be found from the solution. Exactly the same procedure should be followed for the $(d\phi + \delta\phi)$ terms.

15. Apart from numerical considerations, no reason exists why $(d\omega + \delta\omega)$, $(d\phi + \delta\phi)$ should not be considered as independent unknowns and evaluated by the solution, even though the terms contain the independent unknowns $d\omega$, $d\phi$. Such a combination of unknowns does not invalidate any principle of least squares.[1] We can finally determine the deflections $\delta\omega$, $\delta\phi$ by subtracting $d\omega$, $d\phi$. The adjustment will not, however, be very strong unless frequent astronomical measures are made.

[1] See Thompson, E. H. (1962), "The Theory of the Method of Least Squares," *The Photogrammetric Record*, v. 4, 61.

16. If astronomical azimuth is measured, then the $\Delta\alpha$-term is dropped, and any random error in the measurement appears in the residuals. This procedure reduces the number of unknowns in the azimuth equations to the same extent as a measurement of astronomical latitude or longitude, and suggests that, except for the purpose of fixing an origin, astronomical longitudes could be replaced by astronomical azimuths, which are much easier to measure precisely.

17. When it becomes possible to measure the angle of refraction, $\Delta\beta$ can similarly be added to the absolute term. Meanwhile, we cannot treat the angle of refraction $\Delta\beta$ as completely unknown at both ends of all lines if the β-equations are to make any contribution to the solution. Some assumptions must be made. For example, we have seen in Chapter 24 that, unless the two stations are at very different heights, the angle of refraction can reasonably be assumed to be the same at the two ends of the line. In that case, $\Delta\beta$ could be eliminated by subtracting the observation equation for the reverse direction of the line from the equation for the forward direction before solution. This method would have advantages when reciprocal observations have been made at both ends of the line at the same time.

18. Another possibility is to express $\Delta\beta$ as some function of the length s of the line and to assume that the constants in the expression are the same for all lines observed from the same station at about the same time. The solution would then determine the constants, provided there are not too many of them. The simplest assumption, which can give quite good results, is that $\Delta\beta$ is directly proportional to s or to some fixed power of s; in that case, there will be only one constant per station to determine. Zenith distances should be observed along all rays in rapid succession, but the results could be meaned with similar sets taken at a different time.

19. Owing to uncertainty in the refraction, the β-equations should properly be given less weight. However, interaction between the α- and β-equations in normal terrestrial triangulation is so limited that weighting has little effect; indeed, the two sets of equations might be solved separately. The coefficients of $d\omega$, $d\phi$, $d\bar{\omega}$, $d\bar{\phi}$ in the β-equations are all small so that these terms could be omitted in a first solution. The main function of the β-equations, controlled by frequent astronomical observations, is to interpolate deflections and to

determine dh, $d\bar{h}$. The coefficients of these unknowns in the α-equations are, however, small so that fairly large errors in these coefficients would have little effect on the determination of $d\omega$, $d\phi$, $d\bar{\omega}$, $d\bar{\phi}$ from the α-equations. The one exception is the term $(d\omega + \delta\omega) \sin \phi$ in the azimuth equation; it can be inferred from Equation 19.30 that uncertainty in this term would mainly affect the determination of $\Delta\alpha$.

20. In the case of lines radiating from the origin, $d\omega$, $d\phi$, dh are all zero, and astronomical longitude, latitude, and azimuth should be measured so that the $\delta\omega$, $\delta\phi$, $\Delta\alpha$ terms can be evaluated. (If astronomical values are accepted as the initial geodetic elements, then $\delta\omega$, $\delta\phi$, $\Delta\alpha$ would all be zero.) The effect of this procedure on at least two lines will be to ensure proper orientation of the geodetic coordinate system by satisfying Equations 19.29. The inclusion of frequent astronomical observations will similarly preserve orientation of the geodetic system.

Lengths

21. The observation equation in geodetic coordinates for a measured distance between stations is given at once by substituting Equations 25.17 and 25.20 in Equation 26.08 as

(Observed Minus Computed) Distance
$$= (\nu + h) \cos \phi \sin \alpha \sin \beta (d\bar{\omega} - d\omega)$$
$$+ (\bar{\rho} + \bar{h}) \cos \bar{\alpha} \sin \bar{\beta} \, d\bar{\phi} + \cos \bar{\beta} \, d\bar{h}$$
$$- (\rho + h) \cos \alpha \sin \beta \, d\phi - \cos \beta \, dh.$$

26.30

The equation should be divided by a constant of the same order as the average side-length in the network so that the equation may have roughly the same dimensions as the α- and β-equations. The length and angular equations may, of course, be weighted differently if there is reason to do so. Present (1968) experience suggests that electronic distance measurements are generally of about the same order of accuracy as the best angular measurements and that relative weighting is unnecessary.

22. The only correction required in electronic distance measurements is for refraction; the correction reduces the actual measurement to the straight air-line distance between the two stations.

Spirit Levels

23. If the two ends of the line are connected by spirit levels, it is possible to construct a first-order observation equation to reflect the measurement and to include the equation in the general adjustment of the network. The observing procedure virtually frees the spirit leveling from the effects of atmospheric refraction and makes the inclusion of such observation equations in the network adjustment of considerable value.

24. The right-hand side of the β-Equations 26.24 and 26.28 *without the refraction terms* $\Delta\beta$, $\overline{\Delta\beta}$ can be considered as a correction to the computed straight-line geodetic zenith distance, arising from changes in the end coordinates and from the change from the geodetic to the astronomical zenith. Consequently, the "observed" zenith distance in these equations, apart from observational error, is the zenith distance of the straight line measured from the astronomical zenith. To a first order, Equation 25.36 relates these "observed" zenith distances (β), $(\bar{\beta})$ to the rise h_1 in spirit levels from the unbarred to the barred end of the line, except that the zenith distance at the barred point in Equation 25.36 refers to the line produced. In our present notation, Equation 25.36 becomes

$$h_1 = \tfrac{1}{2}s\{\cos(\beta) + \cos[180° - (\bar{\beta})]\}$$
$$\simeq \tfrac{1}{2}s\{(\bar{\beta}) - (\beta)\}$$

because the two zenith distances are nearly 90°. If we subtract Equation 26.24 for the forward direction from Equation 26.28 for the reverse direction, the left-hand side of the resulting equation will be

$$\frac{2h_1}{s} + \begin{pmatrix}\text{computed zenith}\\\text{distance at}\\\text{unbarred end}\end{pmatrix} - \begin{pmatrix}\text{computed zenith}\\\text{distance at}\\\text{barred end}\end{pmatrix}.$$

26.31

The computed zenith distance at the barred end will be $180° - \bar{\beta}$ where $\bar{\beta}$ will have been computed from the initial approximate geodetic coordinates by Equation 25.19. The right-hand side of the final observation equation is similarly derived as Equation 26.28 minus Equation 26.24 without the $\Delta\beta$, $\overline{\Delta\beta}$ terms.

25. We have used only a first-order formula for the difference in potential (or spirit levels), whereas the spirit levels will usually have been measured to a high degree of accuracy which we have not used. However, the effect on all the unknowns except dh, $d\bar{h}$ will be small, and we should expect to evaluate

dh, $d\bar{h}$ within the limits only of the first-order assumption and not to the degree of accuracy of precise spirit leveling. If the required data are available, we could first remove the second-order terms from the measured spirit levels by using Equations 25.33, in which the χ-term should be omitted because, in this case, we are expanding the potential along the straight line. In many cases, it would be sufficient to use geodetic curvatures and standard gravity in the evaluation of the second-order terms. If allowance is made for the second-order terms in this way, the adjustment should provide better values of the geodetic heights.

Initial Values

26. Before the observation equations can be formed, we must have approximate values for the geodetic coordinates of all points in the network. These approximate values can be obtained from formulas given in Chapter 25. Alternatively, we can start with very rough positions, obtained from maps or triangulation charts, and solve some of the observation equations themselves for corrections to the initial positions. For this purpose, we could ignore minor terms, such as deflections in the azimuth equations, and substitute as best we can for the angle of refraction and for deflections in the zenith-distance equations.

OBSERVATION EQUATIONS IN CARTESIAN COORDINATES

27. The invariant terms in the observation Equations 26.24, 26.25, and 26.30 and the equation for spirit levels, that is,

$$\bar{m}_r d\bar{x}^r, \quad m_r dx^r, \quad \bar{n}_r d\bar{x}^r, \quad n_r dx^r, \quad \bar{l}_r d\bar{x}^r, \quad l_r dx^r,$$

can, of course, be evaluated in any coordinate system; all that is needed is to evaluate the components of the vectors in the proposed system. In this case, the unknowns $d\bar{x}^r$, dx^r will be corrections to the end coordinates, not in the geodetic system (ω, ϕ, h), but in the system which has been used to evaluate the vector components. If, for example, we evaluate these invariant terms in Cartesian coordinates, the parallel vectors $\bar{l}_r$, $\bar{m}_r$, $\bar{n}_r$ will have the same components as l_r, m_r, n_r, and the invariant terms in Equation 26.24, for example, become

$$m_1(d\bar{x} - dx)/s, \quad m_2(d\bar{y} - dy)/s, \quad m_3(d\bar{z} - dz)/s.$$

This does not mean, however, that we have reduced the number of unknowns which will appear in different combinations in the observation equations for adjacent lines. Nevertheless, with the exception of the length Equation 26.08, we cannot express in Cartesian coordinates all the observation equations so far discussed because azimuth, zenith distance, and the astronomical latitude and longitude cannot be expressed simply and solely in Cartesian coordinates. We have to find the geodetic coordinates of points, even to express the Cartesian components of the vectors, and we have finally to convert the Cartesian results to the geodetic system. Thus, the only overall advantage of working in Cartesian coordinates in the cases so far considered seems to be that the more elementary Cartesian system is easier to understand than a curvilinear system. This conclusion applies only to observation equations so far discussed for use in connection with horizontal and vertical angular measurements, distances, levels, and astronomical measures. Other forms of measurement, as we shall see, may indicate different coordinate systems.

28. When required, the Cartesian components of the vectors l_r, m_r, n_r are very easily found from Equations 12.013 and 19.22, that is, from

26.32 $\{A_r, B_r, C_r\} = \mathbf{Q}^T\{\lambda_r, \mu_r, \nu_r\}.$

The Cartesian components (a, b, c) of l_r in azimuth α, zenith distance β are found by contracting this last equation with l^r as

$$\{a, b, c\} = \mathbf{Q}^T\{\sin\alpha\sin\beta, \cos\alpha\sin\beta, \cos\beta\},$$

26.33

which agrees with Equations 25.11 and 25.12. The Cartesian components of m_r in azimuth α, zenith distance $(\frac{1}{2}\pi + \beta)$ are given by

26.34 $\mathbf{Q}^T\{\sin\alpha\cos\beta, \cos\alpha\cos\beta, -\sin\beta\};$

the Cartesian components of n_r in azimuth $(\frac{3}{2}\pi + \alpha)$, zenith distance $\frac{1}{2}\pi$ are given by

26.35 $\mathbf{Q}^T\{-\cos\alpha, \sin\alpha, 0\}.$

FLARE TRIANGULATION

29. So far, we have considered only observations made at intervisible ground stations, whereas observations from ground stations that are not intervisible to elevated beacons that cannot be occupied have received much attention in recent years. The object is to increase the distance between ground stations so as to provide a more open network quickly or to bridge wide water gaps. One such system, used, for example, by W. E. Browne

to bridge the Straits of Florida, is to make simultaneous observations from ground stations to parachute flares dropped from aircraft.

30. Whenever observations to the flare consist of horizontal and vertical angular measurements in relation to the astronomical zenith, the observation Equations 26.24 and 26.25 can be used as given. In this case, we start with an approximate position for the flare as well as for the ground stations which we are required to fix; we form two observation equations for each line, containing corrections to the coordinates of the flare and of the ground station as well as the astronomical and refraction corrections. There are, of course, no corrections to the coordinates of known ground stations in these equations. For simultaneous [2] observation of one position of one flare from three known ground stations and one unknown ground station, we have, for example, eight equations between six unknowns, assuming that full astronomical observations have been made at all ground stations and that valid corrections have been made for refraction. Theoretically, we have enough equations to fix the unknown station, and the equations might prove to be sufficient in practice if the stations covered a considerable range in altitude. However, it is usual to observe several flares in widely separated positions from the same ground stations, including several unknown stations, and also to make several observations to the same flare as it falls, treating the position of the flare as unknown for every such additional observation. In this way, we can form enough observation equations to dispense with astronomical measures, if necessary. The determination of geodetic heights from vertical angles is weaker than from reciprocal observations between ground stations because only one end of each line can be occupied. However, if the flares are dropped roughly midway between the known and unknown ground stations, residual errors of refraction tend to cancel as between the heights of ground stations, although the (unwanted) flare heights are seriously affected. Additional observation equations can, of course, be formed and used in the adjustment for observations between such ground stations as may be intervisible.

STELLAR TRIANGULATION

31. Simultaneous photography from two or more ground stations of a luminous beacon—a rocket flash or a flare dropped from an aircraft—against a background of stars was first proposed and extensively used by Väisälä in Finland about 1946. In principle, the direction to the beacon is interpolated by measurements on the photographic plate from the known right ascensions and declinations of the background stars; a single photograph can be considered an observation for the right ascension and declination of the beacon. A simultaneous observation from a second ground station gives the orientation of the plane containing the beacon and the two ground stations. Two such planes for two different positions of the beacon intersect in the line joining the two ground stations, whose direction is accordingly determined in the right ascension-declination system. This direction is, of course, "absolute" in the sense that it does not depend on the local direction of the plumbline, which would be the case if horizontal and vertical angles were measured.

32. To develop the theory in more detail, we shall use the same Earth-fixed, right-handed orthogonal triad of unit Cartesian vectors A^r, B^r, C^r as set up in § 12–8 and § 12–10 to define latitude and longitude. As usual, C^r is parallel to the Earth's axis of rotation, the plane A^r, C^r determines the origin of longitude or hour angle, and B^r completes the right-handed triad A^r, B^r, C^r. We define the *declination* (D) of a unit space vector L^r as the angle between L^r and the plane A^r, B^r — positive north. This definition follows the usual astronomical convention. The *origin-hour angle* (H) of the vector L^r is defined as the angle between the planes A^r, C^r and L^r, C^r — positive in the direction of a positive right-handed rotation about C^r, that is, positive eastward from A^r toward B^r. This definition reverses the sign of the usual astronomical convention for the hour angle, which is positive westward, but enables us to adhere to normal mathematical conventions as used throughout this book, and to relate declination and origin-hour angle directly to latitude and longitude (which also is positive east). It will then be apparent that Equations 12.003, 12.004, and 12.005 hold equally well for declination D and origin-hour angle H in relation to the vector L^r, which can accordingly be expressed as

$$L^r = (\cos D \cos H)A^r + (\cos D \sin H)B^r + (\sin D)C^r.$$

26.36

The origin-hour angle H is the right ascension of the direction L^r *minus* the local sidereal time at the origin, both expressed in angular measure. The local sidereal time at the origin is the Greenwich sidereal time *plus* the astronomical longitude of

[2] The observations are synchronized by radio signals. In some systems, the circle readings are photographed by small cameras operated by the radio signals, and all the observer need do is to keep the flare continuously intersected.

the origin relative to Greenwich, measured as always positive eastward.

33. The right ascension and declination from a ground station to the beacon at a given time, obtained from plate measurements, give H, D for substitution in Equation 26.36. (We shall defer a description of the process until we deal with the modern techniques of satellite triangulation in § 26–43.) A simultaneous observation from another ground station provides a similar equation for the unit vector $\bar{L}^r$ from the second station to the beacon. We know that the unit vector joining the ground stations is coplanar with L^r and $\bar{L}^r$, a fact which gives us one relation between the hour angle and declination of the line joining the ground stations. Repetition of the whole process from the same two ground stations to another position of the beacon will then determine H, D for the line joining the ground stations.

34. The situation is illustrated by the spherical diagram, figure 31, in which the unit vectors to the

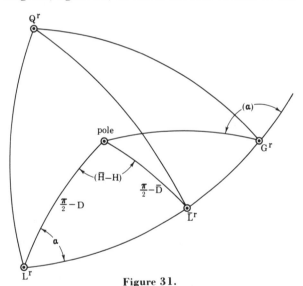

Figure 31.

beacon are represented by L^r, $\bar{L}^r$ and a unit vector perpendicular to the plane of L^r, $\bar{L}^r$ is Q^r, the pole of the great circle $L^r\bar{L}^r$. The unit vector of the line joining the ground stations is shown as G^r, necessarily on the great circle $L^r\bar{L}^r$ because the three vectors are coplanar. The hour angle and declination of Q^r are obtained from the triangle L^r-pole-Q^r in figure 31, and then Equation 26.36 gives

$$Q^r = A^r(\sin H \cos \alpha - \sin D \cos H \sin \alpha)$$
$$+ B^r(-\cos H \cos \alpha - \sin D \sin H \sin \alpha)$$
$$+ C^r(\cos D \sin \alpha)$$

26.37

in which the quantities within parentheses are the Cartesian components of Q^r and must therefore have the same values at all points of the great circle $L^r\bar{L}^rG^r$. We can, of course, compute α from the elements H, D, $\bar{H}$, $\bar{D}$ of figure 31 so that these components (l, m, n) are known. If (H), (D) are the origin-hour angle and declination of G^r, the line joining the ground stations, we then have

$$\sin (H) \cos (\alpha) - \sin (D) \cos (H) \sin (\alpha) = l$$
$$-\cos (H) \cos (\alpha) - \sin (D) \sin (H) \sin (\alpha) = m$$

26.38 $$\cos (D) \sin (\alpha) = n,$$

two equations of which are independent. From the second position of the beacon, when (α) becomes (α^*), we have similarly two independent equations connecting (H), (D), and (α^*) which are easily solved to determine (H), (D), (α), and (α^*). The difference $(\alpha) - (\alpha^*)$ is the angle between the planes containing the ground stations and one angle each of the beacon positions. The magnitude of this "angle of cut" is a measure of the geometrical accuracy of the result.

35. We could compute (H), (D) in this manner for each pair of simultaneous observations to the beacon and use the results as observed values in a system of observation equations. However, (H) and (D) are a long way from the actual observations, which are measures of rectangular coordinates on the photographic plates. Moreover, it would be difficult to ensure a proper weighting of such derived "observations," especially when simultaneous observations are made from more than two ground stations or when it is difficult to select pairs of observations with a good "angle of cut" without using the same observation twice. For these reasons, it will usually be better to form observation equations for each observed direction to the beacon; we shall now do this.

Observation Equations for Directions

36. If H, D are the origin-hour angle and declination to the beacon—unit vector L^r—we define two auxiliary unit vectors M^r (origin-hour angle H, declination $D - \frac{1}{2}\pi$) and N^r (origin-hour angle $H + \frac{1}{2}\pi$, declination zero) as

$$M^r = (\sin D \cos H)A^r + (\sin D \sin H)B^r - (\cos D)C^r$$

26.39

26.40 $$N^r = -(\sin H)A^r + (\cos H)B^r.$$

The triad L^r, M^r, N^r is right-handed in that order. Because the Cartesian vectors A^r, B^r, C^r are fixed, we can then differentiate Equation 26.36 to have

26.41 $d(L^r) = -M^r dD + (\cos D) N^r dH.$

Substituting in Equation 26.10, where the triad l^r, m^r, n^r is any right-handed unit orthogonal set, and equating coefficients of M^r, N^r give us the observation equations

26.42 $\qquad s \, dD = -\overline{M}_s \, d\bar{x}^s + M_s \, dx^s$

26.43 $\qquad (s \cos D) \, dH = \overline{N}_s \, d\bar{x}^s - N_s \, dx^s$

in which dx^s, $d\bar{x}^s$ are, respectively, corrections to initial approximate coordinates of the ground station and of the beacon, whose declination and origin-hour angle are D, H in the direction from the unbarred (ground) to the overbarred (beacon) end of the line. The components of the auxiliary vectors M_s, N_s (and of the parallel vectors $\overline{M}_s$, $\overline{N}_s$ at the beacon end of the line) are computed from Equations 26.39 and 26.40 in the same coordinate system as dx^s, $d\bar{x}^s$. On the left-hand side of the observation equations, s is the length of the line computed from the approximate end coordinates and dD, for example, is the measured declination minus the declination computed from the approximate end coordinates.

37. The observation equations must necessarily contain corrections to the initial approximate position of the beacon, which we do not usually require. These unwanted corrections can, however, be eliminated at some suitable stage—either before or during the formation of the normal equations.

Time Correction

38. In relating the photographic image of the beacon to the stars, we are in effect observing the right ascension of the beacon in the system of the star catalog. The observed origin-hour angle is then obtained by subtracting, from the right ascension of the satellite, the local sidereal time at the origin of the instant when the beacon was photographed, while the computed origin-hour angle is obtained from the approximate end coordinates of the line. If, however, we do not know the precise local sidereal time of the observation, then we must assume an approximate value t_0, which must be corrected to $(t_0 + dt)$. This assumption amounts to adding a time correction dt, expressed in radian measure like dx/s, to the right-hand side of Equation 26.43 and to evaluating this extra unknown together with the corrections to the end coordinates of the line in the solution of the observation equations. The time correction dt would, however, be the same for all stations engaged in the *simul-*

taneous observation of the beacon because it is a correction to the assumed local sidereal time of the observation at the origin, which is common to all stations. This correction could also be the clock correction to one particular (master) station clock used to define t_0. An additional clock correction would have to be included for every other station clock which has not been synchronized to the master clock.

Observation Equations in Cartesian Coordinates

39. In this case, there is evidently some advantage of working in Cartesian coordinates. From Equation 26.36, we have at once the difference in Cartesian coordinates of the two ends of the line referred to the axes A^r, B^r, C^r,

$$\bar{x} - x = s \cos D \cos H$$
$$\bar{y} - y = s \cos D \sin H$$

26.44 $\qquad \bar{z} - z = s \sin D.$

The Cartesian components of the auxiliary vectors from Equations 26.39 and 26.40 are

$$M^r = \overrightarrow{M}^r = (\sin D \cos H, \sin D \sin H, -\cos D)$$
$$N^r = \overline{N}^r = (-\sin H, \cos H, 0)$$

26.45

so that the observation equations become

(Observed Minus Computed) Declination
$$= -\sin D \cos H \, (d\bar{x} - dx)/s$$
$$\quad -\sin D \sin H \, (d\bar{y} - dy)/s$$
$$\quad +\cos D \, (d\bar{z} - dz)/s$$

26.46

(Observed Minus Computed) Origin-Hour Angle
$$= -\sec D \sin H \, (d\bar{x} - dx)/s$$
$$\quad +\sec D \cos H \, (d\bar{y} - dy)/s.$$

26.47

Equations 26.44 are used to obtain computed values of s, H, D from initial approximate values of the end Cartesian coordinates. Either these values of H, D or the observed values may be used for the coefficients on the right of the observation equations.

40. Approximate positions of the ground stations will usually be more accurately known than the position of the beacon. In that case, we could form

Equations 26.44 for the other ground station, solve with Equations 26.44 to determine the two distances to the beacon, and thus obtain the approximate position of the beacon from the observed values of hour angles and declinations. Once we have decided on the approximate positions, we must, of course, use them in Equations 26.44 to obtain accurate "computed" values of D and H. A similar procedure can be followed if the observation equations are formed in geodetic or geocentric coordinates.

Observation Equations in Other Coordinate Systems

41. The observation equations can be solved to give corrections to geodetic coordinates instead of Cartesian coordinates by substituting the geodetic components of the auxiliary vectors in the observation Equations 26.42 and 26.43. From Equation 26.39, we have

$$M_s = (\sin D \cos H, \sin D \sin H, -\cos D)\{A_s, B_s, C_s\},$$

which, by using Equation 19.35, can be written as

$$(M_1, M_2, M_3) = (\sin D \cos H, \sin D \sin H, -\cos D)$$

26.48 $\qquad \times \mathbf{Q}^T\mathbf{S},$

an equation holding true in any (ω, ϕ, N) coordinate system, provided the appropriate **S**-matrix is used from Equation 19.32. In geodetic coordinates, the **S**-matrix is

$$\begin{pmatrix} (\nu+h)\cos\phi & 0 & 0 \\ 0 & (\rho+h) & 0 \\ 0 & 0 & 1 \end{pmatrix},$$

while $\mathbf{Q}^T$ is obtained from Equation 19.26. Expansion of Equation 26.48 then gives

$$M_1 = (\nu+h)\cos\phi\sin D\sin(H-\omega)$$

$$M_2 = -(\rho+h)\{\sin\phi\sin D\cos(H-\omega)$$
$$+ \cos\phi\cos D\}$$

$$M_3 = \cos\phi\sin D\cos(H-\omega) - \sin\phi\cos D.$$
26.49

At the beacon, the components of the parallel vector $\overline{M}_s$, for which D, H are the same, are given by

$$(\overline{M}_1, \overline{M}_2, \overline{M}_3) = (\sin D\cos H, \sin D\sin H, -\cos D)$$

26.50 $\qquad \times \overline{\mathbf{Q}}^T\overline{\mathbf{S}};$

this equation expands to give the same result as Equations 26.49, provided ν, ρ, h, ϕ, ω are overbarred. This fact means simply that the approxi-

mate values of these five quantities at the beacon must be substituted in Equations 26.49. In the same way, we have

26.51 $\qquad (N_1, N_2, N_3) = (-\sin H, \cos H, 0)\mathbf{Q}^T\mathbf{S},$

which expands to

$$N_1 = (\nu+h)\cos\phi\cos(H-\omega)$$

$$N_2 = (\rho+h)\sin\phi\sin(H-\omega)$$

26.52 $\qquad N_3 = -\cos\phi\sin(H-\omega).$

Components of $\overline{N}_s$ are obtained by substitution of the approximate values of ν, ρ, h, ϕ, ω at the beacon in Equations 26.52.

42. The observation equations can also be written in geocentric coordinates, which are more closely related to the observed right ascensions and declinations. In that case, the N-surfaces are spheres of radius r centered on the origin, and latitude and longitude refer not to the astronomical or geodetic zenith, but to the radius vector. Because Equations 26.48 and 26.51 hold true in any (ω, ϕ, N) system, we have merely to substitute r for $(\nu+h)$ or $(\rho+h)$ in Equations 26.49 and 26.52 and interpret (ω, ϕ) as the geocentric longitude and latitude. If computation is to be done directly from Equations 26.48, etc., in matrix form, the appropriate **S**-matrix is now

$$\begin{pmatrix} r\cos\phi & 0 & 0 \\ 0 & r & 0 \\ 0 & 0 & 1 \end{pmatrix},$$

and $\mathbf{Q}^T$ is given by Equation 19.26 for the geocentric latitude and longitude.

SATELLITE TRIANGULATION— DIRECTIONS

43. Although there are other means of fixing positions by observations on near-Earth artificial satellites, we shall understand the term "satellite triangulation" to mean stellar triangulation using the satellite as a beacon, which either emits flashes on command or reflects sunlight. In the latter case of a passive balloonlike satellite, accurate timing is necessary and can be obtained to ensure that observations from two or more ground camera stations are automatically synchronized. If the same "instantaneous" flash or series of flashes is observed by several ground stations, the event still has to be timed, but less accurate timing is necessary because the stars, which are required to determine the orientation of the camera, move more

slowly than the satellite; synchronization of the observation to the satellite is achieved by the flashes themselves. Although some tracking cameras are sidereally mounted so that the stars appear as point images while a continuously illuminated satellite appears as a trail, we shall consider only the case of rigidly fixed cameras so that both the stars and a continuously illuminated satellite form trails on the photographic plate. The trails are "chopped" by shutter closures at accurately recorded times when the image of the star or satellite is considered to be at the break in the trail. Before the operation, the camera is set in altitude and azimuth from predicted orbital data so that the satellite trail will pass close to the center of the plate. The star trails are chopped in a distinctive manner before and after the satellite pass, and between passes. Measurement of the plate coordinates of the breaks in the star trails determines the orientation of the camera and of the photographic plate as well as a number of calibration parameters, and gives assurance that the camera has not moved between star calibrations. Finally, the known orientation and calibration enable the direction to the satellite to be computed from plate coordinates of breaks in the satellite trail. Variations in procedure do not seriously affect the method of reducing the observations now to be given in barest outline. For example, the only difference in the case of a flashing satellite is that measurements are made to point images and not to trail breaks. There are considerably fewer images to measure with a flashing satellite; whereas, a continuously illuminated satellite can be chopped all the way across the plate until it ceases to be illuminated by the Sun.

Choice of Coordinate Systems

44. The first step is to determine the direction of the camera axis in a specified Cartesian coordinate system. There are three main possibilities:

(a) An inertial system whose z-axis is parallel to the axis of rotation of the Earth and whose xz-plane defines the origin of right ascensions.

(b) An Earth-fixed system, as used so far throughout this book, whose z-axis is parallel to the axis of rotation of the Earth and whose xz-plane defines the origin of astronomical longitudes. The base vectors in this system in our usual notation are A^r, B^r, C^r, as defined in Chapter 12; we shall denote coordinates in this system by (X, Y, Z). The relation between this system and the inertial system are described in § 26–32.

(c) A "local" $(\bar{X}, \bar{Y}, \bar{Z})$ system in which the geo-

centric latitude and longitude of the $\bar{Z}$-direction are (ϕ, ω) and the origin in the (X, Y, Z) Earth-fixed system is (X_0, Y_0, Z_0). The $\bar{Y}$-direction will be northward in the plane containing the $\bar{Z}$-direction and the axis of rotation. The $\bar{X}$-direction will be eastward in accordance with our normal right-handed conventions. The coordinate axes are accordingly $(\lambda^r, \mu^r, \nu^r)$ in a spherically symmetric (ω, ϕ, N) system; by contracting Equation 12.013 with a position vector from the new origin, we have

$$\begin{pmatrix} X-X_0 \\ Y-Y_0 \\ Z-Z_0 \end{pmatrix} = \begin{pmatrix} -\sin\omega & -\cos\omega & 0 \\ \cos\omega & -\sin\omega & 0 \\ 0 & 0 & 1 \end{pmatrix}$$

$$\times \begin{pmatrix} 1 & 0 & 0 \\ 0 & \sin\phi & -\cos\phi \\ 0 & \cos\phi & \sin\phi \end{pmatrix} \begin{pmatrix} \bar{X} \\ \bar{Y} \\ \bar{Z} \end{pmatrix}$$

26.53 $\qquad = \mathbf{N}\{\bar{X}, \bar{Y}, \bar{Z}\}.$

In this application, (X_0, Y_0, Z_0) is the camera station and (ω, ϕ) are *approximately* the geocentric coordinates of the camera station in the (X, Y, Z) system. However, both (X_0, Y_0, Z_0) and (ω, ϕ) are independent. We can consider that (ω, ϕ) are two fixed parameters whose values are chosen to be approximately the geocentric coordinates of the camera station in order to facilitate the application of corrections for astronomical refraction. As we have seen in Chapter 24, these fixed parameters are presently based on a spherically symmetric model atmosphere. Indeed, this coordinate system is introduced solely for the purpose of evaluating and applying refraction corrections.

45. The direction of the camera axis and the orientation of the plate can be determined in any of these three systems, provided the star directions are transformed to the same system. If we use the inertial system, updated places derived from the star catalogs can be used after correction for precession, nutation, annual and diurnal aberration, and astronomical refraction; the camera orientation will be in terms of right ascension and declination, as also will be the direction to the satellite. In this case, we shall have to transform to an Earth-fixed system before combining results from different stations at different times.

46. If we use the Earth-fixed system for camera calibration, we shall have to convert right ascensions to origin-hour angles by subtracting the local sidereal time at the origin, which means that we must be in a position to apply clock corrections

before we start, although the observation equations could be modified to include time corrections similar to those given in § 26–38. Alternatively, we could set up a temporary Earth-fixed system with an approximate sidereal time and apply a final correction by means of a longitude rotation of the coordinate system into the definitive Earth-fixed system. The final correction could be applied in conjunction with rotations for polar movement, which will be discussed in § 26–62. The camera orientation and direction to the satellite will be determined in terms of declination and origin-hour angle. There will be no need to transform to any other system for the network adjustment.

47. If we use the "local" system, we must, in addition, transform the declinations D and origin-hour angles H of the stars to azimuths α and zenith distances β in the local system by means of the relation

$$\textbf{26.54} \quad \begin{pmatrix} \sin \alpha \sin \beta \\ \cos \alpha \sin \beta \\ \cos \beta \end{pmatrix} = \mathbf{N}^T \begin{pmatrix} \cos D \cos H \\ \cos D \sin H \\ \sin D \end{pmatrix},$$

which is easily obtained from Equation 26.53. We shall then obtain the camera orientation and direction to the satellite in terms of azimuth and zenith distance, and shall transform to the fixed-Earth system for the network adjustment by means of the inverse of Equation 26.54. As explained in § 26–44(c), we must use the same approximate values of the geocentric coordinates (ω, ϕ) of the camera station in the matrix $\mathbf{N}$ for both direct and inverse transformations.

48. The local system is perhaps most often used for the star calibration. As a means of wider illustration, we shall, nevertheless, start with the Earth-fixed system and transform only the updated places of the stars to the local system in order to evaluate and to apply refraction corrections, while still determining the camera orientation and direction to the satellite in the Earth-fixed system. This system would require less modification if a different method of refraction correction is introduced later; but in any case, once any of the systems is fully understood, it is a simple matter to derive the equations for any other system.

The Basic Photogrammetric Equations

49. If H_c, D_c are the origin-hour angle and declination of the camera axis, it will be clear from Equation 12.012 that

$$\begin{pmatrix} 1 & 0 & 0 \\ 0 & \sin D_c & \cos D_c \\ 0 & -\cos D_c & \sin D_c \end{pmatrix} \begin{pmatrix} -\sin H_c & \cos H_c & 0 \\ -\cos H_c & -\sin H_c & 0 \\ 0 & 0 & 1 \end{pmatrix} \begin{pmatrix} X \\ Y \\ Z \end{pmatrix}$$

gives the Cartesian coordinates of the point (X, Y, Z) in a system whose z-axis is the camera axis and whose y-axis lies in the plane of the z-axis and the original C^r-axis. On the photographic plate in the Northern Hemisphere, the y-axis joins the *principal point* (where the camera axis cuts the plate) to the photographic image of the celestial North Pole. The x- or y-axes, from which measurements are made on the plate, are, however, given by fixed fiducial marks in the camera; to effect a final rotation to this plate system, we introduce a positive rotation κ, known as the *swing*, about the camera axis by premultiplication with the matrix

$$\begin{pmatrix} \cos \kappa & \sin \kappa & 0 \\ -\sin \kappa & \cos \kappa & 0 \\ 0 & 0 & 1 \end{pmatrix}.$$

Also, we change the X, Y, Z origin to the camera station (X_0, Y_0, Z_0) by replacing the vector $\{X, Y, Z\}$ with $\{(X-X_0), (Y-Y_0), (Z-Z_0)\}$. In the result, we shall have coordinates of the original object point (X, Y, Z) in the new system, and we have next to find the corresponding coordinates of the photographic image. If Δ is the distance from the camera to the object point and if d is the distance from the internal perspective center to the photographic image of the point, then we must reduce the transformed coordinates of the object point in the ratio d/Δ to obtain the coordinates of the image point. Finally, we can change the origin of plate coordinates so that coordinates relative to the camera axis become $\{(x-x_0), (y-y_0), f\}$ where (x_0, y_0) are the plate coordinates of the principal point in the new system. In an undistorted perspective, the camera axis — supposedly perpendicular to the plate — cuts the plate in the principal point. The *principal distance* f is the length of the perpendicular between the internal perspective center and the principal point. The final transformation is expressed as

$$\textbf{26.55} \quad \begin{pmatrix} x-x_0 \\ y-y_0 \\ f \end{pmatrix} = \left(\frac{d}{\Delta}\right) \mathbf{M} \begin{pmatrix} X-X_0 \\ Y-Y_0 \\ Z-Z_0 \end{pmatrix}$$

where the rotation matrix is given by

$$\mathbf{M} = \begin{pmatrix} \cos \kappa & \sin \kappa & 0 \\ -\sin \kappa & \cos \kappa & 0 \\ 0 & 0 & 1 \end{pmatrix}$$

$$\times \begin{pmatrix} 1 & 0 & 0 \\ 0 & \sin D_c & \cos D_c \\ 0 & -\cos D_c & \sin D_c \end{pmatrix} \begin{pmatrix} -\sin H_c & \cos H_c & 0 \\ -\cos H_c & -\sin H_c & 0 \\ 0 & 0 & 1 \end{pmatrix}$$

26.56

and

$$\left(\frac{d}{\Delta}\right)^2 = \frac{(x-x_0)^2 + (y-y_0)^2 + f^2}{(X-X_0)^2 + (Y-Y_0)^2 + (Z-Z_0)^2}.$$

This equation gives (x, y, f) in the same general sense as (X, Y, Z) for small rotations so that x, y are considered to be measured on a positive print covering the object space. If we measure coordinates on the original negative — emulsion side up — in relation to the same fiducial mark as the positive x-direction, then we would measure $(x, -y)$ and should change the sign of y before insertion in Equation 26.53. This rule, of course, assumes normal right-handed coordinate conventions.

50. An alternative form of Equation 26.55 is useful in the present application. If we write the expanded rotation matrix as

26.57
$$\mathbf{M} = \begin{pmatrix} m_{11} & m_{12} & m_{13} \\ m_{21} & m_{22} & m_{23} \\ m_{31} & m_{32} & m_{33} \end{pmatrix}$$

and eliminate d/Δ, we have

$$\frac{x-x_0}{f} = \frac{m_{11}(X-X_0) + m_{12}(Y-Y_0) + m_{13}(Z-Z_0)}{m_{31}(X-X_0) + m_{32}(Y-Y_0) + m_{33}(Z-Z_0)}$$

$$\frac{y-y_0}{f} = \frac{m_{21}(X-X_0) + m_{22}(Y-Y_0) + m_{23}(Z-Z_0)}{m_{31}(X-X_0) + m_{32}(Y-Y_0) + m_{33}(Z-Z_0)}.$$

26.58

Equations 26.58 are equivalent to the original equations, only two of which are independent, because the scale factor d/Δ has the effect of reducing the vectors in Equation 26.55 to unit vectors, while all the rotation matrices are orthogonal.

51. Equation 26.55 or Equations 26.58 are usually known as the projective equations of photogrammetry or as the conditions of collinearity. In deriving these equations as coordinate transformations, we have, indeed, assumed collinearity of the image and object points and of the perspective center, so that either set of equations represents an undistorted perspective. Many different conventions for the rotation angles and coordinate systems are used in photogrammetric literature, including some left-handed systems, but the formulas can be reconciled with the normal mathematical conventions used throughout this book by reversing the signs of some coordinates and the directions of some rotations; in whatever order the rotations are made, the final matrix $\mathbf{M}$, connecting the same two coordinate systems, must be the same.

Calibration

52. The process of obtaining the orientation of the camera and certain camera constants is very similar to the method of camera calibration from stars described, with a full bibliography, in the *Manual of Photogrammetry*.[3]

53. If the object photographed is a star of declination D and origin-hour angle H, we can write

$$\begin{pmatrix} X-X_0 \\ Y-Y_0 \\ Z-Z_0 \end{pmatrix} = \begin{pmatrix} r \cos D \cos H \\ r \cos D \sin H \\ r \sin D \end{pmatrix}$$

in which r is very large, but is cancelled by Δ. Equation 26.55 for stars is accordingly

26.59
$$\frac{1}{d} \begin{pmatrix} x-x_0 \\ y-y_0 \\ f \end{pmatrix} = \mathbf{M} \begin{pmatrix} \cos D \cos H \\ \cos D \sin H \\ \sin D \end{pmatrix},$$

with the alternative form from Equations 26.58 of

$$\frac{x-x_0}{f} = \frac{m_{11} \cos D \cos H + m_{12} \cos D \sin H + m_{13} \sin D}{m_{31} \cos D \cos H + m_{32} \cos D \sin H + m_{33} \sin D}$$

$$\frac{y-y_0}{f} = \frac{m_{21} \cos D \cos H + m_{22} \cos D \sin H + m_{23} \sin D}{m_{31} \cos D \cos H + m_{32} \cos D \sin H + m_{33} \sin D}.$$

26.60

54. Theoretically, these equations are soluble for $\kappa, D_c, H_c, x_0, y_0, f$ from three stars, but even then the solution would not be simple because the equations are not linear in the unknowns. In practice, we require the use of more than three stars to achieve precise results, and we shall have to increase the number of unknowns to allow for the fact that we are not dealing with an undistorted perspec-

---

[3] American Society of Photogrammetry (1966), *Manual of Photogrammetry*, 3d ed., v. 1, 180–194.

tive. Accordingly, the next step is to form differential observation equations in the usual way by partial differentiation of Equations 26.60 with respect to all six unknowns and the measured (x, y). In the result, dx, for example, will be the measured x minus the computed x, obtained by substituting preliminary values of the unknowns in the first equation of Equations 26.60. We are then able to solve a large number of such observation equations, formed for a large number of stars and appropriately weighted, by the usual least-square processes to provide corrections $d\kappa$, dD_c, etc., to the preliminary values of the unknowns.

55. We can also add other unknown parameters to the observation equations before solution by expressing their effect on the measured (x, y). For example, considerations of symmetry indicate that the radial lens distortion can be expressed as

$$\Delta r = k_1 r^3 + k_2 r^5 + k_3 r^7$$

in which Δr is the outward displacement from a true perspective position, r is the radius vector from the principal point, and k_1, k_2, k_3 are unknown parameters to be derived from the calibration. From similar triangles, we have

$$\frac{\Delta x}{(x - x_0)} = \frac{\Delta y}{(y - y_0)} = \frac{\Delta r}{r} = k_1 r^2 + k_2 r^4 + k_3 r^6.$$

The component Δx of the distortion must, for example, be subtracted from the measured x to give the value of x which would be measured on an undistorted photograph. But the observed x in the observation equation is measured on a true undistorted perspective. Accordingly, if we insert the actual measured x in the observation equation, we must subtract

$$\Delta x = (x - x_0)(k_1 r^2 + k_2 r^4 + k_3 r^6)$$

from the (observed minus computed) x in the original equation, and similarly must do the same for y. This relation adds three unknowns to each observation equation.

56. In addition to the use of three parameters to determine the radial lens distortion, it is usual in current practice to introduce parameters to allow for

(a) nonperpendicularity of the coordinate axes and other sources of error in the plate-measuring instrument;

(b) difference in scale in the x- and y-directions arising from emulsion creep, which is equivalent to the determination of two principal distances; and

(c) lens deviation or decentering, nonradial distortion (involving five extra parameters), and correction for nonperpendicularity of the optical axis and the plate.

Residual Atmospheric Refraction

57. We have not yet included any correction to the apparent places of the stars for astronomical refraction. One possibility is to convert the apparent places from hour angle and declination to approximate azimuth and zenith distance by Equation 26.54, using approximate values ϕ, ω of the geocentric latitude and longitude of the camera station. The zenith distances are then corrected for refraction from tables, and the corrected star positions are converted back to hour angle and declination, *using the same values of ϕ, ω*, before insertion into Equations 26.60 where H, D would then be held constant during differentiation. Errors in the assumed values of ϕ, ω, affecting only the refraction correction through the corresponding error in zenith distance, are of little consequence. However, it is usual in current practice to determine residual refraction parameters—in much the same way as lens distortion and other parameters—from the solution of the calibration observation equations. For this purpose, we simply combine Equations 26.54 and 26.59 to give

26.61 $\quad \dfrac{1}{d}\begin{pmatrix} x - x_0 \\ y - y_0 \\ f \end{pmatrix} = \mathbf{MN}\begin{pmatrix} \sin \alpha \sin \beta \\ \cos \alpha \sin \beta \\ \cos \beta \end{pmatrix}$

in which the rotation matrix is now

$$\mathbf{MN} = \begin{pmatrix} n_{11} & n_{12} & n_{13} \\ n_{21} & n_{22} & n_{23} \\ n_{31} & n_{32} & n_{33} \end{pmatrix},$$

whose components are obtained from Equations 26.56 and 26.53 and contain κ, D_c, H_c, ω, ϕ. Equations 26.60 become

$$\frac{x - x_0}{f} = \frac{n_{11} \sin \alpha \sin \beta + n_{12} \cos \alpha \sin \beta + n_{13} \cos \beta}{n_{31} \sin \alpha \sin \beta + n_{32} \cos \alpha \sin \beta + n_{33} \cos \beta}$$

$$\frac{y - y_0}{f} = \frac{n_{21} \sin \alpha \sin \beta + n_{22} \cos \alpha \sin \beta + n_{23} \cos \beta}{n_{31} \sin \alpha \sin \beta + n_{32} \cos \alpha \sin \beta + n_{33} \cos \beta}.$$

26.62

In forming the observation equations by differentiation, we hold ω, ϕ, α fixed and equate $d\beta$ to the expression for the refraction correction. If we insert apparent zenith distances into Equations 26.62 to derive the computed (x, y), $d\beta$ will be the (true minus apparent) zenith distance, which is the same as the normal convention for refraction. The sign of $d\beta$ is of little importance, however, because a wrong sign would simply result in reversed signs for the parameters in the refraction equation, which we shall now consider.

58. The expression for astronomical refraction, introduced by Hellmut Schmid, is

$$T^{1/2}W[K_1 \tan \tfrac{1}{2}\theta + K_2 \tan^3 \tfrac{1}{2}\theta$$
$$+ K_3 \tan^5 \tfrac{1}{2}\theta + k_4 \tan^7 \tfrac{1}{2}\theta]$$

where the refraction is in seconds of arc, and

$T = t/273.16$,

t = observed temperature at camera station in °C.,

$W = P_0/(760T^2)$,

P_0 = observed pressure at camera station in mm., Hg.,

$\tan \theta = 0.1147618 T^{1/2} \tan \beta$,

β = apparent zenith distance.

The formula is to some extent empirical, but does follow Garfinkel's theory (§ 24–67) by using a modified zenith distance in the classical expansion in powers of the tangent. In fact, the formula fits Garfinkel's model very accurately for zenith distances of less than 75°. In using the formula for satellite triangulation, the four parameters K_1, K_2, K_3, K_4 are determined at each calibration from the observation equations.

Direction to Satellite

59. The camera calibration provides data for correcting the (x, y) coordinates of each satellite image through the now-known parameters for various distortions, etc., listed in § 26–55 and § 26–56, and for atmospheric refraction. Also, a correction should be applied for differential aberration, that is, for the traveltime of light to the camera station from the satellite in relation to the stars. In addition, the parallax correction (Equation 24.72) for differential refraction has to be applied in a sense opposite to the astronomical refraction. Finally, a correction is applied for phase angle, arising from unsymmetrical illumination of a passive satellite by the Sun.

60. In current (1968) U.S. Coast and Geodetic Survey practice on the worldwide satellite triangulation, the next step is to reduce all the satellite images, which are exposed (or chopped) at equal intervals of time on each pass, to a single equivalent or "fictitious" image. Other organizations naturally use somewhat different procedures, especially when there are fewer images, but the principles are much the same. The reduction to a single "fictitious" image is done by fitting the corrected x- and y-coordinates of the images separately to polynomial functions of time, usually of the fifth order. A time is then selected for all simultaneous observations of the satellite involving two or more plates, so that the satellite image at that time would have been formed as near as possible to the center of each plate. The actual (x, y) of the satellite at this selected time is then computed from the polynomial, after applying clock corrections and after adding the time that light takes to travel from the satellite to the camera. The result is equivalent to a single meaned position of the satellite, simultaneously observed from two or more ground stations, at a given time.

Net Adjustment

61. The origin-hour angle H and declination D of the satellite at this mean position may now be computed from the inverse of Equation 26.59, that is,

$$\textbf{26.63} \qquad \begin{pmatrix} \cos D \cos H \\ \cos D \sin H \\ \sin D \end{pmatrix} = \mathbf{M}^T \begin{pmatrix} (x-x_0)/d \\ (y-y_0)/d \\ f/d \end{pmatrix}$$

where we have $d^2 = (x-x_0)^2 + (y-y_0)^2 + f^2$, using, of course, the calibrated values of κ, H_c, D_c, x_0, y_0, f. If the difference in scale for x and y is significant, $(x-x_0)$ and $(y-y_0)$ could first be corrected to a mean f.

62. We have so far worked in coordinate systems, oriented with respect to the actual "instantaneous" pole or rotation at the time of observation. If polar movements, as discussed in § 21–55, are found to be significant, the coordinate system could be changed at this stage by applying the appropriate rotation matrices to the left-hand side of Equation 26.63, or by applying the transpose of these rotation matrices to the right-hand side, with consequent modification of $\mathbf{M}^T$.

63. Explicit formulas in terms of the components of the original matrix $\mathbf{M}$ of Equation 26.57 are

$$\tan H = \frac{m_{12}(x-x_0) + m_{22}(y-y_0) + m_{32}(f)}{m_{11}(x-x_0) + m_{21}(y-y_0) + m_{31}(f)}$$

$$\tan D = \sin H \times \frac{m_{13}(x-x_0) + m_{23}(y-y_0) + m_{33}(f)}{m_{12}(x-x_0) + m_{22}(y-y_0) + m_{32}(f)}$$

$$= \cos H \times \frac{m_{13}(x-x_0) + m_{23}(y-y_0) + m_{33}(f)}{m_{11}(x-x_0) + m_{21}(y-y_0) + m_{31}(f)}.$$

26.64

64. Observation equations for the network can now be formed exactly as, for example, in § 26–36 and combined with duly weighted equations for such measured distances, etc., as are to be included in the adjustment of the network.

65. An alternative method is to form observation equations for the net adjustment by differentiating Equations 26.58 with respect to x, y, X, Y, Z, X_0, Y_0, Z_0, holding all other quantities fixed by the calibration and thus deriving corrections to initial approximate positions of the satellite (X, Y, Z) and of the ground station (X_0, Y_0, Z_0). Corrections to the satellite position are not, of course, required for triangulation purposes and can be eliminated during the solution.

66. The choice between the two methods does not involve any question of principle; we are entitled to consider that (H, D) are observed as much as the averaged (x, y). A decision will, no doubt, rest on what programs are available; if, for example, programs designed primarily for photogrammetric purposes are available, the choice will probably fall on the second method.

SATELLITE TRIANGULATION – DISTANCES

Observation Equations

67. If electronic distance measurements are made to the satellite from ground stations, the observation Equation 26.08 can be used in any coordinates; we have simply to assume initial coordinates for the satellite and for the ground station, and then use these coordinates to compute components of the unit vector joining the two ends of the line in the same system. In Cartesian coordinates, for example, if quantities at the satellite are overbarred, we have

(Observed Minus Computed) Distance

$$= (d\bar{x} - dx)(\bar{x} - x)/s + (d\bar{y} - dy)(\bar{y} - y)/s$$
$$+ (d\bar{z} - dz)(\bar{z} - z)/s.$$

26.65

68. To derive the observation equations in any (ω, ϕ, N) system, we have, for a unit vector in azimuth α, zenith distance β,

$$l_r = \lambda_r \sin\alpha \sin\beta + \mu_r \cos\alpha \sin\beta + \nu_r \cos\beta$$

so that, using Equations 25.13 and 19.32, we can write

$$s\{l_1, l_2, l_3\} = \mathbf{S}^T\{s\sin\alpha\sin\beta, s\cos\alpha\sin\beta, s\cos\beta\}$$
26.66 $$= \mathbf{S}^T\mathbf{Q}[\{\bar{x}, \bar{y}, \bar{z}\} - \{x, y, z\}];$$

by interchanging the overbars and by reversing the sign of s, we have for the components at the satellite

26.67 $$s\{\bar{l}_1, \bar{l}_2, \bar{l}_3\} = \bar{\mathbf{S}}^T\bar{\mathbf{Q}}[\{\bar{x}, \bar{y}, \bar{z}\} - \{x, y, z\}].$$

In any (ω, ϕ, N) coordinates, $\mathbf{Q}$ is obtained from Equation 19.26. In geodetic coordinates, we substitute Equations 25.15 for (x, y, z) or use Equations 25.18 and 25.19. The $\mathbf{S}$-matrix is given by

$$\mathbf{S} = \mathbf{S}^T = \begin{pmatrix} (\nu + h)\cos\phi & 0 & 0 \\ 0 & (\rho + h) & 0 \\ 0 & 0 & 1 \end{pmatrix}.$$

69. In geocentric coordinates, which are often the most suitable in dealing with satellites, we have

$$x = r \cos\phi \cos\omega$$
$$y = r \cos\phi \sin\omega$$
$$z = r \sin\phi;$$

the $\mathbf{S}$-matrix is given by

$$\mathbf{S} = \mathbf{S}^T = \begin{pmatrix} r\cos\phi & 0 & 0 \\ 0 & r & 0 \\ 0 & 0 & 1 \end{pmatrix}.$$

70. In some systems, such as SECOR, only distance measurements are made and must be made simultaneously from a number of ground stations. For example, if simultaneous measurements are made from four ground stations and the positions of three ground stations are known, we have only four observation equations and six unknowns. If observations are made from the same ground stations to another, widely different position of the satellite, we add four equations and only three unknowns – that is, corrections to the second position of the satellite – so that the problem of fixing the position of the unknown ground station becomes soluble from three satellite positions. In practice, many observations are made over a long period to many satellite positions.

Net Adjustment

71. Observation equations for distances can be combined with observation equations for directions, only if simultaneous measurements are made to the same position of the satellite. However, it is possible to form normal equations separately for the direction and distance measurements. The two sets of normal equations could be appropriately weighted and solved together, but the extent to which such a

combined adjustment could be done without vitiating the more accurate measurements would require statistical study in each case.

72. If distances are measured in conjunction with directions, the same coordinate system would have to be used for both sets of observation equations. If distances are measured separately, there would be some advantage in using the simpler Cartesian form of the observation equations. Simultaneous measurement of both distance and direction would give the complete vector to the satellite and, by subtraction, would give the complete vector between ground stations, which could be treated as an observation without deriving corrections to the satellite position. Each such ground vector would provide two observation equations for direction and one observation equation for distance.

LUNAR OBSERVATIONS

73. We can fix positions on the Earth by photographing the Moon against a background of stars, in much the same way as by photography of any other Earth satellite. One difficulty is that the stars and the Moon require different exposures, but this difficulty has been successfully overcome by the Markowitz moon-camera, designed for and widely used during and following the International Geophysical Year 1957–58. The camera is equatorially mounted to hold the exposure of the stellar background. Moonlight is reduced by a parallel-plate filter which can be rotated, in much the same way as the parallel-plate micrometer of a precise surveying level, to hold the photographic image of the Moon fixed in relation to the stars. The time of an observation is considered to occur when the rotating filter introduces no relative displacement between the Moon and the stars. Another difficulty arises from irregularities in the Moon's limb; these irregularities have always limited the accuracy of geodetic observations, such as the determination of longitude from lunar occultations of stars. Improved knowledge of the topography of the Moon may before long enable us to correct these irregularities; meanwhile, the Markowitz system reduces the effect of these irregularities by obtaining the right ascension (or hour angle) and declination of the Moon's center from photographic measurement of a large number of stars. Apart from the fact that the Moon costs **nothing to launch, a considerable advantage of** the system is that the elements of the Moon's orbit are accurately known; this advantage makes simultaneous observation unnecessary, although the observation must be accurately timed. Photography

of the Moon in at least two different positions from the same station will fix the position of that station in all three coordinates, relative to the center of mass of the Earth. At this time (1968), the results will be of lower accuracy than those obtainable from artificial satellites, but this fact may not be always true.

74. The *Ephemeris* [1] gives the right ascension of the Moon. We shall reduce the right ascension to origin-hour angle by subtracting the local sidereal time at the origin, which may, of course, be one of the points we propose to fix. The origin-hour angle will be the longitude $\bar{\omega}$ in a geocentric system whose zero of longitude is the plane parallel to the axis of rotation of the Earth and parallel to the *astronomical* zenith at the origin. The listed declination of the Moon will be the same as its geocentric latitude $\bar{\phi}$. In addition, the *Ephemeris* gives us the parallax π of the Moon's center; the parallax being related to the radius vector $\bar{r}$ from the center of mass of the Earth by the formula

26.68 $$\bar{r} = d \operatorname{cosec} \pi$$

in which d is an assumed equatorial radius of the Earth.

75. As usual, we start with initial approximate values of $(\bar{\omega}, \bar{\phi}, \bar{r})$ for the Moon at the time of observation and also of (ω, ϕ, r) for the ground station in the same geocentric (spherical polar) coordinate system. The origin of longitudes ω is the plane containing the axis of rotation and the astronomical zenith at the station selected as origin. The approximate values $(\bar{\omega}, \bar{\phi}, \bar{r})$ are used to find computed values H, D, s of the origin-hour angle, declination, and length of the line joining the ground station to the Moon's center from the equations

$$s \cos D \cos H = \bar{r} \cos \bar{\phi} \cos \bar{\omega} - r \cos \phi \cos \omega$$

$$s \cos D \sin H = \bar{r} \cos \bar{\phi} \sin \bar{\omega} - r \cos \phi \sin \omega$$

26.69 $$s \sin D = \bar{r} \sin \bar{\phi} - r \sin \phi,$$

obtained by projecting the line on the three Cartesian axes. Subtraction of these computed values of H, D from the values obtained by measurement of the photographic plate gives us the dD, dH of the observation Equations 26.42 and 26.43 in which we must use the geocentric components of the auxiliary

---

[1] See, for example, U.S. Naval Observatory (1966), *The American Ephemeris and Nautical Almanac for the Year 1968*, or Royal Greenwich Observatory (1966), *The Astronomical Ephemeris*. Beginning with the editions for 1960, both publications are unified, but issued separately as a joint publication by the United Kingdom and the United States.

vectors, as given by Equations 26.49 and 26.52, with $r = (\nu + h) = (\rho + h)$. The final observation equations will be in the form

(Observed Minus Computed) Declination of the Line Joining the Ground Station to the Moon's Center

$$= -\bar{M}_1 d\bar{\omega}/s - \bar{M}_2 d\bar{\phi}/s - \bar{M}_3 d\bar{r}/s$$
$$+ M_1 d\omega/s + M_2 d\phi/s + M_3 dr/s$$

26.70

(Observed Minus Computed) Right Ascension (or Origin-Hour Angle) of the Same Line

$$= \bar{N}_1 \sec D d\bar{\omega}/s$$
$$+ \bar{N}_2 \sec D d\bar{\phi}/s + \bar{N}_3 \sec D d\bar{r}/s$$
$$- N_1 \sec D d\omega/s$$
$$- N_2 \sec D d\phi/s - N_3 \sec D dr/s.$$

26.71

It is assumed that the local sidereal time at the origin for the instant of observation is accurately known so that in this case there is no need to include a time correction in the second observation equation.

76. If the position of the Moon really were accurately known at the instant of observation, we could put $d\bar{\omega}$, $d\bar{\phi}$, $d\bar{r}$ equal to zero in these equations. Unfortunately, we cannot be sure that the Universal Time of the observation is exactly the same as the Ephemeris Time used as an argument in the Lunar *Ephemeris*; there is a difference, which varies slowly, between the two times. The simplest way to overcome the difficulty is to envisage a correction dt to the time of observation, to find $d\bar{\omega}/dt$, etc., from the tabular differences, and to replace $d\bar{\omega}$, etc., in the observation equations by $(d\bar{\omega}/dt)dt$. This procedure reduces the number of unknowns by two. The four unknowns dt, $d\omega$, $d\phi$, dr can be determined from observations to two widely separated positions of the Moon, provided dt can be taken as the same for both. In practice, the Moon will be photographed in many positions from several ground stations; it may also be possible to derive corrections to the orbital elements, or to the position of the Moon's center, by expressing $d\bar{\omega}$, etc., in terms of these elements.

77. Another difficulty arises from the indefiniteness of the constant d in Equation 26.68. However, we can take d as unity, thereby reducing the scale of the whole model so that we finally determine the

radius vector of a ground station as r/d. We must also start with an approximate value of r/d, then s in Equations 26.69 becomes s/d. A measured terrestrial distance between ground stations would then serve to scale the model and to determine the constant d.

LINE-CROSSING TECHNIQUES

78. As a final example of the formation of differential observation equations, we shall consider such systems as hiran where slant radar ranges are measured from two ground stations (S_1, S_2) to an aircraft (A) flying a straight-and-level course across the line joining the two ground stations, which are usually not intervisible. Continuous measurements are made during the crossing; the minimum sum of the two ranges, corrected for refraction, is used to determine the distance between the two ground stations. It is assumed in the usual method of reduction that the minimum position occurs when the plane S_1AS_2 is vertical at A. The limitations of this assumption can be seen at once by considering the aircraft course as tangential to a prolate spheroid whose foci are S_1, S_2. The sum $(S_1P + PS_2)$ is the same for any point P on this spheroid and is less than for any point Q on the straight aircraft course external to the spheroid, so that the minimum position occurs at the point of contact of the course with the spheroid. The usual assumption is accordingly justified only if (a) the aircraft course is perpendicular to S_1S_2 (this situation is usually not the case), or (b) the aircraft crosses in the midway position. The problem can, however, be solved simply and rigorously in three dimensions without making any such assumptions.

79. We shall denote values of quantities at the aircraft position A by an overbar, and at the ground station S_2 by a double overbar. The coordinates of S_1, A, S_2 are then x^r, $\bar{x}^r$, $\bar{\bar{x}}^r$. Unit vectors in the directions S_1A, AS_2 are p^r, q^r, and the unit aircraft course vector is a^r. Parallel vectors at the three points are denoted by appropriate overbars; for example, parallels to the course vector at S_1, A, S_2, respectively, are a^r, $\bar{a}^r$, $\bar{\bar{a}}^r$. The slant ranges S_1A, AS_2, corrected for refraction, are u, v.

80. Equation 26.08 for the variation of the two slant ranges is then

26.72 $\qquad du = \bar{p}_r d\bar{x}^r - p_r dx^r$

26.73 $\qquad dv = \bar{\bar{q}}_r d\bar{\bar{x}}^r - \bar{q}_r d\bar{x}^r.$

To establish the minimum position, we first assume that S_1, S_2 are fixed and that the aircraft alone moves by $d\bar{x}^r$, while dx^r, $d\bar{\bar{x}}^r$ are zero. At the minimum position, we have also $du + dv = 0$ so that the minimum condition is

26.74 $$\bar{p}_r d\bar{x}^r = \bar{q}_r d\bar{x}^r.$$

But $d\bar{x}^r$ is proportional to the contravariant course vector $\bar{a}^r$, which reduces the minimum condition to

26.75 $$\bar{p}_r \bar{a}^r = \bar{q}_r \bar{a}^r = \cos P = \cos Q$$

where P and Q are the angles that the aircraft course makes with S_1A and AS_2, respectively. The equality of these angles is the correct minimum condition.

81. Next, we suppose that the aircraft course a^r remains fixed, and we seek corrections dx^r, $d\bar{x}^r$, $d\bar{\bar{x}}^r$ to initial approximate positions of S_1, A, S_2. The correction positions of the three points must satisfy the minimum condition, Equation 26.75. The changes in $\cos P$, $\cos Q$ arising from dx^r, $d\bar{x}^r$, $d\bar{\bar{x}}^r$ are given by

$u \times \{$final $(\cos P)$ minus initial $(\cos P)\}$

$$= ud(\cos P) = ud(a_r p^r) = ua_r d(p^r)$$
$$= a_r(d\bar{x}^r - dx^r) - (\cos P)du$$

where we have used Equation 26.07 and

$v \times \{$final $(\cos Q)$ minus initial $(\cos Q)\}$

$$= vd(\cos Q) = vd(a_r q^r) = va_r d(q^r)$$
$$= a_r(d\bar{\bar{x}}^r - d\bar{x}^r) - (\cos Q)dv.$$

Subtraction of these two equations, after equating the final values of $\cos P$ and $\cos Q$ to satisfy the minimum condition, gives

initial $(\cos Q)$ minus initial $(\cos P)$

26.76
$$= -\frac{1}{u} a_r dx^r + \left(\frac{1}{u} + \frac{1}{v}\right) \bar{a}_r d\bar{x}^r$$
$$- \frac{1}{v} \bar{\bar{a}}_r d\bar{\bar{x}}^r - \frac{du}{u} \cos P + \frac{dv}{v} \cos Q$$

in which $\cos P$, $\cos Q$ are initial values computed from the initial approximate coordinates and du (or dv) is the observed minus the computed value of u (or v). The P, Q, u, v and the components of the vectors need to be accurately computed even though the aircraft course is only roughly known. Equations 26.76, 26.72, and 26.73 can be used either as condition equations or as observation equations in conjunction with any other measurements which may have been made to connect S_1, S_2. If one end of the line is fixed, for example S_1, then we have $dx^r = 0$, and the equations are somewhat simplified.

82. Although the equations are true in any coordinate system, provided components of the vectors in the same system are used, it will be usual to work in geodetic coordinates. Azimuths, zenith distances, and distances between the initial approximate positions of the ground stations and the aircraft are computed from Equations 25.18. We can then expand Equations 26.72 and 26.73 exactly as in Equation 26.30. If the azimuth of the level aircraft course is $\bar{A}$, then we have

$$\bar{a}_1 = (\bar{\nu} + \bar{h}) \cos \bar{\phi} \sin \bar{A}$$
$$\bar{a}_2 = (\bar{\rho} + \bar{h}) \cos \bar{A}$$
$$\bar{a}_3 = 0,$$

and components of the parallel vectors a_r, $\bar{a}_r$ are found as often before from Equation 19.39. Lastly, if α, β are the azimuth and zenith distance from S_1 to A and if $\bar{\alpha}$, $\bar{\beta}$ refer as usual to the same direction at A in the same sense, then we have

$$\cos P = \bar{p}^r \bar{a}_r = \sin \bar{A} \sin \bar{\alpha} \sin \bar{\beta} + \cos \bar{A} \cos \bar{\alpha} \sin \bar{\beta}$$

26.77 $$= \sin \bar{\beta} \cos (\bar{A} - \bar{\alpha}),$$

with a similar equation for $\cos Q$.

83. If the only measurements connecting the ground stations are aircraft crossings, it will be impossible to determine corrections to geodetic heights, and the terms containing dh, $d\bar{h}$, $d\bar{\bar{h}}$ must be dropped. In a simple trilateration, for example, where a third ground point is to be fixed from two known points, there would be only the three Equations 26.72, 26.73, and 26.76 for each of the two sides; these six equations could do no more than determine corrections to the latitudes and longitudes of the third point and of the two aircraft positions. Even though we do not require the aircraft positions, corrections to them must, of course, be left in the equations. The result is not very sensitive to height changes, but the omission of the dh-terms must to some extent affect the determination of latitude and longitude; this omission must be accounted as a weakness of the method.

84. If the initial approximate positions are within 15 seconds of the truth, and this degree of approximation can usually be arranged by rough spherical computation and by placing the aircraft along the line in simple proportion to the measured ranges, then a single solution provides results correct to about 2 feet. In a test case of a single trilateral,

deliberately rough initial values of latitude and longitude of the unknown ground station proved to be, respectively, 8 minutes and 5 minutes adrift, and the initial aircraft position was 3 minutes adrift. The first solution averaged about 14 seconds adrift, the largest difference being 47 seconds in the longitude of the unknown ground station. The second solution gave results within 0.025 second of correct values. Movements of the aircraft are not very sensitive. Equation 26.76 is soon satisfied; when that situation occurs, the corrections to the aircraft position have the same coefficients in the remaining equations because of Equation 26.74, and thus can be eliminated.

CHAPTER 27

External Adjustment of Networks

CHANGE OF SPHEROID

1. If we retain the same origin and the same Cartesian vectors, it is evident that the (x, y, z) coordinates of all points in space will be unchanged. To derive the changes in geodetic coordinates resulting from changes da, de in the major axis and in the eccentricity of the base spheroid, we will need to differentiate Equations 25.15 for $dx = dy = dz = 0$. Because we have $\tan \omega = y/x$, there will be no change in longitude, and so we will need to differentiate only

$$(x^2 + y^2)^{1/2} = (\nu + h) \cos \phi \qquad \text{and}$$

27.01 $$z = (\bar{e}^2 \nu + h) \sin \phi,$$

with x, y, z constant. In the last equation, $\bar{e}$ is the complementary eccentricity given by $\bar{e}^2 = 1 - e^2$.

2. From Equations 18.55 and 18.54, we have

$$\partial \nu / \partial a = \nu/a$$

$$\partial \nu / \partial e = (e/\bar{e}^2)\rho \sin^2 \phi;$$

from Equations 22.16, 22.17, and 22.18, we have

$$\partial (\nu \cos \phi)/\partial \phi = -\rho \sin \phi$$

$$\partial (\nu \sin \phi)/\partial \phi = \rho \cos \phi/\bar{e}^2$$

$$\partial \nu / \partial \phi = (\nu - \rho) \tan \phi.$$

Differentiation of Equations 27.01 then gives

$$(\rho + h) \sin \phi \, d\phi - \cos \phi \, dh$$

27.02 $$= (\nu/a) \cos \phi \, da + (e/\bar{e}^2)\rho \sin^2 \phi \cos \phi \, de$$

and

$$0 = \{\bar{e}^2(\nu - \rho) \tan \phi \sin \phi + \bar{e}^2 \nu \cos \phi + h \cos \phi\}d\phi$$

$$+ \sin \phi \, dh + (\nu/a)\bar{e}^2 \sin \phi \, da$$

$$+ \{e\rho \sin^3 \phi - 2e\nu \sin \phi\}de.$$

The last equation, with the help of Equations 18.54 and 18.55, simplifies to

$$(\rho + h) \cos \phi \, d\phi + \sin \phi \, dh$$

$$= -(\nu/a)\bar{e}^2 \sin \phi \, da + (e/\bar{e}^2)(\rho \cos^2 \phi + \nu \bar{e}^2) \sin \phi \, de;$$

27.03

Equations 27.02 and 27.03 are readily solved to give finally

$$d\omega = 0$$

$$(\rho + h)d\phi = (e^2 \nu/a) \sin \phi \cos \phi \, da$$

$$+ (e/\bar{e}^2)(\rho + \nu \bar{e}^2) \sin \phi \cos \phi \, de$$

27.04 $$dh = -(a/\nu)da + e\nu \sin^2 \phi \, de.$$

If preferred, we can include the *flattening*

$$f = (a - b)/a = (1 - \bar{e})$$

instead of the eccentricity by using the relation

$$df = (e/\bar{e})de.$$

CHANGE OF ORIGIN

3. Next, we introduce a change (dX_0, dY_0, dZ_0) in the Cartesian origin, involving a corresponding translation of the base spheroid in the geodetic coordinate system. The effect will be the same if we keep the Cartesian origin and the spheroid fixed and if we alter the Cartesian coordinates of each point in space by $(-dX_0, -dY_0, -dZ_0)$. The corresponding changes in the geodetic coordinates could then be found by differentiating Equations 25.15, with a, e fixed, and by solving the resulting three equations for $d\omega$, $d\phi$, dh. However, we can in this case obtain directly the changes in geodetic coordinates from results already given.

4. We have, for example,

$$d\omega = -\frac{\partial \omega}{\partial x} dX_0 - \frac{\partial \omega}{\partial y} dY_0 - \frac{\partial \omega}{\partial z} dZ_0$$

$$= -A^1 dX_0 - B^1 dY_0 - C^1 dZ_0$$

where A^1, B^1, C^1 are the 1-components of the Cartesian vectors in geodetic coordinates; similarly, we have

$$d\phi = -A^2 dX_0 - B^2 dY_0 - C^2 dZ_0$$

$$dh = -A^3 dX_0 - B^3 dY_0 - C^3 dZ_0.$$

Using the notation of Equation 19.36, we then have

$$\{d\omega,\, d\phi,\, dh\} = -(\mathbf{Q}^T\mathbf{R})^T\{dX_0,\, dY_0,\, dZ_0\}$$

27.05 $$= -\mathbf{R}^T\mathbf{Q}\{dX_0,\, dY_0,\, dZ_0\},$$

an equation which would be true in any $(\omega,\, \phi,\, N)$ system, with the appropriate values of the matrices from Equations 19.26 and 19.31. In geodetic coordinates, we have

$$\mathbf{R}^T = \mathbf{R} = \begin{pmatrix} 1/\{(\nu + h)\cos\phi\} & 0 & 0 \\ 0 & 1/(\rho + h) & 0 \\ 0 & 0 & 1 \end{pmatrix};$$

expansion of Equation 27.05 gives

$$(\nu + h)\cos\phi\, d\omega = (\sin\omega)dX_0 - (\cos\omega)dY_0$$

$$(\rho + h)d\phi = (\sin\phi\cos\omega)dX_0 + (\sin\phi\sin\omega)dY_0$$

$$- (\cos\phi)dZ_0$$

$$dh = -(\cos\phi\,\cos\omega)dX_0$$

27.06 $$- (\cos\phi\,\sin\omega)dY_0 - (\sin\phi)dZ_0.$$

If there is both a change of spheroid and a change of origin, these first-order results should be added to Equations 27.04. We may write Equations 27.06 in matrix form as

$$\{(\nu + h)\cos\phi\, d\omega,\, (\rho + h)d\phi,\, dh\}$$

27.07 $$= -\mathbf{Q}\{dX_0,\, dY_0,\, dZ_0\}$$

where $\mathbf{Q}$ is given by Equation 19.26. If the new spheroid is to be parallel to the old at the origin, then we have $d\omega = d\phi = 0$ in the observation Equation 27.07 for the origin.

CHANGES OF CARTESIAN AXES

5. It has been assumed throughout this book that all $(\omega,\, \phi,\, N)$ systems—in particular, the astronomical and geodetic systems—share the same Cartesian axes, which in the geodetic applications are physically related to the axis of rotation of the Earth and to the astronomical meridian at a fixed datum or origin. The conditions to ensure common Cartesian axes at the origin of a survey have been investigated in § 19–13 through § 19–15; this situation will be continuously preserved if frequent astronomical observations are made throughout a network which has been adjusted by using the observation equations developed in § 26–12. If this procedure has been followed, there should be no need to consider reorientation of the Cartesian axes. Unfortunately, many surveys of considerable extent have not followed this rigorous procedure. At most, a few Laplace azimuths have been used in the adjustment; as we have seen in § 19–14 and § 19–15, this procedure is not sufficient to ensure correct orientation. Whenever it becomes necessary to join two such surveys or to adjust them into a correctly oriented system, we should include orientation parameters to allow for a change of Cartesian axes and for a corresponding change in the orientation of the base spheroid of the geodetic coordinate system.

6. Large rotations of the coordinate axes must be made in a prescribed order to provide unique results, although the many ways of prescribing the order can lead to some confusion. For our purposes, it would be advantageous to adopt the most common definition of *Euler's angles* because these angles are used in celestial mechanics and in satellite geodesy.[1] Unfortunately, two of the three Euler angles are indistinguishable in the case of small rotations which concern us in the present application. On the other hand, small rotations can be made in any order and compounded as vectors so that we have no need to specify the order. Nevertheless, we prescribe an order required for large rotations so that the results may be used for other applications.

7. We begin with one set of Cartesian axes $(A^r,\, B^r,\, C^r)$ and derive others $(\bar{A}^r,\, \bar{B}^r,\, \bar{C}^r)$ by right-handed rotations, which are positive if clockwise, when looking outward from the origin along the positive direction of the axis of rotation, as follows:

First, a rotation of ω_1 about the x-axis, A^r,

Second, a rotation of ω_2 about the *new* y-axis, and

Third, a rotation of ω_3 about the *new* z-axis.

The combined effect of these three independent rotations is described by the following product matrix, which premultiplies the initial vectors $(A^r,\, B^r,\, C^r)$ or the initial Cartesian coordinate vector $(x,\, y,\, z)$ to obtain the final vectors $(\bar{A}^r, \bar{B}^r, \bar{C}^r)$ or $(\bar{x},\, \bar{y},\, \bar{z})$. The product matrix is

---

[1] See Kaula (1966), *Theory of Satellite Geodesy*, 17–18.

27.08
$$\mathbf{M} = \begin{pmatrix} \cos\omega_3 & \sin\omega_3 & 0 \\ -\sin\omega_3 & \cos\omega_3 & 0 \\ 0 & 0 & 1 \end{pmatrix} \begin{pmatrix} \cos\omega_2 & 0 & -\sin\omega_2 \\ 0 & 1 & 0 \\ \sin\omega_2 & 0 & \cos\omega_2 \end{pmatrix} \begin{pmatrix} 1 & 0 & 0 \\ 0 & \cos\omega_1 & \sin\omega_1 \\ 0 & -\sin\omega_1 & \cos\omega_1 \end{pmatrix},$$

which expands to

27.09
$$\begin{pmatrix} \cos\omega_2\cos\omega_3 & (\cos\omega_1\sin\omega_3+\sin\omega_1\sin\omega_2\cos\omega_3) & (\sin\omega_1\sin\omega_3-\cos\omega_1\sin\omega_2\cos\omega_3) \\ -\cos\omega_2\sin\omega_3 & (\cos\omega_1\cos\omega_3-\sin\omega_1\sin\omega_2\sin\omega_3) & (\sin\omega_1\cos\omega_3+\cos\omega_1\sin\omega_2\sin\omega_3) \\ \sin\omega_2 & -\sin\omega_1\cos\omega_2 & \cos\omega_1\cos\omega_2 \end{pmatrix}.$$

For small rotations, the expanded matrix reduces to

27.10
$$\mathbf{N} = \begin{pmatrix} 1 & \omega_3 & -\omega_2 \\ -\omega_3 & 1 & \omega_1 \\ \omega_2 & -\omega_1 & 1 \end{pmatrix}.$$

It may be noted that $\mathbf{M}$ is an orthogonal matrix because its three component matrices are orthogonal, so that the inverse transformation is given by the transpose $\mathbf{M}^T$. The approximate matrix $\mathbf{N}$ is not orthogonal, but the inverse will, nevertheless, be given by $\mathbf{N}^T$, which is the approximate form of $\mathbf{M}^T$. Because of the antisymmetric properties of $\mathbf{N}$, the transpose $\mathbf{N}^T$ is equivalent to rotations $(-\omega_1, -\omega_2, -\omega_3)$ which restore the original situation.

8. Next, we have to find the changes in the geodetic coordinates of a point (ω, ϕ, h) resulting from these rotations. If the new Cartesian coordinates of the point are $(\bar{x}, \bar{y}, \bar{z})$, we have

$$\{\bar{x}, \bar{y}, \bar{z}\} = \mathbf{N}\{x, y, z\};$$

the change in Cartesian coordinates is given by

$$\{dx, dy, dz\} = \mathbf{N}\{x, y, z\} - \mathbf{I}\{x, y, z\}$$
27.11
$$= \mathbf{N}_0\{x, y, z\}$$

where $\mathbf{I}$ is the identity matrix and

27.12
$$\mathbf{N}_0 = \begin{pmatrix} 0 & \omega_3 & -\omega_2 \\ -\omega_3 & 0 & \omega_1 \\ \omega_2 & -\omega_1 & 0 \end{pmatrix}.$$

But, from Equation 27.07 in which the changes of coordinates of the point are $\{-dX_0, -dY_0, -dZ_0\}$, we have

$$\{(\nu+h)\cos\phi\, d\omega, (\rho+h)d\phi, dh\} = \mathbf{Q}\{dx, dy, dz\}$$
27.13
$$= \mathbf{Q}\mathbf{N}_0\{x, y, z\}.$$

Expanding and substituting for the Cartesian coordinates from Equations 25.15, we have after

some simplification

$$(\nu+h)\cos\phi\, d\omega = -\omega_3(\nu+h)\cos\phi$$
$$+ (\omega_1\cos\omega + \omega_2\sin\omega)$$
$$\times (\bar{e}^2\nu+h)\sin\phi$$
$$(\rho+h)d\phi = (\omega_2\cos\omega - \omega_1\sin\omega)$$
$$\times (h + a^2/\nu)$$
$$dh = (\omega_2\cos\omega - \omega_1\sin\omega)$$
27.14
$$\times (e^2\nu\sin\phi\cos\phi),$$

which are in a suitable form to add to Equations 27.04 and 27.06 in those cases where there are changes in the shape and size of the base spheroid, in the Cartesian origin, and in the orientation of the Cartesian axes.

9. An interesting alternative way of deriving the same result is to start with the equation

$$\{\bar{A}_r, \bar{B}_r, \bar{C}_r\} = \mathbf{N}\{A_r, B_r, C_r\}$$

or with the equation

$$\{(\bar{A}_r-A_r), (\bar{B}_r-B_r), (\bar{C}_r-C_r)\} = \mathbf{N}_0\{A_r, B_r, C_r\}$$
$$= \mathbf{N}_0\mathbf{Q}^T\{\lambda_r, \mu_r, \nu_r\}$$

from Equations 12.013 and 19.23. If we contract this last equation with a position vector ρ^r and use Equation 12.169, we have

$$\{dx, dy, dz\} = \mathbf{N}_0\mathbf{Q}^T\{(\sec\phi)(\partial p/\partial\omega), \partial p/\partial\phi, p\}$$

in which p is the perpendicular from the origin to the tangent plane to the N-surface (or h-surface in geodetic coordinates) through the point under consideration. Using Equation 27.07, we have

$$\{(\nu+h)\cos\phi\, d\omega, (\rho+h)d\phi, dh\}$$
27.15
$$= \mathbf{Q}\mathbf{N}_0\mathbf{Q}^T\{(\sec\phi)(\partial p/\partial\omega), \partial p/\partial\phi, p\}$$

in which $\mathbf{Q}\mathbf{N}_0\mathbf{Q}^T$ contains only the three rotation angles and the latitude and longitude, while the last vector contains the spheroidal elements. From

Equations 12.170, etc., in geodetic coordinates, we have

$$p = (\nu + h)\cos^2\phi + (\bar{e}^2\nu + h)\sin^2\phi$$

$$= (h + a^2/\nu)$$

$$\partial p/\partial\phi = -e^2\nu\sin\phi\cos\phi$$

27.16 $\partial p/\partial\omega = 0.$

Equation 27.15 then directly expands to Equations 27.14.

CHANGE OF SCALE
AND ORIENTATION

10. We have now dealt with all possible changes in the basic geodetic coordinate system and with the effect of such changes on the coordinates of all points in a network. In addition to the initial choice of a discordant system of geodetic coordinates, the network itself may have systematic errors of scale and orientation for which an allowance should be made before we adjust the network to adjacent work or into the fixed system of a worldwide triangulation. Any discrepancies in the coordinates of common points should then be due to random error, which can be reduced in a subsequent adjustment by least squares, provided we have enough common points.

11. Most of the systematic error in scale of a network could be eliminated by altering the size of the base spheroid in the geodetic coordinate system, that is, by evaluating the parameter da in observation equations which include Equations 27.04. However, this procedure would vitiate the height dimension and would result in some inaccuracy even in a two-dimensional adjustment which ignores geodetic heights, especially if the network covers a considerable area. The size of the base spheroid will almost always be known, and the effect of a change da to another spheroid of known size can be evaluated and removed by means of Equations 27.04 before the formation of the observation equations. In much the same way, the effect of a systematic orientation error in the network could be concealed by evaluating false values of the rotation parameters ω_1, ω_2, ω_3, but this procedure would be even more unsound. We shall accordingly investigate separately the effect of systematic error of scale and orientation within the network by holding the origin fixed, or by holding some central point of the network fixed if there is no origin. We shall choose as parameters (a) a proportional scale change ds/s, where s is the straight-line dis-

tance of the point under consideration from the origin, and (b) changes $d\alpha_0$, $d\beta_0$ in the azimuth and zenith distance at the origin of the straight line to the point under consideration. The parameters ds/s, $d\alpha_0$, $d\beta_0$ will, of course, be given the same values for all lines radiating from the origin. The straight-line distances, azimuths, and zenith distances of all points from the origin are first computed from Equation 25.18 in which the unbarred point is the origin, and are used in the coefficients of the observation equations that we shall now form.

12. We could simply differentiate Equation 25.18, with the unbarred origin and therefore the matrix **Q** fixed; we could then obtain three equations connecting ds/s, $d\alpha = d\alpha_0$, $d\beta = d\beta_0$ with changes $d\bar{\omega}$, $d\bar{\phi}$, $d\bar{h}$ in the geodetic coordinates of the point under consideration. These three equations could then be solved to give $d\bar{\omega}$, $d\bar{\phi}$, $d\bar{h}$ explicitly in terms of the parameters ds/s, $d\alpha_0$, $d\beta_0$. However, we shall find it more instructive to proceed from first principles and to derive the results in matrix form.

13. We make dx^r, $d\omega$, $d\phi$ all zero in Equations 26.07 and 26.14 and obtain

$$l^r(ds/s) + m^r d\beta_0 - n^r\sin\beta\,d\alpha_0 = d\bar{x}^r/s.$$

27.17

In this equation, $d\bar{x}^r$ are corrections to the *Cartesian* coordinates of the point under consideration arising from changes $d\alpha_0$, $d\beta_0$ in the azimuth α and zenith distance β of l^r. The auxiliary vectors m^r, n^r are defined by Equations 26.13; we must use the *Cartesian* components of all vectors in Equation 27.17, which is a vector equation only in Cartesian coordinates because of the derivation of Equation 27.17 from Equation 26.06. If we form the orthogonal matrix

$$\mathbf{A} = \begin{pmatrix} \sin\alpha\sin\beta & \sin\alpha\cos\beta & -\cos\alpha \\ \cos\alpha\sin\beta & \cos\alpha\cos\beta & \sin\alpha \\ \cos\beta & -\sin\beta & 0 \end{pmatrix}$$

27.18

and if we refer to Equations 26.33, 26.34, and 26.35, we find that the matrix of Cartesian components of l^r, m^r, n^r is

$$\mathbf{Q}^T\mathbf{A}$$

where **Q** is as usual given by Equation 19.26. Accordingly, the left-hand side of Equation 27.17 can be written in matrix form as

$$\mathbf{Q}^T\mathbf{A}\{ds/s,\,d\beta_0,\,-\sin\beta\,d\alpha_0\};$$

from Equation 27.07 in which we must substitute

$d\bar{x}$ for $-dX_0$, etc., the right-hand side is

$$\bar{\mathbf{Q}}^T\{(\bar{\nu}+\bar{h})\ \cos\ \bar{\phi}\ d\bar{\omega},\ (\bar{\rho}+\bar{h})d\bar{\phi},\ d\bar{h}\}/s$$

so that we have finally

$$\{(\bar{\nu}+\bar{h})\ \cos\ \bar{\phi}\ d\bar{\omega},\ (\bar{\rho}+\bar{h})d\bar{\phi},\ d\bar{h}\}$$

27.19 $$= s\bar{\mathbf{Q}}\mathbf{Q}^T\mathbf{A}\{ds/s,\ d\beta_0,\ -\sin\ \beta\ d\alpha_0\}.$$

The overbars in this last equation refer to the point under consideration, while the unbarred quantities and $d\alpha_0$, $d\beta_0$ refer to the origin. The matrix $\bar{\mathbf{Q}}\mathbf{Q}^T$ is given by Equation 19.25; by using Equation 19.27 for each of the three vectors l^r, m^r, n^r, we can write

27.20 $$\bar{\mathbf{Q}}\mathbf{Q}^T\mathbf{A} = \bar{\mathbf{A}}$$

where $\bar{\mathbf{A}}$ is the same matrix as $\mathbf{A}$ but formed from the azimuth and zenith distance at the overbarred point, that is, at the point under consideration. If O is the origin, we must as usual form this matrix by using the azimuth and zenith distance at P of the line OP produced, which could have been computed just as easily from Equation 25.19 as the azimuth and zenith distance at O. The parameters $d\alpha_0$, $d\beta_0$ still refer to the origin, but once the parameters are known, they can be substituted in the same equation to give the changes in coordinates of other points which have not been used in the adjustment, regardless of their actual meaning. We can accordingly drop the overbars and rewrite Equation 27.19 as

$$\{(\nu+h)\ \cos\ \phi\ d\omega,\ (\rho+h)d\phi,\ dh\}$$

27.21 $$= s\mathbf{A}\{ds/s,\ d\beta_0,\ -\sin\ \beta\ d\alpha_0\},$$

provided we form the matrix $\mathbf{A}$ from the azimuth α and zenith distance β at the point P under consideration of the line OP produced. In this final form, the equation is suitable for combining with the equations for changes in the geodetic coordinate system.

EXTENSION TO ASTRONOMICAL COORDINATES

14. Most of the preceding analysis applies equally well to a general $(\omega,\ \phi,\ N)$ system, including the astronomical system in which N is the geopotential, provided we use the more general $\mathbf{R}$-matrices given in Equation 19.31. The derivation of Equation 27.05, for example, shows that for changes $(dx,\ dy,\ dz)$ in the Cartesian coordinates of a point, we have

27.22 $$\{d\omega,\ d\phi,\ dN\} = \mathbf{R}^T\mathbf{Q}\{dx,\ dy,\ dz\}$$

where

$$\mathbf{R}^T = \begin{pmatrix} -k_1\ \sec\ \phi & -t_1\ \sec\ \phi & \gamma_1\ \sec\ \phi \\ -t_1 & -k_2 & \gamma_2 \\ 0 & 0 & n \end{pmatrix},$$

and $\mathbf{Q}$ is given by Equation 19.26. Equation 27.22 gives, for example, the changes in $(\omega,\ \phi,\ N)$ coordinates for an origin shift of $(dX_0,\ dY_0,\ dZ_0)$ by simply substituting $dx = -dX_0$, etc.

15. The change in $(\omega,\ \phi,\ N)$ coordinates, arising from operation of the rotation matrix $\mathbf{N}_0$ (Equation 27.12) on the Cartesian axes, is obtained from Equations 27.11 as

27.23 $$\{d\omega,\ d\phi,\ dN\} = \mathbf{R}^T\mathbf{Q}\mathbf{N}_0\{x,\ y,\ z\}.$$

To apply this result, we must know the Cartesian coordinates of the point; in the case of a general $(\phi,\ \omega,\ N)$ system, there are no such integral formulas as Equations 25.15. However, the Cartesian coordinates appear only in the coefficients of the first-order rotations ω_1, ω_2, ω_3, and approximate values would suffice.

16. The result of changes in the scale and orientation of the network corresponding to Equation 27.21 is similarly given by

$$\{d\omega,\ d\phi,\ dN\} = s\mathbf{R}^T\mathbf{A}\{ds/s,\ d\beta_0,\ -\sin\ \beta\ d\alpha_0\}.$$

27.24

To apply this equation in the astronomical system, we need to know the length s and the *astronomical* azimuth and zenith distance at the point P under consideration of the line OP produced, where O is the origin. Approximate values, such as geodetic values, would suffice, corrected if possible for the deflection at P.

17. There is, of course, no corresponding equation to reflect changes da, de in the base-spheroid parameters, which arise solely from the special choice of a $(\omega,\ \phi,\ h)$ system. We make such a special choice in the case of a general $(\omega,\ \phi,\ N)$ system by identifying N, for example, with the geopotential, which settles all the components of the $\mathbf{R}$-matrices at their actual physical values. To apply the system, we accordingly need values of gravity and of the curvature parameters at all points of the network.

ADJUSTMENT PROCEDURE

18. The total change in the geodetic coordinates $(d\omega,\ d\phi,\ dh)$ arising from application of the four sets of parameters $(da,\ de)$, $(dX_0,\ dY_0,\ dZ_0)$, $(\omega_1,\ \omega_2,\ \omega_3)$, and $(ds/s,\ d\beta_0,\ d\alpha_0)$ in Equations 27.04, 27.06, 27.14, and 27.21 can be obtained by adding these equations. This procedure assumes that the parameters are independent and that second-order effects can be either neglected or removed by some

process of iteration, although in some cases, the parameters, especially the rotations, will be strongly correlated (see § 27–27). In the result, we have three equations for each point containing 11 parameters. In most cases, the two spheroids will be known so that the (da, de) terms can be computed and removed from the equations. For the remainder of this section, we shall assume that this procedure has been followed and that we are left with three equations for each point containing nine parameters.

19. We shall consider the case of two adjacent networks which are to be adjusted into sympathy through common points. If one network (overbarred) is held fixed, we substitute

$$d\omega = \bar{\omega} - \omega,$$

etc., for the difference in coordinates of each common point and solve for the parameters to correct the unbarred system. All the coefficient matrices are computed in the unbarred system. We need at least three common points for a solution; if there are more points, the equations can be treated as observation equations and appropriately weighted in a least-squares adjustment. For a stable solution, the common points must, of course, be widely separated.

20. If neither network is to be held fixed, we suppose that the final values of the coordinates will be ω^*, etc. We can then form equations in each network, whose absolute terms are $\omega^* - \bar{\omega}$ and $\omega^* - \omega$, and subtract these equations in pairs to eliminate ω^*. We are left with three equations for each common point containing 18 independent parameters, and we shall need at least six common points. An extension of the same procedure would enable us to connect several networks.

21. We have supposed that all three geodetic coordinates of each common point are known in both adjacent systems. Unfortunately, geodetic heights will seldom be known. Vertical angles, controlled by frequent astronomical observations as proposed in Chapter 26, have not been measured in several major triangulations because of the (excessive) fear of the effects of atmospheric refraction and in the expectation that the stations would be connected by lines of spirit levels. However, for economic reasons, spirit leveling has for the most part been confined to roads, and triangulation stations sited on hills still have no accurate heights. Where accurate vertical angles have been measured, there are usually too few astronomical observations to provide adequate geodetic heights, and

the vertical angles have been reduced as indicated in § 25–19 to provide a first-order approximation to spirit levels.

22. If spirit levels, or an approximation to spirit levels, are available for the common points, the best procedure would be to replace the dh-equations by dN-equations, formed as in § 27–14, using geodetic values of (ω, ϕ) in the coefficients and the best possible values of the gravitational parameters in the **R**-matrix. An additional parameter may be required to allow for difference of level datums in the networks. The unknown parameters are otherwise the same in the dN-equations, which can accordingly be used in conjunction with the $d\omega$, $d\phi$ geodetic equations.

23. If no adequate heights are available in any defined system for the common points, no valid adjustment is possible; the points of the network are, in fact, located in three-dimensional space, and we cannot expect to achieve a rational answer by arbitrarily stripping a dimension, even though such procedures have been common in classical geodesy. The most we can do is to drop the dh-equations and to solve for the unknown parameters from the $d\omega$, $d\phi$ equations only, using the best available values for h in the coefficients. In that case, we should need at least 50 percent more common points, and even so we could not expect to derive valid values for some of the parameters. For example, dX_0, dY_0, dZ_0 would probably be fictitious because we should not have taken any definite steps toward positioning the spheroids. It would be better to defer the adjustment altogether until adequate observations have been made.

FIGURE OF THE EARTH

24. In modern language, the old problem of determining a "Figure of the Earth" becomes the problem of finding a geodetic coordinate system which best fits the astronomical system. The problem is very easily solved if we substitute the astronomical minus the geodetic longitude (or latitude) for $d\omega$ (or $d\phi$) in the observation equations of this chapter and retain the parameters da, de of Equations 27.04. All the points used in the adjustment should be in the same network, although the network may have been formed by joining adjacent networks as proposed in the last section. In addition to da, de, other parameters may be included in the adjustment, depending on the kind of network we are using.

25. The parameters $(dX_0,\ dY_0,\ dZ_0)$ should normally be included in order to locate the origin of the final system as near as possible at the *center of figure*; we should be unable to locate the origin at the *center of mass* by any geometrical adjustment. However, if we know the positions of some of the stations of the network in relation to the center of mass, whether by lunar observations as described in Chapter 26 or by dynamic observations to artificial satellites, we can relate the origin derived from the geometrical adjustment to the center of mass and so can shift the origin to the center of mass. For example, if the geocentric coordinates of a point in relation to the center of mass as origin are $(\bar{\omega},\ \bar{\phi},\ r)$ and if the geodetic coordinates of the same point are $(\omega,\ \phi,\ h)$, then

$$dx = (\nu + h)\cos\phi\cos\omega - r\cos\bar{\phi}\cos\bar{\omega}$$

$$dy = (\nu + h)\cos\phi\sin\omega - r\cos\bar{\phi}\sin\bar{\omega}$$

27.25 $\qquad dz = (\bar{e}^2\nu + h)\sin\phi - r\sin\bar{\phi}$

give the coordinates of the center of mass from the origin of the geodetic system. Mean values of the shift from a number of points should ultimately provide a close result. As always, we require the geocentric and geodetic systems to share the same Cartesian axes. If we know $dx,\ dy,\ dz$ from Equations 27.25, then we can substitute $dx = dX_0$, etc., in the observation equations and so can derive a geodetic system whose origin is the center of mass.

26. The Cartesian rotations $(\omega_1,\ \omega_2,\ \omega_3)$ should be included in the observation equations if we have any reason to suspect the initial orientation of the network. These rotations should not be included in a passive satellite triangulation network where every line, apart from observational error, has been correctly oriented.

27. Scale and orientation parameters $(ds/s,\ d\beta_0,\ d\alpha_0)$ could be included, but would be confused with da and $(\omega_1,\ \omega_2,\ \omega_3)$ unless the network is of great extent. These parameters should not be included in a worldwide satellite triangulation network which has been closed and internally adjusted, but should be included in the adjustment of an existing triangulation to satellite control.

28. We have so far considered only the observation equations for latitude and longitude in determining a Figure of the Earth. The question arises whether we also can include equations for the third dimension. If we know the geopotential at points of the network, whether by spirit leveling or by other means, we can find a point whose geodetic coordinates are $(\omega,\ \phi,\ \bar{h})$ where the standard potential has the same value. If h is the geodetic height of the network point, we could write $(\bar{h} - h)$ for dh in an observational equation. Inclusion of this equation in the adjustment would result in values of the parameters which would minimize $(\bar{h} - h)$ as well as the astronomical minus the geodetic latitude and longitude. The adjustment would thus bring the standard gravitational field into closer accord with actuality.

29. There are, of course, certain advantages in adopting a geodetic system close to the astronomical system. It is convenient to confuse the two systems within allowable limits of error for such purposes as small-scale mapping; it is essential that first-order transformations between the two systems should be sufficiently accurate for even the most refined geodetic work. However, there are serious practical and economic disadvantages in changing the geodetic system too often. The next justifiable occasion to make the change may well be on completion of the worldwide satellite triangulation.

CHAPTER 28

Dynamic Satellite Geodesy

GENERAL REMARKS

1. The static use of artificial satellites as elevated beacons has been described in § 26–43 through § 26–72. In addition, it is possible to derive much geodetic information by observing and analyzing the motion of the satellite in orbit. The lower harmonics of the gravitational field can be obtained more accurately from satellites than by any other method, until it becomes possible to cover the entire globe with gravity observations to a high degree of accuracy and with uniform density; corrections to the positions of tracking stations may be obtained in a worldwide reference system, supplementing direct geometrical fixation by satellite triangulation; and the origin of the reference system can be located at the center of mass of the Earth, which is impossible by any other method until gravity surveys are completed over the entire globe. But to obtain all this information, as well as the changing elements of the satellite orbits from a growing number of satellites, necessarily involves some complexity.

2. Methods initially were taken from the astronomers — who did not have quite the same problem of a close satellite of an unsymmetrical rotating parent body — with the result that considerable extensions and modifications have been found necessary. As in astronomical calculations, analytical methods, which must, nevertheless, be studied to gain any understanding of the problem, are giving way to numerical and statistical methods, using larger computers on more sophisticated programs. Against this background of rapid development and of growing complexity, the most explanation which can be provided in one chapter is a fairly detailed account of the basic equations and elementary theory, followed by notes in bare outline on current methods of solution.

EQUATIONS OF MOTION– INERTIAL AXES

3. Newton's second law of motion for a particle of mass m is usually expressed in Cartesian coordinates as

28.001
$$m \frac{d^2x}{dt^2} = \frac{d(mv_x)}{dt} = F_x$$

with two similar equations for the other coordinates y and z. In these equations, the derivatives are with respect to time t, which is assumed to be independent of the space coordinates; v_x, F_x are, respectively, the x-components of the velocity (dx/dt) and of the applied force. If the equations are to hold in the same Cartesian system over some finite region of space, then that space must be flat (§ 5–2). Moreover, if the Cartesian equations of motion are to express a law of nature, these equations must be invariant with respect to manmade coordinate transformations; it can be shown that the equations are invariant, provided the mass does not change either with time or with the coordinate system and provided the two sets of Cartesian axes are fixed or, at most, are moving relative to each other with a constant velocity of translation. The equations do not hold true in any coordinate system if one set of axes is accelerating (or rotating) with respect to the other set.

4. A coordinate or reference system which is either fixed or moving with a constant velocity of

translation is known as an *inertial system;* we can say that Equation 28.001 holds true only in such a system. The inertial system which most concerns us in satellite geodesy has the *z*-axis parallel to, and in the northward direction of, the Earth's axis of rotation; the *x*-axis is parallel to the plane of the Earth's orbit around the Sun—the plane of the *ecliptic*—in the direction of the vernal *equinox*. We must also specify a time or epoch and must correct our observations accordingly because the axis of rotation and the ecliptic vary slightly in time, mainly as a result of lunar and planetary perturbations. Even then, we cannot say that we have a true inertial system. A recent description of the astronomical determination of an inertial frame of reference has been given by Wayman.[1] Nevertheless, it has been said that the only valid definition of an inertial system is one which would make Newton's laws true, and because these laws are not true on the cosmic scale, there is no such thing as an inertial system. However, for our present purposes, the concept is a good approximation. We shall also assume that the origin of the inertial system is the center of mass of the Earth, in which case as we have seen in § 21–42 that first-degree harmonics must necessarily be absent from the expression of the Earth's potential in spherical harmonics derived from the Cartesian inertial system.

5. To express Equation 28.001 in a general coordinate system x^r, we must first generalize the velocity vector. In (overbarred) Cartesian coordinates, the contravariant velocity vector is $d\bar{x}^s/dt$, expressing the time-rate of change of each coordinate. By the ordinary transformation law, the velocity vector in any other coordinate system (unbarred) is then

28.002 $\qquad v^r = \dfrac{\partial x^r}{\partial \bar{x}^s}\, \bar{v}^s = \dfrac{\partial x^r}{\partial \bar{x}^s}\dfrac{d\bar{x}^s}{dt} = \dfrac{dx^r}{dt} = \dfrac{ds}{dt}\dfrac{dx^r}{ds} = vl^r$

where $v = ds/dt$ is the linear velocity, ds is the arc element of the path of motion or orbit, and l^r is the unit tangent to the path of motion. The covariant velocity vector is obtained by simply lowering the indices in the first and last members of Equation 28.002. In Cartesian coordinates, the velocity vector is also the time-rate of change of the position vector ρ^r, and we may generalize this statement to

28.003 $\qquad \dfrac{\delta \rho^r}{\delta t} = vl^r$

with a covariant equation obtained by lowering the indices, provided that we now take the *intrinsic* derivative (§ 4–1) of the position vector. Because

[1] Wayman (1966), "Determination of the Inertial Frame of Reference," *The Quarterly Journal of the Royal Astronomical Society*, v. 7, 138–156.

Equation 28.003 is a tensor equation which is true in Cartesian coordinates, it is true in any coordinate system.

6. The equations of motion can now be generalized to

28.004 $\qquad m\dfrac{\delta^2 \rho_r}{\delta t^2} = m\dfrac{\delta v_r}{\delta t} = \dfrac{\delta(mvl_r)}{\delta t} = F_r$

where F_r is the applied force vector and (mvl_r) is defined as the *momentum* vector. Equation 28.004 reduces to Equation 28.001 and to the two similar equations in Cartesian coordinates, as a tensor equation, Equation 28.004 is therefore true in any coordinate system derived from an inertial system. If we consider F_r to be the force per unit mass or, alternatively, if we consider that we are dealing with a particle of unit mass, we may drop the m in the last equation and write

28.005 $\qquad \dfrac{\delta^2 \rho_r}{\delta t^2} = \dfrac{\delta v_r}{\delta t} = \dfrac{\delta(vl_r)}{\delta t} = F_r,$

which expresses the *acceleration* vector. If the applied force is derived from a scalar potential V, we have

$$F_r = -V_r$$

from the generalization of Equation 20.05; we can write

28.006 $\qquad \dfrac{\delta^2 \rho_r}{\delta t^2} = \dfrac{\delta v_r}{\delta t} = \dfrac{\delta(vl_r)}{\delta t} = F_r = -V_r.$

7. The tensor Equation 28.006 can be written in yet another form more suitable for expanding the equations of motion in a particular coordinate system. We have

$$-V_r = F_r = \frac{\delta(vl_r)}{\delta t} = \frac{d(vl_r)}{dt} - \Gamma^s_{rk}\,(vl_s)\frac{dx^k}{dt}$$

$$= \frac{d(vl_r)}{dt} - \Gamma^s_{rk}\, v^2 g_{sq} l^q l^k$$

$$= \frac{d(vl_r)}{dt} - [rk, q]v^2 l^q l^k$$

$$= \frac{d(vl_r)}{dt} - \tfrac{1}{2}\left(\frac{\partial g_{rq}}{\partial x^k} + \frac{\partial g_{kq}}{\partial x^r}\right.$$

$$\left. - \frac{\partial g_{rk}}{\partial x^q}\right) v^2 l^q l^k$$

$$= \frac{d(vl_r)}{dt} - \tfrac{1}{2}\left(\frac{\partial g_{rq}}{\partial x^k} + \frac{\partial g_{kq}}{\partial x^r}\right.$$

$$\left. - \frac{\partial g_{rq}}{\partial x^k}\right) v^2 l^q l^k$$

on interchanging the dummy indices (k, q) in the last term and by using Equations 28.002, 3.02, and 3.01. Finally, we have

28.007 $-V_r = F_r = \dfrac{d}{dt}\left(g_{rs}\dfrac{dx^s}{dt}\right) - \tfrac{1}{2}\dfrac{\partial g_{kq}}{\partial x^r}\dfrac{dx^k}{dt}\dfrac{dx^q}{dt},$

which enables us to write at once the components of force in any coordinate system from the metric alone.

8. For example, suppose that we wish to work in the symmetrical (ω, ϕ, h) coordinate system of Chapter 18. By direct substitution of the metric given in Equations 18.03 and 18.04, we have

$$-\frac{\partial V}{\partial \omega} = \frac{d}{dt}\{(\bar{R}_1 + h)^2 \cos^2 \phi\, \dot{\omega}\}$$

$$-\frac{\partial V}{\partial \phi} = \frac{d}{dt}\{(\bar{R}_2 + h)^2 \dot{\phi}\} - \tfrac{1}{2}\frac{\partial\{(\bar{R}_1 + h)^2 \cos^2 \phi\}}{\partial \phi}\,\dot{\omega}^2$$

$$\qquad - \tfrac{1}{2}\frac{\partial\{(\bar{R}_2 + h)^2\}}{\partial \phi}\,\dot{\phi}^2$$

$$-\frac{\partial V}{\partial h} = \frac{d}{dt}\{\dot{h}\} - \tfrac{1}{2}\frac{\partial\{(\bar{R}_1 + h)^2 \cos^2 \phi\}}{\partial h}\,\dot{\omega}^2$$

$$\qquad - \tfrac{1}{2}\frac{\partial\{(\bar{R}_2 + h)^2\}}{\partial h}\,\dot{\phi}^2$$

28.008

in which we have adopted the usual convention of denoting differentiations with respect to time by dots, for example, $\dot{\omega} = d\omega/dt$. Equations 28.008 apply to any choice of axially symmetrical base surface whose principal radii of curvature $\bar{R}_1$, $\bar{R}_2$ are functions of the latitude ϕ only. To obtain the equations in geodetic coordinates with a spheroidal base, we have only to use the special values of $\bar{R}_1$, $\bar{R}_2$ given by Equations 18.55 and 18.54. We can also obtain the equations in spherical polar coordinates by choosing a spherical base surface of radius

$$r_0 = \bar{R}_1 = \bar{R}_2$$

so that we have

$$(\bar{R}_1 + h) = (\bar{R}_2 + h) = r,$$

the radius vector of the point under consideration. Expansion of Equations 28.008 in this case give immediately the well-known formulas

$$-\frac{\partial V}{\partial \omega} = \frac{d}{dt}(r^2 \cos^2 \phi\, \dot{\omega})$$

$$-\frac{\partial V}{\partial \phi} = \frac{d}{dt}(r^2 \dot{\phi}) + r^2 \sin \phi \cos \phi\, \dot{\omega}^2$$

28.009 $-\dfrac{\partial V}{\partial r} = \ddot{r} - r \cos^2 \phi\, \dot{\omega}^2 - r\dot{\phi}^2.$

EQUATIONS OF MOTION – MOVING AXES

9. Next, we shall suppose that the motion of the particle or satellite is referred to the usual Cartesian axes A_r, B_r, C_r, fixed in the Earth but rotating around the C_r-axis with constant angular velocity $\tilde{\omega}$ relative to the inertial axes $\bar{A}_r, \bar{B}_r, \bar{C}_r$ ($C_r = \bar{C}_r$). If t is elapsed time since the two sets of axes coincided, we have from Equations 20.10

$$A_r = \bar{A}_r \cos \tilde{\omega}t + \bar{B}_r \sin \tilde{\omega}t$$

$$B_r = -\bar{A}_r \sin \tilde{\omega}t + \bar{B}_r \cos \tilde{\omega}t$$

28.010 $C_r = \bar{C}_r.$

Because ordinary and covariant differentiation are the same in Cartesian coordinates and because $\bar{A}_r, \bar{B}_r, \bar{C}_r$ are fixed, we have

$$\frac{dA_r}{dt} = \tilde{\omega}B_r\,; \qquad \frac{dB_r}{dt} = -\tilde{\omega}A_r\,; \qquad \frac{dC_r}{dt} = 0.$$

28.011

10. The position vector of a satellite at (x, y, z) in the moving system is

$$\rho_r = xA_r + yB_r + zC_r;$$

using Equations 28.011, the absolute velocity vector relative to the inertial axes is

$$\frac{d\rho_r}{dt} = \dot{x}A_r + \dot{y}B_r + \dot{z}C_r + \tilde{\omega}(xB_r - yA_r),$$

the last two terms arising from the motion of the axes and the first three terms giving the apparent velocity vector v_r relative to the moving axes. In the same way, the absolute acceleration vector is given by

$$\frac{d^2\rho_r}{dt^2} = (\ddot{x}A_r + \ddot{y}B_r + \ddot{z}C_r)$$

$$\qquad + 2\tilde{\omega}(\dot{x}B_r - \dot{y}A_r) - \tilde{\omega}^2(xA_r + yB_r).$$

We may equate the absolute acceleration to the applied force vector per unit mass F_r by Newton's second law. The first group of terms in parentheses on the right is the apparent acceleration relative to the moving axes; this group can be expressed in tensor form as $\delta v_r/\delta t$ in which v_r is the apparent velocity vector. The second group of terms can be written as the vector product

$$2\tilde{\omega}\epsilon_{rpq}C^p v^q,$$

if we remember that covariant and contravariant components are the same in rectangular Cartesian coordinates. The third group of terms is the gradient of $-\frac{1}{2}\tilde{\omega}^2(x^2+y^2)$; this group can be written as

$$-\tfrac{1}{2}\tilde{\omega}^2(x^2+y^2)_r,$$

using Equations 12.009.

We have finally

28.012 $\qquad F_r = \dfrac{\delta v_r}{\delta t} + 2\tilde{\omega}\epsilon_{rpq}C^p v^q - \tfrac{1}{2}\tilde{\omega}^2(x^2+y^2)_r.$

This last equation is a tensor equation which holds true in any coordinate system transformed from the *moving A_r, B_r, C_r system*, if we note that (x^2+y^2) is the square of the distance of the satellite from the axis of rotation and is therefore an invariant under such transformations. Moreover, the vector C^p symbolizes any axis of rotation and need no longer have anything to do with the coordinate system. It will be seen that Equation 28.012 differs from the Newtonian equations of motion relative to inertial axes by the addition of the last two terms on the right. The first of these terms is known as the *Coriolis* force (or acceleration); the second is known as the *centripetal* force. However, these are fictitious forces arising from the motion of the axes, unlike the applied force F_r, the idea being that if we "correct" the applied force by the Coriolis and centripetal "forces," the ordinary Newtonian equations of motion apply to the apparent velocity. Another way of handling the matter is to forget that the axes are rotating and to use Equation 28.012 instead of Equation 28.005. It may be emphasized that the covariant velocity vector $v_r = vl_r$ is not the gradient of the scalar velocity v, whether in an inertial or moving coordinate system. The scalar velocity v has so far been defined only as ds/dt along the orbit and can have a gradient only along the orbit. At the end of this chapter, we shall define the scalar velocity of a family of orbits in space, but meanwhile there need be no confusion.

11. If the impressed force F_r is derived from a scalar potential V, we have

$$F_r = -V_r$$

from the generalization of Equation 20.05. Also, if W is the geopotential defined in § 20–10, we have

$$W_r = V_r - \tfrac{1}{2}\tilde{\omega}^2(x^2+y^2)_r$$

from Equation 20.08, so that Equation 28.012 in this case can be written as

28.013 $\qquad -W_r = \dfrac{\delta v_r}{\delta t} + 2\tilde{\omega}\epsilon_{rpq}C^p v^q.$

If the Coriolis force — the last term on the right — could be written as the gradient of a scalar S, then the equations of motion would take the normal Newtonian form with a potential $(W+S)$. However, this is generally impossible; the Newtonian equations of motion simply do not apply to accelerating or moving axes even with a modified potential.

12. The equations of motion in Cartesian coordinates, referred to the Earth-fixed A_r, B_r, C_r system, are easily obtained by contracting Equation 28.012 successively with A^r, B^r, and C^r, which are constant vectors in this system so that the x-component of the applied force is, for example,

$$F_x = F_r A^r = A^r \frac{\delta^2 \rho_r}{\delta t^2} + 2\tilde{\omega}\epsilon_{rpq}A^r C^p v^q - \tilde{\omega}^2 x x_r A^r$$

$$= \frac{\delta^2(A^r \rho_r)}{\delta t^2} - 2\tilde{\omega}B_q \frac{dx^q}{dt} - \tilde{\omega}^2 x$$

$$= \frac{d^2 x}{dt^2} - 2\tilde{\omega}\frac{dy}{dt} - \tilde{\omega}^2 x.$$

The three equations of motion are then

$$\ddot{x} - 2\tilde{\omega}\dot{y} = F_x + \tilde{\omega}^2 x = -\partial W/\partial x$$

$$\ddot{y} + 2\tilde{\omega}\dot{x} = F_y + \tilde{\omega}^2 y = -\partial W/\partial y$$

28.014 $\qquad \ddot{z} \qquad\quad = F_z \qquad\quad = -\partial W/\partial z.$

The last three members of these equations assume that the impressed force can be expressed as the gradient of a scalar potential $-V$, in which case W is the geopotential.

INERTIAL AXES — FIRST INTEGRALS

13. It is apparent from Equation 28.002 that the magnitude of the velocity vector v^r is v because l^r is a unit vector. Accordingly, we have

$$v^r v_r = v^2,$$

which can be differentiated intrinsically to give

$$\frac{d(v^2)}{dt} = v^r \frac{\delta v_r}{\delta t} + v_r \frac{\delta v^r}{\delta t}$$

$$= v^r \frac{\delta v_r}{\delta t} + g_{rs}v^s \frac{\delta v^r}{\delta t}$$

$$= v^r \frac{\delta v_r}{\delta t} + v^s \frac{\delta(g_{rs}v^r)}{\delta t}$$

$$= v^r \frac{\delta v_r}{\delta t} + v^s \frac{\delta v_s}{\delta t}$$

28.015 $\qquad = 2v^r \dfrac{\delta v_r}{\delta t},$

remembering that the metric tensor g_{rs} is constant under covariant or intrinsic differentiation.

14. If we take the equations of motion in the form of Equation 28.006 as

28.016
$$\frac{\delta(v_r)}{\delta t} = -V_r,$$

contract with the contravariant velocity vector $v^r = dx^r/dt$, and use Equation 28.015, we have

28.017
$$v^r \frac{\delta v_r}{\delta t} = \frac{1}{2}\frac{d(v^2)}{dt} = -V_r \frac{dx^r}{dt}.$$

The total time differential of V is

28.018
$$\frac{dV}{dt} = \frac{\partial V}{\partial x^r}\frac{dx^r}{dt} + \frac{\partial V}{\partial t} = V_r \frac{dx^r}{dt} + \frac{\partial V}{\partial t};$$

if V does not contain the time explicitly ($\partial V/\partial t = 0$), we can write Equation 28.017 as

28.019
$$\frac{d}{dt}\left(\tfrac{1}{2}v^2 + V\right) = 0,$$

which shows that

28.020
$$H^* = \tfrac{1}{2}v^2 + V$$

is a constant of the motion and provides a first integral of the equations of motion. The potential V, as we have seen in § 20–3, can be considered a form of energy; whereas $(\tfrac{1}{2}v^2)$, remembering that we are dealing with a particle of unit mass, is the kinetic energy of the particle. We say that $(\tfrac{1}{2}v^2 + V)$ represents the total energy of the particle, which is *conserved* during the motion. The integral $(\tfrac{1}{2}v^2 + V)$ is sometimes known in the literature as the *vis viva*.

15. If, on the other hand, the potential is time-dependent in the sense that its expression contains the time explicitly, then there is generally no simple law of conservation of energy. In that case, if we add Equations 28.017 and 28.018 and integrate, we have

28.021
$$\tfrac{1}{2}v^2 + V = \int \frac{\partial V}{\partial t}\, dt + \text{constant};$$

the integral on the right cannot generally be evaluated unless we can express V completely in terms of the single time variable. Equation 28.021 can, in some cases, be solved by successive approximation; as we shall see in § 28–91, the equation can be given a definite expression in the case of a uniformly rotating, attracting body such as the Earth.

16. The attraction potential of the Earth is not symmetrical about the axis of rotation and will therefore contain tesseral harmonics when expressed in spherical harmonics related to Earth-fixed, but rotating, axes A_r, B_r, C_r. The longitude ω in the spherical harmonics is related to the inertial longitude $\bar{\omega}$ by the relation

28.022
$$\omega = \bar{\omega} - \tilde{\omega}t,$$

if t is the elapsed time since the two sets of axes coincided and if $\tilde{\omega}$ is the constant angular velocity of rotation, as we can see at once from figure 16, Chapter 20. To express the potential in spherical harmonics related to the inertial system, as we must do if we are going to use Newtonian equations of motion, we can substitute Equation 28.022, for example, in Equation 21.035, which would then contain the time explicitly. Another way of considering this matter is to note that the field at a fixed point in inertial space will vary with time as the Earth rotates; the potential is time-dependent, whether we express the potential in spherical harmonics or in any other coordinate system derived from the inertial system. We conclude that Equation 28.021, and not Equation 28.020, holds true in this case.

17. Another law which might assist a solution of the equations of motion is the conservation of angular momentum. In figure 32, the origin is at S, the

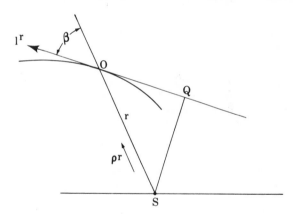

Figure 32.

satellite is at O, and the unit tangent l_r to the orbit is as shown in the plane of the paper. The line SQ is perpendicular to the tangent; the magnitude of the angular momentum or moment of momentum for unit mass is defined as

$$v(SQ) = vr\sin\beta,$$

which is the magnitude of the vector product

28.023
$$\epsilon^{rst}\rho_s v_t = v\epsilon^{rst}\rho_s l_t = \epsilon^{rst}\rho_s \dot{\rho}_t,$$

known as the *angular momentum* vector, whose direction is perpendicular to the plane of the paper and toward the reader. If we assume that both the magnitude and direction of this vector must be constant in time to satisfy a conservation law, we have

$$\epsilon^{rst}\rho_s v_t = \text{constant.}$$

Obviously, this law cannot be a universal law of nature because it depends on the origin S of the coordinate system through the position vector ρ_s. To determine the circumstances in which the supposed law can apply, we differentiate intrinsically with respect to time, remembering that we have $\delta\rho_s/\delta t = v_s$ and that the vector product of two parallel or identical vectors is zero. The result, using Equation 28.005, is

28.024 $\epsilon^{rst}\rho_s F_t = 0,$

which implies that the force — or the gradient of the potential — must be parallel to the position vector. In the case we are considering, this result restricts the potential to the elementary form GM/r; $(vr \sin \beta)$ is then constant. Also, the orbit must lie entirely in a plane passing through the origin, that is, the plane of the paper in figure 32, because the angular momentum vector is normal to this plane and is a constant vector. There is a clear analogy with the situation discussed in § 24–10 for the path of a light ray in a spherically symmetrical refracting medium, an analogy first noted by Newton [2] himself.

18. We shall now indicate briefly that the same situation would occur if the supposed law required the magnitude, but not the direction, of the angular momentum vector to be constant in time. In that case, we have

$$\epsilon^{rst}\rho_s v_t \epsilon_{rpq}\rho^p v^q = \text{constant;}$$

by intrinsic time differentiation, we have after some manipulation and use of Equations 2.18, 2.19, and 2.21

28.025 $\rho_p V_q \rho^p v^q = \rho_q V_p \rho^p v^q.$

We now set up the usual triad $(\lambda_r, \mu_r, \nu_r)$ of parallel, meridian, and normal vectors in a spherical polar (ω, ϕ, r) system. The gradient vector of the potential, like any other vector, can be expressed in terms of the triad as

28.026 $V_q = l\lambda_q + m\mu_q + n\nu_q.$

If the azimuth and zenith distance of the orbit in

the (ω, ϕ, r) system are α, β, we have

$$v^q = vl^q = v(\lambda^q \sin \alpha \sin \beta + \mu^q \cos \alpha \sin \beta + \nu^q \cos \beta)$$

and also

$$\rho^q = rv^q.$$

Substitution in Equation 28.025 gives after some manipulation

$$vr^2 \sin \beta(l \sin \alpha + m \cos \alpha) = 0,$$

which clearly cannot be satisfied for a general orbit (α, β arbitrary) unless we have $l = m = 0$, again requiring V_q in Equation 28.026 to be parallel to the position vector. In this case also, angular momentum is conserved only in an elementary potential field GM/r. The orbit is then plane, and

28.027 $vr \sin \beta = \text{constant}$

is an integral of the equations of motion.

MOVING AXES — FIRST INTEGRALS

19. In our present problem, the geopotential W in Equation 28.013 does not contain the time explicitly. For example, the attraction potential in spherical harmonics given by Equation 21.035 contains only spherical polar coordinates derived from the Earth-fixed A_r, B_r, C_r system, and the same applies to the expression of the potential in any other coordinates derived from the A_r, B_r, C_r system. The centripetal part $\frac{1}{2}\tilde{\omega}^2(x^2 + y^2)$ of the geopotential contains only rectangular coordinates in the A_r, B_r, C_r system. The total time differential of the geopotential is accordingly

$$\frac{dW}{dt} = W_r \frac{dx^r}{dt}.$$

If we contract Equation 28.013 with the velocity vector $v^r = dx^r/dt$, the Coriolis force is eliminated. Using Equation 28.015 and integrating with respect to time as in § 28–14, we have

28.028 $\frac{1}{2}v^2 + W = \text{constant}$

as a first integral even though the geopotential contains tesseral harmonics. In this expression, v is the magnitude of the apparent velocity relative to the rotating axes fixed in the Earth. We shall consider in § 28–87 and § 28–88 how to transform this result to the inertial system, and so to obtain a first integral of the *inertial* equations of motion.

20. The rotating system can be considered an inertial system in which the ordinary Newtonian equations of motion would apply, if we interpret the impressed force as the gradient of the geopotential

[2] Quoted by Forsyth (Dover ed. of 1960), *Calculus of Variations*, original ed. of 1926, 256–257.

plus the Coriolis force. Therefore, we cannot expect angular momentum to be conserved in the rotating system unless the total force, thus compounded, is directed toward the origin. As we found from Equation 28.024, we should require

$$-W_r + 2\tilde{\omega}\epsilon_{rpq}C^p v^q = \kappa\rho_r$$

in which κ is a scalar; this equation cannot possibly be satisfied for general values of W_r and v^q, any more than Equation 28.024 could be satisfied by general values of the potential. Accordingly, no first integral can be derived from a conservative law of angular momentum except in special cases.

THE LAGRANGIAN

21. In an inertial system, the space coordinates are independent of time — an essential feature of the Newtonian system — and are therefore independent also of the velocity components. Generally, we can associate any velocity components with any space coordinates, although the two sets of variables will, of course, be related for a particular orbit. Instead of considering our present problem in terms of three space variables and of their variation with time, we can consider the problem in terms of seven independent variables $(x, y, z, \dot{x}, \dot{y}, \dot{z}, t)$, which can be transformed in various ways, and we derive solutions of the equations of motion for particular orbits in the form of relations between these seven variables. A complete solution, for example, would consist of x, y, z as functions of time from which $\dot{x}, \dot{y}, \dot{z}$ could be obtained by differentiation or, alternatively, $\dot{x}, \dot{y}, \dot{z}$ as functions of time from which x, y, z could be obtained by integration.

22. Next, we introduce an expression

28.029 $\qquad L^* = \frac{1}{2}(\dot{x}^2 + \dot{y}^2 + \dot{z}^2) - V(x, y, z, t),$

known as the *Lagrangian*, in which $(\dot{x}, \dot{y}, \dot{z}, x, y, z, t)$ are considered as independent variables. The first term on the right is the kinetic energy, and V is a scalar potential. We then have

$$\frac{d}{dt}\left(\frac{\partial L^*}{\partial \dot{x}}\right) = \frac{d\dot{x}}{dt} = \ddot{x} = -\frac{\partial V}{\partial x} = \frac{\partial L^*}{\partial x},$$

using the Cartesian form of Equation 28.006 for the equations of motion in a scalar potential field, plus two similar equations for y and z which are equivalent to the Newtonian equations of motion. These three equations can be put into index form as

28.030 $\qquad \dfrac{d}{dt}\left(\dfrac{\partial L^*}{\partial \dot{q}^r}\right) = \dfrac{\partial L^*}{\partial q^r},$

which is a tensor equation only if the coordinates and the transforming factors

$$\frac{\partial q^r}{\partial \bar{q}^s} = \frac{\partial \dot{q}^r}{\partial \dot{\bar{q}}^s}$$

are independent of time. The equations of motion may be written in this Lagrangian form for the positions and velocities of any number of particles in a general dynamic system.

THE CANONICAL EQUATIONS

23. Although a first integral of the inertial equations of motion in the form of Equation 28.020 will not generally exist, there will, nevertheless, be a quantity H^*—known as the *Hamiltonian*—given by

28.031 $\qquad H^* = \frac{1}{2}v^2 + V.$

The H^* will be constant in time in accordance with Equation 28.020, only if the applied force is the gradient of a scalar, $-V$, which does not explicitly contain the time. However, in the general circumstances of our problem, H^* can be written in Cartesian coordinates in the form

28.032 $\qquad H^* = \frac{1}{2}(\dot{x}^2 + \dot{y}^2 + \dot{z}^2) + V(x, y, z, t),$

containing seven variables. Differentiation with respect to these variables and substitution in the Cartesian form of Equation 28.006 give three sets of equations of the form

$$\frac{\partial H^*}{\partial \dot{x}} = \dot{x} = \frac{dx}{dt}\,; \qquad \frac{\partial H^*}{\partial x} = \frac{\partial V}{\partial x} = -\frac{d\dot{x}}{dt},$$

which can be written in index notation as

28.033 $\qquad \dfrac{\partial H^*}{\partial \dot{x}_r} = \dfrac{dx^r}{dt}\,; \qquad \dfrac{\partial H^*}{\partial x^r} = -\dfrac{d\dot{x}_r}{dt}.$

These last sets of equations are evidently equivalent to the Newtonian equations of motion, except that we now have six first-order equations connecting the six variables x^r, $\dot{x}_r$ and the time, instead of three second-order equations connecting the x^r and the time. The symmetrical first-order form of the equations of motion in Equations 28.033 is known as the *canonical* form. We shall see later that these equations can be transformed to others having the same form by a suitable change of variables.

24. The canonical form of the equations of motion has been derived from and is equivalent to the inertial equations. We can derive a similar canonical form for the equations, referred to moving (Earth-fixed) axes from Equations 28.014, only if the Coriolis force can be expressed as the gradient of a

scalar which could be used to modify the Hamiltonian. Generally, this is not possible. Otherwise, the most we can do is to transform back to the inertial system (x_0, y_0, z_0) by the relations

$$x = x_0 \cos \tilde{\omega}t + y_0 \sin \tilde{\omega}t$$

$$y = -x_0 \sin \tilde{\omega}t + y_0 \cos \tilde{\omega}t$$

28.034 $z = z_0$

in which t is the time since the two sets of axes coincided. We can then write the canonical equations in the variables $(x_0, y_0, z_0, \dot{x}_0, \dot{y}_0, \dot{z}_0, t)$ and can transform to other canonical variables, as will be explained later.

THE KEPLER ELLIPSE

25. If the attracting body were a single particle of mass M situated at the origin of inertial coordinates or, alternatively, a sphere of uniform density and total mass M centered on the origin, then the external potential from Equation 20.01 would be minus $(GM)/r$, which in this chapter we shall denote as minus μ/r. In that case, the equations of motion of a satellite can be integrated easily and completely from the first integrals already obtained. The potential is not time-dependent; therefore, Equation 28.020 holds true as

28.035 $\tfrac{1}{2}v^2 - \mu/r = H^*$

with H^* the constant energy of the system. The angular momentum is also constant from § 28–17, and we can write

28.036 $vr \sin \beta = N$

in which β (fig. 32) is the zenith distance of the orbit in a spherical polar coordinate system. Also, we know from § 28–17 that the orbit is a plane curve. If (r, f) (fig. 33) are polar coordinates in this plane

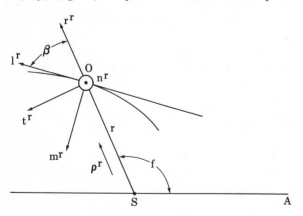

Figure 33.

and ds is an element of length of the orbit, then for any orbit, we have

$$dr/ds = \cos \beta$$

28.037 $rdf/ds = \sin \beta;$

multiplying these equations by the linear velocity $v = ds/dt$, we have

$$\dot{r} = v \cos \beta$$

28.038 $r\dot{f} = v \sin \beta$

which, substituted in Equations 28.035 and 28.036, give

$$r^2\dot{f} = N$$

28.039 $(\dot{r})^2 + (r\dot{f})^2 = v^2 = 2(\mu/r + H^*).$

These equations could also have been obtained from Equations 28.009 for motion in a plane by substituting $V = -\mu/r$, $\phi = 0$, $\omega = f$ and integrating.

26. Eliminating $\dot{f}$ in Equations 28.039, we have

$$\dot{r} = \left(2H^* + \frac{2\mu}{r} - \frac{N^2}{r^2}\right)^{1/2}$$

$$= \left\{2H^* + \left(\frac{\mu}{N}\right)^2 - \left(\frac{N}{r} - \frac{\mu}{N}\right)^2\right\}^{1/2},$$

which is directly integrable to give r as a function of time. However, we require the equation of the orbit in polar coordinates as a relation between r and f, for which purpose we substitute

$$\dot{r} = \frac{dr}{df}\frac{df}{dt} = \frac{dr}{df}\left(\frac{N}{r^2}\right) = -\frac{d}{df}\left(\frac{N}{r}\right) = -\frac{d}{df}\left(\frac{N}{r} - \frac{\mu}{N}\right).$$

The equation can now be integrated as a standard form to give

$$\left(\frac{N}{r} - \frac{\mu}{N}\right) = \left(2H^* + \frac{\mu^2}{N^2}\right)^{1/2} \cos (f - f_0)$$

in which f_0 is a constant of integration. Comparing this last equation with Equation 22.21, we see that the orbit is an ellipse, one of whose foci S is at the origin. If f is measured from the nearest point A of the major axis (fig. 26, Chapter 22), known as *perigee* in this subject, then we have $f_0 = 0$. The semimajor axis a and eccentricity e of the ellipse are then obtained by comparison with Equation 22.21 and are given by

$$\frac{1}{a(1-e^2)} = \frac{\mu}{N^2}$$

$$\frac{e}{a(1-e^2)} = \frac{1}{N}\left(2H^* + \frac{\mu^2}{N^2}\right)^{1/2},$$

from which we have

28.040 $N = \sqrt{\mu a(1-e^2)}$

28.041
$$H^* = -\mu/2a;$$

also, from Equation 28.035 we have

28.042
$$v^2 = \mu\left(\frac{2}{r} - \frac{1}{a}\right) = \frac{\mu r'}{ar}$$

where r' is the radius vector to the other focus.

27. The constant N is customarily expressed in a different way. An element of area swept out by the radius vector to the satellite is $\frac{1}{2}r^2 df$, so that the first equation of Equations 28.039 expresses the fact that the time-rate of change of this area is constant, which is Kepler's second law. Moreover, if T is the time required to describe the whole orbit from perigee to perigee, the total area of the ellipse is

$$\pi ab = \pi a^2(1-e^2)^{1/2} = \int_0^T \frac{1}{2}r^2\dot{f}dt = \frac{1}{2}NT.$$

But if n, known as the *mean motion*, is the mean angular velocity of description of the orbit over a complete revolution, then we have

28.043
$$n = \frac{2\pi}{T};$$

combining the last two equations with Equation 28.040, we have

28.044
$$n = \mu^{1/2}a^{-3/2},$$

which expresses Kepler's third law. In terms of n, Equation 28.040 becomes

28.045
$$N = \sqrt{\mu a(1-e^2)} = na^2(1-e^2)^{1/2}.$$

28. Next, we introduce the *eccentric anomaly E*, which is the same as the reduced latitude u for the meridian ellipse of figure 26, Chapter 22. By differentiating the purely geometric Equation 22.21 along the ellipse (a, e fixed) with respect to time, we have

$$\frac{dr}{dt} = ae \sin E \frac{dE}{dt} = \frac{ae(1-e^2)\sin f}{(1+e\cos f)^2}\frac{df}{dt} = \frac{r^2 e \sin f}{a(1-e^2)}\frac{N}{r^2}.$$

28.046

Using Equations 22.20, 28.045, and 22.21, the last two members of Equation 28.046 reduce to

28.047
$$\frac{dE}{dt} = \frac{na}{r} = \frac{n}{(1-e\cos E)},$$

which integrates to

$$(E - e \sin E) = n(t - t_0)$$

where t_0 is a constant of integration equal to the time of passing perigee ($E=0$). The right-hand side

of this equation is defined as the *mean anomaly M*, giving the position of the satellite as if it were moving at the mean angular velocity n about the focus or origin. We have finally

28.048
$$(E - e \sin E) = n(t - t_0) = M,$$

usually known in the literature as Kepler's equation.

29. We have now completed the dynamical examination of the elliptic orbit, although we also can use any of the purely geometrical relations for an ellipse, as given in § 22–3 through § 22–10, in which case the notation may require some translation. For example, we shall use β in this chapter for the "zenith distance" of the orbit, relative to the focal radius vector as the zenith direction, shown in figures 32 and 33. This symbol is the complement of the angle β, shown in figure 26, Chapter 22, and used in Chapter 22 as the angle between the normal to the ellipse and either focal radius vector. We shall also use α as the azimuth of the orbit in this chapter, whereas α is an elliptic constant in Chapter 22. For example, the second equation of Equations 22.03, translated into our present notation, gives the zenith distance of the orbit in the form

28.049
$$\cot\beta = \frac{e\sin E}{(1-e^2)^{1/2}},$$

which can also be obtained in the equivalent form

28.050
$$\cot\beta = \frac{e\sin f}{(1+e\cos f)} = \frac{re\sin f}{a(1-e^2)}$$

from Equations 28.037 and 28.046—the two forms being shown to be equivalent from Equations 22.20 and 22.21. Equation 22.21 is repeated for convenience as

28.051
$$r = a(1-e\cos E) = \frac{a(1-e^2)}{(1+e\cos f)}.$$

The rectangular coordinates of the satellite in the plane of the Kepler ellipse are repeated from Equations 22.20 as

$$q_1 = r\cos f = a(\cos E - e)$$

28.052
$$q_2 = r\sin f = a(1-e^2)^{1/2}\sin E.$$

We have also from Equations 28.038, 28.046, and 28.045

28.053
$$v\cos\beta = \frac{\mu^{1/2}e\sin f}{a^{1/2}(1-e^2)^{1/2}} = \frac{\mu^{1/2}a^{1/2}e\sin E}{r}$$

which, together with Equation 28.050, gives

$$v\sin\beta = \frac{N}{r} = \frac{\mu^{1/2}a^{1/2}(1-e^2)^{1/2}}{r} = \frac{\mu^{1/2}(1+e\cos f)}{a^{1/2}(1-e^2)^{1/2}}.$$

28.054

Other useful formulas, easily verified, are

$$\cos E = \frac{\cos f + e}{1 + e \cos f}$$

28.055 $$\cos f = \frac{\cos E - e}{1 - e \cos E}$$

$$v^2 = \frac{\mu^2(1 + 2e \cos f + e^2)}{N^2} = \frac{\mu(1 + e \cos E)}{r}.$$

28.056

The components of velocity in and perpendicular to the semimajor axis are

$$v \cos (f + \beta) = \dot{q}_1 = -\frac{na \sin f}{(1 - e^2)^{1/2}} = -\frac{na^2 \sin E}{r}$$

$$v \sin (f + \beta) = \dot{q}_2 = \frac{na(e + \cos f)}{(1 - e^2)^{1/2}} = \frac{na^2(1 - e^2)^{1/2} \cos E}{r}.$$

28.057

30. In the centrally symmetric field we are considering, the orbital characteristics (a, e, r, v, f, M, etc.) will evidently be the same whatever the attitude of the orbital plane in a three-dimensional coordinate system. Nevertheless, even in this special case, we must define the orbital plane if we are to locate the satellite in the inertial system or in any system. To do this, we introduce three angular elements Ω, i, w as shown in the spherical diagram, figure 34. The inertial system specified in § 28–4 is shown as X, Y, Z, the origin being lettered S to agree with figure 33 and to indicate that the origin is a focus of the Kepler ellipse. The point Z is the North Pole of the axis of rotation; the great circle XY represents the plane of the Equator. The satellite is represented at O moving in the direction shown in figure 34; the great circle PAO represents the orbital plane intersecting the Equator at P, which is known as the *ascending node* for the direction of motion shown. The *descending node* is 180°

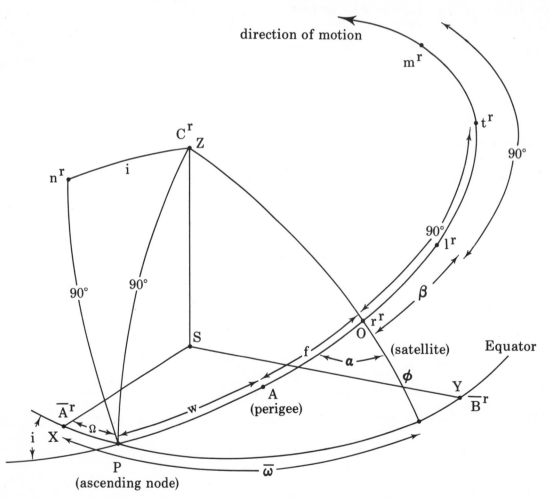

Figure 34.

in longitude away from P, and the line SP is known as the *line of nodes*. The line SA is the direction to perigee, already defined as the point on the major axis nearest S. The other end of the major axis is known as *apogee*. The angle $\Omega = XP$ is accordingly the *right ascension of the ascending node* or longitude of the ascending node in the inertial system; i is the orbital *inclination*; and $w = PA$ is known as the *argument of perigee*, usually denoted in the literature by ω, which, however, is required throughout this book for various forms of longitude. We also use the term longitude in the geodetic sense as measured in the equatorial plane, whereas astronomers often measure longitude, wholly or partly, in the plane of the ecliptic.

Auxiliary Vectors

31. We shall require certain unit vectors which are shown in both figure 33, representing the plane of the ellipse, and figure 34. The unit radius vector to the satellite is shown as $r^s = \rho^s/r$. The unit tangent to the orbit, represented at l^r in figure 34, is the direction of the radius Sl^r; the representative point l^r must lie in the great circle representing the orbital plane. The angle between l^r and r^r, shown as β, is the zenith distance of the orbit relative to a spherical polar system of coordinates. The azimuth of the orbit in the same system is the spherical angle α. Unit vectors t^r, m^r in the orbital plane perpendicular, respectively, to r^r, l^r are as shown in both figures 33 and 34. Finally, a unit vector n^r perpendicular to the orbital plane, shown in both figures 33 and 34, is used to complete either of the right-handed triads (l^r, m^r, n^r) or (r^r, t^r, n^r). In figure 34, n^r is the pole of the orbital plane.

32. From figure 33, representing the plane of the orbit, we have

$$l^k = r^k \cos \beta + t^k \sin \beta$$

28.058 $\qquad m^k = -r^k \sin \beta + t^k \cos \beta.$

In terms of the usual meridian, parallel, and normal vectors $(\mu^k, \lambda^k, \nu^k)$ of the spherical polar coordinate system, the vectors are easily found to be

$$l^k = \lambda^k \sin \alpha \sin \beta + \mu^k \cos \alpha \sin \beta + \nu^k \cos \beta$$

$$m^k = \lambda^k \sin \alpha \cos \beta + \mu^k \cos \alpha \cos \beta - \nu^k \sin \beta$$

$$n^k = -\lambda^k \cos \alpha + \mu^k \sin \alpha$$

$$r^k = \nu^k$$

$$t^k = \lambda^k \sin \alpha + \mu^k \cos \alpha.$$

28.059

Inertial Cartesian components are

$$r^k = \begin{pmatrix} \cos(w+f) \cos \Omega - \sin(w+f) \sin \Omega \cos i \\ \cos(w+f) \sin \Omega + \sin(w+f) \cos \Omega \cos i \\ \sin(w+f) \sin i \end{pmatrix}$$

28.060

$$t^k = \begin{pmatrix} -\sin(w+f) \cos \Omega - \cos(w+f) \sin \Omega \cos i \\ -\sin(w+f) \sin \Omega + \cos(w+f) \cos \Omega \cos i \\ \cos(w+f) \sin i \end{pmatrix}$$

28.061

28.062 $\qquad n^k = \begin{pmatrix} \sin \Omega \sin i \\ -\cos \Omega \sin i \\ \cos i \end{pmatrix}$

28.063 $\qquad l^r = \begin{pmatrix} \cos(w+f+\beta) \cos \Omega - \sin(w+f+\beta) \sin \Omega \cos i \\ \cos(w+f+\beta) \sin \Omega + \sin(w+f+\beta) \cos \Omega \cos i \\ \sin(w+f+\beta) \sin i \end{pmatrix}$

28.064 $\qquad m^r = \begin{pmatrix} -\sin(w+f+\beta) \cos \Omega - \cos(w+f+\beta) \sin \Omega \cos i \\ -\sin(w+f+\beta) \sin \Omega + \cos(w+f+\beta) \cos \Omega \cos i \\ \cos(w+f+\beta) \sin i \end{pmatrix},$

as we can easily verify by expressing the scalar products of each vector with the Cartesian vectors $\bar{A}^r$, $\bar{B}^r$, C^r in terms of elements of spherical triangles in figure 34.

33. We can obtain alternative formulas in much the same way as we did from § 12–15 by applying the following positive rotations to the inertial $(\bar{A}^k, \bar{B}^k, C^k)$ system:

(a) *First*, Ω about the z-axis,
(b) *Second*, i about the new x-axis, and
(c) *Third*, $(w+f)$ about the new z-axis.

The result is

$$
\begin{pmatrix} r^k \\ t^k \\ n^k \end{pmatrix} = \begin{pmatrix} \cos\,(w+f) & \sin\,(w+f) & 0 \\ -\sin\,(w+f) & \cos\,(w+f) & 0 \\ 0 & 0 & 1 \end{pmatrix} \begin{pmatrix} 1 & 0 & 0 \\ 0 & \cos i & \sin i \\ 0 & -\sin i & \cos i \end{pmatrix} \begin{pmatrix} \cos\Omega & \sin\Omega & 0 \\ -\sin\Omega & \cos\Omega & 0 \\ 0 & 0 & 1 \end{pmatrix} \begin{pmatrix} \bar{A}^k \\ \bar{B}^k \\ C^k \end{pmatrix}
$$

28.065 $= \mathbf{K}\{\bar{A}^k,\ \bar{B}^k,\ C^k\}$

$$
\mathbf{K} = \begin{pmatrix} \cos\,(w+f)\cos\Omega - \sin\,(w+f)\sin\Omega\cos i & \cos\,(w+f)\sin\Omega + \sin\,(w+f)\cos\Omega\cos i & \sin i \sin\,(w+f) \\ -\sin\,(w+f)\cos\Omega - \cos\,(w+f)\sin\Omega\cos i & -\sin\,(w+f)\sin\Omega + \cos\,(w+f)\cos\Omega\cos i & \sin i \cos\,(w+f) \\ \sin\Omega\sin i & -\cos\Omega\sin i & \cos i \end{pmatrix}.
$$

28.066

Because the component matrices of $\mathbf{K}$ and therefore $\mathbf{K}$ itself are orthogonal matrices, we can also write

28.067 $\{\bar{A}^k,\ \bar{B}^k,\ C^k\} = \mathbf{K}^T\{r^k,\ t^k,\ n^k\}.$

34. By putting $f = 0$ in Equation 28.065, we obtain a triad of vectors $(j^r,\ k^r,\ n^r)$ in which j^r (the x-axis) is the unit radius vector to perigee and k^r (the y-axis) is in the orbital plane. We have

$$\{j^r,\ k^r,\ n^r\} = \mathbf{K}_{f=0}\{\bar{A}^r,\ \bar{B}^r,\ C^r\};$$

contracting this equation with the position vector of the satellite, we have

28.068 $\{q_1, q_2, 0\} = \mathbf{K}_{f=0}\{x, y, z\}$

where q_1, q_2 are given by Equations 28.052 and x, y, z are the inertial coordinates of the satellite. The reverse equation is

28.069 $\{x, y, z\} = \mathbf{K}_{f=0}^T\{q_1, q_2, 0\},$

which enables us to express the inertial coordinates in terms of orbital elements. By splitting the third rotation $(w+f)$ in Equation 28.065 into two successive rotations, we have also

$$
\mathbf{K} = \begin{pmatrix} \cos f & \sin f & 0 \\ -\sin f & \cos f & 0 \\ 0 & 0 & 1 \end{pmatrix} \mathbf{K}_{f=0}
$$

28.070 $= \mathbf{F}\mathbf{K}_{f=0}.$

35. In deriving Equation 28.065, if the third rotation were $(w+f+\beta)$, it is clear from figure 34 that we should arrive at the triad $\{l^k,\ m^k,\ n^k\}$. By substituting $(w+f+\beta)$ for $(w+f)$, we accordingly have

28.071 $\{l^k,\ m^k,\ n^k\} = \mathbf{K}_{w+f+\beta}\{\bar{A}^k,\ \bar{B}^k,\ C^k\}$

and a corresponding inverse. Moreover, by applying a *fourth* rotation of β about the z-axis to Equation

28.065, we have

28.072 $\mathbf{K}_{w+f+\beta} = \begin{pmatrix} \cos\beta & \sin\beta & 0 \\ -\sin\beta & \cos\beta & 0 \\ 0 & 0 & 1 \end{pmatrix} \mathbf{K}.$

36. The velocity vector is given by

$$\dot{\rho}^k = vl^k = (v\cos\beta,\ v\sin\beta,\ 0)\mathbf{K}\{\bar{A}^k,\ \bar{B}^k,\ C^k\};$$

28.073

the three Cartesian components of the velocity vector are given by

$$\dot{\rho}^k(\bar{A}_k,\ \bar{B}_k,\ C_k) = (\dot{\rho}^k\bar{A}_k,\ \dot{\rho}^k\bar{B}_k,\ \dot{\rho}^kC_k) = (\dot{x},\ \dot{y},\ \dot{z})$$

28.074 $= (v\cos\beta,\ v\sin\beta,\ 0)\mathbf{K}$

in which we can substitute Equations 28.053 and 28.054 and so can obtain the velocity vector and its components in terms of the orbital elements. We can, of course, transpose the last equation as

$$\{\dot{x},\ \dot{y},\ \dot{z}\} = \mathbf{K}^T\{v\cos\beta,\ v\sin\beta,\ 0\}$$

$$= \mathbf{K}_{f=0}^T\mathbf{F}^T\{v\cos\beta,\ v\sin\beta,\ 0\}$$

28.075 $= \mathbf{K}_{f=0}^T\{v\cos\,(f+\beta),\ v\sin\,(f+\beta),\ 0\},$

using the transpose of Equation 28.070. But the last vector in this equation evidently gives the components of the velocity vector vl^k in and perpendicular to the radius vector to perigee, that is,

$$\{v\cos\,(f+\beta),\ v\sin\,(f+\beta),\ 0\} = \{vl^rj_r,\ vl^rk_r,\ vl^rn_r\}$$

$$= \{q_1,\ q_2,\ 0\},$$

so that finally we have

28.076 $\{\dot{x},\ \dot{y},\ \dot{z}\} = \mathbf{K}_{f=0}^T\{\dot{q}_1,\ \dot{q}_2,\ 0\}.$

Comparison of this result with Equation 28.069 shows that the matrix $\mathbf{K}_{f=0}$ can be considered as constant during time differentiation, as we should expect in a Kepler ellipse because the components of the matrix are all constant. This result holds true for the osculating ellipse of a perturbed orbit, as we shall see in § 28–40.

37. The latitude and longitude of the satellite in a spherical polar system, based on the inertial Cartesian system, are marked as $(\phi, \bar{\omega})$ in figure 34, and the following spherical relations will often be found useful,

28.077 $$\cos i = \cos \phi \sin \alpha$$

28.078 $$\cos (w+f) = \cos \phi \cos (\bar{\omega} - \Omega)$$

$$\sin (w+f) = \sin (\bar{\omega} - \Omega) \csc \alpha = \sin \phi \csc i$$

28.079

$$\cos \alpha = \tan \phi \cot (w+f) = \sin \phi \sin \alpha \cot (\bar{\omega} - \Omega)$$

$$= \sin i \cos (\bar{\omega} - \Omega) = \sin i \sec \phi \cos (w+f).$$

28.080

PERTURBED ORBITS

38. If the mass M of a heavy particle located at the origin or if the total mass of a homogeneous sphere centered on the origin is the same as the total mass of the actual Earth, then for the symmetrical potential we have been considering,

$$-\frac{GM}{r} = -\frac{\mu}{r}$$

is the first and largest term in the expansion of the actual potential expressed by Equation 21.035 in spherical harmonics. We can write the actual potential as

28.081 $$-V = \mu/r + R$$

so that R represents all the terms which must be added to μ/r to give the true potential, whether or not R is expressed in spherical harmonics. Moreover, R may contain other small gravitational potentials contributed by the Sun and the Moon. The effect of dissipative and discontinuous forces, such as atmospheric drag and solar radiation pressure which cannot be expressed as continuous derivatives of a scalar potential, cannot be included in R; separate treatment is required. We have seen that if R were zero, the orbit would be a Kepler ellipse, defined as an unperturbed orbit. Accordingly, R is a measure of the departure of the actual perturbed orbit from a Kepler ellipse; we call

minus R the *perturbing or disturbing potential* and call the gradient R_k the disturbing force.

39. If we are given the position, and the magnitude and direction of the velocity of a satellite at a given time, then it is possible to find a unique Kepler orbit in which the satellite would have the same position and velocity. The position and direction of motion (or direction of the velocity vector) of the satellite, together with the origin of inertial coordinates, settle uniquely the plane of a Kepler orbit. Within this plane, we are given the radius vector r, the zenith distance β relative to the radius vector as zenith, and the linear velocity v. These three quantities enable us to determine uniquely a, e, and f from Equations 28.042, 28.054, and 28.053, and so to specify a Kepler ellipse in which the satellite would have the same position and velocity, in magnitude and direction, as in the actual orbit; the *true anomaly f* applied to the direction of the radius vector settles the direction of the major axis, and a, e settle the size and shape of the ellipse. Another way of considering this matter is to note that the satellite has six *degrees of freedom*; that is, we can choose arbitrarily three position coordinates and three components of velocity. Having chosen these six quantities, we can find six, and no more than six Kepler elements Ω, i, w, f, a, e which are necessary and sufficient to establish the same instantaneous motion in a Kepler orbit. The Kepler ellipse which satisfies these conditions is known as the *osculating ellipse*. (However, this is an incorrect description because the two orbits do not have more than two-point contact.) Instead of the true anomaly f, we may choose either the eccentric or the mean anomaly (E or M) to describe the position of the satellite within the osculating ellipse. There are some advantages in choosing the mean anomaly M. It is sometimes stated, although this is not a very realistic approach to the problem, that the satellite would travel in the osculating ellipse if at any time all perturbing forces were removed.

40. We can say that such relations as Equation 28.076 are true for a perturbed orbit (although derived for a Kepler orbit), provided osculating elements are used in such equations, because nothing more is involved than the elements and velocity components which are the same for the actual and osculating orbits. The energy (which is $-\mu/2a$ in the osculating orbit) is not the same for the two orbits; the kinetic energy is the same, but the potential energy differs by the perturbing potential. The accelerations are not the same because the components of force are not the same. Accordingly,

the satellite will depart from a plane osculating orbit and will follow a more complicated curve in space under the action of the more complicated forces. Nevertheless, at any subsequent time, we can fit another osculating ellipse to the actual orbit, so that we can describe the actual motion by means of time differentials of the osculating elements rather than by changes in the actual position and velocity of the satellite. In the next section, we derive expressions for the time differentials of the osculating elements, leading to another form of the equations of motion.

VARIATION OF THE ELEMENTS

41. We shall suppose that the total force F_r per unit mass is composed of a central force—directed toward the origin or focus of the osculating ellipse and of magnitude μ/r^2—together with a *disturbing force* R_r, so that we have

28.082 $$F_r = -\frac{\mu}{r^3}\rho_r + R_r.$$

The central force, if acting alone, would maintain the satellite in the Kepler ellipse, although R_r may, of course, have a central component in addition. In cases where the disturbing force is the gradient of a scalar, Equation 28.081 differentiated shows that R_r is the gradient of the scalar R; but in this section, we shall assume F_r and R_r to be forces which are not necessarily derived from a scalar potential.

42. The linear acceleration in the direction of the orbit is the component of total force in that direction, giving

28.083 $$\frac{dv}{dt} = F_r l^r = -\frac{\mu \cos \beta}{r^2} + R_r l^r.$$

As in Equation 28.003, the velocity vector is $\dot\rho^r = v l^r$; from Equation 28.015, we have

28.084 $$\frac{d(r^2)}{dt} = 2r\frac{dr}{dt} = \frac{\delta(\rho_r \rho^r)}{\delta t} = 2\rho_r \dot\rho^r = 2\rho_r(v l^r)$$

28.085 $$\frac{dr}{dt} = \rho_r \dot\rho^r / r = v \cos \beta.$$

Semimajor Axis

43. To obtain the time differentials of the elements, we differentiate any suitable Kepler equation without holding any of the elements fixed. For example, if we differentiate Equation 28.042 with respect to time, we have

$$2v\frac{dv}{dt} = -\frac{2\mu}{r^2}\frac{dr}{dt} + \frac{\mu}{a^2}\frac{da}{dt};$$

Equations 28.083 and 28.085 then give

28.086 $$\left(\frac{\mu}{2a^2}\right)\frac{da}{dt} = vR_r l^r = R_r \dot\rho^r.$$

As we should expect, if there is no perturbing force, the semimajor axis a remains constant; whereas, in the presence of a perturbing force R_r, this last equation gives the rate of change of a between two successive osculating ellipses.

44. From figure 33 or 34, either of which illustrates the osculating ellipse as well as a Kepler ellipse, we have

$$l^r = r^r \cos \beta + t^r \sin \beta$$

so that an alternative equation is

$$\frac{da}{dt} = \frac{2a^2}{N}\left\{ e \sin f (R_r r^r) + \frac{a(1-e^2)}{r}(R_r t^r) \right\},$$

28.087

using Equations 28.053, 28.054, and 28.045.

Angular Momentum

45. As in §28–17, we can write the angular momentum vector as

28.088 $$(vr \sin \beta) n^r = Nn^r = \epsilon^{rpq}\rho_p \dot\rho_q$$

in which n^r is the unit vector normal to the plane of the osculating ellipse. Differentiating intrinsically with respect to time, we have

$$\frac{dN}{dt} n^r + N\frac{\delta n^r}{\delta t} = \epsilon^{rpq}\dot\rho_p\dot\rho_q + \epsilon^{rpq}\rho_p\ddot\rho_q.$$

The first term on the right is the vector product of two parallel vectors and is therefore zero. The equations of motion can be written in the form

$$\ddot\rho_q = F_q = -\frac{\mu}{r^3}\rho_q + R_q$$

so that the last equation becomes

$$\frac{dN}{dt} n^r + N\frac{\delta n^r}{\delta t} = \epsilon^{rpq}\rho_p F_q$$

$$= -\frac{\mu}{r^3}\epsilon^{rpq}\rho_p\rho_q + \epsilon^{rpq}\rho_p R_q$$

28.089 $$= \epsilon^{rpq}\rho_p R_q$$

because the vector product of two parallel vectors again is zero. Because n^r is a unit vector, as in Equation 3.19, $\delta n^r / \delta t$ must be perpendicular to n^r and must therefore be coplanar with r^r and t^r in figure 33 so that we can write

$$\frac{\delta n^r}{\delta t} = P r^r + Q t^r;$$

contracting with r_r, we have

$$P = r_r \frac{\delta n^r}{\delta t} = \frac{1}{r} \rho_r \frac{\delta n^r}{\delta t} = -\frac{1}{r} n^r \frac{\delta \rho_r}{\delta t} = -\frac{v}{r} n^r l_r = 0$$

because n^r and l^r are perpendicular. In deriving this result, we have used the fact that ρ_r and n_r are perpendicular so that we have

$$\rho_r n^r = 0,$$

and by intrinsic differentiation, we have

$$\rho_r \frac{\delta n^r}{\delta t} = -n^r \frac{\delta \rho^r}{\delta t}.$$

Substitution in Equation 28.089 and successive contraction with n_r and t_r yield

28.090 $\qquad \dfrac{dN}{dt} = \epsilon^{rpq} n_r \rho_p R_q = r R_q t^q,$

using the formula for a vector product given in Equation 2.24. Also, we have

$$NQ = \epsilon^{rpq} t_r \rho_p R_q = -r R_q n^q$$

so that

28.091 $\qquad \dfrac{\delta n^r}{\delta t} = -\dfrac{r}{N} (R_q n^q) t^r.$

As we found in §28–17, both the magnitude and direction of the angular momentum vector are constant in unperturbed motion ($R_q = 0$).

Eccentricity

46. We are now able to find the variation of the eccentricity e by differentiating Equation 28.045, that is,

$$N^2 = \mu a (1 - e^2).$$

Substituting Equations 28.090 and 28.086 in the result, we have

$$\mu a e \frac{de}{dt} = \tfrac{1}{2} \mu (1 - e^2) \frac{da}{dt} - N \frac{dN}{dt}$$

28.092 $\qquad = \{ v a^2 (1 - e^2) (l^q R_q) - N_r (t^q R_q) \},$

which can be expressed in terms of the perpendicu-

lar vectors r^q, t^q as

$$\frac{de}{dt} = \frac{a^{1/2} (1 - e^2)^{1/2}}{\mu^{1/2}} \{ \sin f (r^q R_q)$$

28.093 $\qquad\qquad + (\cos f + \cos E) (t^q R_q) \}$

by substituting

$$l^q = r^q \cos \beta + t^q \sin \beta$$

and by using Equations 28.053, 28.054, and 28.051. An expression in terms of the perpendicular vectors l^q, m^q can be obtained similarly as

$$\frac{de}{dt} = \frac{(1 - e^2)}{v} \left\{ \frac{2 \cos E (l^q R_q)}{1 - e \cos E} - \frac{\sin E (m^q R_q)}{(1 - e^2)^{1/2}} \right\}.$$

28.094

Zenith Distance

47. Although the zenith distance β is not one of the usual six osculating elements, its variation is sometimes useful and is easily found by differentiating

$$N = v r \sin \beta$$

and by using Equations 28.090, 28.083, 28.085, and 28.042. We have then

28.095 $\quad v r \dfrac{d\beta}{dt} = \mu \sin \beta \left(\dfrac{1}{a} - \dfrac{1}{r} \right) + r (m^q R_q).$

In this last equation, β, of course, varies even in an unperturbed orbit where its variation is given by the first term on the right.

True Anomaly

48. Although only one of the anomalies (f, E, or M) may be taken as one of the six elements, it is convenient to have time derivatives of all three. These three time derivations may be obtained by straight differentiation of any elliptic formula containing any other quantities whose time derivatives have already been found. The time derivative of the true anomaly is, for example, easily obtained by differentiating Equation 28.051 in the form

$$(1 + e \cos f) = \frac{N^2}{\mu r}$$

and by using Equations 28.093, 28.090, and 28.085.

We have after some manipulation the alternative expressions

$$\frac{df}{dt} = \frac{N}{r^2} + \frac{(N\cos f)(R_q r^q)}{\mu e}$$

$$- \frac{N(2 - \cos^2 f - \cos E \cos f)(R_q t^q)}{\mu e \sin f}$$

$$= \frac{N}{r^2} + \frac{(N\cos f)(R_q r^q)}{\mu e}$$

28.096
$$- \frac{(N\sin f)(R_q t^q)}{\mu e}\left\{1 + \frac{r}{a(1-e^2)}\right\}$$

$$= \frac{N}{r^2} - \frac{(2\sin f)(R_q l^q)}{ev}$$

28.097
$$- \frac{(\cos E + e)(R_q m^q)}{ev}$$

in which the term

28.098
$$\frac{N}{r^2} = \frac{\mu^{1/2}a^{1/2}(1-e^2)^{1/2}}{a^2(1-e\cos E)^2} = \frac{n(1+e\cos f)^2}{(1-e^2)^{3/2}}$$

is evidently the unperturbed rate of change, as we have already found in Equation 28.046.

Eccentric Anomaly

49. In the same way, by differentiating

$$r = a(1 - e\cos E)$$

and by using Equations 28.085, 28.087, and 28.093, we have

$$\frac{dE}{dt} = \frac{na}{r} + \frac{a^{1/2}(\cos f - e)(R_r r^r)}{e\mu^{1/2}}$$

28.099
$$- \frac{(a^{1/2}\sin E)(2 - e^2 + e\cos f)(R_r t^r)}{e\mu^{1/2}(1-e^2)^{1/2}}$$

$$= \frac{na}{r} - \frac{(2\sin f)(R_r l^r)}{ve(1-e^2)^{1/2}}$$

28.100
$$- \frac{(1-e^2)^{1/2}\cos E(R_r m^r)}{ve}$$

in which the term

$$\frac{na}{r} = \frac{n}{(1 - e\cos E)}$$

is the unperturbed rate, as already found in Equation 28.047.

Mean Anomaly

50. By differentiating the defining equation

$$M = E - e\sin E$$

and by using Equations 28.099 and 28.093 or Equations 28.100 and 28.092, we have after some manipulation

$$\frac{dM}{dt} = n + \frac{\{(1-e^2)\cos f - 2er/a\}(R_r r^r)}{nae}$$

28.101
$$- \frac{\{(1-e^2)^{1/2}\sin E(2 + e\cos f)\}(R_r t^r)}{nae}$$

$$= n + \frac{\{a(1-e^2)\cos f - 2er\}(R_r r^r)}{e\mu^{1/2}a^{1/2}}$$

28.102
$$- \frac{\{(1-e^2)\sin f\}(R_r t^r)}{e\mu^{1/2}a^{1/2}}\left(a + \frac{r}{1-e^2}\right)$$

$$= n - \frac{2\sin E(1 + e\cos f + e^2)(R_r l^r)}{ev}$$

28.103
$$- \frac{(1-e^2)^{1/2}r\cos f(R_r m^r)}{vae}$$

in which the unperturbed value is the mean motion

$$n = \mu^{1/2}a^{-3/2}$$

as defined.

Inclination

51. Variation of the orbital inclination i is obtained by contracting Equation 28.091 with the Cartesian vector C^r. Remembering that the fixed vector C^r is constant under covariant differentiation, we have

$$C_r\frac{\delta n^r}{\delta t} = \frac{\delta(C_r n^r)}{\delta t} = \frac{d(\cos i)}{dt} = -\frac{r}{N}(R_q n^q)t^r C_r.$$

From the spherical triangle $C^r t^r P$ in figure 34, we have

$$t^r C_r = \sin(w + f + 90°)\sin i = \cos(w + f)\sin i$$

so that we have finally

28.104
$$\frac{di}{dt} = \frac{r}{N}(R_q n^q)\cos(w + f).$$

Right Ascension of the Ascending Node

52. If we contract Equation 28.091 similarly with the fixed Cartesian vector $\bar{A}^r$, we have

$$\frac{\delta(n^r\bar{A}_r)}{\delta t} = \frac{d(\sin\Omega\sin i)}{dt} = -\frac{r}{N}(R_q n^q)t^r\bar{A}_r$$

and

$$t^r\bar{A}_r = \cos\Omega\cos(w + f + 90°)$$

$$- \sin\Omega\sin(w + f + 90°)\cos i$$

$$= -\cos\Omega\sin(w + f)$$

$$- \sin\Omega\cos(w + f)\cos i.$$

Substitution of Equation 28.104 yields

28.105 $\quad \dfrac{d\Omega}{dt} = \dfrac{r}{N} (R_q n^q) \sin(w+f) \operatorname{cosec} i,$

showing that the variation of both i and Ω depends on the component of force perpendicular to the osculating orbital plane.

Argument of Perigee

53. The scalar product of the unit vectors $\bar{A}_r$ and $r^r = \rho^r / r$ in figure 34 gives

$(1/r)\bar{A}_r \rho^r = \cos\Omega \cos(w+f) - \sin\Omega \sin(w+f)\cos i.$

Differentiation of this equation with respect to time gives on the left side

$-\dfrac{v\cos\beta}{r^2}\bar{A}_r\rho^r + \dfrac{v}{r}\bar{A}_r l^r = -\dfrac{v\cos\beta}{r}\bar{A}_r r^r$

$\qquad\qquad + \dfrac{v}{r}\bar{A}_r(r^r\cos\beta + t^r\sin\beta)$

$\qquad\qquad = \dfrac{v\sin\beta}{r}\bar{A}_r t^r$

$\qquad\qquad = \dfrac{v\sin\beta}{r}(-\cos\Omega\sin(w+f)$

$\qquad\qquad\quad - \sin\Omega\cos(w+f)\cos i),$

and gives on the right side

$(-\sin\Omega\cos(w+f) - \cos\Omega\sin(w+f)\cos i)(d\Omega/dt)$

$- (\cos\Omega\sin(w+f)$

$+ \sin\Omega\cos(w+f)\cos i)(dw/dt + df/dt)$

$+ \sin\Omega\sin(w+f)\sin i\,(di/dt);$

substituting

$\qquad di/dt = \cot(w+f)\sin i\,(d\Omega/dt)$

from Equations 28.104 and 28.105, we have finally

$\dfrac{dw}{dt} + \dfrac{df}{dt} = \dfrac{v\sin\beta}{r} - \cos i\,\dfrac{d\Omega}{dt}$

28.106 $\qquad = \dfrac{N}{r^2} - \dfrac{r}{N}(R_q n^q)\sin(w+f)\cot i.$

Subtraction of df/dt in Equation 28.096 or 28.097 gives dw/dt explicitly in terms of three components of the disturbing force. For example, we have

$\dfrac{dw}{dt} = -\dfrac{(N\cos f)(R_q r^q)}{\mu e}$

$\qquad + \dfrac{(N\sin f)(R_q t^q)}{\mu e}\left(1 + \dfrac{r}{a(1-e^2)}\right)$

28.107 $\qquad - \dfrac{r\sin(w+f)\cot i\,(R_q n^q)}{N}.$

THE GAUSS EQUATIONS

54. Time derivatives of the six elements in terms of the disturbing force components $R_r r^r$, $R_r t^r$, $R_r n^r$ — usually known in the literature as R, S, W or S, T, W with various sign conventions — were first given by Gauss. However, it is convenient to have these components in vector form which can easily be transformed to the alternative and sometimes simpler set $R_r l^r$, $R_r m^r$, $R_r n^r$. If we neglect the effect of atmospheric rotation, the drag of the atmosphere will be against the direction l^r and will have no component in directions m^r, n^r; expressions in terms of this alternative set accordingly show at a glance which perturbations are least likely to be affected by drag. For example, the effect on da/dt is total; perturbation of the semimajor axis is accordingly of more use for studying drag than for determining the gravitational field. On the other hand, di/dt and $d\Omega/dt$ are virtually drag-free in a nonrotating atmosphere, although drag effects do appear in second-order terms through the other elements. In some derivations, the disturbing force R_q is restricted to the gradient of a scalar potential, which is unnecessary and confusing. It will be clear from the derivation given in this section that the disturbing force need not be conservative and that the equations hold equally true for dissipative forces or even for such discontinuous forces as radiation pressure, provided the equations are integrated between points of discontinuity.

55. The six first-order Gauss equations are exact alternatives to the three Newtonian second-order differential equations of motion given earlier in various forms. First integrals of the Newtonian equations of motion would give the three components of velocity; second integrals would give the three coordinates of the satellite. Solution of the Gauss equations would give all six osculating elements from which components of velocity and coordinates could be calculated by the ordinary formulas for the Kepler ellipse.

DERIVATIVES WITH RESPECT TO THE ELEMENTS

56. In cases where the force F_r is the gradient of a scalar F, we shall require the partial derivatives of F with respect to the elements (a, e, i, M, w, Ω). The partial derivative $\partial F/\partial a$, for example, implies that the other five elements e, i, M, w, Ω are constant during the differentiation. The process can in places be simplified if we consider f or E constant instead of M; a glance at Equations 28.048

and 28.055 shows that we can always do this, *except* when we are evaluating $\partial F/\partial e$. Although we shall usually identify F as the negative of a scalar potential, whether the actual potential or a disturbing potential, the equations obtained in this section hold true if F is any scalar whatsoever defined in relation to the orbit; this fact will be clear from the derivation in each case. We shall also require partial derivatives of the velocity vector; the method of obtaining these derivatives will be explained in each case.

Semimajor Axis

57. If we suppose that a alone varies and if in this case f remains constant, the only possible virtual displacement of the satellite is radial and proportional to the change da in a; the osculating ellipse remains in the same plane and is simply enlarged in the ratio da/a. The vector displacement is accordingly

28.108
$$\left(\frac{da}{a} \times r\right) r^r,$$

and we have

28.109
$$\frac{\partial F}{\partial a} = \frac{r(F_r r^r)}{a} = \frac{F_r \rho^r}{a}.$$

58. To determine the change in the velocity vector between the two osculating ellipses, we have by differentiating Equation 28.042

$$2v\frac{\partial v}{\partial a} = -\frac{2\mu}{r^2}\frac{\partial r}{\partial a} + \frac{\mu}{a^2} = -\frac{2\mu}{ar} + \frac{\mu}{a^2} = -\frac{v^2}{a}$$

because the enlargement of the osculating ellipse implies that we have $dr/r = da/a$. If the radius vector to a consecutive point is $\bar{r}$, then we have $d\bar{r}/\bar{r} = dr/r$. Also, it is clear from similar triangles that the direction of the unit tangent l^r is unaltered by enlargement of the osculating ellipse. The derivative of the velocity vector is then

$$\frac{\partial \dot{\rho}^r}{\partial a} = \frac{\partial(vl^r)}{\partial a} = v\frac{\partial l^r}{\partial a} + \frac{\partial v}{\partial a}l^r = -\frac{vl^r}{2a} = -\frac{\dot{\rho}^r}{2a}.$$

28.110

In deriving this equation, we have assumed that the components of l^r have not changed during a parallel displacement. Accordingly, the equation holds true only in Cartesian coordinates, as will also be the case for the other partial derivatives. The corresponding equation in terms of the vectors

r^r, t^r is obtained from Equations 28.058, 28.053, and 28.054 as

$$\frac{\partial \dot{\rho}^r}{\partial a} = \frac{\partial(vl^r)}{\partial a} = -\frac{\mu^{1/2}}{2a^{1/2}r}\{(e\sin E)r^r + (1-e^2)^{1/2}\,t^r\}.$$

28.111

Eccentricity

59. In this case, we must take special precautions to ensure that M, and not f or E, is constant while e varies. Differentiation of Equation 28.048 with M constant relates the changes in e and E by

28.112
$$dE = \frac{\sin E\,de}{(1-e\cos E)}.$$

The change in the radius vector is then obtained by differentiating Equation 28.051 with a constant. We have

$$dr = -a\cos E\,de + ae\sin E\,dE = -a\cos f\,de$$

28.113

on substituting Equation 28.112, simplifying, and using Equations 28.052. The change in the true anomaly f is then obtained by differentiating either of Equations 28.052, and after some simplification is given by

28.114
$$rdf = \left(a\sin f + \frac{r\sin f}{(1-e^2)}\right)de.$$

The total vector displacement of the satellite, which must occur in the plane of the osculating ellipse in relation to a fixed major axis because Ω, i, w are constant, is then

$$\left\{-(a\cos f)r^r + \left(a\sin f + \frac{r\sin f}{(1-e^2)}\right)t^r\right\}de;$$

28.115

the required partial derivative is

28.116
$$\frac{\partial F}{\partial e} = -(a\cos f)(F_r r^r) + \left(a + \frac{r}{1-e^2}\right)(F_r t^r)\sin f.$$

60. The partial derivative of the unit tangent l^r is easily found by differentiating Equation 28.063 to be

$$\frac{\partial l^r}{\partial e} = m^r\frac{\partial(f+\beta)}{\partial e};$$

by differentiating Equation 28.042, we have

$$v \frac{\partial v}{\partial e} = -\frac{\mu}{r^2} \frac{\partial r}{\partial e} = \frac{\mu a \cos f}{r^2}$$

in which we have used Equation 28.113. The derivative of the velocity vector is accordingly

$$\frac{\partial (v l^r)}{\partial e} = \frac{\mu a \cos f}{v r^2} l^r + \frac{\partial (f + \beta)}{\partial e} v m^r.$$

From Equations 28.057, we have

$$\tan (f + \beta) = -(1 - e^2)^{1/2} \cot E.$$

Differentiation and use of Equation 28.112 give after some manipulation

$$\frac{\partial (f + \beta)}{\partial e} = \frac{n^2 a^4 \sin E}{v^2 r^2} \left\{ \frac{e \cos E}{(1 - e^2)^{1/2}} + \frac{(1 - e^2)^{1/2}}{(1 - e \cos E)} \right\}$$

$$= \frac{\mu a \sin f}{v^2 r^2} \left\{ 1 + \frac{r e \cos E}{a (1 - e^2)} \right\}$$

so that we have finally

$$\frac{\partial \dot{\rho}^r}{\partial e} = \frac{\partial (v l^r)}{\partial e}$$

$$= \frac{\mu a}{v r^2} \left\{ (\cos f) l^r + \left(1 + \frac{r e \cos E}{a (1 - e^2)} \right) m^r \sin f \right\}.$$

28.117

A somewhat simpler expression in terms of the r^r, t^r vectors can easily be obtained as

28.118 $\quad \dfrac{\partial \dot{\rho}^r}{\partial e} = \dfrac{N}{r(1 - e^2)} \{ -r^r \sin f + t^r \cos E \}.$

61. It may be noted that these last two vector equations hold true in any *Cartesian* coordinate system whose transformation factors are constants in space and are therefore independent of the elements e, etc. For example, in the plane of the osculating orbit, the components of the vectors in Equation 28.118 are

$$r^r = (\cos f, \sin f, 0)$$

$$t^r = (-\sin f, \cos f, 0)$$

so that we have

$$\frac{\partial \dot{q}_1}{\partial e} = -\frac{N \sin f}{r(1 - e^2)} \{ \cos f + \cos E \}$$

$$\frac{\partial \dot{q}_2}{\partial e} = \frac{N}{r(1 - e^2)} \{ -\sin^2 f + \cos E \cos f \},$$

28.119

which may be verified by direct differentiation of Equations 28.052.

Mean Anomaly

62. If the mean anomaly alone varies, the only possible virtual displacement of the satellite is tangential to the (fixed) osculating ellipse. By differentiating Equation 28.048 for constant a (and therefore n) and for constant t_0, we have

$$dM = n dt = (n/v) ds$$

where ds is the magnitude of the displacement. The vector displacement is accordingly

$$(v/n) l^r dM,$$

and the partial derivative is

28.120 $\quad \dfrac{\partial F}{\partial M} = \dfrac{v}{n} (F_r l^r) = \dfrac{1}{n} (F_r \dot{\rho}^r).$

By substituting

$$l^r = r^r \cos \beta + t^r \sin \beta$$

and Equations 28.053 and 28.054, we have the alternative equation

$$\frac{\partial F}{\partial M} = \frac{(ae \sin f)(F_r r^r)}{(1 - e^2)^{1/2}} + \frac{a(1 + e \cos f)(F_r t^r)}{(1 - e^2)^{1/2}}.$$

28.121

63. The partial derivative of the velocity vector can be found in the same way as for the eccentricity. However, in this case, the only possible displacement is along the fixed osculating ellipse, and we may accordingly consider that the virtual motion is unperturbed. We have

$$\frac{\partial \dot{\rho}^r}{\partial M} = \frac{\partial (v l^r)}{\partial M} = \frac{1}{n} \frac{d \dot{\rho}^r}{dt} = -\frac{\mu}{n r^3} \rho^r = -\frac{\mu}{n r^2} r^r,$$

28.122

using the unperturbed equations of motion with $R_r = 0$ and $\ddot{\rho}_r = F_r$ in Equation 28.082.

Inclination

64. In this case, the virtual displacement of the satellite arises from a rotation of di about the line of nodes, everything else remaining fixed. The vector displacement is

$$r \sin (w + f) n^r di,$$

and the partial derivative is

28.123 $\quad \dfrac{\partial F}{\partial i} = r \sin (w + f)(F_r n^r).$

65. From Equations 28.042 and 28.051, it is evi-

dent that we have $\partial v/\partial i = 0$; by differentiating Equation 28.063, we have

$$\frac{\partial l^r}{\partial i} = \sin (w+f+\beta) n^r$$

so that the derivative of the velocity vector is

$$\frac{\partial \dot{\rho}^r}{\partial i} = \frac{\partial (v l^r)}{\partial i} = v \sin (w+f+\beta) n^r$$

28.124 $\qquad = \dfrac{\mu n^r}{N} \{\cos (w+f) + e \cos w\}.$

Right Ascension of the Ascending Node

66. The virtual displacement arises solely from a rotation $d\Omega$ about the inertial C^r-axis. If the position vector of the satellite is ρ^r, the vector displacement is then

$$\epsilon^{rst} C_s \rho_t d\Omega.$$

We can express C_s in terms of the orthogonal triad (r_s, t_s, n_s) as

$$C_s = \sin i \sin (w+f) r_s$$
$$+ \sin i \cos (w+f) t_s + (\cos i) n_s,$$

which is easily verified by forming scalar products and by using spherical relations obtained at sight from figure 34. The vector displacement is then

$$\{-r \sin i \cos (w+f) n^r + (r \cos i) t^r\} d\Omega,$$

and the partial derivative is

$$\frac{\partial F}{\partial \Omega} = \epsilon^{rst} F_r C_s \rho_t$$
$$= (r \cos i)(F_r t^r) - r \sin i \cos (w+f)(F_r n^r).$$

28.125

67. The derivative of the velocity vector is

$$\frac{\partial \dot{\rho}^r}{\partial \Omega} = v \frac{\partial l^r}{\partial \Omega}$$

$$= v \begin{pmatrix} -\cos (w+f+\beta) \sin \Omega - \sin (w+f+\beta) \cos \Omega \cos i \\ \cos (w+f+\beta) \cos \Omega - \sin (w+f+\beta) \sin \Omega \cos i \\ 0 \end{pmatrix}$$

$$= (v \cos i) m^r - v \sin i \cos (w+f+\beta) n^r$$

$$= \frac{N}{a(1-e^2)} \{-\cos i(1+e \cos f) r^r + (e \cos i \sin f) t^r$$

28.126 $\qquad + [\sin i \sin (w+f) + e \sin i \sin w] n^r\}.$

Argument of Perigee

68. In this case, the plane and the shape and size of the osculating ellipse remain fixed. The whole

ellipse, and with it the position of the satellite, is given a rotation dw about the unit vector n^r perpendicular to the osculating plane. The virtual displacement of the satellite is

$$\epsilon^{rst} n_s \rho_t dw = r t^r dw,$$

and the partial derivative is

28.127 $\qquad \dfrac{\partial F}{\partial w} = r F_r t^r.$

69. The derivative of the velocity vector is

$$\frac{\partial \dot{\rho}^r}{\partial w} = v \frac{\partial l^r}{\partial w} = v m^r$$

28.128 $\qquad = \dfrac{\mu^{1/2} a^{1/2}}{r} \{-(1-e^2)^{1/2} r^r + (e \sin E) t^r\}.$

Relations Between Partial Derivatives

70. All six partial derivatives of a scalar F with respect to the six elements cannot be independent because they can all be expressed in terms of the *three* components of the scalar gradient $F_r r^r$, $F_r t^r$, $F_r n^r$. Accordingly, there must be three relations between the partial derivatives, obtainable by equating alternative expressions for each of the three components. For example, after some manipulation, we can express the partial derivatives with respect to each (a, e, i) in terms of the partial derivatives with respect to (M, w, Ω) as

$$(ae \sin f) \frac{\partial F}{\partial a} = \frac{r(1-e^2)^{1/2}}{a} \frac{\partial F}{\partial M}$$
$$- (1+e \cos f) \frac{\partial F}{\partial w}$$

$$\{e(1-e^2)^{1/2} \sin E\} \frac{\partial F}{\partial e} = (e+\cos E) \frac{\partial F}{\partial w}$$
$$+ (1-e^2)^{1/2}(e-\cos E) \frac{\partial F}{\partial M}$$

$$\sin i \cot (w+f) \frac{\partial F}{\partial i} = -\frac{\partial F}{\partial \Omega} + \cos i \frac{\partial F}{\partial w}.$$

28.129

Derivatives of Cartesian Coordinates

71. We have seen in §28–56 that F (as used in Equations 28.109 through 28.129) may be any scalar. For example, if in Equation 28.123 we take F as the inertial Cartesian coordinate x, then F_r is the Cartesian vector $\bar{A}_r$ (fig. 34) and $F_r n^r$ is the Cartesian x-component of the vector n^r, with similar results for the other coordinates (y and z). Combining the three resulting equations, we can say

that the following vector equation—in which ρ^r is the position vector of the satellite—holds true in Cartesian coordinates,

$$\frac{\partial \rho^r}{\partial i} = r \sin (w+f) n^r.$$

In the same way, the complete set of partial derivatives of the position vector can be written at once as

$$\frac{\partial \rho^r}{\partial a} = \frac{\rho^r}{a} = \frac{r r^r}{a}$$

$$\frac{\partial \rho^r}{\partial e} = -(a \cos f) r^r + \left(a + \frac{r}{1-e^2}\right) t^r \sin f$$

$$\frac{\partial \rho^r}{\partial i} = r \sin (w+f) n^r$$

$$\frac{\partial \rho^r}{\partial M} = \frac{(ae \sin f) r^r}{(1-e^2)^{1/2}} + \frac{a(1+e \cos f) t^r}{(1-e^2)^{1/2}} = \frac{\dot\rho^r}{n}$$

$$\frac{\partial \rho^r}{\partial w} = r t^r$$

28.130 $\quad \dfrac{\partial \rho^r}{\partial \Omega} = (r \cos i) t^r - r \sin i \cos (w+f) n^r.$

Individual derivatives can, of course, be obtained from Equations 28.130 by substituting Cartesian components given in Equations 28.060, 28.061, and 28.062. For example, we have

$$\frac{\partial x}{\partial a} = \frac{r}{a} \{\cos (w+f) \cos \Omega - \sin (w+f) \sin \Omega \cos i\}.$$

72. It is convenient at this stage to collect and to compare the partial derivatives of the velocity vector with respect to the elements in terms of the vectors r^r, t^r, n^r. From Equations 28.111 through 28.128, we have

$$\frac{\partial \dot\rho^r}{\partial a} = -\frac{\mu^{1/2}}{2a^{1/2}r} \{(e \sin E) r^r + (1-e^2)^{1/2} t^r\}$$

$$\frac{\partial \dot\rho^r}{\partial e} = \frac{N}{r(1-e^2)} \{-r^r \sin f + t^r \cos E\}$$

$$\frac{\partial \dot\rho^r}{\partial i} = \frac{\mu n^r}{N} \{\cos (w+f) + e \cos w\}$$

$$\frac{\partial \dot\rho^r}{\partial M} = -\frac{\mu r^r}{nr^2}$$

$$\frac{\partial \dot\rho^r}{\partial w} = v m^r = \frac{\mu^{1/2} a^{1/2}}{r} \{-(1-e^2)^{1/2} r^r + (e \sin E) t^r\}$$

$$\frac{\partial \dot\rho^r}{\partial \Omega} = \frac{N}{a(1-e^2)} \{-\cos i(1+e \cos f) r^r$$
$$+ (e \cos i \sin f) t^r$$
$$+ [\sin i \sin (w+f)$$
28.131 $\qquad + e \sin i \sin w] n^r\}$

from which individual components may be obtained by substituting Cartesian components given in Equations 28.060, 28.061, and 28.062. For example, we have

$$\frac{\partial \dot x}{\partial i} = \frac{\mu \sin \Omega \sin i}{N} \{\cos (w+f) + e \cos w\}.$$

73. As in the case of the scalar equations, not all equations of Equations 28.131 are independent. We can, for example, solve either the first three equations or the second three equations for the three vectors r^r, t^r, n^r, and can equate the results to obtain three relations between partial derivatives of the velocity vector. Corresponding to Equations 28.130, we have

$$(2ae \sin f) \frac{\partial \dot\rho^r}{\partial a} = (1-e^2)^{1/2}(1-e^2 \cos^2 E) \frac{\partial \dot\rho^r}{\partial M}$$
$$-\frac{a(1-e^2)}{2r} \frac{\partial \dot\rho^r}{\partial w}$$

$$\{e(1-e^2)^{1/2} \sin E\} \frac{\partial \dot\rho^r}{\partial e} = \cos E \frac{\partial \dot\rho^r}{\partial w}$$
$$+ (1-e^2)^{1/2}(e - \cos E) \frac{\partial \dot\rho^r}{\partial M}$$

$$[\sin i \sin (w+f) + e \sin i \sin w] \frac{\partial \dot\rho^r}{\partial i}$$
$$= \{\cos (w+f) + e \cos w\}$$
28.132 $\qquad \times \left(\dfrac{\partial \dot\rho^r}{\partial \Omega} - \cos i \dfrac{\partial \dot\rho^r}{\partial w}\right).$

74. If we differentiate with respect to time along the osculating ellipse, considered fixed (a, e, i, w, Ω constant), we have from Equations 28.038, 28.060, 28.061, and 28.062

$$\frac{dr}{dt} = v \cos \beta$$

$$\frac{df}{dt} = \frac{v \sin \beta}{r} = \frac{N}{r^2}$$

$$\frac{dr^r}{dt} = \frac{df}{dt} t^r$$

$$\frac{dt^r}{dt} = -\frac{df}{dt} r^r$$

28.133 $\qquad \dfrac{dn^r}{dt} = 0.$

By differentiating in this way the right-hand sides of Equations 28.130, we obtain after a little manipulation the right-hand sides of Equations 28.131, *except* in the case of the $\partial/\partial a$-equation. We conclude that, with this exception, time derivatives commute with partial derivatives with respect to the elements, although the reason for this is not immediately obvious; we could not have assumed that time differences remain the same in a different orbit, formed by variation of the elements. However, if s is any orbital element other than a, we have

$$\frac{\partial}{\partial s}\left(\frac{d}{dt}\right) = \frac{\partial}{\partial s}\left(n\frac{\partial}{\partial M}\right) = n\frac{\partial^2}{\partial s \partial M} = n\frac{\partial^2}{\partial M \partial s}$$

$$= n\frac{\partial}{\partial M}\left(\frac{\partial}{\partial s}\right) = \frac{d}{dt}\left(\frac{\partial}{\partial s}\right),$$

using Equations 28.048 and 28.044; whereas, we have

$$\frac{\partial}{\partial a}\left(\frac{d}{dt}\right) = n\frac{\partial^2}{\partial a \partial M} + \frac{\partial n}{\partial a}\frac{\partial}{\partial M} = n\frac{\partial^2}{\partial a \partial M} - \frac{3}{2}\frac{n}{a}\frac{\partial}{\partial M},$$

which does not commute but is easily verified from Equations 28.130 and 28.131 for components of the position vector.

75. Kaula[3] simply and elegantly obtains results which are equivalent to Equations 28.130 and 28.131 by forming and differentiating coordinate transformation matrices, such as Equation 28.069. There are, however, advantages in deriving and exhibiting these equations in vectors: In some cases, the results are simpler; the same formulas can be used to find the derivatives of quantities other than coordinates and velocity components, such as the derivatives of a disturbing potential, and the geometrical meaning of the derivatives is more evident. Both methods are likely to be required in future developments.

THE LAGRANGE PLANETARY EQUATIONS

76. If the scalar F in Equations 28.109 through 28.127 is the negative of the perturbing potential, that is, R, we can combine these equations with the time derivatives in Equations 28.086 through 28.107 and write

$$\frac{da}{dt} = \frac{2}{na}\frac{\partial R}{\partial M}$$

$$\frac{de}{dt} = \frac{(1-e^2)}{na^2e}\frac{\partial R}{\partial M} - \frac{(1-e^2)^{1/2}}{na^2e}\frac{\partial R}{\partial w}$$

$$\frac{di}{dt} = \frac{\cot i}{N}\frac{\partial R}{\partial w} - \frac{\operatorname{cosec} i}{N}\frac{\partial R}{\partial \Omega}$$

$$\frac{dM}{dt} = n - \frac{2}{na}\frac{\partial R}{\partial a} - \frac{(1-e^2)}{na^2e}\frac{\partial R}{\partial e}$$

$$\frac{dw}{dt} = \frac{N}{\mu ae}\frac{\partial R}{\partial e} - \frac{\cot i}{N}\frac{\partial R}{\partial i}$$

28.134
$$\frac{d\Omega}{dt} = \frac{\operatorname{cosec} i}{N}\frac{\partial R}{\partial i}$$

---

[3] Kaula (1966), *Theory of Satellite Geodesy*, 67–68.

$$\frac{dN}{dt} = \frac{\partial R}{\partial w}$$

$$\frac{\delta n^r}{\delta t} = -\frac{t^r}{N \sin(w+f)}\frac{\partial R}{\partial i}$$

$$\frac{df}{dt} = \frac{N}{r^2} - \frac{N}{\mu ae}\frac{\partial R}{\partial e}$$

$$\frac{dE}{dt} = \frac{na}{r} + \frac{1}{na^2e}\left\{-\frac{\partial R}{\partial e} - \frac{ae(1+e\cos f)}{(1-e^2)}\frac{\partial R}{\partial a}\right.$$

28.135
$$\left. + \frac{e^2 \sin f}{(1-e^2)}\frac{\partial R}{\partial w}\right\}.$$

The first six of these first-order equations are the Lagrange planetary equations, and are equivalent to either the six first-order Gauss equations or the three second-order Newtonian equations of motion.

CURVATURE AND TORSION OF THE ORBIT

77. If we expand the equations of motion in the form of Equation 28.006, we have

28.136
$$\left(\frac{dv}{dt}\right)l_r + v^2 l_{rs}l^s = F_r.$$

Contraction with l^r gives the linear acceleration

28.137
$$\frac{dv}{dt} = F_r l^r$$

as in Equation 28.083; contraction with $\bar{m}^r$, the principal normal to the orbit, gives

28.138
$$v^2\chi = F_r\bar{m}^r$$

in which χ is the curvature of the orbit, and we have used the Frenet Equations 4.06. It should be noted that $\bar{m}^r$ is not necessarily in the plane of the "osculating" ellipse, which has only first-order contact with the orbit, and that $\bar{m}^r$ does not necessarily coincide with m^r in figure 33. Nevertheless, $\bar{m}^r$ must lie in the plane of m^r and n^r because $\bar{m}^r$ is perpendicular to l^r, and we can accordingly write

28.139
$$\bar{m}^r = m^r \cos\gamma + n^r \sin\gamma$$

so that we have

28.140
$$v^2\chi = (F_rm^r)\cos\gamma + (F_rn^r)\sin\gamma.$$

If $\bar{n}^r$ is the binormal to the orbit, completing the right-handed orthogonal triad $(l^r, \bar{m}^r, \bar{n}^r)$, we must have from figure 35

28.141
$$\bar{n}^r = n^r \cos\gamma - m^r \sin\gamma.$$

The two vectors m^r, n^r are as shown in figure 33 or 34.

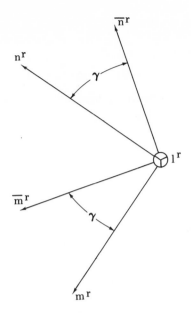

Figure 35.

78. If we contract the basic Equation 28.136 with the binormal $\bar{n}^r$, we have

28.142 $\qquad F_r \bar{n}^r = 0 = (F_r n^r) \cos \gamma - (F_r m^r) \sin \gamma$

so that

28.143 $\qquad \tan \gamma = \dfrac{F_r n^r}{F_r m^r}$

28.144 $\quad F_r m^r = v^2 \chi \cos \gamma = (\mu \sin \beta)/r^2 + R_r m^r$

28.145 $\qquad F_r n^r = v^2 \chi \sin \gamma = R_r n^r$

in which we have used Equations 28.140 and 28.082 for the disturbing force R_r. These equations enable us to find both γ and χ from the force components. In an unperturbed orbit $(R_r = 0)$, we have $\gamma = 0$; the radius of curvature is

$$\frac{1}{\chi} = \frac{v^2 r^2}{\mu \sin \beta} = \frac{r(2 - r/a)}{\sin \beta}$$

$$= r \operatorname{cosec} \beta (1 + \cos E) = a \operatorname{cosec} \beta (1 - e^2 \cos^2 E)$$

in terms of the Kepler elements. Allowing for difference in notation, this last equation is easily verified from Equation 22.12 as the radius of curvature of an ellipse.

79. For the perturbed curvature vector, we can now rewrite Equation 28.136 as

$$v^2 \chi \bar{m}_r = F_r - (F_s l^s) l_r$$

$$= (F_s m^s) m_r + (F_s n^s) n_r$$

28.146 $\qquad = \left(\dfrac{\mu \sin \beta}{r^2} + R_s m^s \right) m_r + (R_s n^s) n_r.$

80. The torsion (τ) of the orbit involves derivatives of the force. For example, by taking the covariant derivative of Equation 28.142 along the orbit and by using the third equation of the Frenet Equations 4.06, we have

28.147 $\qquad F_{rs} \bar{n}^r l^s = \tau F_r \bar{m}^r = v^2 \chi \tau$

after substituting Equation 28.138. We can also differentiate Equation 28.141 covariantly along the orbit and can substitute Equation 28.139 to give

$$-\tau \bar{m}_r = n_{rs} l^s \cos \gamma - m_{rs} l^s \sin \gamma - \bar{m}_r (d\gamma/ds)$$

in which ds is the arc element $(= v \, dt)$ of the orbit. Contracting this last equation with $\bar{m}_r$ and using Equations 28.139 and 3.19, we have

28.148 $\qquad \tau = (d\gamma/ds) - n_{rs} m^r l^s.$

There are various ways of evaluating the invariant on the right. An interesting method is to use Equations 28.062 and 28.064 and to evaluate in Cartesian coordinates from

$$v n_{rs} m^r l^s = m^r \frac{dn_r}{dt}$$

$$= -\sin (w + f + \beta) \sin i \, \frac{d\Omega}{dt}$$

$$- \cos (w + f + \beta) \frac{di}{dt}$$

$$= -\frac{r}{N} (R_q n^q) \cos \beta$$

by substituting Equations 28.105 and 28.104. Using Equations 28.145 and 28.054, we have finally

$$n_{rs} m^r l^s = -\chi \sin \gamma \cot \beta$$

28.149 $\qquad \tau = (d\gamma/ds) + \chi \sin \gamma \cot \beta.$

Evaluation of $(d\gamma/ds)$ by differentiating Equation 28.143 or Equations 28.144 and 28.145 along the orbit again introduces derivatives of the force or second derivatives of a perturbing potential. The torsion of an unperturbed orbit $(\gamma = 0)$ is, of course, zero.

THE DELAUNAY VARIABLES

81. Instead of the elements (a, e, i), it is sometimes convenient to use three new variables

$$L = \sqrt{\mu a}$$

$$G = \sqrt{\mu a (1 - e^2)} = N$$

$$H = \sqrt{\mu a (1 - e^2)} \cos i = N \cos i,$$

first introduced by Delaunay, and still retain the other three elements (M, w, Ω). Unfortunately, every one of these symbols (L, G, H), which are standard in the literature, also means something else, sometimes in the same chapter of the literature. It is also usual in this context to use (l, g, h) instead of (M, w, Ω), the better to exhibit their relationship to (L, G, H). To avoid confusion, so far as possible, we have used L^*, H^* for the Lagrangian and Hamiltonian. The Delaunay variables are not used outside this chapter and are unlikely to be confused with other meanings—of G, g, h, for example—used elsewhere.

Time Derivatives

82. The time derivatives of the new variables are easily obtained by direct differentiation and by use of the formulas for da/dt, de/dt, di/dt already given. We can also relate the results to partial derivatives given in § 28–56 through § 28–76, remembering that in those sections F is any scalar defined in relation to the orbit, such as the disturbing potential R. We have

$$\frac{dL}{dt} = \frac{1}{2}\frac{\mu^{1/2}}{a^{1/2}}\frac{da}{dt} = \frac{1}{2}\frac{\mu^{1/2}}{a^{1/2}}\frac{2a^2}{\mu}vR_r l^r = \frac{vR_r l^r}{n} = \frac{\partial R}{\partial M},$$

28.150

using Equations 28.086 and 28.120; we have

28.151 $\qquad \dfrac{dG}{dt} = \dfrac{dN}{dt} = rR_q t^q = \dfrac{\partial R}{\partial w},$

using Equations 28.090 and 28.127; and we have

$$\frac{dH}{dt} = \cos i\,\frac{dN}{dt} - N\sin i\,\frac{di}{dt}$$
$$= (r\cos i)R_q t^q - r\sin i\cos(w+f)R_q n^q$$

28.152 $\qquad = \dfrac{\partial R}{\partial \Omega},$

using Equations 28.090, 28.104, and 28.125.

83. We can also express the time derivatives of (M, w, Ω), already obtained, in terms of partial derivatives of the disturbing potential R with respect to the new variables (L, G, H). For this purpose, we need partial derivatives of (a, e, i) with respect to (L, G, H). We have

$$a = L^2/\mu$$
$$G^2 = L^2(1-e^2)$$

28.153 $\qquad H = G\cos i.$

For partial derivatives with respect to L, we must have H, G constant (as well as M, w, Ω) so that i is constant and

$$2L(1-e^2)dL - 2eL^2 de = 0,$$

giving, together with the first equation of Equations 28.153,

$$\frac{\partial a}{\partial L} = \frac{2L}{\mu}; \qquad \frac{\partial e}{\partial L} = \frac{(1-e^2)}{eL}; \qquad \frac{\partial i}{\partial L} = 0;$$

28.154

in the same way, we have

$$\frac{\partial a}{\partial G} = 0; \qquad \frac{\partial e}{\partial G} = -\frac{G}{eL^2}; \qquad \frac{\partial i}{\partial G} = \frac{\cot i}{G}$$

28.155

$$\frac{\partial a}{\partial H} = 0; \qquad \frac{\partial e}{\partial G} = 0; \qquad \frac{\partial i}{\partial H} = -\frac{1}{G\sin i}.$$

28.156

84. Next, we have by the ordinary chain rule

$$\frac{\partial R}{\partial L} = \frac{\partial a}{\partial L}\frac{\partial R}{\partial a} + \frac{\partial e}{\partial L}\frac{\partial R}{\partial e} + \frac{\partial i}{\partial L}\frac{\partial R}{\partial i}$$
$$= \frac{2L}{\mu}\frac{r}{a}(R_r r^r) + \frac{(1-e^2)}{eL}\Big\{-(a\cos f)R_r r^r$$

28.157 $\qquad\qquad\qquad + \Big(a + \dfrac{r}{1-e^2}\Big)R_r t^r \sin f\Big\},$

using Equations 28.154, 28.109, and 28.116; by inspection of Equation 28.102, this is

28.158 $\qquad \dfrac{\partial R}{\partial L} = -\dfrac{dM}{dt} + n.$

In the same way, we have

$$\frac{\partial R}{\partial G} = -\frac{G}{eL^2}\Big\{-(a\cos f)R_r r^r + \Big(a + \frac{r}{1-e^2}\Big)R_r t^r \sin f$$
$$\qquad + r\cot i\sin(w+f)(R_r n^r)/G\Big\}$$
$$= -\frac{dw}{dt},$$

28.159

using Equations 28.116, 28.123, and 28.107. Also, we have

28.160 $\qquad \dfrac{\partial R}{\partial H} = -\dfrac{r\sin(w+f)(R_r n^r)}{G\sin i} = -\dfrac{d\Omega}{dt},$

using Equations 28.123 and 28.105.

Canonical Equations

85. In this section, we have defined R as the scalar whose gradient is the disturbing force R_r. To ensure correct signs, we integrate Equation 28.082 and obtain

28.161 $\qquad -V = (\mu/r) + R$

where V is the total potential; therefore, R is, for example, the sum of all the terms in the spherical harmonic expansion of the potential given in Equation 21.035 which must be added to μ/r, thus agreeing with Equation 28.081.

86. The Hamiltonian H^* (not to be confused with the Delaunay variable H), as defined by Equation 28.031, is

28.162 $\qquad H^* = \tfrac{1}{2}v^2 - (\mu/r) - R.$

We can substitute Equation 28.042 for v because the actual velocity is equal to the velocity in the osculating ellipse so that we have

28.163 $\qquad H^* = -\dfrac{\mu}{2a} - R = -\dfrac{\mu^2}{2L^2} - R$

in which L is the Delaunay variable $\sqrt{\mu a}$. Also, we have

$$\frac{\partial H^*}{\partial L} = \frac{\mu^2}{L^3} - \frac{\partial R}{\partial L} = n - \frac{\partial \dot R}{\partial L};$$

whereas, the partial differentials of H^* with respect to the other five Delaunay variables are the same as the partials of $(-R)$. By substitution in Equations 28.150, 28.151, 28.152, 28.158, 28.159, and 28.160 and writing (l, g, h) for (M, w, Ω), we have

$$\frac{dL}{dt} = -\frac{\partial H^*}{\partial l} \;; \qquad \frac{dG}{dt} = -\frac{\partial H^*}{\partial g} \;; \qquad \frac{dH}{dt} = -\frac{\partial H^*}{\partial h}$$

$$\frac{dl}{dt} = \frac{\partial H^*}{\partial L} \;; \qquad \frac{dg}{dt} = \frac{\partial H^*}{\partial G} \;; \qquad \frac{dh}{dt} = \frac{\partial H^*}{\partial H}.$$

28.164

These six equations are in the canonical form of Equations 28.033, with (l, g, h) replacing the Cartesian coordinates (x, y, z) and with (L, G, H) replacing the momenta $(\dot x, \dot y, \dot z)$. The Hamiltonian has the same value, that is, $\tfrac{1}{2}v^2 + V$, whether the Hamiltonian is expressed in Cartesian or Delaunay variables.

FIRST INTEGRALS OF THE EQUATIONS OF MOTION—FURTHER GENERAL CONSIDERATIONS

87. We shall now consider further the Equation 28.028, that is,

28.165 $\qquad \tfrac{1}{2}\bar v^2 + \bar W = \text{constant},$

which was obtained as a first integral of the equations of motion relative to the uniformly rotating axes A^r, B^r, C^r fixed in the Earth. To avoid confusion, we have overbarred all quantities related to this system so that $\bar v$ is the apparent velocity of the satellite relative to axes rotating with constant angular velocity $\tilde\omega$, and

$$\bar W = \bar V - \tfrac{1}{2}\tilde\omega^2 d^2$$

is the geopotential. Also, $\bar V$ is the attraction potential and d is the distance of the satellite from the axis of rotation, as obtained in § 20–10. But the attraction potential, as a physical invariant, has the same value in both the inertial and rotating systems. Also, d has the same value if the axis of rotation is the C^r-axis common to both systems, as we have assumed throughout this book. Accordingly, the geopotential retains the same value on transformation to the inertial system; we can drop the overbars from $\bar V$ and $\bar W$.

88. If ρ^r is the inertial position vector, the apparent velocity vector relative to the rotating axes is

$$\dot\rho^r - (\tilde\omega d)\lambda^r$$

where λ^r is the usual unit vector in the direction of the parallel of spherical polar latitude. The magnitude of the apparent velocity is given by

$$\begin{aligned}
\bar v^2 &= (\dot\rho^r - (\tilde\omega d)\lambda^r)(\dot\rho_r - (\tilde\omega d)\lambda_r) \\
&= \dot\rho^r\dot\rho_r - 2(\tilde\omega d)\dot\rho^r\lambda_r + \tilde\omega^2 d^2 \\
&= v^2 - 2(\tilde\omega d)vl^r\lambda_r + \tilde\omega^2 d^2 \\
&= v^2 - 2(\tilde\omega d)v \sin\alpha \sin\beta + \tilde\omega^2 d^2,
\end{aligned}$$

using Equations 28.003 and 28.059. Substituting this result in Equation 28.165, we find that

$$\tfrac{1}{2}v^2 + V - (\tilde\omega d)v \sin\alpha \sin\beta = \text{constant}$$

applies in the inertial system. Using the fact that we have $d = r \cos\phi$, together with Equations 28.077 and 28.054, we can also write

28.166 $\qquad \tfrac{1}{2}v^2 + V - \tilde\omega N \cos i = \text{constant}$

where N as usual is $\sqrt{\mu a(1-e^2)}$. This equation must be a first integral of the inertial equations of motion, equivalent in this case of uniform rotation to Equation 28.021. We can also write

28.167 $\int \dfrac{\partial V}{\partial t}\,dt = \tilde{\omega}N \cos i + \text{constant}.$

Equation 28.166 can be considered as an expression of the law of conservation of energy in this case and will, in the future, be referred to as the *energy integral* in our particular problem. It will be noted that $(N \cos i)$ in the correcting term is the same as the Delaunay variable H.

89. Equation 28.167 leads us to consider the time variation of $(N \cos i)$. Using Equations 28.090 and 28.104, we have

$$\frac{d(N \cos i)}{dt} = rR_q\{t^q \cos i - n^q \sin i \cos (w+f)\}$$

28.168 $= (r \cos \phi)R_q\lambda^q$

by substituting Equations 28.059 and 28.077, and the last term of Equation 28.080. But $(R_q\lambda^q)$ is the component of disturbing force in the direction of the parallel and is zero only if the resultant disturbing force lies in the plane of the meridian, which would require the field to be axially symmetric. Also, $(r \cos \phi)R_q\lambda^q$ is the moment of this force component about the axis of rotation. We conclude that $(N \cos i)$ is the axial component of the angular momentum vector, which can be verified from Equation 28.023, if we take

$$N \cos i = \epsilon^{rst}C_r\rho_s\dot{\rho}_t$$

$$\frac{d(N \cos i)}{dt} = \epsilon^{rst}C_r\rho_s\ddot{\rho}_t = \epsilon^{rst}C_r\rho_sF_t = \epsilon^{rst}C_r\rho_sR_t$$

28.169

because the central component of force does not contribute to the vector product, and we are therefore left with the disturbing force R_t. We have finally

$$\frac{d(N \cos i)}{dt} = r\epsilon^{rst}C_rr_sR_t = (r \cos \phi)\lambda^tR_t,$$

agreeing with Equation 28.168.

90. We can now verify Equation 28.167 and thus Equation 28.166. If the potential is expressed in the form

$$-V = \sum \frac{\mu}{r^{n+1}} P_n^m(\cos \phi)(C_{nm} \cos m\omega + S_{nm} \sin m\omega)$$

in which ω is the geodetic longitude and in the form

$$\omega = \bar{\omega} - \tilde{\omega}t$$

where $\bar{\omega}$ is the inertial longitude and t is elapsed time since the inertial and geodetic meridians coincided, then we have at once

$$\frac{\partial V}{\partial t} = -\tilde{\omega}\,\frac{\partial V}{\partial \omega} = \tilde{\omega}\,\frac{\partial R}{\partial \omega} = \tilde{\omega}R_q\lambda^q(r \cos \phi)$$

because we have $-V = \mu/r + R$ and therefore $\partial V/\partial \omega = -\partial R/\partial \omega$. From Equation 28.168, we have

28.170 $\dfrac{\partial V}{\partial t} = \tilde{\omega}\,\dfrac{d(N \cos i)}{dt},$

which is equivalent to Equation 28.167.

91. We find therefore that $(N \cos i)$ is a constant of the motion, and thus an integral of the equations of motion, only if the field is axially symmetric, in which case $(N \cos i)$ is clearly an integral of the equations of motion relative to either the inertial or the rotating axes. In the case of an axially symmetrical field (tesseral harmonics absent), we have *both*

28.171 $\tfrac{1}{2}v^2 + V = \text{constant}$

28.172 $N \cos i = \text{constant};$

whereas, in the case of an unsymmetrical field, we have only

28.173 $\tfrac{1}{2}v^2 + V - \tilde{\omega}N \cos i = \text{constant},$

or, using Equations 28.169, we have

28.174 $\tfrac{1}{2}v^2 + V - \tilde{\omega}\epsilon^{rst}C_r\rho_s\dot{\rho}_t = \text{constant}.$

92. An alternative way of looking at the symmetrical field is of some interest. If the disturbing force is axially symmetric, it can be expressed as

$$R_r = AC_r + B\rho_r$$

where A, B are scalars, but not necessarily constants. In that case, we can see at once from the vector product in Equation 28.125 that we have $\partial R/\partial \Omega = 0$; therefore, we have $dH/dt = 0$ from Equation 28.152 where H is the Delaunay variable $(N \cos i)$. Accordingly, we have verified that $(N \cos i)$ is a constant of the motion in an axially symmetrical field. A canonical variable, such as $\Omega = h$ in this case, which makes the associated variable a constant in this way, is said to be *ignorable*.

INTEGRATION OF THE GAUSS EQUATIONS

93. A standard method of solving differential equations is to find an exact solution in a special case which is close to the actual problem; for example, the exact solution of our present problem

for the main term $-\mu/r$ in the potential is the Kepler ellipse. This exact solution results in a number of arbitrary constants which, in this case, are six Kepler elements from the three second-order equations of motion or the equivalent six first-order equations. We then obtain more general solutions by writing equations for the (small) variations of the constants required to accommodate the difference between the exact and actual problems—in this case, the perturbing potential—and we solve these equations by successive approximation. Astronomers can claim to have invented this perturbation method for this particular purpose, but it is now very generally applied to most of the equations of mathematical physics, usually in the form of an integral equation. A clear introduction to the subject, supported by further references, has been given by the Jeffreys.[4]

94. The first Gauss Equation 28.086 can be written as

$$\frac{\mu}{2a^2}\frac{da}{dt}=R_r\frac{dx^r}{dt}=\frac{dR}{dt}-\frac{\partial R}{\partial t}$$

in which dR/dt is the total differential of the disturbing potential, containing explicit time. Integrating this equation, we have

$$-\frac{\mu}{2a}-R+\int\frac{\partial R}{\partial t}\,dt=\text{constant.}$$

But the velocity in the actual and osculating orbits is the same so that Equation 28.042 holds true as

$$\tfrac{1}{2}v^2=\frac{\mu}{r}-\frac{\mu}{2a};$$

we have also from Equation 28.081

$$-V=\frac{\mu}{r}+R$$

so that

$$\tfrac{1}{2}v^2+V-\int\frac{\partial V}{\partial t}\,dt=\text{constant;}$$

or, using Equation 28.167, we have

$$\tfrac{1}{2}v^2+V-\tilde\omega N\cos i=\text{constant,}$$

which is the same as the energy integral Equation 28.166. The first Gauss equation is accordingly equivalent to the energy integral, and will give us no more information.

95. To illustrate the general method of solution, we shall consider Equation 28.105 for the right ascension of the ascending node, perturbed by the

[4] Jeffreys and Jeffreys (reprint of 1962), *Methods of Mathematical Physics*, 3d ed. of 1956, 493–495.

second zonal harmonic of the gravitational field, as

28.175 $$R=\frac{\mu C_{20}P_2(\sin\phi)}{r^3}=\frac{\mu C_{20}}{2r^3}(3\sin^2\phi-1)$$

where C_{20} has the meaning assigned in Chapter 21. Using Equations 28.059 in a spherical polar coordinate system, we first find the invariant

$$R_q n^q=\frac{\sin\alpha}{r}\frac{\partial R}{\partial\phi}$$

$$=\frac{3\mu C_{20}}{r^4}\sin\phi\cos\phi\sin\alpha$$

$$=\frac{3\mu C_{20}}{r^4}\sin(w+f)\sin i\cos i$$

by substituting Equations 28.077 and 28.079 so that we have

28.176 $$\frac{d\Omega}{dt}=\frac{3\mu C_{20}}{Nr^3}\sin^2(w+f)\cos i.$$

To integrate this equation, we must first transform to a single variable of the osculating ellipse, either t or f, or M, or E; the obvious choice in this case is the true anomaly f. Using the unperturbed relation

28.177 $$\frac{d}{dt}=\frac{df}{dt}\frac{d}{df}=\frac{N}{r^2}\frac{d}{df}$$

from Equation 28.098 and substituting the last member of Equation 28.051, we have

$$\frac{d\Omega}{df}=\frac{r^2}{N}\frac{d\Omega}{dt}$$

$$=\frac{3\mu C_{20}(1+e\cos f)\sin^2(w+f)\cos i}{N^2a(1-e^2)}$$

$$=\frac{3C_{20}\cos i}{2a^2(1-e^2)^2}\{1-\cos(2w+2f)+e\cos f$$

$$-\tfrac{1}{2}e\cos(2w+3f)-\tfrac{1}{2}e\cos(2w+f)\}\cdot$$

28.178

To obtain a first-order result, already implicit in the use of the unperturbed Equation 28.177, we assume that the elements a, e, w, i are unchanged during the integration; we then integrate over a complete revolution from f_0 to $f_0+2\pi$. The resulting first-order change $\Delta_1\Omega$ (not to be confused with the Laplacian) in the nodal longitude is

28.179 $$\Delta_1\Omega=\frac{3\pi C_{20}\cos i}{a^2(1-e^2)^2}.$$

Or, adopting an alternative form of the constant C_{20} whereby we have

28.180 $$C_{n0}=-(a_e)^n J_n$$

in which a_e is a mean radius of the Earth, we have

28.181
$$\Delta_1\Omega = -\frac{3\pi a_e^2 \cos i J_2}{a^2(1-e^2)^2}.$$

By the same process, we have for the other elements

$$\Delta_1 a = 0$$

$$\Delta_1 e = 0$$

$$\Delta_1 i = 0$$

$$\Delta_1 w = \frac{6\pi a_e^2 J_2}{a^2(1-e^2)^2}\left(1 - \tfrac{5}{4}\sin^2 i\right)$$

$$\int\left(\frac{dM}{dt} - n\right)dt = \frac{3\pi a_e^2 J_2}{a^2(1-e^2)^{3/2}}\left(1 - \tfrac{3}{2}\sin^2 i\right).$$

28.182

The perturbation of the mean anomaly requires some explanation. If carried from perigee to perigee using Equation 28.043, the integral on the left would be the total change in M minus 2π, on the same assumption as for the other first-order perturbations that a and therefore n are constant during the integration; otherwise, the last equation is not strictly correct. There is little or no effect on the first-order perturbations whether we integrate from perigee to perigee or between ascending nodes, but the distinction does affect and does complicate the second-order perturbations.

96. First-order or linear perturbations $\Delta_1\Omega$, etc., of the elements caused by each higher harmonic can be calculated in the same way; the results can be added to give the final perturbation $\Delta\Omega$ as a series containing only the first powers of the gravitational constants C_{nm}, S_{nm}. If we make enough measurements of the perturbations on different satellites so as to introduce different values of the coefficients of the C_{nm}, S_{nm}, we can accordingly solve the resulting equations for some of the lower order C_{nm}, S_{nm}, assuming that the effect of the higher harmonics on satellites, whose perigee heights are large, can be neglected. The process of integration over a complete revolution will remove some of the higher tesseral harmonics; all the tesseral harmonics will be eliminated if observations of the change in the elements are averaged over a complete day. The method has, in fact, been used most extensively to determine a few of the lower zonal harmonics after suitable corrections for lunisolar perturbations, atmospheric drag, and radiation pressure—the last two of which are small in the case of heavy, compact, high-altitude satellites suitable for determination of the gravitational field.

97. It will be found that the coefficients of J_2,

J_4, J_6, . . . are much larger than the coefficients of J_3, J_5, . . . in the series for Δw and $\Delta\Omega$; these perturbations are accordingly used mostly for the determination of the even harmonics. The Δe- and Δi-perturbations are best used for the determination of the odd harmonics, and can also be used for the higher even harmonics J_4, J_6, ... The integration of Equation 28.178 over a complete revolution has removed the *short-period* terms, consisting of constants multiplied by sines or cosines of angles containing multiples of the true anomaly f. The resulting first-order perturbations—averaged over a complete revolution, caused by J_2, and given in Equations 28.181 and 28.182—do not contain any periodic terms (because $\Delta i = 0$) and are known as *secular* terms, the effect of which increases steadily with time. From Equations 28.182, we see that the argument of perigee w changes secularly so that perigee will eventually complete a whole revolution in the orbit. For this reason, terms containing sines and cosines of w, which appear in the perturbations caused by some higher harmonics, are known as *long-period* terms.

98. First-order perturbation by J_2 of the argument of perigee, $\Delta_1 w$ in Equations 28.182, becomes zero for an inclination given by $\sin^2 i = \tfrac{4}{5}$ or $\cos^2 i = \tfrac{1}{5}$. Close to this critical inclination, perigee oscillates instead of precessing secularly. This case has attracted much attention, but seems to be of importance in geodetic applications only insofar as the critical inclination slightly limits the use of perturbation in perigee.

99. The Kepler elements are not very suitable for orbits having small inclination or eccentricity because then Ω, w, M and their perturbations are not well defined. The difficulty, which has been encountered in a different context in § 27–6, may be overcome by using suitable combinations of the elements as variables.

100. As long ago as 1884, Helmert determined J_2 from the orbit of the Moon, using a formula comparable with $\Delta_1\Omega$ in Equation 28.181, after allowance for the large perturbation of the Moon's orbit by the Sun. However, the accuracy of the result, which depends on $(a_e/a)^2$, is much greater from nearer artificial satellites even though the higher harmonics have more effect.

Second-Order Perturbations

101. In common with other perturbation methods of solving differential equations, integration of

the Gauss equations runs into trouble when one of the perturbing terms, in this case C_{20} or J_2, is much larger than the other terms. It is well established that C_{20} is about one thousand times larger than any of the other C_{nm}, S_{nm}; second-order perturbations containing C_{20}^2 or J_2^2 have about the same magnitude as first-order perturbations caused by the other C_{nm}, S_{nm}. Consequently, we cannot hope to obtain values of the other harmonics unless we includes J_2^2-terms and possibly also such terms as J_2J_3, etc. To do this, we must not continue to assume that elements occurring in the coefficients of Equation 28.178, for example, are constant during the integration, and we must use a perturbed relation instead of Equation 28.177. The process will be illustrated by the same example as used for the first-order perturbations, that is, perturbation of Ω by the second zonal harmonic.

102. We begin with Equation 28.176 and consider necessary modifications arising from the inconstancy of w. We have

$$\frac{d\Omega}{dt} = \left\{\frac{d\Omega}{dt}\right\} + \frac{\partial(d\Omega/dt)}{\partial w}\, dw$$

$$= \left\{\frac{d\Omega}{dt}\right\} - \frac{6\mu C_{20}}{Nr^3} \sin(w+f)\cos(w+f)\cos i\, dw$$

28.183

in which the term in braces is the same as we have used on the assumption that the elements are constant. From Equations 28.175 and 28.059, we have

$$R_r r^r = \frac{\partial R}{\partial r} = -\frac{3\mu C_{20}}{2r^4}(3\sin^2\phi - 1)$$

$$R_r t^r = \frac{\cos\alpha}{r}\frac{\partial R}{\partial\phi} = \frac{3\mu C_{20}}{r^4}\sin\phi\cos\phi\cos\alpha$$

$$= \frac{3\mu C_{20}}{r^4}\sin(w+f)\cos(w+f)\sin^2 i,$$

using Equation 28.079 and the last term of Equations 28.080. Substitution in Equation 28.096 then gives an equation of the form

$$\frac{df}{dt} = \frac{N}{r^2}\left(1 - \frac{3C_{20}X}{2ea^2(1-e^2)}\right)$$

in which X is a function containing e, $\sin^2 i$, and trigonometric functions of multiples of w and f. To a first order in C_{20}, we can write

$$\frac{dt}{df} = \frac{r^2}{N}\left(1 + \frac{3C_{20}X}{2ea^2(1-e^2)}\right);$$

combining this equation with Equation 28.183, we have

$$\frac{d\Omega}{df} = \frac{r^2}{N}\left\{\frac{d\Omega}{dt}\right\}$$

$$-\frac{r^2}{N}\frac{6\mu C_{20}}{Nr^3}\sin(w+f)\cos(w+f)\cos i\, dw$$

$$+\frac{r^2}{N}\frac{3C_{20}X}{2ea^2(1-e^2)}\left\{\frac{d\Omega}{dt}\right\}$$

in which we have omitted the term containing C_{20}^2, leading to a third-order term. Integration around a complete revolution will give, for the first term on the right,

$$\int\frac{r^2}{N}\left\{\frac{d\Omega}{dt}\right\} = \Delta_1\Omega,$$

already evaluated in Equation 28.181. The second-order perturbation to be added to $\Delta_1\Omega$ will accordingly be

$$\Delta_2\Omega = -\int\frac{6\mu C_{20}\sin(w+f)\cos(w+f)\cos i}{Nr^3}$$

$$\times\left(\frac{r^2}{N}\frac{dw}{df}\right)df$$

$$+\int\frac{3C_{20}X}{2ea^2(1-e^2)}\times\frac{r^2}{N}\left\{\frac{d\Omega}{dt}\right\}df.$$

In these integrals, we have to substitute Equation 28.178 and a corresponding equation for dw/df, and then convert to trigonometric functions of multiple angles. During the evaluation of these second-order integrals we can consider the elements constant, just as we did in the evaluation of the first-order integrals to find the first-order perturbation $\Delta_1\Omega$, so that the integration follows the same lines as the integration of Equation 28.178.

103. In addition, we have to include terms in Equation 28.183, such as

$$\frac{\partial(d\Omega/dt)}{\partial e}\, de,$$

to allow for variation in the other elements; each such term would lead to a second-order integral containing, for example, de/df. These terms have to be evaluated, even though the first-order perturbation $\Delta_1 e$ taken between limits is zero.

104. First- and second-order perturbations for a number of harmonics have been derived by Merson,[5]

[5] Merson (1961), "The Motion of a Satellite in an Axi-symmetric Gravitational Field," *Geophysical Journal of the Royal Astronomical Society*, v. 4, 17–52.

Kozai,[6] Zhongolovitch and Pellinen,[7] and others. The algebraic equations, even those of the final results, are involved; the labor required to obtain these equations must have been immense. It is probable that the method has served its purpose in the evaluation of a few low zonal harmonics and that future developments will be more in the direction of numerical integration. Meanwhile, other attempts have been made to avoid the complexity introduced by the magnitude of J_2.

INTEGRATION OF THE LAGRANGE EQUATIONS

105. The Lagrange Equations 28.134 require the disturbing potential R to be expressed in terms of the elements (a, e, i, M, w, Ω). This expression has been given by Kaula[8] in the form

$$R_{nm} = \frac{\mu a_e^n}{a^{n+1}} \sum_{p=0}^{n} F_{nmp}(i) \sum_{q=-\infty}^{\infty} G_{npq}(e)$$

28.184 $\hspace{3cm} \times S_{nmpq}(w, M, \Omega, \theta)$

where R_{nm} is the harmonic of order m and degree n in the disturbing potential R, and

$$S_{nmpq} = \begin{bmatrix} C_{nm} \\ -S_{nm} \end{bmatrix}_{\substack{n-m \text{ even} \\ n-m \text{ odd}}} \cos\left[(n-2p)w\right.$$

$$\left. + (n-2p+q)M + m(\Omega-\theta)\right]$$

$$+ \begin{bmatrix} S_{nm} \\ C_{nm} \end{bmatrix}_{\substack{n-m \text{ even} \\ n-m \text{ odd}}} \sin\left[(n-2p)w\right.$$

28.185 $\hspace{3cm} \left. + (n-2p+q)M + m(\Omega-\theta)\right].$

Also, θ is the sidereal time at the origin of longitude—for example, Greenwich—in the original expression for the potential in spherical harmonics. The angle $(\Omega-\theta)$ is accordingly the (Greenwich) longitude of the ascending node. The terms $F_{nmp}(i)$ and $G_{npq}(e)$ are known functions, respectively, of the inclination and eccentricity, which appear in the literature of classical astronomy, and have been tabulated for a number of harmonics by Kaula.[9] The symbol a_e is a mean radius of the Earth, the inclusion of which requires the C_{nm}, S_{nm} of Chapter 21 to be divided by a_e^n before substitution in Equation 28.185. It is hardly necessary to say that Equations 28.184

---

[6] Kozai (1959), "The Motion of a Close Earth Satellite," *The Astronomical Journal*, v. 64, 367–377.

[7] Zhongolovitch and Pellinen (1962), "Mean Elements of Artificial Earth Satellites," *Biulleten' Instituta Teoreticheskoĭ Astronomii*, v. 8, 381–395.

[8] Kaula, *op. cit. supra* note 3, 37.

[9] *Ibid.*, 34–35, 38.

and 28.185 are merely indicial equations and have no tensor significance any more than the constants C_{nm}, S_{nm}. Transformation of the ordinary expression of the potential in spherical harmonics to the pole of the osculating orbital plane is not difficult; the complexity arises almost entirely from the use of M as one of the elements rather than a purely geometrical quantity such as f, but this complexity is necessary if we expect to use the canonical Equations 28.164.

106. Because the Lagrange equations, like the Gauss equations, are linear, we can substitute differentials of individual harmonics R_{nm} on the right side of these equations and can integrate term-by-term. For example, the contribution to $d\Omega/dt$ of one term R_{nmpq} in the double summation of Equation 28.184, substituted in the last equation of Equations 28.134, is

28.186 $\quad \dfrac{d\Omega}{dt} = \dfrac{1}{N \sin i} \dfrac{\mu a_e^n}{a^{n+1}} \dfrac{dF_{nmp}}{di} G_{npq} S_{nmpq},$

which can be integrated to find the first-order or linear perturbation on much the same assumptions as are made for the integration of the Gauss equations. In this case, we assume that (a, e, i) are constant during the integration and that $\dot{w} = dw/dt$, $\dot{M} = dM/dt$, $\dot{\Omega} = d\Omega/dt$ are also constant, which implies that $\dot{w}$, $\dot{M}$, $\dot{\Omega}$ have either unperturbed or average values obtainable from the corresponding Lagrange equations. The only variable in Equation 28.186 is then S_{nmpq}; we have

$$\int S_{nmpq} \, dt$$

$$= \int \frac{S_{nmpq} \, d\{(n-2p)w + (n-2p+q)M + m(\Omega-\theta)\}}{(n-2p)\dot{w} + (n-2p+q)\dot{M} + m(\dot{\Omega}-\dot{\theta})}$$

$$= \frac{\bar{S}_{nmpq}}{(n-2p)\dot{w} + (n-2p+q)\dot{M} + m(\dot{\Omega}-\dot{\theta})}$$

where $\bar{S}_{nmpq}$ is the integral of S_{nmpq} in Equation 28.185, with respect to the argument $(n-2p)w + (n-2p+q)M + m(\Omega-\theta)$. In this result, $\dot{\theta} = \bar{\omega}$ is the constant rate of rotation of the Earth. The final contribution to the change in the element is

$$\Delta\Omega_{nm} = \frac{1}{N \sin i} \frac{\mu a_e^n}{a^{n+1}}$$

$$\times \sum_{pq} \frac{(\partial F_{nmp}/\partial i) G_{npq} \bar{S}_{nmpq}}{(n-2p)\dot{w} + (n-2p+q)\dot{M} + m(\dot{\Omega}-\dot{\theta})}.$$

28.187

In this equation, n is, of course, an index and not the mean motion.

107. First-order perturbations are found to be the same as those obtainable from the Gauss equations. The second-order perturbations may be obtained in much the same way, allowing for variation in $(a, e, i, \dot{w}, \dot{M}, \dot{\Omega})$, but are just as complicated and just as necessary.

Resonance

108. If the denominator

$$(n-2p)\dot{w}+(n-2p+q)\dot{M}+m(\Omega-\dot{\theta})$$

of equations, such as Equation 28.187, for the first-order perturbations is near zero, the corresponding term in the perturbation will become very large and the first-order theory will break down. These cases are of considerable importance in the orbits of geostationary communications satellites and in the accurate determination of some higher harmonics. One case, considered by Kaula,[10] occurs when

$$\dot{w}+\dot{M}+\Omega-\dot{\theta}$$

is nearly zero; this situation can happen for certain terms in the disturbing function S_{nmpq} of Equation 28.185. Another case arises when the ratio of the mean motion of the satellite $(\dot{M})$ to the Earth's rotation rate $(\dot{\theta})$ is nearly equal to

$$m/(n-2p+q)$$

because, for such a term, the denominator will contain only the small perturbations $\dot{w}, \dot{\Omega}$. The orbit is then said to be *commensurable*. There is already a large and rapid growing literature on the subject by such authors as Allan, Anderle, Morando, Wagner, and Yionoulis. One of the latest, which gives reasonably full references to earlier work, is a paper by Gedeon, Douglas, and Palmiter.[11]

INTEGRATION OF THE CANONICAL EQUATIONS

Contact Transformations

109. In this book, we have so far used only *point transformations*, either to a different set of coordinates or to a point in another space related by one-to-one correspondence. We now briefly consider *contact transformations*, whereby both the coordinates of a point and a vector associated with the point are transformed in such a way that the

canonical form of equations connecting the coordinates and components is preserved. The transformation from the six independent variables $(x, y, z, \dot{x}, \dot{y}, \dot{z})$ in Equations 28.033 to the Delaunay variables (L, G, H, l, g, h) in Equations 28.164 is a contact transformation. For our present purposes, we need to consider the position and velocity of a single particle only in three-dimensional space with six independent variables. However, the same methods apply to dynamical systems consisting of any number of particles, each of which will contribute three *coordinates* and three components of velocity or *momenta*. The transformed variables may no longer represent position and velocity separately—the Delaunay variables do not—although the transformed variables are sufficient to determine position and velocity either directly or by another transformation. Nevertheless, it is usual to call three of the variables coordinates and to call the other three momenta to fix their position in the canonical equations with the correct sign. We shall denote coordinates by q^r and momenta by p_r so that the canonical equations are, as in Equations 28.033,

28.188 $$\dot{q}^r=\frac{\partial H^*}{\partial p_r}\;;\qquad \dot{p}_r=-\frac{\partial H^*}{\partial q^r}$$

in which it is assumed that the Hamiltonian H^* can be expressed as a function of p_r, q^r and of the time t. In writing these equations, we have used index notation and can use the summation convention, but the canonical equations are generally not tensor equations because the variables do not transform in the same way.

The total time differential of the Hamiltonian is

$$\frac{dH^*}{dt}=\frac{\partial H^*}{\partial p_r}\dot{p}_r+\frac{\partial H^*}{\partial q^r}\dot{q}^r+\frac{\partial H^*}{\partial t}$$

in which the first two terms on the right cancel by Equations 28.188. If the Hamiltonian does not contain the time explicitly $(\partial H^*/\partial t=0)$, then we have $dH^*/dt=0$; the Hamiltonian is a constant of the motion and therefore an integral of the equations of motion.

110. A contact transformation to new variables Q^r, P_r will result in the canonical equations

28.189 $$\dot{Q}^r=\frac{\partial K^*}{\partial P_r}\;;\qquad \dot{P}_r=-\frac{\partial K^*}{\partial Q^r}$$

in which the new Hamiltonian K^* expressed in terms of P_r, Q^r need not necessarily have the same value as H^*. It can be shown[12] that the transforma-

[10] *Ibid.*, 49–56.
[11] Gedeon, Douglas, and Palmiter (1967), "Resonance Effects on Eccentric Satellite Orbits," *The Journal of the Astronautical Sciences*, v. XIV, no. 4, 147–157.

[12] A fuller treatment of the subject for different forms of the transforming function is given by Goldstein (1950), *Classical Mechanics*, 237–243.

tion equations from Equations 28.188 and 28.189 are

$$p_r = \frac{\partial S}{\partial q^r} ; \qquad Q^r = \frac{\partial S}{\partial P_r} ; \qquad K^* = H^* + \frac{\partial S}{\partial t}$$

28.190

in which the *transforming function* S may be a function of time and is a function of the mixed variables q^r, P_r, so that we have

28.191 $\qquad S = f(q^r, P_r, t)$.

There are alternative transformations in which S can be a function of other variables, for example q^r, Q_r, but this form in Equations 28.190 and 28.191 is the most useful for our present purposes. The Hamiltonian remains unchanged in value, even though expressed in terms of different variables, if the transforming function does not explicitly contain the time.

The Hamilton-Jacobi Equation

111. Next, we seek a contact transformation which will make the new Hamiltonian K^* zero so that we have

$$H^*(q^r, p_r, t) + \frac{\partial S}{\partial t} = 0;$$

or, using the transforming equation $p_r = \partial S/\partial q^r$, we have

28.192 $\qquad H^*\left(q^r, \frac{\partial S}{\partial q^r}, t\right) + \frac{\partial S}{\partial t} = 0,$

known as the Hamilton-Jacobi equation. If we can solve this last equation for S, the whole problem is solved because the new canonical Equations 28.189 then show that the new P_r, Q^r are arbitrary constants of the motion α_r, β^r. The transforming function in Equation 28.191 can then be written

$$S = f(q^r, \alpha_r, t);$$

the transforming Equations 28.190 become

$$p_r = \frac{\partial S(q^r, \alpha_r, t)}{\partial q^r}$$

28.193 $\qquad Q^r = \beta^r = \frac{\partial S(q^r, \alpha_r, t)}{\partial \alpha_r},$

which enable us to express p_r and q^r as functions of α_r, β^r and t. We can finally choose the arbitrary constants α_r, β^r to fit given values of p_r, q^r at a given time, that is, to fit the starting conditions in the orbit. The coordinates and momenta p_r, q^r are then calculable at any later time.

112. In the form of Equation 28.192, the Hamilton-Jacobi equation applies to general dynamical prob-

lems containing any number of coordinates q^r. For our particular problem of a single particle in three dimensions, we can use Equation 28.032 for the Hamiltonian in Cartesian coordinates and write the equation as

$$V(x, y, z, t) + \frac{1}{2}\left\{\left(\frac{\partial S}{\partial x}\right)^2 + \left(\frac{\partial S}{\partial y}\right)^2 + \left(\frac{\partial S}{\partial z}\right)^2\right\} + \frac{\partial S}{\partial t} = 0;$$

or, using Equation 3.13, we have

28.194 $\qquad V + \frac{1}{2}\nabla S + \frac{\partial S}{\partial t} = 0.$

But this last equation is a space invariant which holds true in any space coordinates, provided we can write the potential V in the same coordinates and provided the space coordinates in S are independent of time — as we are entitled to assume in any Newtonian system. If the associated metric tensor of the coordinate system is g^{rs}, all we need do is to use Equation 3.13 and write

28.195 $\qquad \nabla S = g^{rs}S_r S_s.$

113. If the potential does not contain explicit time t, the Hamilton-Jacobi Equation 28.194 can evidently be satisfied without any other loss of generality by

28.196 $\qquad S = W^* - \alpha_1 t$

in which W^* is a scalar not containing explicit time and α_1 is an arbitrary constant; W^* is not to be confused with the geopotential. The equation then becomes

28.197 $\qquad H^* = V + \frac{1}{2}\nabla W^* = \alpha_1.$

We can consider W^* as the transforming function (replacing S in § 28–111 and § 28–112) for a contact transformation which makes the new Hamiltonian the same as the old (because $\partial W^*/\partial t = 0$), both being equal to the constant α_1. The new canonical Equations 28.189 are then

$$\dot{P}_r = -\frac{\partial \alpha_1}{\partial Q^r} = 0$$

which integrates to

28.198 $\qquad P_r = \alpha_r,$

a set of constants, one of which may be taken as α_1; we have

$$Q^r = \frac{\partial \alpha_1}{\partial P_r} = \frac{\partial \alpha_1}{\partial \alpha_r} = \delta_1^r,$$

using the Kronecker delta. This last equation integrates to

28.199 $\qquad Q^r = \delta_1^r t + \beta^r$

in which β^r are arbitrary constants. All the new coordinates and momenta are constants except

$$Q^1 = t + \beta^1.$$

Combining these results with the transforming Equations 28.190 and with the transforming function W^* instead of S, we have finally

$$P_r = \alpha_r$$

$$Q^r = \delta_1^r t + \beta^r = \frac{\partial W^*}{\partial \alpha_r}$$

28.200 $\qquad K^* = H^* = \alpha_1.$

This W^*-transformation, where W^* is time-independent and the Hamiltonian is unchanged and a constant of the motion, is quite different from the S-transformation where the transforming function is time-dependent and the new Hamiltonian is zero. Nevertheless, both Equations 28.194 and 28.197 are known as the Hamilton-Jacobi equation; S is known as Hamilton's *principal function* and W^* is known as Hamilton's *characteristic function*.

114. The Hamilton-Jacobi equation in the time-independent form of Equation 28.197 can be solved exactly in a few coordinate systems, provided the equation can be separated into three ordinary differential equations, each containing only one variable, in much the same way as the Laplace equation was solved in spheroidal coordinates in § 22–17. For example, the equation can be solved in spherical polar coordinates for the unperturbed potential $-\mu/r$; the transformed coordinates and momenta Q^r, P_r are then found to be the Delaunay variables. Plummer [13] gives a complete solution.

The Vinti Potential

115. Vinti [14] has shown that the Hamilton-Jacobi Equation 28.197, in the case of a time-independent potential, is separable in the spheroidal coordinates of § 22–10 and § 22–11, provided the potential has the form

$$\frac{b_0 \cot \alpha - b_1 \sin u}{\cot^2 \alpha + \sin^2 u}$$

---

[13] Plummer (Dover ed. of 1960), *An Introductory Treatise on Dynamical Astronomy*, original ed. of 1918, 142.

[14] Vinti (1959), "New Method of Solution for Unretarded Satellite Orbits," *Journal of Research of the National Bureau of Standards, Section B*, v. 63, 105–116; (1961), "Mean Motions in Conditionally Periodic Separable Systems," v. 65, 131–135; (1961), "Theory of an Accurate Intermediary Orbit for Satellite Astronomy," v. 65, 169–201; and (1962), "Intermediary Equatorial Orbits of an Artificial Satellite," v. 66, 5–13.

in which b_0, b_1 are arbitrary constants and the constant (ae) of the spheroidal coordinate system—not to be confused with the Kepler elements of any orbit—is also available as an arbitrary constant. For equatorial symmetry, the potential does not change for $\pm u$, and b_1 must be zero. The potential is then

$$\frac{b_0 \cot \alpha}{\cot^2 \alpha + \sin^2 u} = \frac{\frac{1}{2} i b_0}{i \cot \alpha - \sin u} + \frac{\frac{1}{2} i b_0}{i \cot \alpha + \sin u},$$

which can be expanded to within a scale constant by Heine's Theorem [15] as

$$i b_0 \sum_{n=0}^{\infty} (2n+1) Q_n (i \cot \alpha) P_n (\sin u) \qquad (n \text{ even}).$$

This result is transformed to spherical harmonics—for the same mass distribution, whatever that may be—by Equation 23.15 as

$$i b_0 \left(\frac{ae}{ir} - \frac{(ae)^3}{ir^3} P_2(\sin \phi) + \frac{(ae)^5}{ir^5} P_4(\sin \phi) - \ \ldots \right).$$

We may choose the harmonic of zero order to be $-\mu/r$ as usual if we make

28.201 $\qquad b_0 = -\dfrac{\mu}{ae};$

then, the potential is

$$-\frac{\mu}{r} \left\{ 1 - \left(\frac{ae}{r} \right)^2 P_2(\sin \phi) + \left(\frac{ae}{r} \right)^4 P_4(\sin \phi) - \ldots \right\}.$$

Also, we can make the second zonal harmonic the same as in the actual potential of the Earth, if we use Equation 28.180 and make

28.202 $\qquad (ae)^2 = -C_{20} = +a_e^2 J_2,$

which is Vinti's convention, so that finally the potential is

$$-\frac{\mu}{r} \left\{ 1 - \left(\frac{a_e}{r} \right)^2 J_2 P_2(\sin \phi) + \left(\frac{a_e}{r} \right)^4 J_2^2 P_4(\sin \phi) \right.$$
$$\left. - \left(\frac{a_e}{r} \right)^6 J_2^3 P_4(\sin \phi) + \ldots \right\}.$$

28.203

It is of interest to note that Equation 28.202 leads to a real spheroidal coordinate system only if J_2 (in Vinti's convention) is positive or if C_{20} (in our convention of Equation 21.035) is negative, but in the case of the actual Earth, this condition is met.

116. The transforming function W^* is obtained from the solution of the Hamilton-Jacobi equation

---

[15] Whittaker and Watson (reprint of 1962), *A Course of Modern Analysis*, 4th ed. of 1927, 321.

by Vinti in the form of elliptic integrals containing the constant momenta α_r, which appear during the process of separation; W^* is differentiated with respect to these constants to provide the transformed coordinates Q^r from Equations 28.200 also in the form of elliptic integrals. The constants α_r, β^r describe the motion completely in much the same way as initial values of the Delaunay variables do for the potential $-\mu/r$, although not as simply. Nor are the constants α_r, β^r as easily related to the Kepler elements, although this relation has been accomplished by Izsak [16] and Vinti.[17] The solution completely takes care of the large second zonal harmonic which causes trouble in the integration of the Gauss and Lagrange equations, but first-order perturbation methods are still necessary to evaluate the higher harmonics. The higher zonal harmonics are evaluated as differences from the corresponding harmonics in the Vinti potential.

The von Zeipel Transformation

117. Instead of making the transformed Hamiltonian zero as in § 28–111, the von Zeipel transformation of the canonical equations successively eliminates the time and the Delaunay angular variables from the Hamiltonian. In the final transformation represented by Equations 28.189, for example, the $\partial K^*/\partial Q^r$ are zero; therefore, the final momenta P_r are arbitrary constants. Working backward from the now-known P_r and $\dot{Q}^r$, we can, at any rate theoretically, recover the original p_r, q^r in terms of arbitrary constants which can be related to the starting conditions. The method has been used to account for the lower-order zonal harmonics, and is complicated enough in this favorable symmetrical case where explicit time and one Delaunay coordinate are absent in the initial Hamiltonian. (We have seen in Equation 28.172 that, in this axially symmetrical case, the Delaunay variable $H = N \cos i$ is constant in time; therefore, the Hamiltonian in Equations 28.164 cannot contain the Delaunay coordinate $h = \Omega$.) An outline description, covering only the C_{20}- or J_2-disturbing potential, is given by

[16] Izsak (1960), "A Theory of Satellite Motion About an Oblate Planet. I. A Second-Order Solution of Vinti's Dynamical Problem," *Smithsonian Institution Astrophysical Observatory. Research in Space Science. Special Report No. 52.*

[17] Vinti (1961), "The Formulae for an Accurate Intermediary Orbit of an Artificial Satellite," *The Astronomical Journal,* v. 66, 514–516; and (1966), "Invariant Properties of the Spheroidal Potential of an Oblate Planet," *Journal of Research of the National Bureau of Standards, Section B,* v. 70, 1–16.

Kaula;[18] a fuller description, including the application to other zonal harmonics, is given by Brouwer.[19]

DIFFERENTIAL OBSERVATION EQUATIONS – DIRECTION AND RANGE

118. A solution, which is more in line with current geodetic practice, is to assume an approximate orbit in much the same way as we start with approximate positions in a geodetic network adjustment. The "computed" value of an observed quantity is then obtained from this approximate model and enters the observed minus computed side of a differential observation equation. On the other side of the equation are various terms giving the effect on the observed quantity of the application of corrections to the approximate orbital elements. These terms are broken down into corrections to the gravitational constants assumed in the approximate orbit, together with a number of parameters in expressions for the drag, etc., which the solution is required to provide. The observation equations at different times to a number of satellites are then solved by least squares for the corrections and parameters. The method differs only from a normal geodetic adjustment in that the observations are made at different times to a moving object, so that the coefficients of the corrections will usually contain the time of observation. The approximate orbit is usually a Kepler ellipse perturbed by the large C_{20}- or J_2-gravitational term; this orbit ensures that corrections to the gravitational constants will be uniformly small.

119. The most useful observations to artificial satellites for geodetic purposes consist of:

(a) photography of the satellite against a stellar background with, for example, the Baker-Nunn tracking cameras or the BC-4 cameras used for satellite triangulation, as described in § 26–43 through § 26–66;

(b) ranging by radio; or, optical-distance measurement to the satellite using lasers; and

(c) range-rate measurement by Doppler-tracking systems or by continuous range measurement.
Other methods, such as measurement of horizontal and vertical angles to the satellite at a known time by kinetheodolite, for example, are generally less accurate, but the appropriate observation equa-

[18] Kaula, *op. cit. supra* note 3, 43–49.

[19] Brouwer (1959), "Solution of the Problem of Artificial Satellite Theory Without Drag," *The Astronomical Journal,* v. 64, 378–397.

tions can easily be formed if required by suitable modification of equations given in Chapter 26.

120. The reduction of photographic observations has already been fully treated in § 26–43 through § 26–66, although fewer refinements are usually required in orbital analysis. The end result consists of observational equations connecting observed minus computed plate or film measurements—or deduced right ascensions and declinations—with corrections to the Cartesian coordinates of the satellite and of the ground-tracking station, such as Equations 26.46 and 26.47. For range observations, we can use Equation 26.65. Although these equations were drawn up for the Earth-fixed A^r, B^r, C^r system, the equations apply equally well in the inertial $\bar{A}^r$, $\bar{B}^r$, C^r system, provided we replace the origin-hour angle H (as defined in § 26–32) by $(H + \theta)$ where θ is the sidereal time at the origin of longitudes in the Earth-fixed system—in other words, if we interpret H as right ascension. The inertial coordinates of the tracking station change as the Earth rotates and are different for each observation. To derive corrections to the Earth-fixed coordinates dx_0, dy_0 of the tracking station, we must replace the inertial coordinates x, y of the tracking station in the modified Equations 26.46, 26.47, and 26.65 by

28.204
$$\begin{pmatrix} x \\ y \end{pmatrix} = \begin{pmatrix} \cos\theta & -\sin\theta \\ \sin\theta & \cos\theta \end{pmatrix} \begin{pmatrix} x_0 \\ y_0 \end{pmatrix},$$

and must replace the inertial differentials dx, dy by

28.205
$$\begin{pmatrix} dx \\ dy \end{pmatrix} = \begin{pmatrix} \cos\theta & -\sin\theta \\ \sin\theta & \cos\theta \end{pmatrix} \begin{pmatrix} dx_0 \\ dy_0 \end{pmatrix}.$$

We can replace θ by $\bar{\omega}t$ in which $\bar{\omega}$ is the rotation rate of the Earth and t is elapsed time since the initial meridians of the Earth-fixed and inertial systems coincided. These transformations do not alter the Cartesian origin. Accordingly, if first harmonics are omitted from the expression for the potential used in forming the observation equations, the corrections dx_0, dy_0 to be found by solving the observation equations will give the final coordinates of the tracking station in relation to the center of mass as origin, as we have seen in § 21–42.

121. We are not interested in obtaining corrections to initial values of the inertial coordinates (x^r or ρ^r) of the satellite, which also would be quite different for each observation. Instead, we seek corrections to approximate values of the orbital elements (a, e, i, M, w, Ω), which would have been used to compute x^r from Equation 28.069 and so to obtain the computed value of the observed direc-

tion or range. The orbital elements (other than M) vary much more slowly than the Cartesian coordinates, and can be considered constant in first-order observational equations covering observations over considerable periods of time. Accordingly, we replace dx, for example, by

$$dx = \frac{\partial x}{\partial a} da + \frac{\partial x}{\partial e} de + \ldots$$

and use Equations 28.130 for the $\partial x / \partial a$, etc. Moreover, the corrections da, etc., to the orbital elements are themselves composed of:

(a) Corrections da_0 to the values assumed for the approximate orbit. If the approximate orbit takes account of certain perturbations, such as C_{20} or J_2, then the osculating elements of the approximate orbit will vary with time. Integration of the approximate orbit will give values of the elements $\bar{a}_0$ at a particular time t_0. If the time of observation t is very different, we may have to replace the correction da_0 in the observation equations by

$$d\bar{a}_0 + (\partial a / \partial t)_0 (t - t_0),$$

using the Gauss equations for $(\partial a / \partial t)$, etc., at t_0; that is, we have to substitute $\bar{a}_0$, etc., in the Gauss equations.

(b) Corrections arising from the Earth's gravitational perturbations. These may be obtained from the integrated Lagrange equations, such as Equation 28.187, by partial differentiation with respect to the C_{nm}, S_{nm}. The results will contain sine or cosine terms with arguments

$$(n - 2p)w + (n - 2p + q)M + m(\Omega - \theta).$$

Again, the elements will vary with time if the approximate orbit is not a Kepler ellipse (M will do so anyway). However, if the correcting terms are small, we can write the argument as

$$(n - 2p)(w_0 + \dot{w}\Delta t) + (n - 2p + q)(M_0 + \dot{M}\Delta t)$$
$$+ m\{\Omega_0 - \theta_0 + (\dot{\Omega} - \dot{\theta})\Delta t\}$$

where the zero suffix denotes the initial approximate value of the element at t_0, Δt is the time of the observation since t_0, and $\dot{w}$, $\dot{M}$, $\dot{\Omega}$ are considered constant; C_{20} or J_2 is now well enough known to be included in the approximate orbit, in which case the remaining terms, such as

$$\left(\frac{\partial \Omega}{\partial C_{nm}}\right) dC_{nm},$$

could then include such higher zonal and tesseral harmonics as can be handled by computer capacity.

(c) Other corrections to the elements arising from atmospheric drag, radiation pressure, and lunisolar perturbations. These corrections will be considered very briefly in the following three sections.

Drag

122. Correction terms to the Gauss or Lagrange equations for $\dot{a}$, $\dot{e}$, $\dot{w}$, and $\dot{M}$ have been given by Sterne[20] and applied by Izsak[21] to an atmospheric model in which the density decreases exponentially with height. More realistic high-altitude atmospheric models derived from satellite observations, which among other solar effects show a large diurnal bulge toward the Sun with a pronounced lag caused by the Earth's rotation, have been described by Jacchia,[22] by King-Hele,[23] and by Priester, Roemer, and Volland.[24] The results can be used to provide first-order corrections, such as

$$\Delta a = \dot{a}\Delta t,$$

to the preliminary values a_0 of the elements. However, it has been shown by Kaula[25] that the principal effect is a perturbation ΔM of the mean anomaly which can be described by a few terms of a polynomial in time as

$$\Delta M = p(\Delta t)^2 + q(\Delta t)^3 + \ldots$$

Kaula also obtains the drag perturbations Δa, Δe, Δw, $\Delta \Omega$ in terms of the same coefficients p, q, which can accordingly be considered as parameters or unknowns in the observation equations in much the same way as the atmospheric parameters K_1, K_2, K_3, K_4 (§ 26–58) are determined in the solution of the observation equations in satellite triangulation.

Radiation Pressure

123. Solar radiation pressure as a nongravitational force can have a considerable effect on the large, light, balloonlike satellites used for satellite triangulation, but, in that case, a correction is required

only for orbital prediction. The effect is much less on small, heavy satellites suitable for the determination of the gravitational field, but, nevertheless, some allowance must usually be made. The satellite is affected only in sunlight; this intermittent effect requires in practice some form of numerical integration or harmonic analysis designed to include discontinuity. The effect can then be integrated over the time covered by a batch of observations, and can be applied as a correction to the a_0, e_0, etc., adopted as constant for the batch. A complete treatment has been given by, among others, Musen[26] and by Walters, Koskela, and Arsenault.[27]

Lunisolar Perturbations

124. We have thus far considered only the attraction exerted by the Earth on the satellite, and we have justifiably assumed that the attraction exerted by the small satellite on the Earth has no effect on the motion of the Earth. However, if we introduce a massive body such as the Sun into the system, the effect on the motion of the Earth relative to the satellite is by no means negligible. The force of attraction on the Earth is $GM_SM_E/\bar{r}^2$ where M_S, M_E are, respectively, the masses of the Sun and the Earth and where $\bar{r}$ (fig. 36) is the distance between

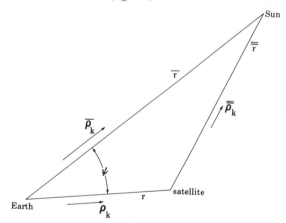

Figure 36.

the two bodies. We have assumed, as we can do because of the great distance $\bar{r}$, that the Earth can, for this purpose, be represented by a point mass at its center of mass (or a uniform sphere centered

[20] Sterne (1959), "Effect of the Rotation of a Planetary Atmosphere Upon the Orbit of a Close Satellite," *ARS* [*American Rocket Society*] *Journal*, v. 29, 777–782.

[21] Izsak (1960), "Periodic Drag Perturbations of Artificial Satellites," *The Astronomical Journal*, v. 65, 355–357.

[22] Jacchia (1960), "A Variable Atmospheric-Density Model from Satellite Accelerations," *Journal of Geophysical Research*, v. 65, 2775–2782.

[23] King-Hele (1964), *Theory of Satellite Orbits in an Atmosphere*.

[24] Priester, Roemer, and Volland (1967), "The Physical Behavior of the Upper Atmosphere Deduced from Satellite Drag Data," *Space Science Reviews*, v. 6, 707–780.

[25] Kaula, *op. cit. supra* note 3, 57–59.

[26] Musen (1960), "The Influence of the Solar Radiation Pressure on the Motion of an Artificial Satellite," *Journal of Geophysical Research*, v. 65, 1391–1396.

[27] Walters, Koskela, and Arsenault (1961), "Solar Radiation Pressure Perturbations," *Handbook of Astronautical Engineering*, 8–33, 8–34.

on the center of mass of the Earth). The Earth, along with the origin of the "inertial" coordinate system we have used throughout this book, is now subjected to an acceleration of $GM_S/\bar{r}^2$ toward the Sun; the coordinate system is no longer inertial, and the Newtonian equations of motion do not apply. However, we can restore the inertial system by applying an equal and opposite acceleration to all bodies in the system without affecting their relative motion. The satellite (of unit mass) is then subject to the following forces or accelerations:

(a) the attraction F_k of the Earth, whatever that may be (we do not assume that this force is directed toward the center of mass of the Earth);

(b) the attraction of the Sun $GM_S/\bar{\bar{r}}^2$ toward the center of mass of the Sun; and

(c) an acceleration of $GM_S/\bar{r}^2$, parallel to the direction of the Earth from the Sun, required to cancel the acceleration of the coordinate system.

The *disturbing* force on the satellite is the vector sum of (b) and (c), that is,

28.206 $$GM_S\left(\frac{\bar{\bar{\rho}}_k}{\bar{\bar{r}}^3} - \frac{\bar{\rho}_k}{\bar{r}^3}\right),$$

which is equivalent to a disturbing potential at the satellite of

$$-GM_S\left(\frac{1}{\bar{\bar{r}}} - \frac{\rho^j\bar{\rho}_j}{\bar{r}^3}\right),$$

as we can see at once by taking the negative gradient of the latter expression at the satellite with $\bar{\rho}_j$ fixed. Expansion of the disturbing potential, as in Equation 21.010, gives

$$-\frac{GM_S}{\bar{r}}\left(1 + \frac{r}{\bar{r}}\cos\psi\right.$$
$$+ \ldots \frac{r''}{\bar{r}''}P_n(\cos\psi)\ldots - \frac{r}{\bar{r}}\cos\psi\right)$$
$$= -\frac{GM_S}{\bar{r}}\left(1 + \frac{r^2}{\bar{r}^2}P_2(\cos\psi) + \ldots\right).$$

The term not containing ψ drops out on differentiation of the potential to form the equations of motion; the remaining terms of the order $(1/\bar{r}^3)$ are small, even though M_S is large.

125. Perturbation of the satellite by any number of other bodies, such as the Moon, can be handled by adding accelerations in the same way. Because the Newtonian equations of motion are linear, we can achieve the same result by considering the effect of each body in turn. The disturbing potential in each case can be expanded in spherical harmonics related to the inertial system, as in Equation 21.035, and so in terms of the orbital elements of the satellite and of the Sun (or Moon) in a double

series similar to Equation 28.184. The full expansion has been given by Kaula.[28] The same methods can then be used as for perturbations of the satellite by terms in the Earth's potential. However, it is now more usual to integrate the Cartesian equations of motion numerically for each small perturbation, using Equation 28.206.

DIFFERENTIAL OBSERVATION EQUATIONS – RANGE RATE

126. Continuous measurement of range to the satellite provides a measure of range rate. The range rate is also related to the Doppler frequency of signals emitted by the moving satellite and received by a ground station, after correction for atmospheric refraction and ionospheric refraction by a two-wavelength technique, although the large number of Doppler observations made on even a short orbital arc requires special initial treatment. Accordingly, we need a form of observation equation for the time rate of change of range, which we shall denote as P. If the inertial position vectors to the satellite and to the tracking station are ρ^r, $\bar{\rho}^r$, and if the range and unit vector from the tracking station to the satellite are s, u^r so that we have

28.207 $$su^r = \rho^r - \bar{\rho}^r,$$

then the range rate is the component of relative velocity in the direction u^r, giving

28.208 $$P = (\dot{\rho}^r - \dot{\bar{\rho}}^r)u_r.$$

Proceeding exactly as in § 26–5 and § 26–6, we find that we have

28.209 $$sd\mathrm{P} = (d\dot{\rho}^r - d\dot{\bar{\rho}}^r)(\rho_r - \bar{\rho}_r)$$
$$+ (p_k p_r + q_k q_r)(\dot{\rho}^k - \dot{\bar{\rho}}^k)(d\rho^r - d\bar{\rho}^r)$$

in which p_k, q_k are any unit vectors forming a right-handed orthogonal triad (u_k, p_k, q_k) with u_k — for example, the m_r, n_r of § 26–7 and § 26–8 evaluated in spherical polar coordinates. The position and velocity vectors of the satellite ρ_r, ρ^k are given by Equations 28.130 and 28.131 in terms of the orbital elements. Position and velocity vectors of the tracking station are easily obtained in terms of Earth-fixed coordinates (x_0, y_0, z_0) from Equation 28.204 in the form

28.210 $$\bar{\rho}^r = \begin{pmatrix} \cos\bar{\omega}t & -\sin\bar{\omega}t & 0 \\ \sin\bar{\omega}t & \cos\bar{\omega}t & 0 \\ 0 & 0 & 1 \end{pmatrix}\bar{\rho}_0^r$$

[28] Kaula (1962), "Development of the Lunar and Solar Disturbing Functions for a Close Satellite," *The Astronomical Journal*, v. 67, 300–303.

and

28.211 $\qquad \dot{\rho}^r = \tilde{\omega} \begin{pmatrix} -\sin \tilde{\omega}t & -\cos \tilde{\omega}t & 0 \\ \cos \tilde{\omega}t & -\sin \tilde{\omega}t & 0 \\ 0 & 0 & 0 \end{pmatrix} \bar{\rho}_0^r$

where t is elapsed time since the inertial and Earth-fixed meridians coincided.

127. Finally, we must express corrections to the position and velocity of the satellite in terms of corrections to the orbital elements as

$$d\rho^r = \frac{\partial \rho^r}{\partial a} \, da + \frac{\partial \rho^r}{\partial e} \, de + \ldots$$

$$d\dot{\rho}^r = \frac{\partial \dot{\rho}^r}{\partial a} \, da + \frac{\partial \dot{\rho}^r}{\partial e} \, de + \ldots,$$

and then substitute Equations 28.130 and 28.131. As in the case of the observation equations for direction and range, da, etc., are then expressed in terms of da_0, dC_{nm}, dS_{nm}, etc. Corrections to the position and velocity of the tracking station are expressed in terms of corrections to the Earth-fixed coordinates $\bar{\rho}_0^r$ by differentiating Equations 28.210 and 28.211 with the time fixed.

128. As in the case of the observation equations for direction and range, the omission of first-degree gravitational harmonics will ensure that corrections to the position of tracking stations are derived in an inertial or Earth-fixed system whose origin is located at the center of mass of the Earth. We have seen in § 21–57 that C_{21}- and S_{21}-harmonics should also be omitted, although for test purposes these harmonics are sometimes included and the results are compared with the theoretical zero. The large number of Doppler observations, which can be made on short arcs, makes this form of measurement particularly suitable, and indeed essential, for the determination of the tesseral harmonics.

THE VARIATIONAL METHOD

129. We shall now consider a different approach which yields no fresh results, but affords a deeper insight into the whole problem. So far, we have considered only one orbit, and have defined the linear velocity in this orbit alone. Now we consider velocity as a scalar in three dimensions, defined in some way in a domain surrounding the orbit; this we can do by supposing that the orbit is one of a family, all of whose members have some characteristic in common. We shall assume a time-independent potential V and shall choose the common

characteristic of the family to be the same constant energy α_1 or the Hamiltonian

28.212 $\qquad \frac{1}{2}v^2 + V = \alpha_1.$

Because the potential V is defined in space, so is v; we can introduce the space gradient v_r of v, which is not to be confused with the velocity vector vl_r in one of the orbits.

130. We can also transform the orbit space conformally with scale factor v to a space in which the line element is $d\bar{s}$ so that we have

28.213 $\qquad d\bar{s} = vds;$

the velocity vector transforms to

28.214 $\qquad \bar{l}_r = vl_r$

in accordance with Equation 10.13, provided we use the same coordinate system in both spaces. This transformation implies that the point corresponding to the satellite is traveling in the overbarred conformal space with velocity $\bar{l}_r$, that is, with constant (unit) linear velocity. We might suppose therefore that the line corresponding to the orbit is a geodesic of the conformal space, just as the free path of a point moving with uniform velocity in ordinary space is a straight line. At present, we introduce this geodesic property as a reasonable hypothesis; later we shall show that it is equivalent to Newton's second law.

131. It is evident that all members of the family of orbits will transform in the same way to a family of geodesics, which will cut orthogonally a family of geodesic parallel surfaces generated by assigning different (constant) values to a scalar M^*, as in § 10–19 and § 10–20. Given the family of geodesics, it is always possible to construct one surface which cuts the family orthogonally; the other geodesic parallels are then constructed by joining points at equal distances along the geodesics from the initial surface.

132. We can now use any of the results in Chapter 10. Corresponding to Equation 10.27, the equations of the orbits can be written in the vector form

28.215 $\qquad M_r^* = vl_r = \bar{l}_r.$

From this last equation, we have

$$\frac{\partial M^*}{\partial \bar{s}} = M_r^* \bar{l}^r = 1$$

so that M^* is the distance between geodesic parallel surfaces ($M^* = $ constant) measured along the geodesics, as we found in § 10–19. We can rewrite Equation 28.213 as

$$M^* = \int v\,ds = \int v^2\,dt.$$

Because the length of a geodesic is, in general, less than the length of any other neighboring curve joining two fixed points, we can say that the value of the integral

$$\int v\,ds = \int v^2\,dt$$

between two fixed points on an orbit is less if taken along the orbit than along any neighboring path between the fixed points. This is the classical *principle of least action*, which is now seen to be equivalent to the geodesic property in the conformal transformation. We can call M^*, integrated along a section of the orbit, the *action*.

133. The acceleration vector is given by intrinsic differentiation of Equation 28.215 as

$$\frac{\delta(vl_r)}{\delta t} = M^*_{rs}\frac{dx^s}{dt} = vM^*_{rs}l^s.$$

Because M^* is a scalar, we have $M^*_{rs} = M^*_{sr}$ and also

$$\frac{\delta(vl_r)}{\delta t} = vM^*_{sr}l^s = v(vl_s)_r l^s = vv_r + v^2 l_{sr}l^s$$

in which the last term is zero by Equation 3.19, so that we have

28.216 $\qquad \dfrac{\delta(vl_r)}{\delta t} = vv_r = (\tfrac{1}{2}v^2)_r = -V_r$

by using Equation 28.212; this last equation is Newton's second law as expressed in Equation 28.006 (in which, however, v_r is the velocity vector and is not the gradient of the linear velocity). Accordingly, the geodesic principle, the principle of least action, and Newton's second law are all three equivalent.

134. Another way of demonstrating the equivalence of the principle of least action and Newton's second law is to write

$$v^2 = (\tfrac{1}{2}v^2 + V) + (\tfrac{1}{2}v^2 - V)$$
$$= \alpha_1 + L^*$$

where L^* is the Lagrangian, defined in Equation 28.029, and α_1 is the constant energy of Equation 28.212. The principle of least action is accordingly equivalent to the assertion that

$$\int (\alpha_1 + L^*)\,dt$$

is a minimum for the actual orbit, compared with any neighboring curve between the same points. The Euler-Lagrange equations in the calculus of variations, expressing the condition for this integral to be a minimum, are the same as the Lagrangian equations of motion in Equation 28.030, which we have seen are equivalent to the Newtonian equations of motion.

135. Equation 28.216 can also be written as

$$\frac{\delta(vl_r)}{\delta s} = v_r$$

in which v_r is the gradient of v and s is the arc length of the orbit. This last equation is entirely analogous to Equation 24.07 for the path of a light ray in a medium of refractive index μ. Instead of v in the dynamical problem, we write c/v from Equation 24.01 in the optical problem. We are not at present concerned to reconcile these two problems further.

136. From Equation 28.215, we have

28.217 $\qquad \nabla M^* = g^{rs}M^*_r M^*_s = v^2 g^{rs}l_r l_s = v^2$

because l_r is a unit vector. This result should be compared with the eikonal Equation 24.05 in the optical analogy. Substituting Equation 28.217 in Equation 28.212, we have

$$V + \tfrac{1}{2}\nabla M^* = \alpha_1;$$

this equation is the Hamilton-Jacobi Equation 28.197 for a time-independent potential, if we take M^*, with any of its various meanings, as the transforming function or Hamilton's characteristic function in the Hamilton-Jacobi theory. Moreover, in all cases where we can solve the Hamilton-Jacobi equation for M^*, we can differentiate the result in any coordinate system, can substitute in Equation 28.215, and can obtain components of the velocity vector in the same system as a complete first integral of the equations of motion. This approach offers a more geometrical alternative to the canonical solution.

137. Unfortunately, there seems to be no obvious way within the framework of Riemannian three-dimensional geometry to extend this conception to time-dependent potentials. For example, in the geodetic case of a uniformly rotating unsymmetrical field, we could replace Equation 28.212 by Equation 28.174 as a means of defining scalar velocity; but this course at once introduces a preferred direction as well, that is, the tangent to the orbit, which takes the problem out of point transformations into contact transformations. On the other hand, if we

replace Equation 28.212 by Equation 28.028, that is, by the first integral of the equations of motion referred to rotating axes, we are able to define scalar velocity in the rotating space without the introduction of a preferred direction, but this course does not lead to the correct equations of motion referred to rotating axes. The fact remains that the whole conception of least action as we have defined it is Newtonian, and the equations of motion referred to accelerated (rotating) axes are not Newtonian.

CHAPTER 29

Integration of Gravity Anomalies— The Poisson-Stokes Approach

GENERAL REMARKS

1. In 1849, Stokes produced his classical paper [1] on the determination of the potential at points on a nearly spherical surface by integrating values of gravity or gravity anomalies over that surface. Much work has been done by geodesists on the extension and application of Stokes' result to such problems as determining the form of the geoid and the deflection of the vertical—with the object of transforming astronomical to geodetic coordinates—which has resulted in a considerable literature where the basic equations are not always proved or critically examined. As in Chapter 28, we shall accordingly concentrate on deriving the basic equations, and shall indicate methods of solution in bare outline only. Some modern applications are based on even earlier work by Poisson who determined the potential in a field external to a sphere from given boundary values of the potential over that sphere. A considerable simplification of the subject results from deriving Poisson's and Stokes' integrals by the same method, and we shall therefore approach the subject in this way.

SURFACE INTEGRALS OF SPHERICAL HARMONICS

2. We shall require and shall collect here for easy reference some well-known formulas for the integrals of products of spherical harmonics over the surface of a sphere of unit radius or over the whole

solid angle subtended at the origin. If $d\Omega$ is an element of solid angle, if $d\phi$, $d\omega$ are, respectively, elements of (geocentric) latitude and longitude in a spherical polar coordinate system, and if Y is the integrand, these two equivalent forms of integration can be written as

29.01 $$\int Y d\Omega = \int_{\omega=0}^{2\pi} \int_{\phi=-\pi/2}^{\pi/2} Y \cos \phi \, d\phi d\omega.$$

We shall also use the following abbreviations for spherical harmonics,

$$\{u_n^m\} = P_n^m(\sin \phi)(C_{nm} \cos m\omega + S_{nm} \sin m\omega)$$

29.02

$$\{\bar{u}_n^m\} = P_n^m(\sin \phi)(\bar{C}_{nm} \cos m\omega + \bar{S}_{nm} \sin m\omega),$$

29.03

including the case $m = 0$ as

29.04 $$\{u_n\} = C_{n0}P_n(\sin \phi).$$

In these expressions, the braces are intended to show that u_n^m is not necessarily a tensor and that the summation convention is not applied to the index m on the right side of Equations 29.02 and 29.03. Summation will be indicated as, for example,

$$\sum_{n=0}^{\infty} \sum_{m=0}^{n} \{u_n^m\} \quad \text{or} \quad \sum_{n, m} \{u_n^m\}.$$

3. The following results are then easily derivable from the standard mathematical texts,

$$\int \{u_n^m\} \{\bar{u}_q^p\} d\Omega = 0 \text{ if } (m, p) \text{ are different}$$

29.05 or if (n, q) are different.

---

[1] Stokes (1849), "On the Variation of Gravity at the Surface of the Earth," *Transactions of the Cambridge Philosophical Society*, v. 8, 672–695.

The only nonzero values of the integral are

$$\int \{u_n^m\} \{\bar{u}_n^m\} d\Omega = \frac{2\pi}{(2n+1)} \frac{(n+m)!}{(n-m)!} (C_{nm}\bar{C}_{nm} + S_{nm}\bar{S}_{nm})$$

29.06 $(m \neq 0)$

and

$$\int \{u_n\} \{\bar{u}_n\} d\Omega = \frac{4\pi}{(2n+1)} C_{n0}\bar{C}_{n0} \qquad (m=0).$$

29.07

Special cases of these formulas are easily obtained by giving the C's and S's particular values, for example,

$$\int [P_n^m(\sin\phi)\cos m\omega]^2 d\Omega = \int [P_n^m(\sin\phi)\sin m\omega]^2 d\Omega$$
$$= \frac{2\pi}{(2n+1)} \frac{(n+m)!}{(n-m)!}$$

29.08 $(m \neq 0)$

29.09 $\int [P_n(\sin\phi)]^2 d\Omega = \frac{4\pi}{(2n+1)}.$

4. Another important integral can be obtained more directly than in most of the literature. In figure 37, $\bar{P}$ is a *fixed* point in (geocentric) longitude

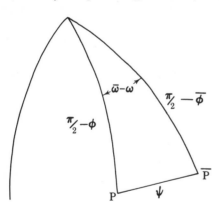

Figure 37.

and latitude $(\bar{\omega}, \bar{\phi})$, P is a current point at (ω, ϕ), and the angular distance between the two is given by

$$\cos\psi = \sin\phi \sin\bar{\phi} + \cos\phi \cos\bar{\phi} \cos(\bar{\omega}-\omega).$$

The expression $\{u_n^m\}$ is the value at P of a spherical harmonic, defined over the whole solid angle, and we require the value of the integral

$$\int \{u_n^m\} P_n(\cos\psi) d\Omega.$$

Using the expression for $\{u_n^m\}$ given by Equation 29.02 and the Addition theorem for $P_n(\cos\psi)$ in terms of ϕ, $\bar{\phi}$, etc., and taking $(\bar{\phi}, \bar{\omega})$ as constant

during the integration, we find without difficulty, on using Equation 29.08, that we have

$$\int \{u_n^m\} P_n(\cos\psi) d\Omega = \frac{4\pi}{2n+1} P_n^m(\sin\bar{\phi})(C_{nm}\cos m\bar{\omega}$$
$$+ S_{nm}\sin m\bar{\omega}$$

29.10 $= \frac{4\pi}{2n+1} \{u_n^m\}_{\bar{P}}$

where $\{u_n^m\}_{\bar{P}}$ is the value of the spherical harmonic at $\bar{P}$. This result also holds for $m = 0$.

SERIES EXPANSIONS

5. The summations of some infinite series containing Legendre functions are required in this subject and are easily obtained from the following well-known formula, which is often considered to be the defining equation of the Legendre functions,

29.11 $\dfrac{1}{(1-2k\cos\psi+k^2)^{1/2}} = \displaystyle\sum_{n=0}^{\infty} k^n P_n(\cos\psi).$

This equation is absolutely and uniformly convergent if $k < 1$ (see, for example, § 21–11). Usually k is considered a constant, but because the equation is true for all values of $k < 1$, we can consider k to be an independent variable—independent, that is, of ψ—so that the equation can be differentiated with respect to k.

6. If we differentiate Equation 29.11 with respect to k, multiply the result by $2k$, and add to the original equation, we have

$$\frac{(1-k^2)}{(1-2k\cos\psi+k^2)^{3/2}} = \sum_{n=0}^{\infty} (2n+1)k^n P_n(\cos\psi),$$

29.12

which can be expressed in the equivalent form

$$\sum_{n=2}^{\infty} (2n+1)k^{n-2}P_n(\cos\psi) = \frac{1}{k^2}\left[\frac{(1-k^2)}{(1-2k\cos\psi+k^2)^{3/2}}\right.$$
$$\left. -1-3k\cos\psi\right].$$

Integration of this equation with respect to k between the limits k, 0, using the standard forms contained in most tables of integrals, gives

$$\sum_{n=2}^{\infty} \frac{(2n+1)}{(n-1)} k^{n-1}P_n(\cos\psi) = \left[\frac{1}{k} - \frac{1-6k\cos\psi+3k^2}{k\Phi^{1/2}}\right.$$
$$\left. -3\cos\psi \ln(2-2k\cos\psi+2\Phi^{1/2})\right]_0^k$$

in which, for brevity, we have written

29.13 $\Phi = (1 - 2k \cos \psi + k^2)$.

After expansion and some manipulation, the value of the expression within brackets for $k = 0$ is found to be

$$(5 \cos \psi - 3 \cos \psi \ln 4)$$

so that we have finally

$$S(k, \psi) = \sum_{n=2}^{\infty} \frac{(2n+1)}{(n-1)} k^{n+1} P_n(\cos \psi)$$

$$= k - 5k^2 \cos \psi$$

$$- k(1 - 6k \cos \psi + 3k^2)/\Phi^{1/2}$$

29.14 $-3k^2 \cos \psi \ln \tfrac{1}{2}(1 - k \cos \psi + \Phi^{1/2})$.

7. The basic Equation 29.11, considered as a power series in k, can be differentiated term-by-term, and the differentiated series has the same radius of convergence $k < 1$. The subsequent operations of deriving Equation 29.12 do not affect convergence, and Equation 29.12 is accordingly convergent for $k < 1$. The series in Equation 29.14 is also convergent for $k < 1$ because each term is less than the corresponding term in Equation 29.12.

8. The case $k = 1$ requires some proof, which we shall not consider, of at least conditional convergence, except at the point $\psi = 0$. Assuming such a degree of convergence, Equation 29.14 reduces to

$$S(\psi) = \sum_{n=2}^{\infty} \frac{(2n+1)}{(n-1)} P_n(\cos \psi)$$

$$= 1 - 5 \cos \psi - (2 - 3 \cos \psi) \operatorname{cosec} \tfrac{1}{2}\psi$$

29.15 $-3 \cos \psi \ln (\sin \tfrac{1}{2}\psi + \sin^2 \tfrac{1}{2}\psi)$,

known in gravimetric geodesy as Stokes' function, with the symbol $S(\psi)$. For a particular value of k, which we shall consider in § 29–31, the expression in Equation 29.14 is known as Pizzetti's extension of Stokes' function. However, the even more general Equation 29.14 is simply an identity, although this identity does have important applications in gravimetry.

9. We shall also require two other expansions which can easily be obtained by integration of Equation 29.11, using the identity

$$\frac{(2n+1)}{(n+1)} = 2 - \frac{1}{(n+1)}.$$

These expansions, which are similar to Equations 29.14 and 29.15, are

$$\bar{S}(k, \psi) = \sum_{n=0}^{\infty} \frac{(2n+1)}{(n+1)} k^{n+1} P_n(\cos \psi)$$

29.16 $= \dfrac{2k}{\Phi^{1/2}} - \ln\left(\dfrac{\Phi^{1/2} + k - \cos \psi}{1 - \cos \psi}\right)$,

in which Φ is given by Equation 29.13, and

$$\bar{S}(\psi) = \sum_{n=0}^{\infty} \frac{(2n+1)}{(n+1)} P_n(\cos \psi)$$

29.17 $= \operatorname{cosec} \tfrac{1}{2}\psi - \ln (1 + \operatorname{cosec} \tfrac{1}{2}\psi)$.

These modified functions are convergent to the same extent as Equations 29.14 and 29.15.

INTRODUCTION OF THE STANDARD FIELD

Potential Anomaly

10. If the actual potential is W and if the standard potential—usually the potential of the standard field described in Chapter 23—is U, the difference

29.18 $T = W - U$

is known as the *potential anomaly*. Because the actual and standard fields are supposed to be rotating about the same axis with the same angular velocity $\bar{\omega}$, the terms in the geopotentials containing $\bar{\omega}$ cancel; and it is immaterial whether W, U are both attraction potentials or both geopotentials. In either case, the potential anomaly T is harmonic. By suitable choice of the standard field, T can be made a small quantity more amenable to approximate solutions. In the literature, T is usually called the disturbing potential, which is too easily confused with the disturbing or perturbing potential affecting satellite orbits (§ 28–38).

Curvature and Deflection

11. At a point P in space (fig. 38), the unit normals to the actual and standard equipotential surfaces, respectively, are ν^r, $\bar{\nu}^r$. The unit vector $\bar{\bar{\nu}}^r$ in figure 38, which is not necessarily in the same plane as ν^r, $\bar{\nu}^r$, is the unit normal to the coordinate surface through P. We shall assume in this section that $\bar{\bar{\nu}}^r$ refers to the geodetic (ω, ϕ, h) system in which the meridian and parallel vectors will be denoted by $\bar{\bar{\mu}}^r$, $\bar{\bar{\lambda}}^r$. We shall also assume that the standard field is as described in Chapter 23 and that the equipotential spheroid coincides with the base spheroid of the coordinate system. From Equation 19.42, we then have in the notation of figure 38

$$\Delta^r = \nu^r - \bar{\bar{\nu}}^r \backsimeq (\cos \phi \; \delta\omega)\bar{\bar{\lambda}}^r + (\delta\phi)\bar{\bar{\mu}}^r = \eta\bar{\bar{\lambda}}^r + \xi\bar{\bar{\mu}}^r$$

29.19

where Δ^r is the astronomical minus the geodetic deflection vector and $\delta\omega$ ($\delta\phi$) is the astronomical

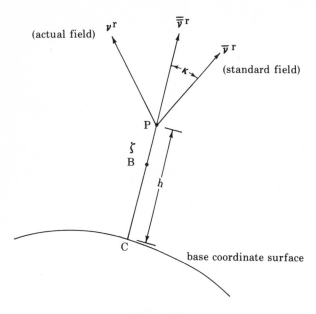

Figure 38.

minus the geodetic longitude (latitude). In this equation, $\delta\omega$, $\delta\phi$ are supposed to be small, and the equation holds true to the first order in these quantities. The first-order meridian and parallel components of deflection are denoted by ξ, η, as usual in the literature.

12. We shall call the angle κ between $\bar{\nu}^r$ and $\bar{\bar{\nu}}^r$ the *standard curvature correction* because it arises from the curvature of the standard line of force when the base coordinate surface is a standard equipotential. There are several ways of finding κ from the geometry of the standard field. One method is to convert the geodetic coordinates of P to geocentric coordinates, compute the latitude of the standard line of force ($\bar{\nu}^r$) at the same time as standard gravity from Equations 23.40 and 23.41, and subtract from the geodetic latitude of P to obtain the curvature correction κ. With the sign convention of figure 38, we then have

29.20 $\qquad \bar{\nu}^r = \bar{\bar{\nu}}^r \cos\kappa - \bar{\bar{\mu}}^r \sin\kappa.$

The meridian component of standard gravity γ, given by g_m in Equation 23.37 for a spheroidal field, is

$$U_r\bar{\bar{\mu}}^r = \gamma\bar{\nu}_r\bar{\bar{\mu}}^r = -\gamma\sin\kappa,$$

which is another way of computing κ. If the base coordinate surface is a standard equipotential, κ is zero on that surface and is also zero along the axes of symmetry of the standard field.

Gradient of the Potential Anomaly

13. By differentiating the scalar Equation 29.18, we have

29.21 $\qquad T_r = W_r - U_r = g\nu_r - \gamma\bar{\nu}_r$

where W, U are now considered to be geopotentials and g, γ are, respectively, actual and standard gravity. In this equation, we have used Equation 20.05 and the physical definition of the potential (§ 20–3). Equations 29.19 and 29.20 enable us to express the gradient of the potential anomaly in terms of the geodetic parallel, meridian, and normal vectors as

$$T_r = (g\eta)\bar{\lambda}_r + (g\xi + \gamma\sin\kappa)\bar{\bar{\mu}}_r + (g - \gamma\cos\kappa)\bar{\bar{\nu}}_r.$$
29.22

This equation is exact within the first-order definition of (ξ, η). At points not too far removed from the Earth's surface, the curvature correction κ will be no larger than the deflection components, and to the same degree of accuracy we can write

29.23 $\qquad T_r \simeq (g\eta)\bar{\lambda}_r + g(\xi + \kappa)\bar{\bar{\mu}}_r + (g - \gamma)\bar{\bar{\nu}}_r.$

Equations 29.22 and 29.23 hold true for any (ω, ϕ, h) coordinate system, provided that $\bar{\lambda}_r$, $\bar{\bar{\mu}}_r$, $\bar{\bar{\nu}}_r$ are the parallel, meridian, and normal vectors of the system and provided that the deflections and curvature correction refer to the same system. For example, in a spherical polar system, $\bar{\bar{\nu}}_r$ is the unit radius vector and Equation 29.19 gives ξ, η as the meridian and parallel components of the astronomical zenith in the spherical polar system. The vector $\bar{\lambda}_r$ is the same in the spherical polar system as in the geodetic system, but the meridian vector $\bar{\bar{\mu}}_r$ is not the same; the deflection component η is the same, but $(\xi + \kappa)$ is not the same; and if κ is ignored, as usual in the literature, then the meridian deflection ξ is not the same.

Gravity Disturbance

14. We define the *gravity disturbance* at the point P as

29.24 $\qquad g_D = g - \gamma.$

Equation 29.23 then shows that we have

29.25 $\qquad g_D = T_r\bar{\bar{\nu}}^r = \partial T/\partial h;$

that is, the gravity disturbance is the component of the gradient of the potential anomaly in the direction of the geodetic normal. In the literature, the gravity disturbance is usually denoted by δg, which, however, might be confused in this book with any increment of g.

15. If the potential anomaly is expressible in spherical harmonics as

$$T = \sum_{n,\,m} \{T_n^m\}/r^{n+1},$$

then the radial component of the gradient is

$$\frac{\partial T}{\partial r} = -\sum_{n,\,m} \frac{(n+1)\{T_n^m\}}{r^{n+2}}.$$

The geodetic normal can be considered as not far removed from the radius vector in the case of the Earth, and the gravity disturbance will, in any case, be a small quantity if the standard field has been chosen close to the actual field. Subject to these approximations, we can combine the last equation with Equation 29.25 and can write

29.26 $\qquad g_D \simeq -\sum_{n,\,m} (n+1)\{T_n^m\}/r^{n+2}.$

Gravity Anomaly

16. The actual potential at P (fig. 38) is W_P. From formulas given in Chapter 23 or from tables based on these formulas, we can find a number of points where the standard potential U is equal to W_P, and we choose such a point B in the direction of the geodetic normal $\bar{\bar{\nu}}^r$ so that $W_P = U_B$. The *gravity anomaly* is then defined as

29.27 $\qquad g_A = g_P - \gamma_B,$

and the length $BP = \zeta$ is known as the *height anomaly*. The gravity anomaly g_A is usually denoted by Δg, which can, however, be confused in this book with a Laplacian. To a first order, we have

$$W_P = T_P + U_P = T_P + U_B + (\partial U/\partial h)_B \zeta,$$

and because $W_P = U_B$, this equation reduces to

$$T_P \simeq -(\partial U/\partial h)_B \zeta.$$

If we ignore the distinction between $\bar{\bar{\nu}}^r$ and $\bar{\nu}^r$, which means neglecting the curvature correction, we have

29.28 $\qquad T_P \simeq -\gamma_B \zeta,$

usually known as Bruns' equation. Very often this equation is approximated further by assuming that $\gamma_B = \gamma_P$, so that at any point in space we have

29.29 $\qquad T \simeq -\gamma \zeta.$

17. Next, we combine Equations 29.24 and 29.25 to give to first-order accuracy

$$\left(\frac{\partial T}{\partial h}\right)_P = g_P - \gamma_P = g_P - \gamma_B - \left(\frac{\partial \gamma}{\partial h}\right)_B \zeta$$

$$= g_A - \left(\frac{\partial \gamma}{\partial h}\right)_B \zeta = g_A + \left(\frac{\partial \gamma}{\partial h}\right)_B \frac{T}{\gamma_B}.$$

We assume further that PB is small and ignore the distinction between P and B in this last equation, which becomes then for any point in space

29.30 $\qquad g_A \simeq \dfrac{\partial T}{\partial h} - \left(\dfrac{\partial \ln \gamma}{\partial h}\right) T.$

Equation 29.30 is usually known in the literature as the "fundamental equation of physical geodesy." All the approximations in this formula are covered by the single assumption that the potential anomaly T is small. One further approximation is often made. If we ignore the centrifugal part of the standard potential, which is then harmonic, and confuse $\bar{\bar{\nu}}^r$ with $\bar{\nu}^r$ (fig. 38), we have from Equation 20.17

$$\frac{\partial \ln \gamma}{\partial h} = 2H$$

where H is the mean curvature of the standard equipotential surface. Moreover, the standard field differs little from a spherically symmetrical field in which we have $2H = -2/r$, so that we can write

29.31 $\qquad g_A \simeq \dfrac{\partial T}{\partial r} + \dfrac{2T}{r}.$

We should obtain the same result from Equation 29.30 by assuming that the standard field is static and spherically symmetrical with a potential of minus μ/r.

18. If T is expressed in spherical harmonics as

$$T = \sum_{n,\,m} \{T_n^m\}/r^{n+1}$$

where $\{T_n^m\}$ is given by Equation 29.02, substitution in Equation 29.31 gives for each harmonic

$$\{g_{A\,n}^{\,m}\} = -\frac{(n+1)\{T_n^m\}}{r^{n+2}} + \frac{2\{T_n^m\}}{r^{n+2}} = -\frac{(n-1)\{T_n^m\}}{r^{n+2}}.$$

29.32

This formula was first obtained by Stokes,[2] who made equivalent but different assumptions in deriving it. Summing over m, n, we have

29.33 $\qquad g_A = -\sum_{n,\,m} \dfrac{(n-1)\{T_n^m\}}{r^{n+2}}.$

[2] Stokes, *op. cit. supra* note 1, 693.

19. Various interpretations are given to the points P, B in figure 38, subject to the requirement $W_P = U_B$. For example, P is often a point on the geoid and B is a point on the standard spheroidal equipotential, an interpretation which implies that the geoid and spheroid must have the same potential. In that case, measurements of gravity made on the topographic surface are reduced to corresponding values at P on the geoid by making various assumptions about crustal densities.[3] The value of standard gravity at B on the spheroid is subtracted to give the gravity anomaly. In Chapter 30, we shall take P as a point on the topographic surface of the Earth, in which case the locus of the point B is a surface named by Hirvonen the *telluroid*. To compute the gravity anomaly in this case, W_P would have to be measured by spirit leveling.

20. We may wonder why the more complicated gravity anomaly is used in preference to the simpler, and more logically geometrical, gravity disturbance which compares the two fields at the same point in space. One reason is that, in the earlier applications, P is a point on the geoid and tables of standard gravity are required only for points on the equipotential spheroid to compute the gravity anomaly. Another reason is that the geodetic height h is initially known only approximately—in fact, one of the objects of the whole exercise is to find h—so that we cannot calculate standard gravity accurately at P. These arguments are less significant today when standard gravity is readily calculable at any point in space and when h can be, and usually is, found by successive approximation. If the gravity disturbance is used, some iterative procedure, starting with approximate values of geodetic heights, would be necessary and would probably require more computation than the use of the gravity anomaly; there is no certainty that the operation would converge, but this has not yet (1968) been fully investigated. Equation 29.30 for the gravity anomaly has the form of one of the boundary conditions of classical potential theory, and this fact has probably attracted theoretical investigators. However, Equation 29.25 is a much simpler boundary condition and is more accurate.

THE SPHERICAL STANDARD FIELD

21. It will be apparent throughout this chapter and Chapter 30 that this branch of geodesy could be simplified by using spherical polar coordinates

[3] See also § 29–42. For full details, see Heiskanen and Moritz (1967), *Physical Geodesy*, 126–159.

and a spherically symmetrical standard field instead of the geodetic system. If all the standard equipotentials are to be spheres, we can eliminate the leading term in the attraction potential from the potential anomaly by suitable choice of constants in the formulas of § 20–24, but we cannot eliminate the centrifugal term. However, we can eliminate both terms by making one equipotential surface a sphere which coincides with the base surface of the spherical polar system $(r = R)$. In that case, the standard geopotential is symmetrical about the z-axis and is given by Equation 23.01 as

$$-U = \sum_{n=0}^{\infty} \frac{GC_{n0}P_n(\sin\phi)}{r^{n+1}} + \tfrac{1}{3}\tilde{\omega}^2 r^2 - \tfrac{1}{3}\tilde{\omega}^2 r^2 P_2(\sin\phi).$$

29.34

If the geopotential is to be constant (U_0) for all values of the spherical polar latitude ϕ over the base sphere $(r = R)$, we must have

$$-U_0 = GC_{00}/R + \tfrac{1}{3}\tilde{\omega}^2 R^2$$

29.35 $$0 = GC_{20}/R^3 - \tfrac{1}{3}\tilde{\omega}^2 R^2,$$

and all other C_{n0} must be zero. For the leading term to be the same as the leading term in the actual potential, we must have C_{00} equal to M—the total mass of the Earth. The centrifugal terms will cancel in the potential anomaly if the origin of spherical polar coordinates lies on the axis of rotation. The first harmonics (absent in the standard potential) will not appear in the potential anomaly if the origin is located at the actual center of gravity; this condition is compatible with cancellation of the centrifugal terms. If the standard geopotential U_0 of the base sphere is to be equal to the actual geopotential W_0 of the geoid, this requirement would settle the value of R in accordance with the first equation of Equations 29.35. Standard gravity and the latitude of the tangent to the standard line of force, and thus the curvature correction, are given by Equations 23.02 and 23.03 or by Equations 23.04 and 23.05. All the formulas and remarks in the last four subsections (§ 29–11 through § 29–20) apply if we use the elements of this spherical system in place of the geodetic system, provided we use one complete system or the other. The disadvantage of this spherical system, compared with the use of geodetic coordinates and a spheroidal standard field, is that the anomalies and meridian deflections are generally larger, although probably still within the limits of the usual first-order assumptions; there is not the same necessity in this branch of geodesy as there is in satellite geodesy (§ 28–101) to provide a model field which eliminates most of the second harmonics. We could, of course, choose a sphere as base coordinate surface and a spheroid as standard equipotential, but, in that case, the angle κ in figure 38 will be large in mid-latitudes, and Equations 29.25 and 29.30 for the gravity disturbance and the gravity anomaly might no longer be sufficiently accurate; nothing would be gained.

POISSON'S INTEGRAL

22. We shall now suppose that values of a harmonic function H are given at all points Q (fig. 39)

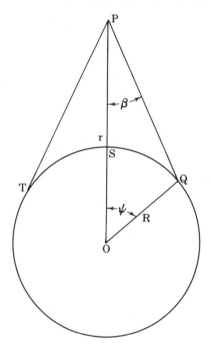

Figure 39.

on the surface of a sphere of radius R. We suppose that H is defined at all points outside as well as on the sphere, and we must find the value of the harmonic function at a point P outside the sphere at a distance r from the center O of the sphere. The angle between OQ and OP is shown as ψ in figure 39, and the distance PQ is shown as l.

23. First, we put $k = R/r$ in Equation 29.12 to give

29.36 $\qquad \dfrac{(r^2 - R^2)}{l^3} = \sum_{n=0}^{\infty} (2n+1) \dfrac{R^n}{r^{n+1}} P_n(\cos \psi).$

Next, we suppose that H is expressible as a convergent series of spherical harmonics with O as origin so that we have

29.37 $\qquad H_Q = \sum_{n=0}^{\infty} \sum_{m=0}^{n} \{H_n^m\}/R^{n+1}.$

Multiplying these last two equations, integrating over the whole solid angle, and using Equation 29.10 on the right-hand side give

29.38 $\qquad \int \dfrac{(r^2 - R^2)}{l^3} H_Q d\Omega = \sum_{n=0}^{\infty} \sum_{m=0}^{n} \dfrac{4\pi R^n}{r^{n+1}} \dfrac{\{H_n^m\}_S}{R^{n+1}}$

in which we have interchanged the order of summation and integration on the right, and $\{H_n^m\}_S$ is the value of the spherical harmonic $\{H_n^m\}$ at S on the radius vector to P (fig. 39). Because P is fixed during the integration, r and the spherical radius R are both constant during the integration. But $\{H_n^m\}$ contains only geocentric latitude and longitude, which are the same at P and S, so that we have

$$\{H_n^m\}_S = \{H_n^m\}_P.$$

Moreover, the value of H at P is

$$H_P = \sum_{n=0}^{\infty} \sum_{m=0}^{n} \{H_n^m\}_P/r^{n+1}$$

so that Equation 29.38 reduces finally to

29.39 $\qquad H_P = \dfrac{R}{4\pi} \int \dfrac{(r^2 - R^2)}{l^3} H_Q d\Omega,$

known as Poisson's integral.

24. This important result enables us, for example, to determine the attraction potential H_P at any point in space external to a sphere from the boundary values H_Q of the attraction potential on the sphere. We have assumed that H is expressible in a convergent series of spherical harmonics in the space external to the sphere, which, as we have seen in §21–11, implies that the sphere contains all the mass. Poisson's integral may be obtained without using spherical harmonics,[4] but the potential must be assumed to be regular outside the sphere, which again is equivalent to the assumption that there are no masses outside the sphere.

25. Equation 29.39 applies to any harmonic function H which is regular outside the sphere, and many useful formulas may be derived by giving H special values. For example, if H is the reciprocal of the radius vector, we have, in the notation of figure 39,

$$\frac{1}{r} = \frac{R}{4\pi} \int \frac{(r^2 - R^2)}{l^3} \frac{d\Omega}{R};$$

---

[4] See, for example, Bateman (Dover ed. of 1944), *Partial Differential Equations of Mathematical Physics*, original ed. of 1932, 367–368. Bateman obtains Poisson's integral by using the Green's function for a sphere.

and because r, R are both constant during the integration, we have

29.40 $$\frac{4\pi}{r(r^2-R^2)}=\frac{4\pi}{r(PT)^2}=\int\frac{d\Omega}{l^3}$$

where PT is the length of the tangent to the sphere from the point P.

26. If the point P lies inside the sphere, then for Equation 29.12 to be convergent, we must make $k=r/R$; and in place of Equation 29.36, we have

29.36A $$\frac{R^2-r^2}{l^3}=\sum_{n=0}^{\infty}(2n+1)\frac{r^n}{R^{n+1}}P_n(\cos\psi).$$

We now deal with harmonic functions of the form $r^n\{H_n^m\}$, defined on the sphere as

29.37A $$H_Q=\sum_{n=0}^{\infty}\sum_{m=0}^{n}R^n\{H_n^m\}$$

instead of Equation 29.37; and proceeding as in § 29–23, we find that Poisson's integral for this case is

29.39A $$H_P=\frac{R}{4\pi}\int\frac{(R^2-r^2)}{l^3}H_Q d\Omega$$

instead of Equation 29.39. In physical geodesy, we are not very interested in this case, which can, however, lead to some useful geometrical results. For example, each Cartesian coordinate—that is, each Cartesian component of the position vector ρ^r—is harmonic and regular inside the sphere, and we have

29.41 $$\rho_P^r=\frac{R}{4\pi}\int\frac{(R^2-r^2)}{l^3}\rho_Q^r d\Omega;$$

contracting this equation with $(\rho_r)_P$, which is constant during the integration, we have

29.42 $$r=\frac{R^2}{4\pi}\int\frac{(R^2-r^2)}{l^3}\cos\psi\,d\Omega.$$

27. The Cartesian derivatives of a harmonic potential V are also harmonic so that we have in Cartesian coordinates

29.43 $$(V_r)_P=\frac{R(r^2-R^2)}{4\pi}\int(V_r)_Q\frac{d\Omega}{l^3}.$$

If ν_r is the direction of the potential gradient and g is the gravitational force, this last equation is

$$(g\nu_r)_P=\frac{R(r^2-R^2)}{4\pi}\int(g\nu_r)_Q\frac{d\Omega}{l^3};$$

and because $(\nu_r)_P$ is constant during the integration, we have

29.44 $$g_P=\frac{R(r^2-R^2)}{4\pi}\int g_Q(\nu_r)_Q(\nu^r)_P\frac{d\Omega}{l^3}.$$

If V is the potential anomaly, it would be assumed to a usual degree of accuracy that ν_r is radial, and therefore $(\nu_r)_Q(\nu^r)_P=\cos\psi$. However, the formula is exact only if ν_r is the direction and g is the magnitude of the gradient of V.

28. If we assume that the harmonic potential V is expressible in spherical harmonics as

29.45 $$V=\sum_{n=0}^{\infty}\sum_{m=0}^{n}\{V_n^m\}/r^{n+1}$$

on and outside the sphere, which is equivalent to assuming that there are no masses outside the sphere, then the radial component of the gradient of V, denoted by $\bar{g}$, is given by

$$\bar{g}=\frac{\partial V}{\partial r}=-\sum_{n=0}^{\infty}\sum_{m=0}^{n}\frac{n+1}{r}\frac{\{V_n^m\}}{r^{n+1}}$$

or

29.46 $$r\bar{g}=-\sum_{n=0}^{\infty}\sum_{m=0}^{n}(n+1)\{V_n^m\}/r^{n+1}.$$

But each term of the series on the right is a harmonic function, and therefore $r\bar{g}$ is a harmonic function. Substitution in Poisson's integral, Equation 29.39, gives

29.47 $$\bar{g}_P=\frac{R^2(r^2-R^2)}{4\pi r}\int\bar{g}_Q\frac{d\Omega}{l^3},$$

which is exact only for the radial component of the gradient of V. If $V=1/r$, Equation 29.47 gives

$$\frac{1}{r^2}=\frac{(r^2-R^2)}{4\pi r}\int\frac{d\Omega}{l^3}$$

as we found in Equation 29.40. But if $V=1/r$, Equation 29.44 gives

$$\frac{1}{r^2}=\frac{(r^2-R^2)}{4\pi R}\int\frac{\cos\psi}{l^3}\,d\Omega.$$

These last two equations must accordingly be equivalent, and in fact we can prove from Equations 29.36 and 29.09 that we have

$$\frac{r}{R}\int\frac{\cos\psi}{l^3}\,d\Omega=\int\frac{d\Omega}{l^3},$$

which reconciles the two equations.

29. If the potential anomaly is expressible in spherical harmonics on and outside the sphere, which will be the case if both the actual and standard potentials can be so expressed, it follows from Equation 29.33 or 29.26 that rg_A or rg_D is harmonic so that Equation 29.47 holds true for the gravity anomaly or for the gravity disturbance as

29.48 $$(g_A)_P=\frac{R^2(r^2-R^2)}{4\pi r}\int(g_A)_Q\frac{d\Omega}{l^3}.$$

This last equation is usually known as the *upward continuation integral* because it enables us to calculate the gravity anomaly (or gravity disturbance) at any point in space by numerical integration, if we have values of the gravity anomaly (or gravity disturbance) at a large number of points on a sphere.

STOKES' INTEGRAL

30. If we multiply Equation 29.15 for the Stokes' function $S(\psi)$ by a bounded function, such as the gravity anomaly g_A in Equation 29.33, we have

$$S(\psi)g_A = -\sum_{n=2}^{\infty} \frac{(2n+1)}{(n-1)} P_n (\cos \psi)$$
$$\times \sum_{p=0}^{\infty} \sum_{m=0}^{p} \frac{(p-1)\{T_p^m\}}{r^{p+2}},$$

assuming that g_A is expressible as a convergent series of spherical harmonics. Integrating this equation over the whole solid angle or the sphere in figure 39, noting that the terms of the product on the right are zero unless $p=n$ (Equation 29.05), and using Equation 29.10, we have

$$\int S(\psi)(g_A)_Q d\Omega = -4\pi \sum_{n=2}^{\infty} \sum_{m=0}^{n} \frac{\{T_n^m\}_S}{R^{n+2}}$$

where $\{T_n^m\}_S$ is the value of the harmonic $\{T_n^m\}$ at S on the radius vector OP (fig. 39). But we have

29.49 $$T_S = \sum_{n=2}^{\infty} \sum_{m=0}^{n} \frac{\{T_n^m\}_S}{R^{n+1}},$$

omitting the first- and zero-degree harmonics, so that we then have

29.50 $$T_S = -\frac{R}{4\pi} \int S(\psi)(g_A)_Q d\Omega,$$

known as Stokes' integral, which enables us to find the potential anomaly by numerical integration of gravity anomalies over the sphere, using Stokes' function $S(\psi)$ given by Equation 29.15. At the point $S(\psi=0)$, Stokes' function becomes infinite, and special methods of integration are necessary in the immediate vicinity of the point S.[5]

31. A similar operation on Equation 29.14 gives

$$\int S(k, \psi)(g_A)_Q d\Omega = -\sum_{n=2}^{\infty} \sum_{m=0}^{n} \frac{4\pi k^{n+1}\{T_n^m\}_S}{R^{n+2}}.$$

If we substitute $k=R/r$ (fig. 39) and note that we have

$$T_P = \sum_{n=2}^{\infty} \sum_{m=0}^{n} \frac{\{T_n^m\}_S}{r^{n+1}},$$

omitting the first- and zero-degree harmonics, we then have

29.51 $$T_P = -\frac{R}{4\pi} \int S(R/r, \psi)(g_A)_Q d\Omega,$$

known as Pizzetti's extension of Stokes' integral, which enables us to find the potential anomaly at any point in space by numerical integration of gravity anomalies over the sphere, using Equation 29.14 for the special value $k=R/r$.

32. The Stokes' functions $S(\psi)$, $S(k, \psi)$ do not contain terms for $n=0, 1$, sometimes known as the "forbidden" harmonics. The term for $n=1$ would be infinite and cannot be included; the term for $n=0$ could be included but is conventionally omitted. Equation 29.49, used to derive the Stokes' integral, shows then that the potential anomaly obtained from the Stokes' integral cannot contain zero- or first-degree harmonics, which means that these harmonics must be the same, or zero, in the actual and standard potentials. For the zero-degree harmonics to be the same, we must assume the same total mass (§21–41); for the first-degree harmonics to be the same, we must assume that the two mass distributions have the same center of mass (§21–42)—as we have already assumed, but usually with less effect, in supposing that the centrifugal terms in the geopotential are the same. There are no present means of accurately ensuring either of these conditions or of satisfying the condition $W_P = U_Q$, required in the definition of the gravity anomaly by Equation 29.27. Considerable ingenuity has accordingly been applied to correcting the results after Stokes' integration[6] has been carried out over the entire globe. Equation 29.33 shows further that the gravity anomalies used in Stokes' integration should not contain either of the "forbidden" harmonics $n=0, 1$, although analysis of the observed gravity data does not necessarily indicate absence of these harmonics.[7]

33. We can similarly obtain integral formulas for the gravity disturbance g_D instead of the gravity anomaly g_A if we use Equations 29.17, 29.16, and 29.26. It will be found that the Stokes' integral,

---

[5] Detailed methods of integration are given in Heiskanen and Moritz, *op. cit. supra* note 3, 117–123.

[6] *Ibid.*, 98–111.

[7] See Lambert (1957), "Inadmissible Spherical Harmonics in the Expansion of Gravity Anomalies," *Festschrift zum 75. Geburtstag von Prof. Dr. C. F. Baeschlin*, 149–154.

Equation 29.50, holds true if we use the simpler function $\bar{S}(\psi)$, given by Equation 29.17, instead of the Stokes' function $S(\psi)$. Pizzetti's extension, Equation 29.51, holds true if we use the modified function $\bar{S}(R/r, \psi)$, obtained from Equation 29.16, for $k = R/r$. Use of the gravity disturbance instead of the gravity anomaly avoids trouble over the "forbidden" harmonics because the modified functions $\bar{S}(\psi)$, $\bar{S}(R/r, \psi)$ do not require suppression of the terms $n = 0$, 1 nor do we have to satisfy the condition $W_P = U_Q$, required in the definition of the gravity anomaly by Equation 29.27.

34. Bruns' Equation 29.28 enables us to find the separation between an actual equipotential surface and a standard equipotential surface if both surfaces have the same potential number. This separation (usually denoted by N) is

29.52 $$N = \frac{R}{4\pi G} \int S(R/r, \psi)(g_A)_Q d\Omega$$

in which G is any reasonable value of standard gravity near the point P. If P is on the geoid or equipotential spheroid, we make $R = r$, and the corresponding formula for the separation of geoid and spheroid is then

29.53 $$N = \frac{R}{4\pi G} \int S(\psi)(g_A)_Q d\Omega,$$

always assuming that the potential of the geoid is equal to the potential of the spheroid. The same formulas apply to the gravity disturbance, provided we use the modified functions $\bar{S}(R/r, \psi)$, and $\bar{S}(\psi)$ given by Equations 29.16 and 29.17.

DEFLECTION OF THE VERTICAL

35. If we refer to figure 39 and differentiate the equation

$$l^2 = r^2 + R^2 - 2rR \cos \psi$$

covariantly for a displacement of P with Q fixed, we have after some simplification

29.54 $$l_r = r_r \cos \beta + \psi_r(r \sin \beta)$$

in which β is the angle OPQ—that is, the zenith distance of the direction $\overrightarrow{QP}$ in the spherical polar (ω, ϕ, r) system. If we take Q as a temporary Cartesian origin and QP as the x-axis, the components of the vector l_r are

$$l_r = (\partial l / \partial x, 0, 0) = (dl/dl, 0, 0) = (1, 0, 0)$$

so that l_r is a unit vector in this temporary Cartesian system and therefore in any system. Also,

r_r is a unit vector, being the unit normal ν_r in the spherical polar system. Equation 29.54 then shows that $(r\psi_r)$ is a unit vector perpendicular to r_r. Moreover, if α is the spherical polar azimuth at P of the direction $\overrightarrow{QP}$, we have as usual

$$l_r = \lambda_r \sin \alpha \sin \beta + \mu_r \cos \alpha \sin \beta + r_r \cos \beta$$

29.55

in which λ_r, μ_r are the parallel and meridian vectors in the spherical polar system. Combining Equations 29.54 and 29.55, we have

29.56 $$r\psi_r = \lambda_r \sin \alpha + \mu_r \cos \alpha.$$

36. Next, we differentiate Equation 29.51 covariantly for a displacement of P *with Q fixed* to give

$$(T_r)_P = -\frac{R}{4\pi} \int \left(\frac{\partial S}{\partial r} r_r + \frac{\partial S}{\partial \psi} \psi_r \right) (g_A)_Q d\Omega.$$

Contracting this equation in turn with the spherical polar parallel and meridian vectors at P (which are fixed during the surface integration) and using Equation 29.23 for a spherical polar system, we have

$$g\eta = -\frac{R}{4\pi r} \int \frac{\partial S}{\partial \psi} \sin \alpha (g_A)_Q d\Omega$$

29.57 $$g(\xi + \kappa) = -\frac{R}{4\pi r} \int \frac{\partial S}{\partial \psi} \cos \alpha (g_A)_Q d\Omega$$

where we have also used Equation 29.56. These equations, with κ assumed to be zero, were originally given by Vening-Meinesz; the function $\partial S/\partial \psi$, obtained by straight differentiation of the Stokes' function, Equation 29.15, is usually known as the Vening-Meinesz function. However, in the form given by Equations 29.57, the equations hold true for Pizzetti's extension of the Stokes' function and also hold true for the integration of gravity disturbances (instead of gravity anomalies), provided the modified functions $\bar{S}$, given by Equation 29.16 or 29.17, are used. The azimuth α in Equations 29.57 refers to the azimuth at P of the direction $\overrightarrow{QP}$. If we use the azimuth of the direction $\overrightarrow{PQ}$, we must change both the minus signs in Equations 29.57 to plus.

37. However, we must realize that Equations 29.57 give the first-order meridian and parallel components of deflection (ξ, η) at the point P in relation to a geocentric spherical polar system; the second equation does not, as discussed in §29–13, give the meridian deflection in relation to the geodetic system, and the difference may be quite considerable.

It is by no means easy to discern this fact in the maze of approximations usually made in deriving the Vening-Meinesz integrals. The difficulty arises not so much from first-order approximations as from the nature and multiplicity of first-order approximations.

38. The assumption that κ is zero in the Vening-Meinesz form of Equations 29.57 is in order if we are dealing solely with points on the base coordinate sphere, which is taken as a standard equipotential. Otherwise κ should be computed for the standard field described in §29–21. The usual assumption that κ is zero everywhere implies that all the standard equipotential surfaces are spheres, and this interpretation is possible only if the standard field is not rotating. A nonrotating standard field is incompatible with the definition of the potential anomaly and with the harmonic properties of the potential anomaly on which the entire theory is based, although a nonrotating standard field is assumed in deriving the approximate formula for the gravity anomaly in Equation 29.31.

39. We do not obtain deflections in the geodetic system from the Vening-Meinesz integrals by using gravity anomalies computed for a spheroidal standard field, although the effect may well be disguised by doing so. It is true that in the derivation of the Stokes and Pizzetti Equations 29.50 and 29.51 from which the Vening-Meinesz equations are obtained by differentiation, the gravity anomalies are merely assumed to be any function related to a harmonic function by Equation 29.32. Nevertheless, as soon as we identify this harmonic function with the potential anomaly, we introduce a standard field; for example, the use of the approximate formula for the gravity anomaly in terms of the potential anomaly, Equation 29.31, introduces a spherical nonrotating standard field, which we must use if we are to be consistent. It is better to use the spherically symmetrical rotating standard field described in §29–21, especially in the more accurate formulas containing the gravity disturbance, and so retain the harmonic properties of the potential anomaly. Such a standard field lies within legitimate first-order approximation in this branch of geodesy (unlike the potential disturbance of satellite geodesy, discussed in §28–101), and the resulting geocentric deflections can very easily be converted to geodetic deflections.

GRAVITY AND DEFLECTION FROM POISSON'S INTEGRAL

40. We are now able to differentiate Poisson's integral, Equation 29.39, for the potential anomaly

T_P at P. Because r and l (fig. 39) are functions which can be considered as defined at Q in the same way as at P and because Q is fixed for a displacement of P, we have

$$(T_r)_P = \frac{R}{4\pi} \int^P \left(\frac{2r}{l^3} r_r - \frac{3(r^2 - R^2)}{l^4} l_r \right) T_Q d\Omega$$

which, on substitution of Equation 29.54, becomes

$$(T_r)_P = \frac{R}{4\pi} \int \left[\left\{ \frac{2r}{l^3} - \frac{3(r^2 - R^2)\cos\beta}{l^4} \right\} r_r \right.$$
$$\left. - \left\{ \frac{3(r^2 - R^2)\sin\beta}{l^4} \right\} r\psi_r \right] T_Q d\Omega.$$

Contraction with the spherical polar meridian, parallel, and normal (r_r) vectors at P (which are constant during the surface integration) and use of Equations 29.23 and 29.56 give

$$g\xi = -\frac{3R(r^2 - R^2)}{4\pi} \int \frac{\sin\beta\cos\alpha}{l^4} T_Q d\Omega$$

$$g\eta = -\frac{3R(r^2 - R^2)}{4\pi} \int \frac{\sin\beta\sin\alpha}{l^4} T_Q d\Omega$$

$$(g_D)_P = \frac{R}{4\pi} \int \left\{ \frac{2r}{l^3} - \frac{3(r^2 - R^2)\cos\beta}{l^4} \right\} T_Q d\Omega.$$

29.58

These equations give the geocentric deflections and gravity disturbance, relative to a spherically symmetrical standard field, at any point in space from given values of the potential anomaly over the reference sphere. The only assumption made is that the geocentric deflections are of the first order. The equations do not determine gravity and deflection at points on the reference sphere $(r = R)$ any more than the original Poisson equation determines potential, although the third equation does apply on the sphere, apart from the singularity in the neighborhood of $P(l = 0)$. Heiskanen and Moritz[8] remove this singularity by an ingenious device which we shall consider next.

41. The third equation of Equations 29.58 applies to any potential function T and the radial component of its gradient. If we apply this equation in space to the potential function $-R/r$, which becomes -1 on the sphere, we have

$$\frac{\partial}{\partial r}\left(-\frac{R}{r} \right) = \frac{R}{r^2} = -\frac{R}{4\pi} \int \left\{ \frac{2r}{l^3} - \frac{3(r^2 - R^2)\cos\beta}{l^4} \right\} d\Omega;$$

[8] Heiskanen and Moritz, *op. cit. supra* note 3, 37–39.

multiplying this equation by T_P, which remains constant during the surface integration, and adding to the third equation of Equations 29.58, we have

$$\left(\frac{\partial T}{\partial r}\right)_P + \frac{R}{r^2}T_P = \frac{R}{4\pi}\int\left\{\frac{2r}{l^3} - \frac{3(r^2-R^2)\cos\beta}{l^4}\right\}$$

29.59 $\times (T_Q - T_P)\,d\Omega.$

Next, we make the substitution $r = R + h$, where h is small, and find that the contribution of the second term in the integrand over a small area in the neighborhood of P is approximately

$$-\frac{6Rh\cos\beta}{l^4}\left(l\frac{\partial T}{\partial l}\right)\left(\frac{\pi l^2}{R^2}\right) \simeq -\frac{6\pi\cos^2\beta}{R}\left(\frac{\partial T}{\partial l}\right),$$

which becomes zero in the limit when P lies on the sphere. The contribution of the second term is zero everywhere else for $r = R$, so that when P lies on the sphere we have

29.60 $\left(\dfrac{\partial T}{\partial r}\right)_P + \dfrac{T_P}{R} = \dfrac{R^2}{2\pi}\displaystyle\int \dfrac{(T_Q - T_P)}{l^3}\,d\Omega.$

The contribution of a small area in the neighborhood of P to the area integral is

$$\left(l\frac{\partial T}{\partial l}\right)\left(\frac{1}{l^3}\right)\left(\frac{\pi l^2}{R^2}\right),$$

which remains finite as $l \to 0$, so that there is no singularity at P in Equation 29.60.

EXTENSION TO A SPHEROIDAL BASE SURFACE

42. The commonest application of the formulas given in this chapter is to find the separation between the geoid and the standard spheroidal equipotential surface having the same potential number as the geoid. Usually the spheroid is also the geodetic coordinate base surface. In that case, the point P (in fig. 39 and §29–14) is on the geoid, Q is on the spheroid, and h is the required separation which enables us to locate the geoid with reference to the spheroid. To compute the gravity anomaly from Equation 29.27, we require gravity on the geoid where it cannot usually be measured. Reduction of the value of gravity measured on the topographic surface to the value of gravity on the geoid requires, in the first place, a knowledge of where the geoid is in relation to the topographic surface—that is, the height of the topographic surface above the geoid. Moreover, all the formulas in this chapter require the potential to be regular

(or, as an equivalent condition, require the potential to be expressible in spherical harmonics) on and outside the surface of integration—in this case, the geoid—which implies that this surface must contain all the attracting matter. Numerous attempts have been made to solve this problem by calculating the effect on gravity of removing all masses external to the geoid, using various hypotheses relating to the mass and density distribution. The operation usually shifts the position of the geoid itself to what is known as the *co-geoid* or *regularized geoid* for a particular hypothesis. Next, the separation h is calculated by Stokes' integration of reduced gravity anomalies over the co-geoid by Equation 29.53. Finally, the effect on h of replacing the external masses is calculated. Fortunately, much of the error in the hypotheses is removed by using the same hypotheses for the replacement of the external masses. A good account of the various processes has been given by Heiskanen and Moritz.[9]

43. A further difficulty arises from the fact that all the formulas in this chapter, including Stokes' integral, require integration not over the irregular geoid or co-geoid but over a sphere. Stokes[10] himself shows that his formula is valid to a high degree of accuracy for nearly spherical surfaces. In the hope of improving Stokes' results, Zagrebin[11] modified Stokes' integral for a spheroidal, in place of a spherical, reference surface. Some errors in Zagrebin's results were later corrected by Bjerhammar,[12] using a different method. The results are complicated, and the conclusion is that there is little or no difference in the potential (or separation), as Stokes himself showed, but a considerable difference in the Vening-Meinesz integrals for deflection. The difference may, however, arise in part from misinterpretation of the Vening-Meinesz integrals, as discussed in §29–37. We shall now consider a simpler method of approaching this problem.

[9] See Heiskanen and Moritz, *loc. cit. supra* note 3.

[10] Stokes, *loc. cit. supra* note 1.

[11] Zagrebin (1956), "Die Theorie des Regularisierten Geoids," *Geodätischen Instituts*, Potsdam, Veröffentlichungen no. 9, 1–129. This is a German translation of an article that originally appeared in a Soviet journal. See (1952), "Teoriia Reguliarizirovannogo Geoida," *Trudy Instituta Teoreticheskoĭ Astronomii*, v. 1, 87–222.

[12] Bjerhammar (1962), "On an Explicit Solution of the Gravimetric Boundary Value Problem for an Ellipsoidal Surface of Reference," *The Royal Institute of Technology, Geodesy Division*, Stockholm, 1–95, and (1966), "On the Determination of the Shape of the Geoid and the Shape of the Earth From an Ellipsoidal Surface of Reference," *Bulletin Géodésique*, new series, no. 81, 235–265.

44. The simplicity of using a spherical base co-ordinate surface, as in Poisson's and Stokes' integrals, arises not only from the fact that the radius vector—the third coordinate—is constant during the surface integration, but also from the fact that functions of the radius vector in the potential and gravity anomalies depend only on the degree n and not on the order m of the spherical harmonics used to express the potential anomaly. We can obtain some, but not all, of this advantage by integrating over a base spheroid in the spheroidal coordinates of Chapter 22. The potential anomaly can be expressed in spheroidal coordinates (ω, u, α) by Equation 22.50 as

$$-T/G = \sum_{n=0}^{\infty} \sum_{m=0}^{n} Q_n^m(i \cot \alpha) P_n^m(\sin u)$$

29.61 $\times \{A_{nm} \cos m\omega + B_{nm} \sin m\omega\};$

the gravity disturbance g_D on the base spheroid is then obtained from Equations 29.25, 22.28, and 22.29 as

$$g_D = \frac{\partial T}{\partial s} = -\frac{\tan \alpha}{\nu} \frac{\partial T}{\partial \alpha}$$

$$= -\frac{G \tan \alpha}{\nu} \sum_{n=0}^{\infty} \sum_{m=0}^{n} (i \operatorname{cosec}^2 \alpha) Q_n^{m\prime}(i \cot \alpha)$$

29.62 $\times P_n^m (\sin u)\{A_{nm} \cos m\omega + B_{nm} \sin m\omega\}.$

The (m, n) harmonics are accordingly related by the equation

$$\{(g_D \nu)_n^m\} = i \tan \alpha \operatorname{cosec}^2 \alpha \frac{Q_n^{m\prime}(i \cot \alpha)}{Q_n^m(i \cot \alpha)} \{T_n^m\}$$

$$= \frac{i \tan \alpha \{(n+1)(i \cot \alpha) Q_n^m(i \cot \alpha)\}}{Q_n^m(i \cot \alpha)} \{T_n^m\}$$

$$+ \frac{i \tan \alpha \{-(n-m+1) Q_{n+1}^m(i \cot \alpha)\}}{Q_n^m(i \cot \alpha)} \{T_n^m\}$$

$$= -(n+1)\{T_n^m\}$$

$$- \frac{i \tan \alpha (n-m+1) Q_{n+1}^m(i \cot \alpha)}{Q_n^m(i \cot \alpha)} \{T_n^m\};$$

by summation over m, n, we have

$$g_D \nu = -\sum_{n=0}^{\infty} \sum_{m=0}^{n} (n+1)\{T_n^m\}$$

$$- \sum_{n=0}^{\infty} \sum_{m=0}^{n} \frac{i \tan \alpha (n-m+1) Q_{n+1}^m(i \cot \alpha)}{Q_n^m(i \cot \alpha)} \{T_n^m\}$$

29.63

which is an extension of Equation 29.26, except that the harmonics are now in terms of the reduced latitude u and not the geocentric latitude. We multiply this last equation by the modified Stokes' function, Equation 29.17,

$$\bar{S}(\psi) = \sum_{n=0}^{\infty} \frac{2n+1}{n+1} P_n (\cos \psi)$$

$$= \operatorname{cosec} \tfrac{1}{2} \psi - \ln (1 + \operatorname{cosec} \tfrac{1}{2} \psi)$$

where $\cos \psi$ is now calculated from the reduced latitudes $u, \bar{u}$ as

$$\cos \psi = \sin u \sin \bar{u} + \cos u \cos \bar{u} \cos (\bar{\omega} - \omega),$$

29.64

and integrate over the whole solid angle

$$d\Omega = \cos u \, du d\omega.$$

We then have

$$\int (g_D \nu) \bar{S}(\psi) d\Omega = -4\pi T_P$$

$$- \int \sum_{n=0}^{\infty} \sum_{m=0}^{n} \frac{i \tan \alpha (n-m+1) Q_{n+1}^m(i \cot \alpha)}{Q_n^m (i \cot \alpha)}$$

29.65 $\times \bar{S}(\psi)\{T_n^m\} d\Omega$

which is an extension of Stokes' integral for the gravity disturbance. From Equation 22.49, we have

$$\frac{Q_{n+1}^m(i \cot \alpha)}{Q_n^m(i \cot \alpha)} = \frac{(-)^m(n+m+1)}{(2n+3)i \cot \alpha}\left[1 + O\left(\frac{1}{i \cot \alpha}\right)^2\right],$$

and the integral on the right side of Equation 29.65 becomes

$$- \sum_{n=0}^{\infty} \sum_{m=0}^{n} \frac{(-)^m \tan^2 \alpha (n+m+1)(n-m+1)}{(2n+3)}$$

29.66 $\times \bar{S}(\psi)\{T_n^m\} d\Omega,$

ignoring the fourth and higher powers of $\tan \alpha$, which is roughly the eccentricity of the base spheroid. This last integral can accordingly be considered as a correction to the Stokes' integral to allow for the gravity disturbance being given over a spheroid instead of over a sphere. The correction is of the second order in the eccentricity. The other difference from the Stokes' integral in Equation 29.65—the use of the principal radius ν instead of a mean spherical radius R—is also a second-order effect, so that the spherical Stokes' integral holds true for integration of gravity disturbances over a spheroid to a first order in the eccentricity, provided we use the reduced latitude and, in effect, integrate over the auxiliary sphere.

45. To calculate the correction in Equation 29.66, we need to expand a first approximation to the

potential anomaly in spheroidal harmonics, converted if necessary from spherical harmonics by Equation 22.59. However, in practice, the zero- and first-degree harmonics are usually assumed to be absent in the potential anomaly because the total mass and center of mass are assumed to be the same in the actual and standard fields. We need usually consider only the comparatively large second-degree zonal harmonic for which the correcting term in Equation 29.66 is

$$-(9/7)\tan^2\alpha\int\{T_2\}(5/3)P_2(\cos\psi)\,d\Omega$$
$$=-(15/7)\tan^2\alpha(4\pi/5)\{T_2\}_P$$
$$=-(12\pi/7)\tan^2\alpha\{T_2\},$$

using Equation 29.10. The second-degree zonal harmonic, in the actual potential and therefore in the potential anomaly, is already (1968) well known.

46. A formula in terms of the gravity anomaly g_A instead of the gravity disturbance g_D may be obtained from Equation 29.30, which in our present notation gives

$$\nu g_D = \nu g_A + \nu\left(\frac{\partial\ln\gamma}{\partial s}\right)T.$$

On the base equipotential spheroid, the Bruns' Equation 20.23 in our present notation gives

$$\nu\left(\frac{\partial\ln\gamma}{\partial s}\right)=-\frac{\nu}{\rho}-1-\frac{2\tilde\omega^2\nu}{\gamma}$$
$$=-2-\sin^2\alpha\,\cos^2 u-2\tilde\omega^2\nu/\gamma$$

to a second order in the eccentricity, using Equations 22.10 and 22.12. It is usual, as in the approximate formula for the gravity anomaly (Equation 29.31), to ignore the centrifugal term when multiplied by the small potential anomaly. However, the magnitude of this term in the last equation is about 1/150, which is about the square of the eccentricity, so that we have no right to ignore this term in working to a second order. Equation 29.63 can now be replaced by

$$g_A\nu = -\sum_{n=0}^{\infty}\sum_{m=0}^{n}(n-1)\{T_n^m\}$$
$$+\sum_{n=0}^{\infty}\sum_{m=0}^{n}\sin^2\alpha\cos^2 u\{T_n^m\}$$
$$+\sum_{n=0}^{\infty}\sum_{m=0}^{n}(2\tilde\omega^2\nu/\gamma)\{T_n^m\}$$
$$-\sum_{n=0}^{\infty}\sum_{m=0}^{n}\frac{i\tan\alpha(n-m+1)Q_{n+1}^m(i\cot\alpha)}{Q_n^m(i\cot\alpha)}\{T_n^m\}.$$

29.67

When multiplied by the Stokes' function

$$S(\psi)=\sum_{n=2}^{\infty}\frac{2n+1}{n-1}P_n(\cos\psi),$$

where $\cos\psi$ is given by Equation 29.64, and integrated over the whole solid angle, this last equation gives an extension of Stokes' integral similar to Equation 29.65 with three correcting terms on the right which can be evaluated numerically for the main second-degree zonal harmonic as in § 29–43. In evaluating the centrifugal correcting term, it is reasonable to assume that $(2\tilde\omega^2\nu/\gamma)$ is constant at its mean value, which is about 1/145.

47. Equations 29.65 and the corresponding equation for the gravity anomaly are in the form of integral equations whose solution gives the potential anomaly at a particular point P on the spheroid; this form best illustrates the analogy with the Stokes' integrals for the sphere. However, these integral equations are exactly equivalent to the system of linear equations in Equations 29.63 and 29.67, expressing the gravity disturbance or anomaly as an infinite series of spheroidal harmonics of the potential anomaly. We cannot, of course, solve an infinite number of these equations for the coefficients A_{nm}, B_{nm} of Equation 29.61 any more than we can evaluate the integrals in the integral equations for all points of the spheroid; the most we can do is to integrate numerically the gravity disturbance or anomaly at a number of discrete points, which represent average conditions in the locality and are well spaced over the spheroid. In much the same way, we can suppose that the potential anomaly is sufficiently well represented by a finite number of the coefficients A_{nm}, B_{nm} in Equation 29.61, and we can solve Equation 29.63 or 29.67 for these coefficients. The number of coefficients for which we can solve will naturally be limited by computer capacity; we must, of course, have at least as many observations for g_D or g_A as unknown coefficients, preferably many more so that we may solve the observation equations derived from Equation 29.63 or 29.67 by least squares. The advantage of this method is that we are not limited to points on the spheroid; we can substitute all three coordinates of the observation points in the coefficients of the unknown A_{nm}, B_{nm} in Equations 29.63 and 29.67, and have no need of Pizzetti extensions to the integral Equation 29.65 or the corresponding equation for the gravity anomaly. The same method can be used in geocentric coordinates to solve Equation 29.26 or 29.33 for the C_{nm}, S_{nm} of the potential anomaly expressed in spherical harmonics. In § 29–49, we shall consider yet another application of this method.

BJERHAMMAR'S METHOD

48. Realizing the essential simplicity of the classical spherical approach, Bjerhammar,[13] in one of the most modern methods, uses a spherical

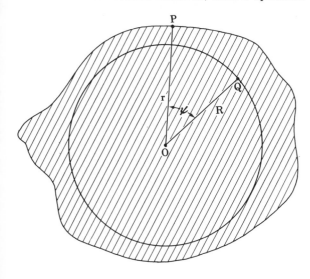

P

Q

r

ψ

R

O

Figure 40.

reference surface completely embedded in the Earth (fig. 40). He then uses the upward continuation integral in Equation 29.48, that is,

29.68 $(g_A)_P = \dfrac{R^2(r^2 - R^2)}{4\pi r} \displaystyle\int \dfrac{(g_A)_Q}{l^3} \, d\Omega,$

first, to determine values of the gravity anomaly $(g_A)_Q$ on the reference surface from measured values $(g_A)_P$ on the topographic surface, and second, to determine values in the external field generally from values on the reference surface. The first operation involves inversion or solution of the integral Equation 29.68 and results in quantities which can no longer be physically identified with gravity anomalies because of the intervening matter, but do, nevertheless, satisfy the integral equation. The method is applicable without modification to gravity disturbances or to any function derivable from Poisson's integral in the same way as Equation 29.48. Once the gravity anomaly, or preferably the gravity disturbance, has been found at points in the external field, it is a simple matter to compute actual gravity at such points; the result could be compared with, and be used to supplement,

gravity determination from satellites. The external potential could be found by harmonic analysis of gravity, followed by integration or by Stokes' integration.

49. The integral Equation 29.68 can be solved approximately by the standard method of transformation to a finite number of simultaneous linear equations.[14] For example, we can express $(g_A)_Q$ approximately over the reference sphere by a sufficient number of spherical harmonics as

29.69 $(g_A)_Q = \displaystyle\sum_{n,\,m} \{u_n^m\},$

even if the function $(g_A)_Q$ contains simple discontinuities. Expressing Equation 29.36 in the form

$$\frac{r(r^2 - R^2)}{l^3} = \sum_{n=0}^{\infty} \frac{R^n}{r^n} (2n+1) P_n(\cos\psi)$$

and substituting in the integral Equation 29.68, we have

$$(g_A)_P = \int \frac{R^{n+2}}{r^{n+2}} \frac{(2n+1)}{4\pi} \sum_{n,\,m} \{u_n^m\} P_n(\cos\psi) \, d\Omega$$

29.70 $\quad = \displaystyle\sum_{n,\,m} \frac{R^{n+2}}{r^{n+2}} \{u_n^m\}_P,$

using Equation 29.10. For each point P where gravity is measured or averaged on the topographic surface, we have one linear Equation 29.70 connecting a finite number of the spherical harmonic coefficients C_{nm}, S_{nm} in $\{u_n^m\}$ by Equation 29.02. Given enough observations, we can solve these equations for the C_{nm}, S_{nm} by least squares, thereby fitting the function $(g_A)_Q$ in Equation 29.69 in a reasonable way to the observed values on the topographic surface. There is no need to exclude the "forbidden" harmonics $n = 0$, 1 from the expression for $(g_A)_Q$. Convergence difficulties, caused by matter external to the reference sphere and discussed in § 12–73, do not arise because we are not dealing with an infinite series of spherical harmonics, but are concerned solely to find a finite series which fits a finite number of observations.

50. Members of the Stockholm school [15] have proposed various other polynomial representations of

[13] Bjerhammar (1962), "Gravity Reduction to a Spherical Surface," *Technical Report, The Royal Institute of Technology, Geodesy Division*, Stockholm, 1–2, and (1964), "A New Theory of Geodetic Gravity," *Kungliga Tekniska Högskolans Handlingar*, Stockholm, no. 243, 3–76. Details are provided in several other publications of *The Royal Institute of Technology*.

[14] For a clear introduction to the method, see Jeffreys and Jeffreys (reprint of 1962), *Methods of Mathematical Physics*, 3d ed. of 1956, 167–168.

[15] See, for example, among other publications of *The Royal Institute of Technology*, Reit (1967), "On the Numerical Solution of the Gravimetrical Integral Equation of Bjerhammar," *The Royal Institute of Technology, Geodesy Division*, Stockholm, 1–36.

the function $(g_A)_Q$ as alternatives to expression in spherical harmonics by Equation 29.69. One proposal is to use a finite series in powers of the topographic height h above the point Q, that is,

$$(g_A)_Q = \sum_n c_n h^n.$$

Substitution of this series in the integral Equation 29.68 gives

29.71 $(g_A)_P = \sum_n c_n \int \frac{h^n}{l^3} \frac{R^2(r^2 - R^2)}{4\pi r} d\Omega,$

the integrals in which equation can be evaluated numerically. The resulting system of linear equations is then solved for the coefficients c_n. Anomalies $(g_A)_P$ on the topographic surface or in the external field appear also as power series in h, an interpretation which implies that gravity anomalies are constant over level plains. But this result is contrary to experience, as members of the Stockholm school themselves realize; variations in the anomalies over the Gangetic Plain in India have, for example, yielded valuable geophysical results, and the same could be said for many large oilfields. However, representation of $(g_A)_Q$ by a power series serves well to illustrate the principles of the method, which can be applied to more sophisticated polynomials.

51. An alternative method of solving the integral Equation 29.68 has been given by Moritz.[16] From Equation 29.40, we have

$$\frac{R^2}{r^2} = \frac{R^2(r^2 - R^2)}{4\pi r} \int \frac{d\Omega}{l^3}.$$

If we multiply this equation by $(g_A)_S$—the value of the gravity anomaly at S in figure 39—which is a constant during the surface integration, and subtract from Equation 29.68, we have

$$\frac{R^2}{r^2}(g_A)_S = (g_A)_P - \frac{R^2(r^2 - R^2)}{4\pi r} \int \frac{(g_A)_Q - (g_A)_S}{l^3} d\Omega.$$

The factor (R^2/r^2) on the left is near unity and is ignored, and the last equation is then solved for $(g_A)_S$ by iteration. For the first approximation, the anomalies $(g_A)_Q$, $(g_A)_S$ on the sphere in the surface integral are taken to be their observed values on the topographic surface. Second approximations to the values on the sphere—for example, $(g_A)_S$ on the left—are then obtained from the integral equation and are used in the surface integral to obtain a third approximation. Similar iterative methods have been proposed in various publications of the

---

[16] Heiskanen and Moritz, *op. cit. supra* note 3, 318.

Stockholm school, including Bjerhammar's first paper on the subject, published in 1962.

52. The method is based on Poisson's integral, which requires an absence of matter outside the reference sphere if the quantities g_A are to be interpreted as gravity anomalies. It is possible in the case of many mass distributions to remove matter external to the reference sphere and to add matter inside the reference sphere without effect on the total mass, on the center of mass, or on the external field, but there is no guarantee that this is possible in the case of such an irregular body as the Earth; if it were possible, the $(g_A)_Q$ would then be gravity anomalies of the alternative mass distribution in which all the matter external to the reference sphere has been removed. The existence of a solution of the integral Equation 29.68 could then certainly be justified on physical grounds. We have no need to interpret values of $(g_A)_Q$ on the reference sphere as gravity anomalies. We could consider $(g_A)_Q$ simply a function defined on the reference sphere which, when substituted in the integral Equation 29.68, correctly reproduces the observed quantities $(g_A)_P$, but we still have to show that such a function can be found by solving the integral equation and is expressible to sufficient accuracy by a practicable number of terms. For example, there are considerable fluctuations in the anomalies over the topographic surface which could lead to even more violent fluctuations of the $(g_A)_Q$, requiring a very large number of polynomial terms for adequate representation. Failing justification on physical grounds by an alternative mass distribution, the only way of settling the question is by numerical trials on simulated and unfavorably irregular mass distributions. Members of the Stockholm school are still (1968) engaged in such trials, but their results so far seem to indicate that the method will be satisfactory when applied to the actual Earth and will be as good as any other method, in addition to being much simpler.

THE EQUIVALENT SPHERICAL LAYER

53. We know that the external potential of a solid body can arise from an infinite variety of mass distributions, and the question arises whether we can replace the actual mass distribution by a coating of density σ spread over a given surface without effect on the external potential. In some modern geodetic applications, such replacement is assumed possible for any surface; we shall consider this

generalization in more detail in § 30–55. In this chapter, we shall consider, as an introduction to the more general case, the classical problem of whether, and in what circumstances, the mass distribution of a given external potential can be replaced by a surface density σ spread over a sphere. An obvious advantage would be that we can then obtain any required elements of the external field straight from the surface mass distribution by surface integration. In fact, we can obtain alternative, but equivalent, forms of all the integral formulas in this chapter, no more and no less, and the alternatives are subject to the same limitations.

54. Any bounded function, including functions with simple discontinuities, can be represented over the surface of a sphere in a series of spherical harmonics; we can accordingly express a surface density σ in geocentric coordinates (ω, ϕ) as

$$\sigma = \sum_{n=0}^{\infty} \sum_{m=0}^{n} P_n^m(\sin \phi) \{c_{nm} \cos m\omega + s_{nm} \sin m\omega\}$$

29.72

where c_{nm}, s_{nm} are constants. If dS is an element of area of the spherical surface, the corresponding element of mass is σdS; we can then obtain the C_{nm}, S_{nm} of the external attraction potential from Equations 21.037. For example, we have

$$\bar{C}_{n0} = R \int \sigma P_n(\sin \phi) dS$$

$$= R^{n+2} \int_{\omega=0}^{\omega=2\pi} \int_{\phi=-\pi/2}^{\phi=+\pi/2} \sigma P_n(\sin \phi) \cos \phi \, d\omega d\phi.$$

If we substitute Equation 29.72 for σ, the variables are found to be separable and in accordance with the ordinary rules for integration of trigonometric and Legendre functions; we have then

$$C_{n0} = \frac{4\pi R^{n+2}}{(2n+1)} c_{n0}.$$

Integration of the other two equations of Equations 21.037 in the same way shows that the same relation holds between the other coefficients, and we can write

29.73 $$\binom{C_{nm}}{S_{nm}} = \frac{4\pi R^{n+2}}{(2n+1)} \binom{c_{nm}}{s_{nm}}.$$

If V is the external potential, we can write this equation in the notation of § 29–2 and with the physical definition of the potential as

29.74 $$\{V_n^m\} = -\frac{4\pi R^{n+2}}{(2n+1)} \{\sigma_n^m\},$$

which can be summed over m and n to give the required relation between the potential and the surface density. It is assumed that units have been chosen to make the gravitational constant G unity in Equation 21.035. However, Equation 29.74 would hold true if we consider σ to be the density multiplied by the gravitational constant.

55. If we are given the surface density in spherical harmonics, the potential is obtained as a series of spherical harmonics, convergent right down to the surface of the sphere, which in this case is the sphere of convergence defined in § 21–11. However, if we preassign values to C_{nm}, S_{nm} to represent the attraction potential of an actual body, such as the Earth, the corresponding series of solid harmonics is certainly convergent only outside the sphere of convergence for that body; it is only in that domain that the equivalent spherical coating, given by Equation 29.74, can be said to give rise to the actual potential of the Earth. Equation 29.74 is accordingly limited in the same way as the expression of the actual potential in spherical harmonics, no more and no less. Subject to this limitation on Equation 29.74, we can always use Equation 29.74 to find a spherical coating which will give rise to the actual potential.

56. The total mass M of the coating is

29.75 $$\int \sigma dS = 4\pi R^2 c_{00} = M = C_{00},$$

in agreement with Equation 29.73. Moreover, if the origin is at the center of mass of the actual body so that the first harmonics C_{10}, C_{11}, S_{11} are zero, so then are c_{10}, c_{11}, and s_{11} zero, and the center of mass of the coating is at the same origin. Equation 29.73 automatically ensures that the actual body and the coating have the same center of mass, whether this common center of mass is at the origin or not.

57. The potential at P (fig. 39), arising from the element of mass $\sigma dS = \sigma R^2 d\Omega$ at Q, is

$$-\sigma R^2 d\Omega / l;$$

the total potential at P is accordingly

29.76 $$V_P = -\int \frac{\sigma R^2}{l} d\Omega,$$

which is easily verified from Equations 29.74, 29.11 (for $k = R/r$), and 29.10. This formula is an alternative to Poisson's integral.

58. As another example, the vector force at P (fig. 39), arising from the coating, is the negative of

the potential gradient at P by the generalization of Equation 20.05; and so we have

29.77 $$(V_r)_P = + \int \frac{\sigma R^2}{l^2} \, l_r d\Omega$$

where l_r is a unit vector in the direction $\overrightarrow{QP}$ given by Equations 29.54 and 29.55. This equation can be contracted with the meridian, parallel, and normal vectors (which remain fixed during the integration) in the spherical polar system at P to give three components of force and thus the magnitude and direction of the total force. If V is the potential anomaly, the magnitude of the total force to a high degree of accuracy is the gravity disturbance.

59. Another formula, frequently found in the literature, connects the gravity anomaly g_A with the density σ of a spherical coating, giving rise to the potential anomaly T. Both T and g_A have their values on the sphere. From Equations 29.74 and 29.32, we have

$$
\begin{aligned}
(2\pi\sigma - g_A) &= \sum_{n=0}^{\infty} \sum_{m=0}^{n} \left[-\frac{(2n+1)}{2R^{n+2}} \{T_n^m\} + \frac{(n-1)}{R^{n+2}} \{T_n^m\} \right] \\
\mathbf{29.78} \qquad &= -\frac{3T}{2R}
\end{aligned}
$$

in which we have also used Equations 29.33 and 29.45. A similar formula for the gravity disturbance g_D on the sphere is obtained from Equation 29.26 as

29.79 $$(2\pi\sigma - g_D) = \frac{T}{2R}.$$

These formulas are subject to the usual limitation of absence of matter outside the sphere and to the first-order assumptions inherent in Equations 29.30 and 29.32 for the gravity anomaly. Equation 29.78 is often applied to the co-geoid as being sufficiently near a sphere.

CHAPTER 30

Integration of Gravity Anomalies — The Green-Molodenskii Approach

GENERAL REMARKS

1. In the last chapter, we considered the integration of gravity disturbances and gravity anomalies over regular mathematical surfaces which are no more complicated than a spheroid. We cannot, however, measure gravity on such a reference surface, and so are compelled to reduce measurements of gravity actually made on the topographic surface of the Earth, or derived from satellites, to calculated values which would be obtained on the reference surface if we could measure them on the reference surface. The calculation, which is described in outline in § 29–42, must assume some distribution of mass in the Earth's crust. To avoid making any such assumptions about crustal densities, which are certainly a source of weakness in the method, much work has been done, mainly by Molodenskii [1] and his associates, on the formation and solution of integral equations requiring integration of the anomalies, not over a regular mathematical surface, but over the actual topographic surface where the measurements are made.

2. Unfortunately, this imaginative conception introduces other, and perhaps equivalent, difficulties. In dealing with such regular surfaces as spheres and spheroids or Newtonian equipotentials in free air, we have not been bothered much by questions of continuity, but this situation is no longer true in the case of the highly irregular topographic surface of the Earth. For the proper application of Green's theorem (for example, Equation 9.19), which is used throughout this branch of geodesy, the unit normal vector of the surface should vary continuously over the surface; in addition, any function used in Green's theorem should have continuous first derivatives on and outside the surface as well as continuous second derivatives outside the surface. These last conditions are satisfied in the case of the topographic surface by gravitational potentials, but are not necessarily satisfied by the distance between two points, one or both of which lie on the surface. Some smoothing of the surface is accordingly necessary; in mountainous regions, smoothing will usually involve at least some of the density assumptions which the method seeks to avoid. Moreover, Molodenskii's integrals contain the slopes of the topographic surface relative to the astronomical or geodetic zenith, and if these slopes are excessive, the integrals will not converge; again, some smoothing of the surface is necessary in mountainous regions.

3. Recognizing these limitations, de Graaff-Hunter [2] has proposed the introduction of a Model

[1] A fairly complete summary and bibliography are given in Molodenskii, Eremeev, and Yurkina (1960), "Methods for Study of the External Gravitational Field and Figure of the Earth," 1–248. Translated from "Metod Izucheniya Vneshnego Gravitatsionnogo Polya i Figury Zemli," in *Trudȳ Tsentral'nogo Nauchno-Issledovatel'skogo Instituta Geodezii, Aéros"emki i Kartografii*, no. 131, 3–251, and published in 1962 by the Israel Program for Scientific Translations for the National Science Foundation and the U.S. Department of Commerce.

[2] de Graaff-Hunter (1960), "The Shape of the Earth's Surface Expressed in Terms of Gravity at Ground Level," *Bulletin Géodésique*, new series, no. 56, 191–200.

Earth, obtained by smoothing the actual topography and defined in relation to the topography, not in relation to the coordinate base surface; the surface of the Model Earth, for example, coincides with Mean Sea Level in ocean areas. The slopes of the Model Earth do not exceed one percent by much, and the surface is sufficiently continuous for the application of Green's theorem. Unfortunately, it is necessary to reduce measurements of gravity and potential made on the topographic surface to equivalent values on the surface of the Model Earth; this reduction requires crustal density assumptions between the topographic surface and the Model Earth which are similar to those required in reductions to the geoid, although not as extensive. Members of the Russian school, who require the equivalent of such reductions only in mountainous areas, consider that this degree of smoothing is unnecessary; the subject is still (1968) controversial.

4. The positions of points on the topographic surface, and therefore the form of the topographic surface, are known at present (1968) only in a relative sense, not in a single worldwide coordinate system. Geometrical heights, such as the third coordinate in the geodetic (ω, ϕ, h) system or in a spherical polar system, are mostly unknown even in a relative sense. Available heights are usually obtained from spirit leveling or vertical angle measurements, which, as we have seen in § 25–19, give, in combination with gravity measurements, an approximation to the geopotential. The main object of the global integration of gravity anomalies is to determine deflections and geometrical heights, which are not vitiated by errors of atmospheric refraction, and so to simplify the more precise calculation of distances and directions by making possible the transformation to geodetic coordinates from measurable astronomical coordinates. In this sense, gravimetric methods are in direct competition with satellite methods, which provide positions in a worldwide geometrical coordinate system without requiring measurement of astronomical latitude, longitude, and potential. A disadvantage of the gravimetric method is the difficulty of obtaining sufficiently dense and accurate gravity measurements over the oceans and over the polar regions, while satellite methods are unlikely to be an economical means of fixing dense networks on land. Gravimetric methods may accordingly be most usefully employed in the future on regional or local surveys in conjunction with surface triangulation, trilateration, or traverse. Little work has so far been done on these lines, but no doubt the general principles of methods described in Chapters 29 and

30 for global gravimetric surveys will still apply to surveys of more limited extent. For example, the low harmonics of the potential may be determined globally from satellites while the higher harmonics are obtained from regional ground gravimetric surveys—both being used to determine deflections for substitution in the observation Equations 26.24 and 26.25 of ground networks.

5. We cannot obtain an answer to these problems by simply integrating gravity anomalies over the unknown topographic surface as Stokes did over a known sphere. Some extra data are required, and, in practice, it is assumed that both gravity and geopotential are measured. This requirement constitutes another serious disadvantage of the gravimetric method. At present (1968), accurate measurements of potential, obtained from spirit leveling in conjunction with gravity measurements, exist only in developed areas along roads or railroads and would be very costly in mountainous areas. Vertical angle measurements, which would provide at least approximate values of potential differences, are missing in many of the main triangulation networks of the world through fear of the effects of atmospheric refraction and through the unrealized hope that heights would eventually be provided by spirit leveling. It may be easier to remedy this deficiency in regional, rather than in global, gravimetric surveys.

6. The usual method of utilizing the potential has already been given in § 29–16 (fig. 38), but is restated now for convenience in a slightly different notation. In figure 41, Q is a current point on the

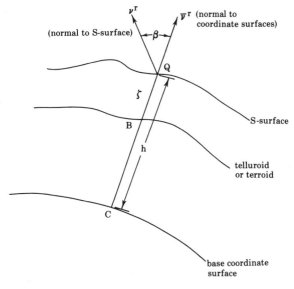

Figure 41.

S-surface, which is either the topographic surface smoothed as necessary or the Model Earth. In this chapter, we shall be dealing solely with (ω, ϕ, h) coordinate systems, usually the spheroidal geodetic system; and $\bar{\nu}^r$ is the straight normal through Q to the h-coordinate surfaces. The point B on this normal is chosen to make the actual potential at $Q(W_Q)$ equal to the standard potential at $B(U_B)$. Because W is supposed to be known at all points of the *S*-surface, the locus of the point B is a known surface and is called the *telluroid* if S is the topographic surface, or the *terroid* if S is the Model Earth surface. The *height anomaly* $BQ = \zeta$ and the *gravity anomaly* $g_Q - \gamma_B$ are as defined in § 29–16. The unit normal to the *S*-surface is shown in figure 41 as ν^r.

7. As usual, we shall provide full derivations of the basic equations, which are not easy to find expressed in simple terms in the literature, and an outline only of the methods for approximating and solving the basic equations; descriptions of these methods are all too prolific in the literature. First, however, we must investigate some geometrical properties of the *S*-surface in (ω, ϕ, h) coordinates to avoid breaking the argument later.

THE *S*-SURFACE IN (ω, ϕ, h) COORDINATES

8. The longitude and latitude (ω, ϕ) are constant along the straight h-surface normal CQ (fig. 41) and therefore have definite values at Q so that (ω, ϕ) can be taken as *S*-surface coordinates. Coordinates of the space in which S is embedded will be taken as the (ω, ϕ, h) system. The equation of the *S*-surface can then be expressed in Monge's form (§ 6–5) as

30.01 $$h_Q = f(\omega, \phi).$$

The x^r_α of the surface (§ 6–5) are then given by

30.02 $$x^3_\alpha = f_\alpha ; \qquad x^r_\alpha = \delta^r_\alpha \qquad (r = 1, 2)$$

in which f_α is the derivative of the scalar f with respect to x^α, that is, with respect to ω or ϕ, and δ^r_α is the Kronecker delta. It should be emphasized that f is interpreted as a height only on the *S*-surface; otherwise, f is simply a function of (ω, ϕ).

The Metric Tensor

9. Substitution of the space metric tensor (Equation 17.04) in Equation 6.06 gives the metric tensor of the *S*-surface as

30.03 $$a_{\alpha\beta} = \bar{a}_{\alpha\beta} + f_\alpha f_\beta$$

in which the overbar refers to the coordinate h-surface passing through Q (fig. 41), not to the base coordinate surface $(h = 0)$ as in Equation 17.09, which, however, enables us to evaluate $\bar{a}_{\alpha\beta}$ in terms of the fundamental forms of the base surface. The determinant of the metric tensor by direct calculation is

$$a = (\bar{a}_{11} + f_1^2)(\bar{a}_{22} + f_2^2) - (\bar{a}_{12} + f_1 f_2)^2$$
$$= \bar{a} + \bar{a}\bar{a}^{22} f_2^2 + \bar{a}\bar{a}^{11} f_1^2 + 2\bar{a}a^{12} f_1 f_2$$
$$= \bar{a}(1 + \overline{\nabla f})$$

30.04 $$= \bar{a}(1 + \nabla f).$$

The invariant $\overline{\nabla f}$ (§ 3–9) is a surface invariant obtained from the metric of the h-surface passing through Q, but because f is a function of (ω, ϕ) only, $f_3 = 0$, and the invariant has the same value as the space invariant ∇f.

The Unit Normal

10. We can obtain the covariant components of the unit normal to the *S*-surface by giving dissimilar values to the indices s and t in Equation 6.11. For example, for $s = 2$, $t = 3$, we have

$$\nu_1 \epsilon^{123} = \epsilon^{2\beta} f_\beta = \epsilon^{21} f_1$$

which, using Equations 2.15, 17.05, and 2.30, gives

$$\nu_1 = -(\bar{a}/a)^{1/2} f_1;$$

obtaining the other components in the same way, we have

30.05 $$\nu_r = (\bar{a}/a)^{1/2}\{-f_1, -f_2, 1\}.$$

Raising the index with the space metric tensor in Equation 17.05 gives the contravariant components as

$$\nu^r = \{\bar{a}^{11}\nu_1, \bar{a}^{22}\nu_2, \nu_3\}$$

30.06 $$= (\bar{a}/a)^{1/2}\{-\bar{a}^{11} f_1, -\bar{a}^{22} f_2, 1\}.$$

But ν^r is a unit vector, and we must have

$$1 = \nu_r \nu^r = (\bar{a}/a)\{\bar{a}^{11} f_1^2 + \bar{a}^{22} f_2^2 + 1\}$$
$$= (\bar{a}/a)(1 + \overline{\nabla f}),$$

agreeing with Equation 30.04. But from Equation 17.28, the unit normal $\bar{\nu}_r$ to the h-surface is $(0, 0, 1)$; if β is the angle between the two normals, as in figure 41, we have

$$\cos \beta = \bar{\nu}_r \nu^r = (\bar{a}/a)^{1/2}$$

so that

30.07 $$a/\bar{a} = 1 + \nabla f = 1 + \overline{\nabla f} = \sec^2 \beta$$

30.08 $$\nabla f = \overline{\nabla f} = \tan^2 \beta.$$

Moreover, by making the space indices both 3 in Equation 6.10 for the S-surface, we have

$$1 = a^{\alpha\beta} f_\alpha f_\beta + (\bar{a}/a)$$

or

30.09 $\nabla_S f = \sin^2 \beta = \overline{\nabla f} \cos^2 \beta = \nabla f \cos^2 \beta$

in which the invariant ∇_S is obtained from the S-surface metric. All the Equations 30.01 through 30.09 hold true in a general (ω, ϕ, h) system whose properties are given in Chapter 17.

11. The angle β is the zenith distance in the (ω, ϕ, h) coordinate system of the S-surface normal and is also the maximum slope of the tangent plane to the S-surface in relation to the coordinate h-surface, which usually will be the geodetic horizontal. If the azimuth of the direction of maximum slope is α, we can write the unit normal ν_r of the S-surface in terms of the usual parallel, meridian, and normal vectors $(\bar{\lambda}_r, \bar{\mu}_r, \bar{\nu}_r)$ as

$$\nu_r = \bar{\lambda}_r \sin \alpha \sin \beta + \bar{\mu}_r \cos \alpha \sin \beta + \bar{\nu}_r \cos \beta.$$

30.10

In a general (ω, ϕ, h) system, we can use Equations 17.26, 17.27, 17.28, and 17.13 to find the components of ν_r in terms of h and the curvatures of the base coordinate surface; we can compare the results with Equation 30.05 and so can express f_1, f_2 in terms of α, β. For a spheroidal base surface with principal radii of curvature ρ, ν, we can use Equations 18.11 and can express the unit normal to the S-surface as

$$\nu_r = \{(\nu + h) \cos \phi \sin \alpha \sin \beta,$$

30.11 $(\rho + h) \cos \alpha \sin \beta, \cos \beta\}$

so that we have

$$f_1 = -(\nu + h) \cos \phi \sin \alpha \tan \beta$$

30.12 $f_2 = -(\rho + h) \cos \alpha \tan \beta.$

In these equations, h is the geodetic height of the point Q on the S-surface (fig. 41). Instead of working in terms of the azimuth and zenith distance of the maximum slope, it is usual in the literature to make $\sin \alpha \tan \beta = -\tan \beta_2$ and $\cos \alpha \tan \beta = -\tan \beta_1$ where β_1, β_2 are, respectively, the inclinations to the geodetic horizontal in north-south, east-west direction of the tangent plane to the S-surface. However, by working in terms of the azimuth α and zenith distance β of the normal to the S-surface, with the sign conventions used throughout this book, we avoid any ambiguity as to whether an inclination or slope of the tangent plane means an elevation or depression.

The Associated Tensor

12. The associated metric tensor of the S-surface is given by Equations 2.44 and 2.30 as

$$a^{\alpha\beta} = \epsilon^{\alpha\gamma} \epsilon^{\beta\delta} a_{\gamma\delta}$$

$$= (\bar{a}/a) \bar{\epsilon}^{\alpha\gamma} \bar{\epsilon}^{\beta\delta} (\bar{a}_{\gamma\delta} + f_\gamma f_\delta)$$

30.13 $= \cos^2 \beta \{ \bar{a}^{\alpha\beta} + \bar{\epsilon}^{\alpha\gamma} \bar{\epsilon}^{\beta\delta} f_\gamma f_\delta \}.$

An alternative expression is obtained from Equation 6.10 for the S-surface immersed in (ω, ϕ, h) space. By giving the indices r, s in Equation 6.10 the surface values γ, δ, we have

30.14 $\bar{a}^{\gamma\delta} = a^{\gamma\delta} + \nu^\gamma \nu^\delta,$

which can be shown to be equivalent to Equation 30.13.

Normal Gradients

13. The component of the gradient of a scalar F along the normal to the S-surface is given by

$$\frac{\partial F}{\partial s} = F_r \nu^r = \cos \beta (-\bar{a}^{11} f_1 F_1 - \bar{a}^{22} f_2 F_2 + F_3)$$

30.15 $= \cos \beta \left\{ \dfrac{\partial F}{\partial h} - \overline{\nabla}(F, f) \right\}$

on substituting Equations 30.06 and 30.07. The invariant $\overline{\nabla}(F, f)$ is obtained from the metric of the h-surface passing through Q, and it may be more convenient to calculate the S-surface invariant. From the definition of the invariant in Equation 3.14, it is evident that the space invariant $\nabla(F, f)$ is the same as the h-surface invariant because f is a function of ω, ϕ only. But if we set up another (ω, ϕ, h) coordinate system with S as a base surface and use the metric in Equation 17.05, the S-surface invariant $\nabla_S(F, f)$ is given by

30.16 $\nabla(F, f) = \nabla_S(F, f) + (\partial F/\partial s)(\partial f/\partial s),$

whatever the surface coordinates on S may be. Substituting f for F in Equation 30.15 and remembering that $\partial f/\partial h = 0$ because f is a function of ω, ϕ only, we have

30.17 $\partial f/\partial s = -\overline{\nabla f} \cos \beta = -\sin \beta \tan \beta,$

using Equation 30.08. From the last two equations, we then have

$$\nabla(F, f) = \overline{\nabla}(F, f) = \nabla_S(F, f) - \sin \beta \tan \beta \, (\partial F/\partial s);$$

substituting in Equation 30.15, we have finally

30.18 $\dfrac{\partial F}{\partial s} = \sec \beta \left\{ \dfrac{\partial F}{\partial h} - \nabla_S(F, f) \right\}.$

Equations 30.15 and 30.18 have been obtained in a

slightly different form by Moritz,[3] whose $\bar{D}(F, f)$ is $\nabla_s(F, f) \cos^2 \beta$ and is accordingly an *S*-surface invariant, although not the standard invariant used here. Moritz' $D(F, f)$ is, however, the same as our *h*-surface invariant $\overline{\nabla}(F, f)$ or $\nabla(F, f)$. We can replace f by h in the *S*-surface invariant of Equation 30.18, but we are not entitled to do so in Equation 30.15 for the reasons given in § 30–8.

The Invariant $\overline{\nabla}(T, f)$

14. Next, we evaluate the invariants in Equations 30.15 and 30.18 when the arbitrary scalar F is taken as the potential anomaly T. We have already seen that the *h*-surface invariant in Equation 30.15 is the same as the space invariant, and therefore can be evaluated in the (ω, ϕ, h) space system as

30.19 $\qquad \overline{\nabla}(T, f) = \nabla(T, f) = g^{pq}(W_p - U_p)f_q.$

If the components of standard gravity in the directions $(\bar{\lambda}^r, \bar{\mu}^r, \bar{\nu}^r)$ of the coordinate system are $(\gamma_1, \gamma_2, \gamma_3)$, the second term is

$$-(\gamma_1\bar{\lambda}^q + \gamma_2\bar{\mu}^q + \gamma_3\bar{\nu}^q)f_q$$

in which the last term is zero because $\bar{\nu}^q = (0, 0, 1)$ and $f_3 = 0$. In a symmetrical standard field $\gamma_1 = 0$, and the remaining term in the case of a spheroidal field is

30.20 $\qquad -\gamma_2\bar{\mu}^q f_q = -\gamma_2\bar{\mu}^2 f_2 = \gamma_2 \cos \alpha \tan \beta,$

using Equations 18.10 and 30.12. The component γ_2 is the g_m of Equation 23.37. This term is ignored altogether in the literature on the assumption that there is no meridian component of standard gravity close to the spheroidal equipotential, but γ_2 can easily be computed and allowed for in extreme cases.

15. If, as in § 19–23, we define the vector deflection Δ^q as

$$\Delta^q = (\nu^q) - \bar{\nu}^q$$

in which (ν^q), $\bar{\nu}^q$ are, respectively, the unit vectors in the direction of the astronomical zenith and of the normal to the geodetic coordinate system, then again $\bar{\nu}^q f_q = 0$, and the first term on the right side of Equation 30.19 is to a first order

$$g(\nu^q)f_q = g\Delta^q f_q = (g \cos \phi \; \delta\omega) \bar{\lambda}^q f_q + (g\delta\phi) \bar{\mu}^q f_q$$
$$= -(g \cos \phi \; \delta\omega) \sin \alpha \tan \beta$$
$$-(g\delta\phi) \cos \alpha \tan \beta,$$

using Equations 19.42, 18.10, and 30.12. In this equation, $\delta\omega$ $(\delta\phi)$ is the astronomical minus the geodetic longitude (latitude). In terms of the usual components of deflection $\xi = \delta\phi$, $\eta = \cos \phi \; \delta\omega$, we can finally write Equation 30.19 as

$$\overline{\nabla}(T, f) = \nabla(T, f) = -g\eta \sin \alpha \tan \beta$$

30.21 $\qquad\qquad\qquad -(g\xi - \gamma_2) \cos \alpha \tan \beta$

in which γ_2 is the meridian component of standard gravity obtainable from Equation 23.37 (not to be confused with the curvature parameter γ_2 of either a general (ω, ϕ, N) system or the gravitational field as defined in § 12–17).

16. The use of Equation 30.15 and of the *h*-surface invariant $\overline{\nabla}(T, f)$ accordingly requires a knowledge of the deflection components ξ, η. Suitable choice of a reference spheroid would make ξ, η, and β small in flat country. In mountainous country, measurement of vertical angles in a triangulation network, combined with an open astronomical control, would provide sufficiently accurate deflections by methods discussed in Chapter 26. Nevertheless, it is a defect of the method to require a knowledge of deflections, in addition to potential and gravity, at all stations. For this reason, Molodenskii uses Equation 30.18 with the *S*-surface invariant $\nabla_s(T, f)$, which we shall evaluate next. However, Molodenskii[4] and Moritz[5] (following Molodenskii) use a special form of invariant instead of the standard form of two-dimensional tensor invariants without reaping any apparent advantage. For example, Molodenskii's *S*-surface invariant $\Delta_2 f$ for the function f of Equation 30.01 can be shown, not without some difficulty, to be

$$\Delta_2 f = \sec^2 \beta \; \Delta f$$

where Δf is the ordinary *S*-surface Laplacian $a^{\alpha\beta}f_{\alpha\beta}$. We shall use the ordinary tensor invariants throughout this chapter, and we shall find that the gain in simplicity is considerable.

The Invariant $\nabla_s(T, f)$

17. If we substitute Equation 30.18 for $F = T$ in the basic integral equation for the potential

---

[3] Moritz (1964), *The Boundary Value Problem of Physical Geodesy*. Report No. 46 of the Institute of Geodesy, Photogrammetry and Cartography, The Ohio State University Research Foundation, Columbus, Ohio, 1–66. Republished with the same title in 1965 in the *Annales Academiæ Scientiarum Fennicæ*, series A. III. Geologica-Geographica, no. 83, 1–48.

[4] Molodenskii, Eremeev, and Yurkina, *op. cit. supra* note 1, 81–85.

[5] Moritz, *op. cit. supra* note 3, 20. See also Moritz (1966), *Linear Solutions of the Geodetic Boundary-Value Problem*. Report No. 79 of the Department of Geodetic Science, The Ohio State University Research Foundation, Columbus, Ohio, 21–22. Republished with the same title in 1968 in *Deutsche Geodätische Kommission bei der Bayerischen Akademie der Wissenschaften*, series A, no. 58, 16–18.

anomaly, which we shall derive as Equation 30.50, we find that the term containing the S-surface invariant $\nabla_S(T, f)$ is

30.22 $\qquad \nabla_S(T, f) \sec \beta / l.$

This term accordingly contains differentials of T which must be removed if the integral equation is to be linear in T. We propose to do this by transforming the term with the two-dimensional form of Green's Equation 9.18; that is, for any two scalars ϕ, ψ, we have

30.23 $\qquad \displaystyle\int \{\nabla(\phi, \psi) + \phi \Delta\psi\} dS = \int \phi \psi_\alpha j^\alpha ds,$

connecting the surface integral on the left side with the contour integral on the right side, in which j^α is a unit surface vector, normal and outward-drawn to the contour (away from the area covered by the surface integral). Using the same argument as in § 9–7, we can say also that over any *closed* surface, we have

30.24 $\qquad \displaystyle\int \{\nabla(\phi, \psi) + \phi \Delta\psi\} dS = 0$

in which the invariants are two-dimensional surface invariants. From the definition $\nabla(\phi, \psi) = a^{\alpha\beta}\phi_\alpha\psi_\beta$ of the first-order invariant, we can rewrite Equation 30.22 as

$$\frac{\nabla_S(T, f)}{l \cos \beta} = \nabla_S\left(\frac{T}{l \cos \beta}, f\right) - T\nabla_S\left(\frac{1}{l \cos \beta}, f\right).$$

If we integrate this last equation over the closed S-surface and use Equation 30.24, we have

$$\int \frac{\nabla_S(T, f)}{l \cos \beta} dS = -\int \frac{T}{l \cos \beta} \Delta f dS$$

30.25 $\qquad \displaystyle - \int T\nabla_S\left(\frac{1}{l \cos \beta}, f\right) dS,$

which removes differentials of T from the integral equation.

18. Next, we must express the S-surface Laplacian Δf in terms of known or measurable quantities. If we continue to overbar all quantities related to the coordinate h-surface passing through the point Q of figure 41, we have

30.26 $\qquad \bar{\nu}_r x_\alpha^r = x_\alpha^3 = f_\alpha,$

using Equation 17.28 for the components of $\bar{\nu}_r$ (the unit normal to the h-surface) and Equations 30.02. Taking the tensor derivative of this last equation over the S-surface, we have

$$\bar{\nu}_{rs} x_\alpha^r x_\beta^s + \bar{\nu}_r x_{\alpha\beta}^r = f_{\alpha\beta}.$$

According to § 17–18, there are no 3-components of

$\bar{\nu}_{rs}$ in a (ω, ϕ, h) coordinate system, and $\bar{\nu}_{\alpha\beta} = -\bar{b}_{\alpha\beta}$. From Equation 6.16, we have also $x_{\alpha\beta}^r = b_{\alpha\beta}\nu^r$ so that we have

30.27 $\qquad -\bar{b}_{\alpha\beta} + b_{\alpha\beta} \cos \beta = f_{\alpha\beta}$

connecting the second fundamental forms of the h-surface and the S-surface. Contracting this last equation with Equation 30.14 and using Equation 8.13, we have

30.28 $\qquad \Delta f = 2H \cos \beta - 2\bar{H} + \bar{b}_{\alpha\beta}\nu^\alpha\nu^\beta,$

the last two terms of which can be evaluated from Equation 30.06 or 30.10 in any particular (ω, ϕ, h) coordinate system. In the geodetic system with principal curvatures ρ, ν of the base spheroid in and perpendicular to the meridian, Equations 30.10 and 18.10 give components of the unit normal to the S-surface as

$$\nu^r = \left\{\frac{\sec \phi \sin \alpha \sin \beta}{(\nu + h)}, \frac{\cos \alpha \sin \beta}{(\rho + h)}, \cos \beta\right\}$$

which, together with Equations 18.01, 18.02, and 18.05, give the last two terms of Equation 30.28 as

$$\frac{1}{(\nu + h)} + \frac{1}{(\rho + h)} - \frac{\sin^2 \alpha \sin^2 \beta}{(\nu + h)} - \frac{\cos^2 \alpha \sin^2 \beta}{(\rho + h)},$$

so that Equation 30.28 finally becomes

$$\Delta f = 2H \cos \beta + \frac{(1 - \sin^2 \alpha \sin^2 \beta)}{(\nu + h)}$$

30.29 $\qquad \displaystyle + \frac{(1 - \cos^2 \alpha \sin^2 \beta)}{(\rho + h)}.$

In addition to the azimuth α and zenith distance β of the normal to the S-surface, that is, the direction and magnitude of the maximum slope of the tangent plane to the S-surface, this equation also contains the mean curvature H of the S-surface. There is no way of avoiding some expression for the curvature of the S-surface in a formula for Δf, and this limitation must be considered the price for avoiding inclusion of the deflection components ξ, η. If the S-surface is the actual surface of the Earth, $(2H)$ may be obtained by estimating the sum of normal curvatures in two perpendicular directions from contoured maps.

Deformation of the S-Surface

19. Next, we consider a family of surfaces obtained by progressive deformation of the S-surface; each member of the family is obtained by reducing the h-coordinates of points on the S-surface in the constant ratio k while retaining the (ω, ϕ) coordi-

nates so that corresponding points between two members of the family lie on the same normal to the h-coordinate surfaces. For $k=1$, the member of the family is evidently the original S-surface; for $k=0$, the member is the base coordinate surface. We can take any relation obtained in this section for the S-surface and simply substitute kh for h to obtain the corresponding relation for the deformed surface. If we enclose quantities relating to the deformed surface in parentheses, we have, for example, from Equations 30.01 and 30.02

30.30 $$(f) = kf$$

30.31 $$(f_\alpha) = kf_\alpha.$$

20. In particular, we shall require the azimuth (α) and zenith distance (β) of the line of greatest slope on the deformed surface relative to the normal of the h-coordinate surface. From Equations 30.12, we have in geodetic coordinates

$$(\nu + kh) \sin(\alpha) \tan(\beta) = -(f_1) \sec \phi$$

$$= k(\nu + h) \sin \alpha \tan \beta$$

$$(\rho + kh) \cos(\alpha) \tan(\beta) = -(f_2)$$

30.32 $$= k(\rho + h) \cos \alpha \tan \beta.$$

In spherical polar coordinates $(\rho = \nu = R)$, these equations reduce to

$$(\alpha) = \alpha$$

30.33 $$\tan(\beta) = \frac{k(R + h)}{R + kh} \tan \beta;$$

if we neglect h/R, the last equation becomes

30.34 $$\tan(\beta) \simeq k \tan \beta.$$

21. We shall also require an expression for the distance (l) between two points (P) and (Q) on the deformed surface. Quantities relating to Q are overbarred. From either Equation 25.18 or 25.19, after some manipulation with the formulas given in § 19–7, we have in geodetic coordinates

$$(l)^2 = (\bar{\nu} + k\bar{h})^2 - 2(\bar{\nu} + k\bar{h})(\nu + kh) \cos \sigma + (\nu + kh)^2$$

$$- 2e^2 k(\bar{\nu} \sin \bar{\phi} - \nu \sin \phi)(\bar{h} \sin \bar{\phi} - h \sin \phi)$$

$$+ (e^4 - 2e^2)(\bar{\nu} \sin \bar{\phi} - \nu \sin \phi)^2$$

30.35

where σ is the angle between the spherical representation of the points (P) and (Q). For the azimuth $(\bar{\alpha})$ and zenith distance $(\bar{\beta})$ of the direction $\overrightarrow{(P)(Q)}$

at (Q), we have from Equation 25.19

$$(l) \sin(\bar{\alpha}) \sin(\bar{\beta}) = (\nu + kh) \sin \sigma \sin \bar{\alpha}^*$$

$$(l) \cos(\bar{\alpha}) \sin(\bar{\beta}) = (\nu + kh) \sin \sigma \cos \bar{\alpha}^*$$

$$- e^2 \cos \bar{\phi}(\bar{\nu} \sin \bar{\phi} - \nu \sin \phi)$$

$$(l) \cos(\bar{\beta}) = -(\nu + kh) \cos \sigma + (\bar{\nu} + k\bar{h})$$

30.36 $$- e^2 \sin \bar{\phi}(\bar{\nu} \sin \bar{\phi} - \nu \sin \phi)$$

where σ and $\bar{\alpha}^*$ are functions of the geodetic latitude and longitude of corresponding points of the deformed surfaces given by Equations 19.01, 19.07, and 19.08. In spherical polar coordinates $(\nu = \bar{\nu} = R, e = 0)$, Equations 30.35 and 30.36 reduce to

$$(l)^2 = 4 \sin^2 \tfrac{1}{2}\psi(R + kh)(R + k\bar{h}) + k^2(h - \bar{h})^2$$

$$= l_0^2 \left(1 + \frac{k(h + \bar{h})}{R} + \frac{k^2 h\bar{h}}{R^2}\right) + k^2(h - \bar{h})^2$$

30.37

where we have written ψ for σ and l_0 for $2R \sin \tfrac{1}{2}\psi$ $(k=0)$ to agree with the notation of Chapter 29. We have also

$$(l) \sin(\bar{\alpha}) \sin(\bar{\beta}) = (R + kh) \sin \psi \sin \bar{\alpha}^*$$

$$= (R + kh) \cos \phi \sin(\bar{\omega} - \omega)$$

$$(l) \cos(\bar{\alpha}) \sin(\bar{\beta}) = (R + kh) \sin \psi \cos \bar{\alpha}^*$$

$$= (R + kh)(- \sin \phi \cos \bar{\phi}$$

$$+ \cos \phi \sin \bar{\phi}$$

$$\times \cos(\bar{\omega} - \omega))$$

$$(l) \cos(\bar{\beta}) = (R + k\bar{h}) - (R + kh) \cos \psi$$

30.38 $$= 2 \sin^2 \tfrac{1}{2}\psi(R + kh) + k(\bar{h} - h).$$

APPLICATION OF GREEN'S THEOREM

22. In this section, we shall apply Green's theorem in the form of Equation 9.19 to a volume bounded in part by an arbitrary surface S (fig. 42), which is somewhere near the actual surface of the Earth E, and shall obtain an expression for the potential at a point P on S. Later, we shall make S coincide with the actual surface of the Earth, but for the present we consider the more general case where there are masses external to S. One of the scalars in Equation 9.19 will be the reciprocal of the distance $(1/l)$ from the fixed point P to a current point Q within the volume, and the other scalar will be V (the attraction potential at Q) so that Equation 9.19 becomes

$$\int_S \left\{V \frac{\partial}{\partial s}\left(\frac{1}{l}\right) - \frac{1}{l}\frac{\partial V}{\partial s}\right\} dS = \int_v \left\{V\Delta\left(\frac{1}{l}\right) - \frac{1}{l}\Delta V\right\} dv$$

30.39

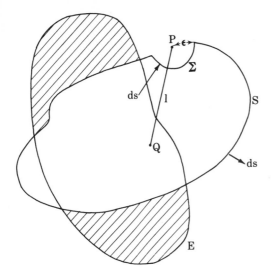

Figure 42.

in which dv is an element of volume and ds is the arc element in the direction of the normal to S, drawn outward from the volume considered.

23. In the first place, we shall consider the internal volume bounded by S, and shall consider only the attraction potential V_1 arising from the matter outside S (shaded in fig. 42) so that mathematically we may suppose all the matter inside S has been removed. But in applying Equation 30.39 to this case, we notice that the surface integrand at least becomes infinite when $l=0$, that is, when Q coincides with P, as it must do for some. part of the integration; therefore, we cannot apply Equation 30.39 as it stands to the whole region bounded by S. To overcome this difficulty, we remove a *small* hemisphere Σ of radius ϵ, centered on P, from the volume enclosed by S and integrate over the remaining volume, the surface S minus Σ, and the curved surface of Σ. For this area and volume, Equation 30.39 becomes

$$\int_{S-\Sigma}\left\{V_1\frac{\partial}{\partial s}\left(\frac{1}{l}\right)-\frac{1}{l}\frac{\partial V_1}{\partial s}\right\}dS+\int_{\Sigma}\left\{V_1\frac{\partial}{\partial s}\left(\frac{1}{l}\right)-\frac{1}{l}\frac{\partial V_1}{\partial s}\right\}dS$$

30.40
$$=\int\left\{V_1\Delta\left(\frac{1}{l}\right)-\frac{1}{l}\Delta V_1\right\}dv.$$

Throughout the volume, both $1/l$ and V_1 are harmonic and the volume integral is zero. Next, we consider the surface integral over Σ. If (V_1) is an average value of V_1 over Σ and if $d\Omega$ is an element of solid angle at P, the first term is

$$-(V_1)\int\frac{1}{l^2}\frac{\partial l}{\partial s}\times\epsilon^2 d\Omega=+2\pi(V_1)$$

because $l=\epsilon$ on Σ and $\partial l/\partial s$ is minus 1 on Σ. (Note that for the proper application of Green's theorem, as derived in § 9–12 through § 9–14, the positive direction of ds must be in the direction of the normal to the boundary surface exterior to the volume over which the volume integral is taken, as shown in fig. 42.) In the second term of the integral over Σ, $\partial V_1/\partial s$ is the normal component of the force of attraction arising from V_1; for physical reasons, this force must be finite and have a maximum value $(\partial V_1/\partial s)$ over Σ so that the second term is less than

$$-\left(\frac{\partial V_1}{\partial s}\right)\int\frac{1}{\epsilon}\,\epsilon^2 d\Omega=-2\pi\epsilon\left(\frac{\partial V_1}{\partial s}\right),$$

which is zero in the limit when $\epsilon\to0$. The average value (V_1) of V_1 on Σ becomes in the limit the potential V_{1P} at P. We may also consider that the remaining surface integral is taken over the whole surface *except at the actual point* P, although it will require special treatment in the immediate neighborhood of P as in the case of Stokes' integral (§ 29–30). Equation 30.40 finally becomes

30.41 $$-2\pi V_{1P}=\int\left\{V_1\frac{\partial}{\partial s}\left(\frac{1}{l}\right)-\frac{1}{l}\frac{\partial V_1}{\partial s}\right\}dS.$$

24. In deriving this result, we have assumed that the volume integrand in Equation 30.40 remains finite as $\epsilon\to0$, or in other words, the volume integral

$$\int\left\{V_1\Delta\left(\frac{1}{l}\right)-\frac{1}{l}\Delta V_1\right\}dv$$

taken over the hemisphere becomes zero as $\epsilon\to0$. Throughout the small volume, bounded by the hemisphere Σ and the continuation of the surface S, ΔV_1, by Poisson's Equation 20.14, is either zero or at least finite, even if P lies just inside the matter on and external to S. If (ΔV_1) is the maximum value of ΔV_1, the second term of the volume integral is accordingly less than

$$-(\Delta V_1)\int_0^\epsilon\frac{1}{l}\times2\pi l^2 dl=-(\Delta V_1)\pi\epsilon^2$$

which is zero as $\epsilon\to0$. In regard to the first term of the volume integral, we can consider that $(-1/l)$ is the potential at Q of a particle of mass $1/G$ situated at P (G is the gravitational constant). When Q is within Σ, $\Delta(1/l)$ is therefore zero except actually at the particle of mass $1/G$, that is, when Q coincides with P. For physical reasons, we must suppose that the actual attraction potential V_1 of the external masses is finite within Σ. Accordingly, the first term of the volume integral becomes zero as $\epsilon\to0$, provided we exclude the actual point

P ($\epsilon = 0$) as we have already done in deriving Equation 30.41. The exclusion of the point P, and of any matter actually at P, from the volume and the surface, although mathematically necessary, makes no significant physical difference to the mass distribution and to the external field. Subject to these considerations, we are justified in assuming that the volume integral over the hemisphere becomes zero as $\epsilon \to 0$.

25. Next, we shall consider the potential V_2 arising from matter within the same surface S (shaded in fig. 43), and shall evaluate the potential

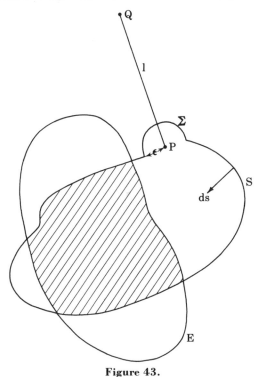

Figure 43.

at the same point P on S by applying Green's theorem to the volume enclosed between S and a sphere $\bar{S}$ of infinite radius (not indicated in fig. 43). To isolate the singularity in $1/l$ at P, we take a small hemisphere Σ of radius ϵ out of this volume, as shown in figure 43. Equation 30.39 for the remaining area and volume then becomes

$$\int_{S-\Sigma} \left\{ V_2 \frac{\partial}{\partial s}\left(\frac{1}{l}\right) - \frac{1}{l}\frac{\partial V_2}{\partial s} \right\} dS$$
$$+ \int_{\bar{S}} \left\{ V_2 \frac{\partial}{\partial s}\left(\frac{1}{l}\right) - \frac{1}{l}\frac{\partial V_2}{\partial s} \right\} dS$$
$$+ \int_{\Sigma} \left\{ V_2 \frac{\partial}{\partial s}\left(\frac{1}{l}\right) - \frac{1}{l}\frac{\partial V_2}{\partial s} \right\} dS$$

30.42
$$= \int \left\{ V_2 \Delta\left(\frac{1}{l}\right) - \frac{1}{l}\Delta V_2 \right\} dv.$$

As in the case of V_1 arising from the external matter, we find that the volume integral is zero, even when $\epsilon \to 0$; and so also is the integral zero over the infinite sphere $\bar{S}$ because V_2 behaves like $1/l$ at infinity. The second term of the surface integral over Σ is similarly zero, and the first term is

$$- (V_2) \int \frac{1}{l^2}\frac{\partial l}{\partial s} \, \epsilon^2 d\Omega$$

where (V_2) is an average value of V_2 over the hemispherical surface. In this case, the positive direction of ds is inward away from the volume over which the volume integral is taken, as shown in figure 43, so that $\partial l/\partial s = -1$ on the boundary of the hemisphere, and the surface integral as $\epsilon \to 0$ is $2\pi V_{2P}$ where V_{2P} is the value of V_2 at P. Equation 30.42 thus reduces to

30.43
$$-2\pi V_{2P} = \int_S \left\{ V_2 \frac{\partial}{\partial s}\left(\frac{1}{l}\right) - \frac{1}{l}\frac{\partial V_2}{\partial s} \right\} dS,$$

which has exactly the same form as Equation 30.41 for the potential V_{1P} arising from the external masses. A glance at figures 42 and 43 shows, however, that the positive directions of ds are opposite in the two cases. If we wish to combine Equations 30.41 and 30.43, we must change the sign of ds in one of these equations. We shall do so in Equation 30.43, thereby ensuring that the positive direction of ds is away from the main mass of the Earth in both cases. Equation 30.43 then becomes

30.44
$$2\pi V_{2P} = \int \left\{ V_2 \frac{\partial}{\partial s}\left(\frac{1}{l}\right) - \frac{1}{l}\frac{\partial V_2}{\partial s} \right\} dS.$$

Because there are no volume integrals in Equations 30.41 and 30.44, the current point Q is now restricted to the surface S. The potentials (V_1 or V_2) and the component of the forces of attraction in the direction of the normal to S, drawn toward the main mass of the Earth ($\partial V_1/\partial s$ or $\partial V_2/\partial s$ in accordance with Equation 20.05), must be evaluated or observed at points Q on S. The distance l is PQ between two points on S; one point is fixed at P and the other is the current point Q in the surface integration.

26. Next, we consider the potential Ω of the centrifugal force, given by Equation 20.08 as

30.45
$$\Omega = \tfrac{1}{2}\tilde{\omega}^2(x^2 + y^2)$$

in which $\tilde{\omega}$ is the angular velocity of rotation of the Earth and $(x^2 + y^2)$ is the square of the perpendicular distance of the point considered from the axis of rotation. If W, V are, respectively, the geopotential and the attraction potential at the same point, then Equation 20.08 with suitable change of notation also gives

30.46
$$W = V - \Omega = V_1 + V_2 - \Omega$$

in which we have applied the principle of super-position (§20–7) by making the total potential $V = V_1 + V_2$. It is clear from Equation 30.45 that Ω has no singularities on or inside the surface S of figure 42 so that we can use Equation 30.40 simply by replacing V_1 with Ω. The volume integral in Equation 30.40 is now

$$- \int \frac{2\tilde{\omega}^2 dv}{l},$$

taken over the whole volume enclosed by S; allow-ing for the singularity of $1/l$ at $l = 0$ as in §30–23, we have

$$- 2\pi \Omega_P = \int \left\{ \Omega \frac{\partial}{\partial s} \left(\frac{1}{l} \right) - \frac{1}{l} \frac{\partial \Omega}{\partial s} \right\} dS + \int \frac{2\tilde{\omega}^2}{l} \, dv.$$

30.47

By adding Equations 30.41 and 30.44, subtracting Equation 30.47, and using Equation 30.46, we have

$$\int \left\{ W \frac{\partial}{\partial s} \left(\frac{1}{l} \right) - \frac{1}{l} \frac{\partial W}{\partial s} \right\} dS - \int \frac{2\tilde{\omega}^2}{l} \, dv$$

$$= 2\pi (V_{2P} - V_{1P}) + 2\pi \Omega_P$$

$$= 2\pi (W_P + \Omega_P - 2V_{1P}) + 2\pi \Omega_P$$

30.48 $= 2\pi (W_P - 2V_{1P}) + 2\pi \tilde{\omega}^2 (x_P^2 + y_P^2).$

This equation, which is fundamental to the subject, has been given explicitly by de Graaff-Hunter[6] and in various approximate or special forms by several other writers.

27. It can be argued that V_1 and V_2 in Equation 30.46 are harmonic and therefore $V = V_1 + V_2$ is harmonic—for example, in the sense that if V_1 and V_2 can be validly expressed in solid spherical harmonics, so can V—even when P lies inside the attracting matter, where V should satisfy not the Laplace equation but Poisson's Equation 20.14. This question, which does not appear to be satis-factorily answered anywhere in the literature, requires an answer even though, for reasons given in §21–74, we are not concerned in geodesy with potential and force inside matter. We have already noted in §30–23 and §30–24 that the point P, and with P any particle of matter at P, must be excluded from both the surface and the volume considered in Green's Equation 30.39. The point P must there-fore be considered as lying within a small cavity where the potential is harmonic. This argument is even clearer if we consider the potential at P in the form of a volume integral

$$V = - \int \frac{G\rho dv}{l}$$

---

[6] de Graaff-Hunter, *op. cit. supra* note 2.

in which l is the distance between P and a current point Q, G is the gravitational constant, ρ is the density, and the integral is taken over the whole volume occupied by attracting matter. The inte-grand becomes infinite when Q coincides with P ($l = 0$), and the integral does not therefore con-verge unless we exclude the particle actually at P. If we do exclude this particle (and we can do so without significant effect on either the mass dis-tribution, the external field, or the internal field), V becomes a sum of harmonic functions and there-fore itself a harmonic function. Nevertheless, we are not entitled to differentiate the relation $V = V_1 + V_2$—once to find the force, or twice to find the density—unless the resulting differentials are continuous; differentiation implies a displace-ment from the cavity at P into the surrounding matter, and we must expect some discontinuity to result from this process. In the case of a continu-ous distribution of matter—except in the cavity at P—we can argue physically from the principle of superposition (§20–7) of potential and of force, implying that a relation similar to $V = V_1 + V_2$ exists for the force components, that the potential and its first derivatives are continuous at P, but the second derivatives are not continuous and Poisson's equation provides a measure of the discontinuity (§20–18). This question of discontinuous derivatives will become clearer when we consider single- and double-layer distributions in §30–31 through §30–41. We shall find that in the case of a single layer the potential is continuous across the surface, whereas the force is discontinuous and cannot be obtained by differentiating the potential; in the case of a double layer, both the potential and the force are discontinuous.

28. It is usual to simplify Equation 30.48 by intro-ducing the potential anomaly T as defined in §29–10. To do this, we write Equation 30.48 for the actual geopotential W and for the standard geopotential U and subtract, remembering that the centrifugal terms are the same for both actual and standard fields and will cancel. We assume further that the mass giving rise to the standard field is entirely contained within the surface S so that V_{1P} for the standard field is zero. The result is

30.49 $2\pi (T_P - 2V_{1P}) = \int \left\{ T \frac{\partial}{\partial s} \left(\frac{1}{l} \right) - \frac{1}{l} \frac{\partial T}{\partial s} \right\} dS.$

It is usually assumed that the mass giving rise to the standard field of Chapter 23 is contained within the equipotential base spheroid of this field, so that the field external to the spheroid can be ex-pressed in the form of a convergent series of spheroidal harmonics as discussed in §23–9 and §22–23. In that case, we must ensure that the spheroid lies entirely within the surface S of Equation 30.49.

29. If the surface S coincides with or lies entirely outside the topographic surface of the Earth, we have $V_{1P} = 0$, and Equation 30.49 becomes

30.50 $2\pi T_P = \int \left\{ T \frac{\partial}{\partial s} \left(\frac{1}{l} \right) - \frac{1}{l} \frac{\partial T}{\partial s} \right\} dS.$

This equation applies also to the co-geoid, or regularized geoid, outside which all masses have been removed. On the other hand, if we do not remove the external masses, we must estimate their potential V_{1P} at P and substitute in Equation 30.49, which then applies to the actual or nonregularized geoid. In the same way, we can estimate the potential of masses external to the Model Earth (or the telluroid or the terroid), but with less drastic assumptions; Equation 30.49 can then be applied to the surface of the Model Earth (or the telluroid or the terroid). Unless S coincides with the actual topographic surface, and for reasons given in §30–2 this situation is not altogether possible, some estimate of the potential of masses external to S is necessary.

30. In applications involving satellites, we may require the attraction potential at a point P not on S but external to S, which, for this purpose, we shall assume contains all the matter. We apply Green's Equation 30.39 to the volume bounded by S and the infinite sphere. The integrand becomes infinite when the current point Q coincides with P $(l = 0)$, and to deal with this situation, we exclude a small *sphere* Σ of radius ϵ centered on P from the area and volume considered. As in §30–25, we find that the volume integral is zero (even when $\epsilon \to 0$), the integral over the infinite sphere is zero, and the second term of the surface integral over Σ is zero. The remaining integral over Σ, as in §30–23, is

$$\int_{\Sigma} V \frac{\partial}{\partial s} \left(\frac{1}{l} \right) dS = \int \frac{V}{\epsilon^2} \epsilon^2 d\Omega = 4\pi V_P.$$

The positive direction of ds in Equation 30.39 is away from the volume considered, and we must accordingly change the sign of ds to follow the convention of §30–25, that is, positive ds away from the main mass of the Earth. We have finally

30.51 $4\pi V_P = \int \left\{ V \frac{\partial}{\partial s} \left(\frac{1}{l} \right) - \frac{1}{l} \frac{\partial V}{\partial s} \right\} dS$

in which we may substitute for V the harmonic potential anomaly T, so that Equation 30.50 holds for an exterior point P with the substitution of 4π

for 2π. If P is an exterior point, the singularity at P has to be removed by excluding a small sphere of radius ϵ, whereas if P is confined to the surface S, a small hemisphere serves to remove the singularity. The difference in area between a sphere and a hemisphere accounts for the factor of 2 between Equations 30.51 and 30.50.

Equations 30.41, 30.44, and 30.51 are equivalent to three of the six relations, usually known as *Green's third identities*, obtained from Equation 30.39 for the volumes external and internal to the closed surface S when P is outside, on, or inside S. The other three identities can easily be obtained similarly if required. If V in Equation 30.39 is not harmonic, the volume integral

$$-\int \frac{\Delta V}{l} \, dv$$

must be retained in deriving these identities as we have done in deriving Equation 30.47; V must still be finite and continuous, and have finite and continuous first and second derivatives throughout the volume considered. *Green's first identity* is Equation 9.18, and *Green's second identity* is Equation 9.19 with Equation 30.39 as a special case.

POTENTIAL AND ATTRACTION OF A SINGLE LAYER

31. We shall now develop further the ideas in §29–53 through §29–59 by considering the field arising from a layer or coating of surface density σ spread over an arbitrary S-surface.

At External Points

32. Omitting the gravitational constant or considering σ to be the surface density multiplied by the gravitational constant, the potential at an external point P arising from an element of mass at Q on the surface is $-\sigma dS/l$ where l as usual is the distance PQ. The total potential at P is accordingly

30.52 $V_P = -\int \frac{\sigma dS}{l} = -\int \frac{\sigma}{Kl} \, d\Omega$

where K is the Gaussian curvature of the surface and $d\Omega$ is an element of solid angle enclosed by normals to the surface, that is, an element of solid angle or area in the unit spherical representation of the surface. In deriving this result, we have used Equation 13.14.

33. The vector attraction at an external point P arising from an element of mass at Q is

$$-\frac{\sigma dS}{l^2}\, l_r$$

where l_r is a unit vector in the direction $\overrightarrow{QP}$ and is also the gradient of l for a displacement of P with Q fixed. The gradient of the potential at P—the negative of the total force of attraction from the generalization of Equation 20.05—is then

30.53 $(V_r)_P = +\int \frac{\sigma dS}{l^2}\, l_r = +\int \frac{\sigma}{Kl^2}\, l_r d\Omega,$

which could have been obtained by differentiating Equation 30.52 for a displacement of P, but only because there are no singularities in either the potential or gravity at an external point P. If we wish to combine Equation 30.53 with other equations in which l_r is the unit vector in the direction $\overrightarrow{PQ}$, we must change the sign of l_r and write Equation 30.53 as

30.53A $(V_r)_P = -\int \frac{\sigma dS}{l^2}\, l_r = -\int \frac{\sigma}{Kl^2}\, l_r d\Omega.$

At Points on the Surface

34. Equations 30.52 and 30.53 are valid if the S-surface has a unique spherical representation (§ 11–2) and continuous curvature. However, if the point P lies on the surface, the integrands become infinite when P and Q coincide ($l = 0$), and we must investigate this case further. We do so by considering part of the coating to be a small circular disc centered on P, the potential and attraction of which is a stock case in the literature;[7] the potential and attraction of the remainder of the coating presents no problem. The potential of the disc, of radius ϵ, is $-2\pi\sigma\epsilon$ which diminishes to zero as ϵ decreases. Moreover, this result is true whether we consider P to be outside or inside the coating, so that the potential is continuous across the coating and Equation 30.52 holds true whether P lies on the surface or not, although the integral will need special evaluation when Q is in the neighborhood of P just as Stokes' integral needs special evaluation in that case (§ 29–30).

35. The attraction of the disc at P on the surface is $2\pi\sigma$, directed along the surface normal at P if the disc is small enough for the density to be considered uniform. The attraction of the disc is down-

---

[7] See, for example, Heiskanen and Moritz (1967), *Physical Geodesy*, 129.

ward if P is on the outside (and upward if P is on the inside) of the surface so that there is a discontinuity of $4\pi\sigma$ across the surface. If, as usual in this application, P is on the outside of the surface, the gradient of the potential at P or the negative of the total force of attraction at P is given by

$$(V_r)_P = +2\pi\sigma(\nu_r)_P + \int \frac{\sigma dS}{l^2}\, l_r$$

30.54 $= +2\pi\sigma(\nu_r)_P + \int \frac{\sigma}{Kl^2}\, l_r d\Omega$

instead of by Equation 30.53. In Equation 30.54, $(\nu_r)_P$ is the unit outward-drawn or exterior normal to the surface at P, and l_r is the unit vector in the direction $\overrightarrow{QP}$. If we wish to combine Equation 30.54 with other equations in which l_r is the unit vector in the direction $\overrightarrow{PQ}$, we must change the sign of l_r and write Equation 30.54 as

$$(V_r)_P = +2\pi\sigma(\nu_r)_P - \int \frac{\sigma dS}{l^2}\, l_r$$

30.54A $= +2\pi\sigma(\nu_r)_P - \int \frac{\sigma}{Kl^2}\, l_r d\Omega.$

POTENTIAL AND ATTRACTION OF A DOUBLE LAYER

36. In this section, we develop further the ideas in § 21–101 through § 21–103 by considering an outer surface layer of density σ and an inner surface layer of density minus σ. The notion of negative density has, of course, no physical significance except in connection with the analogous magnetic dipole distribution, but the notion is, nevertheless, of value as a mathematical device. In figure 44, we locate an element of mass (minus

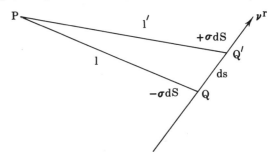

Figure 44.

σdS) at the current point Q on the S-surface and an element of mass (plus σdS) at a point Q' on the surface normal distant ds from Q. Because ds is small and in the limit will be zero, we can suppose that the two elements of area dS at Q and Q' are bounded by surface normals and are equal. In proceeding to the limit $ds \to 0$, we assume that σds remains finite and equal to μ so that $\sigma \to \infty$ as $ds \to 0$. The whole arrangement is accordingly analogous to a surface distribution of dipoles of moment density μ, oriented in the direction of the surface normals.

At External Points

37. The potential at an external point P arising from the elements $\pm \sigma dS$ is

$$-\frac{\sigma dS}{l'} + \frac{\sigma dS}{l} = -\frac{\mu}{ds}\left(\frac{1}{l'} - \frac{1}{l}\right) dS.$$

In the limit $ds \to 0$, this last expression becomes

$$-\mu \frac{\partial}{\partial s}\left(\frac{1}{l}\right) dS$$

so that the total potential at P is

30.55 $$V_P = -\int \mu \frac{\partial}{\partial s}\left(\frac{1}{l}\right) dS,$$

which contains no singularities as long as P lies outside the surface ($l \neq 0$). Partial differentiation with respect to s implies differentiation along the surface normal at Q with P fixed, so that we have

30.56 $$\frac{\partial}{\partial s}\left(\frac{1}{l}\right) = \left(\frac{1}{l}\right)_r \nu^r = -\frac{1}{l^2}(l_r \nu^r)$$

in which l_r is now a unit vector in the direction $\overrightarrow{PQ}$.

38. The attraction at P is

$$\frac{\sigma dS}{(l')^2} - \frac{\sigma dS}{l^2} = \frac{\mu}{ds}\left(\frac{1}{(l')^2} - \frac{1}{l^2}\right) dS,$$

which becomes in the limit

$$\mu \frac{\partial}{\partial s}\left(\frac{1}{l^2}\right) dS$$

in the direction $\overrightarrow{PQ} = l_r$. The gradient of the total potential at P is the negative of the total attraction at P,

30.57 $$(V_r)_P = -\int \mu \frac{\partial}{\partial s}\left(\frac{1}{l^2}\right) l_r dS = \int \frac{2\mu}{l^3}(l_t \nu^t) l_r dS.$$

At Points on the Surface

39. If P is on the surface, there are strong singularities when P and Q coincide ($l = 0$) and the integrands become infinite. As in the case of a single layer, we consider small circular discs of radius ϵ taken out of the two layers, as shown in figure 45, where we have located P on the outside of the top layer. The potential of the top disc is $-2\pi\sigma\epsilon$ and

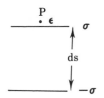

Figure 45.

the potential of the bottom disc is $2\pi\sigma\,(\epsilon - ds)$ to a first order in ds/ϵ, so that the total potential at P of the double disc is $-2\pi\sigma ds$ which becomes $-2\pi\mu$ in the limit $ds \to 0$. Instead of Equation 30.55 for the potential of the whole double layer, we have

30.58 $$V_P = -2\pi\mu_P - \int \mu \frac{\partial}{\partial s}\left(\frac{1}{l}\right) dS.$$

If we had located P on the inside of the bottom layer, the potential of the double disc would be $+2\pi\mu_P$; accordingly, there is a discontinuity of $4\pi\mu_P$ in the potential on crossing a double layer.

40. If we use the same method to evaluate the attraction of the double layer at a point P on the surface, we find that the attraction is indeterminate when both ϵ and ds tend to zero. Moreover, the singularity in the potential of Equation 30.58 suggests that there must also be a singularity in the attraction containing differentials of the moment distribution μ, which we cannot introduce if we suppose that the distribution is uniform over the small discs. We can overcome the difficulty by a device similar to that used in § 29–41, which has also been used by Koch [8] in the present application.

41. We can evaluate the integral

$$\int \frac{\partial}{\partial s}\left(\frac{1}{l}\right) dS$$

by the divergence theorem, Equation 9.17, provided we remove the singularity at P, where the integrand becomes infinite, by the device used in § 30–23. Or, we can use Equation 30.41 for V_1 equal to unity and obtain the result at once as

30.59 $$\int \frac{\partial}{\partial s}\left(\frac{1}{l}\right) dS = -2\pi,$$

which can be used to rewrite the potential of the double layer at P, given by Equation 30.58, as

30.60 $$V_P = -\int (\mu - \mu_P) \frac{\partial}{\partial s}\left(\frac{1}{l}\right) dS.$$

[8] Koch (1967), *Determination of the First Derivatives of the Disturbing Potential by Green's Fundamental Formula*, Report No. 90 of the Department of Geodetic Science, The Ohio State University Research Foundation, Columbus, Ohio, 12–13.

If we differentiate this last equation for a displacement of P in a direction m^r (line element dm) with Q fixed, we have

$$\frac{\partial V_P}{\partial m} = \int \frac{\partial \mu_P}{\partial m} \frac{\partial}{\partial s}\left(\frac{1}{l}\right) dS - \int (\mu - \mu_P) \frac{\partial}{\partial m}\frac{\partial}{\partial s}\left(\frac{1}{l}\right) dS$$

30.61
$$= -2\pi \frac{\partial \mu_P}{\partial m} - \int (\mu - \mu_P) \frac{\partial}{\partial m}\frac{\partial}{\partial s}\left(\frac{1}{l}\right) dS$$

where we have used Equation 30.59. This equation gives the negative of the component of attraction in the direction m^r, provided we can show there are no singularities in the integrals of both Equations 30.60 and 30.61. Using Equation 30.56, we can rewrite Equation 30.60 as

30.62 $\qquad V_P = \int (\mu - \mu_P) \frac{(l_r \nu^r)}{l^2} dS$

where l_r is a unit vector in the direction $\overrightarrow{PQ}$ and ν^r is the unit normal to the S-surface at Q. We can show, as in § 29–41, that this equation contains no singularity at P. The change in the vector (ll_r) for a displacement dm of P in the direction m^r with Q fixed is $-m_r dm$ (fig. 46), so that we have

$$\frac{\partial}{\partial m}(ll_r) = -m_r.$$

Accordingly, the value of the integral in Equation 30.61, obtained by differentiating Equation 30.62

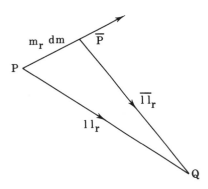

Figure 46.

for a displacement of P with Q (and therefore ν^r, dS) fixed, is

$$-\int (\mu - \mu_P) \frac{\partial}{\partial m}\frac{\partial}{\partial s}\left(\frac{1}{l}\right) dS$$

$$= \int (\mu - \mu_P) \frac{\partial}{\partial m}\left(\frac{ll_r}{l^3}\right) \nu^r dS$$

30.63 $\qquad = \int \frac{(\mu - \mu_P)}{l^3}\{3(l_t \nu^t)(l_r m^r) - m_r \nu^r\} dS,$

remembering that the gradient l at P with Q fixed is in the direction $\overrightarrow{QP}$ and is therefore minus l_r. As in § 29–41, we can show that there is no singularity in this integral at P so that Equation 30.61, with the alternative expression in Equation 30.63, correctly gives the component in the direction m^r of the potential gradient (or the negative of the force vector) at P when P is on the surface. Because m^r is an arbitrary vector which can be considered constant during the surface integration, we can rewrite Equations 30.61 and 30.63 in the vector form

$$(V_r)_P = -2\pi(\mu_r)_P + \int \frac{\mu - \mu_P}{l^3}\{3(l_t \nu^t)l_r - \nu_r\} dS$$

30.64

in which l_r is the unit vector in the direction $\overrightarrow{PQ}$. Because the moment density μ can vary only along the surface, its gradient μ_r has no normal component. If we contract Equation 30.64 with an arbitrary unit vector m^r, we must accordingly ignore the normal component of m^r in evaluating the $(\mu_r)_P$-term. For example, if q^r is a unit surface vector in the plane of ν^r and m^r, we may write

$$m^r = \nu^r \cos \beta + q^r \sin \beta,$$

and the value of the $(\mu_r)_P$-term will then be $-2\pi(\mu_r q^r \sin \beta)$.

THE EQUIVALENT SURFACE LAYERS

42. One object of the diversion on single and double layers in the last two sections, apart from the fact that these notions appear often in the literature, is to show that any harmonic potential can be considered as arising from a combination of single and double layers spread over a surface S which contained all the original mass distribution. If P is an external point and Q a current point on the surface as usual and if we suppose that we are given the values of V_Q and $(\partial V/\partial s)_Q$ over the surface, we can take the moment density of the double layer to be $\mu_Q = -V_Q/(4\pi)$ and the density of the single layer to be $\sigma_Q = (\partial V/\partial s)_Q/(4\pi)$. From Equations 30.55 and 30.52, the total potential at the *external* point P will be

$$V_P = \frac{1}{4\pi}\int\int\left\{V_Q \frac{\partial}{\partial s}\left(\frac{1}{l}\right) - \frac{1}{l}\left(\frac{\partial V}{\partial s}\right)_Q\right\} dS,$$

30.65

which agrees with Equation 30.51, so that the two mass distributions can be considered equivalent in the sense that they give rise to the same external field.

43. From Equation 30.58 and from the fact that Equation 30.52 continues to hold true for a point P on the surface (§ 30–34), we find that the total potential of both layers at a point P on the S-surface is

$$V_P = \tfrac{1}{2} V_P + \frac{1}{4\pi} \int \left\{ V_Q \frac{\partial}{\partial s}\left(\frac{1}{l}\right) - \frac{1}{l}\left(\frac{\partial V}{\partial s}\right)_Q \right\} dS,$$

giving the same answer as Equation 30.50, in which T can be considered a general harmonic potential. The same two layers accordingly give the correct potential at a point on the surface as well as at an external point. The same restrictions must, however, be applied as in the derivation of Equations 30.50 and 30.51 in regard to the continuity of the surface, which must contain all the original mass distribution.

44. If the S-surface is an equipotential, such as the co-geoid or regularized geoid, V_Q is a constant V_0 over the surface, and the first term of the integral of Equation 30.65 becomes

$$\frac{1}{4\pi} V_0 \int \frac{\partial}{\partial s}\left(\frac{1}{l}\right) dS.$$

If P is an external point, there are no singularities in this surface integral or in the volume integral of the divergence theorem (Equation 9.17) over the space enclosed by the surface. The integral is therefore zero. In this case, the potential arising from the constant moment density is zero; we can consider that the equivalent coating is a single layer of density $(\partial V/\partial s)_Q/(4\pi)$, known as Green's equivalent layer.

45. To obtain the deflections and gravity disturbance, whether at external points or on the surface, we shall have to differentiate Equation 30.50 or 30.51 for a displacement of the point P, substitute Equation 29.23 for the gradient of the potential anomaly, and contract with the coordinate vectors as we did to derive Equations 29.58 in the case of the Poisson integral. The best procedure, which takes care of all the singularities, is to use the same two equivalent layers as we used for the potential in § 30–42. If P is external to the surface, we add the vector Equations 30.53 and 30.57 to obtain the potential gradient; if P is on the surface, we add Equations 30.54 and 30.64.

THE BASIC INTEGRAL EQUATIONS IN GEODETIC COORDINATES

46. Our next task will be to express Green's Equation 30.50 or 30.51 in a form in which they can be solved. We shall concentrate on Equation 30.50

for the potential anomaly at a point P on the S-surface (fig. 47), considering that the modifications required to use Equation 30.51 when P is outside the S-surface are self-evident. In figure 47, the

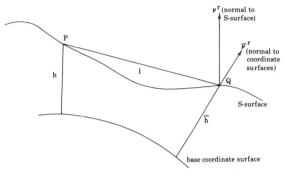

Figure 47.

normal to the S-surface at the current point Q is shown as ν^r and the normal through Q to the h-coordinate surface is shown as $\bar{\nu}^r$. The plane of the paper in figure 47 may be considered as containing $\bar{\nu}^r$ and PQ, but this plane does not necessarily contain ν^r or either normal at P, although the heights of P and Q are shown as $h, \bar{h}$, respectively.

47. If α, β are the geodetic azimuth and zenith distance of ν^r, and the geodetic parallel, meridian, and normal vectors are $\bar{\lambda}^r$, $\bar{\mu}^r$, $\bar{\nu}^r$, we have as usual

$$\nu^r = \bar{\lambda}^r \sin \alpha \sin \beta + \bar{\mu}^r \cos \alpha \sin \beta + \bar{\nu}^r \cos \beta.$$

30.66

We can consider that the maximum slope of the S-surface relative to the geodetic zenith is a depression of β in azimuth α, and, for the present purpose, it will be sufficient to take α, β as the astronomical azimuth and zenith distance of ν^r. If $\bar{\alpha}$, $\bar{\beta}$ are the geodetic azimuth and zenith distance at Q of the unit vector in the direction $\vec{PQ}$, which we have seen in § 29–35 is the same as the covariant gradient vector l_r for displacements of Q with P fixed, we have

$$l_r = \bar{\lambda}_r \sin \bar{\alpha} \sin \bar{\beta} + \bar{\mu}_r \cos \bar{\alpha} \sin \bar{\beta} + \bar{\nu}_r \cos \bar{\beta}.$$

30.67

We can obtain $\bar{\alpha}$, $\bar{\beta}$ direct from Equations 25.19 by writing l for s and by taking the overbarred point as Q. For substitution in Equation 30.50, we then have

$$\frac{\partial}{\partial s}\left(\frac{1}{l}\right) = -\frac{l_r \nu^r}{l^2}$$

$$= -\frac{1}{l^2} \{\cos \beta \cos \bar{\beta}$$

30.68
$$+ \cos (\bar{\alpha} - \alpha) \sin \beta \sin \bar{\beta}\}.$$

From Equations 30.66 and 29.23 in our present notation, we have also

$$\frac{\partial T}{\partial s} = T_r \nu^r = g\eta \sin \alpha \sin \beta$$

30.69 $+ g(\xi + \kappa) \cos \alpha \sin \beta + (g - \gamma) \cos \beta$

where g is actual gravity, γ is standard gravity, κ is the curvature correction (§ 29–12), and ξ, η are the usual components of deflection, all at Q. Equation 30.69 is suitable if we use the gravity disturbance $g_D = (g - \gamma)$ at Q during the surface integration. If we use the gravity anomaly g_A and Equations 29.25 and 29.30, we have

30.70 $\frac{\partial T}{\partial h} = (g - \gamma) = g_A + \frac{\partial \ln \gamma}{\partial h} T$

and

$$\frac{\partial T}{\partial s} = g\eta \sin \alpha \sin \beta + g(\xi + \kappa) \cos \alpha \sin \beta$$

30.71 $+ \left(g_A + \frac{\partial \ln \gamma}{\partial h} T \right) \cos \beta.$

Formulas equivalent to Equations 30.69 and 30.71 can also be obtained from Equation 30.15 for $F = T$ with Equation 30.21, which shows that $(g\kappa)$ is minus the meridian component of standard gravity, as indeed we have already shown in § 29–12 to a first order in κ and in the gravity disturbance. If we wish to avoid introducing the deflections, we can use Equation 30.18 for $F = T$ with Equations 30.25 and 30.29, after substitution in the basic integral Equation 30.50. To avoid breaking the argument, we shall not write this alternative in full; instead, we shall concentrate on using Equations 30.69 and 30.71.

48. We have finally to express in geodetic coordinates the element of area dS of the S-surface at Q. If we construct normals to the h-coordinate surfaces through points on the boundary of dS, the element of area of the h-surface through Q enclosed by these normals can be expressed in two ways as

$$\cos \beta \, dS = (\bar{\nu} + \bar{h})(\bar{\rho} + \bar{h}) \cos \bar{\phi} \, d\bar{\omega} d\bar{\phi}$$

30.72 $= (\bar{\nu} + \bar{h})(\bar{\rho} + \bar{h}) d\Omega,$

using Equations 9.01 and 18.04 with $\bar{\rho}$, $\bar{\nu}$ as the principal radii of curvature of the base spheroid in the latitude $\bar{\phi}$ of Q. As shown in figure 47, $\bar{h}$ is the geodetic height of Q. The element of solid angle $d\Omega$ from Equation 29.01 refers to the spherical representation of the base coordinate spheroid and can be expressed as

30.73 $d\Omega = \cos \bar{\phi} \, d\bar{\omega} d\bar{\phi}.$

49. Substituting Equations 30.68, 30.71, and 30.72 in Equation 30.50 gives

30.74 $2\pi T_P + \int J T_Q d\Omega = \int L d\Omega$

where

$$J = \left\{ \cos \bar{\beta} + \cos (\bar{\alpha} - \alpha) \tan \beta \sin \bar{\beta} \right.$$
$$\left. + l \frac{\partial \ln \gamma}{\partial h} \right\} (\bar{\rho} + \bar{h})(\bar{\nu} + \bar{h})/l^2$$
$$L = -\{ g_A + g\eta \sin \alpha \tan \beta$$

30.75 $+ g(\xi + \kappa) \cos \alpha \tan \beta\}(\bar{\rho} + \bar{h})(\bar{\nu} + \bar{h})/l.$

Equation 30.74 is an integral equation for the unknown potential anomaly with J as kernel. All quantities in the surface integrands J, L refer to the current point Q, and the integrands contain the geodetic heights $\bar{h}$. But if we know the geodetic heights of all points as well as the potential, we should also know the standard potential and thus the potential anomaly; there would be no problem. Accordingly, the integral equation can only be solved by successive approximation. We could start with assumed heights and solve the equation for a first approximation to the potential anomaly T, which enables us to calculate the corresponding geodetic height at P. This operation would have to be repeated for the height of a network of points P to be used in a second approximation, so that ultimately we should end with a network of consistent heights which do satisfy the integral equation. Unfortunately, this direct numerical method is excessively complicated and involves so much computation that it could hardly be used in preference to corresponding data provided by satellite methods.

50. Many attempts have accordingly been made to derive integral formulas for the second and higher approximations. The most elegant method is a parametric method proposed by Molodenskii [9] who uses it to solve the simpler integral equation derived for a single layer in the next section, although the method could be used to solve the present problem. The integral equation is rewritten for a deformed surface, as discussed in § 30–19 through § 30–21, which simply means substitution of the formulas given in § 30–19 through § 30–21 and expansion in powers of k. In addition, the potential anomaly is expanded in powers of k as

30.76 $T = T_0 + kT_1 + k^2 T_2 + k^3 T_3 + \ldots.$

Because k is arbitrary in the sense that any deformed surface intermediate between the S-surface

---

[9] Molodenskii, Eremeev, and Yurkina, *op. cit. supra* note 1, 120–124.

and the base coordinate surface can be used, we can equate powers of k in the result and so can obtain a number of integral equations for T_0, T_1, T_2 .... The final answer for the potential anomaly on the S-surface ($k=1$) is obtained from Equation 30.76 as

30.77 $T = T_0 + T_1 + T_2 + T_3 + \ldots$

We may ask why the term containing the gravity anomaly and the deflections is not also expanded in powers of k; to do so would amount to defining the gravity anomaly, etc., on the base surface and on all intermediate k-surfaces, involving some form of height reduction for gravity and deflection which the entire Molodenskii approach seeks to avoid. However, we can consider that the gravity anomaly term is defined only on the S-surface; the term is therefore expressible as a function of two coordinates only—the geodetic latitude and longitude—and retains the same value at corresponding points of all the k-surfaces, although the term does not represent the gravity anomaly, etc., on these intermediate surfaces. The term $(\partial \ln \gamma / \partial h)$ also requires special consideration. The usual assumption is that the h-coordinate surfaces are standard equipotentials and the centrifugal term is assumed to be zero in Bruns' Equation 20.17, so that we have

30.78 $\dfrac{\partial \ln \gamma}{\partial h} = 2H = -\dfrac{1}{(\bar{\rho} + \bar{h})} - \dfrac{1}{(\bar{\nu} + \bar{h})}.$

These assumptions may be justified in view of the usual assumptions made in defining the gravity anomaly itself (for example, by Equation 29.31), especially when the term $(\partial \ln \gamma / \partial h)$ is multiplied by the small potential anomaly in the integral equation; but, by the time a number of other approximations have been made, it is not unreasonable to doubt the value of the T_2, T_3, etc., terms in Equation 30.77. If we work in terms of the gravity disturbance instead of the gravity anomaly, it is evident from Equation 30.70 that the term $(\partial \ln \gamma / \partial h)$ simply disappears from the integral equation, but in that case it would be necessary to compute the gravity disturbances from approximate geodetic heights and to repeat the whole computation later from more accurate heights.

51. Other approximations which have been introduced in the integral equation are too numerous to detail here. One very common—almost universal—approximation is to replace the $\bar{\rho}$, $\bar{\nu}$ of the base spheroid by a constant mean radius of curvature R, which amounts to changing the coordinate system to spherical polar coordinates. There is no objection to this procedure which is sometimes described as

a spherical approximation and is justified by rather unconvincing geometry, but to be consistent we should evaluate the slopes β and the deflections ξ, η in the same system; we should also use appropriate values for κ and $(\partial \ln \gamma / \partial h)$ which depend on the adopted standard field. These logical consequences of the spherical approximation are almost always ignored. Another common approximation is to neglect h/R in order to simplify further the expressions for l, $\bar{\alpha}$, $\bar{\beta}$, etc. The best reference for these approximate solutions is Moritz,[10] but other approximate solutions are given by de Graaff-Hunter [11] and by Levallois,[12] the latter using a spherical base surface in conjunction with gravity disturbances on the topographic surface. Iterative methods of approximate solution have been discussed fully by Koch [13] for the case of a single equivalent layer, and could be extended to cover the case of both single and double layers.

52. If we evaluate anomalies over the base spheroid instead of over the S-surface, we have $\beta = 0$, $\bar{h} = 0$, and Equations 30.75 become

$$J = \left\{ \cos \bar{\beta} + l\,\frac{\partial \ln \gamma}{\partial h} \right\} \frac{\bar{\rho}\bar{\nu}}{l^2}$$

$$L = -g_A \bar{\rho}\bar{\nu}/l.$$

The resulting integral equation, with the usual assumptions relating to $(\partial \ln \gamma / \partial h)$ unless gravity disturbances are used, can be used to solve the Zagrebin-Bjerhammar problem (§ 29–43) or to provide results equivalent to those derived in § 29–44 through § 29–47. If, in addition, we assume that the base surface is a sphere so that $\bar{\rho} = \bar{\nu} = R$, $l = 2R \sin \frac{1}{2}\psi$, $\cos \bar{\beta} = \sin \frac{1}{2}\psi$, $\partial \ln \gamma / \partial h \approx -2/R$, the integral equation can be solved by spherical harmonics to give Stokes' Equation 29.32.

Gradient Equations

53. Integral equations for the gradient of the potential anomaly can be obtained by the method outlined in § 30–45. For example, by adding Equations 30.54A and 30.64 for the potential anomaly T at a point P on the S-surface and by using the layer

[10] Moritz, *loc. cit. supra* note 5.

[11] de Graaff-Hunter, *loc. cit. supra* note 2.

[12] Levallois (1958), "Sur une Équation Intégrale Très Générale de la Gravimétrie," *Bulletin Géodésique*, new series, no. 50, 36–49.

[13] Koch (1967), *Successive Approximation of Solutions of Molodensky's Basic Integral Equation.* Report No. 85 of the Department of Geodetic Science, The Ohio State University Research Foundation, Columbus, Ohio, 1–34.

densities given in § 30–42, that is,

$$\sigma = \frac{1}{4\pi}\left(\frac{\partial T}{\partial s}\right), \quad \mu = -\frac{T}{4\pi},$$

we have

$$(T_r)_P = \frac{1}{2}\left(\frac{\partial T}{\partial s}\right)_P (\nu_r)_P - \frac{1}{4\pi}\int \frac{1}{l^2}\frac{\partial T}{\partial s} l_r dS$$

30.79 $\qquad + \frac{1}{2}(\bar{T}_r)_P - \frac{1}{4\pi}\int \frac{T-T_P}{l^3}\{3(l^t\nu_t)l_r - \nu_r\}dS$

where the overbar in the third term on the right implies the S-surface gradient of T for reasons given at the end of § 30–41. This equation can be contracted with any vector fixed at P during the integration. The simplest results are obtained by contraction with the S-surface normal and with the surface vectors at P because we are then able to assimilate the nonintegral terms on the right. For example, if we contract with $(\nu_r)_P$ (the S-surface normal at P), we have

$$(T_r\nu^r)_P = \left(\frac{\partial T}{\partial s}\right)_P$$

$$= -\frac{1}{2\pi}\int\left[\frac{1}{l^2}\frac{\partial T}{\partial s} l_r(\nu^r)_P\right.$$

30.80 $\qquad\left. + \frac{T-T_P}{l^3}\{3(l^t\nu_t)l_r(\nu^r)_P - \nu_r(\nu^r)_P\}\right]dS$

where as usual quantities which are not suffixed P refer to Q, and l_r is a unit vector in the direction $\overrightarrow{PQ}$. Contraction with an S-surface vector $(m^r)_P$ (line element dm) produces exactly the same result with the substitution of $(m^r)_P$ for $(\nu^r)_P$ and $\partial T/\partial m$ for $\partial T/\partial s$. Equivalent unexpanded formulas not in vector form have been obtained by Koch [14] who has priority for these formulas. The vector Equation 30.79 is, however, more general and can be contracted with the coordinate vectors at P to obtain the deflections and gravity disturbance at P, using Equation 29.23. Invariants in contractions of Equation 30.79 are best calculated from Cartesian components which, of course, are the same at P and Q for parallel vectors. Theoretically, the deflections and gravity disturbance at P can be calculated from the three simpler components of T_r, given by contraction with the S-surface normal and surface vectors; but, if S is the topographic surface, the results would be completely invalidated by uncertainty in the slope of the surface.

54. If the S-surface is a sphere, the equations are, of course, much simpler and are often given in the

[14] Koch, *op. cit. supra* note 8, 18–21.

literature, but they tell us nothing which has not already been obtained even more simply in Chapter 29. For example, Equation 30.80 can be reduced to Equation 29.60, using only results which have been obtained in Chapter 29.

THE EQUIVALENT SINGLE LAYER

55. The extra complication involved in the representation of the basic Green's Equation 30.50 by both single and double layers, especially in the gradient equations and when the point P is on the surface, has led Molodenskii to propose using only a single layer, spread over the topographic S-surface, as an equivalent mass distribution giving rise to the actual potential anomaly. The density σ of this single layer is, of course, no longer $(\partial V/\partial s)/(4\pi)$, but has to be determined to agree with the actual potential anomaly. We have seen in § 29–55 that this arrangement is possible for a general Newtonian potential if the S-surface is a sphere containing all the attracting matter, but some justification is needed in the case of a more general surface. The potential of a single layer at a point P, which is either on or outside the surface, is from Equation 30.52 and § 30–34

30.81 $\qquad V_P = -\int \frac{\sigma dS}{l}.$

If we hold the current point Q fixed so that σ and dS are fixed, differentiate twice covariantly for a displacement of an *external* point P, and contract with the associated metric tensor, all in Cartesian coordinates, we have

30.82 $\qquad (\Delta V)_P = -\int \Delta(1/l)\sigma dS = 0,$

provided σ is bounded. Moreover, the potential at P when P is at a great distance L from S tends toward

30.83 $\qquad V_P = -\frac{1}{L}\int \sigma dS = -\frac{M}{L}$

where M is the total mass of the coating. The coating accordingly does give rise to a Newtonian potential throughout the space outside the S-surface, and it is not unreasonable to suppose that we have sufficient freedom in the choice of σ to represent any Newtonian potential in this way. Similar justification when P is on the surface presents more difficulty. Differentiating Equation 30.54A again in Cartesian coordinates, we have

$$(V_{rs})_P = 2\pi(\bar{\sigma}_s)_P(\nu_r)_P + 2\pi\sigma_P(\nu_{rs})_P + \int (1/l)_{rs}\sigma dS$$

30.84

in which the overbar implies the surface gradient of σ because σ can vary only over the surface. We are entitled to assume that the surface integral derives from a Newtonian potential in free space at P, which is analytic at P, because the integral is not taken over the small disc at P (§ 30–35), so that there are no singularities in any of the derivatives of the potential represented by the integral. If we contract Equation 30.84 with the metric tensor and use Equation 7.19, we have

30.85 $$(\Delta V)_P = -4\pi H_P \sigma_P$$

in which H_P is the mean curvature of the surface at P. If the coating is to give rise to a Newtonian potential at a point P on the surface, we must assume, as indeed we have done in § 30–34 and § 30–35, that the small disc at P can be considered flat; in other words, that a small part of the surface at P, where we wish to find the potential, can be replaced by a plane. In practice, this conception presents no difficulty in the case of a sufficiently smooth surface; we do not avoid, and cannot expect to avoid, the necessity for some smoothing of the topographic surface by adopting the single layer device.

56. Brovar [15] has noticed that Equation 30.82 is satisfied if we use a more general harmonic function E instead of $1/l$ and a more general bounded function ϕ of the position of the current point Q on the surface instead of the surface density σ. In that case,

30.86 $$V_P = \int \phi E \, dS$$

represents a harmonic potential. But if V_P is to represent a general Newtonian potential throughout the free space external to the surface, Equation 30.83 must also be satisfied, and it has to be shown that a particular choice of E does so. For example, the spheroidal coordinate α does so (§ 22–35) and could be used in the representaion of a general Newtonian potential; so could Pizzetti's extension of the Stokes' function (Equation 29.14 for $k = R/r$), provided the zero- and first-degree harmonics are omitted. The use of Pizzetti's function does, in fact, result in some simplification in the formation and solution of the basic integral Equation 30.90 for a single layer. But the Cartesian coordinates of P and many functions of the Cartesian coordinates, which become infinite at great distances, cannot be used.

[15] Brovar (1963), "Solutions of the Molodenskiy Boundary Problem," American Geophysical Union translation of *Geodeziya i Aerofotos"yemka*, no. 4, 237–240.

The Basic Integral Equations

57. Writing Equation 30.54A for the potential anomaly, contracting with the coordinate vectors at P (a point on the surface), and using Equations 29.23, 29.25, 29.30, 30.66, and 30.67, we have

$$(g_D)_P = (g_A)_P + \left(\frac{\partial \ln \gamma}{\partial h}\right)_P T_P$$

30.87 $$= 2\pi\sigma_P \cos \beta_P - \int \frac{\sigma \cos \bar{\beta}_P}{l^2} \, dS$$

$$(g\eta)_P = 2\pi\sigma_P \sin \alpha_P \sin \beta_P$$

30.88 $$- \int \frac{\sigma \sin \bar{\alpha}_P \sin \bar{\beta}_P}{l^2} \, dS$$

$$\{g(\xi + \kappa)\}_P = 2\pi\sigma_P \cos \alpha_P \sin \beta_P$$

30.89 $$- \int \frac{\sigma \cos \bar{\alpha}_P \sin \bar{\beta}_P}{l^2} \, dS$$

where $(g_D)_P$, $(g_A)_P$ are as usual the gravity disturbance and gravity anomaly at P; α_P, β_P are the azimuth and zenith distance of the normal to the S-surface at P, that is, the azimuth α_P of the greatest slope, a depression of β_P; and $\bar{\alpha}_P$, $\bar{\beta}_P$ are the azimuth and zenith distance at P of the line $\overrightarrow{PQ}$ obtained in geodetic coordinates from Equation 25.18. Equation 30.87 can be combined with Equation 30.81 and written as

$$2\pi\sigma_P \cos \beta_P - \int \left[\frac{\cos \bar{\beta}_P}{l^2} - \left(\frac{\partial \ln \gamma}{\partial h}\right)_P \frac{1}{l}\right] \sigma \, dS = (g_A)_P,$$

30.90

which is the basic integral equation to determine σ from gravity anomalies. The corresponding equation for the gravity disturbance is obtained by omitting the term containing $(\partial \ln \gamma/\partial h)_P$. If P is outside the S-surface, we use Equation 30.53A instead of Equation 30.54A, which amounts simply to dropping the terms containing σ_P from Equations 30.87, 30.88, and 30.89.

58. The integral Equation 30.90 can be solved by any of the methods outlined in § 30–50 and § 30–51. It is usual to solve the equation in spherical polar coordinates with the usual approximation $\partial \ln \gamma/\partial h = -2/(R+h)$ (Equation 30.78). In that case, the first- or zero-order approximation, obtained by ignoring all heights or by solving the integral equation resulting from terms not containing k in Molodenskii's parametric solution, must be given by any of the results obtained for a spherical layer in § 29–53 through § 29–59. Equation 30.90 in spher-

ical polar coordinates with all heights ignored ($\beta_P = 0$, $\bar\beta_P = \frac{1}{2}\pi + \frac{1}{2}\psi$, $l = 2R\sin\frac{1}{2}\psi$, $dS = R^2 d\Omega$) becomes

$$(g_A)_P = 2\pi\sigma_P - \frac{3}{2}\int (\frac{1}{2}\operatorname{cosec}\frac{1}{2}\psi)\sigma\,d\Omega$$

30.91
$$= 2\pi\sigma_P - \frac{3}{2}\int \sigma \sum_{n=0}^{\infty} P_n(\cos\psi)\,d\Omega,$$

using Equation 29.11 for $k=1$. Using Equation 29.10, this last equation can be solved in spherical harmonics as

$$\{g_{A_n}^m\}_P = 2\pi\{\sigma_n^m\}_P - \frac{3}{2}\frac{4\pi}{2n+1}\{\sigma_n^m\}_P$$

30.92
$$= \frac{4\pi(n-1)}{2n+1}\{\sigma_n^m\}_P,$$

which is equivalent to

$$4\pi\sigma_P = \sum_{n,\,m}\frac{2n+1}{n-1}\{g_{A_n}^m\}_P$$

$$= \sum_{n,\,m}\frac{2n+1}{n-1}\frac{2n+1}{4\pi}\int\{g_{A_n}^m\}P_n(\cos\psi)\,d\Omega$$

30.93
$$= \frac{1}{4\pi}\int g_A \sum_{n=2}^{\infty}\frac{(2n+1)^2}{n-1}P_n(\cos\psi),$$

using Equations 29.10, 29.05, and 29.06 and noting that terms in the expansion of g_A in spherical harmonics make no contribution to the integral except the term of the nth degree. Terms of zero and first degree must be dropped from the summation, and are not included or determined in either g_A or σ for reasons given in §29–32. However, when these harmonics are suppressed in the potential anomaly, as always assumed, they will not appear in g_A (Equation 29.32) or σ. The function

$$\bar{\bar{S}}(\psi) = \sum_{n=2}^{\infty}\frac{(2n+1)^2}{n-1}P_n(\cos\psi)$$

is easily found by writing

$$\frac{(2n+1)^2}{n-1} = 4n+2+\frac{3(2n+1)}{n-1}.$$

Using Equation 29.11 (for $k=1$), Equation 29.11 differentiated (for $k=1$), and Equation 29.15, we have

$$\bar{\bar{S}}(\psi) = 1 + 3\operatorname{cosec}\tfrac{1}{2}\psi - 18\sin\tfrac{1}{2}\psi - 21\cos\psi$$
$$- 9\cos\psi\,\ln(\sin\tfrac{1}{2}\psi + \sin^2\tfrac{1}{2}\psi).$$

The final equation for determining the first approximation to the density σ from gravity anomalies is

30.94
$$16\pi^2\sigma_P = \int \bar{\bar{S}}(\psi)g_A\,d\Omega.$$

The density would have to be calculated from this equation if we wish to use Equations 30.88 and 30.89 for the deflections or to calculate the external field. However, if we merely require the potential anomaly T at a surface point P, we can use Equations 30.92 and 29.32 and write

$$4\pi\{\sigma_n^m\}_P = -\frac{2n+1}{n-1}\frac{(n-1)\{T_n^m\}_P}{R^{n+2}},$$

which is the same as Equation 29.74 for a spherical layer. We then have

$$\frac{T_P}{R} = -\sum_{n,\,m}\frac{4\pi}{2n+1}\{\sigma_n^m\}_P$$

$$= -\sum_{n,\,m}\int\{\sigma_n^m\}P_n(\cos\psi)\,d\Omega$$

$$= -\frac{1}{4\pi}\int g_A \sum_n \frac{2n+1}{n-1}P_n(\cos\psi)\,d\Omega$$

again using Equation 30.92. If we exclude zero- and first-degree harmonics, as we must, this last equation is the same as Stokes' integral, Equation 29.50. In other words, we may use Stokes' integral to find the first approximation to the potential anomaly. To derive this result, we use values of g_A observed on the topographic surface, for reasons given in §30–50, without attempting to apply any reduction to the base sphere; the resulting potential anomaly T is a first approximation to the potential anomaly on the topographic surface. Neither g_A nor T refers to values on the base sphere, although these quantities are connected by equations applicable to values on the base sphere. The same conclusion applies to the first approximation to the density σ. It will be found that the integral equations for the higher approximations have the same form with functions containing heights instead of g_A, and can be solved in the same way. The whole operation is simpler than solving Equation 30.74, and should give the same results.

Index of Symbols

(Only main uses of the symbols on frequent occasions are given; minor use for some other quantity in only one context is not given in the index, but is fully explained in the text. References are to the first significant appearance or explanation in the text; later references are sometimes added to a fuller treatment or to an equally important use of the symbol.)

347

Summary of Formulas

Metric:

1.06
$$ds^2 = g_{rs}dx^r dx^s \qquad (r, s = 1, 2, 3)$$
$$\text{(in three dimensions)}$$

$$ds^2 = a_{\alpha\beta}dx^\alpha dx^\beta \qquad (\alpha, \beta = 1, 2)$$
$$\text{(in two dimensions)}$$

Unit Contravariant Vector:

1.08
$$l^r = dx^r/ds$$

Unit Covariant Vector:

1.12
$$l_s = g_{rs}l^r = g_{sr}l^r$$

Vector of Magnitude λ:

1.09; 1.13
$$L^r = \lambda l^r; \qquad L_r = \lambda l_r$$

Scalar Product:

1.17
$$L^r M_r = \lambda \mu \cos \theta$$

Gradient of a Scalar N:

1.20; 1.21
$$N_r = \partial N/\partial x^r = n\nu_r$$

Transformation of Vectors:

1.18
$$\bar{L}^r = \frac{\partial \bar{x}^r}{\partial x^s} L^s$$

1.19
$$\bar{L}_r = \frac{\partial x^s}{\partial \bar{x}^r} L_s$$

Kronecker Delta:

$$\delta_t^s = 1 \quad \text{if} \quad s = t$$

1.24
$$\delta_t^s = 0 \quad \text{if} \quad s \neq t$$

Chapter 2

Transformation of Tensors:

2.01
$$\bar{A}_{rs} = \frac{\partial x^p}{\partial \bar{x}^r} \frac{\partial x^q}{\partial \bar{x}^s} A_{pq}$$

2.02
$$\bar{A}^{rs} = \frac{\partial \bar{x}^r}{\partial x^p} \frac{\partial \bar{x}^s}{\partial x^q} A^{pq}$$

2.03
$$\bar{A}_s^r = \frac{\partial \bar{x}^r}{\partial x^p} \frac{\partial x^q}{\partial \bar{x}^s} A_q^p$$

Addition of Tensors:

2.04
$$C_{st}^r = A_{st}^r + B_{st}^r$$

Multiplication of Tensors:

2.05
$$C_{st}^r = A_{st}B^r$$

2.06
$$C_s = A_{st}B^t$$

The Metric Tensor as Product of Unit Orthogonal Vectors:

2.07
$$\lambda^r \lambda_s + \mu^r \mu_s + \nu^r \nu_s = \delta_s^r = g^{rt}g_{st}$$

2.08
$$\lambda_r \lambda_s + \mu_r \mu_s + \nu_r \nu_s = g_{rs}$$

2.09; 2.10
$$\lambda^r \lambda^t + \mu^r \mu^t + \nu^r \nu^t = g^{rt} = G^{rt}/g$$

Raising and Lowering Indices:

$$g^{rs}A_{rt} = A_{\cdot t}^s$$

$$g_{rs}A_{\cdot t}^s = A_{rt}$$

Determinants:

2.12
$$A e_{rst} = e_{ijk}A_r^i A_s^j A_t^k$$

2.16
$$3!A = e^{ijk}e^{rst}A_{ir}A_{js}A_{kt}$$

2.17
$$2!A^{ir} = e^{ijk}e^{rst}A_{js}A_{kt}$$

The ϵ-Systems:

$$\left| \frac{\partial x^p}{\partial \bar{x}^r} \right| = \sqrt{\bar{g}}$$

2.14
$$\bar{\epsilon}_{rst} = \sqrt{\bar{g}}e_{rst}$$

2.15
$$\epsilon^{rst} = e^{rst}/\sqrt{g}$$

2.18
$$\delta_{rst}^{lmn} = \epsilon^{lmn}\epsilon_{rst} = e^{lmn}e_{rst}$$

2.19
$$\delta_{st}^{mn} = \delta_{stp}^{mnp}$$

2.22 $\delta_s^m = \frac{1}{2}\delta_{sn}^{mn}$

2.20 $\delta_{st}^{mn}A_{mnp} = A_{stp} - A_{tsp}$

2.21 $\delta_{st}^{mn}A_{\cdot\cdot p}^{st} = A_{\cdot\cdot p}^{mn} - A_{\cdot\cdot p}^{nm}$

Vector Products:

2.24 $\epsilon^{rst}A_s B_t = (ab\ \sin\theta)\lambda^r$

2.25 $\epsilon^{str}A_s B_t C_r = abc\ \sin\theta\ \sin\phi$

2.26 $\epsilon^{rst}\lambda_r\mu_s\nu_t = 1$

(λ_r, μ_r, ν_r unit orthogonal right-handed vectors.)

Further Properties of ϵ-Systems:

$\epsilon^{rst} = \lambda^r(\mu^s\nu^t - \nu^s\mu^t) + \mu^r(\nu^s\lambda^t - \lambda^s\nu^t)$

2.27 $\quad + \nu^r(\lambda^s\mu^t - \mu^s\lambda^t)$

2.28 $g_{ri}\epsilon^{rst}\epsilon^{ijk} = g^{sj}g^{tk} - g^{sk}g^{jt}$

Two-Dimensional Formulas:

2.29 $\bar{A}_{\alpha\beta} = \dfrac{\partial x^\gamma}{\partial \bar{x}^\alpha}\dfrac{\partial x^\delta}{\partial \bar{x}^\beta}A_{\gamma\delta}$

2.30 $\epsilon^{\alpha\beta} = e^{\alpha\beta}/\sqrt{a}; \qquad \epsilon_{\alpha\beta} = \sqrt{a}\,e_{\alpha\beta}$

2.32 $\epsilon^{\alpha\beta} = \lambda^\alpha\mu^\beta - \mu^\alpha\lambda^\beta$

(λ^α, μ^β unit orthogonal vectors.)

2.32 $\epsilon_{\alpha\beta} = \lambda_\alpha\mu_\beta - \mu_\alpha\lambda_\beta$

2.37 $\mu_\beta = \epsilon_{\alpha\beta}\lambda^\alpha$

2.34 $a_{\alpha\beta} = \lambda_\alpha\lambda_\beta + \mu_\alpha\mu_\beta$

2.35 $a^{\alpha\beta} = \lambda^\alpha\lambda^\beta + \mu^\alpha\mu^\beta$

2.36 $a^{\alpha\beta}a_{\beta\gamma} = \delta_\gamma^\alpha = \lambda^\alpha\lambda_\gamma + \mu^\alpha\mu_\gamma$

2.38 $\delta_{\gamma\delta}^{\alpha\beta} = \epsilon^{\alpha\beta}\epsilon_{\gamma\delta}$

2.39 $\delta_\delta^\beta = \delta_{\alpha\delta}^{\alpha\beta}$

2.41 $\delta_{\gamma\delta}^{\alpha\beta}A_{\alpha\beta\rho\sigma} = A_{\gamma\delta\rho\sigma} - A_{\delta\gamma\rho\sigma}$

2.42 $2!A = e^{\alpha\gamma}e^{\beta\delta}A_{\alpha\beta}A_{\gamma\delta}$

2.43 $A^{\alpha\beta} = e^{\alpha\gamma}e^{\beta\delta}A_{\gamma\delta}$

2.44 $a^{\alpha\beta} = \epsilon^{\alpha\gamma}\epsilon^{\beta\delta}a_{\gamma\delta}$

2.45 $a_{\alpha\beta} = \epsilon_{\alpha\gamma}\epsilon_{\beta\delta}a^{\gamma\delta}$

Chapter 3

Christoffel Symbols:

3.01 $[ij, k] = \frac{1}{2}\left(\dfrac{\partial g_{jk}}{\partial x^i} + \dfrac{\partial g_{ik}}{\partial x^j} - \dfrac{\partial g_{ij}}{\partial x^k}\right)$

3.02 $\Gamma_{ij}^l = g^{lk}[ij, k]$

Covariant Derivatives of a Vector λ^i, λ_j:

3.07 $\lambda_j^i = \dfrac{\partial \lambda^i}{\partial x^j} + \Gamma_{jk}^i\lambda^k$

3.08 $\lambda_{ij} = \dfrac{\partial \lambda_i}{\partial x^j} - \Gamma_{ij}^l\lambda_l$

Covariant Derivative of a Tensor λ_{st}^r:

3.09 $\lambda_{stu}^r = \dfrac{\partial \lambda_{st}^r}{\partial x^u} + \Gamma_{uj}^r\lambda_{st}^j - \Gamma_{us}^j\lambda_{jt}^r - \Gamma_{ut}^j\lambda_{sj}^r$

(Rules follow Equation 3.09.)

Covariant Derivative of a Scalar Gradient ϕ_r:

3.10; 3.11 $\phi_{r, s} = \dfrac{\partial^2 \phi}{\partial x^r \partial x^s} - \Gamma_{rs}^t\phi_t = \phi_{s, r}$

Laplacian of a Vector F_r:

3.12; 3.17 $\Delta F = g^{rs}F_{rs} = F_{\cdot s}^s = \dfrac{1}{\sqrt{g}}\dfrac{\partial}{\partial x^s}\left(\sqrt{g}F^s\right)$

Other Differential Invariants:

3.13 $\nabla(F) = g^{rs}F_r F_s$

3.14 $\nabla(F, G) = g^{rs}F_r G_s$

Curl of a Vector F_t:

3.15 $\epsilon^{rst}F_{ts}$

Differentials of Determinant of Metric Tensor:

3.16 $\dfrac{\partial(\ln\sqrt{g})}{\partial x^u} = \Gamma_{ku}^k$

Covariant Derivatives of Unit Perpendicular Vectors:

3.19; 3.20 $l_{r, s}\,l^r = 0; \qquad l_{r, s}\,j^r = -j_{r, s}\,l^r$

Chapter 4

Frenet Equations of a Curve in Three Dimensions:

$l_{rs}l^s = \chi m_r$

$m_{rs}l^s = -\chi l_r + \tau n_r$

4.06 $n_{rs}l^s = -\tau m_r$

Curvature of Orthogonal Surface Curves l_α, j_α:

$l_{\alpha\beta} = \sigma j_\alpha l_\beta + \sigma^* j_\alpha j_\beta$

4.11 $j_{\alpha\beta} = -\sigma l_\alpha l_\beta - \sigma^* l_\alpha j_\beta$

$$\epsilon^{\alpha\beta}l_{\alpha\beta}=-\sigma$$

4.12
$$\epsilon^{\alpha\beta}j_{\alpha\beta}=-\sigma^*$$

Chapter 5

Riemann-Christoffel Tensors:

5.03
$$R^l_{\cdot ijk}=\frac{\partial}{\partial x^j}\,\Gamma^l_{ik}-\frac{\partial}{\partial x^k}\,\Gamma^l_{ij}+\Gamma^m_{ik}\Gamma^l_{mj}-\Gamma^m_{ij}\Gamma^l_{mk}$$

5.02
$$\lambda_{i,\,jk}-\lambda_{i,\,kj}=R^l_{\cdot ijk}\lambda_l$$

5.04
$$R^l_{\cdot ijk}=-R^l_{\cdot ikj}$$

5.05
$$R^l_{\cdot ijk}+R^l_{\cdot jki}+R^l_{\cdot kij}=0$$

5.06
$$R_{mijk}=g_{lm}R^l_{\cdot ijk}$$

5.07
$$R_{mijk}=\frac{\partial}{\partial x^j}\,[ik,\,m]-\frac{\partial}{\partial x^k}\,[ij,\,m]$$
$$+\Gamma^l_{ij}[mk,\,l]-\Gamma^l_{ik}[mj,\,l]$$

5.08
$$R_{mijk}=\tfrac{1}{2}\left(\frac{\partial^2 g_{mk}}{\partial x^i\partial x^j}+\frac{\partial^2 g_{ij}}{\partial x^m\partial x^k}-\frac{\partial^2 g_{mj}}{\partial x^i\partial x^k}-\frac{\partial^2 g_{ik}}{\partial x^m\partial x^j}\right)$$
$$+g^{pq}\{[mk,\,p][ij,\,q]-[mj,\,p][ik,\,q]\}$$

5.09
$$R_{mijk}=R_{jkmi}$$

Ricci Tensor:

5.11
$$R_{ij}=g^{mk}R_{mijk}=R^k_{\cdot ijk}$$

5.12
$$=\frac{\partial}{\partial x^j}\,\Gamma^l_{il}-\frac{\partial}{\partial x^l}\,\Gamma^l_{ij}+\Gamma^m_{il}\Gamma^l_{mj}-\Gamma^m_{ij}\,\Gamma^l_{ml}$$

Lamé Tensor:

5.13
$$S^{pq}=\tfrac{1}{4}\epsilon^{pmi}\epsilon^{qjk}R_{mijk}$$

5.14
$$\epsilon_{prs}\epsilon_{qtu}S^{pq}=R_{rstu}$$

5.15
$$R_{ij}=S_{ij}-Sg_{ij}$$

Gaussian Curvature of a Surface:

5.16; 5.17
$$K=\tfrac{1}{4}\,\epsilon^{\alpha\beta}\epsilon^{\gamma\delta}R_{\alpha\beta\gamma\delta}=R_{1212}/a$$

5.18
$$=-\frac{1}{2\sqrt{a}}\left[\frac{\partial}{\partial x^1}\left(\frac{1}{\sqrt{a}}\frac{\partial a_{22}}{\partial x^1}\right)\right.$$
$$\left.+\frac{\partial}{\partial x^2}\left(\frac{1}{\sqrt{a}}\frac{\partial a_{11}}{\partial x^2}\right)\right]\qquad(a_{12}=0)$$

5.19
$$R_{\epsilon\rho\sigma\tau}=K\epsilon_{\epsilon\rho}\epsilon_{\sigma\tau}$$

5.20
$$R_{\rho\sigma}=-Ka_{\rho\sigma}$$

Unit Orthogonal Surface Vectors $\lambda_\alpha,\,\mu_\alpha$:

5.22; 5.23
$$\lambda_{\alpha,\,\beta\gamma}-\lambda_{\alpha,\,\gamma\beta}=\lambda_\delta R^\delta_{\cdot\alpha\beta\gamma}=\lambda^\delta R_{\delta\alpha\beta\gamma}=K\mu_\alpha\epsilon_{\beta\gamma}$$

5.24
$$\epsilon^{\beta\gamma}\lambda_{\alpha,\,\beta\gamma}=K\mu_\alpha$$

Riemannian Curvature:

5.25; 5.26
$$C=R_{mijk}\lambda^m\mu^i\lambda^j\mu^k=S^{pq}\nu_p\nu_q$$

Chapter 6

General:

6.02
$$\frac{\partial x^r}{\partial x^\alpha}=x^r_\alpha$$

6.06
$$a_{\alpha\beta}=g_{rs}x^r_\alpha x^s_\beta$$

Surface Vectors:

6.07
$$l^r=x^r_\alpha l^\alpha$$

6.08
$$l_s x^s_\beta=l_\beta$$

6.09
$$x^r_\alpha=l^r l_\alpha+j^r j_\alpha$$

The Unit Normal:

6.10
$$g^{rs}=a^{\alpha\beta}x^r_\alpha x^s_\beta+\nu^r\nu^s$$

6.11
$$\nu_r\epsilon^{rst}=\epsilon^{\alpha\beta}x^s_\alpha x^t_\beta$$

6.12
$$\nu_p=\tfrac{1}{2}\,\epsilon^{\alpha\beta}\epsilon_{pst}x^s_\alpha x^t_\beta$$

Covariant Derivatives:

6.13
$$\frac{\partial(\ln\sqrt{a})}{\partial x^\alpha}=\Gamma^\beta_{\alpha\beta}$$

6.14
$$x^r_{\alpha\beta}=\frac{\partial^2 x^r}{\partial x^\alpha\partial x^\beta}+\Gamma^r_{st}x^t_\alpha x^s_\beta-\Gamma^\gamma_{\alpha\beta}x^r_\gamma$$

The Gauss Equations:

6.16
$$x^r_{\alpha\gamma}=b_{\alpha\gamma}\nu^r$$

The Weingarten Equations:

6.17
$$\nu^r_\gamma=-a^{\alpha\beta}b_{\beta\gamma}x^r_\alpha$$

The Fundamental Forms:

6.18
$$a_{\alpha\beta}=g_{rs}x^r_\alpha x^s_\beta$$
$$b_{\alpha\beta}=-g_{rs}x^r_\alpha\nu^s_\beta$$
$$c_{\alpha\beta}=g_{rs}\nu^r_\alpha\nu^s_\beta=a^{\gamma\delta}b_{\alpha\gamma}b_{\beta\delta}$$

The Mainardi-Codazzi Equations:

6.21
$$b_{\alpha\beta\gamma}=b_{\alpha\gamma\beta}\qquad\text{(flat space)}$$

6.22
$$b_{\alpha\beta\gamma}=b_{\alpha\gamma\beta}-R_{urst}\nu^u x^r_\alpha x^s_\beta x^t_\gamma$$

Gaussian Curvature:

6.26
$$K\epsilon_{\delta\alpha}\epsilon_{\beta\gamma}=R_{\delta\alpha\beta\gamma}=(b_{\alpha\gamma}b_{\beta\delta}-b_{\delta\gamma}b_{\alpha\beta})\qquad\text{(flat space)}$$

6.27 $\qquad aK = R_{1212} = b \qquad$ (flat space)

6.28 $K\epsilon_{\delta\alpha}\epsilon_{\beta\gamma} = R_{\delta\alpha\beta\gamma} = b_{\alpha\gamma}b_{\beta\delta} - b_{\delta\gamma}b_{\alpha\beta} + R_{urst}x_\delta^u x_\alpha^r x_\beta^s x_\gamma^t$

Chapter 7

Curvature (Meusnier's Equations):

7.03 $\qquad l_{rs}\nu^r l^s = -\nu_{rs}l^r l^s = b_{\alpha\beta}l^\alpha l^\beta = \chi\cos\theta = k$

7.04 $\qquad l_{rs}j^r l^s = \sigma = \chi\sin\theta$

Torsion:

$$t = \tau + (d\theta/ds) = b_{\alpha\beta}l^\alpha j^\beta = b_{\alpha\beta}j^\alpha l^\beta$$

7.08 $\qquad = -\nu_{rs}l^r j^s = -\nu_{rs}j^r l^s$

Curvature and Torsion:

7.09 $\qquad \nu_{rs}l^s = -kl_r - tj_r$

7.10 $\qquad b_{\alpha\beta}l^\beta = +kl_\alpha + tj_\alpha$

7.12 $\qquad b_{\alpha\beta} = kl_\alpha l_\beta + t(l_\alpha j_\beta + j_\alpha l_\beta) + k^* j_\alpha j_\beta$

7.14 $\qquad c_{\alpha\beta} = (k^2 + t^2)l_\alpha l_\beta + 2Ht(l_\alpha j_\beta + j_\alpha l_\beta) + (k^{*2} + t^2)j_\alpha j_\beta$

Invariants:

7.15 $\qquad a^{\alpha\beta}b_{\alpha\beta} = k + k^* = 2H$

7.18 $\qquad K = b/a = c/b = (kk^* - t^2)$

7.19 $\qquad 2H = -\nu_{,r}^r$

7.20 $\qquad Ka_{\alpha\beta} - 2Hb_{\alpha\beta} + c_{\alpha\beta} = 0$

Principal Curvatures:

7.21 $\qquad 2H = \kappa_1 + \kappa_2$

7.22 $\qquad K = \kappa_1\kappa_2$

7.23 $\qquad a_{\alpha\beta} = u_\alpha u_\beta + v_\alpha v_\beta$

7.24 $\qquad b_{\alpha\beta} = \kappa_1 u_\alpha u_\beta + \kappa_2 v_\alpha v_\beta$

7.25 $\qquad c_{\alpha\beta} = \kappa_1^2 u_\alpha u_\beta + \kappa_2^2 v_\alpha v_\beta$

7.26; 7.27 $\qquad \nu_{rs}u^s = -\kappa_1 u_r; \qquad \nu_{rs}v^s = -\kappa_2 v_r$

Chapter 8

Contravariant Fundamental Forms:

8.01 $\qquad Kb^{\alpha\beta} = \epsilon^{\alpha\gamma}\epsilon^{\beta\delta}b_{\gamma\delta}$

8.02 $\qquad = k^* l^\alpha l^\beta - t(l^\alpha j^\beta + j^\alpha l^\beta) + kj^\alpha j^\beta$

8.03 $\qquad = \kappa_2 u^\alpha u^\beta + \kappa_1 v^\alpha v^\beta$

8.04 $\qquad K^2 c^{\alpha\beta} = \epsilon^{\alpha\gamma}\epsilon^{\beta\delta}c_{\gamma\delta}$

$$K^2 c^{\alpha\beta} = (k^{*2} + t^2)l^\alpha l^\beta - 2Ht(l^\alpha j^\beta + j^\alpha l^\beta)$$
$$+ (k^2 + t^2)j^\alpha j^\beta$$

8.05 $\qquad = \kappa_2^2 u^\alpha u^\beta + \kappa_1^2 v^\alpha v^\beta$

8.07 $\qquad a^{\alpha\beta} - 2Hb^{\alpha\beta} + Kc^{\alpha\beta} = 0$

8.08 $\qquad b^{\alpha\beta}b_{\alpha\gamma} = \delta_\gamma^\beta; \qquad c^{\alpha\beta}c_{\alpha\gamma} = \delta_\gamma^\beta$

8.09; 8.12 $\qquad b^{\alpha\beta}c_{\beta\gamma} = a^{\alpha\beta}b_{\beta\gamma}; \qquad c^{\alpha\beta}b_{\beta\gamma} = b^{\alpha\beta}a_{\beta\gamma}$

8.10; 8.11 $\qquad b^{\alpha\beta}\nu_\beta^r = -a^{\alpha\beta}x_\beta^r; \qquad c^{\alpha\beta}\nu_\beta^r = -b^{\alpha\beta}x_\beta^r$

8.13 $\qquad 2H = a^{\alpha\beta}b_{\alpha\beta} = b^{\alpha\beta}c_{\alpha\beta} = Kc^{\alpha\beta}b_{\alpha\beta} = Kb^{\alpha\beta}a_{\alpha\beta}$

8.14 $\qquad a^{\alpha\beta}c_{\alpha\beta} = K^2 c^{\alpha\beta}a_{\alpha\beta} = (4H^2 - 2K) = \kappa_1^2 + \kappa_2^2$

Covariant Derivatives:

$$b_{\alpha\beta\gamma} = (\kappa_1)_\gamma u_\alpha u_\beta + (\kappa_2)_\gamma v_\alpha v_\beta$$

8.16 $\qquad + (\kappa_1 - \kappa_2)(\sigma u_\gamma + \sigma^* v_\gamma)(u_\alpha v_\beta + v_\alpha u_\beta)$

$$c_{\alpha\beta\gamma} = (\kappa_1^2)_\gamma u_\alpha u_\beta + (\kappa_2^2)_\gamma v_\alpha v_\beta$$

8.17 $\qquad + (\kappa_1^2 - \kappa_2^2)(\sigma u_\gamma + \sigma^* v_\gamma)(u_\alpha v_\beta + v_\alpha u_\beta)$

$$b_{\cdot\cdot\gamma}^{\alpha\beta} = (1/\kappa_1)_\gamma u^\alpha u^\beta + (1/\kappa_2)_\gamma v^\alpha v^\beta$$

8.18 $\qquad + (1/\kappa_1 - 1/\kappa_2)(\sigma u_\gamma + \sigma^* v_\gamma)(u^\alpha v^\beta + v^\alpha u^\beta)$

$$c_{\cdot\cdot\gamma}^{\alpha\beta} = (1/\kappa_1^2)_\gamma u^\alpha u^\beta + (1/\kappa_2^2)_\gamma v^\alpha v^\beta$$

8.19 $\qquad + (1/\kappa_1^2 - 1/\kappa_2^2)(\sigma u_\gamma + \sigma^* v_\gamma)(u^\alpha v^\beta + v^\alpha u^\beta)$

8.20

$a^{\alpha\beta}b_{\alpha\beta\gamma} = (2H)_\gamma$	$a^{\alpha\beta}c_{\alpha\beta\gamma} = (4H^2 - 2K)_\gamma$
$b^{\alpha\beta}b_{\alpha\beta\gamma} = (\ln K)_\gamma$	$b^{\alpha\beta}c_{\alpha\beta\gamma} = (4H)_\gamma$
$c^{\alpha\beta}b_{\alpha\beta\gamma} = -(2H/K)_\gamma$	$c^{\alpha\beta}c_{\alpha\beta\gamma} = 2(\ln K)_\gamma$

Mainardi-Codazzi Equations:

$$(\kappa_1 - \kappa_2)\sigma = (\kappa_1)_\gamma v^\gamma$$

8.22 $\qquad (\kappa_1 - \kappa_2)\sigma^* = (\kappa_2)_\gamma u^\gamma$

$$\sigma(k - k^*) = (k)_\gamma j^\gamma - (t)_\gamma l^\gamma - 2t\sigma^*$$

8.23 $\qquad \sigma^*(k - k^*) = (k^*)_\gamma l^\gamma - (t)_\gamma j^\gamma + 2t\sigma$

Space and Surface Tensors and Invariants:

8.25 $\qquad F_{rs}x_\alpha^r x_\beta^s = F_{\alpha\beta} - (F_r\nu^r)b_{\alpha\beta}$

8.26 $\qquad F_{rs}u^r v^s = F_{\alpha\beta}u^\alpha v^\beta$

8.27 $\qquad F_{\cdot r}^r = F_{\cdot\alpha}^\alpha - 2H(F_r\nu^r) + F_{rs}\nu^r\nu^s$

8.29 $\qquad \Delta F = \overline{\Delta F} - 2H(\partial F/\partial s) + (\partial^2 F/\partial s^2) - \chi(F_r w^r)$

8.30 $\qquad \nabla(F, G) = \overline{\nabla(F, G)} + \left(\dfrac{\partial F}{\partial s}\right)\left(\dfrac{\partial G}{\partial s}\right)$

Space Curved:

8.31 $\qquad K = (kk^* - t^2) + C$

Chapter 9

General:

9.01 $$dS = \sqrt{a}\,dx^1 dx^2$$

9.02 $$dV = \sqrt{g}\,dx^1 dx^2 dx^3$$

Surface and Contour Integrals:

9.04 $$\int_S \epsilon^{\alpha\beta} F_{\beta,\,\alpha}\,dS = \int_C F_\alpha l^\alpha ds$$

9.06 $$\int_S \epsilon^{lmn}\nu_l T_{ijk,\,m}\,dS = \int_C T_{ijk} l^n ds$$

9.07 $$\int_S \nu_l \epsilon^{lmn} F_{n,\,m}\,dS = \int_C F_n l^n ds$$

9.08 $$\int_S \nu_l \epsilon^{lmn} F_{n,\,m}\,dS = 0 \qquad \text{(closed surface)}$$

9.09 $$\int_S (\nu_p T_{ijk,\,q} - \nu_q T_{ijk,\,p})\,dS = \int_C \epsilon_{npq} T_{ijk} l^n ds$$

9.10 $$\int_S (\nu_p G^q_{,q} - \nu_q G^q_{,p})\,dS = \int_C \epsilon_{npq} G^q l^n ds$$

9.11 $$\int_S (2H\nu^l U_{jk} + a^{\alpha\beta} x^q_\alpha x^l_\beta U_{jk,\,q})\,dS = -\int_C j^l U_{jk}\,ds$$

9.12 $$\int_S \overline{\Delta\phi}\,dS = -\int_C \phi_l j^l ds$$

9.13 $$\int_S \overline{\Delta\phi}\,dS = 0 \qquad \text{(closed surface)}$$

Volume and Surface Integrals:

9.15 $$\int_V T_{ijk,m}\,dV = \int_S T_{ijk}\nu_m\,dS$$

9.16 $$\int_V F^m_{,m}\,dV = \int_S F^m \nu_m\,dS = \int_S F_m \nu^m\,dS$$

9.17 $$\int_V (\Delta\phi)\,dV = \int_S (\partial\phi/\partial s)\,dS$$

9.18 $$\int_V \{\nabla(\phi,\psi) + \phi\Delta\psi\}\,dV = \int_S \phi(\partial\psi/\partial s)\,dS$$

9.19 $$\int_V \{\phi\Delta\psi - \psi\Delta\phi\}\,dV = \int_S \left(\phi\frac{\partial\psi}{\partial s} - \psi\frac{\partial\phi}{\partial s}\right) dS$$

Chapter 10

Metrical Relations:

10.01 $$d\bar{s}^2 = m^2 ds^2$$

10.02 $$\bar{g}_{rs} = m^2 g_{rs}$$

10.03 $$|\bar{g}_{rs}| = m^6 |g_{rs}|$$

10.04 $$\bar{g}^{rs} = m^{-2} g^{rs}$$

10.05 $$m^{-2}\overline{[ij,k]} = [ij,k] + g_{ik}(\ln m)_j + g_{jk}(\ln m)_i - g_{ij}(\ln m)_k$$

$$\bar{\Gamma}^l_{ij} = \Gamma^l_{ij} + \delta^l_i(\ln m)_j + \delta^l_j(\ln m)_i - g_{ij}g^{lk}(\ln m)_k$$

10.06

10.07 $$m^{-2}\bar{R}_{qrst} - R_{qrst} = mg_{qs}(1/m)_{rt} - mg_{qt}(1/m)_{rs}$$
$$- mg_{rs}(1/m)_{qt} + mg_{rt}(1/m)_{qs}$$
$$+ m^2(g_{rs}g_{qt} - g_{rt}g_{qs})\nabla(1/m)$$

10.09 $$\bar{R}_{rs} - R_{rs} = -m(1/m)_{rs} + (1/m)(\Delta m)g_{rs}$$

10.11 $$\bar{S}_{rs} - S_{rs} = -m(1/m)_{rs} - (\Delta \ln m)g_{rs}$$

Transformation of Tensors:

10.12 $$\bar{l}^r = m^{-1} l^r$$

10.13 $$\bar{l}_r = m l_r$$

10.14 $$m^{-1}\bar{l}_{r,\,s} = l_{r,\,s} - (\ln m)_r l_s + g_{rs}(\ln m)_t l^t$$

10.15 $$m\bar{l}^r_{,s} = l^r_{,s} + \delta^r_s(\ln m)_t l^t - g^{rt}(\ln m)_t l_s$$

10.16 $$\bar{\phi}_{rs} = \phi_{rs} - \phi_r(\ln m)_s - \phi_s(\ln m)_r + g_{rs}\nabla(\ln m, \phi)$$

10.17 $$m^2\overline{\Delta\phi} = \Delta\phi + (\delta^r_r - 2)\nabla(\ln m, \phi)$$

10.18 $$m^2\overline{\Delta\phi} = \Delta\phi + \nabla(\ln m, \phi) \qquad \text{(three dimensions)}$$

Correspondence of Lines:

10.19 $$\bar{l}_{rs}\bar{l}^s = l_{rs}l^s - (\ln m)_r + \{(\ln m)_t l^t\}l_r$$

10.20 $$\bar{\chi}\bar{n}_r = m\chi n_r = \{\chi - (\ln m)_t p^t\}p_r - \{(\ln m)_t q^t\}q_r$$

10.21 $$m\bar{\chi}\cos\theta = \chi - (\ln m)_t p^t$$
$$m\bar{\chi}\sin\theta = -(\ln m)_t q^t$$

10.22 $$m\bar{\tau} = \tau + (d\theta/ds)$$

10.23 $$m\bar{\chi}(d\theta/ds) = -\sin\theta(\partial\chi/\partial s) + \tau(\ln m)_r n^r + m(1/m)_{rs}b^r l^s$$

10.24 $$m^2\bar{\chi}\bar{\tau} = \chi\tau\cos\theta - \sin\theta(\partial\chi/\partial s) + m(1/m)_{rs}b^r l^s$$

$$m^2(\partial\bar\chi/\partial\bar s)=\cos\theta(\partial\chi/\partial s)-\tau(\ln m)_r b^r$$
10.25
$$+m(1/m)_{rs}n^r l^s$$

Surface Normals:

10.27 $\qquad\qquad N_r=n\nu_r$

10.28 $\qquad \nu_{rs}=\nu_{sr}+\nu_s(\ln n)_r-\nu_r(\ln n)_s$

10.29 $\qquad \nu_{rs}\nu^s=(\ln n)_r-\nu_r(\ln n)_s\nu^s$

Transformation of Surfaces:

$$\bar a_{\alpha\beta}=m^2 a_{\alpha\beta}$$
$$|\bar a_{\alpha\beta}|=m^4|a_{\alpha\beta}|$$
10.30 $\qquad \bar a^{\alpha\beta}=m^{-2}a^{\alpha\beta}$

10.31 $\qquad \Delta(\ln m)=K-m^2\bar K$

10.32 $\qquad \Delta(\ln m)=K \qquad$ (plane to curved surface)

Geodesic Curvatures:

10.33 $\qquad \sigma-m\bar\sigma=(\ln m)_\alpha j^\alpha$

Extrinsic Properties:

10.34 $\qquad\qquad \bar x^r_\alpha=x^r_\alpha$

10.35 $\qquad\qquad m\bar\nu^r_\alpha=\nu^r_\alpha+nx^r_\alpha$

10.36 $\qquad$ In Equation 10.35, $\quad n=(\ln m)_r\nu^r.$

10.37 $\qquad\qquad m^{-1}\bar b_{\alpha\beta}=b_{\alpha\beta}-na_{\alpha\beta}$

10.38 $\qquad\qquad \bar c_{\alpha\beta}=c_{\alpha\beta}-2nb_{\alpha\beta}+n^2 a_{\alpha\beta}$

10.39 $\qquad\qquad m\bar k=k-n$

10.40 $\qquad\qquad m\bar k^*=k^*-n$

10.41 $\qquad\qquad m\bar t=t$

10.42 $\qquad m^2(\bar k\bar k^*-\bar t^2)=(kk^*-t^2)-2Hn+n^2$

10.43 $\qquad m^2\bar C=C-\{\Delta(\ln m)-2Hn+n^2\}$

$$m^{-1}\bar b_{\alpha\beta\gamma}-b_{\alpha\beta\gamma}=a_{\alpha\beta}m(1/m)_{st}\nu^s x^t_\gamma$$

$$-\sum_{\alpha\beta\gamma}(\ln m)_\alpha b_{\beta\gamma}$$

10.44 $\qquad\qquad\qquad +a^{\delta\epsilon}(\ln m)_\epsilon\sum_{\alpha\beta\gamma}a_{\alpha\beta}b_{\gamma\delta}$

$$m^{-1}R_{qrst}\bar\nu^q\bar x^r_\alpha\bar x^s_\beta\bar x^t_\gamma-R_{qrst}\nu^q x^r_\alpha x^s_\beta x^t_\gamma$$

10.45 $\qquad =-ma_{\alpha\beta}(1/m)_{qt}\nu^q x^t_\gamma+ma_{\alpha\gamma}(1/m)_{qs}\nu^q x^s_\beta$

Gauss-Bonnet Theorem:

10.46 $\qquad \int_C\sigma ds-\int_C\bar\sigma d\bar s=-\int_S KdS$

$$\int_C\sigma ds+\int_S KdS=2\pi \qquad \text{(continuous contour)}$$
10.47

$$\int_C\sigma ds+\int_S KdS=2\pi-n\pi+\sum_n\theta_n \qquad \text{(n-corners)}$$
10.48

$$\int_C\sigma ds+\int_S KdS=A+B+C-\pi \qquad \text{(triangle)}$$
10.49

$$\int_S KdS=A+B+C-\pi \qquad \text{(geodesic triangle)}$$
10.50

Chapter 11

Metrical Relations:

(Overbarred quantities refer to the sphere.)

11.01 $\qquad\qquad \nu^r=\bar\rho^r=\bar\nu^r$

11.02 $\qquad\qquad \nu^r_\alpha=\bar\rho^r_\alpha=\bar x^r_\alpha=\bar\nu^r_\alpha$

11.03 $\qquad\qquad \bar a_{\alpha\beta}=c_{\alpha\beta}$

11.04 $\qquad\qquad \bar b_{\alpha\beta}=-c_{\alpha\beta}=-\bar a_{\alpha\beta}$

11.05 $\qquad\qquad \bar c_{\alpha\beta}=c_{\alpha\beta}=\bar a_{\alpha\beta}$

11.06 $\qquad |\bar a_{\alpha\beta}|=|c_{\alpha\beta}|=K^2|a_{\alpha\beta}|=K|b_{\alpha\beta}|$

11.07 $\qquad\qquad \bar a^{\alpha\beta}=c^{\alpha\beta}=-\bar b^{\alpha\beta}=\bar c^{\alpha\beta}$

11.08 $\qquad\qquad b^{\beta\gamma}x^r_\gamma=\bar b^{\beta\gamma}\bar x^r_\gamma$

(Scale factor $m=d\bar s/ds$.)

11.11 $\qquad\qquad m^2=k^2+t^2$

11.12 $\qquad\qquad l^\alpha=m\bar l^\alpha$

11.13 $\qquad\qquad m\bar l_\beta=c_{\alpha\beta}l^\alpha=m^2 l_\beta+2Htj_\beta$

11.14 $\qquad\qquad \epsilon_{\alpha\beta}=\bar\epsilon_{\alpha\beta}/K; \qquad \epsilon^{\alpha\beta}=K\bar\epsilon^{\alpha\beta}$

11.15 $\qquad\qquad j_\beta=(m/K)\bar{\bar j}_\beta$

Principal Directions and Curvatures:

$$m=-\kappa_1 \qquad \text{(in u^α-direction)}$$

11.18 $\qquad m=-\kappa_2 \qquad \text{(in v^α-direction)}$

11.19 $\qquad u^\alpha=-\kappa_1\bar u^\alpha; \qquad u_\beta=-\bar u_\beta/\kappa_1$

11.20 $\qquad v^\alpha=-\kappa_2\bar v^\alpha; \qquad v_\beta=-\bar v_\beta/\kappa_2$

Direction $l^\alpha(l^\alpha u_\alpha=\cos\psi)$:

11.21 $\qquad m^2=\kappa_1^2\cos^2\psi+\kappa_2^2\sin^2\psi$

11.22 $\qquad \cos\bar\psi=\dfrac{-\kappa_1\cos\psi}{(\kappa_1^2\cos^2\psi+\kappa_2^2\sin^2\psi)^{1/2}}$

11.23 $\quad \sin \bar{\psi} = \dfrac{-\kappa_2 \sin \psi}{(\kappa_1^2 \cos^2 \psi + \kappa_2^2 \sin^2 \psi)^{1/2}}$

11.24 $\quad \tan \bar{\psi} = (\kappa_2/\kappa_1) \tan \psi$

Christoffel Symbols:

11.30 $\quad \Gamma^\gamma_{\alpha\beta} - \bar{\Gamma}^\gamma_{\alpha\beta} = -b^{\gamma\delta} b_{\alpha\beta\delta}$

11.31 $\quad \Gamma^\gamma_{\alpha\beta} + b^{\gamma\delta} b_{\alpha\beta\delta} = \quad$ same overbarred

Chapter 12

Base Vectors:

12.001 $\qquad N_r = n \nu_r$

$l^r = \lambda^r \sin \alpha \sin \beta + \mu^r \cos \alpha \sin \beta + \nu^r \cos \beta$

12.007

$\lambda_r = -A_r \sin \omega + B_r \cos \omega$

$\mu_r = -A_r \sin \phi \cos \omega - B_r \sin \phi \sin \omega + C_r \cos \phi$

$\nu_r = A_r \cos \phi \cos \omega + B_r \cos \phi \sin \omega + C_r \sin \phi$

12.008

$$x_r = A_r = -\lambda_r \sin \omega - \mu_r \sin \phi \cos \omega$$
$$+ \nu_r \cos \phi \cos \omega$$
$$y_r = B_r = \lambda_r \cos \omega - \mu_r \sin \phi \sin \omega$$
$$+ \nu_r \cos \phi \sin \omega$$
$$z_r = C_r = \mu_r \cos \phi + \nu_r \sin \phi$$

12.009

$$\bar{x} = -(x - x_0) \sin \omega + (y - y_0) \cos \omega$$
$$\bar{y} = -(x - x_0) \sin \phi \cos \omega$$
$$- (y - y_0) \sin \phi \sin \omega + (z - z_0) \cos \phi$$
$$\bar{z} = (x - x_0) \cos \phi \cos \omega$$

12.010 $\quad + (y - y_0) \cos \phi \sin \omega + (z - z_0) \sin \phi$

$(x - x_0) = -\bar{x} \sin \omega - \bar{y} \sin \phi \cos \omega + \bar{z} \cos \phi \cos \omega$

$(y - y_0) = \bar{x} \cos \omega - \bar{y} \sin \phi \sin \omega + \bar{z} \cos \phi \sin \omega$

$(z - z_0) = \bar{y} \cos \phi + \bar{z} \sin \phi$

12.011

$$\begin{pmatrix} \lambda_r \\ \mu_r \\ \nu_r \end{pmatrix} = \begin{pmatrix} 1 & 0 & 0 \\ 0 & \sin \phi & \cos \phi \\ 0 & -\cos \phi & \sin \phi \end{pmatrix} \begin{pmatrix} -\sin \omega & \cos \omega & 0 \\ -\cos \omega & -\sin \omega & 0 \\ 0 & 0 & 1 \end{pmatrix} \begin{pmatrix} A_r \\ B_r \\ C_r \end{pmatrix}$$

12.012

$$\begin{pmatrix} A_r \\ B_r \\ C_r \end{pmatrix} = \begin{pmatrix} -\sin \omega & -\cos \omega & 0 \\ \cos \omega & -\sin \omega & 0 \\ 0 & 0 & 1 \end{pmatrix} \begin{pmatrix} 1 & 0 & 0 \\ 0 & \sin \phi & -\cos \phi \\ 0 & \cos \phi & \sin \phi \end{pmatrix} \begin{pmatrix} \lambda_r \\ \mu_r \\ \nu_r \end{pmatrix}$$

12.013

Derivatives of Base Vectors:

$$\lambda_{rs} = (-A_r \cos \omega - B_r \sin \omega) \omega_s$$

12.014 $\qquad = (\mu_r \sin \phi - \nu_r \cos \phi) \omega_s$

12.015 $\qquad \mu_{rs} = -\sin \phi \, \lambda_r \omega_s - \nu_r \phi_s$

12.016 $\qquad \nu_{rs} = \cos \phi \, \lambda_r \omega_s + \mu_r \phi_s$

12.017 $\qquad N_{rs} = n_s \nu_r + n \nu_{rs}$

12.020 $\qquad \nu_{rs}\nu^s = \{(\ln n)_s \lambda^s\} \lambda_r + \{(\ln n)_s \mu^s\} \mu_r$

12.021 $\qquad = \gamma_1 \lambda_r + \gamma_2 \mu_r$

12.022 $\qquad \lambda_{\alpha\beta} = \mu_\alpha \omega_\beta \sin \phi$

12.023 $\qquad \mu_{\alpha\beta} = -\lambda_\alpha \omega_\beta \sin \phi$

12.024 $\qquad \nu_{\alpha\beta} = -b_{\alpha\beta}$

Components of Base Vectors:

12.025 $\qquad \phi_s = -\mu_{rs} \nu^r$

12.026 $\qquad (\cos \phi) \omega_s = -\lambda_{rs} \nu^r$

12.029 $\qquad \begin{aligned} \lambda^r &= (\omega_s \lambda^s, \phi_s \lambda^s, N_s \lambda^s) \\ &= (-k_1 \sec \phi, -t_1, 0) \end{aligned}$

12.030 $\qquad \begin{aligned} \mu^r &= (\omega_s \mu^s, \phi_s \mu^s, N_s \mu_s) \\ &= (-t_1 \sec \phi, -k_2, 0) \end{aligned}$

12.034 $\qquad \begin{aligned} \nu^r &= (\omega_s \nu^s, \phi_s \nu^s, N_s \nu^s) \\ &= (\gamma_1 \sec \phi, \gamma_2, n) \end{aligned}$

12.035 $\qquad \lambda^\alpha = (-k_1 \sec \phi, -t_1)$

12.036 $\qquad \mu^\alpha = (-t_1 \sec \phi, -k_2)$

12.041 $\quad K\lambda_r = (-k_2 \cos \phi, +t_1, K \sec \phi \, \partial(1/n)/\partial\omega)$

12.042 $\quad K\mu_r = (+t_1 \cos \phi, -k_1, K\partial(1/n)/\partial\phi)$

12.043 $\qquad \nu_r = (0, 0, 1/n)$

$$\left\{ \begin{aligned} K\lambda_3 &= (k_2\gamma_1 - t_1\gamma_2)/n = -(1/n)_s(k_2\lambda^s - t_1\mu^s) \\ K\mu_3 &= (k_1\gamma_2 - t_1\gamma_1)/n = -(1/n)_s(-t_1\lambda^s + k_1\mu^s) \end{aligned} \right\}$$

12.039; 12.040

12.044 $\qquad K\lambda_\alpha = (-k_2 \cos \phi, +t_1)$

12.045 $\qquad K\mu_\alpha = (+t_1 \cos \phi, -k_1)$

12.046 $\quad (\cos \phi)\omega_r = -k_1\lambda_r - t_1\mu_r + \gamma_1\nu_r$

12.047 $\quad \phi_r = -t_1\lambda_r - k_2\mu_r + \gamma_2\nu_r$

12.048 $\quad (\ln n)_r = \gamma_1\lambda_r + \gamma_2\mu_r + \{(\ln n)_s\nu^s\}\nu_r$

Curvatures of N-Surfaces:

$$k = k_1 \sin^2 \alpha + 2t_1 \sin \alpha \cos \alpha + k_2 \cos^2 \alpha$$

12.049

$$t = (k_2 - k_1) \sin \alpha \cos \alpha - t_1(\cos^2 \alpha - \sin^2 \alpha)$$

12.050

12.051 $\quad \tan 2A = +2t_1/(k_2 - k_1)$

$$\kappa_1 = k_1 \sin^2 A + 2t_1 \sin A \cos A + k_2 \cos^2 A$$

$$\kappa_2 = k_1 \cos^2 A - 2t_1 \sin A \cos A + k_2 \sin^2 A$$

12.052

12.053 $\quad H = \frac{1}{2}(\kappa_1 + \kappa_2) = \frac{1}{2}(k_1 + k_2)$

$$(\kappa_1 - \kappa_2) = (k_2 - k_1)\sec 2A = 2t_1 \operatorname{cosec} 2A$$

12.054

12.055 $\quad K = \kappa_1\kappa_2 = k_1k_2 - t_1^2$

12.056 $\quad k = \kappa_1 \cos^2 (A - \alpha) + \kappa_2 \sin^2 (A - \alpha)$

12.057 $\quad t = \frac{1}{2}(\kappa_1 - \kappa_2) \sin 2(A - \alpha)$

$$k_1 = \kappa_1 \sin^2 A + \kappa_2 \cos^2 A$$

$$k_2 = \kappa_1 \cos^2 A + \kappa_2 \sin^2 A$$

12.058 $\quad t_1 = (\kappa_1 - \kappa_2) \sin A \cos A$

$$(\cos \phi)\partial\omega/\partial l = -k_1 \sin \alpha - t_1 \cos \alpha$$
$$= -k \sin \alpha + t \cos \alpha$$
$$\partial\phi/\partial l = -t_1 \sin \alpha - k_2 \cos \alpha$$
$$= -k \cos \alpha - t \sin \alpha$$
$$(\cos \phi)\partial\omega/\partial j = k_1 \cos \alpha - t_1 \sin \alpha$$
$$= k^* \cos \alpha - t \sin \alpha$$
$$\partial\phi/\partial j = t_1 \cos \alpha - k_2 \sin \alpha$$

12.060 $\quad = -k^* \sin \alpha - t \cos \alpha$

$$(\cos \phi)\omega_r = (-k \sin \alpha + t \cos \alpha)l_r$$

12.061 $\quad + (k^* \cos \alpha - t \sin \alpha)j_r + \gamma_1\nu_r$

$$\phi_r = -(k \cos \alpha + t \sin \alpha)l_r$$

12.062 $\quad - (k^* \sin \alpha + t \cos \alpha)j_r + \gamma_2\nu_r$

Geodesic Curvatures:

12.063 $\quad l_{\beta\gamma} = j_\beta(\omega_\gamma \sin \phi - \alpha_\gamma)$

12.064 $\quad \sigma l_\gamma + \sigma^* j_\gamma = \omega_\gamma \sin \phi - \alpha_\gamma$

12.065 $\quad \sigma = \sin \phi(\partial\omega/\partial l) - (\partial\alpha/\partial l)$

$$\sigma_1 = -k_1 \tan \phi; \qquad \sigma_2 = -t_1 \tan \phi$$

12.066; 12.067

$$\sigma = \sigma_1 \sin \alpha + \sigma_2 \cos \alpha - (\partial\alpha/\partial l)$$

12.068

Metric Tensor:

$$g_{11} = a_{11} = (k_2^2 + t_1^2) \cos^2 \phi/K^2$$

$$g_{12} = a_{12} = -2Ht_1 \cos \phi/K^2$$

$$g_{22} = a_{22} = (k_1^2 + t_1^2)/K^2$$

$$g_{13} = -\frac{k_2}{K} \frac{\partial(1/n)}{\partial\omega} + \frac{t_1 \cos \phi}{K} \frac{\partial(1/n)}{\partial\phi}$$

$$= -[\gamma_1(k_2^2 + t_1^2) - 2H\gamma_2 t_1]/(nK^2 \sec \phi)$$

$$g_{23} = \frac{t_1 \sec \phi}{K} \frac{\partial(1/n)}{\partial\omega} - \frac{k_1}{K} \frac{\partial(1/n)}{\partial\phi}$$

$$= -[\gamma_2(k_1^2 + t_1^2) - 2H\gamma_1 t_1]/nK^2$$

$$g_{33} = \sec^2 \phi \left(\frac{\partial(1/n)}{\partial\omega}\right)^2 + \left(\frac{\partial(1/n)}{\partial\phi}\right)^2 + \frac{1}{n^2}$$

$$= [\gamma_1^2(k_2^2 + t_1^2) + \gamma_2^2(k_1^2 + t_1^2)$$

$$- 4Ht_1\gamma_1\gamma_2 + K^2]/(n^2K^2)$$

12.069 $\quad = \sec^2 \beta/n^2$

12.070 $\quad g = \cos^2 \phi/(n^2K^2); \qquad a = \cos^2 \phi/K^2$

$$g^{11} = (k_1^2 + t_1^2 + \gamma_1^2) \sec^2 \phi$$

$$g^{12} = (\gamma_1\gamma_2 + 2Ht_1) \sec \phi$$

$$g^{22} = (k_2^2 + t_1^2 + \gamma_2^2)$$

$$g^{13} = n\gamma_1 \sec \phi$$

$$g^{23} = n\gamma_2$$

12.071 $\quad g^{33} = n^2$

$$a^{11} = (k_1^2 + t_1^2) \sec^2 \phi$$

$$a^{12} = 2Ht_1 \sec \phi$$

12.072 $\quad a^{22} = (k_2^2 + t_1^2)$

12.073 $\quad |g^{rs}| = n^2K^2 \sec^2 \phi; \qquad |a^{\alpha\beta}| = K^2 \sec^2 \phi$

Second Fundamental Form:

$$b_{\alpha\beta} = -(\cos \phi)\lambda_\alpha\omega_\beta - \mu_\alpha\phi_\beta$$

12.074

12.075 $\quad = (k_2 \cos^2 \phi/K, -t_1 \cos \phi/K, k_1/K)$

12.076 $\qquad b = \cos^2 \phi / K$

12.077 $\qquad b^{\alpha\beta} = (k_1 \sec^2 \phi, \, t_1 \sec \phi, \, k_2)$

12.079 $\qquad b_{1\alpha} = -(\cos \phi)\lambda_\alpha: \quad b_{2\alpha} = -\mu_\alpha$

12.080 $\qquad b^{1\alpha} = -(\sec \phi)\lambda^\alpha: \quad b^{2\alpha} = -\mu^\alpha$

12.081 $\qquad (\ln n)_\alpha = -b_{\alpha\beta}\nu^\beta$

12.082 $\qquad \nu^\alpha = -b^{\alpha\beta}(\ln n)_\beta$

Third Fundamental Form:

12.083 $\qquad c_{\alpha\beta} = (\cos^2 \phi, \, 0, \, 1)$

12.084 $\qquad c = \cos^2 \phi$

12.085 $\qquad c^{\alpha\beta} = (\sec^2 \phi, \, 0, \, 1)$

Coordinate Directions:
   Longitude:

12.086 $\qquad i^r = (1/\sqrt{g_{11}}, \, 0, \, 0)$

$$\cos \alpha_1 = t_1/(k_2^2 + t_1^2)^{1/2} = t_1/m_2$$

12.087 $\quad \sin \alpha_1 = -k_2/(k_2^2 + t_1^2)^{1/2} = -k_2/m_2$

$$m_2 = (k_2^2 + t_1^2)^{1/2} = (\kappa_2^2 \sin^2 A + \kappa_1^2 \cos^2 A)^{1/2}$$

$$\cos \alpha_1 = (\kappa_1 - \kappa_2) \sin A \cos A/m_2$$

12.088 $\quad \sin \alpha_1 = -(\kappa_2 \sin^2 A + \kappa_1 \cos^2 A)/m_2$

$$\sin (A - \alpha_1) = \kappa_1 \cos A/m_2$$

12.089 $\qquad \cos (A - \alpha_1) = -\kappa_2 \sin A/m_2$

Coordinate Directions:
   Latitude:

12.090 $\qquad j^r = (0, \, 1/\sqrt{g_{22}}, \, 0)$

$$\cos \alpha_2 = -k_1/(k_1^2 + t_1^2)^{1/2} = -k_1/m_1$$

12.091 $\quad \sin \alpha_2 = t_1/(k_1^2 + t_1^2)^{1/2} = t_1/m_1$

$$m_1 = (k_1^2 + t_1^2)^{1/2} = (\kappa_1^2 \sin^2 A + \kappa_2^2 \cos^2 A)^{1/2}$$

$$\cos \alpha_2 = -(\kappa_1 \sin^2 A + \kappa_2 \cos^2 A)/m_1$$

12.092 $\quad \sin \alpha_2 = (\kappa_1 - \kappa_2) \sin A \cos A/m_1$

$$\sin (A - \alpha_2) = -\kappa_1 \sin A/m_1$$

12.093 $\qquad \cos (A - \alpha_2) = -\kappa_2 \cos A/m_1$

The Isozenithal:

12.095 $\qquad k^r = (0, \, 0, \, 1/\sqrt{g_{33}})$

$$\sin \alpha \sin \beta = \{\sec \phi \; \partial(1/n)/\partial\omega\}/\sqrt{g_{33}}$$

$$\cos \alpha \sin \beta = \{\partial(1/n)/\partial\phi\}/\sqrt{g_{33}}$$

$$\cos \beta = (1/n)/\sqrt{g_{33}}$$

12.096

$$\sin \alpha \tan \beta = -(\sec \phi)\partial(\ln n)/\partial\omega$$

12.097 $\qquad \cos \alpha \tan \beta = -\partial(\ln n)/\partial\phi$

12.098 $\qquad \lambda_{rs}k^s = \mu_{rs}k^s = \nu_{rs}k^s = 0$

Laplacians of Coordinates:

12.099 $\qquad N_{rs} = n_s\nu_r + n\nu_{rs}$

12.100 $\qquad \Delta N = \partial n/\partial s - 2Hn$

12.101 $\qquad (\cos \phi)\omega_s = (1/n)N_{rs}\lambda^r$

12.102 $\qquad \phi_s = (1/n)N_{rs}\mu^r$

12.103 $\qquad n_s = N_{rs}\nu^r$

$$(\cos \phi)\Delta\omega = 2 \sin \phi \, \nabla(\omega, \phi) - 2 \cos \phi \, \nabla(\omega, \ln n)$$

12.104 $\qquad + (1/n)(\Delta N)_r\lambda^r$

$$\Delta\phi = -2\nabla(\phi, \ln n) - \sin \phi \cos \phi \, \nabla(\omega)$$

12.105 $\qquad + (1/n)(\Delta N)_r\mu^r$

$$\Delta n = n\{\cos^2 \phi \, \nabla(\omega) + \nabla(\phi)\} + (\Delta N)_r\nu^r$$

12.106

12.109 $\qquad \cos^2 \phi \, \nabla(\omega) = k_1^2 + t_1^2 + \gamma_1^2$

12.110 $\qquad \nabla(\phi) = k_2^2 + t_1^2 + \gamma_2^2$

12.111 $\quad \cos \phi \, \nabla(\omega, \phi) = 2Ht_1 + \gamma_1\gamma_2$

$$\cos \phi \, \nabla(\omega, \ln n) = -k_1\gamma_1 - t_1\gamma_2 + 2H\gamma_1 + (\gamma_1\Delta N)/n$$

12.112 $\qquad = k_2\gamma_1 - t_1\gamma_2 + (\gamma_1\Delta N)/n$

$$\nabla(\phi, \ln n) = -t_1\gamma_1 - k_2\gamma_2 + 2H\gamma_2 + (\gamma_2\Delta N)/n$$

12.113 $\qquad = k_1\gamma_2 - t_1\gamma_1 + (\gamma_2\Delta N)/n$

$$\cos^2 \phi \, \nabla(\omega) + \nabla(\phi) = 4H^2 - 2K + (\gamma_1^2 + \gamma_2^2)$$

12.114 $\qquad = \kappa_1^2 + \kappa_2^2 + (\gamma_1^2 + \gamma_2^2)$

$$(1/n)\Delta n = 4H^2 - 2K + (\gamma_1^2 + \gamma_2^2)$$

12.115 $\qquad + (1/n)(\Delta N)_r\nu^r$

Surface Invariants:

$$(\cos \phi)\overline{\Delta\omega} = 2(\sin \phi)\overline{\nabla}(\omega, \phi) - (2H)_\alpha\lambda^\alpha$$

12.118

12.119 $\overline{\nabla}(\omega, \phi) = 2Ht_1 \sec \phi$

12.120 $\overline{\Delta\phi} = -(\sin\phi\cos\phi)\overline{\nabla}(\omega) - (2H)_\alpha\mu^\alpha$

12.121 $\overline{\nabla}(\omega) = (k_1^2 + t_1^2)\sec^2\phi$

$(1/n)\overline{\Delta n} = (4H^2 - 2K) + 2(\gamma_1^2 + \gamma_2^2) - \partial(2H)/\partial s$

12.122

Christoffel Symbols:

$\Gamma^3_{\alpha\beta} = nb_{\alpha\beta}$; $\Gamma^3_{3\alpha} = 0$; $\Gamma^3_{33} = -\partial(\ln n)/\partial N$

12.124

12.127 $\Gamma^\alpha_{\beta 3} = b^{\alpha\gamma}\dfrac{\partial b_{\beta\gamma}}{\partial N} = -b_{\beta\gamma}\dfrac{\partial b^{\alpha\gamma}}{\partial N}$

12.128 $\Gamma^\alpha_{33} = (1/n)b^{\alpha\beta}\dfrac{\partial^2(\ln n)}{\partial x^\beta \partial N}$

12.129
$\Gamma^\gamma_{\alpha\beta}$ (space) $= \dfrac{\partial\lambda_\alpha}{\partial x^\beta}\lambda^\gamma + \dfrac{\partial\mu_\alpha}{\partial x^\beta}\mu^\gamma$
$\qquad\qquad\qquad - \omega_\beta\sin\phi(\mu_\alpha\lambda^\gamma - \lambda_\alpha\mu^\gamma) + b_{\alpha\beta}\nu^\gamma$

12.130
$\Gamma^\gamma_{\alpha\beta}$ (surface) $= \dfrac{\partial\lambda_\alpha}{\partial x^\beta}\lambda^\gamma + \dfrac{\partial\mu_\alpha}{\partial x^\beta}\mu^\gamma$
$\qquad\qquad\qquad - \lambda_{\alpha\beta}\lambda^\gamma - \mu_{\alpha\beta}\mu^\gamma$

12.131
$\Gamma^\gamma_{\alpha\beta}$ (space) $- \Gamma^\gamma_{\alpha\beta}$ (surface) $= -\nu_{\alpha\beta}\nu^\gamma$
$\qquad\qquad\qquad\qquad\qquad\qquad = b_{\alpha\beta}\nu^\gamma$

Mainardi-Codazzi Equations:

$\partial b_{11}/\partial\phi - \partial b_{12}/\partial\omega + b_{11}\tan\phi + b_{22}\sin\phi\cos\phi = 0$

12.134

12.135 $\partial b_{12}/\partial\phi - \partial b_{22}/\partial\omega - b_{12}\tan\phi = 0$

12.143 $\dfrac{\partial b_{\alpha\beta}}{\partial N} = -\dfrac{\partial^2(1/n)}{\partial x^\alpha \partial x^\beta} + \overline{\Gamma}^\gamma_{\alpha\beta}\dfrac{\partial(1/n)}{\partial x^\gamma} - \dfrac{c_{\alpha\beta}}{n}$

12.144 $= -\left(\dfrac{1}{n}\right)_{\alpha\beta} + b^{\gamma\delta}b_{\alpha\beta\delta}\left(\dfrac{1}{n}\right)_\gamma - \dfrac{c_{\alpha\beta}}{n}$

12.142 $\overline{\Gamma}^2_{11} = \sin\phi\cos\phi$; $\overline{\Gamma}^1_{12} = -\tan\phi$

Mainardi-Codazzi Equations in Tangential Coordinates:

12.145 $p = \rho_r\nu^r$

12.146 $p_\alpha = \rho_r\nu^r_\alpha$

$p_{\alpha\beta} = -b_{\alpha\beta} + \rho_r(b^{\gamma\delta}b_{\alpha\beta\delta}\nu^r_\gamma - c_{\alpha\beta}\nu^r)$

12.147
$b_{\alpha\beta} = -p_{\alpha\beta} + b^{\gamma\delta}b_{\alpha\beta\delta}p_\gamma - pc_{\alpha\beta}$
$= -\dfrac{\partial^2 p}{\partial x^\alpha \partial x^\beta} + \overline{\Gamma}^\gamma_{\alpha\beta}p_\gamma - pc_{\alpha\beta}$

12.148 $\dfrac{\partial p}{\partial N} = \dfrac{1}{n}$

12.151 $-b_{\alpha\beta} = \bar{p}_{\alpha\beta} + pc_{\alpha\beta}$

Higher Derivatives of Base Vectors:

12.153 $\lambda_{3\alpha} = \left(\sin\phi\,\dfrac{\partial(1/n)}{\partial\phi} - \dfrac{\cos\phi}{n}\right)\delta^1_\alpha$

12.154 $\mu_{3\alpha} = -\tan\phi\,\dfrac{\partial(1/n)}{\partial\omega}\delta^1_\alpha - \dfrac{1}{n}\delta^2_\alpha$

12.155 $\nu_{3\alpha} = (1/n)_\alpha$

$\lambda_{\alpha\beta 3} = \lambda_{\alpha 3\beta} = -(\sin\phi)\mu_\alpha b^{1\gamma}(\partial b_{\beta\gamma}/\partial N)$

$\mu_{\alpha\beta 3} = \mu_{\alpha 3\beta} = (\sin\phi)\lambda_\alpha b^{1\gamma}(\partial b_{\beta\gamma}/\partial N)$

12.159 $\nu_{\alpha\beta 3} = \nu_{\alpha 3\beta} = \partial b_{\alpha\beta}/\partial N$

$\lambda_{\alpha 33} = \mu_\alpha(1/n)\tan\phi\,\lambda^\delta\{\partial^2(\ln n)/\partial x^\delta \partial N\}$

$\mu_{\alpha 33} = -\lambda_\alpha(1/n)\tan\phi\,\lambda^\delta\{\partial^2(\ln n)/\partial x^\delta \partial N\}$

$\nu_{\alpha 33} = (1/n)\{\partial^2(\ln n)/\partial x^\alpha \partial N\}$

12.160

12.161 $\nu_{\alpha\beta\gamma} = -b_{\alpha\beta\gamma} - b_{\beta\gamma}(\ln n)_\alpha$

The Marussi Tensor:

$N_{rs}\lambda^r\lambda^s = -nk_1$

$N_{rs}\mu^r\mu^s = -nk_2$

$N_{rs}\lambda^r\mu^s = -nt_1$

$N_{rs}\lambda^r\nu^s = n\gamma_1$

$N_{rs}\mu^r\nu^s = n\gamma_2$

12.162 $N_{rs}\nu^r\nu^s = n(\ln n)_s\nu^s$

The Position Vector:

12.169 $\rho_r = (\sec\phi)(\partial p/\partial\omega)\lambda_r + (\partial p/\partial\phi)\mu_r + p\nu_r$

$p = x\cos\phi\cos\omega + y\cos\phi\sin\omega + z\sin\phi$

12.170

$\partial p/\partial\phi = -x\sin\phi\cos\omega - y\sin\phi\sin\omega + z\cos\phi$

12.171

$(\sec\phi)\partial p/\partial\omega = -x\sin\omega + y\cos\omega$

12.172

Chapter 13

Curvatures and Azimuths:

13.02
$$k = -m \cos(\alpha - \bar{\alpha})$$

13.03
$$t = -m \sin(\alpha - \bar{\alpha})$$

$$m \cos \bar{\alpha} = -k \cos \alpha - t \sin \alpha$$
$$= -k_2 \cos \alpha - t_1 \sin \alpha$$

13.04
$$= \partial \phi / \partial s$$

$$m \sin \bar{\alpha} = -k \sin \alpha + t \cos \alpha$$
$$= -k_1 \sin \alpha - t_1 \cos \alpha$$

13.05
$$= (\cos \phi) \partial \omega / \partial s$$

Geodesic Curvatures:

$$m\bar{\sigma} - \sigma = (\alpha - \bar{\alpha})_\beta l^\beta$$

13.10
$$= \left(\frac{k^2}{m^2}\right) \frac{\partial (t/k)}{\partial l}$$

Covariant Derivatives:

$$(m/K)\bar{l}_{\alpha\beta} = l_{\alpha\beta} + j_\alpha(\alpha - \bar{\alpha})_\beta$$

13.12
$$= l_{\alpha\beta} + j_\alpha \left(\frac{k^2}{m^2}\right) \frac{\partial (t/k)}{\partial x^\beta}$$

13.13
$$F_{\alpha\beta} - \bar{F}_{\alpha\beta} = b^{\gamma\delta} b_{\alpha\beta\delta} F_\gamma$$

Double Spherical Representation:

$$\frac{m}{m^*} = \frac{k_2 \cos \alpha + t_1 \sin \alpha}{k_2^* \cos \alpha^* + t_1^* \sin \alpha^*}$$

13.19
$$= \frac{k_1 \sin \alpha + t_1 \cos \alpha}{k_1^* \sin \alpha^* + t_1^* \cos \alpha^*}$$

13.20
$$\tan \alpha = -\frac{a + b \tan \alpha^*}{c + d \tan \alpha^*}$$

13.21
$$\tan \alpha^* = -\frac{a + c \tan \alpha}{b + d \tan \alpha}$$

$$a = (k_2 t_1^* - t_1 k_2^*) ; \qquad b = (k_2 k_1^* - t_1 t_1^*)$$
$$c = (t_1 t_1^* - k_1 k_2^*) ; \qquad d = (t_1 k_1^* - k_1 t_1^*)$$

13.22
$$ad - bc = KK^*$$

$$(m/m^*)K^* \sin \alpha^* = -(a \cos \alpha + c \sin \alpha)$$
$$(m/m^*)K^* \cos \alpha^* = (b \cos \alpha + d \sin \alpha)$$
$$(m^*/m)K \sin \alpha = (a \cos \alpha^* + b \sin \alpha^*)$$

13.25
$$(m^*/m)K \cos \alpha = -(c \cos \alpha^* + d \sin \alpha^*)$$

Chapter 14

(In some cases, the formulas have been extended or rearranged to give the isozenithal derivatives explicitly and can be obtained at sight from the textual references on the left.)

Fundamental Forms:

$$\partial a_{\alpha\beta}/\partial N = b^{\gamma\delta} a_{\beta\gamma}(\partial b_{\alpha\delta}/\partial N) + b^{\gamma\delta} a_{\alpha\gamma}(\partial b_{\beta\delta}/\partial N)$$

14.03

12.127
$$\partial b_{\alpha\beta}/\partial N = b_{\alpha\gamma}\Gamma^\gamma_{\beta 3}$$

12.144
$$= -\left(\frac{1}{n}\right)_{\alpha\beta} + b^{\gamma\delta} b_{\alpha\beta\delta}\left(\frac{1}{n}\right)_\gamma - \frac{c_{\alpha\beta}}{n}$$

12.143
$$= -\frac{\partial^2(1/n)}{\partial x^\alpha \partial x^\beta} + \Gamma^\gamma_{\alpha\beta}\frac{\partial(1/n)}{\partial x^\gamma} - \frac{c_{\alpha\beta}}{n}$$

$$= -\overline{(1/n)}_{\alpha\beta} - c_{\alpha\beta}/n$$

(Covariant derivatives refer to surface metric; overbars refer to metric of spherical representation. Only nonzero values of spherical Christoffel symbols are

12.142
$$\overline{\Gamma}^2_{11} = \sin \phi \cos \phi ; \qquad \overline{\Gamma}^1_{12} = -\tan \phi.)$$

14.08
$$\frac{\partial c^{\alpha\beta}}{\partial N} = 0$$

14.06
$$\partial a^{\alpha\beta}/\partial N = -(a^{\alpha\gamma} b^{\beta\delta} + a^{\beta\gamma} b^{\alpha\delta})(\partial b_{\gamma\delta}/\partial N)$$

$$\frac{\partial b^{\alpha\beta}}{\partial N} = -b^{\alpha\gamma} b^{\beta\delta}(\partial b_{\gamma\delta}/\partial N)$$

14.07; 12.127
$$= -b^{\alpha\gamma}\Gamma^\beta_{\gamma 3}$$

14.08
$$\frac{\partial c_{\alpha\beta}}{\partial N} = 0$$

14.04; 3.16
$$\frac{\partial \ln \sqrt{a}}{\partial N} = \frac{\partial \ln b}{\partial N} = -\frac{\partial \ln K}{\partial N} = \Gamma^\alpha_{\alpha 3}$$

12.084
$$\frac{\partial \ln c}{\partial N} = 0$$

Curvature Invariants:

(Overbars refer to surface metric.)

$$\partial(2H)/\partial N = -a^{\alpha\beta}(\partial b_{\alpha\beta}/\partial N)$$
$$= \overline{\Delta(1/n)} + (4H^2 - 2K)(1/n)$$

14.32; 14.28
$$- b^{\alpha\beta}(2H)_\alpha(1/n)_\beta$$

$$\partial(\ln K)/\partial N = -b^{\alpha\beta}(\partial b_{\alpha\beta}/\partial N)$$
$$= b^{\alpha\beta}\overline{(1/n)}_{\alpha\beta} + 2H(1/n)$$

14.32; 14.29
$$- b^{\alpha\beta}(\ln K)_\alpha(1/n)_\beta$$

$$\partial(2H/K)/\partial N = c^{\alpha\beta}(\partial b_{\alpha\beta}/\partial N)$$

$$= -c^{\alpha\beta}\overline{(1/n)}_{\alpha\beta} - 2(1/n)$$

14.32; 14.30; 14.37 $\qquad - b^{\alpha\beta}(2H/K)_\alpha(1/n)_\beta$

Christoffel Symbols:

$$\frac{\partial}{\partial N}\,\Gamma^\alpha_{\beta\gamma} = (\Gamma^\alpha_{\beta 3})_\gamma$$

$$= (\Gamma^\alpha_{\gamma 3})_\beta$$

$$= \left(b^{\alpha\delta}\frac{\partial b_{\beta\delta}}{\partial N}\right)_\gamma$$

14.14; 14.15 $\qquad = -\left(b_{\beta\delta}\dfrac{\partial b^{\alpha\delta}}{\partial N}\right)_\gamma$

Curvature Parameters:

$$b_{\alpha\beta\gamma}\lambda^\alpha\lambda^\beta = (k_1)_\gamma - 2t_1\omega_\gamma\sin\phi$$

$$b_{\alpha\beta\gamma}\lambda^\alpha\mu^\beta = (t_1)_\gamma + (k_1-k_2)\omega_\gamma\sin\phi$$

14.35 $\qquad b_{\alpha\beta\gamma}\mu^\alpha\mu^\beta = (k_2)_\gamma + 2t_1\omega_\gamma\sin\phi$

$$\frac{\partial k_1}{\partial N} = -\frac{\partial b_{\alpha\beta}}{\partial N}\lambda^\alpha\lambda^\beta = \cos^2\phi\,\frac{\partial b^{11}}{\partial N}$$

$$\frac{\partial t_1}{\partial N} = -\frac{\partial b_{\alpha\beta}}{\partial N}\lambda^\alpha\mu^\beta = \cos\phi\,\frac{\partial b^{12}}{\partial N}$$

14.34; 12.077 $\qquad \dfrac{\partial k_2}{\partial N} = -\dfrac{\partial b_{\alpha\beta}}{\partial N}\mu^\alpha\mu^\beta = \dfrac{\partial b^{22}}{\partial N}$

$$\frac{\partial}{\partial N}\left(\frac{k_1}{K}\right) = \frac{\partial b_{22}}{\partial N}$$

$$\frac{\partial}{\partial N}\left(\frac{t_1}{K}\right) = -\sec\phi\,\frac{\partial b_{12}}{\partial N}$$

12.075 $\qquad \dfrac{\partial}{\partial N}\left(\dfrac{k_2}{K}\right) = \sec^2\phi\,\dfrac{\partial b_{11}}{\partial N}$

14.40 $\qquad \partial\gamma_1/\partial N = -\Gamma^1_{3s}\nu^s\cos\phi$

14.41 $\qquad \partial\gamma_2/\partial N = -\Gamma^2_{3s}\nu^s$

Principal Curvatures:

$$b_{\alpha\beta\gamma}u^\alpha u^\beta = (\kappa_1)_\gamma$$

$$b_{\alpha\beta\gamma}v^\alpha v^\beta = (\kappa_2)_\gamma$$

14.43 $\qquad b_{\alpha\beta\gamma}u^\alpha v^\beta = (\kappa_1 - \kappa_2)(\omega_\gamma\sin\phi - A_\gamma)$

$$\partial\kappa_1/\partial N = -(\partial b_{\alpha\beta}/\partial N)u^\alpha u^\beta$$

$$\partial\kappa_2/\partial N = -(\partial b_{\alpha\beta}/\partial N)v^\alpha v^\beta$$

14.42 $\qquad (\kappa_1 - \kappa_2)(\partial A/\partial N) = (\partial b_{\alpha\beta}/\partial N)u^\alpha v^\beta$

Miscellaneous Point Functions:

14.09 $\qquad \partial\epsilon_{\alpha\beta}/\partial N = -\epsilon_{\alpha\beta}\partial(\ln K)/\partial N$

14.10 $\qquad \partial\epsilon^{\alpha\beta}/\partial N = +\epsilon^{\alpha\beta}\partial(\ln K)/\partial N$

14.11 $\qquad \partial(K\epsilon_{\alpha\beta})/\partial N = \partial(\epsilon^{\alpha\beta}/K)/\partial N = 0$

13.14; 14.05 $\qquad \partial(KdS)/\partial N = 0$

14.50 $\qquad \partial x^r_\alpha/\partial N = \Gamma^\gamma_{\alpha 3}x^r_\gamma$

14.51 $\qquad \partial\nu^r_\alpha/\partial N = 0$

14.52 $\qquad \partial\nu^r_{\alpha\beta}/\partial N = -(\Gamma^\gamma_{\alpha 3})_\beta\nu^r_\gamma$

(The space coordinates are Cartesian in the last three equations.)

14.16 $\qquad \dfrac{\partial b_{\alpha\beta\gamma}}{\partial N} = b_{\alpha\rho}b_{\beta\sigma}\left(\dfrac{\partial b^{\rho\sigma}}{\partial N}\right)_\gamma$

Surface Vectors Defined in Space:

$$l_{r3} = -j_r(\partial\alpha/\partial N)$$

14.17 $\qquad j_{r3} = l_r(\partial\alpha/\partial N)$

Projection of Surface Vectors:
Length:

$$\frac{\partial(\ln\delta s)}{\partial N} = -\frac{\partial(\ln m)}{\partial N} = -\frac{\partial\{\ln(k^2+t^2)^{1/2}\}}{\partial N} = \Gamma^\gamma_{\alpha 3}l^\alpha l_\gamma$$

14.53; 14.54

14.56 $\qquad \partial\{\ln(m/K)\}/\partial N = \Gamma^\gamma_{\alpha 3}j^\alpha j_\gamma$

Azimuth:

$$(\partial\alpha/\partial N) = -\Gamma^\gamma_{\alpha 3}l^\alpha j_\gamma = (k^2/m^2)\{\partial(t/k)/\partial N\}$$

14.61; 14.67

Components:

14.59 $\qquad \partial l^\alpha/\partial N = -\Gamma^\beta_{\gamma 3}l^\gamma l_\beta l^\alpha$

14.64 $\qquad \partial l_\alpha/\partial N = \Gamma^\beta_{\alpha 3}l_\beta - j_\alpha(\partial\alpha/\partial N)$

Curvatures:

14.65 $\qquad \partial k/\partial N = k\{\partial(\ln m)/\partial N\} - t(\partial\alpha/\partial N)$

14.66 $\qquad \partial t/\partial N = t\{\partial(\ln m)/\partial N\} + k(\partial\alpha/\partial N)$

14.69 $\qquad \dfrac{\partial\sigma}{\partial N} = \sigma\,\dfrac{\partial(\ln m)}{\partial N} - \dfrac{\partial^2\alpha}{\partial x^\beta\partial N}\,l^\beta$

Covariant Derivatives:

14.70 $\qquad \dfrac{\partial l_{\alpha\beta}}{\partial N} = l_{\alpha\beta}\,\dfrac{\partial\{\ln(m/K)\}}{\partial N} - j_\alpha\,\dfrac{\partial^2\alpha}{\partial x^\beta\partial N}$

14.71 $\qquad \dfrac{\partial F_{\alpha\beta}}{\partial N} = \left(\dfrac{\partial F}{\partial N}\right)_{\alpha\beta} - (\Gamma^\gamma_{\alpha 3})_\beta F_\gamma$

(*F* is a scalar defined in space.)

Chapter 15

Normal Coordinates:
Metric:

15.02 $\qquad ds^2 = a_{\alpha\beta}dx^\alpha dx^\beta + (1/n)^2 dN^2$

15.04 $\qquad g = (1/n^2)a$

15.05 $\qquad g^{rs} = (a^{\alpha\beta}, n^2)$

Unit Normals:

15.07 $\qquad \nu_r = (0, 0, 1/n)$

15.08 $\qquad \nu^r = (0, 0, n)$

15.10 $\quad \nu^3_\alpha = 0; \qquad \nu^\alpha_\beta = -a^{\alpha\gamma}b_{\beta\gamma} = -b^{\alpha\gamma}c_{\beta\gamma}$

Surface Vectors:

$$l_3 = 0; \qquad l^3 = 0$$

Christoffel Symbols:

$$\Gamma^\gamma_{\alpha\beta} \quad \text{(space)} = \Gamma^\gamma_{\alpha\beta} \quad \text{(surface)}$$

$$\Gamma^\alpha_{33} = (1/n^2)a^{\alpha\beta}(\ln n)_\beta; \qquad \Gamma^\alpha_{\beta3} = -(1/n)a^{\alpha\gamma}b_{\beta\gamma}$$

$$\Gamma^3_{\alpha\beta} = nb_{\alpha\beta}; \qquad \Gamma^3_{3\alpha} = -(\ln n)_\alpha; \qquad \Gamma^3_{33} = -\partial(\ln n)/\partial N$$

15.11

15.12 $\qquad \dfrac{\partial}{\partial N} = \left(\dfrac{1}{n}\right)\dfrac{\partial}{\partial s}$

Derivatives of Unit Normal:

15.18 $\qquad \nu_{\alpha\beta} = -b_{\alpha\beta}$

$$\nu_{\alpha3} = -(1/n)_\alpha$$
$$\nu_{3\alpha} = 0$$

15.19 $\qquad \nu_{33} = 0$

15.20 $\qquad \nu^3_{\alpha\beta} = -nc_{\alpha\beta}$

15.21 $\qquad \nu^\gamma_{\alpha\beta} = -a^{\gamma\delta}b_{\alpha\beta\delta}$

Mainardi-Codazzi Equations:

15.24 $\qquad b_{\alpha\beta\gamma} = b_{\alpha\gamma\beta}$

15.25 $\qquad \dfrac{\partial b_{\alpha\beta}}{\partial s} = n\overline{\left(\dfrac{1}{n}\right)}_{\alpha\beta} - c_{\alpha\beta}$

Normal Differentiation:

Fundamental Forms:

15.13 $\qquad \partial a_{\alpha\beta}/\partial s = -2b_{\alpha\beta}$

15.25 $\qquad \dfrac{\partial b_{\alpha\beta}}{\partial s} = n\overline{\left(\dfrac{1}{n}\right)}_{\alpha\beta} - c_{\alpha\beta}$

15.26 $\qquad \dfrac{\partial c_{\alpha\beta}}{\partial s} = na^{\gamma\delta}b_{\alpha\gamma}\overline{\left(\dfrac{1}{n}\right)}_{\beta\delta} + na^{\gamma\delta}b_{\beta\gamma}\overline{\left(\dfrac{1}{n}\right)}_{\alpha\delta}$

$$\dfrac{\partial a^{\alpha\beta}}{\partial s} = 2a^{\alpha\gamma}a^{\beta\delta}b_{\gamma\delta} = 4Ha^{\alpha\beta} - 2Kb^{\alpha\beta}$$

15.14; 15.15

15.27 $\qquad \dfrac{\partial b^{\alpha\beta}}{\partial s} = -nb^{\alpha\gamma}b^{\beta\delta}\overline{\left(\dfrac{1}{n}\right)}_{\gamma\delta} + a^{\alpha\beta}$

15.28 $\qquad \dfrac{\partial c^{\alpha\beta}}{\partial s} = -nb^{\alpha\gamma}c^{\beta\delta}\overline{\left(\dfrac{1}{n}\right)}_{\gamma\delta} - nb^{\beta\gamma}c^{\alpha\delta}\overline{\left(\dfrac{1}{n}\right)}_{\gamma\delta}$

15.16 $\qquad \dfrac{\partial(\ln a)}{\partial s} = -4H$

15.25 $\quad \partial(\ln b)/\partial s = b^{\alpha\beta}(\partial b_{\alpha\beta}/\partial s) = nb^{\alpha\beta}\overline{(1/n)}_{\alpha\beta} - 2H$

$$\partial(\ln c)/\partial s = c^{\alpha\beta}(\partial c_{\alpha\beta}/\partial s) = 2nb^{\alpha\beta}\overline{(1/n)}_{\alpha\beta}$$

Surface Invariants:

15.30 $\qquad \dfrac{\partial(2H)}{\partial s} = n\overline{\Delta(1/n)} + (4H^2 - 2K)$

15.29 $\qquad \dfrac{\partial(\ln K)}{\partial s} = nb^{\alpha\beta}\overline{\left(\dfrac{1}{n}\right)}_{\alpha\beta} + 2H$

15.31 $\qquad \dfrac{\partial(2H/K)}{\partial s} = -nc^{\alpha\beta}\overline{\left(\dfrac{1}{n}\right)}_{\alpha\beta} - 2$

Christoffel Symbols:

$$\dfrac{\partial\Gamma^\alpha_{\beta\gamma}}{\partial s} = -a^{\alpha\delta}b_{\beta\gamma\delta} + a^{\alpha\delta}b_{\beta\delta}(\ln n)_\gamma$$

15.32 $\qquad + a^{\alpha\delta}b_{\gamma\delta}(\ln n)_\beta - a^{\alpha\delta}b_{\beta\gamma}(\ln n)_\delta$

Curvature Parameters:

(See § 15-35.)

$$\partial k_1/\partial s = n\overline{(1/n)}_{\alpha\beta}\lambda^\alpha\lambda^\beta + (k_1^2 + t_1^2)$$
$$+ 2\gamma_1 t_1 \tan\phi$$
$$\partial k_2/\partial s = n\overline{(1/n)}_{\alpha\beta}\mu^\alpha\mu^\beta + (k_2^2 + t_1^2)$$
$$- 2\gamma_1 t_1 \tan\phi$$
$$\partial t_1/\partial s = n\overline{(1/n)}_{\alpha\beta}\lambda^\alpha\mu^\beta + 2Ht_1$$

14.36 $\qquad - \gamma_1(k_1 - k_2)\tan\phi$

Principal Curvatures:

(See § 15-35.)

14.45 $\qquad \partial\kappa_1/\partial s = n\overline{(1/n)}_{\alpha\beta}u^\alpha u^\beta + \kappa_1^2$

14.46 $\qquad \partial\kappa_2/\partial s = n\overline{(1/n)}_{\alpha\beta}v^\alpha v^\beta + \kappa_2^2$

14.44 $\quad (\kappa_1 - \kappa_2)(\gamma_1 \tan\phi - \partial A/\partial s) = n\overline{(1/n)}_{\alpha\beta}u^\alpha v^\beta$

Miscellaneous Point Functions:

$$\dfrac{\partial\epsilon_{\alpha\beta}}{\partial s} = -2H\epsilon_{\alpha\beta}$$

15.17 $\qquad \dfrac{\partial\epsilon^{\alpha\beta}}{\partial s} = +2H\epsilon^{\alpha\beta}$

15.39 $\qquad \partial(\delta S)/\partial s = -2H\delta S \qquad \text{(area)}$

$$\partial(b_{\alpha\beta\gamma})/\partial s = n\overline{(1/n)}_{\alpha\beta\gamma} - c_{\alpha\beta}(\ln n)_\gamma$$
$$- c_{\beta\gamma}(\ln n)_\alpha - c_{\gamma\alpha}(\ln n)_\beta$$

15.33 $\qquad + a^{\delta\epsilon}(\ln n)_\epsilon(b_{\alpha\gamma}b_{\delta\beta} + b_{\beta\gamma}b_{\delta\alpha})$

Surface Vectors Defined in Space:

$$\partial l_\alpha/\partial s = -kl_\alpha + j_\alpha(\gamma_1 \tan\phi - t - \partial\alpha/\partial s)$$

15.36 $\qquad \partial l^\alpha/\partial s = kl^\alpha + j^\alpha(\gamma_1 \tan\phi + t - \partial\alpha/\partial s)$

Meridian and Parallel:

$$\partial\lambda_\alpha/\partial s = (\gamma_1 \tan\phi - t_1)\mu_\alpha - k_1\lambda_\alpha$$

$$\partial\lambda^\alpha/\partial s = (\gamma_1 \tan\phi + t_1)\mu^\alpha + k_1\lambda^\alpha$$

$$\partial\mu_\alpha/\partial s = -(\gamma_1 \tan\phi + t_1)\lambda_\alpha - k_2\mu_\alpha$$

15.35 $\qquad \partial\mu^\alpha/\partial s = -(\gamma_1 \tan\phi - t_1)\lambda^\alpha + k_2\mu^\alpha$

Principal Directions:

$$\partial u_\alpha/\partial s = -\kappa_1 u_\alpha + v_\alpha(\gamma_1 \tan\phi - \partial A/\partial s)$$

$$\partial u^\alpha/\partial s = +\kappa_1 u^\alpha + v^\alpha(\gamma_1 \tan\phi - \partial A/\partial s)$$

$$\partial v_\alpha/\partial s = -\kappa_2 v_\alpha - u_\alpha(\gamma_1 \tan\phi - \partial A/\partial s)$$

15.37 $\qquad \partial v^\alpha/\partial s = +\kappa_2 v^\alpha - u^\alpha(\gamma_1 \tan\phi - \partial A/\partial s)$

Normal Projection of Surface Vectors:
Length:

15.38 $\qquad \partial(\ln\,\delta l)/\partial s = -k$

Azimuth:

15.43 $\qquad \partial\alpha/\partial s = \gamma_1 \tan\phi + t$

Components:

15.40 $\qquad \dfrac{\partial l^\alpha}{\partial s} = kl^\alpha$

15.41 $\qquad \partial l_\alpha/\partial s = -kl_\alpha - 2tj_\alpha$

Curvatures:

15.44 $\qquad \partial k/\partial s = n\overline{(1/n)}_{\alpha\beta}l^\alpha l^\beta + (k^2 - t^2)$

15.46 $\qquad \partial t/\partial s = n\overline{(1/n)}_{\alpha\beta}j^\alpha l^\beta + 2kt$

$$\partial\sigma/\partial s = k\sigma + 2t(\ln n)_\beta l^\beta - k(\ln n)_\beta j^\beta - t_\beta l^\beta$$

15.54

Covariant Derivatives:

15.51 $\qquad \partial l_{\alpha\beta}/\partial s = -k^* l_{\alpha\beta} + j_\alpha\{Q_\beta + t(\ln n)_\beta - t_\beta\}$

with

15.49 $\qquad Q_\beta = -\gamma_1\phi_\beta + (\gamma_2 \cos\phi)\omega_\beta$

15.49; 15.50 $\qquad = Kb^{\gamma\delta}(\ln\,n)_\gamma\epsilon_{\delta\beta} = \epsilon^{\gamma\alpha}(\ln\,n)_\gamma b_{\alpha\beta}$

15.52 $\qquad j_\alpha Q_\beta = b_{\alpha\beta}(\ln n)_\gamma l^\gamma - b_{\beta\delta}(\ln n)_\alpha l^\delta$

$$\frac{\partial F_{\alpha\beta}}{\partial s} = n\left(\frac{1}{n}\frac{\partial F}{\partial s}\right)_{\alpha\beta} + F^\gamma\{b_{\alpha\beta\gamma} - b_{\alpha\gamma}(\ln n)_\beta$$

15.53 $\qquad\qquad\qquad -b_{\beta\gamma}(\ln n)_\alpha + b_{\alpha\beta}(\ln n)_\gamma\}$

Chapter 16

Darboux Equation:

$$\overline{(1/n)}_{\alpha\beta}u^\alpha v^\beta \ \text{(surface)} = (1/n)_{rs}u^r v^s \ \text{(space)} = 0$$

16.03; 16.04

16.05 $\qquad \partial A/\partial s = \gamma_1 \tan\phi$

16.06 $\qquad \dfrac{\partial^2(1/n)}{\partial x^1\partial x^2} = \Gamma^1_{12}\dfrac{\partial(1/n)}{\partial x^1} + \Gamma^2_{12}\dfrac{\partial(1/n)}{\partial x^2}$

(Surface coordinate lines are lines of curvature.)

Particular Solutions:

16.07 $\qquad a + bx + cy + dz + er^2$

Chapter 17

The (ω, ϕ, h) Coordinate System:
Metric:

17.04 $\qquad ds^2 = a_{\alpha\beta}dx^\alpha dx^\beta + dh^2$

17.05 $\qquad g^{rs} = (a^{\alpha\beta}, 1)$

Fundamental Forms:

$$a_{11} = (k_2^2 + t_1^2)\cos^2\phi/K^2 \qquad b_{11} = k_2\cos^2\phi/K$$

$$a_{12} = -2Ht_1\cos\phi/K^2 \qquad b_{12} = -t_1\cos\phi/K$$

$$a_{22} = (k_1^2 + t_1^2)/K^2 \qquad b_{22} = k_1/K$$

17.12 $\qquad c_{\alpha\beta} = (\cos^2\phi, 0, 1)$

$$a^{11} = (k_1^2 + t_1^2)\sec^2\phi \qquad b^{11} = k_1\sec^2\phi$$

$$a^{12} = 2Ht_1\sec\phi \qquad b^{12} = t_1\sec\phi$$

$$a^{22} = (k_2^2 + t_1^2) \qquad b^{22} = k_2$$

17.20 $\qquad c^{\alpha\beta} = (\sec^2\phi, 0, 1)$

17.21 $\qquad \dfrac{a}{a} = \dfrac{b^2}{b^2} = \dfrac{\overline{K}^2}{K^2}$

Base Vectors:

17.23 $\qquad \lambda^r = (-k_1\sec\phi, -t_1, 0)$

17.24 $\qquad \mu^r = (-t_1\sec\phi, -k_2, 0)$

17.25 $\qquad \nu^r = (0, 0, 1)$

17.26 $\qquad K\lambda_r = (-k_2\cos\phi, +t_1, 0)$

17.27 $\qquad K\mu_r = (+t_1\cos\phi, -k_1, 0)$

17.28 $\qquad \nu_r = (0, 0, 1)$

17.29 $\qquad (\cos\phi)\omega_r = -k_1\lambda_r - t_1\mu_r$

17.30 $\qquad \phi_r = -t_1\lambda_r - k_2\mu_r$

$$\lambda_{\alpha\beta} = \mu_\alpha\omega_\beta \sin\phi$$

$$\mu_{\alpha\beta} = -\lambda_\alpha\omega_\beta \sin\phi$$

17.31 $\qquad \nu_{\alpha\beta} = -b_{\alpha\beta} = (\cos\phi)\lambda_\alpha\omega_\beta + \mu_\alpha\phi_\beta$

17.32 $\qquad \lambda_{31} = -\cos\phi ; \qquad \mu_{32} = -1$

Christoffel Symbols:

$$\Gamma^\gamma_{\alpha\beta} \qquad \text{(space)} = \Gamma^\alpha_{\alpha\beta} \qquad \text{(surface)}$$

17.36 $\qquad \Gamma^3_{\alpha\beta}=b_{\alpha\beta} \qquad \Gamma^\alpha_{\beta3}=-a^{\alpha\gamma}b_{\beta\gamma}=\nu^\alpha_\beta$

(All other 3-index symbols are zero.)

Laplacians:

17.37 $\qquad\qquad \Delta h=-2H$

17.38 $\qquad (\cos\phi)\Delta\omega=2(\sin\phi)\nabla(\omega,\phi)-(2H)_\alpha\lambda^\alpha$

$\qquad\qquad\qquad$ (space or surface)

17.39 $\qquad \Delta\phi=-(\sin\phi\cos\phi)\nabla(\omega)-(2H)_\alpha\mu^\alpha$

$\qquad\qquad\qquad$ (space or surface)

17.40 $\qquad$ with $\quad \nabla(\omega,\phi)=a^{12}=2Ht_1\sec\phi$

17.41 $\qquad \nabla(\omega)=a^{11}=(k_1^2+t_1^2)\sec^2\phi$

$$\Delta F=\overline{\Delta F}-2H\frac{\partial F}{\partial h}+\frac{\partial^2 F}{\partial h^2}=\overline{\Delta F}+K\frac{\partial}{\partial h}\left(\frac{1}{K}\frac{\partial F}{\partial h}\right)$$

17.42; 17.43

The *h*-Differentiation:

(References may be to formulas in (ω,ϕ,N) or in normal coordinates from which the formulas given now are derived. See § 17–32. The corresponding formulas given now in (ω,ϕ,h) coordinates are not, of course, the same in all cases.)

The Fundamental Forms:

15.13 $\qquad\qquad \partial a_{\alpha\beta}/\partial h=-2b_{\alpha\beta}$

15.25 $\qquad\qquad \partial b_{\alpha\beta}/\partial h=-c_{\alpha\beta}$

15.26 $\qquad\qquad \partial c_{\alpha\beta}/\partial h=0$

$$\partial a^{\alpha\beta}/\partial h=2a^{\alpha\gamma}a^{\beta\delta}b_{\gamma\delta}=4Ha^{\alpha\beta}-2Kb^{\alpha\beta}$$

15.14; 15.15

15.27 $\qquad\qquad \partial b^{\alpha\beta}/\partial h=a^{\alpha\beta}$

15.28 $\qquad\qquad \partial c^{\alpha\beta}/\partial h=0$

17.09 $\qquad\qquad a_{\alpha\beta}=\bar{a}_{\alpha\beta}-2h\bar{b}_{\alpha\beta}+h^2\bar{c}_{\alpha\beta}$

17.10 $\qquad\qquad b_{\alpha\beta}=\bar{b}_{\alpha\beta}-h\bar{c}_{\alpha\beta}$

17.11 $\qquad\qquad c_{\alpha\beta}=\bar{c}_{\alpha\beta}$

17.17 $\qquad a^{\alpha\beta}/K^2=\bar{a}^{\alpha\beta}/\bar{K}^2-2h\bar{b}^{\alpha\beta}/\bar{K}+h^2\bar{c}^{\alpha\beta}$

17.18 $\qquad\qquad b^{\alpha\beta}/K=\bar{b}^{\alpha\beta}/\bar{K}-h\bar{c}^{\alpha\beta}$

17.19 $\qquad\qquad c^{\alpha\beta}=\bar{c}^{\alpha\beta}$

§ 17–14 $\qquad \dfrac{\partial\ln\sqrt{a}}{\partial h}=\dfrac{\partial\ln b}{\partial h}=-2H$

§ 17–14 $\qquad\qquad \dfrac{\partial\ln c}{\partial h}=0$

Curvature Invariants:

15.30 $\qquad\qquad \partial(2H)\partial h=4H^2-2K$

15.29; 17.22 $\qquad \partial(\ln K)/\partial h=2H$

15.31 $\qquad\qquad \partial(2H/K)\partial h=-2$

$$\bar{K}/K=1-2\bar{H}h+\bar{K}h^2=(1-h\bar\kappa_1)(1-h\bar\kappa_2)$$

17.14; 17.15

17.16 $\qquad\qquad 2H/K=2\bar{H}/\bar{K}-2h$

§ 17–14 $\qquad K^2a=Kb=c=\cos^2\phi=\bar{c}=\bar{K}\bar{b}=\bar{K}^2\bar{a}$

Christoffel Symbols:

15.32; 17.52 $\qquad \dfrac{\partial}{\partial h}\Gamma^\alpha_{\beta\gamma}=-a^{\alpha\delta}b_{\beta\gamma\delta}$

$$\frac{\partial}{\partial h}\Gamma^3_{\alpha\beta}=-c_{\alpha\beta}$$

17.36 $\qquad\qquad \dfrac{\partial}{\partial h}\Gamma^\alpha_{\beta3}=-a^{\alpha\gamma}c_{\beta\gamma}$

Curvature Parameters:

$$\partial k_1/\partial h=(k_1^2+t_1^2)$$

$$\partial k_2/\partial h=(k_2^2+t_1^2)$$

14.34; 14.36 $\qquad \partial t_1/\partial h=2Ht_1$

$$k_1/K=\bar{k}_1/\bar{K}-h$$

$$t_1/K=\bar{t}_1/\bar{K}$$

17.13 $\qquad\qquad k_2/K=\bar{k}_2/\bar{K}-h$

Principal Curvatures:

14.44; § 17–21 $\qquad \partial A/\partial h=0$

14.45; 14.46 $\qquad \dfrac{\partial}{\partial h}\left(\dfrac{1}{\kappa_1}\right)=\dfrac{\partial}{\partial h}\left(\dfrac{1}{\kappa_2}\right)=-1$

$$(1/\kappa_1)=(1/\bar\kappa_1)-h$$

17.35 $\qquad\qquad (1/\kappa_2)=(1/\bar\kappa_2)-h$

Miscellaneous Point Functions:

$$\partial\epsilon_{\alpha\beta}/\partial h=-2H\epsilon_{\alpha\beta}$$

15.17 $\qquad\qquad \partial\epsilon^{\alpha\beta}/\partial h=+2H\epsilon^{\alpha\beta}$

15.39 $\qquad \partial(\delta S)/\partial h=-2H\delta S \qquad$ (area)

13.14 $\qquad\qquad \partial(K\delta S)/\partial h=0$

14.11 $\qquad \partial(K\epsilon_{\alpha\beta})/\partial h=\partial(\epsilon^{\alpha\beta}/K)/\partial h=0$

14.50; 17.36 $\qquad \partial x^r_\alpha/\partial h=\nu^r_\alpha$

14.51 $\qquad\qquad \partial\nu^r_\alpha/\partial h=0$

14.52 $\qquad\qquad \partial\nu^r_{\alpha\beta}/\partial h=a^{\gamma\delta}b_{\alpha\beta\gamma}\nu^r_\delta$

(Space coordinates in the last three equations are Cartesian.)

17.53 $\qquad\qquad \partial b_{\alpha\beta\gamma}/\partial h=0$

Surface Vectors Defined in Space:

$$\partial l_\alpha/\partial h=-kl_\alpha-j_\alpha(t+\partial\alpha/\partial h)$$

15.36 $\qquad \partial l^\alpha/\partial h=kl^\alpha+j^\alpha(t-\partial\alpha/\partial h)$

(The vector is defined in space; it is not projected.)

Meridian and Parallel:

$$\partial\lambda_\alpha/\partial h = -t_1\mu_\alpha - k_1\lambda_\alpha = -b_{\alpha\beta}\lambda^\beta$$

$$\partial\lambda^\alpha/\partial h = \quad t_1\mu^\alpha + k_1\lambda^\alpha = a^{\alpha\beta}b_{\beta\gamma}\lambda^\gamma$$

$$\partial\mu_\alpha/\partial h = -t_1\lambda_\alpha - k_2\mu_\alpha = -b_{\alpha\beta}\mu^\beta$$

15.35 $\qquad \partial\mu^\alpha/\partial h = \quad t_1\lambda^\alpha + k_2\mu^\alpha = a^{\alpha\beta}b_{\beta\gamma}\mu^\gamma$

Principal Directions:

$$\partial u_\alpha/\partial h = -\kappa_1 u_\alpha \qquad \partial v_\alpha/\partial h = -\kappa_2 v_\alpha$$

15.37 $\qquad \partial u^\alpha/\partial h = \kappa_1 u^\alpha \qquad \partial v^\alpha/\partial h = \kappa_2 v^\alpha$

Normal Projection of Surface Vectors:
Length:
(*m* = scale factor of spherical representation.)

14.53; 15.38 $\qquad \partial(\ln m)/\partial h = -\partial(\ln \delta l)/\partial h = k$

14.56; 17.36 $\qquad \dfrac{\partial \ln (m/K)}{\partial h} = -k^*$

Azimuth:

15.43 $\qquad\qquad \partial\alpha/\partial h = t$

Components:

15.40 $\qquad\qquad \partial l^\alpha/\partial h = kl^\alpha$

15.41 $\qquad\qquad \partial l_\alpha/\partial h = -kl_\alpha - 2tj_\alpha$

Curvatures:

15.44 $\qquad\qquad \partial k/\partial h = k^2 - t^2$

15.46 $\qquad\qquad \partial t/\partial h = 2kt$

15.54 $\qquad\qquad \partial\sigma/\partial h = k\sigma - t_\beta l^\beta$

Covariant Derivatives:

14.70; 15.51 $\qquad \partial l_{\alpha\beta}/\partial h = -k^* l_{\alpha\beta} - j_\alpha t_\beta$

17.54 $\qquad \dfrac{\partial F_{\alpha\beta}}{\partial h} = \overline{\left(\dfrac{\partial F}{\partial h}\right)}_{\alpha\beta} + a^{\gamma\delta}F_\delta b_{\alpha\beta\gamma}$

17.55 $\qquad \alpha^{\alpha\beta}\dfrac{\partial F_{\alpha\beta}}{\partial h} = \overline{\Delta}\left(\dfrac{\partial F}{\partial h}\right) + \overline{\nabla}(2H, F)$

$$\dfrac{\partial(\overline{\Delta}F)}{\partial h} = \overline{\Delta}\left(\dfrac{\partial F}{\partial h}\right) + \overline{\nabla}(2H, F) + 4H\overline{\Delta}F - 2Kb^{\alpha\beta}\overline{F}_{\alpha\beta}$$

17.56

Normal Projection — Integral Equations:
(Overbars denote values on base surface.)

$$\Delta\alpha = (\bar\alpha - \alpha)$$

$$(ds/d\bar s) \sin \Delta\alpha = -h\bar t$$

17.47 $\qquad (ds/d\bar s) \cos \Delta\alpha = (1 - h\bar k)$

$$(ds/d\bar s)^2 = 1 - 2h\bar k + h^2(\bar k^2 + \bar t^2)$$

$$(ds/d\bar s)^2 k = \bar k - h(\bar k^2 + \bar t^2)$$

17.44 $\qquad (ds/d\bar s)^2(k^2 + t^2) = \bar k^2 + \bar t^2$

17.48 $\qquad\qquad (ds/d\bar s)^2 t = \bar t$

The Position Vector:

17.64 $\qquad\qquad \rho^r = \bar\rho^r + h\nu^r$

17.65 $\qquad \bar\rho^r = (\sec \phi \ \partial\bar p/\partial\omega)\bar\lambda^r + (\partial\bar p/\partial\phi)\bar\mu^r + \bar p\bar\nu^r$

$$\rho^r = (\sec \phi \ \partial\bar p/\partial\omega)\lambda^r + (\partial\bar p/\partial\phi)\mu^r + (\bar p + h)\nu^r$$

17.66

17.67 $\qquad\qquad p = \bar p + h$

Chapter 18

Radii of Curvature:

18.01 $\qquad R_1 = -1/k_1 = -1/\kappa_1 = \bar R_1 + h$

18.02 $\qquad R_2 = -1/k_2 = -1/\kappa_2 = \bar R_2 + h$

Fundamental Forms:

18.03 $\qquad g^{rs} = (a^{\alpha\beta}, 1) ; \qquad g_{rs} = (a_{\alpha\beta}, 1)$

18.04 $\qquad a_{\alpha\beta} = \{(\bar R_1 + h)^2 \cos^2 \phi, 0, (\bar R_2 + h)^2\}$

18.05 $\qquad b_{\alpha\beta} = \{-(\bar R_1 + h) \cos^2 \phi, 0, -(\bar R_2 + h)\}$

18.06 $\qquad c_{\alpha\beta} = \{\cos^2 \phi, 0, 1\}$

18.07 $\qquad a^{\alpha\beta} = \{\sec^2 \phi/(\bar R_1 + h)^2, 0, 1/(\bar R_2 + h)^2\}$

18.08 $\qquad b^{\alpha\beta} = \{-\sec^2 \phi/(\bar R_1 + h), 0, -1/(\bar R_2 + h)\}$

18.09 $\qquad c^{\alpha\beta} = \{\sec^2 \phi, 0, 1\}$

Base Vectors:

$$\lambda^r = u^r = \{\sec \phi/(\bar R_1 + h), 0, 0\}$$

$$\mu^r = v^r = \{0, 1/(\bar R_2 + h), 0\}$$

18.10 $\qquad \nu^r = \quad \{0, 0, 1\}$

$$\lambda_r = u_r = \{(\bar R_1 + h) \cos \phi, 0, 0\}$$

$$\mu_r = v_r = \{0, (\bar R_2 + h), 0\}$$

18.11 $\qquad \nu_r = \quad \{0, 0, 1\}$

18.12 $\qquad (\cos \phi)\omega_r = \lambda_r/(\bar R_1 + h)$

18.13 $\qquad\qquad \phi_r = \mu_r/(\bar R_2 + h)$

$$l^r = \left\{\frac{\sec \phi \sin \alpha \sin \beta}{(\bar R_1 + h)}, \frac{\cos \alpha \sin \beta}{(\bar R_2 + h)}, \cos \beta\right\}$$

$$l_r = \{(\bar R_1 + h)\cos \phi \sin \alpha \sin \beta,$$

18.14 $\qquad (\bar R_2 + h) \cos \alpha \sin \beta, \cos \beta\}$

Derivatives of Base Vectors:

18.15 $\quad \lambda_{21} = (\bar{R}_2 + h) \sin \phi : \quad \lambda_{31} = -\cos \phi$

18.16 $\quad \mu_{11} = -(\bar{R}_1 + h) \sin \phi \cos \phi : \quad \mu_{32} = -1$

18.17 $\quad \nu_{11} = (\bar{R}_1 + h) \cos^2 \phi : \quad \nu_{22} = \bar{R}_2 + h$

Surface Curvatures:

$$-k = 1/R$$

18.18 $\quad = \sin^2 \alpha/(\bar{R}_1 + h) + \cos^2 \alpha/(\bar{R}_2 + h)$

18.19 $\quad t = \dfrac{(\bar{R}_2 - \bar{R}_1) \sin \alpha \cos \alpha}{(\bar{R}_1 + h)(\bar{R}_2 + h)}$

18.20 $\quad \sigma_1 = \tan \phi/(\bar{R}_1 + h)$

18.21 $\quad \sigma = \tan \phi \sin \alpha/(\bar{R}_1 + h) - \partial \alpha/\partial l$

Codazzi Equations:

18.22 $\quad \dfrac{\partial \bar{R}_1}{\partial \phi} = (\bar{R}_1 - \bar{R}_2) \tan \phi$

18.23 $\quad \dfrac{\partial \bar{R}_2}{\partial \omega} = 0$

18.24 $\quad \dfrac{\partial b_{\alpha\beta}}{\partial h} = -c_{\alpha\beta}$

Christoffel Symbols:

$$\Gamma_{11}^2 = (\bar{R}_1 + h) \sin \phi \cos \phi/(\bar{R}_2 + h)$$

$$\Gamma_{12}^1 = -(\bar{R}_2 + h) \tan \phi/(\bar{R}_1 + h)$$

18.34 $\quad \Gamma_{22}^2 = \dfrac{\partial \ln (\bar{R}_2 + h)}{\partial \phi}$

$$\Gamma_{11}^3 = -(\bar{R}_1 + h) \cos^2 \phi$$

$$\Gamma_{22}^3 = -(\bar{R}_2 + h)$$

$$\Gamma_{13}^1 = 1/(\bar{R}_1 + h)$$

18.35 $\quad \Gamma_{23}^2 = 1/(\bar{R}_2 + h)$

Higher Derivatives of Base Vectors:

18.36 $\quad \lambda_{213} = -(\bar{R}_2 + h) \sin \phi/(\bar{R}_1 + h)$

18.37 $\quad \mu_{113} = \sin \phi \cos \phi$

18.38 $\quad \nu_{\alpha\beta3} = -c_{\alpha\beta}$

18.39 $\quad \lambda_{\alpha33} = \mu_{\alpha33} = \nu_{\alpha33} = 0$

18.40 $\quad \nu_{\alpha\beta\gamma} = -b_{\alpha\beta\gamma}$

$$\nu_{\alpha\beta\gamma} = \delta_\alpha^1 \delta_\beta^1 (\bar{R}_1)_\gamma \cos^2 \phi + \delta_\alpha^2 \delta_\beta^2 (\bar{R}_2)_\gamma$$

18.41 $\quad + (\bar{R}_1 - \bar{R}_2) \sin \phi \cos \phi (\delta_\alpha^1 \delta_\beta^2 + \delta_\alpha^2 \delta_\beta^1) \delta_\gamma^1$

The Position Vector:

18.25 $\quad R_1 \cos \phi = -\displaystyle\int R_2 \sin \phi \, d\phi$

$$x = R_1 \cos \phi \cos \omega$$

18.28 $\quad y = R_1 \cos \phi \sin \omega$

$$z = \int R_2 \cos \phi \, d\phi$$

$$= -R_1 \cos \phi \cot \phi - \int R_1 \cos \phi \, \mathrm{cosec}^2 \phi \, d\phi$$

$$= R_1 \sin \phi - \int (R_1 - R_2) \sec \phi \, d\phi$$

18.30

$$p = R_1 \cos^2 \phi + \sin \phi \int R_2 \cos \phi \, d\phi$$

$$= -\sin \phi \int R_1 \cos \phi \, \mathrm{cosec}^2 \phi \, d\phi$$

18.31 $\quad = R_1 - \sin \phi \displaystyle\int (R_1 - R_2) \sec \phi \, d\phi$

$$dp/d\phi = -R_1 \sin \phi \cos \phi + \cos \phi \int R_2 \cos \phi \, d\phi$$

$$= -R_1 \cot \phi - \cos \phi \int R_1 \cos \phi \, \mathrm{cosec}^2 \phi \, d\phi$$

$$= -\cos \phi \int (R_1 - R_2) \sec \phi \, d\phi$$

18.32

18.33 $\quad \rho^r = (d\bar{p}/d\phi) \mu^r (\bar{p} + h) \nu^r$

Laplacians:

18.42 $\quad \Delta h = -2H$

18.45 $\quad \Delta \omega = 0$

$$\Delta \phi = -\tan \phi/(\bar{R}_1 + h)^2 - (2H)_\alpha \mu^\alpha$$

18.46 $\quad = -\dfrac{\tan \phi}{(\bar{R}_1 + h)(\bar{R}_2 + h)} - \dfrac{1}{(\bar{R}_2 + h)^3} \dfrac{d\bar{R}_2}{d\phi}$

Surface Geodesics:

$$\cot \phi \frac{\partial \alpha}{\partial \phi} = \frac{k_1 \sin \alpha + t_1 \cos \alpha}{k_2 \cos \alpha + t_1 \sin \alpha}$$

18.49 $\quad = \dfrac{k \sin \alpha - t \cos \alpha}{k \cos \alpha + t \sin \alpha} \qquad$ (any surface)

$$R_1 \cos \phi \sin \alpha = (\bar{R}_1 + h) \cos \phi \sin \alpha = \text{constant}$$

18.50; 18.51 $\qquad$ (surfaces of revolution)

The Spheroidal Base:

(Eccentricity e; $\quad$ semiaxes a, b.)

18.53 $\quad \bar{e} = b/a = +(1 - e^2)^{1/2}$

18.55 $\quad \bar{R}_1(=N=\nu)=a(1-e^2\sin^2\phi)^{-1/2}$

$\qquad \bar{R}_2(=M=\rho)=a\bar{e}^2(1-e^2\sin^2\phi)^{-3/2}$

18.54 $\qquad\qquad =\bar{e}^2\bar{R}_1^3/a^2$

18.56 $\qquad\qquad \bar{z}=\bar{e}^2\bar{R}_1\sin\phi$

18.57 $\qquad\qquad \bar{p}=a^2/\bar{R}_1$

18.58 $\quad d\bar{p}/d\phi=-e^2\bar{R}_1\sin\phi\cos\phi$

$\quad x=\bar{x}+h\cos\phi\cos\omega=(\bar{R}_1+h)\cos\phi\cos\omega$

$\quad y=\bar{y}+h\cos\phi\sin\omega=(\bar{R}_1+h)\cos\phi\sin\omega$

$\quad z=\bar{z}+h\sin\phi\qquad =(\bar{e}^2\bar{R}_1+h)\sin\phi$

18.59

$\quad \rho^r=-(e^2\bar{R}_1\sin\phi\cos\phi)\mu^r+(a^2/\bar{R}_1+h)\nu^r$

18.60

Chapter 19

Auxiliary Spherical Formulas:

$\quad \cos\sigma=\sin\phi\sin\bar{\phi}+\cos\phi\cos\bar{\phi}\cos\delta\omega$

19.01

$\quad \cos\tau=\cos\phi\cos\bar{\phi}+\sin\phi\sin\bar{\phi}\cos\delta\omega$

19.02 $\quad =\sin\alpha^*\sin\bar{\alpha}^*+\cos\alpha^*\cos\bar{\alpha}^*\cos\sigma$

$\quad \cos\delta\omega=\cos\alpha^*\cos\bar{\alpha}^*$

19.03 $\qquad\qquad +\sin\alpha^*\sin\bar{\alpha}^*\cos\sigma$

$\quad \sin\phi\sin\delta\omega=-\sin\alpha^*\cos\bar{\alpha}^*$

19.04 $\qquad\qquad +\cos\alpha^*\sin\bar{\alpha}^*\cos\sigma$

$\quad \sin\bar{\phi}\sin\delta\omega=\cos\alpha^*\sin\bar{\alpha}^*$

19.05 $\qquad\qquad -\sin\alpha^*\cos\bar{\alpha}^*\cos\sigma$

$\quad \sin\sigma\cos\alpha^*=\cos\phi\sin\bar{\phi}$

19.06 $\qquad\qquad -\sin\phi\cos\bar{\phi}\cos\delta\omega$

$\quad \sin\sigma\cos\bar{\alpha}^*=-\sin\phi\cos\bar{\phi}$

19.07 $\qquad\qquad +\cos\phi\sin\bar{\phi}\cos\delta\omega$

19.08 $\quad \sin\sigma\sin\bar{\alpha}^*=\cos\phi\sin\delta\omega$

19.09 $\quad \sin\sigma\sin\alpha^*=\cos\bar{\phi}\sin\delta\omega$

$\quad \cos\bar{\phi}\cos\bar{\alpha}^*=-\sin\phi\sin\sigma$

19.10 $\qquad\qquad +\cos\phi\cos\sigma\cos\alpha^*$

$\quad \cos\phi\cos\alpha^*=\sin\bar{\phi}\sin\sigma$

19.11 $\qquad\qquad +\cos\bar{\phi}\cos\sigma\cos\bar{\alpha}^*$

$\quad \cos\bar{\phi}\cos\delta\omega=\cos\phi\cos\sigma$

19.12 $\qquad\qquad -\sin\phi\sin\sigma\cos\alpha^*$

$\quad \cos\phi\cos\delta\omega=\cos\bar{\phi}\cos\sigma$

19.13 $\qquad\qquad +\sin\bar{\phi}\sin\sigma\cos\bar{\alpha}^*$

$\quad \cot\alpha^*\sin\delta\omega=\cos\phi\tan\bar{\phi}$

19.14 $\qquad\qquad -\sin\phi\cos\delta\omega$

$\quad \cot\bar{\alpha}^*\sin\delta\omega=-\cos\bar{\phi}\tan\phi$

19.15 $\qquad\qquad +\sin\bar{\phi}\cos\delta\omega$

$\quad \sin\sigma\,d\alpha^*=\sin\alpha^*\cos\sigma\,d\phi+\cos\bar{\phi}\cos\bar{\alpha}^*\,d(\delta\omega)$

19.16 $\qquad -\cos\phi\sec\bar{\phi}\sin\alpha^*\,d\bar{\phi}$

$\quad \sin\sigma\,d\bar{\alpha}^*=\sin\bar{\alpha}^*\sec\phi\cos\bar{\phi}\,d\phi$

19.17 $\qquad +\cos\phi\cos\alpha^*d(\delta\omega)-\sin\bar{\alpha}^*\cos\sigma\,d\bar{\phi}$

$\quad d\sigma=-\cos\alpha^*\,d\phi$

19.18 $\qquad +\cos\phi\sin\alpha^*\,d(\delta\omega)+\cos\bar{\alpha}^*\,d\bar{\phi}$

Rotation Matrices:

19.20 $\qquad \mathbf{\Phi}=\begin{pmatrix} 1 & 0 & 0 \\ 0 & \sin\phi & \cos\phi \\ 0 & -\cos\phi & \sin\phi \end{pmatrix}$

19.21 $\qquad \mathbf{\Omega}=\begin{pmatrix} -\sin\omega & \cos\omega & 0 \\ -\cos\omega & -\sin\omega & 0 \\ 0 & 0 & 1 \end{pmatrix}$

$\quad \mathbf{Q}=\mathbf{\Phi\Omega}=\begin{pmatrix} -\sin\omega & \cos\omega & 0 \\ -\sin\phi\cos\omega & -\sin\phi\sin\omega & \cos\phi \\ \cos\phi\cos\omega & \cos\phi\sin\omega & \sin\phi \end{pmatrix}$

19.22; 19.26

$\quad \bar{\mathbf{Q}}\mathbf{Q}^T=\begin{pmatrix} \cos\delta\omega & \sin\phi\sin\delta\omega & -\cos\phi\sin\delta\omega \\ -\sin\bar{\phi}\sin\delta\omega & \cos\tau & -\sin\sigma\cos\bar{\alpha}^* \\ \cos\bar{\phi}\sin\delta\omega & \sin\sigma\cos\alpha^* & \cos\sigma \end{pmatrix}$

19.25

Base Vectors:

19.24 $\qquad \{\bar{\lambda}_r,\ \bar{\mu}_r,\ \bar{\nu}_r\}=\bar{\mathbf{Q}}\mathbf{Q}^T\{\lambda_r,\ \mu_r,\ \nu_r\}$

Azimuths and Zenith Distances:

$\{\sin\bar{\alpha}\sin\bar{\beta},\ \cos\bar{\alpha}\sin\bar{\beta},\ \cos\bar{\beta}\}$

19.27 $\qquad =\bar{\mathbf{Q}}\mathbf{Q}^T\{\sin\alpha\sin\beta,\ \cos\alpha\sin\beta,\ \cos\beta\}$

Orientation Conditions:

$\quad \bar{\mathbf{Q}}\mathbf{Q}^T=\mathbf{I}+\begin{pmatrix} 0 & \sin\phi\,\delta\omega & -\cos\phi\,\delta\omega \\ -\sin\phi\,\delta\omega & 0 & -\delta\phi \\ \cos\phi\,\delta\omega & \delta\phi & 0 \end{pmatrix}$

19.28

$$\delta\alpha = \sin\phi\,\delta\omega + \cot\beta\,(\sin\alpha\,\delta\phi - \cos\alpha\cos\phi\,\delta\omega)$$

$$\delta\beta = -\cos\phi\sin\alpha\,\delta\omega - \cos\alpha\,\delta\phi$$

19.29

The (ω, ϕ, N) Components of Base Vectors:

$$\mathbf{R} = \begin{pmatrix} \lambda^1 & \lambda^2 & \lambda^3 \\ \mu^1 & \mu^2 & \mu^3 \\ \nu^1 & \nu^2 & \nu^3 \end{pmatrix} = \begin{pmatrix} -k_1\sec\phi & -t_1 & 0 \\ -t_1\sec\phi & -k_2 & 0 \\ \gamma_1\sec\phi & \gamma_2 & n \end{pmatrix}$$

19.31

$$\mathbf{S} = \begin{pmatrix} \lambda_1 & \lambda_2 & \lambda_3 \\ \mu_1 & \mu_2 & \mu_3 \\ \nu_1 & \nu_2 & \nu_3 \end{pmatrix}$$

$$= \begin{pmatrix} -k_2\cos\phi/K & t_1/K & \sec\phi\,\partial(1/n)/\partial\omega \\ t_1\cos\phi/K & -k_1/K & \partial(1/n)/\partial\phi \\ 0 & 0 & (1/n) \end{pmatrix}$$

19.32

19.33 $$\mathbf{R}\mathbf{S}^T = \mathbf{S}\mathbf{R}^T = \mathbf{I}$$

19.34 $$\mathbf{R}^{-1} = \mathbf{S}^T; \qquad \mathbf{S}^{-1} = \mathbf{R}^T$$

Tensor Transformation Matrices:

$$\begin{pmatrix} \partial x/\partial\omega & \partial x/\partial\phi & \partial x/\partial N \\ \partial y/\partial\omega & \partial y/\partial\phi & \partial y/\partial N \\ \partial z/\partial\omega & \partial z/\partial\phi & \partial z/\partial N \end{pmatrix} = \begin{pmatrix} A_1 & A_2 & A_3 \\ B_1 & B_2 & B_3 \\ C_1 & C_2 & C_3 \end{pmatrix} = \mathbf{Q}^T\mathbf{S}$$

19.35

$$\begin{pmatrix} \partial\omega/\partial x & \partial\phi/\partial x & \partial N/\partial x \\ \partial\omega/\partial y & \partial\phi/\partial y & \partial N/\partial y \\ \partial\omega/\partial z & \partial\phi/\partial z & \partial N/\partial z \end{pmatrix} = \begin{pmatrix} A^1 & A^2 & A^3 \\ B^1 & B^2 & B^3 \\ C^1 & C^2 & C^3 \end{pmatrix} = \mathbf{Q}^T\mathbf{R}$$

19.36

$$\begin{pmatrix} \partial\bar\omega/\partial\omega & \partial\bar\omega/\partial\phi & \partial\bar\omega/\partial N \\ \partial\bar\phi/\partial\omega & \partial\bar\phi/\partial\phi & \partial\bar\phi/\partial N \\ \partial\bar N/\partial\omega & \partial\bar N/\partial\phi & \partial\bar N/\partial N \end{pmatrix} = \bar{\mathbf{R}}^T\bar{\mathbf{Q}}\mathbf{Q}^T\mathbf{S}$$

19.37

Parallel Transport of Vectors:

$$\{\bar l^1, \bar l^2, \bar l^3\} = \bar{\mathbf{R}}^T\bar{\mathbf{Q}}\mathbf{Q}^T\mathbf{S}\{l^1, l^2, l^3\}$$

19.38 $$= \bar{\mathbf{R}}^T\bar{\mathbf{Q}}\mathbf{Q}^T\{\sin\alpha\sin\beta, \cos\alpha\sin\beta, \cos\beta\}$$

$$\{\bar l_1, \bar l_2, \bar l_3\} = \bar{\mathbf{S}}^T\bar{\mathbf{Q}}\mathbf{Q}^T\mathbf{R}\{l_1, l_2, l_3\}$$

19.39 $$= \bar{\mathbf{S}}^T\bar{\mathbf{Q}}\mathbf{Q}^T\{\sin\alpha\sin\beta, \cos\alpha\sin\beta, \cos\beta\}$$

The Deflection Vector:

19.40 $$\Delta^r = \bar\nu^r - \nu^r$$

19.41 $$\Delta^r l_r = \cos\bar\beta - \cos\beta$$

$$\Delta^r = (\cos\bar\phi\,\sin\delta\omega)\lambda^r$$

19.43 $$+ (\sin\sigma\cos\alpha^*)\mu^r - 2\sin^2(\sigma/2)\nu^r$$

Change in Coordinates:

19.44 $$\{\bar\omega_r, \bar\phi_r, \bar N_r\} = \bar{\mathbf{R}}^T\bar{\mathbf{Q}}\mathbf{Q}^T\mathbf{S}\{\omega_r, \phi_r, N_r\}$$

$$\{(\delta\omega)_r, (\delta\phi)_r, (\delta N)_r\} = (\bar{\mathbf{S}}^{-1}\bar{\mathbf{Q}}\mathbf{Q}^T\mathbf{S} - \mathbf{I})\{\omega_r, \phi_r, N_r\}$$

19.45 $$= (\bar{\mathbf{R}}^T\bar{\mathbf{Q}}\mathbf{Q}^T - \mathbf{R}^T)\{\lambda_r, \mu_r, \nu_r\}$$

$$\mathbf{M} = \begin{pmatrix} \dfrac{\partial(\delta\omega)}{\partial\lambda} & \dfrac{\partial(\delta\omega)}{\partial\mu} & \dfrac{\partial(\delta\omega)}{\partial\nu} \\[2ex] \dfrac{\partial(\delta\phi)}{\partial\lambda} & \dfrac{\partial(\delta\phi)}{\partial\mu} & \dfrac{\partial(\delta\phi)}{\partial\nu} \\[2ex] \dfrac{\partial(\delta N)}{\partial\lambda} & \dfrac{\partial(\delta N)}{\partial\mu} & \dfrac{\partial(\delta N)}{\partial\nu} \end{pmatrix} = \bar{\mathbf{R}}^T\bar{\mathbf{Q}}\mathbf{Q}^T - \mathbf{R}^T$$

19.46

19.47 $$\mathbf{R} + \mathbf{M}^T = \mathbf{Q}\bar{\mathbf{Q}}^T\bar{\mathbf{R}}$$

$$\left\{\frac{\partial(\delta\omega)}{\partial l}, \frac{\partial(\delta\phi)}{\partial l}, \frac{\partial(\delta N)}{\partial l}\right\}$$

$$= (\bar{\mathbf{R}}^T\bar{\mathbf{Q}}\mathbf{Q}^T - \mathbf{R}^T)\{\sin\alpha\sin\beta, \cos\alpha\sin\beta, \cos\beta\}$$

19.48

Chapter 20

Attraction Potential (Free Space):

20.01 $$N = \sum -Gm/r$$

20.03 $$\Delta N = 0$$

Force:

20.05 $$F_s = -N_s = -n\nu_s$$

Geopotential:

20.08 $$M = N - \tfrac{1}{2}\tilde\omega^2(x^2 + y^2)$$

20.09 $$\Delta M = -2\tilde\omega^2 \qquad \text{(free space)}$$

20.15 $$\Delta M = 4\pi G\rho - 2\tilde\omega^2 \qquad \text{(at density } \rho)$$

Equations of Motion:

20.11 $$\frac{\delta^2\rho_r}{\delta t^2} = \frac{\delta v_r}{\delta t} = -V_r \qquad \text{(fixed axes)}$$

$$\frac{\delta\bar v_r}{\delta t} = -W_r - 2\epsilon_{rst}(\tilde\omega C^s)\bar v^t$$

20.12 $$\text{(rotating axes)}$$

Gravity Differentials (Free Space):

20.17 $$\partial n/\partial s = 2Hn - 2\tilde\omega^2$$

20.32 $\quad (\ln n)_r \nu^r = (k_1 + k_2) - 2\tilde{\omega}^2/n$

$$\frac{\partial(1/n)}{\partial N} = -2H\left(\frac{1}{n}\right)^2 + 2\tilde{\omega}^2\left(\frac{1}{n}\right)^3 - b^{\alpha\beta}\left(\frac{1}{n}\right)_\alpha\left(\frac{1}{n}\right)_\beta$$

20.27

Flux:

$$f = -n\delta S$$

20.30 $\qquad \partial f/\partial s = -(\Delta N)\delta S$

Torque:

$$-(2ml^2 \sin^2\beta)n\{(k_1 - k_2)\sin\alpha\cos\alpha$$
$$+ t_1(\cos^2\alpha - \sin^2\alpha)$$

20.36 $\qquad - \gamma_1 \cos\alpha\cot\beta + \gamma_2 \sin\alpha\cot\beta\}$

20.37 $\qquad = -(2mnl^2 \sin\beta)(\nu_{rs}j^r l^s)$

20.38 $\qquad = (2mnl^2 \sin\beta)\{t\sin\beta - (\ln n)_r j^r \cos\beta\}$

$$= (2mnl^2 \sin\beta)\{t\sin\beta + \gamma_1 \cos\alpha\cos\beta$$
20.39 $\qquad\qquad\qquad - \gamma_2 \sin\alpha\cos\beta\}$

Chapter 21

Generalized Harmonic Functions:

21.003 $\qquad A^{rst \cdots (n)}H_{rst \cdots (n)}$

21.004 $\qquad CL^r M^s N^t \cdots Q^{(n)}H_{rst \cdots (n)}$

$$B_{rst \cdots (n)}\rho^r\rho^s\rho^t \cdots \rho^{(n)}: \qquad g^{kl}B_{klt \cdots (n)} = 0$$
21.009

Potential at Distant Points:

Maxwell's Form:

$$-\frac{V}{G} = \sum_{n=0}^{\infty} \frac{(-)^n}{n!} I^{stu \cdots (n)}\left(\frac{1}{r}\right)_{stu \cdots (n)}$$

21.017

21.012 $\qquad I^{stu \cdots (n)} = \sum \bar{m}\bar{x}^s\bar{x}^t\bar{x}^u \cdots \bar{x}^{(n)}$

21.019 $\qquad\qquad = \int_V \rho\bar{\rho}^s\bar{\rho}^t\bar{\rho}^u \cdots \bar{\rho}^{(n)}dv$

Successive Derivatives of $(1/r)$:

$$\frac{(-)^n(1/r)_{pqrst \cdots (n)}r^{n+1}}{1 \cdot 3 \cdot 5 \cdots (2n-1)} = \nu_p\nu_q\nu_r\nu_s\nu_t \cdots \nu_{(n)}$$

$$- \frac{\{g_{pq}\nu_r\nu_s\nu_t \cdots \nu_{(n)}\}}{(2n-1)}$$

$$+ \frac{\{g_{pq}g_{rs}\nu_t \cdots \nu_{(n)}\}}{(2n-1)(2n-3)}$$

21.025 $\qquad\qquad - \cdots$

$$\frac{(-)^n(1/r)_{pqrst \cdots (n)}r^{n+1}}{1 \cdot 3 \cdot 5 \cdots (2n-1)}$$
$$= \nu_p\nu_q\nu_r\nu_s\nu_t \cdots \nu_{(n)}$$
$$- \frac{n(n-1)}{2(2n-1)}g_{pq}\nu_r\nu_s\nu_t \cdots \nu_{(n)}$$
$$+ \frac{n(n-1)(n-2)(n-3)}{2 \cdot 4(2n-1)(2n-3)}g_{pq}g_{rs}\nu_t \cdots \nu_{(n)}$$
$$- \cdots \qquad \text{(symmetrical form)}$$

21.026

$$\left(\frac{1}{r}\right)_{333 \cdots (n)} = \frac{(-)^n n!}{r^{n+1}}P_n(\sin\phi)$$

21.027

$$\left(\frac{1}{r}\right)_{111 \cdots (n)} = \frac{(-)^n n!}{r^{n+1}}P_n(\cos\phi\cos\omega)$$

21.028

$$\left(\frac{1}{r}\right)_{222 \cdots (n)} = \frac{(-)^n n!}{r^{n+1}}P_n(\cos\phi\sin\omega)$$

21.029

$$\frac{(-)^n r^{2n+1}}{1 \cdot 3 \cdots (2n-1)}f_n\left(\frac{\partial}{\partial x}, \frac{\partial}{\partial y}, \frac{\partial}{\partial z}\right)\left(\frac{1}{r}\right)$$
$$= \left[1 - \frac{r^2\Delta}{2(2n-1)} + \frac{r^4\Delta^2}{2 \cdot 4(2n-1)(2n-3)}\right.$$

21.031 $\qquad \left. - \cdots \right]f_n(x, y, z)$

Potential in Spherical Harmonics:

$$-\frac{V}{G} = \sum_{n=0}^{\infty}\sum_{m=0}^{n} P_n^m(\sin\phi)\{C_{nm}\cos m\omega$$

21.035 $\qquad\qquad + S_{nm}\sin m\omega\}/r^{n+1}$

$$C_{n0} = \sum \bar{m}\bar{r}^n P_n(\sin\bar\phi)$$
$$\binom{C_{nm}}{S_{nm}} = 2\sum \bar{m}\bar{r}^n \frac{(n-m)!}{(n+m)!}P_n^m(\sin\bar\phi)\binom{\cos m\bar\omega}{\sin m\bar\omega}$$

21.037

Normalized Coefficients:
$$\bar{C}_{n0} = C_{n0}/(2n+1)^{1/2}$$

$$\binom{\bar{C}_{nm}}{\bar{S}_{nm}} = \left[\frac{(n+m)!}{2(2n+1)(n-m)!}\right]^{1/2}\binom{C_{nm}}{S_{nm}}$$

21.038

Inertia Tensors (First and Second Orders):

21.062A; 21.062B $\qquad I^s = Mx_0^s = M\rho_0^s$

21.064 $\qquad I = g_{rs}I^{rs} = \sum \bar{m}\bar{r}^2$

21.065 $\qquad I_{OP} = I^{rs}(g_{rs} - \nu_r\nu_s) = I^{rs}(\lambda_r\lambda_s + \mu_r\mu_s)$

$$I_{OP} = I - I^{11}\cos^2\phi\cos^2\omega - I^{22}\cos^2\phi\sin^2\omega$$
$$- I^{33}\sin^2\phi - 2I^{12}\cos^2\phi\sin\omega\cos\omega$$
$$- 2I^{13}\sin\phi\cos\phi\cos\omega$$
$$- 2I^{23}\sin\phi\cos\phi\sin\omega$$

21.066

$$I^{12} = \sum \bar{m}\bar{x}\bar{y}$$

$$I^{13} = \sum \bar{m}\bar{x}\bar{z}$$

21.067 $\qquad I^{23} = \sum \bar{m}\bar{y}\bar{z}$

21.073 $\quad \frac{1}{2}I^{st}(1/r)_{st} = (2I - 3I_{OP})/(2r^3)$

Potential at Near Points:

$$V_P = V_0 + (V_s)_0\rho^s + \tfrac{1}{2}(V_{st})_0\rho^s\rho^t + \ldots$$

21.085 $\qquad + \dfrac{1}{n!}(V_{st\ldots(n)})_0\rho^s\rho^t\ldots\rho^{(n)} + \ldots$

$$-\frac{V}{G} = \sum_{n=0}^{\infty}\sum_{m=0}^{n} r^n P_n^m(\sin\phi)\{[C_{nm}]\cos m\omega$$

21.086 $\qquad\qquad\qquad + [S_{nm}]\sin m\omega\}$

$$[C_{n0}] = \sum \frac{\bar{m}}{\bar{r}^{(n+1)}} P_n(\sin\bar{\phi})$$

$$\begin{pmatrix}[C_{nm}]\\[S_{nm}]\end{pmatrix} = 2\sum \frac{\bar{m}}{\bar{r}^{(n+1)}}\frac{(n-m)!}{(n+m)!} P_n^m(\sin\bar{\phi})\begin{pmatrix}\cos m\bar{\omega}\\\sin m\bar{\omega}\end{pmatrix}$$

21.087

Potential at Internal Points:

$$-\frac{V}{G} = \sum_{n=0}^{\infty}\sum_{m=0}^{n} P_n^m(\sin\phi)\{\bar{C}_{nm}\cos m\omega + \bar{S}_{nm}\sin m\omega\}$$

21.096 $\qquad \bar{C}_{nm} = (C_{nm})_I/r^{(n+1)} + r^n[C_{nm}]_E$

Alternative Expressions:

$$\frac{P_n^m(\sin\phi)}{r^{(n+1)}}\begin{pmatrix}\cos m\omega\\\sin m\omega\end{pmatrix}$$

21.100 $\quad = \dfrac{(-)^n}{(n-m)!}\dfrac{\partial^n}{\partial z^n}\left[\dfrac{1}{r}\left\{\dfrac{r-z}{r+z}\right\}^{m/2}\begin{pmatrix}\cos m\omega\\\sin m\omega\end{pmatrix}\right]$

$$\frac{P_n^m(\sin\phi)}{r^{(n+1)}}e^{\pm im\omega} = \frac{(-)^n}{(n-m)!}\frac{\partial^n}{\partial z^n}\left[\left(\frac{1}{r}\right)e^{-m(\psi\mp i\omega)}\right]$$

21.103; 21.104

Isometric Latitude:

$$e^\psi = \cosh\psi + \sinh\psi = \sec\phi + \tan\phi = \tan(\tfrac{1}{4}\pi + \tfrac{1}{2}\phi)$$
$$= \frac{1+\sin\phi}{\cos\phi} = \left(\frac{1+\sin\phi}{1-\sin\phi}\right)^{1/2}$$

21.101

21.102 $\qquad \psi = \displaystyle\int_0^\phi \sec\phi\, d\phi$

21.107 $\quad V_0 = \dfrac{1}{r}\{f(\psi + i\omega) + g(\psi - i\omega)\}$

21.107A $\quad V_0 = \left(\dfrac{1}{r}\right) F\left(\dfrac{x+iy}{r+z}\right) + \left(\dfrac{1}{r}\right) G\left(\dfrac{x-iy}{r+z}\right)$

The (ξ, η, z) System:

$$\xi = x + iy = r\cos\phi\, e^{iw}$$
$$\eta = x - iy = r\cos\phi\, e^{-iw}$$
$$r^2 = \xi\eta + z^2$$
$$e^{iw} = (\xi/\eta)^{1/2}$$

21.108 $\qquad e^\psi = (r+z)/(\xi\eta)^{1/2}$

$$e^{\psi+i\omega} = (r+z)/\eta = \xi/(r-z)$$

21.109 $\quad e^{\psi-i\omega} = (r+z)/\xi = \eta/(r-z)$

$$\frac{\partial r}{\partial\xi} = \tfrac{1}{2}\frac{\eta}{r}$$

$$\frac{\partial r}{\partial\eta} = \tfrac{1}{2}\frac{\xi}{r}$$

21.110 $\qquad \dfrac{\partial r}{\partial z} = \dfrac{z}{r}$

$$\frac{\partial(\psi+i\omega)}{\partial\xi} = \frac{1}{2r}e^{-(\psi+i\omega)}\; ; \qquad \frac{\partial(\psi-i\omega)}{\partial\xi} = -\frac{1}{2r}e^{(\psi-i\omega)}$$

$$\frac{\partial(\psi+i\omega)}{\partial\eta} = -\frac{1}{2r}e^{(\psi+i\omega)}\; ; \qquad \frac{\partial(\psi-i\omega)}{\partial\eta} = \frac{1}{2r}e^{-(\psi-i\omega)}$$

$$\frac{\partial(\psi+i\omega)}{\partial z} = \frac{1}{r}\; ; \qquad \frac{\partial(\psi-i\omega)}{\partial z} = \frac{1}{r}$$

21.111

$$2\frac{\partial}{\partial\xi} = \frac{\partial}{\partial x} - i\frac{\partial}{\partial y}$$

21.112 $\qquad 2\dfrac{\partial}{\partial\eta} = \dfrac{\partial}{\partial x} + i\dfrac{\partial}{\partial y}$

21.113 $\qquad ds^2 = d\xi\, d\eta + dz^2$

$$g_{12} = \tfrac{1}{2}; \qquad g_{33} = 1; \qquad |g| = -\tfrac{1}{4};$$
$$g^{12} = 2; \qquad g^{33} = 1$$

21.114 $\qquad \Delta = 4\dfrac{\partial^2}{\partial\xi\,\partial\eta} + \dfrac{\partial^2}{\partial z^2}$

21.115 $\quad 2\dfrac{\partial}{\partial\xi}\left(\dfrac{1}{r}e^{-m(\psi-i\omega)}\right) = -\dfrac{\partial}{\partial z}\left(\dfrac{1}{r}e^{-(m-1)(\psi-i\omega)}\right)$

21.116 $\quad 2\dfrac{\partial}{\partial \xi}\left(\dfrac{1}{r}\,e^{-m(\psi+i\omega)}\right)=\dfrac{\partial}{\partial z}\left(\dfrac{1}{r}\,e^{-(m+1)(\psi+i\omega)}\right)$

21.117 $\quad 2\dfrac{\partial}{\partial \eta}\left(\dfrac{1}{r}\,e^{-m(\psi-i\omega)}\right)=\dfrac{\partial}{\partial z}\left(\dfrac{1}{r}\,e^{-(m+1)(\psi-i\omega)}\right)$

21.118 $\quad 2\dfrac{\partial}{\partial \eta}\left(\dfrac{1}{r}\,e^{-m(\psi+i\omega)}\right)=-\dfrac{\partial}{\partial z}\left(\dfrac{1}{r}\,e^{-(m-1)(\psi+i\omega)}\right)$

$2\dfrac{\partial}{\partial \xi}\left\{\dfrac{P_n^m(\sin\phi)}{r^{(n+1)}}\,e^{im\omega}\right\}$

$\qquad = (n-m+2)(n-m+1)\dfrac{P_{n+1}^{m-1}(\sin\phi)}{r^{(n+2)}}\,e^{i(m-1)\omega}$

21.119

$2\dfrac{\partial}{\partial \eta}\left\{\dfrac{P_n^m(\sin\phi)}{r^{(n+1)}}\,e^{im\omega}\right\}=-\dfrac{P_{n+1}^{m+1}(\sin\phi)}{r^{(n+2)}}\,e^{i(m+1)\omega}$

21.122

Gravity:

$$\dfrac{g\cos\bar\phi\cos\bar\omega}{G}=\sum_{n=0}^{\infty}\sum_{m=0}^{n+1}\dfrac{P_{n+1}^m(\sin\phi)}{r^{(n+2)}}$$

$$\times(\bar C_{(n+1),\,m}\cos m\omega$$

21.136 $\qquad\qquad +\bar S_{(n+1),\,m}\sin m\omega)$

$\bar C_{(n+1),\,0}=\tfrac{1}{2}n(n+1)C_{n1}$

$\bar C_{(n+1),\,1}=-C_{n0}+\tfrac{1}{2}n(n-1)C_{n2}$

$\bar S_{(n+1),\,1}=\tfrac{1}{2}n(n-1)S_{n2}$

- - - - - - - - - - - - - - - - - -

$\left\{\begin{array}{l}\bar C_{(n+1),\,m}=-\tfrac{1}{2}C_{n,\,(m-1)}\\ \qquad\quad +\tfrac{1}{2}(n-m+1)(n-m)C_{n,\,(m+1)}\\ \bar S_{(n+1),\,m}=-\tfrac{1}{2}S_{n,\,(m-1)}\\ \qquad\quad +\tfrac{1}{2}(n-m+1)(n-m)S_{n,\,(m+1)}\end{array}\right\}$

$\qquad\qquad\qquad (m=2,3,\ldots (n-1))$

- - - - - - - - - - - - - - - - - -

$\bar C_{(n+1),\,n}=-\tfrac{1}{2}C_{n,\,(n-1)}$

$\bar S_{(n+1),\,n}=-\tfrac{1}{2}S_{n,\,(n-1)}$

$\bar C_{(n+1),\,(n+1)}=-\tfrac{1}{2}C_{n,\,n}$

$\bar S_{(n+1),\,(n+1)}=-\tfrac{1}{2}S_{n,\,n}$

21.137

$$\dfrac{g\cos\bar\phi\sin\bar\omega}{G}=\sum_{n=0}^{\infty}\sum_{m=0}^{n+1}\dfrac{P_{n+1}^m(\sin\phi)}{r^{(n+2)}}$$

$$\times(\bar C_{(n+1),\,m}\cos m\omega$$

21.138 $\qquad\qquad +\bar S_{(n+1),\,m}\sin m\omega)$

$\bar C_{(n+1),\,0}=\tfrac{1}{2}n(n+1)S_{n1}$

$\bar C_{(n+1),\,1}=\tfrac{1}{2}n(n-1)S_{n2}$

$\bar S_{(n+1),\,1}=-C_{n0}-\tfrac{1}{2}n(n-1)C_{n2}$

- -

$\left\{\begin{array}{l}\bar C_{(n+1),\,m}=\tfrac{1}{2}S_{n,\,(m-1)}\\ \qquad\quad +\tfrac{1}{2}(n-m+1)(n-m)S_{n,\,(m+1)}\\ \bar S_{(n+1),\,m}=-\tfrac{1}{2}C_{n,\,(m-1)}\\ \qquad\quad -\tfrac{1}{2}(n-m+1)(n-m)C_{n,\,(m+1)}\end{array}\right\}$

$\qquad\qquad\qquad (m=2,3,\ldots (n-1))$

- -

$\bar C_{(n+1),\,n}=\tfrac{1}{2}S_{n,\,(n-1)}$

$\bar S_{(n+1),\,n}=-\tfrac{1}{2}C_{n,\,(n-1)}$

$\bar C_{(n+1),\,(n+1)}=\tfrac{1}{2}S_{n,\,n}$

$\bar S_{(n+1),\,(n+1)}=-\tfrac{1}{2}C_{n,\,n}$

21.139

$$\dfrac{g\sin\bar\phi}{G}=\sum_{n=0}^{\infty}\sum_{m=0}^{n+1}\dfrac{P_{n+1}^m(\sin\phi)}{r^{(n+2)}}$$

21.140 $\qquad\times(\bar C_{(n+1),\,m}\cos m\omega+\bar S_{(n+1),\,m}\sin m\omega)$

$\qquad\bar C_{(n+1),\,m}=-(n-m+1)C_{nm}$

21.141 $\qquad\bar S_{(n+1),\,m}=-(n-m+1)S_{nm}$

Spherical Harmonic Coefficients in Second
Differentials of the Potential:

$\dfrac{\partial^2}{\partial x^2}\left(-\dfrac{V}{G}\right)$:

$\bar{\bar C}_{(n+2),\,0}=-\tfrac{1}{2}(n+1)(n+2)C_{n0}$
$\qquad\qquad +\tfrac{1}{2}(n-1)n(n+1)(n+2)C_{n2}$

$\bar{\bar C}_{(n+2),\,1}=-\tfrac{3}{4}n(n+1)C_{n1}+\tfrac{1}{4}(n-2)(n-1)n(n+1)C_{n3}$

$\bar{\bar S}_{(n+2),\,1}=-\tfrac{1}{4}n(n+1)S_{n1}$
$\qquad\qquad +\tfrac{1}{4}(n-2)(n-1)n(n+1)S_{n3}$

$\bar{\bar C}_{(n+2),\,2}=\tfrac{1}{2}C_{n0}-\tfrac{1}{2}n(n-1)C_{n2}$
$\qquad\qquad +\tfrac{1}{4}(n-3)(n-2)(n-1)nC_{n4}$

$\bar{\bar S}_{(n+2),\,2}=-\tfrac{1}{2}n(n-1)S_{n2}$
$\qquad\qquad +\tfrac{1}{4}(n-3)(n-2)(n-1)nS_{n4}$

$\bar{\bar C}_{(n+2),\,m}=\tfrac{1}{4}C_{n,\,(m-2)}-\tfrac{1}{2}(n-m+1)(n-m+2)C_{nm}$
$\qquad\qquad +\tfrac{1}{4}(n-m-1)(n-m)(n-m+1)(n-m+2)$
$\qquad\qquad \times C_{n,\,(m+2)}$

$\bar{\bar S}_{(n+2),\,m}=\tfrac{1}{4}S_{n,\,(m-2)}-\tfrac{1}{2}(n-m+1)(n-m+2)S_{nm}$
$\qquad\qquad +\tfrac{1}{4}(n-m-1)(n-m)(n-m+1)(n-m+2)$

21.145 $\qquad\times S_{n,\,(m+2)}$ $\qquad\qquad (m>2)$

$$\frac{\partial^2}{\partial y^2}\left(-\frac{V}{G}\right): \quad \bar{\bar{C}}_{(n+2),\,0}=-\tfrac{1}{2}(n+1)(n+2)C_{n0}-\tfrac{1}{2}(n-1)n(n+1)(n+2)C_{n2}$$

$$\bar{\bar{C}}_{(n+2),\,1}=-\tfrac{1}{4}n(n+1)C_{n1}-\tfrac{1}{4}(n-2)(n-1)n(n+1)C_{n3}$$

$$\bar{\bar{S}}_{(n+2),\,1}=-\tfrac{3}{4}n(n+1)S_{n1}-\tfrac{1}{4}(n-2)(n-1)n(n+1)S_{n3}$$

$$\bar{\bar{C}}_{(n+2),\,2}=-\tfrac{1}{2}C_{n0}-\tfrac{1}{2}n(n-1)C_{n2}-\tfrac{1}{4}(n-3)(n-2)(n-1)nC_{n4}$$

$$\bar{\bar{S}}_{(n+2),\,2}=-\tfrac{1}{2}n(n-1)S_{n2}-\tfrac{1}{4}(n-3)(n-2)(n-1)nS_{n4}$$

$$\bar{\bar{C}}_{(n+2),\,m}=-\tfrac{1}{4}C_{n,\,(m-2)}-\tfrac{1}{2}(n-m+1)(n-m+2)C_{nm}-\tfrac{1}{4}(n-m-1)(n-m)(n-m+1)(n-m+2)C_{n,\,(m+2)}$$

$$\bar{\bar{S}}_{(n+2),\,m}=-\tfrac{1}{4}S_{n,\,(m-2)}-\tfrac{1}{2}(n-m+1)(n-m+2)S_{nm}-\tfrac{1}{4}(n-m-1)(n-m)(n-m+1)(n-m+2)S_{n,\,(m+2)}$$

21.146 $\qquad\qquad\qquad\qquad\qquad\qquad\qquad\qquad\qquad\qquad\qquad\qquad\qquad (m>2)$

$$\frac{\partial^2}{\partial z^2}\left(-\frac{V}{G}\right): \quad \bar{\bar{C}}_{(n+2),\,0}=(n+1)(n+2)C_{n0}$$

$$\bar{\bar{C}}_{(n+2),\,1}=n(n+1)C_{n1}$$

$$\bar{\bar{S}}_{(n+2),\,1}=n(n+1)S_{n1}$$

$$\bar{\bar{C}}_{(n+2),\,2}=n(n-1)C_{n2}$$

$$\bar{\bar{S}}_{(n+2),\,2}=n(n-1)S_{n2}$$

$$\bar{\bar{C}}_{(n+2),\,m}=(n-m+1)(n-m+2)C_{nm}$$

$$\bar{\bar{S}}_{(n+2),\,m}=(n-m+1)(n-m+2)S_{nm}$$

21.147 $\qquad\qquad\qquad\qquad\qquad\qquad\qquad\qquad\qquad\qquad\qquad\qquad\qquad (m>2)$

$$\frac{\partial^2}{\partial x\partial y}\left(-\frac{V}{G}\right): \quad \bar{\bar{C}}_{(n+2),\,0}=\tfrac{1}{4}(n-1)n(n+1)(n+2)S_{n2}$$

$$\bar{\bar{C}}_{(n+2),\,1}=-\tfrac{1}{4}n(n+1)S_{n1}+\tfrac{1}{4}(n-2)(n-1)n(n+1)S_{n3}$$

$$\bar{\bar{S}}_{(n+2),\,1}=-\tfrac{1}{4}n(n+1)C_{n1}-\tfrac{1}{4}(n-2)(n-1)n(n+1)C_{n3}$$

$$\bar{\bar{C}}_{(n+2),\,2}=\tfrac{1}{4}(n-3)(n-2)(n-1)nS_{n4}$$

$$\bar{\bar{S}}_{(n+2),\,2}=\tfrac{1}{2}C_{n0}-\tfrac{1}{4}(n-3)(n-2)(n-1)nC_{n4}$$

$$\bar{\bar{C}}_{(n+2),\,m}=-\tfrac{1}{4}S_{n,\,(m-2)}+\tfrac{1}{4}(n-m-1)(n-m)(n-m+1)(n-m+2)S_{n,\,(m+2)}$$

$$\bar{\bar{S}}_{(n+2),\,m}=\tfrac{1}{4}C_{n,\,(m-2)}-\tfrac{1}{4}(n-m-1)(n-m)(n-m+1)(n-m+2)C_{n,\,(m+2)}$$

21.148 $\qquad\qquad\qquad\qquad\qquad\qquad\qquad\qquad\qquad\qquad\qquad\qquad\qquad (m>2)$

$$\frac{\partial^2}{\partial y \partial z}\left(-\frac{V}{G}\right): \quad \bar{\bar{C}}_{(n+2),\,0} = -\tfrac{1}{2}n(n+1)(n+2)S_{n1}$$

$$\bar{\bar{C}}_{(n+2),\,1} = -\tfrac{1}{2}(n-1)n(n+1)S_{n2}$$

$$\bar{\bar{S}}_{(n+2),\,1} = (n+1)C_{n0} + \tfrac{1}{2}(n-1)n(n+1)C_{n2}$$

$$\bar{\bar{C}}_{(n+2),\,2} = -\tfrac{1}{2}nS_{n1} - \tfrac{1}{2}(n-2)(n-1)nS_{n3}$$

$$\bar{\bar{S}}_{(n+2),\,2} = \tfrac{1}{2}nC_{n1} + \tfrac{1}{2}(n-2)(n-1)nC_{n3}$$

$$\bar{\bar{C}}_{(n+2),\,m} = -\tfrac{1}{2}(n-m+2)S_{n,\,(m-1)} - \tfrac{1}{2}(n-m)(n-m+1)(n-m+2)S_{n,\,(m+1)}$$

$$\bar{\bar{S}}_{(n+2),\,m} = \tfrac{1}{2}(n-m+2)C_{n,\,(m-1)} + \tfrac{1}{2}(n-m)(n-m+1)(n-m+2)C_{n,\,(m+1)}$$

21.149 $\hspace{10cm} (m > 2)$

$$\frac{\partial^2}{\partial z \partial x}\left(-\frac{V}{G}\right): \quad \bar{\bar{C}}_{(n+2),\,0} = -\tfrac{1}{2}n(n+1)(n+2)C_{n1}$$

$$\bar{\bar{C}}_{(n+2),\,1} = (n+1)C_{n0} - \tfrac{1}{2}(n-1)n(n+1)C_{n2}$$

$$\bar{\bar{S}}_{(n+2),\,1} = -\tfrac{1}{2}(n-1)n(n+1)S_{n2}$$

$$\bar{\bar{C}}_{(n+2),\,2} = \tfrac{1}{2}nC_{n1} - \tfrac{1}{2}(n-2)(n-1)nC_{n3}$$

$$\bar{\bar{S}}_{(n+2),\,2} = \tfrac{1}{2}nS_{n1} - \tfrac{1}{2}(n-2)(n-1)nS_{n3}$$

$$\bar{\bar{C}}_{(n+2),\,m} = \tfrac{1}{2}(n-m+2)C_{n,\,(m-1)} - \tfrac{1}{2}(n-m)(n-m+1)(n-m+2)C_{n,\,(m+1)}$$

$$\bar{\bar{S}}_{(n+2),\,m} = \tfrac{1}{2}(n-m+2)S_{n,\,(m-1)} - \tfrac{1}{2}(n-m)(n-m+1)(n-m+2)S_{n,\,(m+1)}$$

21.150 $\hspace{10cm} (m > 2)$

Chapter 22

The Meridian Ellipse (fig. 26):

22.03 $\quad \sin \beta = \sin \alpha \sin \phi$

$\tan \beta = \tan \alpha \sin u$

22.04 $\quad \tan u = \cos \alpha \tan \phi$

$\sin u = \cos \alpha \sec \beta \sin \phi$

22.05 $\quad = \cos \alpha \sin \phi/(1 - \sin^2 \alpha \sin^2 \phi)^{1/2}$

$\cos u = \sec \beta \cos \phi$

22.06 $\quad = \cos \phi/(1 - \sin^2 \alpha \sin^2 \phi)^{1/2}$

22.07 $\quad (1 - \sin^2 \alpha \sin^2 \phi)(1 - \sin^2 \alpha \cos^2 u) = \cos^2 \alpha$

22.08 $\quad (1 - \sin^2 \alpha \cos^2 u)^{1/2} = \cos \alpha \sec \beta$

$\nu = a \cos u \sec \phi = a \sec \beta$

$\quad = a \sec \alpha/(1 + \tan^2 \alpha \cos^2 \phi)^{1/2}$

$\quad = a/(1 - \sin^2 \alpha \sin^2 \phi)^{1/2}$

$\quad = a \sec \alpha (1 - \sin^2 \alpha \cos^2 u)^{1/2}$

22.10 $\quad = a^2/(a^2 \cos^2 \phi + b^2 \sin^2 \phi)^{1/2}$

$\rho = a \cos^2 \alpha \sec^3 \beta$

$\quad = a \sec \alpha/(1 + \tan^2 \alpha \cos^2 \phi)^{3/2}$

$\quad = a \cos^2 \alpha/(1 - \sin^2 \alpha \sin^2 \phi)^{3/2}$

22.12 $\quad = a \sec \alpha (1 - \sin^2 \alpha \cos^2 u)^{3/2}$

22.13 $\quad d\beta/d\phi = \sin \alpha \cos u$

22.14 $\quad d\beta/du = \tan \alpha \cos^2 \beta \cos u$

22.15 $\quad d(\ln \rho)/d\phi = 3 \sin \alpha \tan \alpha \sin u \cos u$

22.16 $\quad d(\nu \cos \phi)/d\phi = -\rho \sin \phi$

22.17 $\quad d(\nu \sin \phi)/d\phi = \rho \sec^2 \alpha \cos \phi$

22.18 $\quad d\nu/d\phi = (\nu - \rho) \tan \phi$

$K = 1/(\rho\nu)$

22.19 $\quad 2H = -(1/\rho + 1/\nu)$

$q_1 = OS \sin f = b \sin E = a(1 - e^2)^{1/2} \sin E$

$q_2 = OS \cos f = (a \cos E - ae) = a(\cos E - e)$

22.20

22.21 $\quad r = OS = a(1 - e \cos E) = \dfrac{a(1 - e^2)}{(1 + e \cos f)}$

Spheroidal Coordinates:

$$x = (ae) \operatorname{cosec} \alpha \cos u \cos \omega$$

$$y = (ae) \operatorname{cosec} \alpha \cos u \sin \omega$$

22.22 $\quad z = (ae) \cot \alpha \sin u$

22.23 $\quad r = (ae)(\cos u + i \cot \alpha)^{1/2}(\cos u - i \cot \alpha)^{1/2}$

22.24 $\quad$ geocentric latitude $= \cos \alpha \tan u$

22.25 $\quad ds^2 = (a^2 \cos^2 u) d\omega^2 + (\nu^2 \cos^2 \alpha) du^2$
$\qquad\qquad + (\nu^2 \cot^2 \alpha) d\alpha^2$

$$g^{11} = 1/(a^2 \cos^2 u) : \qquad g^{22} = 1/(\nu^2 \cos^2 \alpha) :$$

22.26 $\qquad\qquad g^{33} = 1/(\nu^2 \cot^2 \alpha)$

22.27 $\qquad\qquad \alpha_r = n\nu_r$

22.28 $\qquad\qquad \dfrac{\partial}{\partial \alpha} = \dfrac{1}{n} \dfrac{\partial}{\partial s}$

22.29 $\qquad\qquad n = -\dfrac{\tan \alpha}{\nu}$

22.30 $\quad \dfrac{\partial(\ln a)}{\partial \alpha} = -\cot \alpha \ ; \qquad \dfrac{\partial(\ln a)}{\partial s} = \dfrac{1}{\nu}$

22.31 $\qquad \dfrac{\partial \beta}{\partial \alpha} = \sec \alpha \cos \beta \sin \phi$

22.32 $\qquad \dfrac{\partial \phi}{\partial \alpha} = \tan \alpha \sin \phi \cos \phi$

22.33 $\quad \dfrac{\partial \ln(\nu \cos \phi)}{\partial \alpha} = \dfrac{\partial \ln(a \cos u)}{\partial \alpha} = -\cot \alpha$

22.34 $\quad \dfrac{\partial \ln \nu}{\partial \alpha} = -\cot \alpha + \tan \alpha \sin^2 \phi$

22.35 $\quad \dfrac{\partial \ln \rho}{\partial \alpha} = -\cot \alpha - 2 \tan \alpha + 3 \tan \alpha \sin^2 \phi$

22.36 $\quad b_{\alpha\beta} = (-\nu \cos^2 \phi, 0, -a^2/\nu)$

22.37 $\quad c_{\alpha\beta} = (\cos^2 \phi, 0, a^2 K)$

$\Gamma^1_{13} = -\cot \alpha$

$\Gamma^2_{23} = -a^2/(\nu^2 \sin \alpha \cos \alpha) = -1/(n\rho)$

$\Gamma^2_{33} = -\sec \alpha \sin \phi \cos \phi$

$\Gamma^3_{11} = \tan \alpha \cos^2 \phi$

$\Gamma^3_{22} = (a^2 \tan \alpha)/\nu^2$

$\Gamma^3_{33} = -\dfrac{\partial \ln n}{\partial \alpha} = -\cot \alpha - \dfrac{a^2}{\nu^2 \sin \alpha \cos \alpha} = \dfrac{2H}{n}$

$\Gamma^3_{32} = -\dfrac{\partial \ln n}{\partial u} = \sin \alpha \tan \alpha \sin \phi \cos \phi$

22.38

$\Gamma^1_{12} = -\tan u$

$\Gamma^2_{11} = \sec \alpha \sin \phi \cos \phi$

$\Gamma^2_{22} = -\dfrac{\partial \ln n}{\partial u} = \dfrac{\partial \ln \nu}{\partial u} = \sin \alpha \tan \alpha \sin \phi \cos \phi$

22.39

$\qquad n \overline{(1/n)}_{11} = -\tan^2 \alpha \sin^2 \phi \cos^2 \phi$

$\qquad n \overline{(1/n)}_{12} = 0$

22.40 $\quad n \overline{(1/n)}_{22} = \tan^2 \alpha \cos^2 \beta \cos 2\phi$

External Potential:

$$-\frac{V}{G} = \sum_{n=0}^{\infty} \sum_{m=0}^{n} Q_n^m(i \cot \alpha) P_n^m(\sin u)(A_{nm} \cos m\omega + B_{nm} \sin m\omega)$$

22.50

Internal Potential:

$$-\frac{V}{G} = \sum_{n=0}^{\infty} \sum_{m=0}^{n} P_n^m(i \cot \alpha) P_n^m(\sin u)([A_{nm}] \cos m\omega + [B_{nm}] \sin m\omega)$$

22.51

$\quad Q_0(i \cot \alpha) = -i\alpha$

$\quad Q_1(i \cot \alpha) = \alpha \cot \alpha - 1$

$\quad Q_2(i \cot \alpha) = \tfrac{1}{2}i(\alpha + 3\alpha \cot^2 \alpha - 3 \cot \alpha)$

22.52

$\quad (n+1)Q_{n+1} - (2n+1)i \cot \alpha \, Q_n + nQ_{n-1} = 0$

22.53

$\quad Q_n^m(i \cot \alpha) = \operatorname{cosec}^m \alpha \, \dfrac{d^m Q_n(i \cot \alpha)}{d(i \cot \alpha)^m}$

22.54

Mass Distribution:

$$A_{n0} = \sum \frac{i(2n+1)}{ae} \, \bar{m} P_n(i \cot \bar{\alpha}) P_n(\sin \bar{u})$$

$$\binom{A_{nm}}{B_{nm}} = \sum \frac{2i(2n+1)}{ae}(-)^m \left(\frac{(n-m)!}{(n+m)!}\right)^2 \bar{m} P_n^m(i \cot \bar{\alpha})$$

22.56 $\qquad\qquad \times P_n^m(\sin \bar{u}) \binom{\cos m\bar{\omega}}{\sin m\bar{\omega}}$

$$[A_{n0}] = \sum \frac{i(2n+1)}{ae} \, \bar{m} Q_n(i \cot \bar{\alpha}) P_n(\sin \bar{u})$$

$$\binom{[A_{nm}]}{[B_{nm}]} = \sum \frac{2i(2n+1)}{ae}(-)^m \left(\frac{(n-m)!}{(n+m)!}\right)^2 \bar{m}$$

22.65 $\qquad\qquad \times Q_n^m(i \cot \bar{\alpha}) P_n^m(\sin \bar{u}) \binom{\cos m\bar{\omega}}{\sin m\bar{\omega}}$

Spherical and Spheroidal Coefficients:

$$\binom{A_{nm}}{B_{nm}} = \frac{1 \cdot 3 \cdot 5 \ldots (2n+1)}{(n+m)!} \, i^{(m+n+1)} \left[\frac{1}{(ae)^{n+1}} \binom{C_{nm}}{S_{nm}} \right.$$

$$+ \frac{(n-m)(n-m-1)}{2 \cdot (2n-1)} \frac{1}{(ae)^{n-1}} \binom{C_{(n-2),\, m}}{S_{(n-2),\, m}}$$

$$+ \frac{(n-m)(n-m-1)(n-m-2)(n-m-3)}{2 \cdot 4(2n-1)(2n-3)}$$

$$\left. \times \frac{1}{(ae)^{n-3}} \binom{C_{(n-4),\, m}}{S_{(n-4),\, m}} + \ldots \right]$$

22.59

$$i^{(m+n+1)} \binom{C_{nm}}{S_{nm}} = \frac{(ae)^{n+1}(n-m)!}{1 \cdot 3 \cdot 5 \ldots (2n+1)} \left[\frac{(n+m)!}{(n-m)!} \binom{A_{nm}}{B_{nm}} \right.$$

$$+ \frac{2n+1}{2} \frac{(n+m-2)!}{(n-m-2)!} \binom{A_{(n-2),\, m}}{B_{(n-2),\, m}}$$

$$+ \frac{(2n+1)(2n-1)}{2 \cdot 4} \frac{(n+m-4)!}{(n-m-4)!} \binom{A_{(n-4),\, m}}{B_{(n-4),\, m}}$$

$$+ \frac{(2n+1)(2n-1)(2n-3)}{2 \cdot 4 \cdot 6} \frac{(n+m-6)!}{(n-m-6)!} \binom{A_{(n-6),\, m}}{B_{(n-6),\, m}}$$

22.60 $\left. + \ldots \right]$

Inertial Properties:

22.61 $M = C_{00} = -i(ae)A_{00}$

$$I^s/M = (C_{11}/M, \, S_{11}/M, \, C_{10}/M)$$

22.63 $= \left(\frac{2}{3} i (ae)^2 \frac{A_{11}}{M}, \, \frac{2}{3} i (ae)^2 \frac{B_{11}}{M}, \, -\frac{1}{3}(ae)^2 \frac{A_{10}}{M} \right)$

$$C_{20} = I^{33} - \frac{1}{2}(I^{11} + I^{22}) = \frac{1}{3} i (ae)^3 (\frac{2}{5} A_{20} + A_{00})$$

$$C_{21} = I^{13} = \frac{2}{5}(ae)^3 A_{21}$$

$$S_{21} = I^{23} = \frac{2}{5}(ae)^3 B_{21}$$

$$C_{22} = \frac{1}{4}(I^{11} - I^{22}) = -\frac{8}{5} i (ae)^3 A_{22}$$

$$S_{22} = \frac{1}{2} I^{12} = -\frac{8}{5} i (ae)^3 B_{22}$$

22.64

Differential Form of the Potential:

22.66 $-\dfrac{V}{G} = \displaystyle\sum_{n=0}^{\infty} J^{rst \ldots (n)}(\alpha)_{rst \ldots (n)}$

Chapter 23

Symmetrical Models:

23.01 $-\dfrac{W}{G} = \displaystyle\sum_{n=0}^{\infty} \dfrac{C_{n0} P_n(\sin \phi)}{r^{n+1}} + \dfrac{\frac{1}{2}\tilde{\omega}^2(x^2+y^2)}{G}$

$$g \cos \bar{\phi} = \sum_{n=0}^{\infty} \frac{GC_{n0}}{r^{n+2}} P_{n+1}^1(\sin \phi) - \tilde{\omega}^2 r P_1^1(\sin \phi)$$

23.02

23.03 $g \sin \bar{\phi} = \displaystyle\sum_{n=0}^{\infty} \dfrac{(n+1)GC_{n0}}{r^{n+2}} P_{n+1}(\sin \phi)$

$$g \sin (\bar{\phi} - \phi) = -\sum_{n=1}^{\infty} \frac{GC_{n0}}{r^{n+2}} P_n^1(\sin \phi)$$

23.04 $+ \tilde{\omega}^2 r \sin \phi \cos \phi$

$$g \cos (\bar{\phi} - \phi) = \sum_{n=0}^{\infty} \frac{(n+1)GC_{n0}}{r^{n+2}} P_n(\sin \phi)$$

23.05 $- \tilde{\omega}^2 r \cos^2 \phi$

Standard Potential:

$$-W = GM\alpha/(ae) + GA_{20}Q_2(i \cot \alpha)P_2(\sin u)$$

23.13 $+ \{ \frac{1}{3}\tilde{\omega}^2 a^2 - \frac{1}{3}\tilde{\omega}^2 a^2 P_2(\sin u) \}$

23.11 $-W_0 = GM\alpha_0/(a_0 \sin \alpha_0) + \frac{1}{3} \tilde{\omega}^2 a_0^2$

23.12 $GA_{20} = \dfrac{\frac{2}{3} i \tilde{\omega}^2 a_0^2}{3 \cot \alpha_0 - \alpha_0(1 + 3 \cot^2 \alpha_0)}$

$$(ae) = a_0 \sin \alpha_0$$

23.14 $a = a_0 \sin \alpha_0 \, \mathrm{cosec}\, \alpha$

$$-\frac{W}{G} = \sum_{n=1}^{\infty} (-)^n \frac{(2n+1)iA_{00} + (2n-2)iA_{20}}{(2n-1)(2n+1)}$$

23.18 $\times \dfrac{(ae)^{2n-1}}{r^{2n-1}} P_{2n-2}(\sin \phi) + \dfrac{\frac{1}{2}\tilde{\omega}^2(x^2+y^2)}{G}$

23.19 $A_{00} = iM/(ae)$

Standard Gravity:

23.24 $g_n = \dfrac{ag_e \cos^2 \phi + bg_p \sin^2 \phi}{(a^2 \cos^2 \phi + b^2 \sin^2 \phi)^{1/2}}$

$$\frac{g_p}{b} - \frac{g_e}{a} = \frac{5\tilde{\omega}^2}{2} \left(1 + \frac{9}{35} \tan^2 \alpha_0 - \frac{16}{245} \tan^4 \alpha_0 + \ldots \right)$$

23.28

23.33 $\dfrac{2g_e}{a} + \dfrac{g_p}{b} = 4\pi G\rho - 2\tilde{\omega}^2$

23.34 $g = g_e(1 + B_2 \sin^2 \phi + B_4 \sin^2 2\phi + \ldots)$

$$B_2 = -f + \frac{5}{2} q - \frac{17}{14} qf + \frac{15}{4} q^2$$

23.35 $B_4 = \frac{1}{8} f^2 - \frac{5}{8} qf$

$$f = (a-b)/a; \qquad q = \tilde{\omega}^2 a/g_e$$

$$g_m = \frac{3 \sin u \cos u}{\nu \cos \alpha}\left[GA_{20}Q_2(i \cot \alpha) - \tfrac{1}{3}\tilde{\omega}^2 a^2\right]$$

23.37

23.39 $\qquad g = (g_m^2 + g_n^2)^{1/2}$

$$g \cos \bar{\phi} = \sum_{n=1}^{\infty} G(-)^n \frac{(2n+1)iA_{00}+(2n-2)iA_{20}}{(2n-1)(2n+1)}$$

23.40 $\qquad \times \frac{(ae)^{2n-1}}{r^{2n}} P_{2n-1}^1(\sin\phi) - \tilde{\omega}^2 r \cos\phi$

$$g \sin \bar{\phi} = \sum_{n=1}^{\infty} G(-)^n \frac{(2n+1)iA_{00}+(2n-2)iA_{20}}{(2n+1)}$$

23.41 $\qquad \times \frac{(ae)^{2n-1}}{r^{2n}} P_{2n-1}(\sin\phi)$

$$g \sin(\bar{\phi}-\phi) = \sum_{n=2}^{\infty} G(-)^{n+1} \frac{(2n+1)iA_{00}+(2n-2)iA_{20}}{(2n-1)(2n+1)}$$

$$\times \frac{(ae)^{2n-1}}{r^{2n}} P_{2n-2}^1(\sin\phi)$$

23.42 $\qquad + \tilde{\omega}^2 r \sin\phi\cos\phi$

$$g \cos(\bar{\phi}-\phi) = \sum_{n=1}^{\infty} G(-)^n \frac{(2n+1)iA_{00}+(2n-2)iA_{20}}{(2n+1)}$$

23.43 $\qquad \times \frac{(ae)^{2n-1}}{r^{2n}} P_{2n-2}(\sin\phi) - \tilde{\omega}^2 r \cos^2\phi$

$$g_e = -\tilde{\omega}^2 a - \sum_{n=1}^{\infty} G \frac{(2n+1)iA_{00}+(2n-2)iA_{20}}{(2n+1)} \frac{(ae)^{2n-1}}{a^{2n}}$$

23.44 $\qquad \times \frac{1\cdot3\cdot5 \ldots (2n-3)}{2\cdot4\cdot6 \ldots (2n-2)}$

Curvatures:

(For particular values of the coefficients A, B, C, and D given below.)

$$A + G\sum_{n=0}^{\infty}\frac{C_{n0}}{r^{n+3}}\{BP_{n+2}(\sin\phi)$$
$$+CP_{n+2}^1(\sin\phi) + DP_{n+2}^2(\sin\phi)\}$$

For gk_2: $\quad A = \tilde{\omega}^2 \sin^2\bar{\phi}$

$\qquad\qquad B = (n+1)(n+2)(\cos^2\bar{\phi} - \tfrac{1}{2}\sin^2\bar{\phi})$

$\qquad\qquad C = -(n+1)\sin2\bar{\phi}$

23.49 $\qquad D = \tfrac{1}{2}\sin^2\bar{\phi}$

For gk_1: $\quad A = \tilde{\omega}^2$

$\qquad\qquad B = -\tfrac{1}{2}(n+1)(n+2)$

$\qquad\qquad C = 0$

23.50 $\qquad D = -\tfrac{1}{2}$

For $g\gamma_2$: $\quad A = \tfrac{1}{2}\tilde{\omega}^2\sin2\bar{\phi}$

$\qquad\qquad B = -\tfrac{3}{4}(n+1)(n+2)\sin2\bar{\phi}$

$\qquad\qquad C = -(n+1)\cos2\bar{\phi}$

23.51 $\qquad D = \tfrac{1}{4}\sin2\bar{\phi}$

For $\dfrac{\partial g}{\partial s}$: $\quad A = -\tilde{\omega}^2\cos^2\bar{\phi}$

$\qquad\qquad B = -(n+1)(n+2)(\sin^2\bar{\phi} - \tfrac{1}{2}\cos^2\bar{\phi})$

$\qquad\qquad C = -(n+1)\sin2\bar{\phi}$

23.52 $\qquad D = -\tfrac{1}{2}\cos^2\bar{\phi}$

23.53 $\qquad \dfrac{\partial g}{\partial s} = -g\left(\dfrac{1}{\rho}+\dfrac{1}{\nu}\right) - 2\tilde{\omega}^2$

$$\frac{\partial\nu}{\partial W} = -\tan\phi\frac{\partial(1/g)}{\partial\phi} + \frac{1}{g}$$

23.54 $\qquad \dfrac{\partial\rho}{\partial W} = \dfrac{\partial^2(1/g)}{\partial\phi^2} + \dfrac{1}{g}$

23.55 $\qquad \dfrac{\partial}{\partial s} = g\dfrac{\partial}{\partial W} + \dfrac{1}{\rho}\dfrac{\partial(\ln g)}{\partial\phi}\dfrac{\partial}{\partial\phi}$

23.56 $\qquad \dfrac{\partial\gamma_2}{\partial s} = -\dfrac{1}{\rho}\dfrac{\partial}{\partial\phi}\left(\dfrac{1}{\rho}+\dfrac{1}{\nu}\right) + \dfrac{4\tilde{\omega}^2\gamma_2}{g} + \dfrac{\gamma_2}{\nu}$

$$\gamma_2 = \frac{\partial(\ln g)}{\rho\partial\phi}$$

Geocentric to Geodetic Coordinates:

$$r\cos\phi = (\nu+h)\cos\bar{\bar{\phi}}$$

23.58 $\qquad r\sin\phi = (\nu\cos^2\alpha+h)\sin\bar{\bar{\phi}}$

Chapter 24

Laws of Refraction:

24.01 $\qquad\qquad \mu = c/v$

24.03 $\qquad\qquad S = ct = \int\mu ds$

24.04 $\qquad\qquad S_r = \mu l_r$

24.05 $\qquad\qquad \nabla S = \mu^2$

$\qquad\qquad\qquad (\ln\mu)_r m^r = \chi$

24.06 $\qquad\qquad (\ln\mu)_r n^r = 0$

Equations of Refracted Ray:

24.07 $\qquad\qquad \dfrac{\delta(\mu l_r)}{\delta s} = \mu_r$

$\qquad \mu r\sin\beta = $ constant $\qquad$ (spherical symmetry)

24.11

Arc-to-Chord Corrections:

(The $(\omega, \phi, \ln \mu)$ system.)

$$\tau = (k_2 - k_1) \sin \alpha \cos \alpha - t_1(\cos^2 \alpha - \sin^2 \alpha)$$
$$+ (\gamma_1 \cos \alpha - \gamma_2 \sin \alpha) \cot \beta$$

24.23

$$= t - \nu_{rs} n^r \nu^s \cot \beta$$

24.24

24.25
$$(\ln \mu)_r = -q\nu_r$$

$$q = \{\nabla(\ln \mu)\}^{1/2}$$

24.26
$$\chi = (\ln \mu)_r m^r = q \sin \beta$$

24.27
$$\chi\tau = (\ln \mu)_{rs} n^r l^s$$

$$\{(s)/s\} \sin(\alpha) \sin(\beta) = A \sin \alpha \sin \beta$$
$$+ B \sin \alpha \cos \beta - C \cos \alpha$$

$$\{(s)/s\} \cos(\alpha) \sin(\beta) = A \cos \alpha \sin \beta$$
$$+ B \cos \alpha \cos \beta + C \sin \alpha$$

24.28 $\{(s)/s\} \cos(\beta) = A \cos \beta - B \sin \beta$

$$A = 1 - \tfrac{1}{6}\chi^2 s^2$$

$$B = \tfrac{1}{2}s\left\{\chi + \tfrac{1}{3}\left(\frac{\partial \chi}{\partial s}\right)s\right\} = \tfrac{1}{2}s\chi_3$$

$$C = \tfrac{1}{6}\chi\tau s^2$$

24.29 $(s)/s = 1 - \tfrac{1}{24}\chi^2 s^2$

24.30 $\tan\{(\alpha) - \alpha\} = -\dfrac{C}{A \sin \beta + B \cos \beta}$

24.31 $\{(s)/s\} \sin\{(\beta) - \beta\} = B$ (if $C = 0$)

Arc-to-Chord Corrections — Geodetic Model:

24.32 $\tau = \dfrac{(\rho - \nu) \sin \alpha \cos \alpha}{(\rho + h)(\nu + h)}$

24.33 $\Delta\beta = \tfrac{1}{2}s\chi_3$ (τ assumed zero)

24.34 $\Delta\beta = \tfrac{1}{2}s\chi$ (χ assumed constant)

24.35; 24.38 $f = \chi R = 1 + (R/s)(\bar\beta - \beta)$

Velocity Correction:

24.39 $ct = \tfrac{1}{2}s(\bar\mu + \mu) + \tfrac{1}{12}s^2(\bar\mu\bar\chi \cot \bar\beta - \mu\chi \cot \beta)$

24.41 $-\tfrac{1}{12}\dfrac{s^3}{R^2}f(1 - f)$

Equation of State:

24.42 $p = c\rho T$

24.43 $(\mu - 1)/\rho = \text{constant}$

24.44 $dp = -\rho g dh$

24.47 $p = \dfrac{c\rho T}{1 - 0.37803(e/p)}$

Hypsometric Formula:

$$\ln\left(\frac{p_1}{p_2}\right) = \frac{g_m}{cT_m}\{1 - 0.37803(e/p)_m\}(h_2 - h_1)$$

24.49

Index of Refraction:

$$(\mu_s - 1) \times 10^7 = 2876.04 + 16.288\lambda^{-2} + 0.136\lambda^{-4}$$

24.51

$$(\mu_G - 1) \times 10^7 = 2876.04 + (3 \times 16.288)\lambda^{-2}$$

24.53 $+ (5 \times 0.136)\lambda^{-4}$

$$(\mu - 1) = \frac{(\mu_G - 1)}{(1 + \alpha t)}\left(\frac{p}{760}\right) - \frac{55 \times 10^{-9}e}{(1 + \alpha t)}$$

24.54   (optical wavelengths)

24.57 $(1 + \alpha t) = \alpha T$

$$(\mu - 1) \times 10^6 = \frac{103.49}{T}(p - e) + \frac{86.26}{T}\left(1 + \frac{5748}{T}\right)e$$

24.58   (microwaves)

Curvature:

$$\chi = \frac{\sin \beta}{\mu(1 + \alpha t)}\left[(\mu - 1)\alpha \frac{dt}{dh} - \frac{\mu_G - 1}{760}\frac{dp}{dh}\right.$$

24.59 $\left. + 55 \times 10^{-9}\dfrac{de}{dh}\right]$

24.60 $\dfrac{dp}{dh} = -\left(\dfrac{g}{c}\right)\left(\dfrac{p}{T}\right)$

$$\chi = \frac{(\mu - 1) \sin \beta}{\mu T}\left[\frac{dT}{dh} + \frac{g}{c}\right]$$

24.61 $(e = 0)$ (optical waves)

Astronomical Refraction:

$$\int \chi ds = -\int_{\mu_0}^1 \left\{\left(\frac{\mu r}{\mu_0 r_0 \sin \beta_0}\right)^2 - 1\right\}^{-1/2} d(\ln \mu)$$

24.69   (spherical symmetry)

Chapter 25

General Equations of the Line:

25.01 $l^r_{,s}l^s = 0$ $(r = 1, 2, 3)$

25.02
$$\frac{\partial l^r}{\partial s} + \Gamma_{st}^r l^s l^t = 0$$

$$\bar{x} - x = sa$$

$$\bar{y} - y = sb$$

25.03
$$\bar{z} - z = sc$$

25.04
$$\bar{\rho}^r - \rho^r = sl^r$$

$$\sin \alpha \sin \beta = -a \sin \omega + b \cos \omega$$

$$\cos \alpha \sin \beta = -a \sin \phi \cos \omega - b \sin \phi \sin \omega$$
$$+ c \cos \phi$$

$$\cos \beta = + a \cos \phi \cos \omega + b \cos \phi \sin \omega$$

25.06
$$+ c \sin \phi$$

$$(\sec \phi) l_1 = -(k_2/K) \sin \alpha \sin \beta$$
$$+ (t_1/K) \cos \alpha \sin \beta$$

$$l_2 = (t_1/K) \sin \alpha \sin \beta$$
$$- (k_1/K) \cos \alpha \sin \beta$$

$$l_3 = \frac{\partial(1/n)}{\partial \omega} \sec \phi \sin \alpha \sin \beta$$

25.07
$$+ \frac{\partial(1/n)}{\partial \phi} \cos \alpha \sin \beta + \frac{\cos \beta}{n}$$

25.09
$$= (1/n) \sec \bar{\beta} \cos \bar{\sigma}$$

$$(\cos \phi) l^1 = -k_1 \sin \alpha \sin \beta$$
$$- t_1 \cos \alpha \sin \beta + \gamma_1 \cos \beta$$

$$l^2 = -t_1 \sin \alpha \sin \beta$$
$$- k_2 \cos \alpha \sin \beta + \gamma_2 \cos \beta$$

25.08
$$l^3 = n \cos \beta$$

25.10
$$\{\sin \alpha \sin \beta, \cos \alpha \sin \beta, \cos \beta\} = \mathbf{Q}\{a, b, c\}$$

$$a = -\sin \omega \sin \alpha \sin \beta$$
$$- \sin \phi \cos \omega \cos \alpha \sin \beta$$
$$+ \cos \phi \cos \omega \cos \beta$$

$$b = \cos \omega \sin \alpha \sin \beta$$
$$- \sin \phi \sin \omega \cos \alpha \sin \beta$$
$$+ \cos \phi \sin \omega \cos \beta$$

25.12
$$c = \cos \phi \cos \alpha \sin \beta + \sin \phi \cos \beta$$

The Line in Geodetic Coordinates:
$$\{s \sin \alpha \sin \beta, s \cos \alpha \sin \beta, s \cos \beta\}$$

25.13
$$= \mathbf{Q}\{(\bar{x} - x), (\bar{y} - y), (\bar{z} - z)\}$$

$$x = x_0(\omega, \phi) + h \cos \phi \cos \omega$$

$$y = y_0(\omega, \phi) + h \cos \phi \sin \omega$$

25.14
$$z = z_0(\omega, \phi) + h \sin \phi$$

$$x = (\nu + h) \cos \phi \cos \omega$$

$$y = (\nu + h) \cos \phi \sin \omega$$

$$z = (\bar{e}^2 \nu + h) \sin \phi = (\nu + h) \sin \phi - e^2 \nu \sin \phi$$

25.15

$$l_r = \{(\nu + h) \cos \phi \sin \alpha \sin \beta,$$
$$(\rho + h) \cos \alpha \sin \beta, \cos \beta\}$$

25.17
$$l^r = \left\{ \frac{\sin \alpha \sin \beta \sec \phi}{(\nu + h)}, \frac{\cos \alpha \sin \beta}{(\rho + h)}, \cos \beta \right\}$$

$$\{s \sin \alpha \sin \beta, s \cos \alpha \sin \beta, s \cos \beta\}$$

$$= (\bar{\nu} + \bar{h}) \mathbf{Q} \{\cos \bar{\phi} \cos \bar{\omega}, \cos \bar{\phi} \sin \bar{\omega}, \sin \bar{\phi}\}$$
$$- e^2 \bar{\nu} \sin \bar{\phi} \mathbf{Q} \{0, 0, 1\}$$
$$- (\nu + h) \mathbf{Q} \{\cos \phi \cos \omega, \cos \phi \sin \omega, \sin \phi\}$$
$$+ e^2 \nu \sin \phi \mathbf{Q} \{0, 0, 1\}$$
$$= (\bar{\nu} + \bar{h}) \{\sin \sigma \sin \alpha^*, \sin \sigma \cos \alpha^*, \cos \sigma\}$$
$$- (\nu + h) \{0, 0, 1\}$$
$$- e^2 (\bar{\nu} \sin \bar{\phi} - \nu \sin \phi) \{0, \cos \phi, \sin \phi\}$$

25.18

$$\{s \sin \bar{\alpha} \sin \bar{\beta}, s \cos \bar{\alpha} \sin \bar{\beta}, s \cos \bar{\beta}\}$$

$$= (\nu + h) \{\sin \sigma \sin \bar{\alpha}^*, \sin \sigma \cos \bar{\alpha}^*, -\cos \sigma\}$$
$$+ (\bar{\nu} + \bar{h}) \{0, 0, 1\}$$
$$- e^2 (\bar{\nu} \sin \bar{\phi} - \nu \sin \phi) \{0, \cos \bar{\phi}, \sin \bar{\phi}\}$$

25.19

$$\{\bar{x}, \bar{y}, \bar{z}\} = \{x, y, z\}$$
$$+ \mathbf{Q}^T \{s \sin \alpha \sin \beta, s \cos \alpha \sin \beta, s \cos \beta\}$$

25.21

25.22
$$\tan \bar{\omega} = \bar{y}/\bar{x}$$

$$(\bar{\nu} + \bar{h}) \cos \bar{\phi} = (\bar{x}^2 + \bar{y}^2)^{1/2}$$

25.23
$$(\bar{e}^2 \bar{\nu} + \bar{h}) \sin \bar{\phi} = \bar{z}$$

Taylor Expansion Along the Line:

25.31
$$(\bar{F} - F) = \tfrac{1}{2} s (F' + \bar{F}') + \tfrac{1}{12} s^2 (F'' - \bar{F}'')$$

Expansion of the Gravitational Potential:

$$(\bar{N} - N)/n = s \cos \beta + \tfrac{1}{2} s^2 \{ -k \sin^2 \beta - \chi \sin \beta$$
$$+ 2(\ln n)_s q^s \sin \beta \cos \beta$$
25.33
$$+ (\ln n)_s \nu^s \cos^2 \beta \}$$

$$\bar{N} - N = \tfrac{1}{2} s (n \cos \beta + \bar{n} \cos \bar{\beta})$$

25.35
(first order)

Expansion of Geodetic Heights:

$$\bar{h}-h=\tfrac{1}{2}s(\cos\bar{\beta}+\cos\beta)$$

$$+\tfrac{1}{12}s^2(\bar{k}\sin^2\bar{\beta}+\bar{\chi}\sin\bar{\beta}$$

25.39
$$-k\sin^2\beta-\chi\sin\beta)$$

with

25.38
$$-k=\frac{\sin^2\alpha}{(\nu+h)}+\frac{\cos^2\alpha}{(\rho+h)}$$

Astro-Geodetic Leveling:

$$\tfrac{1}{2}s(\Delta+\bar{\Delta})=(1/n)\{\bar{N}-N\}-\{\bar{h}-h\}$$
25.43   (first order)

$$\Delta=(\cos\phi\,\delta\omega)\sin\alpha\sin\beta+(\delta\phi)\cos\alpha\sin\beta$$
25.44

Deflections by Torsion Balance Measurements:

$$I_P=+k_1\sin\beta\operatorname{cosec}\bar{\beta}\,\{\sin\alpha\cos\alpha(1+\cos\sigma)$$

$$-\sin\alpha\cot\beta\sin\sigma\cos\alpha^*\}$$

$$-k_2\sin\beta\operatorname{cosec}\bar{\beta}\,\{\sin\alpha\cos\alpha(1+\cos\sigma)$$

$$-\cos\alpha\cot\beta\sin\sigma\sin\alpha^*\}$$

$$+t_1\sin\beta\operatorname{cosec}\bar{\beta}\,\{(\cos^2\alpha-\sin^2\alpha)(1+\cos\sigma)$$

$$-\cot\beta\sin\sigma\cos(\alpha+\alpha^*)\}$$

$$-\gamma_1\cos\beta\operatorname{cosec}\bar{\beta}\,\{\cos\alpha(1+\cos\sigma)$$

$$-\cot\beta\sin\sigma\cos\alpha^*\}$$

$$+\gamma_2\cos\beta\operatorname{cosec}\bar{\beta}\,\{\sin\alpha(1+\cos\sigma)$$

25.48
$$-\cot\beta\sin\sigma\sin\alpha^*\}$$

$$I_P\simeq\sin\beta\operatorname{cosec}\bar{\beta}\,(1+\cos\sigma)$$

$$\times\{(k_1-k_2)\sin\alpha\cos\alpha+t_1(\cos^2\alpha-\sin^2\alpha)$$

25.50 $-\gamma_1\cos\alpha\cot\beta+\gamma_2\sin\alpha\cot\beta\}$

$$I_P\simeq(1+\cos\sigma)\{(k_1-k_2)\sin\alpha\cos\alpha$$

25.51 $+t_1(\cos^2\alpha-\sin^2\alpha)\}$

25.49 $s(I_P+I_{\bar{P}})=4\sin\lambda$

$$(\lambda_A-\lambda_G)=-\cos\bar{\alpha}\operatorname{cosec}\bar{\beta}\cos\bar{\phi}\,(\bar{\omega}_A-\bar{\omega}_G)$$

$$+\sin\bar{\alpha}\operatorname{cosec}\bar{\beta}\,(\bar{\phi}_A-\bar{\phi}_G)$$

$$+\cos\alpha\operatorname{cosec}\beta\cos\phi\,(\omega_A-\omega_G)$$

25.52 $-\sin\alpha\operatorname{cosec}\beta\,(\phi_A-\phi_G)$

Chapter 26

The Triangle in Space:

26.02 $s_{12}l_{12}^r+s_{23}l_{23}^r-s_{13}l_{13}^r=0$

$$s_{12}\,(\cos\alpha_{13},\,-\sin\alpha_{13},\,0)$$

$$\times\{\sin\alpha_{12}\sin\beta_{12},\,\cos\alpha_{12}\sin\beta_{12},\,\cos\beta_{12}\}$$

$$=-s_{23}\,(\cos\alpha_{13},\,-\sin\alpha_{13},\,0)$$

$$\times\mathbf{Q}\bar{\mathbf{Q}}^T\{\sin\bar{\alpha}_{23}\sin\bar{\beta}_{23},\,\cos\bar{\alpha}_{23}\sin\bar{\beta}_{23},\,\cos\bar{\beta}_{23}\}$$
26.04

$$s_{12}\,(\cos\bar{\alpha}_{23},\,-\sin\bar{\alpha}_{23},\,0)$$

$$\times\bar{\mathbf{Q}}\mathbf{Q}^T\{\sin\alpha_{12}\sin\beta_{12},\,\cos\alpha_{12}\sin\beta_{12},\,\cos\beta_{12}\}$$

$$=s_{13}\,(\cos\bar{\alpha}_{23},\,-\sin\bar{\alpha}_{23},\,0)$$

$$\times\bar{\mathbf{Q}}\mathbf{Q}^T\{\sin\alpha_{13}\sin\beta_{13},\,\cos\alpha_{13}\sin\beta_{13},\,\cos\beta_{13}\}$$
26.05

Variation of Position:

26.08 $ds=\bar{l}_r d\bar{x}^r-l_r dx^r$

$$sd(l^r)=(\bar{m}_s d\bar{x}^s-m_s dx^s)m^r+(\bar{n}_s d\bar{x}^s-n_s dx^s)n^r$$
26.10

Variation of Position in Geodetic Coordinates:

$$l^r=\lambda^r\sin\alpha\sin\beta+\mu^r\cos\alpha\sin\beta+\nu^r\cos\beta$$
26.11

$$m^r=\lambda^r\sin\alpha\cos\beta+\mu^r\cos\alpha\cos\beta-\nu^r\sin\beta$$

$$n^r=-\lambda^r\cos\alpha+\mu^r\sin\alpha$$
26.13

$$sd\beta=\bar{m}_s d\bar{x}^s-m_s dx^s-s\cos\phi\sin\alpha\,d\omega-s\cos\alpha\,d\phi$$
26.15

$$s\sin\beta\,d\alpha=-\bar{n}_s d\bar{x}^s+n_s dx^s$$

$$+s(\sin\phi\sin\beta-\cos\phi\cos\alpha\cos\beta)d\omega$$

26.16 $+s\sin\alpha\cos\beta\,d\phi$

$$\left\{\frac{m_1}{(\nu+h)\cos\phi},\,\frac{m_2}{(\rho+h)},\,m_3\right\}$$

$$=\{\sin\alpha\cos\beta,\cos\alpha\cos\beta,\,-\sin\beta\}$$

$$\left\{\frac{n_1}{(\nu+h)\cos\phi},\,\frac{n_2}{(\rho+h)},\,n_3\right\}$$
26.20 $=\{-\cos\alpha,\,\sin\alpha,\,0\}$

$$\left\{\frac{\bar{m}_1}{(\bar{\nu}+\bar{h})\cos\bar{\phi}},\,\frac{\bar{m}_2}{(\bar{\rho}+\bar{h})},\,\bar{m}_3\right\}$$

$$=\bar{\mathbf{Q}}\mathbf{Q}^T\{\sin\alpha\cos\beta,\cos\alpha\cos\beta,\,-\sin\beta\}$$

$$\left\{\frac{\bar{n}_1}{(\bar{\nu}+\bar{h})\cos\bar{\phi}},\,\frac{\bar{n}_2}{(\bar{\rho}+\bar{h})},\,\bar{n}_3\right\}$$

$$=\bar{\mathbf{Q}}\mathbf{Q}^T\{-\cos\alpha,\,\sin\alpha,\,0\}$$
26.21

26.22 $\quad \dfrac{\bar{m}_1^2}{(\bar{\nu}+\bar{h})^2 \cos^2 \bar{\phi}} + \dfrac{\bar{m}_2^2}{(\bar{\rho}+\bar{h})^2} + \bar{m}_3^2 = 1$

$\bar{m}_1 = m_1 + s \cos \phi \sin \alpha$

$\bar{n}_1 = n_1 + s\,(\sin \phi \sin \beta - \cos \phi \cos \alpha \cos \beta)$

26.23

Observation Equations in Geodetic Coordinates:

Horizontal and Vertical Angles:
(Observed Minus Computed) Zenith Distance

$= -\Delta\beta + \bar{m}_1 d\bar{\omega}/s + \bar{m}_2 d\bar{\phi}/s + \bar{m}_3 d\bar{h}/s$

$\quad - m_1 d\omega/s - m_2 d\phi/s - m_3 dh/s$

$\quad - (d\omega + \delta\omega)\cos\phi\sin\alpha - (d\phi + \delta\phi)\cos\alpha$

26.24

(Observed Minus Computed) Azimuth

$= -\Delta\alpha - \bar{n}_1 d\bar{\omega}\,(\operatorname{cosec}\beta)/s - \bar{n}_2 d\bar{\phi}\,(\operatorname{cosec}\beta)/s$

$\quad - \bar{n}_3 d\bar{h}\,(\operatorname{cosec}\beta)/s$

$\quad + n_1 d\omega\,(\operatorname{cosec}\beta)/s + n_2 d\phi\,(\operatorname{cosec}\beta)/s$

$\quad + n_3 dh\,(\operatorname{cosec}\beta)/s$

$\quad + (d\omega + \delta\omega)(\sin\phi - \cos\phi\cos\alpha\cot\beta)$

$\quad + (d\phi + \delta\phi)\sin\alpha\cot\beta$

26.25

Reverse Equations:
(Observed Minus Computed) Zenith Distance

$= -\overline{\Delta\beta} - \bar{m}_1 d\bar{\omega}/s - \bar{m}_2 d\bar{\phi}/s - \bar{m}_3 d\bar{h}/s$

$\quad + m_1 d\omega/s + m_2 d\phi/s + m_3 dh/s$

$\quad + (d\bar{\omega} + \overline{\delta\omega})\cos\bar{\phi}\sin\bar{\alpha}$

26.28 $\quad + (d\bar{\phi} + \overline{\delta\phi})\cos\bar{\alpha}$

(Observed Minus Computed) Azimuth

$= -\overline{\Delta\alpha} + \bar{n}_1 d\bar{\omega}\,(\operatorname{cosec}\bar{\beta})/s + \bar{n}_2 d\bar{\phi}\,(\operatorname{cosec}\bar{\beta})/s$

$\quad + \bar{n}_3 d\bar{h}\,(\operatorname{cosec}\bar{\beta})/s$

$\quad - n_1 d\omega\,(\operatorname{cosec}\bar{\beta})/s - n_2 d\phi\,(\operatorname{cosec}\bar{\beta})/s$

$\quad - n_3 dh\,(\operatorname{cosec}\bar{\beta})/s$

$\quad + (d\bar{\omega} + \overline{\delta\omega})\,(\sin\bar{\phi} - \cos\bar{\phi}\cos\bar{\alpha}\cot\bar{\beta})$

$\quad + (d\bar{\phi} + \overline{\delta\phi})\sin\bar{\alpha}\cot\bar{\beta}$

26.29

Lengths:
(Observed Minus Computed) Distance

$= (\nu + h)\cos\phi\sin\alpha\sin\beta(d\bar{\omega} - d\omega)$

$\quad + (\bar{\rho} + \bar{h})\cos\bar{\alpha}\sin\bar{\beta}\,d\bar{\phi} + \cos\bar{\beta}\,d\bar{h}$

26.30 $\quad - (\rho + h)\cos\alpha\,\sin\beta\,d\phi - \cos\beta\,dh$

Observation Equations in Cartesian Coordinates— Auxiliary Vectors:

$\{l_1, l_2, l_3\} = \{\bar{l}_1, \bar{l}_2, \bar{l}_3\}$

26.33 $\quad = \mathbf{Q}^T\{\sin\alpha\sin\beta, \cos\alpha\sin\beta, \cos\beta\}$

$\{m_1, m_2, m_3\} = \{\bar{m}_1, \bar{m}_2, \bar{m}_3\}$

26.34 $\quad = \mathbf{Q}^T\{\sin\alpha\cos\beta, \cos\alpha\cos\beta, -\sin\beta\}$

$\{n_1, n_2, n_3\} = \{\bar{n}_1, \bar{n}_2, \bar{n}_3\}$

26.35 $\quad = \mathbf{Q}^T\{-\cos\alpha, \sin\alpha, 0\}$

Observation Equations—Hour Angle and Declination:

$L^r = (\cos D \cos H)A^r + (\cos D \sin H)B^r + (\sin D)C^r$

26.36

$M^r = (\sin D \cos H)A^r + (\sin D \sin H)B^r - (\cos D)C^r$

26.39

26.40 $\quad N^r = -(\sin H)A^r + (\cos H)B^r$

26.42 $\quad s\,dD = -\overline{M}_s d\bar{x}^s + M_s dx^s$

26.43 $\quad (s \cos D)\,dH = \overline{N}_s d\bar{x}^s - N_s dx^s$

Observation Equations—Hour Angle and Declination— Cartesian Coordinates:

$\bar{x} - x = s \cos D \cos H$

$\bar{y} - y = s \cos D \sin H$

26.44 $\quad \bar{z} - z = s \sin D$

$M^r = \overline{M}^r = (\sin D \cos H, \sin D \sin H, -\cos D)$

$N^r = \overline{N}^r = (-\sin H, \cos H, 0)$

26.45

Observation Equations—Hour Angle and Declination—Other Coordinates:

$(M_1, M_2, M_3) = (\sin D \cos H, \sin D \sin H, -\cos D)$

26.48 $\quad \times \mathbf{Q}^T\mathbf{S}$

$(\overline{M}_1, \overline{M}_2, \overline{M}_3) = (\sin D \cos H, \sin D \sin H, -\cos D)$

26.50 $\quad \times \overline{\mathbf{Q}}^T\overline{\mathbf{S}}$

$(N_1, N_2, N_3) = (-\sin H, \cos H, 0)\mathbf{Q}^T\mathbf{S}$

26.51

$(\overline{N}_1, \overline{N}_2, \overline{N}_3) = (-\sin H, \cos H, 0)\overline{\mathbf{Q}}^T\overline{\mathbf{S}}$

Satellite Triangulation—Directions:

Basic Photogrammetric Equations:

26.55 $\quad \begin{pmatrix} x - x_0 \\ y - y_0 \\ f \end{pmatrix} = \left(\dfrac{d}{\Delta}\right)\mathbf{M}\begin{pmatrix} X - X_0 \\ Y - Y_0 \\ Z - Z_0 \end{pmatrix}$

$$\mathbf{M}=\begin{pmatrix}\cos\kappa & \sin\kappa & 0\\ -\sin\kappa & \cos\kappa & 0\\ 0 & 0 & 1\end{pmatrix}$$

$$\times\begin{pmatrix}1 & 0 & 0\\ 0 & \sin D_c & \cos D_c\\ 0 & -\cos D_c & \sin D_c\end{pmatrix}\begin{pmatrix}-\sin H_c & \cos H_c & 0\\ -\cos H_c & -\sin H_c & 0\\ 0 & 0 & 1\end{pmatrix}$$

26.56

$$\left(\frac{d}{\Delta}\right)^2=\frac{(x-x_0)^2+(y-y_0)^2+f^2}{(X-X_0)^2+(Y-Y_0)^2+(Z-Z_0)^2}$$

$$\frac{x-x_0}{f}=\frac{m_{11}(X-X_0)+m_{12}(Y-Y_0)+m_{13}(Z-Z_0)}{m_{31}(X-X_0)+m_{32}(Y-Y_0)+m_{33}(Z-Z_0)}$$

$$\frac{y-y_0}{f}=\frac{m_{21}(X-X_0)+m_{22}(Y-Y_0)+m_{23}(Z-Z_0)}{m_{31}(X-X_0)+m_{32}(Y-Y_0)+m_{33}(Z-Z_0)}$$

26.58

26.57
$$\mathbf{M}=\begin{pmatrix}m_{11} & m_{12} & m_{13}\\ m_{21} & m_{22} & m_{23}\\ m_{31} & m_{32} & m_{33}\end{pmatrix}$$

Photogrammetric Equations — Star Images:

26.59
$$\frac{1}{d}\begin{pmatrix}x-x_0\\ y-y_0\\ f\end{pmatrix}=\mathbf{M}\begin{pmatrix}\cos D\cos H\\ \cos D\sin H\\ \sin D\end{pmatrix}$$

$$d^2=(x-x_0)^2+(y-y_0)^2+f^2$$

$$\frac{x-x_0}{f}=\frac{m_{11}\cos D\cos H+m_{12}\cos D\sin H+m_{13}\sin D}{m_{31}\cos D\cos H+m_{32}\cos D\sin H+m_{33}\sin D}$$

$$\frac{y-y_0}{f}=\frac{m_{21}\cos D\cos H+m_{22}\cos D\sin H+m_{23}\sin D}{m_{31}\cos D\cos H+m_{32}\cos D\sin H+m_{33}\sin D}$$

26.60

$$\begin{pmatrix}\cos D\cos H\\ \cos D\sin H\\ \sin D\end{pmatrix}=\mathbf{N}\begin{pmatrix}\sin\alpha\sin\beta\\ \cos\alpha\sin\beta\\ \cos\beta\end{pmatrix}$$

$$\mathbf{N}=\begin{pmatrix}-\sin\omega & -\cos\omega & 0\\ \cos\omega & -\sin\omega & 0\\ 0 & 0 & 1\end{pmatrix}\begin{pmatrix}1 & 0 & 0\\ 0 & \sin\phi & -\cos\phi\\ 0 & \cos\phi & \sin\phi\end{pmatrix}$$

26.53; 26.54

Alternative Photogrammetric Equations:

$$\frac{x-x_0}{f}=\frac{n_{11}\sin\alpha\sin\beta+n_{12}\cos\alpha\sin\beta+n_{13}\cos\beta}{n_{31}\sin\alpha\sin\beta+n_{32}\cos\alpha\sin\beta+n_{33}\cos\beta}$$

$$\frac{y-y_0}{f}=\frac{n_{21}\sin\alpha\sin\beta+n_{22}\cos\alpha\sin\beta+n_{23}\cos\beta}{n_{31}\sin\alpha\sin\beta+n_{32}\cos\alpha\sin\beta+n_{33}\cos\beta}$$

26.62

$$\mathbf{MN}=\begin{pmatrix}n_{11} & n_{12} & n_{13}\\ n_{21} & n_{22} & n_{23}\\ n_{31} & n_{32} & n_{33}\end{pmatrix}$$

$$\tan H=\frac{m_{12}(x-x_0)+m_{22}(y-y_0)+m_{32}(f)}{m_{11}(x-x_0)+m_{21}(y-y_0)+m_{31}(f)}$$

$$\tan D=\sin H\times\frac{m_{13}(x-x_0)+m_{23}(y-y_0)+m_{33}(f)}{m_{12}(x-x_0)+m_{22}(y-y_0)+m_{32}(f)}$$

$$=\cos H\times\frac{m_{13}(x-x_0)+m_{23}(y-y_0)+m_{33}(f)}{m_{11}(x-x_0)+m_{21}(y-y_0)+m_{31}(f)}$$

26.64

Chapter 27

Change of Spheroid:

$$d\omega=0$$

$$(\rho+h)d\phi=(e^2\nu/a)\sin\phi\cos\phi\,da$$
$$+(e/\bar{e}^2)(\rho+\nu\bar{e}^2)\sin\phi\cos\phi\,de$$

27.04 $dh=-(a/\nu)da+e\nu\sin^2\phi\,de$

Change of Origin:

$$(\nu+h)\cos\phi\,d\omega=(\sin\omega)dX_0-(\cos\omega)dY_0$$

$$(\rho+h)d\phi=(\sin\phi\cos\omega)dX_0+(\sin\phi\sin\omega)dY_0$$
$$-(\cos\phi)dZ_0$$

$$dh=-(\cos\phi\cos\omega)dX_0$$

27.06 $-(\cos\phi\sin\omega)dY_0-(\sin\phi)dZ_0$

Change of Cartesian Axes:

$$(\nu+h)\cos\phi\,d\omega=-\omega_3(\nu+h)\cos\phi$$
$$+(\omega_1\cos\omega+\omega_2\sin\omega)$$
$$\times(\bar{e}^2\nu+h)\sin\phi$$

$$(\rho+h)d\phi=(\omega_2\cos\omega-\omega_1\sin\omega)$$
$$\times(h+a^2/\nu)$$

$$dh=(\omega_2\cos\omega-\omega_1\sin\omega)$$
27.14 $\times(e^2\nu\sin\phi\cos\phi)$

Change of Scale and Orientation:

$$\mathbf{A}=\begin{pmatrix}\sin\alpha\sin\beta & \sin\alpha\cos\beta & -\cos\alpha\\ \cos\alpha\sin\beta & \cos\alpha\cos\beta & \sin\alpha\\ \cos\beta & -\sin\beta & 0\end{pmatrix}$$

27.18

$$\{(\nu+h)\cos\phi\,d\omega,\ (\rho+h)d\phi,\ dh\}$$

27.21
$$=s\mathbf{A}\{ds/s,\ d\beta_0,\ -\sin\beta\,d\alpha_0\}$$

Extension to Astronomical Coordinates:

Change of Origin:

27.22 $\{d\omega, d\phi, dN\} = \mathbf{R}^T\mathbf{Q}\{dx, dy, dz\}$

where

$$\mathbf{R}^T = \begin{pmatrix} -k_1 \sec\phi & -t_1 \sec\phi & \gamma_1 \sec\phi \\ -t_1 & -k_2 & \gamma_2 \\ 0 & 0 & n \end{pmatrix}$$

Change of Cartesian Axes:

27.23 $\{d\omega, d\phi, dN\} = \mathbf{R}^T\mathbf{Q}\mathbf{N}_0\{x, y, z\}$

Change of Scale and Orientation:

$\{d\omega, d\phi, dN\} = s\mathbf{R}^T\mathbf{A}\{ds/s, d\beta_0, -\sin\beta \, d\alpha_0\}$

27.24

Chapter 28

Equations of Motion – Inertial Axes:

28.001 $\quad m\dfrac{d^2x}{dt^2} = \dfrac{d(mv_r)}{dt} = F_r$

28.002 $\quad v^r = \dfrac{\partial x^r}{\partial \bar{x}^s}\,\bar{v}^s = \dfrac{\partial x^r}{\partial \bar{x}^s}\dfrac{d\bar{x}^s}{dt} = \dfrac{dx^r}{dt} = \dfrac{ds}{dt}\dfrac{dx^r}{ds} = vl^r$

28.003 $\quad \dfrac{\delta\rho^r}{\delta t} = vl^r$

28.004 $\quad m\dfrac{\delta^2\rho_r}{\delta t^2} = m\dfrac{\delta v_r}{\delta t} = \dfrac{\delta(mvl_r)}{\delta t} = F_r$

28.005 $\quad \dfrac{\delta^2\rho_r}{\delta t^2} = \dfrac{\delta v_r}{\delta t} = \dfrac{\delta(vl_r)}{\delta t} = F_r$

28.006 $\quad \dfrac{\delta^2\rho_r}{\delta t^2} = \dfrac{\delta v_r}{\delta t} = \dfrac{\delta(vl_r)}{\delta t} = F_r = -V_r$

28.007 $\quad -V_r = F_r = \dfrac{d}{dt}\left(g_{rs}\dfrac{dx^s}{dt}\right) - \tfrac{1}{2}\dfrac{\partial g_{kq}}{\partial x^r}\dfrac{dx^k}{dt}\dfrac{dx^q}{dt}$

$-\dfrac{\partial V}{\partial \omega} = \dfrac{d}{dt}\{(\bar{R}_1 + h)^2 \cos^2\phi\,\dot{\omega}\}$

$-\dfrac{\partial V}{\partial \phi} = \dfrac{d}{dt}\{(\bar{R}_2 + h)^2\dot{\phi}\} - \tfrac{1}{2}\dfrac{\partial\{(\bar{R}_1 + h)^2 \cos^2\phi\}}{\partial\phi}\,\dot{\omega}^2$

$\qquad - \tfrac{1}{2}\dfrac{\partial\{(\bar{R}_2 + h)^2\}}{\partial\phi}\,\dot{\phi}^2$

$-\dfrac{\partial V}{\partial h} = \dfrac{d}{dt}\{\dot{h}\} - \tfrac{1}{2}\dfrac{\partial\{(\bar{R}_1 + h)^2 \cos^2\phi\}}{\partial h}\,\dot{\omega}^2$

$\qquad - \tfrac{1}{2}\dfrac{\partial\{(\bar{R}_2 + h)^2\}}{\partial h}\,\dot{\phi}^2$

28.008

$-\dfrac{\partial V}{\partial\omega} = \dfrac{d}{dt}(r^2 \cos^2\phi\,\dot{\omega})$

$-\dfrac{\partial V}{\partial\phi} = \dfrac{d}{dt}(r^2\dot{\phi}) + r^2 \sin\phi \cos\phi\,\dot{\omega}^2$

28.009 $\quad -\dfrac{\partial V}{\partial r} = \ddot{r} - r\cos^2\phi\,\dot{\omega}^2 - r\dot{\phi}^2$

Equations of Motion – Moving Axes:

$A_r = \bar{A}_r \cos\tilde{\omega}t + \bar{B}_r \sin\tilde{\omega}t$

$B_r = -\bar{A}_r \sin\tilde{\omega}t + \bar{B}_r \cos\tilde{\omega}t$

28.010 $\quad C_r = \bar{C}_r$

$\dfrac{dA_r}{dt} = \tilde{\omega}B_r\,; \qquad \dfrac{dB_r}{dt} = -\tilde{\omega}A_r\,; \qquad \dfrac{dC_r}{dt} = 0$

28.011

28.012 $\quad F_r = \dfrac{\delta v_r}{\delta t} + 2\tilde{\omega}\epsilon_{rpq}C^pv^q - \tfrac{1}{2}\tilde{\omega}^2(x^2 + y^2)_r$

28.013 $\quad -W_r = \dfrac{\delta v_r}{\delta t} + 2\tilde{\omega}\epsilon_{rpq}C^pv^q$

$\ddot{x} - 2\tilde{\omega}\dot{y} = F_x + \tilde{\omega}^2x = -\partial W/\partial x$

$\ddot{y} + 2\tilde{\omega}\dot{x} = F_y + \tilde{\omega}^2y = -\partial W/\partial y$

28.014 $\quad \ddot{z} \qquad = F_z \qquad = -\partial W/\partial z$

Inertial Axes – First Integrals:

28.015 $\quad \dfrac{d(v^2)}{dt} = 2v^r\dfrac{\delta v_r}{\delta t}$

28.016 $\quad \dfrac{\delta(v_r)}{\delta t} = -V_r$

28.020 $\quad H^* = \tfrac{1}{2}v^2 + V$

28.021 $\quad \tfrac{1}{2}v^2 + V = \displaystyle\int \dfrac{\partial V}{\partial t}\,dt + \text{constant}$

28.027 $\quad vr\sin\beta = \text{constant}$

Moving Axes – First Integrals:

28.028 $\quad \tfrac{1}{2}v^2 + W = \text{constant}$

The Lagrangian:

28.029 $\quad L^* = \tfrac{1}{2}(\dot{x}^2 + \dot{y}^2 + \dot{z}^2) - V(x, y, z, t)$

28.030 $\quad \dfrac{d}{dt}\left(\dfrac{\partial L^*}{\partial \dot{q}^r}\right) = \dfrac{\partial L^*}{\partial q^r}$

The Canonical Equations:

28.032 $\quad H^* = \tfrac{1}{2}(\dot{x}^2 + \dot{y}^2 + \dot{z}^2) + V(x, y, z, t)$

28.033 $\quad \dfrac{\partial H^*}{\partial \dot{x}_r} = \dfrac{dx^r}{dt}\,; \qquad \dfrac{\partial H^*}{\partial x^r} = -\dfrac{d\dot{x}_r}{dt}$

The Kepler Ellipse:

28.035 $\qquad \frac{1}{2}v^2 - \mu/r = H^*$

28.036 $\qquad vr \sin \beta = N$

$\qquad\qquad dr/ds = \cos \beta$

28.037 $\qquad rdf/ds = \sin \beta$

$\qquad\qquad \dot{r} = v \cos \beta$

28.038 $\qquad r\dot{f} = v \sin \beta$

$\qquad\qquad r^2\dot{f} = N$

28.039 $\qquad (\dot{r})^2 + (r\dot{f})^2 = v^2 = 2(\mu/r + H^*)$

28.040 $\qquad N = \sqrt{\mu a(1-e^2)}$

28.041 $\qquad H^* = -\mu/2a$

28.042 $\qquad v^2 = \mu\left(\frac{2}{r} - \frac{1}{a}\right) = \frac{\mu r'}{ar}$

28.043 $\qquad n = \frac{2\pi}{T}$

28.044 $\qquad n = \mu^{1/2}a^{-3/2}$

28.045 $\qquad N = \sqrt{\mu a(1-e^2)} = na^2(1-e^2)^{1/2}$

$\frac{dr}{dt} = ae \sin E \frac{dE}{dt} = \frac{ae(1-e^2)\sin f}{(1+e\cos f)^2}\frac{df}{dt} = \frac{r^2 e \sin f}{a(1-e^2)}\frac{N}{r^2}$

28.046

28.047 $\qquad \frac{dE}{dt} = \frac{na}{r} = \frac{n}{(1-e\cos E)}$

28.048 $\qquad (E - e \sin E) = n(t - t_0) = M$

28.049 $\qquad \cot \beta = \frac{e \sin E}{(1-e^2)^{1/2}}$

28.050 $\qquad \cot \beta = \frac{e \sin f}{(1+e\cos f)} = \frac{re \sin f}{a(1-e^2)}$

28.051 $\qquad r = a(1 - e \cos E) = \frac{a(1-e^2)}{(1+e\cos f)}$

$\qquad\qquad q_1 = r \cos f = a(\cos E - e)$

28.052 $\qquad q_2 = r \sin f = a(1-e^2)^{1/2} \sin E$

28.053 $\qquad v \cos \beta = \frac{\mu^{1/2}e \sin f}{a^{1/2}(1-e^2)^{1/2}} = \frac{\mu^{1/2}a^{1/2}e \sin E}{r}$

$v \sin \beta = \frac{N}{r} = \frac{\mu^{1/2}a^{1/2}(1-e^2)^{1/2}}{r} = \frac{\mu^{1/2}(1+e\cos f)}{a^{1/2}(1-e^2)^{1/2}}$

28.054

$\qquad \cos E = \frac{\cos f + e}{1 + e \cos f}$

28.055 $\qquad \cos f = \frac{\cos E - e}{1 - e \cos E}$

$v^2 = \frac{\mu^2(1 + 2e \cos f + e^2)}{N^2} = \frac{\mu(1 + e \cos E)}{r}$

28.056

$v \cos (f+\beta) = \dot{q}_1 = -\frac{na \sin f}{(1-e^2)^{1/2}} = -\frac{na^2 \sin E}{r}$

$v \sin (f+\beta) = \dot{q}_2 = \frac{na(e + \cos f)}{(1-e^2)^{1/2}} = \frac{na^2(1-e^2)^{1/2}\cos E}{r}$

28.057

Auxiliary Vectors:

$\qquad l^k = r^k \cos \beta + t^k \sin \beta$

28.058 $\qquad m^k = -r^k \sin \beta + t^k \cos \beta$

$l^k = \lambda^k \sin \alpha \sin \beta + \mu^k \cos \alpha \sin \beta + \nu^k \cos \beta$

$m^k = \lambda^k \sin \alpha \cos \beta + \mu^k \cos \alpha \cos \beta - \nu^k \sin \beta$

$n^k = -\lambda^k \cos \alpha + \mu^k \sin \alpha$

$r^k = \nu^k$

$t^k = \lambda^k \sin \alpha + \mu^k \cos \alpha$

28.059

$$r^k = \begin{pmatrix} \cos (w+f) \cos \Omega - \sin (w+f) \sin \Omega \cos i \\ \cos (w+f) \sin \Omega + \sin (w+f) \cos \Omega \cos i \\ \sin (w+f) \sin i \end{pmatrix}$$

28.060

$$t^k = \begin{pmatrix} -\sin (w+f) \cos \Omega - \cos (w+f) \sin \Omega \cos i \\ -\sin (w+f) \sin \Omega + \cos (w+f) \cos \Omega \cos i \\ \cos (w+f) \sin i \end{pmatrix}$$

28.061

28.062 $\qquad n^k = \begin{pmatrix} \sin \Omega \sin i \\ -\cos \Omega \sin i \\ \cos i \end{pmatrix}$

28.063 $\qquad l^r = \begin{pmatrix} \cos (w+f+\beta) \cos \Omega - \sin (w+f+\beta) \sin \Omega \cos i \\ \cos (w+f+\beta) \sin \Omega + \sin (w+f+\beta) \cos \Omega \cos i \\ \sin (w+f+\beta) \sin i \end{pmatrix}$

28.064 $\qquad m^r = \begin{pmatrix} -\sin (w+f+\beta) \cos \Omega - \cos (w+f+\beta) \sin \Omega \cos i \\ -\sin (w+f+\beta) \sin \Omega + \cos (w+f+\beta) \cos \Omega \cos i \\ \cos (w+f+\beta) \sin i \end{pmatrix}$

$$\begin{pmatrix} r^k \\ t^k \\ n^k \end{pmatrix} = \begin{pmatrix} \cos(w+f) & \sin(w+f) & 0 \\ -\sin(w+f) & \cos(w+f) & 0 \\ 0 & 0 & 1 \end{pmatrix} \begin{pmatrix} 1 & 0 & 0 \\ 0 & \cos i & \sin i \\ 0 & -\sin i & \cos i \end{pmatrix} \begin{pmatrix} \cos\Omega & \sin\Omega & 0 \\ -\sin\Omega & \cos\Omega & 0 \\ 0 & 0 & 1 \end{pmatrix} \begin{pmatrix} \bar{A}^k \\ \bar{B}^k \\ C^k \end{pmatrix}$$

28.065
$$= \mathbf{K}\{\bar{A}^k, \bar{B}^k, C^k\}$$

$$\mathbf{K} = \begin{pmatrix} \cos(w+f)\cos\Omega - \sin(w+f)\sin\Omega\cos i & \cos(w+f)\sin\Omega + \sin(w+f)\cos\Omega\cos i & \sin i\sin(w+f) \\ -\sin(w+f)\cos\Omega - \cos(w+f)\sin\Omega\cos i & -\sin(w+f)\sin\Omega + \cos(w+f)\cos\Omega\cos i & \sin i\cos(w+f) \\ \sin\Omega\sin i & -\cos\Omega\sin i & \cos i \end{pmatrix}$$

28.066

28.067 $\quad \{\bar{A}^k, \bar{B}^k, C^k\} = \mathbf{K}^T\{r^k, t^k, n^k\}$

28.068 $\quad \{q_1, q_2, 0\} = \mathbf{K}_{f=0}\{x, y, z\}$

28.069 $\quad \{x, y, z\} = \mathbf{K}_{f=0}^T\{q_1, q_2, 0\}$

$$\mathbf{K} = \begin{pmatrix} \cos f & \sin f & 0 \\ -\sin f & \cos f & 0 \\ 0 & 0 & 1 \end{pmatrix} \mathbf{K}_{f=0}$$

28.070 $\quad = \mathbf{F}\mathbf{K}_{f=0}$

28.071 $\quad \{l^k, m^k, n^k\} = \mathbf{K}_{w+f+\beta}\{\bar{A}^k, \bar{B}^k, C^k\}$

28.072 $\quad \mathbf{K}_{w+f+\beta} = \begin{pmatrix} \cos\beta & \sin\beta & 0 \\ -\sin\beta & \cos\beta & 0 \\ 0 & 0 & 1 \end{pmatrix} \mathbf{K}$

$$\dot{\rho}^k = v l^k = (v\cos\beta, v\sin\beta, 0)\mathbf{K}\{\bar{A}^k, \bar{B}^k, C^k\}$$

28.073

$$\dot{\rho}^k(\bar{A}_k, \bar{B}_k, C_k) = (\dot{\rho}^k\bar{A}_k, \dot{\rho}^k\bar{B}_k, \dot{\rho}^kC_k) = (\dot{x}, \dot{y}, \dot{z})$$

28.074 $\quad = (v\cos\beta, v\sin\beta, 0)\mathbf{K}$

$$\{\dot{x}, \dot{y}, \dot{z}\} = \mathbf{K}^T\{v\cos\beta, v\sin\beta, 0\}$$

$$= \mathbf{K}_{f=0}^T\mathbf{F}^T\{v\cos\beta, v\sin\beta, 0\}$$

28.075 $\quad = \mathbf{K}_{f=0}^T\{v\cos(f+\beta), v\sin(f+\beta), 0\}$

28.076 $\quad \{\dot{x}, \dot{y}, \dot{z}\} = \mathbf{K}_{f=0}^T\{q_1, q_2, 0\}$

28.077 $\quad \cos i = \cos\phi\sin\alpha$

28.078 $\quad \cos(w+f) = \cos\phi\cos(\bar{\omega}-\Omega)$

$\sin(w+f) = \sin(\bar{\omega}-\Omega)\,\mathrm{cosec}\,\alpha = \sin\phi\,\mathrm{cosec}\,i$

28.079

$\cos\alpha = \tan\phi\cot(w+f) = \sin\phi\sin\alpha\cot(\bar{\omega}-\Omega)$

$\quad = \sin i\cos(\bar{\omega}-\Omega) = \sin i\sec\phi\cos(w+f)$

28.080

Variation of the Elements:

28.082 $\quad F_r = -\dfrac{\mu}{r^3}\rho_r + R_r$

28.083 $\quad \dfrac{dv}{dt} = F_r l^r = -\dfrac{\mu\cos\beta}{r^2} + R_r l^r$

28.084 $\quad \dfrac{d(r^2)}{dt} = 2r\dfrac{dr}{dt} = \dfrac{\delta(\rho_r\rho^r)}{\delta t} = 2\rho_r\dot{\rho}^r = 2\rho_r(vl^r)$

28.085 $\quad \dfrac{dr}{dt} = \rho_r\dot{\rho}^r/r = v\cos\beta$

Semimajor Axis:

28.086 $\quad \left(\dfrac{\mu}{2a^2}\right)\dfrac{da}{dt} = vR_r l^r = R_r\dot{\rho}^r$

$$\dfrac{da}{dt} = \dfrac{2a^2}{N}\left\{e\sin f(R_r r^r) + \dfrac{a(1-e^2)}{r}(R_r t^r)\right\}$$

28.087

Angular Momentum:

28.088 $\quad (vr\sin\beta)n^r = Nn^r = \epsilon^{rpq}\rho_p\dot{\rho}_q$

28.089 $\quad \dfrac{dN}{dt}n^r + N\dfrac{\delta n^r}{\delta t} = \epsilon^{rpq}\rho_p R_q$

28.090 $\quad \dfrac{dN}{dt} = \epsilon^{rpq}n_r\rho_p R_q = rR_q t^q$

28.091 $\quad \dfrac{\delta n^r}{\delta t} = -\dfrac{r}{N}(R_q n^q)t^r$

Eccentricity:

$$\mu a e\dfrac{de}{dt} = \tfrac{1}{2}\mu(1-e^2)\dfrac{da}{dt} - N\dfrac{dN}{dt}$$

28.092 $\quad = \{va^2(1-e^2)(l^q R_q) - N_r(t^q R_q)\}$

$$\dfrac{de}{dt} = \dfrac{a^{1/2}(1-e^2)^{1/2}}{\mu^{1/2}}\{\sin f(r^q R_q)$$

28.093 $\quad\quad\quad + (\cos f + \cos E)(t^q R_q)\}$

$$\frac{de}{dt} = \frac{(1-e^2)}{v} \left\{ \frac{2 \cos E(l^q R_q)}{1 - e \cos E} - \frac{\sin E(m^q R_q)}{(1-e^2)^{1/2}} \right\}$$

28.094

Zenith Distance:

28.095 $vr \dfrac{d\beta}{dt} = \mu \sin \beta \left(\dfrac{1}{a} - \dfrac{1}{r} \right) + r(m^q R_q)$

True Anomaly:

$$\frac{df}{dt} = \frac{N}{r^2} + \frac{(N \cos f)(R_q r^q)}{\mu e}$$

$$- \frac{N(2 - \cos^2 f - \cos E \cos f)(R_q t^q)}{\mu e \sin f}$$

$$= \frac{N}{r^2} + \frac{(N \cos f)(R_q r^q)}{\mu e}$$

28.096

$$- \frac{(N \sin f)(R_q t^q)}{\mu e} \left\{ 1 + \frac{r}{a(1-e^2)} \right\}$$

$$= \frac{N}{r^2} - \frac{(2 \sin f)(R_q l^q)}{ev}$$

28.097

$$- \frac{(\cos E + e)(R_q m^q)}{ev}$$

28.098 $\dfrac{N}{r^2} = \dfrac{\mu^{1/2} a^{1/2}(1-e^2)^{1/2}}{a^2(1 - e \cos E)^2} = \dfrac{n(1 + e \cos f)^2}{(1-e^2)^{3/2}}$

Eccentric Anomaly:

$$\frac{dE}{dt} = \frac{na}{r} + \frac{a^{1/2}(\cos f - e)(R_r r^r)}{e\mu^{1/2}}$$

28.099

$$- \frac{(a^{1/2} \sin E)(2 - e^2 + e \cos f)(R_r t^r)}{e\mu^{1/2}(1-e^2)^{1/2}}$$

$$= \frac{na}{r} - \frac{(2 \sin f)(R_r l^r)}{ve(1-e^2)^{1/2}}$$

28.100

$$- \frac{(1-e^2)^{1/2} \cos E(R_r m^r)}{ve}$$

Mean Anomaly:

$$\frac{dM}{dt} = n + \frac{\{(1-e^2) \cos f - 2er/a\}(R_r r^r)}{nae}$$

28.101

$$- \frac{\{(1-e^2)^{1/2} \sin E(2 + e \cos f)\}(R_r t^r)}{nae}$$

$$= n + \frac{\{a(1-e^2) \cos f - 2er\}(R_r r^r)}{e\mu^{1/2} a^{1/2}}$$

28.102

$$- \frac{\{(1-e^2) \sin f\}(R_r t^r)}{e\mu^{1/2} a^{1/2}} \left(a + \frac{r}{1-e^2} \right)$$

$$\frac{dM}{dt} = n - \frac{2 \sin E(1 + e \cos f + e^2)(R_r l^r)}{ev}$$

28.103

$$- \frac{(1-e^2)^{1/2} r \cos f(R_r m^r)}{vae}$$

Inclination:

28.104 $\dfrac{di}{dt} = \dfrac{r}{N}(R_q n^q) \cos(w + f)$

Right Ascension of the Ascending Node:

28.105 $\dfrac{d\Omega}{dt} = \dfrac{r}{N}(R_q n^q) \sin(w + f) \csc i$

Argument of Perigee:

$$\frac{dw}{dt} + \frac{df}{dt} = \frac{v \sin \beta}{r} - \cos i \frac{d\Omega}{dt}$$

28.106

$$= \frac{N}{r^2} - \frac{r}{N}(R_q n^q) \sin(w + f) \cot i$$

$$\frac{dw}{dt} = - \frac{(N \cos f)(R_q r^q)}{\mu e}$$

$$+ \frac{(N \sin f)(R_q t^q)}{\mu e} \left(1 + \frac{r}{a(1-e^2)} \right)$$

28.107

$$- \frac{r \sin(w + f) \cot i(R_q n^q)}{N}$$

Derivations With Respect to the Elements:

Semimajor Axis:

28.108 $\left(\dfrac{da}{a} \times r \right) r^r$

28.109 $\dfrac{\partial F}{\partial a} = \dfrac{r(F_r r^r)}{a} = \dfrac{F_r \rho^r}{a}$

$$\frac{\partial \dot{\rho}^r}{\partial a} = \frac{\partial(v l^r)}{\partial a} = v \frac{\partial l^r}{\partial a} + \frac{\partial v}{\partial a} l^r = - \frac{v l^r}{2a} = - \frac{\dot{\rho}^r}{2a}$$

28.110

$$\frac{\partial \dot{\rho}^r}{\partial a} = \frac{\partial(v l^r)}{\partial a} = - \frac{\mu^{1/2}}{2a^{1/2} r} \{(e \sin E)r^r + (1-e^2)^{1/2} t^r\}$$

28.111

Eccentricity:

$$\frac{\partial F}{\partial e} = - (a \cos f)(F_r r^r) + \left(a + \frac{r}{1-e^2} \right)(F_r t^r) \sin f$$

28.116

$$\frac{\partial \dot{\rho}^r}{\partial e} = \frac{\partial (v l^r)}{\partial e}$$

$$= \frac{\mu a}{v r^2} \left\{ (\cos f) \, l^r + \left(1 + \frac{r e \cos E}{a(1-e^2)} \right) m^r \sin f \right\}$$

28.117

28.118 $\quad \dfrac{\partial \dot{\rho}^r}{\partial e} = \dfrac{N}{r(1-e^2)} \{ -r^r \sin f + t^r \cos E \}$

$$\frac{\partial \dot{q}_1}{\partial e} = -\frac{N \sin f}{r(1-e^2)} \{ \cos f + \cos E \}$$

$$\frac{\partial \dot{q}_2}{\partial e} = \frac{N}{r(1-e^2)} \{ -\sin^2 f + \cos E \cos f \}$$

28.119

Mean Anomaly:

28.120 $\quad \dfrac{\partial F}{\partial M} = \dfrac{v}{n} (F_r l^r) = \dfrac{1}{n} (F_r \dot{\rho}^r)$

$$\frac{\partial F}{\partial M} = \frac{(ae \sin f)(F_r r^r)}{(1-e^2)^{1/2}} + \frac{a(1 + e \cos f)(F_r t^r)}{(1-e^2)^{1/2}}$$

28.121

$$\frac{\partial \dot{\rho}^r}{\partial M} = \frac{\partial (v l^r)}{\partial M} = \frac{1}{n} \frac{d \dot{\rho}^r}{dt} = -\frac{\mu}{nr^3} \rho^r = -\frac{\mu}{nr^2} r^r$$

28.122

Inclination:

28.123 $\quad \dfrac{\partial F}{\partial i} = r \sin (w+f)(F_r n^r)$

$$\frac{\partial \dot{\rho}^r}{\partial i} = \frac{\partial (v l^r)}{\partial i} = v \sin (w+f+\beta) n^r$$

28.124 $\quad\quad = \dfrac{\mu n^r}{N} \{ \cos (w+f) + e \cos w \}$

Right Ascension of the Ascending Node:

$$\frac{\partial F}{\partial \Omega} = \epsilon^{rst} F_r C_s \rho_t$$

$$= (r \cos i)(F_r t^r) - r \sin i \cos (w+f)(F_r n^r)$$

28.125

$$\frac{\partial \dot{\rho}^r}{\partial \Omega} = v \frac{\partial l^r}{\partial \Omega}$$

$$= v \begin{pmatrix} -\cos (w+f+\beta) \sin \Omega - \sin (w+f+\beta) \cos \Omega \cos i \\ \cos (w+f+\beta) \cos \Omega - \sin (w+f+\beta) \sin \Omega \cos i \\ 0 \end{pmatrix}$$

$$= (v \cos i) m^r - v \sin i \cos (w+f+\beta) n^r$$

$$= \frac{N}{a(1-e^2)} \{ -\cos i(1+e \cos f) r^r + (e \cos i \sin f) t^r$$

28.126 $\quad + [\sin i \sin (w+f) + e \sin i \sin w] n^r \}$

Argument of Perigee:

28.127 $\quad\quad \dfrac{\partial F}{\partial w} = r F_r t^r$

$$\frac{\partial \dot{\rho}^r}{\partial w} = v \frac{\partial l^r}{\partial w} = v m^r$$

28.128 $\quad = \dfrac{\mu^{1/2} a^{1/2}}{r} \{ -(1-e^2)^{1/2} r^r + (e \sin E) t^r \}$

Relations Between Partial Derivatives:

$$(ae \sin f) \frac{\partial F}{\partial a} = \frac{r(1-e^2)^{1/2}}{a} \frac{\partial F}{\partial M}$$

$$- (1 + e \cos f) \frac{\partial F}{\partial w}$$

$$\{ e(1-e^2)^{1/2} \sin E \} \frac{\partial F}{\partial e} = (e + \cos E) \frac{\partial F}{\partial w}$$

$$+ (1-e^2)^{1/2} (e - \cos E) \frac{\partial F}{\partial M}$$

$$\sin i \cot (w+f) \frac{\partial F}{\partial i} = -\frac{\partial F}{\partial \Omega} + \cos i \frac{\partial F}{\partial w}$$

28.129

Derivatives of Cartesian Coordinates:

$$\frac{\partial \rho^r}{\partial a} = \frac{\rho^r}{a} = \frac{r r^r}{a}$$

$$\frac{\partial \rho^r}{\partial e} = -(a \cos f) r^r + \left(a + \frac{r}{1-e^2} \right) t^r \sin f$$

$$\frac{\partial \rho^r}{\partial i} = r \sin (w+f) n^r$$

$$\frac{\partial \rho^r}{\partial M} = \frac{(ae \sin f) r^r}{(1-e^2)^{1/2}} + \frac{a(1 + e \cos f) t^r}{(1-e^2)^{1/2}} = \frac{\dot{\rho}^r}{n}$$

$$\frac{\partial \rho^r}{\partial w} = r t^r$$

28.130 $\quad \dfrac{\partial \rho^r}{\partial \Omega} = (r \cos i) t^r - r \sin i \cos (w+f) n^r$

$$\frac{\partial \dot{\rho}^r}{\partial a} = -\frac{\mu^{1/2}}{2a^{1/2} r} \{ (e \sin E) r^r + (1-e^2)^{1/2} t^r \}$$

$$\frac{\partial \dot{\rho}^r}{\partial e} = \frac{N}{r(1-e^2)} \{ -r^r \sin f + t^r \cos E \}$$

$$\frac{\partial \dot{\rho}^r}{\partial i} = \frac{\mu n^r}{N} \{ \cos (w+f) + e \cos w \}$$

$$\frac{\partial \dot{\rho}^r}{\partial M} = -\frac{\mu r^r}{nr^2}$$

$$\frac{\partial \dot{\rho}^r}{\partial w} = v m^r = \frac{\mu^{1/2} a^{1/2}}{r} \{ -(1-e^2)^{1/2} r^r + (e \sin E) t^r \}$$

$$\frac{\partial \dot{\rho}^r}{\partial \Omega} = \frac{N}{a(1-e^2)} \{ -\cos i(1+e \cos f) r^r$$

$$+ (e \cos i \sin f) t^r$$

$$+ [\sin i \sin (w+f)$$

28.131 $\quad\quad + e \sin i \sin w] n^r \}$

$$(2ae \sin f) \frac{\partial \dot{\rho}^r}{\partial a} = (1-e^2)^{1/2}(1-e^2 \cos^2 E) \frac{\partial \dot{\rho}^r}{\partial M}$$

$$- \frac{a(1-e^2)}{2r} \frac{\partial \dot{\rho}^r}{\partial w}$$

$$\{e(1-e^2)^{1/2} \sin E\} \frac{\partial \dot{\rho}^r}{\partial e} = \cos E \frac{\partial \dot{\rho}^r}{\partial w}$$

$$+ (1-e^2)^{1/2}(e - \cos E) \frac{\partial \dot{\rho}^r}{\partial M}$$

$$[\sin i \sin (w+f) + e \sin i \sin w] \frac{\partial \dot{\rho}^r}{\partial i}$$

$$= \{\cos (w+f) + e \cos w\}$$

28.132
$$\times \left(\frac{\partial \dot{\rho}^r}{\partial \Omega} - \cos i \frac{\partial \dot{\rho}^r}{\partial w} \right)$$

The Lagrange Planetary Equations:

$$\frac{da}{dt} = \frac{2}{na} \frac{\partial R}{\partial M}$$

$$\frac{de}{dt} = \frac{(1-e^2)}{na^2 e} \frac{\partial R}{\partial M} - \frac{(1-e^2)^{1/2}}{na^2 e} \frac{\partial R}{\partial w}$$

$$\frac{di}{dt} = \frac{\cot i}{N} \frac{\partial R}{\partial w} - \frac{\operatorname{cosec} i}{N} \frac{\partial R}{\partial \Omega}$$

$$\frac{dM}{dt} = n - \frac{2}{na} \frac{\partial R}{\partial a} - \frac{(1-e^2)}{na^2 e} \frac{\partial R}{\partial e}$$

$$\frac{dw}{dt} = \frac{N}{\mu a e} \frac{\partial R}{\partial e} - \frac{\cot i}{N} \frac{\partial R}{\partial i}$$

28.134
$$\frac{d\Omega}{dt} = \frac{\operatorname{cosec} i}{N} \frac{\partial R}{\partial i}$$

$$\frac{dN}{dt} = \frac{\partial R}{\partial w}$$

$$\frac{\delta n^r}{\delta t} = - \frac{t^r}{N \sin (w+f)} \frac{\partial R}{\partial i}$$

$$\frac{df}{dt} = \frac{N}{r^2} - \frac{N}{\mu a e} \frac{\partial R}{\partial e}$$

$$\frac{dE}{dt} = \frac{na}{r} + \frac{1}{na^2 e} \left\{ - \frac{\partial R}{\partial e} - \frac{ae(1+e \cos f)}{(1-e^2)} \frac{\partial R}{\partial a} \right.$$

28.135
$$\left. + \frac{e^2 \sin f}{(1-e^2)} \frac{\partial R}{\partial w} \right\}$$

Curvature and Torsion of the Orbit:

28.136
$$\left(\frac{dv}{dt} \right) l_r + v^2 l_{rs} l^s = F_r$$

28.137
$$\frac{dv}{dt} = F_r l^r$$

28.138
$$v^2 \chi = F_r \bar{m}^r$$

28.139
$$\bar{m}^r = m^r \cos \gamma + n^r \sin \gamma$$

28.140
$$v^2 \chi = (F_r m^r) \cos \gamma + (F_r n^r) \sin \gamma$$

28.141
$$\bar{n}^r = n^r \cos \gamma - m^r \sin \gamma$$

28.143
$$\tan \gamma = \frac{F_r n^r}{F_r m^r}$$

28.144
$$F_r m^r = v^2 \chi \cos \gamma = (\mu \sin \beta)/r^2 + R_r m^r$$

28.145
$$F_r n^r = v^2 \chi \sin \gamma = R_r n^r$$

$$v^2 \chi \bar{m}_r = F_r - (F_s l^s) l_r$$

$$= (F_s m^s) m_r + (F_s n^s) n_r$$

28.146
$$= \left(\frac{\mu \sin \beta}{r^2} + R_s m^s \right) m_r + (R_s n^s) n_r$$

28.147
$$F_{rs} \bar{n}^r l^s = \tau F_r \bar{m}^r = v^2 \chi \tau$$

28.148
$$\tau = (d\gamma/ds) - n_{rs} m^r l^s$$

$$n_{rs} m^r l^s = -\chi \sin \gamma \cot \beta$$

28.149
$$\tau = (d\gamma/ds) + \chi \sin \gamma \cot \beta$$

The Delaunay Variables:

Canonical Equations:

28.163
$$H^* = -\frac{\mu}{2a} - R = -\frac{\mu^2}{2L^2} - R$$

$$\frac{dL}{dt} = -\frac{\partial H^*}{\partial l} \; ; \quad \frac{dG}{dt} = -\frac{\partial H^*}{\partial g} \; ; \quad \frac{dH}{dt} = -\frac{\partial H^*}{\partial h}$$

$$\frac{dl}{dt} = \frac{\partial H^*}{\partial L} \; ; \quad \frac{dg}{dt} = \frac{\partial H^*}{\partial G} \; ; \quad \frac{dh}{dt} = \frac{\partial H^*}{\partial H}$$

28.164

First Integrals of the Equations of Motion—Further General Considerations:

28.166
$$\tfrac{1}{2}v^2 + V - \tilde{\omega} N \cos i = \text{constant}$$

28.167
$$\int \frac{\partial V}{\partial t} \, dt = \tilde{\omega} N \cos i + \text{constant}$$

$$\frac{d(N \cos i)}{dt} = r R_q \{ t^q \cos i - n^q \sin i \cos (w+f) \}$$

28.168
$$= (r \cos \phi) R_q \lambda^q$$

$$N \cos i = \epsilon^{rst} C_r \rho_s \dot{\rho}_t$$

$$\frac{d(N \cos i)}{dt} = \epsilon^{rst} C_r \rho_s \ddot{\rho}_t = \epsilon^{rst} C_r \rho_s F_t = \epsilon^{rst} C_r \rho_s R_t$$

28.169

28.170
$$\frac{\partial V}{\partial t} = \tilde{\omega} \frac{d(N \cos i)}{dt}$$

28.171
$$\tfrac{1}{2}v^2 + V = \text{constant}$$

28.172 $\qquad N \cos i = \text{constant}$

28.173 $\qquad \frac{1}{2}v^2 + V - \bar{\omega}N \cos i = \text{constant}$

28.174 $\qquad \frac{1}{2}v^2 + V - \bar{\omega}\epsilon^{rst}C_r\rho_s\rho_t = \text{constant}$

Integration of the Gauss Equations:

28.180 $\qquad C_{n0} = -(a_e)^n J_n$

28.181 $\qquad \Delta_1\Omega = -\dfrac{3\pi a_e^2 \cos i J_2}{a^2(1-e^2)^2}$

$$\Delta_1 a = 0$$

$$\Delta_1 e = 0$$

$$\Delta_1 i = 0$$

$$\Delta_1 w = \frac{6\pi a_e^2 J_2}{a^2(1-e^2)^2}\left(1 - \tfrac{5}{4}\sin^2 i\right)$$

$$\int\left(\frac{dM}{dt} - n\right)dt = \frac{3\pi a_e^2 J_2}{a^2(1-e^2)^{3/2}}\left(1 - \tfrac{3}{2}\sin^2 i\right)$$

28.182

Integration of the Lagrange Equations:

$$R_{nm} = \frac{\mu a_e^n}{a^{n+1}}\sum_{p=0}^{n}F_{nmp}(i)\sum_{q=-\infty}^{\infty}G_{npq}(e)$$

28.184 $\qquad\qquad\qquad \times S_{nmpq}(w, M, \Omega, \theta)$

$$S_{nmpq} = \begin{bmatrix}C_{nm}\\-S_{nm}\end{bmatrix}_{\substack{n-m\ \text{even}\\n-m\ \text{odd}}}\cos\left[(n-2p)w\right.$$

$$\left. + (n-2p+q)M + m(\Omega - \theta)\right]$$

$$+ \begin{bmatrix}S_{nm}\\C_{nm}\end{bmatrix}_{\substack{n-m\ \text{even}\\n-m\ \text{odd}}}\sin\left[(n-2p)w\right.$$

28.185 $\qquad\qquad\qquad \left. + (n-2p+q)M + m(\Omega - \theta)\right]$

$$\Delta\Omega_{nm} = \frac{1}{N\sin i}\frac{\mu a_e^n}{a^{n+1}}$$

$$\times \sum_{pq}\frac{(\partial F_{nmp}/\partial i)G_{npq}\bar{S}_{nmpq}}{(n-2p)\dot{w} + (n-2p+q)\dot{M} + m(\dot{\Omega} - \dot{\theta})}$$

28.187

Integration of the Canonical Equations:

Contact Transformations:

28.189 $\qquad \dot{Q}^r = \dfrac{\partial K^*}{\partial P_r}\ ; \qquad \dot{P}_r = -\dfrac{\partial K^*}{\partial Q^r}$

$$p_r = \frac{\partial S}{\partial q^r}\ ; \qquad Q^r = \frac{\partial S}{\partial P_r}\ ; \qquad K^* = H^* + \frac{\partial S}{\partial t}$$

28.190

28.191 $\qquad S = f(q^r, P_r, t)$

The Hamilton-Jacobi Equation:

28.192 $\qquad H^*\left(q^r, \dfrac{\partial S}{\partial q^r}, t\right) + \dfrac{\partial S}{\partial t} = 0$

$$p_r = \frac{\partial S(q^r, \alpha_r, t)}{\partial q^r}$$

28.193 $\qquad Q^r = \beta^r = \dfrac{\partial S(q^r, \alpha_r, t)}{\partial \alpha_r}$

28.194 $\qquad V + \frac{1}{2}\nabla S + \dfrac{\partial S}{\partial t} = 0$

28.195 $\qquad \nabla S = g^{rs}S_r S_s$

28.196 $\qquad S = W^* - \alpha_1 t$

28.197 $\qquad H^* = V + \frac{1}{2}\nabla W^* = \alpha_1$

28.198 $\qquad P_r = \alpha_r$

28.199 $\qquad Q^r = \delta_1^r t + \beta^r$

$$P_r = \alpha_r$$

$$Q^r = \delta_1^r t + \beta^r = \frac{\partial W^*}{\partial \alpha_r}$$

28.200 $\qquad K^* = H^* = \alpha_1$

The Vinti Potential:

28.202 $\qquad (ae)^2 = -C_{20} = +a_e^2 J_2$

$$-\frac{\mu}{r}\left\{1 - \left(\frac{a_e}{r}\right)^2 J_2 P_2(\sin\phi) + \left(\frac{a_e}{r}\right)^4 J_2^2 P_4(\sin\phi)\right.$$

$$\left. - \left(\frac{a_e}{r}\right)^6 J_2^3 P_4(\sin\phi) + \ldots\right\}$$

28.203

The Variational Method:

28.212 $\qquad \frac{1}{2}v^2 + V = \alpha_1$

28.213 $\qquad d\bar{s} = v\,ds$

28.214 $\qquad \bar{l}_r = vl_r$

28.215 $\qquad M_r^* = vl_r = \bar{l}_r$

28.217 $\qquad \nabla M^* = g^{rs}M_r^* M_s^* = v^2 g^{rs}l_r l_s = v^2$

Chapter 29

Surface Integrals of Spherical Harmonics:

29.01 $\qquad \int Y\,d\Omega = \int_{\omega=0}^{2\pi}\int_{\phi=-\pi/2}^{\pi/2}Y\cos\phi\,d\phi d\omega$

$$\{u_n^m\} = P_n^m(\sin\phi)(C_{nm}\cos m\omega + S_{nm}\sin m\omega)$$

29.02

$$\{\bar{u}_n^m\} = P_n^m(\sin\phi)(\bar{C}_{nm}\cos m\omega + \bar{S}_{nm}\sin m\omega)$$

29.03

29.04 $\qquad \{u_n\} = C_{n0}P_n(\sin\phi)$

$$\int \{u_n^m\}\{\bar{u}_q^p\}d\Omega = 0 \text{ if } (m, p) \text{ are different}$$

29.05 $\qquad\qquad\qquad$ or if (n, q) are different

$$\int \{u_n^m\}\{\bar{u}_n^m\}d\Omega = \frac{2\pi}{(2n+1)}\frac{(n+m)!}{(n-m)!}(C_{nm}\bar{C}_{nm} + S_{nm}\bar{S}_{nm})$$

29.06 $\qquad\qquad\qquad\qquad\qquad (m \neq 0)$

$$\int \{u_n\}\{\bar{u}_n\}d\Omega = \frac{4\pi}{(2n+1)}C_{n0}\bar{C}_{n0} \qquad (m = 0)$$

29.07

$$\int [P_n^m(\sin\phi)\cos m\omega]^2 d\Omega = \int [P_n^m(\sin\phi)\sin m\omega]^2 d\Omega$$
$$= \frac{2\pi}{(2n+1)}\frac{(n+m)!}{(n-m)!}$$

29.08 $\qquad\qquad\qquad\qquad\qquad (m \neq 0)$

29.09 $\qquad \int [P_n(\sin\phi)]^2 d\Omega = \frac{4\pi}{(2n+1)}$

$$\int \{u_n^m\}P_n(\cos\psi)d\Omega = \frac{4\pi}{2n+1}P_n^m(\sin\bar{\phi})(C_{nm}\cos m\bar{\omega}$$
$$+ S_{nm}\sin m\bar{\omega})$$

29.10 $\qquad\qquad = \frac{4\pi}{2n+1}\{u_n^m\}_{\bar{P}}$

Series Expansions:

29.11 $\qquad \dfrac{1}{(1 - 2k\cos\psi + k^2)^{1/2}} = \displaystyle\sum_{n=0}^{\infty} k^n P_n(\cos\psi)$

$$\frac{(1 - k^2)}{(1 - 2k\cos\psi + k^2)^{3/2}} = \sum_{n=0}^{\infty}(2n+1)k^n P_n(\cos\psi)$$

29.12

29.13 $\qquad \Phi = (1 - 2k\cos\psi + k^2)$

$$S(k, \psi) = \sum_{n=2}^{\infty}\frac{(2n+1)}{(n-1)}k^{n+1}P_n(\cos\psi)$$
$$= k - 5k^2\cos\psi$$
$$- k(1 - 6k\cos\psi + 3k^2)/\Phi^{1/2}$$

29.14 $\qquad -3k^2\cos\psi\ln\tfrac{1}{2}(1 - k\cos\psi + \Phi^{1/2})$

$$S(\psi) = \sum_{n=2}^{\infty}\frac{(2n+1)}{(n-1)}P_n(\cos\psi)$$
$$= 1 - 5\cos\psi - (2 - 3\cos\psi)\operatorname{cosec}\tfrac{1}{2}\psi$$

29.15 $\qquad -3\cos\psi\ln(\sin\tfrac{1}{2}\psi + \sin^2\tfrac{1}{2}\psi)$

$$\bar{S}(k, \psi) = \sum_{n=0}^{\infty}\frac{(2n+1)}{(n+1)}k^{n+1}P_n(\cos\psi)$$

29.16 $\qquad = \dfrac{2k}{\Phi^{1/2}} - \ln\left(\dfrac{\Phi^{1/2} + k - \cos\psi}{1 - \cos\psi}\right)$

$$\bar{S}(\psi) = \sum_{n=0}^{\infty}\frac{(2n+1)}{(n+1)}P_n(\cos\psi)$$

29.17 $\qquad = \operatorname{cosec}\tfrac{1}{2}\psi - \ln(1 + \operatorname{cosec}\tfrac{1}{2}\psi)$

Introduction of the Standard Field:

Potential Anomaly:

29.18 $\qquad\qquad T = W - U$

Curvature and Deflection:

$$\Delta^r = \nu^r - \bar{\bar{\nu}}^r \simeq (\cos\phi\ \delta\omega)\bar{\lambda}^r + (\delta\phi)\bar{\bar{\mu}}^r = \eta\bar{\lambda}^r + \xi\bar{\bar{\mu}}^r$$

29.19

29.20 $\qquad \bar{\nu}^r = \bar{\bar{\nu}}^r\cos\kappa - \bar{\bar{\mu}}^r\sin\kappa$

Gradient of the Potential Anomaly:

29.21 $\qquad T_r = W_r - U_r = g\nu_r - \gamma\bar{\nu}_r$

$$T_r = (g\eta)\bar{\lambda}_r + (g\xi + \gamma\sin\kappa)\bar{\bar{\mu}}_r + (g - \gamma\cos\kappa)\bar{\bar{\nu}}_r$$

29.22

29.23 $\qquad T_r \simeq (g\eta)\bar{\lambda}_r + g(\xi + \kappa)\bar{\bar{\mu}}_r + (g - \gamma)\bar{\bar{\nu}}_r$

Gravity Disturbance:

29.24 $\qquad\qquad g_D = g - \gamma$

29.25 $\qquad\qquad g_D = T_r\bar{\bar{\nu}}^r = \partial T/\partial h$

29.26 $\qquad g_D \simeq -\displaystyle\sum_{n, m}(n+1)\{T_n^m\}/r^{n+2}$

Gravity Anomaly:

29.27 $\qquad\qquad g_A = g_P - \gamma_B$

29.28 $\qquad\qquad T_P \simeq -\gamma_B\zeta$

29.29 $\qquad\qquad T \simeq -\gamma\zeta$

29.30 $\qquad g_A \simeq \dfrac{\partial T}{\partial h} - \left(\dfrac{\partial\ln\gamma}{\partial h}\right)T$

29.31 $\qquad g_A \simeq \dfrac{\partial T}{\partial r} + \dfrac{2T}{r}$

$$\{g_{A\,n}^m\} = -\frac{(n+1)\{T_n^m\}}{r^{n+2}} + \frac{2\{T_n^m\}}{r^{n+2}} = -\frac{(n-1)\{T_n^m\}}{r^{n+2}}$$

29.32

29.33 $\qquad g_A = -\displaystyle\sum_{n, m}\dfrac{(n-1)\{T_n^m\}}{r^{n+2}}$

The Spherical Standard Field:

$$-U = \sum_{n=0}^{\infty} \frac{GC_{n0}P_n(\sin \phi)}{r^{n+1}} + \tfrac{1}{3} \tilde{\omega}^2 r^2 - \tfrac{1}{3} \tilde{\omega}^2 r^2 P_2(\sin \phi)$$

29.34

$$-U_0 = GC_{00}/R + \tfrac{1}{3}\tilde{\omega}^2 R^2$$

29.35
$$0 = GC_{20}/R^3 - \tfrac{1}{3}\tilde{\omega}^2 R^2$$

Poisson's Integral:

29.36
$$\frac{(r^2 - R^2)}{l^3} = \sum_{n=0}^{\infty} (2n+1) \frac{R^n}{r^{n+1}} P_n(\cos \psi)$$

29.37
$$H_Q = \sum_{n=0}^{\infty} \sum_{m=0}^{n} \{H_n^m\}/R^{n+1}$$

29.38
$$\int \frac{(r^2 - R^2)}{l^3} H_Q d\Omega = \sum_{n=0}^{\infty} \sum_{m=0}^{n} \frac{4\pi R^n}{r^{n+1}} \frac{\{H_n^m\}_S}{R^{n+1}}$$

29.39
$$H_P = \frac{R}{4\pi} \int \frac{(r^2 - R^2)}{l^3} H_Q d\Omega$$

29.40
$$\frac{4\pi}{r(r^2 - R^2)} = \frac{4\pi}{r(PT)^2} = \int \frac{d\Omega}{l^3}$$

29.36A
$$\frac{R^2 - r^2}{l^3} = \sum_{n=0}^{\infty} (2n+1) \frac{r^n}{R^{n+1}} P_n(\cos \psi)$$

29.37A
$$H_Q = \sum_{n=0}^{\infty} \sum_{m=0}^{n} R^n\{H_n^m\}$$

29.39A
$$H_P = \frac{R}{4\pi} \int \frac{(R^2 - r^2)}{l^3} H_Q d\Omega$$

29.41
$$\rho_P^r = \frac{R}{4\pi} \int \frac{(R^2 - r^2)}{l^3} \rho_Q^r d\Omega$$

29.42
$$r = \frac{R^2}{4\pi} \int \frac{(R^2 - r^2)}{l^3} \cos \psi \, d\Omega$$

29.43
$$(V_r)_P = \frac{R(r^2 - R^2)}{4\pi} \int (V_r)_Q \frac{d\Omega}{l^3}$$

29.44
$$g_P = \frac{R(r^2 - R^2)}{4\pi} \int g_Q(\nu_r)_Q(\nu^r)_P \frac{d\Omega}{l^3}$$

29.45
$$V = \sum_{n=0}^{\infty} \sum_{m=0}^{n} \{V_n^m\}/r^{n+1}$$

29.46
$$r\bar{g} = -\sum_{n=0}^{\infty} \sum_{m=0}^{n} (n+1)\{V_n^m\}/r^{n+1}$$

29.47
$$\bar{g}_P = \frac{R^2(r^2 - R^2)}{4\pi r} \int \bar{g}_Q \frac{d\Omega}{l^3}$$

29.48
$$(g_A)_P = \frac{R^2(r^2 - R^2)}{4\pi r} \int (g_A)_Q \frac{d\Omega}{l^3}$$

Stokes' Integral:

29.49
$$T_S = \sum_{n=2}^{\infty} \sum_{m=0}^{n} \frac{\{T_n^m\}_S}{R^{n+1}}$$

29.50
$$T_S = -\frac{R}{4\pi} \int S(\psi) (g_A)_Q d\Omega$$

29.51
$$T_P = -\frac{R}{4\pi} \int S(R/r, \psi) (g_A)_Q d\Omega$$

29.52
$$N = \frac{R}{4\pi G} \int S(R/r, \psi) (g_A)_Q d\Omega$$

29.53
$$N = \frac{R}{4\pi G} \int S(\psi) (g_A)_Q d\Omega$$

Deflection of the Vertical:

$$g\eta = -\frac{R}{4\pi r} \int \frac{\partial S}{\partial \psi} \sin \alpha (g_A)_Q d\Omega$$

29.57
$$g(\xi + \kappa) = -\frac{R}{4\pi r} \int \frac{\partial S}{\partial \psi} \cos \alpha (g_A)_Q d\Omega$$

Gravity and Deflection From Poisson's Integral:

$$g\xi = -\frac{3R(r^2 - R^2)}{4\pi} \int \frac{\sin \beta \cos \alpha}{l^4} T_Q d\Omega$$

$$g\eta = -\frac{3R(r^2 - R^2)}{4\pi} \int \frac{\sin \beta \sin \alpha}{l^4} T_Q d\Omega$$

$$(g_D)_P = \frac{R}{4\pi} \int \left\{ \frac{2r}{l^3} - \frac{3(r^2 - R^2) \cos \beta}{l^4} \right\} T_Q d\Omega$$

29.58

$$\left(\frac{\partial T}{\partial r} \right)_P + \frac{R}{r^2} T_P = \frac{R}{4\pi} \int \left\{ \frac{2r}{l^3} - \frac{3(r^2 - R^2) \cos \beta}{l^4} \right\}$$

29.59
$$\times (T_Q - T_P) d\Omega$$

29.60
$$\left(\frac{\partial T}{\partial r} \right)_P + \frac{T_P}{R} = \frac{R^2}{2\pi} \int \frac{(T_Q - T_P)}{l^3} d\Omega$$

Extension to a Spheroidal Base Surface:

$$-T/G = \sum_{n=0}^{\infty} \sum_{m=0}^{n} Q_n^m(i \cot \alpha) P_n^m(\sin u)$$

29.61
$$\times \{A_{nm} \cos m\omega + B_{nm} \sin m\omega\}$$

$$g_D = \frac{\partial T}{\partial s} = -\frac{\tan \alpha}{\nu} \frac{\partial T}{\partial \alpha}$$

$$= -\frac{G \tan \alpha}{\nu} \sum_{n=0}^{\infty} \sum_{m=0}^{n} (i \operatorname{cosec}^2 \alpha) Q_n^{m\prime}(i \cot \alpha)$$

29.62
$$\times P_n^m(\sin u)\{A_{nm} \cos m\omega + B_{nm} \sin m\omega\}$$

$$g_D \nu = - \sum_{n=0}^{\infty} \sum_{m=0}^{n} (n+1)\{T_n^m\}$$

$$- \sum_{n=0}^{\infty} \sum_{m=0}^{n} \frac{i \tan \alpha (n-m+1) Q_{n+1}^m (i \cot \alpha)}{Q_n^m (i \cot \alpha)} \{T_n^m\}$$

29.63

$$\cos \psi = \sin u \, \sin \bar{u} + \cos u \, \cos \bar{u} \, \cos (\bar{\omega} - \omega)$$

29.64

$$\int (g_D \nu) \bar{S}(\psi) d\Omega = -4\pi T_P$$

$$- \int \sum_{n=0}^{\infty} \sum_{m=0}^{n} \frac{i \tan \alpha (n-m+1) Q_{n+1}^m (i \cot \alpha)}{Q_n^m (i \cot \alpha)}$$

29.65 $$\times \bar{S}(\psi)\{T_n^m\} d\Omega$$

$$g_A \nu = - \sum_{n=0}^{\infty} \sum_{m=0}^{n} (n-1)\{T_n^m\}$$

$$+ \sum_{n=0}^{\infty} \sum_{m=0}^{n} \sin^2 \alpha \, \cos^2 u \{T_n^m\}$$

$$+ \sum_{n=0}^{\infty} \sum_{m=0}^{n} (2\tilde{\omega}^2 \nu/\gamma) \{T_n^m\}$$

$$- \sum_{n=0}^{\infty} \sum_{m=0}^{n} \frac{i \tan \alpha (n-m+1) Q_{n+1}^m (i \cot \alpha)}{Q_n^m (i \cot \alpha)} \{T_n^m\}$$

29.67

Bjerhammar's Method:

29.68 $$(g_A)_P = \frac{R^2 (r^2 - R^2)}{4\pi r} \int \frac{(g_A)_Q}{l^3} d\Omega$$

29.69 $$(g_A)_Q = \sum_{n,m} \{u_n^m\}$$

$$(g_A)_P = \int \frac{R^{n+2}}{r^{n+2}} \frac{(2n+1)}{4\pi} \sum_{n,m} \{u_n^m\} P_n (\cos \psi) d\Omega$$

29.70 $$= \sum_{n,m} \frac{R^{n+2}}{r^{n+2}} \{u_n^m\}_P$$

$$(g_A)_Q = \sum_n c_n h^n$$

29.71 $$(g_A)_P = \sum_n c_n \int \frac{h^n}{l^3} \frac{R^2 (r^2 - R^2)}{4\pi r} d\Omega$$

The Equivalent Spherical Layer:

$$\sigma = \sum_{n=0}^{\infty} \sum_{m=0}^{n} P_n^m (\sin \phi) \{c_{nm} \cos m\omega + s_{nm} \sin m\omega\}$$

29.72

29.73 $$\begin{pmatrix} C_{nm} \\ S_{nm} \end{pmatrix} = \frac{4\pi R^{n+2}}{(2n+1)} \begin{pmatrix} c_{nm} \\ s_{nm} \end{pmatrix}$$

29.74 $$\{V_n^m\} = -\frac{4\pi R^{n+2}}{(2n+1)} \{\sigma_n^m\}$$

29.75 $$\int \sigma dS = 4\pi R^2 c_{00} = M = C_{00}$$

29.76 $$V_P = -\int \frac{\sigma R^2}{l} d\Omega$$

29.77 $$(V_r)_P = +\int \frac{\sigma R^2}{l^2} l_r d\Omega$$

$$(2\pi\sigma - g_A) = \sum_{n=0}^{\infty} \sum_{m=0}^{n} \left[-\frac{(2n+1)}{2R^{n+2}} \{T_n^m\} + \frac{(n-1)}{R^{n+2}} \{T_n^m\} \right]$$

29.78 $$= -\frac{3T}{2R}$$

29.79 $$(2\pi\sigma - g_D) = \frac{T}{2R}$$

Chapter 30

The *S*-Surface in (ω, ϕ, h) Coordinates:

30.01 $$h_Q = f(\omega, \phi)$$

30.02 $$x_\alpha^3 = f_\alpha ; \qquad x_\alpha^r = \delta_\alpha^r \qquad (r = 1, 2)$$

The Metric Tensor:

30.03 $$a_{\alpha\beta} = \bar{a}_{\alpha\beta} + f_\alpha f_\beta$$

30.04 $$a = \bar{a}(1 + \overline{\nabla f}) = \bar{a}(1 + \nabla f)$$

The Unit Normal:

30.05 $$\nu_r = (\bar{a}/a)^{1/2}\{-f_1, -f_2, 1\}$$

$$\nu^r = \{\bar{a}^{11}\nu_1, \bar{a}^{22}\nu_2, \nu_3\}$$

30.06 $$= (\bar{a}/a)^{1/2}\{-\bar{a}^{11}f_1, -\bar{a}^{22}f_2, 1\}$$

30.07 $$a/\bar{a} = 1 + \nabla f = 1 + \overline{\nabla f} = \sec^2 \beta$$

30.08 $$\nabla f = \overline{\nabla f} = \tan^2 \beta$$

30.09 $$\nabla_S f = \sin^2 \beta = \overline{\nabla f} \cos^2 \beta = \nabla f \cos^2 \beta$$

$$\nu_r = \bar{\lambda}_r \sin \alpha \sin \beta + \bar{\mu}_r \cos \alpha \sin \beta + \bar{\nu}_r \cos \beta$$

30.10

$$\nu_r = \{(\nu + h) \cos \phi \sin \alpha \sin \beta,$$

30.11 $$(\rho + h) \cos \alpha \sin \beta, \cos \beta\}$$

$$f_1 = -(\nu + h) \cos \phi \sin \alpha \tan \beta$$

30.12 $$f_2 = -(\rho + h) \cos \alpha \tan \beta$$

The Associated Tensor:

$$a^{\alpha\beta} = \epsilon^{\alpha\gamma} \epsilon^{\beta\delta} a_{\gamma\delta}$$

$$= (\bar{a}/a)\bar{\epsilon}^{\alpha\gamma} \bar{\epsilon}^{\beta\delta}(\bar{a}_{\gamma\delta} + f_\gamma f_\delta)$$

30.13 $$= \cos^2 \beta \{\bar{a}^{\alpha\beta} + \bar{\epsilon}^{\alpha\gamma} \bar{\epsilon}^{\beta\delta} f_\gamma f_\delta\}$$

30.14 $\qquad \bar{a}^{\gamma\delta} = a^{\gamma\delta} + \nu^{\gamma}\nu^{\delta}$

Normal Gradients:

$$\frac{\partial F}{\partial s} = F_r \nu^r = \cos\beta(-\bar{a}^{11}f_1 F_1 - \bar{a}^{22}f_2 F_2 + F_3)$$

30.15 $\qquad = \cos\beta\left\{\frac{\partial F}{\partial h} - \overline{\nabla}(F, f)\right\}$

30.16 $\quad \nabla(F, f) = \nabla_S(F, f) + (\partial F/\partial s)(\partial f/\partial s)$

30.17 $\quad \partial f/\partial s = -\overline{\nabla}f \cos\beta = -\sin\beta \tan\beta$

30.18 $\quad \dfrac{\partial F}{\partial s} = \sec\beta\left\{\dfrac{\partial F}{\partial h} - \nabla_S(F, f)\right\}$

The Invariant $\overline{\nabla}(T, f)$:

30.19 $\qquad \overline{\nabla}(T, f) = \nabla(T, f) = g^{pq}(W_p - U_p)f_q$

$\overline{\nabla}(T, f) = \nabla(T, f) = -g\eta \sin\alpha \tan\beta$

30.21 $\qquad\qquad - (g\xi - \gamma_2)\cos\alpha \tan\beta$

The Invariant $\nabla_S T, f)$:

$$\int \frac{\nabla_S(T, f)}{l \cos\beta} dS = -\int \frac{T}{l \cos\beta} \Delta f dS$$

30.25 $\qquad\qquad - \int T\nabla_S\left(\dfrac{1}{l \cos\beta}, f\right) dS$

30.26 $\qquad \bar{\nu}_r x_\alpha^r = x_\alpha^3 = f_\alpha$

30.27 $\qquad -\bar{b}_{\alpha\beta} + b_{\alpha\beta}\cos\beta = f_{\alpha\beta}$

30.28 $\quad \Delta f = 2H\cos\beta - 2\bar{H} + \bar{b}_{\alpha\beta}\nu^\alpha\nu^\beta$

$$\Delta f = 2H\cos\beta + \frac{(1 - \sin^2\alpha \sin^2\beta)}{(\nu + h)}$$

30.29 $\qquad\qquad + \dfrac{(1 - \cos^2\alpha \sin^2\beta)}{(\rho + h)}$

Deformation of the S-Surface:

30.30 $\qquad\qquad (f) = kf$

30.31 $\qquad\qquad (f_\alpha) = kf_\alpha$

$(\nu + kh)\sin(\alpha)\tan(\beta) = -(f_1)\sec\phi$

$\qquad\qquad = k(\nu + h)\sin\alpha \tan\beta$

$(\rho + kh)\cos(\alpha)\tan(\beta) = -(f_2)$

30.32 $\qquad\qquad = k(\rho + h)\cos\alpha \tan\beta$

$\qquad\qquad (\alpha) = \alpha$

30.33 $\qquad \tan(\beta) = \dfrac{k(R + h)}{R + kh}\tan\beta$

30.34 $\qquad \tan(\beta) \simeq k \tan\beta$

$(l)^2 = (\bar{\nu} + k\bar{h})^2 - 2(\bar{\nu} + k\bar{h})(\nu + kh)\cos\sigma + (\nu + kh)^2$

$\qquad - 2e^2 k(\bar{\nu}\sin\bar{\phi} - \nu\sin\phi)(\bar{h}\sin\bar{\phi} - h\sin\phi)$

$\qquad + (e^4 - 2e^2)(\bar{\nu}\sin\bar{\phi} - \nu\sin\phi)^2$

30.35

$(l)\sin(\bar{\alpha})\sin(\bar{\beta}) = (\nu + kh)\sin\sigma \sin\bar{\alpha}^*$

$(l)\cos(\bar{\alpha})\sin(\bar{\beta}) = (\nu + kh)\sin\sigma \cos\bar{\alpha}^*$

$\qquad\qquad - e^2\cos\bar{\phi}(\bar{\nu}\sin\bar{\phi} - \nu\sin\phi)$

$(l)\cos(\bar{\beta}) = -(\nu + kh)\cos\sigma + (\bar{\nu} + k\bar{h})$

30.36 $\qquad\qquad - e^2\sin\bar{\phi}(\bar{\nu}\sin\bar{\phi} - \nu\sin\phi)$

$(l)^2 = 4\sin^2\tfrac{1}{2}\psi(R + kh)(R + k\bar{h}) + k^2(h - \bar{h})^2$

$\qquad = l_0^2\left(1 + \dfrac{k(h + \bar{h})}{R} + \dfrac{k^2 h\bar{h}}{R^2}\right) + k^2(h - \bar{h})^2$

30.37

$(l)\sin(\bar{\alpha})\sin(\bar{\beta}) = (R + kh)\sin\psi \sin\bar{\alpha}^*$

$\qquad\qquad = (R + kh)\cos\phi \sin(\bar{\omega} - \omega)$

$(l)\cos(\bar{\alpha})\sin(\bar{\beta}) = (R + kh)\sin\psi \cos\bar{\alpha}^*$

$\qquad\qquad = (R + kh)(-\sin\phi \cos\bar{\phi}$

$\qquad\qquad\qquad + \cos\phi \sin\bar{\phi}$

$\qquad\qquad\qquad \times \cos(\bar{\omega} - \omega))$

$(l)\cos(\bar{\beta}) = (R + k\bar{h}) - (R + kh)\cos\psi$

30.38 $\qquad = 2\sin^2\tfrac{1}{2}\psi(R + kh) + k(\bar{h} - h)$

Application of Green's Theorem:

$$\int_S\left\{V\frac{\partial}{\partial s}\left(\frac{1}{l}\right) - \frac{1}{l}\frac{\partial V}{\partial s}\right\} dS = \int_r\left\{V\Delta\left(\frac{1}{l}\right) - \frac{1}{l}\Delta V\right\} dv$$

30.39

$$\int_{S-\Sigma}\left\{V_1\frac{\partial}{\partial s}\left(\frac{1}{l}\right) - \frac{1}{l}\frac{\partial V_1}{\partial s}\right\} dS + \int_\Sigma\left\{V_1\frac{\partial}{\partial s}\left(\frac{1}{l}\right) - \frac{1}{l}\frac{\partial V_1}{\partial s}\right\} dS$$

30.40 $\qquad = \int\left\{V_1\Delta\left(\dfrac{1}{l}\right) - \dfrac{1}{l}\Delta V_1\right\} dv$

30.41 $\quad -2\pi V_{1P} = \int\left\{V_1\dfrac{\partial}{\partial s}\left(\dfrac{1}{l}\right) - \dfrac{1}{l}\dfrac{\partial V_1}{\partial s}\right\} dS$

$$\int_{S-\Sigma}\left\{V_2\frac{\partial}{\partial s}\left(\frac{1}{l}\right) - \frac{1}{l}\frac{\partial V_2}{\partial s}\right\} dS$$

$$+ \int_{\bar{S}}\left\{V_2\frac{\partial}{\partial s}\left(\frac{1}{l}\right) - \frac{1}{l}\frac{\partial V_2}{\partial s}\right\} dS$$

$$+ \int_\Sigma\left\{V_2\frac{\partial}{\partial s}\left(\frac{1}{l}\right) - \frac{1}{l}\frac{\partial V_2}{\partial s}\right\} dS$$

30.42 $\qquad = \int\left\{V_2\Delta\left(\dfrac{1}{l}\right) - \dfrac{1}{l}\Delta V_2\right\} dv$

30.43 $\qquad -2\pi V_{2P} = \int_S \left\{ V_2 \frac{\partial}{\partial s}\left(\frac{1}{l}\right) - \frac{1}{l}\frac{\partial V_2}{\partial s} \right\} dS$

30.44 $\qquad 2\pi V_{2P} = \int \left\{ V_2 \frac{\partial}{\partial s}\left(\frac{1}{l}\right) - \frac{1}{l}\frac{\partial V_2}{\partial s} \right\} dS$

30.45 $\qquad \Omega = \frac{1}{2}\tilde{\omega}^2(x^2 + y^2)$

30.46 $\qquad W = V - \Omega = V_1 + V_2 - \Omega$

$-2\pi\Omega_P = \int \left\{ \Omega \frac{\partial}{\partial s}\left(\frac{1}{l}\right) - \frac{1}{l}\frac{\partial \Omega}{\partial s} \right\} dS + \int \frac{2\tilde{\omega}^2}{l} dv$

30.47

$\int \left\{ W \frac{\partial}{\partial s}\left(\frac{1}{l}\right) - \frac{1}{l}\frac{\partial W}{\partial s} \right\} dS - \int \frac{2\tilde{\omega}^2}{l} dv$

$\qquad = 2\pi(V_{2P} - V_{1P}) + 2\pi\Omega_P$

$\qquad = 2\pi(W_P + \Omega_P - 2V_{1P}) + 2\pi\Omega_P$

30.48 $\qquad = 2\pi(W_P - 2V_{1P}) + 2\pi\tilde{\omega}^2(x_P^2 + y_P^2)$

30.49 $\qquad 2\pi(T_P - 2V_{1P}) = \int \left\{ T \frac{\partial}{\partial s}\left(\frac{1}{l}\right) - \frac{1}{l}\frac{\partial T}{\partial s} \right\} dS$

30.50 $\qquad 2\pi T_P = \int \left\{ T \frac{\partial}{\partial s}\left(\frac{1}{l}\right) - \frac{1}{l}\frac{\partial T}{\partial s} \right\} dS$

30.51 $\qquad 4\pi V_P = \int \left\{ V \frac{\partial}{\partial s}\left(\frac{1}{l}\right) - \frac{1}{l}\frac{\partial V}{\partial s} \right\} dS$

Potential and Attraction of a Single Layer:

At External Points:

30.52 $\qquad V_P = -\int \frac{\sigma dS}{l} = -\int \frac{\sigma}{Kl} d\Omega$

30.53 $\qquad (V_r)_P = +\int \frac{\sigma dS}{l^2} l_r = +\int \frac{\sigma}{Kl^2} l_r d\Omega$

30.53A $\qquad (V_r)_P = -\int \frac{\sigma dS}{l^2} l_r = -\int \frac{\sigma}{Kl^2} l_r d\Omega$

At Points on the Surface:

$(V_r)_P = +2\pi\sigma(\nu_r)_P + \int \frac{\sigma dS}{l^2} l_r$

30.54 $\qquad = +2\pi\sigma(\nu_r)_P + \int \frac{\sigma}{Kl^2} l_r d\Omega$

$(V_r)_P = +2\pi\sigma(\nu_r)_P - \int \frac{\sigma dS}{l^2} l_r$

30.54A $\qquad = +2\pi\sigma(\nu_r)_P - \int \frac{\sigma}{Kl^2} l_r d\Omega$

Potential and Attraction of a Double Layer:

At External Points:

30.55 $\qquad V_P = -\int \mu \frac{\partial}{\partial s}\left(\frac{1}{l}\right) dS$

30.56 $\qquad \frac{\partial}{\partial s}\left(\frac{1}{l}\right) = \left(\frac{1}{l}\right)_r \nu^r = -\frac{1}{l^2}(l_r\nu^r)$

30.57 $\qquad (V_r)_P = -\int \mu \frac{\partial}{\partial s}\left(\frac{1}{l^2}\right) l_r dS = \int \frac{2\mu}{l^3}(l_t\nu^t)l_r dS$

At Points on the Surface:

30.58 $\qquad V_P = -2\pi\mu_P - \int \mu \frac{\partial}{\partial s}\left(\frac{1}{l}\right) dS$

30.59 $\qquad \int \frac{\partial}{\partial s}\left(\frac{1}{l}\right) dS = -2\pi$

30.60 $\qquad V_P = -\int (\mu - \mu_P) \frac{\partial}{\partial s}\left(\frac{1}{l}\right) dS$

$\frac{\partial V_P}{\partial m} = \int \frac{\partial \mu_P}{\partial m} \frac{\partial}{\partial s}\left(\frac{1}{l}\right) dS - \int (\mu - \mu_P) \frac{\partial}{\partial m}\frac{\partial}{\partial s}\left(\frac{1}{l}\right) dS$

$\qquad = -2\pi \frac{\partial \mu_P}{\partial m} - \int (\mu - \mu_P) \frac{\partial}{\partial m}\frac{\partial}{\partial s}\left(\frac{1}{l}\right) dS$

30.61

30.62 $\qquad V_P = \int (\mu - \mu_P) \frac{(l_r\nu^r)}{l^2} dS$

$-\int (\mu - \mu_P) \frac{\partial}{\partial m}\frac{\partial}{\partial s}\left(\frac{1}{l}\right) dS$

$\qquad = \int (\mu - \mu_P) \frac{\partial}{\partial m}\left(\frac{ll_r}{l^3}\right) \nu^r dS$

30.63 $\qquad = \int \frac{(\mu - \mu_P)}{l^3} \{3(l_t\nu^t)(l_r m^r) - m_r\nu^r\} dS$

$(V_r)_P = -2\pi(\mu_r)_P + \int \frac{\mu - \mu_P}{l^3} \{3(l_t\nu^t)l_r - \nu_r\} dS$

30.64

The Equivalent Surface Layers:

$\mu_Q = -V_Q/(4\pi)$

$\sigma_Q = (\partial V/\partial s)_Q/(4\pi)$

$V_P = \frac{1}{4\pi} \int \left\{ V_Q \frac{\partial}{\partial s}\left(\frac{1}{l}\right) - \frac{1}{l}\left(\frac{\partial V}{\partial s}\right)_Q \right\} dS$

30.65

The Basic Integral Equations in Geodetic Coordinates:

$\nu^r = \bar{\lambda}^r \sin\alpha \sin\beta + \bar{\mu}^r \cos\alpha \sin\beta + \bar{\nu}^r \cos\beta$

30.66

$l_r = \bar{\lambda}_r \sin\bar{\alpha} \sin\bar{\beta} + \bar{\mu}_r \cos\bar{\alpha} \sin\bar{\beta} + \bar{\nu}_r \cos\bar{\beta}$

30.67

$$\frac{\partial}{\partial s}\left(\frac{1}{l}\right) = -\frac{l_r \nu^r}{l^2}$$

$$= -\frac{1}{l^2}\{\cos\beta\cos\bar\beta$$

30.68
$$+ \cos(\bar\alpha - \alpha)\sin\beta\sin\bar\beta\}$$

$$\frac{\partial T}{\partial s} = T_r \nu^r = g\eta\sin\alpha\sin\beta$$

30.69
$$+ g(\xi+\kappa)\cos\alpha\sin\beta + (g-\gamma)\cos\beta$$

30.70
$$\frac{\partial T}{\partial h} = (g-\gamma) = g_A + \frac{\partial\ln\gamma}{\partial h}T$$

$$\frac{\partial T}{\partial s} = g\eta\sin\alpha\sin\beta + g(\xi+\kappa)\cos\alpha\sin\beta$$

30.71
$$+ \left(g_A + \frac{\partial\ln\gamma}{\partial h}T\right)\cos\beta$$

$$\cos\beta\, dS = (\bar\nu+\bar h)(\bar\rho+\bar h)\cos\bar\phi\,d\bar\omega d\bar\phi$$

30.72
$$= (\bar\nu+\bar h)(\bar\rho+\bar h)d\Omega$$

30.74
$$2\pi T_P + \int JT_Q d\Omega = \int L\, d\Omega$$

$$J = \left\{\cos\bar\beta + \cos(\bar\alpha-\alpha)\tan\beta\sin\bar\beta\right.$$

$$\left. + l\frac{\partial\ln\gamma}{\partial h}\right\}(\bar\rho+\bar h)(\bar\nu+\bar h)/l^2$$

$$L = -\{g_A + g\eta\sin\alpha\tan\beta$$

30.75
$$+ g(\xi+\kappa)\cos\alpha\tan\beta\}(\bar\rho+\bar h)(\bar\nu+\bar h)/l$$

Gradient Equations:

$$(T_r)_P = \tfrac{1}{2}\left(\frac{\partial T}{\partial s}\right)_P (\nu_r)_P - \frac{1}{4\pi}\int\frac{1}{l^2}\frac{\partial T}{\partial s}l_r\,dS$$

30.79
$$+ \tfrac{1}{2}(\bar T_r)_P - \frac{1}{4\pi}\int\frac{T-T_P}{l^3}\{3(l'\nu_t)l_r - \nu_r\}dS$$

$$(T_r\nu^r)_P = \left(\frac{\partial T}{\partial s}\right)_P$$

$$= -\frac{1}{2\pi}\int\left[\frac{1}{l^2}\frac{\partial T}{\partial s}l_r(\nu^r)_P\right.$$

30.80
$$\left. + \frac{T-T_P}{l^3}\{3(l'\nu_t)l_r(\nu^r)_P - \nu_r(\nu^r)_P\}\right]dS$$

The Equivalent Single Layer:

$$(g_D)_P = (g_A)_P + \left(\frac{\partial\ln\gamma}{\partial h}\right)_P T_P$$

30.87
$$= 2\pi\sigma_P\cos\beta_P - \int\frac{\sigma\cos\bar\beta_P}{l^2}dS$$

$$(g\eta)_P = 2\pi\sigma_P\sin\alpha_P\sin\beta_P$$

30.88
$$- \int\frac{\sigma\sin\bar\alpha_P\sin\bar\beta_P}{l^2}dS$$

$$\{g(\xi+\kappa)\}_P = 2\pi\sigma_P\cos\alpha_P\sin\beta_P$$

30.89
$$- \int\frac{\sigma\cos\bar\alpha_P\sin\bar\beta_P}{l^2}dS$$

$$2\pi\sigma_P\cos\beta_P - \int\left[\frac{\cos\bar\beta_P}{l^2} - \left(\frac{\partial\ln\gamma}{\partial h}\right)_P\frac{1}{l}\right]\sigma dS = (g_A)_P$$

30.90

$$(g_A)_P = 2\pi\sigma_P - \tfrac{3}{2}\int(\tfrac{1}{2}\csc\tfrac{1}{2}\psi)\sigma d\Omega$$

30.91
$$= 2\pi\sigma_P - \tfrac{3}{2}\int\sigma\sum_{n=0}^\infty P_n(\cos\psi)d\Omega$$

$$\{g_{A_n}^m\}_P = 2\pi\{\sigma_n^m\}_P - \tfrac{3}{2}\frac{4\pi}{2n+1}\{\sigma_n^m\}_P$$

30.92
$$= \frac{4\pi(n-1)}{2n+1}\{\sigma_n^m\}_P$$

$$4\pi\sigma_P = \sum_{n,m}\frac{2n+1}{n-1}\{g_{A_n}^m\}_P$$

$$= \sum_{n,m}\frac{2n+1}{n-1}\frac{2n+1}{4\pi}\int\{g_{A_n}^m\}P_n(\cos\psi)d\Omega$$

30.93
$$= \frac{1}{4\pi}\int g_A\sum_{n=2}^\infty\frac{(2n+1)^2}{n-1}P_n(\cos\psi)$$

30.94
$$16\pi^2\sigma_P = \int\bar{\bar S}(\psi)g_A d\Omega$$

General Index

Z

U.S. GOVERNMENT PRINTING OFFICE : 1969 OL—306-962